Grade 8 NCTM Focal Points Alignment

S0-BEB-780

Math Triumphs, Grade 8 provides the prerequisite concepts and skills necessary for success with the Grade 8 NCTM Focal Points. Horizontal alignment ensures successful transitions between *Math Connects* and *Math Triumphs*.

Preparation for NCTM Grade 8 **Focal Points**	*Math Triumphs*, Grade 8	Targeted Prerequisite Skills and Concepts	Preparation for *Math Connects*, Course 3
Grade 8 Focal Point 1 Algebra *Math Triumphs* Book 1	**Chapter 1** **Integers**	Use models to understand integer values.	Chapter 1
		Calculate integers using operations. Multiply and divide integers.	Chapter 1
	Chapter 2 **Patterns and Graphs**	Solve simple problems involving functional relationships.	Chapters 8, 9, and 10
		Identify and graph ordered pairs on a coordinate grid.	Chapters 8, 9, and 10
		Graph linear and nonlinear functions.	Chapters 8, 9, and 10
	Chapter 3 **Expressions and Equations**	Use the order of operations to evaluate expressions and solve equations with integer solutions.	Chapters 1, 8, and 9
		Use variables in simple expressions and equations.	Chapters 1, 8, and 9
		Solve simple linear equations for one variable in terms of another.	Chapters 1, 8, 9, and 10
Grade 8 Focal Point 2 Geometry and Measurement *Math Triumphs* Book 2	**Chapter 4** **Angle Measures**	Measure, identify, and draw angles and triangles.	Chapter 6
		Add measures of angles and know the sum of the angles in a triangle and a straight angle.	Chapters 6 and 7
		Identify the measure of an angle, using knowledge about transversals and parallel lines.	Chapter 6
	Chapter 5 **Ratios, Rates, and Similarity**	Determine unit costs and understand ratios and rates.	Chapters 2, 4, and 10
		Use proportions to compare sets of numerical data.	Chapters 2, 4, 5, and 11
		Use proportions to compare figures and solve problems.	Chapters 2, 4, 5, and 11
	Chapter 6 **Squares, Square Roots, and the Pythagorean Theorem**	Find square numbers and positive square roots of positive integers.	Chapter 3
		Know and use the Pythagorean Theorem to find the lengths of unknown sides of a right triangle.	Chapter 3
		Graph linear functions and determine the slope of a line.	Chapters 3 and 9
Grade 8 Focal Point 3 Data Analysis, Number and Operations, and Algebra *Math Triumphs* Book 3	**Chapter 7** **One-Variable Data**	Sort and classify data and find the measures of central tendency.	Chapters 9 and 11
		Interpret and create bar graphs.	Chapters 9 and 11
		Interpret and create line graphs.	Chapters 9 and 11
	Chapter 8 **Percents and Circle Graphs**	Calculate percentages for data in a set.	Chapters 5, 11, and 12
		Interpret and create circle graphs.	Chapters 5 and 11
	Chapter 9 **Two-Variable Data**	Identify and describe the relationship between two variables within an equation of on a graph.	Chapters 9, 10, and 11
		Interpret and make predictions using data in a scatter plot.	Chapters 9, 10, and 11

For a complete correlation to the NCTM Curriculum Focal Points, go to www.glencoe.com and select **Math,** then **Teacher View.** The complete Curriculum Focal Points may be viewed at www.nctm.org/focalpoints.

NCTM Focal Points	Preparation in Math Triumphs, Grade 8
Algebra (G8-FP1) Analyzing and representing linear functions and solving linear equations and systems of linear equations Students use linear functions, linear equations, and systems of linear equations to represent, analyze, and solve a variety of problems. They recognize a proportion ($y/x = k$, or $y = kx$) as a special case of a linear equation of the form $y = mx + b$, understanding that the constant of proportionality (k) is the slope and the resulting graph is a line through the origin. Students understand that the slope (m) of a line is a constant rate of change, so if the input, or x-coordinate, changes by a specific amount, a, the output, or y-coordinate, changes by the amount ma. Students translate among verbal, tabular, graphical, and algebraic representations of functions (recognizing that tabular and graphical representations are usually only partial representations), and they describe how such aspects of a function as slope and y-intercept appear in different representations. Students solve systems of two linear equations in two variables and relate the systems to pairs of lines that intersect, are parallel, or are the same line, in the plane. Students use linear equations, systems of linear equations, linear functions, and their understanding of the slope of a line to analyze situations and solve problems.	**Chapter 1: Integers** **Chapter 2: Patterns and Graphs** **Chapter 3: Expressions and Equations**
Geometry and Measurement (G8-FP2) Analyzing two- and three-dimensional space and figures by using distance and angle Students use fundamental facts about distance and angles to describe and analyze figures and situations in two- and three-dimensional space and to solve problems, including those with multiple steps. They prove that particular configurations of lines give rise to similar triangles because of the congruent angles created when a transversal cuts parallel lines. Students apply this reasoning about similar triangles to solve a variety of problems, including those that ask them to find heights and distances. They use facts about the angles that are created when a transversal cuts parallel lines to explain why the sum of the measures of the angles in a triangle is 180 degrees, and they apply this fact about triangles to find unknown measures of angles. Students explain why the Pythagorean theorem is valid by using a variety of methods—for example, by decomposing a square in two different ways. They apply the Pythagorean theorem to find distances between points in the Cartesian coordinate plane to measure lengths and analyze polygons and polyhedra.	**Chapter 4: Angle Measures** **Chapter 5: Ratios, Rates, and Similarity** **Chapter 6: Squares, Square Roots, and the Pythagorean Theorem**
Data Analysis and Number and Operations and Algebra (G8-FP3) Analyzing and summarizing data sets Students use descriptive statistics, including mean, median, and range, to summarize and compare data sets, and they organize and display data to pose and answer questions. They compare the information provided by the mean and the median and investigate the different effects that changes in data values have on these measures of center. They understand that a measure of center alone does not thoroughly describe a data set because very different data sets can share the same measure of center. Students select the mean or the median as the appropriate measure of center for a given purpose.	**Chapter 7: One-Variable Data** **Chapter 8: Percents and Circle Graphs** **Chapter 9: Two-Variable Data**

Focal Points Connections	Preparation in Math Triumphs, Grade 8
Algebra (G8-FP4C) Students encounter some nonlinear functions (such as the inverse proportions that they studied in grade 7 as well as basic quadratic and exponential functions) whose rates of change contrast with the constant rate of change of linear functions. They view arithmetic sequences, including those arising from patterns or problems, as linear functions whose inputs are counting numbers. They apply ideas about linear functions to solve problems involving rates such as motion at a constant speed.	**Chapter 2: Patterns and Graphs** **Chapter 5: Ratios, Rates, and Similarity**
Geometry (G85-FP5C) Given a line in a coordinate plane, students understand that all "slope triangles" triangles created by a vertical "rise" line segment (showing the change in y), a horizontal "run" line segment (showing the change in x), and a segment of the line itself—are similar. They also understand the relationship of these similar triangles to the constant slope of a line.	**Chapter 2: Patterns and Graphs** **Chapter 6: Squares, Square Roots, and the Pythagorean Theorem**
Data Analysis (G8-FP6C) Building on their work in previous grades to organize and display data to pose and answer questions, students now see numerical data as an aggregate, which they can often summarize with one or several numbers. In addition to the median, students determine the 25th and 75th percentiles (1st and 3rd quartiles) to obtain information about the spread of data. They may use box-and-whisker plots to convey this information. Students make scatter plots to display bivariate data, and they informally estimate lines of best fit to make and test conjectures.	**Chapter 7: One-Variable Data** **Chapter 9: Two-Variable Data**
Number and Operations (G8-FP7C) Students use exponents and scientific notation to describe very large and very small numbers. They use square roots when they apply the Pythagorean theorem.	**Chapter 6: Squares, Square Roots, and the Pythagorean Theorem**

For a complete correlation to the NCTM Curriculum Focal Points, go to www.glencoe.com and select **Math**, then **Teacher View**. The complete Curriculum Focal Points may be viewed at www.nctm.org/focalpoints.

What is *Math Triumphs?*

- Intensive intervention for students two or more years behind grade level.

- Prerequisite Grade 8 concepts and skills that prepare students for the Grade 8 NCTM Focal Points.

- Horizontal alignment with Glencoe/McGraw-Hill's *Math Connects*, a balanced basal program.

The McGraw-Hill Companies

 Glencoe

Send all inquires to:
Glencoe/McGraw-Hill
8787 Orion Place
Columbus, OH 43240-4027

Teacher Edition
ISBN: 978-0-07-888224-1
MHID: 0-07-888224-9

Student Study Guide, Book 1
ISBN: 978-0-07-888213-5
MHID: 0-07-888213-3

Student Study Guide, Book 2
ISBN: 978-0-07-888214-2
MHID: 0-07-888214-1

Student Study Guide, Book 3
ISBN: 978-0-07-888215-9
MHID: 0-07-888215-X

Printed in the United States of America.

4 5 6 7 8 9 10 RMN/LEH 17 16 15 14 13 12 11 10

Contents in Brief

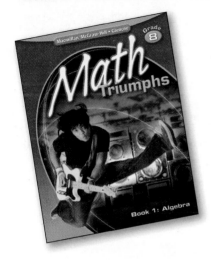

Student Study Guide: Book 1

Chapter 1   Integers   G8-FP1

Chapter 2   Patterns and Graphs   G8-FP1

Chapter 3   Expressions and Equations   G8-FP1

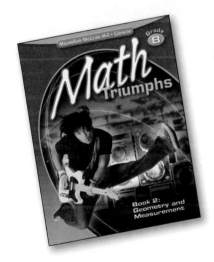

Student Study Guide: Book 2

Chapter 4   Angle Measures   G8-FP2

Chapter 5   Ratios, Rates, and Similarity   G8-FP2

Chapter 6   Squares, Square Roots, and the Pythagorean Theorem   G8-FP2

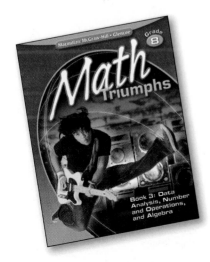

Student Study Guide: Book 3

Chapter 7   One-Variable Data   G8-FP3

Chapter 8   Percents and Circle Graphs   G8-FP3

Chapter 9   Two-Variable Data   G8-FP3

handwritten: MATH M228t 2009 8

AUTHORS

Frances Basich Whitney
Project Director, Mathematics K–12
Santa Cruz County Office of Education
Capitola, California

Kathleen M. Brown
Math Curriculum Staff Developer
Washington Middle School
Long Beach, California

Dixie Dawson
Math Curriculum Leader
Long Beach Unified
Long Beach, California

Philip Gonsalves
Mathematics Coordinator
Alameda County Office of Education
Hayward, California

Robyn Silbey
Math Specialist
Montgomery County Public Schools
Gaithersburg, Maryland

Kathy Vielhaber
Mathematics Consultant
St. Louis, Missouri

CONTRIBUTING AUTHORS

Viken Hovsepian
Professor of Mathematics
Rio Hondo College
Whittier, California

FOLDABLES **Dinah Zike**
Study Organizer Educational Consultant,
Dinah-Might Activities, Inc.
San Antonio, Texas

CONSULTANTS

Assessment

Donna M. Kopenski, Ed.D.
Math Coordinator K–5
City Heights Educational Collaborative
San Diego, California

Instructional Planning and Support

Beatrice Luchin
Mathematics Consultant
League City, Texas

ELL Support and Vocabulary

ReLeah Cossett Lent
Author/Educational Consultant
Alford, Florida

Reviewers

Each person below reviewed at least two chapters of the Student Study Guide, providing feedback and suggestions for improving the effectiveness of the mathematics instruction.

Patricia Allanson
Mathematics Teacher
Deltona Middle School
Deltona, Florida

Debra Allred
Sixth Grade Math Teacher
Wiley Middle School
Leander, Texas

April Chauvette
Secondary Mathematics Facilitator
Leander Independent School District
Leander, Texas

Amy L. Chazarreta
Math Teacher
Wayside Middle School
Fort Worth, Texas

Jeff Denney
Seventh Grade Math Teacher, Mathematics
   Department Chair
Oak Mountain Middle School
Birmingham, Alabama

Franco A. DiPasqua
Director of K-12 Mathematics
West Seneca Central
West Seneca, New York

David E. Ewing
Teacher
Bellview Middle School
Pensacola, Florida

Mark J. Forzley
Eighth Grade Math Teacher
Westmont Junior High School
Westmont, Illinois

Virginia Granstrand Harrell
Education Consultant
Tampa, Florida

Russ Lush
Sixth Grade Math Teacher, Mathematics
   Department Chair
New Augusta - North
Indianapolis, Indiana

Joyce B. McClain
Middle School Math Consultant
Hillsborough County Schools
Tampa, Florida

Suzanne D. Obuchowski
Math Teacher
Proctor School
Topsfield, Massachusetts

Karen L. Reed
Sixth Grade Pre-AP Math
Keller ISD
Keller, Texas

Deborah Todd
Sixth Grade Math Teacher
Francis Bradley Middle School
Huntersville, North Carolina

Susan S. Wesson
Teacher (retired)
Pilot Butte Middle School
Bend, Oregon

TEACHER HANDBOOK

Mathematics Teacher Handbook

Table of Contents

☑ Vertical Alignment

Welcome to *Math Connects* **T3**

*An overview of the vertical alignment of Macmillan/McGraw-Hill's
and Glencoe's PreK–12 mathematics programs*

Implementing Intensive Intervention **T5**

Program Organization **T6**

Balanced approach of concepts, skills, and problem solving

☑ Assessment

Comprehensive Assessment System **T9**

*Diagnostic, Formative, and Summative assessments linked to
Data-Driven Decision Making*

☑ Professional Development

Professional Development **T11**

*Extensive options for purposeful, point-of-use, and consistent
PreK–12 professional development*

Welcome to
Math Connects

Concepts • Skills • Problem Solving

The only true vertically aligned PreK–12 Mathematics Curriculum

Math Connects offers three dimensions of vertical alignment.

❶ Content Design

Vertical content alignment is a process that ensures you and your students experience an articulated, coherent sequence of content from grade level to grade level. This provides you with the assurance that content is introduced, reinforced, and assessed at appropriate times in the series, eliminating gaps and unnecessary duplication. You are able to target your instruction to student needs because you are not teaching content intended to be covered later or that students have previously mastered.

❷ Instructional Design

Our strong vertical alignment in instructional approach from PreKindergarten through Algebra 2 provides a smooth transition for students from elementary to middle school to high school. Our common vocabulary, technology, manipulatives, lesson planning, and Data-Driven Decision Making reduce the confusion students often encounter when transitioning between grade levels without this built-in articulation.

❸ Visual Design

The student pages of *Math Connects* have a consistent visual design from grade to grade. This aids students' transition from elementary school to middle school and from middle school to Algebra 1. Students are more likely to succeed when they are already familiar with how to navigate student pages.

 Intensive Intervention

PreK-2   **3-5**

 Daily Intervention

 Strategic Intervention

5 Keys to Success

❶ Backmapping

According to College Board research, about 80% of students who successfully complete Algebra 1 and Geometry by 10th grade attend and succeed in college. (Changing the Odds: Factors Increasing Access to College, 1990) *Math Connects* was conceived and developed by backmapping with the final result in mind–student success in Algebra 1 and beyond.

❷ Balanced, In-Depth Content

Math Connects was developed to specifically target the skills and topics that give students the most difficulty, such as Problem Solving, in each grade span.

Grades K–2	Grades 3–5
1. Problem Solving 2. Money 3. Time 4. Measurement 5. Fractions 6. Computation	1. Problem Solving 2. Fractions 3. Measurement 4. Decimals 5. Time 6. Algebra
Grades 6–8	**Grades 9–12**
1. Fractions 2. Problem Solving 3. Measurement 4. Algebra 5. Computation	1. Problem Solving 2. Fractions 3. Algebra 4. Geometry 5. Computation 6. Probability

– K–12 Math Market Analysis Survey, Open Book Publishing, 2006

❸ Ongoing Assessment

Math Connects includes diagnostic, formative, and summative assessment; data-driven instruction; intervention options; and performance tracking, as well as remediation, acceleration, and enrichment tools throughout the program.

❹ Intervention and Differentiated Instruction

A three-tiered Response To Intervention (RTI) is provided.

TIER ❶ Daily Intervention Reteach masters and Alternative Strategy suggestions address concepts from a different modality or learning style.

TIER ❷ Strategic Intervention Teachers can use the myriad of intervention tips and ancillary materials, such as the Strategic Intervention Guide (1–5) and Study Guide and Intervention (6–8).

TIER ❸ Intensive Intervention For students who are two or more years below grade level, *Math Triumphs* provides step-by-step instruction, vocabulary support, and data-driven decision making to help students succeed.

❺ Professional Development

Math Connects includes many opportunities for teacher professional development. Additional learning opportunities in various formats–video, online, and on-site instruction–are fully aligned and articulated from Kindergarten through Algebra 2.

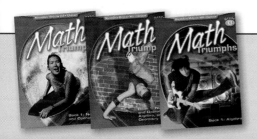

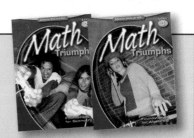

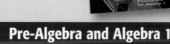

6–8 · **Pre-Algebra and Algebra 1** · **Geometry and Algebra 2**

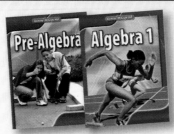

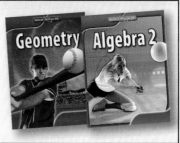

Implementing Intensive Intervention

TIER 3 Data-Driven Intensive Intervention

Ongoing assessment aids the teacher in student placement, progress monitoring, and exit.

Instructional Design

❶ Diagnose and Prescribe
- Course Placement Test
- Online Readiness Quiz
- Chapter Preview
- Chapter Pretest
- Book Pretest

❷ Teach and Practice
- Student Study Guide
- Teacher Edition Strategies
- Vocabulary Cards
- Manipulatives

❸ Advance and Exit
- Assessment Masters
- Chapter Test
- Book Test

Classroom Implementation

Teacher prepares individual or group intervention plan(s).

Teacher modifies instruction based on results of formative assessments.

Test success indicates that a student can progress to another *Math Triumphs* chapter (if needed) or exit the intervention program.

Alignment to NCTM Focal Points

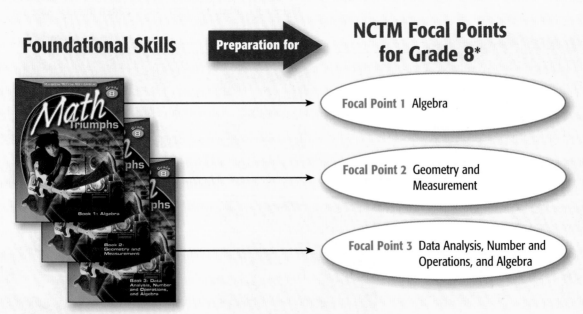

Foundational Skills → **Preparation for** → **NCTM Focal Points for Grade 8***

Focal Point 1 Algebra

Focal Point 2 Geometry and Measurement

Focal Point 3 Data Analysis, Number and Operations, and Algebra

*See front cover folder for key and complete NCTM Focal Points.

Program Organization

Provide Personalized Instruction

Consumable volumes and minimal preparation requirements allow for flexibility and personalized instruction in any setting.

- After school
- Before school
- Tutoring
- Summer school
- Intersession
- Pull-out/Resource room

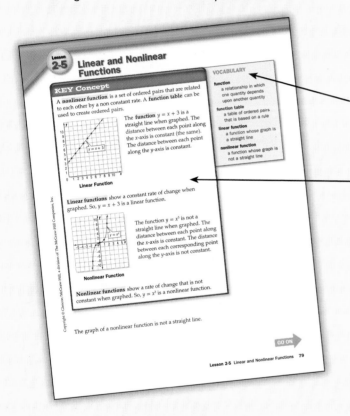

Vocabulary

Vocabulary helps students identify terms presented in the lesson.

Key Concepts

Key Concepts introduce and break mathematics into conceptual steps. Multiple representations demonstrate the skills being presented.

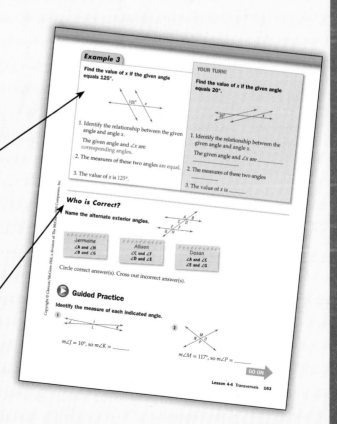

Examples

Fully worked-out **Examples** enable students and parents to see how to solve problems step by step. **Your Turn!** gives students an opportunity to practice skills immediately.

Who is Correct?

Students "grade" sample answers. This formative assessment opportunity generates meaningful classroom discussion and highlights possible misconceptions.

Guided Practice

Guided Practice exercises provide computational practice. They can be used as formative assessment to monitor student progress and guide your instruction.

Step-by-Step Practice guides students to complete a computational problem through a series of conceptual steps. Instructional aids are provided to students in the exercises that follow.

Step-by-Step Problem-Solving Practice walks the student through a four-step problem-solving strategy (Understand, Plan, Solve, Check) that is relevant to the word problem. Aids help the student break down and visualize what the problem is asking and how to solve it.

A **Reflect** question requires the student to think and write about the process of completing a problem.

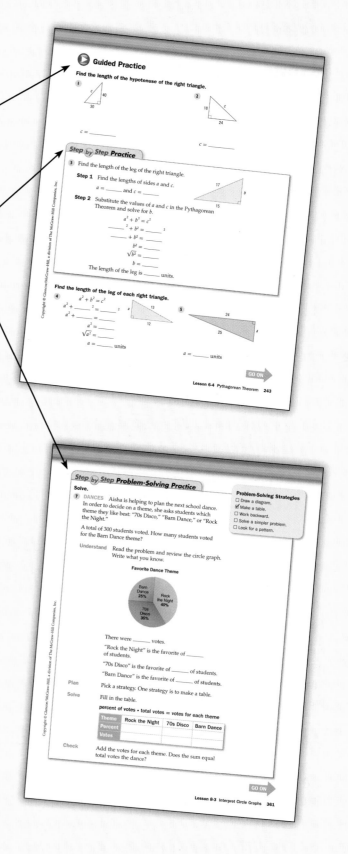

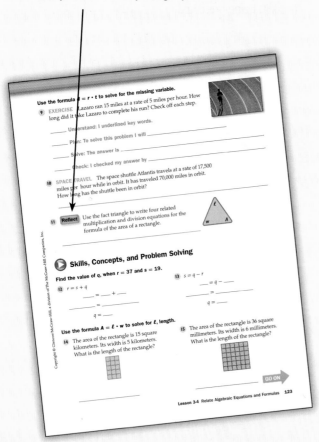

Balance

McGraw-Hill's *Math Triumphs* is designed to provide students a balanced approach to mathematics learning by offering them the opportunity to:

- investigate concepts and build their conceptual understanding;
- review, learn, and practice basic computational and procedural skills; and
- apply mathematics to problem solving in real-world situations.

Independent Practice

Skill, Concepts, and Problem Solving provide homework opportunities and independent practice.

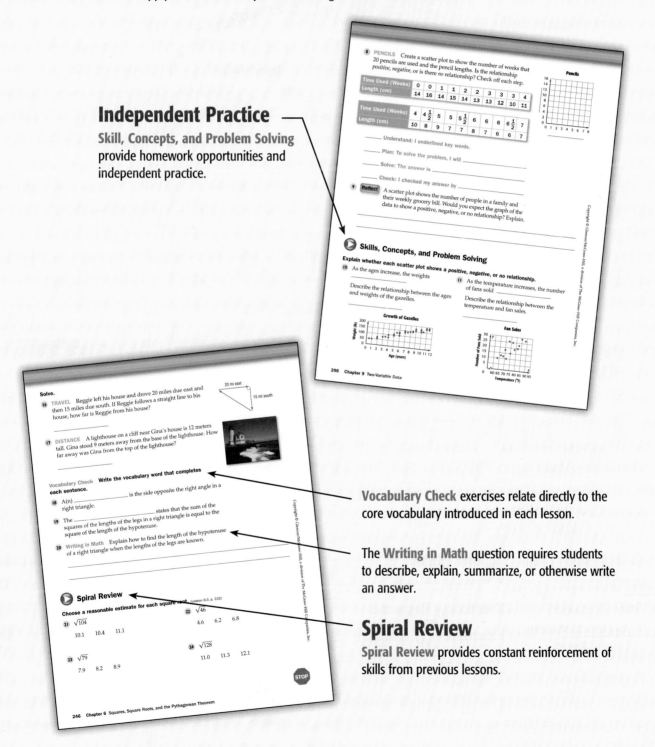

Vocabulary Check exercises relate directly to the core vocabulary introduced in each lesson.

The **Writing in Math** question requires students to describe, explain, summarize, or otherwise write an answer.

Spiral Review

Spiral Review provides constant reinforcement of skills from previous lessons.

Comprehensive Assessment System

Data-Driven Decision Making

Math Triumphs offers frequent and meaningful assessment of student progress within the curriculum structure and teacher support materials.

Assessment and Intervention System

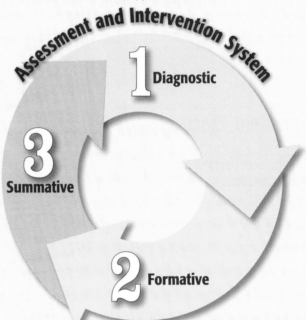

1 Diagnostic

2 Formative

3 Summative

1 Diagnostic

Initial Assessment Assess students' knowledge **at the beginning of the year** with the *Diagnostic and Placement Tests*.

Entry–Level Assessment Assess students' prior knowledge **at the beginning of a chapter** with one of the following options.

Student Study Guide
- Preview

Teacher Edition
- Vocabulary Preview

Print Resources
- Assessment Masters, Chapter Pretest

Technology Resources

ExamView®
Assessment Suite

Math Online > Online Readiness Quiz

Advance TRACKER

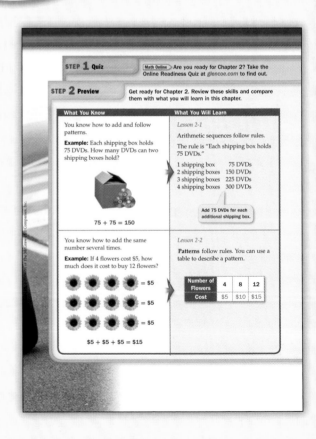

STEP 1 Quiz — Math Online > Are you ready for Chapter 2? Take the Online Readiness Quiz at *glencoe.com* to find out.

STEP 2 Preview — Get ready for Chapter 2. Review these skills and compare them with what you will learn in this chapter.

What You Know	What You Will Learn
You know how to add and follow patterns. **Example:** Each shipping box holds 75 DVDs. How many DVDs can two shipping boxes hold? 75 + 75 = 150	*Lesson 2-1* Arithmetic sequences follow rules. The rule is "Each shipping box holds 75 DVDs." 1 shipping box — 75 DVDs; 2 shipping boxes — 150 DVDs; 3 shipping boxes — 225 DVDs; 4 shipping boxes — 300 DVDs. Add 75 DVDs for each additional shipping box.
You know how to add the same number several times. **Example:** If 4 flowers cost \$5, how much does it cost to buy 12 flowers? = \$5, = \$5, = \$5; \$5 + \$5 + \$5 = \$15	*Lesson 2-2* **Patterns** follow rules. You can use a table to describe a pattern.

Number of Flowers	4	8	12
Cost	\$5	\$10	\$15

Formative

Progress Monitoring Determine if students are progressing adequately as you teach each lesson. Use the assessments to differentiate lesson instruction and practice.

Student Study Guide
- Progress Check
- Who is Correct?
- Study Guide
- Foldables®

Teacher Edition
- Intervention Strategy
- Are They Getting It?
- Ticket Out the Door
- See It, Do It, Say It, Write It
- Data-Driven Decision Making

Print Resources
- Assessment Masters
- Chapter Resource Masters

Technology Resources

Math Online My Math Zone

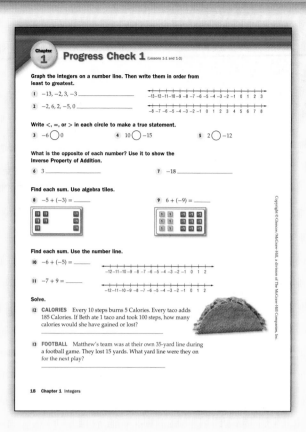

Summative

Summative Evaluation Assess student success in learning the concepts in each chapter.

Student Study Guide
- Chapter Test
- Test Practice
- Foldables®

Teacher Edition
- Data-Driven Decision Making

Print Resources
- Assessment Masters
- Chapter Resource Masters

Technology Resources

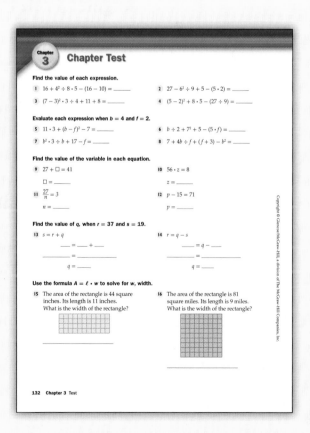

PreK-12 Data-Driven Professional Development

McGraw-Hill Professional Development (MHPD) provides a comprehensive plan for mathematics that is fully aligned and articulated with **Math Connects PreK–8** and the **Glencoe Mathematics** high school series.

Professional Development Needs	Online Courses	DVD Workshops	Video Library	Teach-Use-Succeed	Ready-Access Math
Has immediate classroom application	✓	✓	✓	✓	✓
Builds content knowledge	✓	✓			✓
Promotes best teaching practices		✓	✓		
Supports new and experienced teachers	✓	✓	✓	✓	✓
Allows customization of courses	✓	✓			✓
Can be self-paced	✓	✓		✓	✓
Adaptable for various timeframes	✓	✓	✓	✓	✓
Is grade-level specific			✓	✓	✓
Promotes a learning community	✓	✓			✓
Provides vertically-aligned content	✓	✓	✓		✓
Helps with RTI (Response to Intervention), Tiers 1–3	✓	✓	✓		✓

Use students' mathematics achievement data to help develop a targeted Professional Development Plan.

Accredited Online Courses
(available for purchase)

- Watch video clips of math classrooms.
- Complete interactive exercises.
- Develop electronic portfolios.
- Complete each 3- to 5-hour online module one segment at a time.
- Earn university credit (additional tuition).

DVD Workshops

- Watch video clips of classroom mathematics lessons and commentaries by leading educators.
- Complete lessons and activities.

MHPD Online

- Access this online Professional Development resource for K–12 educators.
- Link to relevant Web sites.
- Download grade-level student resources.

McGraw-Hill Professional

Professional Development Web sites

McGraw-Hill's Experienced Consultants

Ready Access Math Training Materials

Textbook Implementation Modules

Mini Clip Video Library

Video Workshops Mentor-led or Self-Study

Accredited Online Courses

Development Portfolio

Video Library   Math Online

- Access hundreds of K–12 video clips.
- See clips that illustrate mathematics content and instructional strategies.
- Watch demonstrations or commentaries.

Teach-Use-Succeed Textbook Implementation Modules

- Watch an experienced teacher demonstrate the *Math Connects* K–8 Student Editions, Teacher Editions, and program ancillaries—Online or DVD.

Ready-Access Math, Personalized Professional Development

- Access training materials for nearly 300 lessons.
- Create a customized sequence of professional development sessions.
- Deliver 45–60 minute after-school professional development sessions.

Contents

Chapter 1 Integers

Preparation for
Focal Points
and Connections
See front cover folder
for key.

1-1 Model Integers 4   **G8-FP1**

1-2 Add Integers 11   **G8-FP1**

     Progress Check 1 18

1-3 Subtract Integers 19   **G8-FP1**

1-4 Multiply Integers 27   **G8-FP1**

1-5 Divide Integers 33   **G8-FP1**

     Progress Check 2 39

Assessment

     Study Guide..40

     Chapter Test...44

     Test Practice 46

Navajo Bridge, Colorado

Contents

Chapter 2 · Patterns and Graphs

2-1 Number Relationships 50   **G8-FP1**

2-2 Introduction to Functions 57   **G8-FP1**

     Progress Check 1 63

2-3 Ordered Pairs...64   **G8-FP1**

2-4 Coordinate Grids.. 71   **G8-FP1**

2-5 Linear and Nonlinear Functions 79   **G8-FP1**

     Progress Check 2 87

Assessment

     Study Guide 88

     Chapter Test 92

     Test Practice..94

Saint Louis, Missouri

Chapter 3
Expressions and Equations

3-1 Order of Operations..98 **G8-FP1**

3-2 Evaluate Algebraic Expressions...................105 **G8-FP1**

    Progress Check 1 112

3-3 Solve Algebraic Equations 113 **G8-FP1**

3-4 Relate Algebraic Equations and Formulas 119 **G8-FP1**

    Progress Check 2 126

Assessment

    Study Guide 127

    Chapter Test 132

    Test Practice...134

Appalachian Mountains, West Virginia

Contents

Chapter 4 Angle Measures

Preparation for Focal Points and Connections
See front cover folder for key.

4-1 Angles	138	**G8-FP2**
4-2 Triangles	145	**G8-FP2**
Progress Check 1	152	
4-3 Add Angles	153	**G8-FP2**
4-4 Transversals	161	**G8-FP2**
Progress Check 2	168	

Assessment

Study Guide	169
Chapter Test	174
Test Practice	176

Mystic, Connecticut

Contents

Chapter 5 Ratios, Rates, and Similarity

Preparation for Focal Points and Connections
See front cover folder for key.

5-1 Ratios 180   **G8-FP2**

5-2 Rates and Unit Costs 187   **G8-FP2**

Progress Check 1 193

5-3 Proportions 194   **G8-FP2**

5-4 Solve Problems Using Proportions 201   **G8-FP2**

Progress Check 2 208

Assessment

Study Guide 209

Chapter Test 212

Test Practice..214

Stowe, Vermont

Contents

Chapter 6

Squares, Square Roots, and the Pythagorean Theorem

Preparation for Focal Points and Connections
See front cover folder for key.

6-1 Squaring a Number..218   **G8-FP2**

6-2 Square Roots 225   **G8-FP2**

Progress Check 1 231

6-3 Approximate Square Roots....................................232   **G8-FP2**

6-4 Pythagorean Theorem 239   **G8-FP2**

Progress Check 2 247

6-5 Introduction to Slope...248   **G8-FP2**

6-6 Slope Formula...255   **G8-FP2**

Progress Check 3 262

Assessment

Study Guide 263

Chapter Test 268

Test Practice..270

Miami, Florida

Contents

Chapter 7 One-Variable Data

Preparation for Focal Points and Connections See front cover folder for key.

7-1 Sort and Classify 274   **G8-FP3**

7-2 Mode, Median, and Range 281   **G8-FP3**

7-3 Mean 289   **G8-FP3**

Progress Check 1 296

7-4 Interpret Bar Graphs................................297   **G8-FP3**

7-5 Create Bar Graphs.......................................305   **G8-FP3**

Progress Check 2 314

7-6 Interpret Line Graphs................................315   **G8-FP3**

7-7 Create Line Graphs.......................................323   **G8-FP3**

Progress Check 3 330

Assessment

Study Guide..331

Chapter Test..336

Test Practice 338

Surfing in Hawaii

Contents

Chapter 8 — **Percents and Circle Graphs**

8-1 Percents 342   **G8-FP3**

8-2 Percents and Angle Measures 349   **G8-FP3**

Progress Check 1 356

8-3 Interpret Circle Graphs 357   **G8-FP3**

8-4 Create Circle Graphs 365   **G8-FP3**

Progress Check 2 373

Assessment

Study Guide 374

Chapter Test 378

Test Practice 380

Preparation for
**Focal Points
and Connections**
See front cover folder
for key.

Bryce Canyon National Park, Colorado

Chapter 9

Two-Variable Data

9-1 Transition to Two-Variable Data 384

    G8-FP3

9-2 Scatter Plots..391

    G8-FP3

    Progress Check 1 398

9-3 Lines of Best Fit 399

    G8-FP3

    Progress Check 2 406

Assessment

    Study Guide 407

    Chapter Test 410

    Test Practice..412

Jonathan Dickinson State Park, Florida

SCAVENGER HUNT

BOOK 1

Let's Get Started

Use the Scavenger Hunt below to learn where things are located in each chapter.

1. What is the title of Lesson 5-2? Rates and Unit Costs

2. What is the Key Concept of Lesson 4-4? Transversals

3. On what page can you find the vocabulary term *complementary angles* in Lesson 4-3? page 153

4. What are the vocabulary words for Lesson 5-4? proportion, similar figures

5. How many exercises are presented in the Vocabulary and Concept Check section of the Chapter 5 Study Guide? 6

6. What strategy is used in the Step-by-Step Problem-Solving Practice on page 190? Solve a simpler problem.

7. List the first problem-solving step mentioned in exercise #9 on page 245. Understand: I underlined key words.

8. Describe the photo that accompanies Exercise 8 on page 149. It is a square tile, which is cut diagonally.

9. On what pages will you find the Test Practice for Chapter 6? pages 270–271

10. In Chapter 5, find the logo and internet address that tells you where you can take the Online Readiness Quiz. It is found on page 179. The URL is glencoe.com.

SCAVENGER HUNT

BOOK 1

Let's Get Started

Use the Scavenger Hunt below to learn where things are located in each chapter.

1. What is the title of Lesson 3-2? Evaluate Algebraic Expressions

2. What is the Key Concept of Lesson 2-3? Graphing ordered pairs on a coordinate grid

3. On what page can you find the vocabulary term *opposites* in Lesson 1-3? page 19

4. What are the vocabulary words for Lesson 2-3? coordinate grid, ordered pair, origin, x-axis, y-axis

5. How many Examples are presented in the Chapter 3 Study Guide? 8

6. What strategy is used in the Step-by-Step Problem-Solving Practice on page 67? Use a graph.

7. List the integers that are mentioned in Exercise 11 on page 24. 3, −5

8. What is Step 5 in Step-by-Step Practice on page 30? Write the product with the sign.

9. On what pages will you find the Study Guide for Chapter 2? pages 88–91

10. In Chapter 3, find the logo and Internet address that tells you where you can take the Online Readiness Quiz. It is found on page 97. The URL is glencoe.com.

SCAVENGER HUNT

BOOK 1

Let's Get Started

Use the Scavenger Hunt below to learn where things are located in each chapter.

1. What is the title of Lesson 9-3? **Lines of Best Fit**

2. How many examples are provided in Lesson 7-3? **3**

3. On what page can you find the vocabulary term *percent* in Lesson 8-1? **page 342**

4. What are the vocabulary words for Lesson 7-2? **data, median, mode, range**

5. How many exercises are presented in the Chapter 8 Study Guide for Lesson 8-2? **2**

6. What strategy is used in the Step-by-Step Problem-Solving Practice on page 285? **Look for a pattern.**

7. List the operations that are shown in Example 1 on page 289. **add, divide**

8. Describe the art on page 296 that accompanies Exercise 6. **Two overlapping circles, Venn Diagram**

9. On what pages will you find the Test Practice for Chapter 7? **pages 338–339**

10. In Chapter 8, find the logo and Internet address that tells you where you can take the Online Readiness Quiz. **It is found on page 341. The URL is glencoe.com.**

Chapter Overview

Chapter-at-a-Glance

Lesson	Math Objective	State/Local Standards
1-1 Model Integers (pp. 4–10)	Understand and model integers.	
1-2 Add Integers (pp. 11–17)	Find the sum of integers.	
Progress Check 1 (p. 18)		
1-3 Subtract Integers (pp. 19–26)	Find the difference of two or more integers.	
1-4 Multiply Integers (pp. 27–32)	Find the product of two integers.	
1-5 Divide Integers (pp. 33–38)	Find the quotient of two integers.	
Progress Check 2 (p. 39)		

Content-at-a-Glance

The diagram below summarizes and unpacks Chapter 1 content.

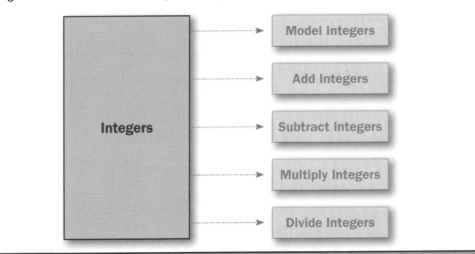

Chapter Assessment Manager

Diagnostic Diagnose students' readiness.

	Student/Teacher Editions	Assessment Masters	Technology
Course Placement Test		1	ExamView® Assessment Suite
Book 1 Pretest		23	ExamView® Assessment Suite
Chapter 1 Pretest		26	ExamView® Assessment Suite
Quiz/Preview	SSG 3		Math Online ▷ glencoe.com StudentWorks™ Plus

Formative Identify students' misconceptions of content knowledge.

	Student/Teacher Editions	Assessment Masters	Technology
Progress Checks	SSG 18, 39		Math Online ▷ glencoe.com StudentWorks™ Plus
Vocabulary Review	SSG 40		Math Online ▷ glencoe.com
Lesson Assessments			ExamView® Assessment Suite
Are They Getting It?	TE 7, 14, 23, 30, 35		Math Online ▷ glencoe.com

Summative Determine student success in learning the concepts in the lesson, chapter, or book.

	Student/Teacher Editions	Assessment Masters	Technology
Chapter 1 Test	SSG 44	29	ExamView® Assessment Suite
Test Practice	SSG 46	32	
Alternative Assessment	TE 44	35	ExamView® Assessment Suite
See It, Do It, Say It, Write It	TE 10, 17, 26, 32, 38		
Book 1 Test		59	ExamView® Assessment Suite

Backmapping and Vertical Alignment McGraw-Hill's *Math Triumphs* intervention program was conceived and developed with the final results in mind: student success in grade-level mathematics, including Algebra 1 and beyond. The authors, using the **NCTM Focal Points and Focal Connections** as their guide, developed this brand-new series by backmapping from grade-level and Algebra 1 concepts, and vertically aligning the topics so that they build upon prior skills and concepts and serve as a foundation for future topics.

Chapter Resource Manager

TeacherWorks™ Plus
All-In-One Planner and Resource Center

	Lesson 1-1	Lesson 1-2	Lesson 1-3	Lesson 1-4
Concept	Model Integers	Add Integers	Subtract Integers	Multiply Integers
Objective	Understand and model integers.	Find the sum of integers.	Find the difference of two or more integers.	Find the product of two integers.
Math Vocabulary	integer negative number opposites positive number whole numbers	Commutative Property of Addition Inverse Property of Addition	absolute value opposites	Associative Properties Commutative Properties Distributive Property factor product
Lesson Resources	**Materials** • Number lines • Rulers • Thermometers **Manipulatives** • Algebra tiles • Counters **Other Resources** [CRM] Vocabulary and English Language Development [CRM] Skills Practice [CRM] Problem-Solving Practice [CRM] Homework Practice	**Materials** • Number lines • Thermometers **Manipulatives** • Algebra tiles • Counters **Other Resources** [CRM] Vocabulary and English Language Development [CRM] Skills Practice [CRM] Problem-Solving Practice [CRM] Homework Practice	**Materials** • Number lines • Money • Thermometers **Manipulatives** • Algebra tiles • Counters • Pattern blocks **Other Resources** [CRM] Vocabulary and English Language Development [CRM] Skills Practice [CRM] Problem-Solving Practice [CRM] Homework Practice	**Materials** • Number lines • Multiplication tables • Hundreds chart **Manipulatives** • Algebra tiles • Geoboards **Other Resources** [CRM] Vocabulary and English Language Development [CRM] Skills Practice [CRM] Problem-Solving Practice [CRM] Homework Practice
Technology	**Math Online** glencoe.com StudentWorks™ Plus ⊙ ExamView® Assessment Suite	**Math Online** glencoe.com StudentWorks™ Plus ⊙ ExamView® Assessment Suite	**Math Online** glencoe.com StudentWorks™ Plus ⊙ ExamView® Assessment Suite	**Math Online** glencoe.com StudentWorks™ Plus ⊙ ExamView® Assessment Suite

Lesson 1-5

Divide Integers	**Concept**
Find the quotient of two integers.	**Objective**
dividend divisor quotient	**Math Vocabulary**

Materials
• Number lines
• Hundreds chart
 	
Manipulatives
• Algebra tiles
• Geoboards
 	
Other Resources
CRM Vocabulary and
    English Language
    Development
CRM Skills Practice
CRM Problem-Solving
    Practice
CRM Homework Practice
	Lesson Resources

Math Online ⟩ glencoe.com StudentWorks™ Plus ⊙ ExamView® Assessment Suite	**Technology**

Intervention Strategy

Operations with Integers

Using concrete materials and physically modeling operations with integers can help give students anchoring experiences that improve their understanding.

Step 1

Have students work in pairs. Write an addition sentence on the board with positive addends. Ask students to model the problem. Some students will use counters, others may use a number line or other strategies.

Step 2

After students share their models, repeat the activity, tell them to try a different strategy.

Step 3

Repeat using one negative addend. Discuss incorrect strategies that lead to an incorrect sum. Repeat until students can easily recognize that the sum has the sign of the largest number.

Step 4

Write an addition sentence with only negative addends. Again, discuss incorrect strategies until students are proficient with all types of integer addition.

Step 5

Repeat Steps 1 through 4 with subtraction.

Step 6

Repeat with multiplication, first with two positive factors, then with different signed factors, and then both negative factors. Have students model the problems and share their strategies. Point out how the Commutative Property lets the order of the factors change to make modeling the number sentence easier.

Step 7

Repeat with division. Have students model using concrete materials or drawings. Remind students how multiplication is the inverse operation of division and can be used to check for a correct answer.

Real-World Applications

Name the Integer   Write an integer for each of the following situations:

The temperature dropped 5 degrees. −5
I dove 3 feet below sea level. −3
He scored 6 points. 6
I found 2 dollars. 2
She owes me 4 dollars. −4

Intervention Strategy
Integer Work

Step 1 Divide students into pairs.

Step 2 Give each pair the following set of integers to work with.
- −9 and 3
- −9 and −3
- 9 and 3
- 9 and −3

Step 3 Have students add, subtract, multiply, and divide each set of integers; therefore, there should be a total of 16 problems.

Step 4 Students should not only have an answer for each problem, but also an explanation.

Step 5 Pairs should share and compare computations with the class.

Chapter 1 Integers

Scuba divers measure altitude with integers.

Different marine animals live at specific altitudes. Scuba divers use integers to find different animals by measuring the depth below sea level.

Chapter 1 Integers

Key Vocabulary

Find interactive definitions in 13 languages in the **eGlossary** at glencoe.com.

English   Español *Introduce the most important vocabulary terms from Chapter 1.*

absolute value   valor absoluto
the distance between a number and 0 on a number line (p. 19)

**Associative Properties
priopedad asociativa**
the way in which numbers are grouped does not change the sum or product (p. 27)

**Commutative Properties
propiedad conmutativa**
the order in which two numbers are added or multiplied does not change the sum or product (p. 27)

integers   enteros
the whole numbers and their opposites (p. 4)

**Inverse Property of Addition
priopedad inversa de la adición**
for any number, the sum of that number and its opposite is zero (p. 11)

negative number   número negativo
a number less than zero (p. 4)

positive number   número positivo
a number that is greater than zero (p. 4)

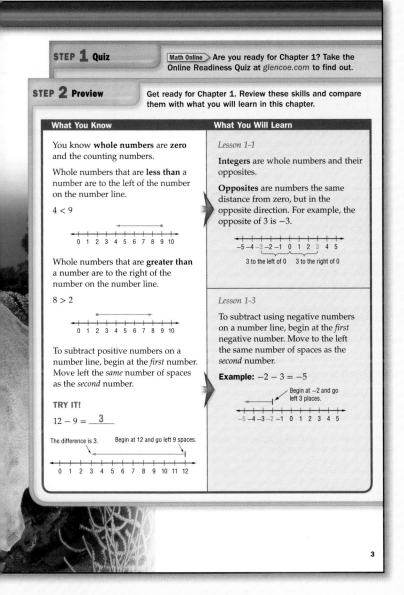

STEP 1 Quiz

Math Online ▷ Are you ready for Chapter 1? Take the Online Readiness Quiz at *glencoe.com* to find out.

STEP 2 Preview

Get ready for Chapter 1. Review these skills and compare them with what you will learn in this chapter.

What You Know	What You Will Learn
You know **whole numbers** are **zero** and the counting numbers.	*Lesson 1-1*
	Integers are whole numbers and their opposites.
Whole numbers that are **less than** a number are to the left of the number on the number line.	**Opposites** are numbers the same distance from zero, but in the opposite direction. For example, the opposite of 3 is −3.
$4 < 9$	

3 to the left of 0   3 to the right of 0

Whole numbers that are **greater than** a number are to the right of the number on the number line.

$8 > 2$

Lesson 1-3

To subtract using negative numbers on a number line, begin at the *first* negative number. Move to the left the same number of spaces as the *second* number.

To subtract positive numbers on a number line, begin at the *first* number. Move left the *same* number of spaces as the *second* number.

Example: $-2 - 3 = -5$

Begin at −2 and go left 3 places.

TRY IT!

$12 - 9 = \underline{\quad 3 \quad}$

The difference is 3.   Begin at 12 and go left 9 spaces.

3

Step 1   Quiz

Pretest/Prescribe   Students can take the Online Readiness Quiz or the Diagnostic Pretest in the Assessment Masters.

Step 2   Preview

Use this pre-chapter activity to activate students' prior knowledge, build confidence, and help students preview the lessons.

 **Dinah Zike's Foldables®**

Guide students through the directions on p. A1 in the Chapter Resource Masters to create their own Foldable graphic organizer for use with this chapter.

Home Connections

- Record the outside temperature every hour for a four-hour period. Describe the hourly change in temperature using integers.

Vocabulary Preview

- As students complete the Chapter Preview, have them make a list of important terms throughout the chapter.

- Have students work in groups to create vocabulary posters. Each poster should list the key vocabulary terms, along with examples and definitions.

- Groups can present their posters to the class.

- Hang posters for reference during the study of Chapter 1.

Professional Development

Targeted professional development has been articulated throughout **McGraw-Hill's *Math Triumphs*** intervention program. **The McGraw-Hill Professional Development Video Library** provides short videos that support the **NCTM Focal Points and Focal Connections**. For more information, visit glencoe.com.

Model Lessons   Instructional Strategies

Lesson Planner

Objective   Understand and model integers.

Vocabulary   integer, negative number, opposites, positive number, whole numbers

Materials/Manipulatives   number lines, rulers, algebra tiles, thermometers, counters

Chapter Resource Masters

- [CRM] Vocabulary and English Language Development (p. A4)
- [CRM] Skills Practice (p. A5)
- [CRM] Problem-Solving Practice (p. A6)
- [CRM] Homework Practice (p. A7)

① Introduce

Vocabulary

Understanding Terms   Explain that −5 is read "negative 5" not "minus 5." Minus indicates the operation of subtraction, and negative indicates a number less than 0.

② Teach

Key Concept

Foundational Skills and Concepts   After students have read through the Key Concept box, have them try these exercises.

I. Write the opposite of each number.

2. Circle the negative integers in the group:

3. Name one whole number that is neither positive nor negative. zero

---

KEY Concept

Whole numbers are zero and the counting numbers.

Opposites are numbers the same distance from zero, but in the opposite direction. For example, the opposite of 5 is −5.

−5 −4 −3 −2 −1 0 1 2 3 4 5
5 to the left of 0   5 to the right of 0

Integers are whole numbers and their opposites, such as 1 and −1, 15 and −15.

Positive numbers are numbers that are greater than zero.
Negative numbers are numbers that are less than zero.

VOCABULARY

integer
the whole numbers and their opposites
Example: ...−3, −2, −1, 0, 1, 2, 3,...

negative number
a number less than zero

opposites
numbers that are the same distance from zero in opposite directions

positive number
a number that is greater than zero

whole numbers
the set of all counting numbers and zero

The number zero is neither positive nor negative.

Example 1

Use <, =, or > to compare −2 and 2.

1. Graph both numbers on the number line.

−5 −4 −3 −2 −1 0 1 2 3 4 5

2. The number farther to the right is 2, so it is the greater number.

3. Write a comparison statement. Since −2 is less than 2, you need to use the *less than* symbol. **−2 < 2**

YOUR TURN!

Use <, =, or > to compare −5 and 0.

1. Graph both numbers on the number line.

−5 −4 −3 −2 −1 0 1 2 3 4 5

2. The number farther to the right is __0__, so it is the greater number.

3. Write a comparison statement. 0 __>__ −5

Additional *Example 1*

Use <, =, or > to compare −4 and −1.

I. Graph both numbers on the number line.

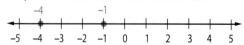

−5 −4 −3 −2 −1 0 1 2 3 4 5

2. The number farther to the right is −1, so it is the greater number.

3. Write a comparison statement. Since −4 is less than −1, you need to use the "less than" symbol. −4 < −1

Example 2

Graph the integers −4, 3, 0, 5, and −2 on a number line. Then write them in order from least to greatest.

1. On the number line, place a dot at each of the numbers.

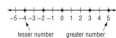

lesser number   greater number

2. Write the graphed numbers in order as they appear from left to right. −4, −2, 0, 3, 5

YOUR TURN!

Graph the integers −3, 2, 1, −5, and −1 on a number line. Then write them in order from least to greatest.

1. On the number line, place a dot at _____ −3, 2, 1, −5, and −1 _____.

−5 −4 −3 −2 −1 0 1 2 3 4 5

2. The numbers in order from least to greatest (as they appear from left to right) are
   −5, −3, −1, 1, 2 .

Example 3

Write an integer to represent the sentence.

"A reef-building coral is found 93 feet below sea level."

1. Underline the key words.

2. Decide if the number is positive or negative.
   negative

   Imagine a number line that is vertical instead of horizontal. Sea level is "0." Below sea level is negative. Above sea level is positive.

3. Write the integer. −93

YOUR TURN!

Write an integer to represent the sentence.

"The temperature in Kansas City one February day is 58°F."

1. Underline key words.

2. Decide if the number is positive or negative. positive

   Imagine a number line that is vertical instead of horizontal. Temperatures above 0°F are positive. Temperatures below 0°F are negative.

3. Write the integer. 58

GO ON

Lesson 1-1 Model Integers **5**

Additional *Example 2*

Graph the integers −5, 0, −3, and 2 on a number line. Then write them in order from least to greatest.

1. On the number line, place a dot at each of the numbers.

   −5   −3   0   2

   −5 −4 −3 −2 −1 0 1 2 3 4 5

2. Write the graphed numbers in order as they appear from left to right. −5, −3, 0, 2

Additional *Example 3*

Write an integer to represent the sentence.

"They dug 25 feet below ground level."

1. Underline the key words. 25 feet below ground level

2. Decide if the number is positive or negative. negative
   Imagine a number line that is vertical instead of horizontal. The ground level is 0. Below ground level is negative. Above ground level is positive.

3. Write the integer. −25

Intervention Strategy

Visual/Logical/Interpersonal Learners

Make a Table Have students work in pairs to classify the group of integers in the table below. Students should take turns placing an X in every box that describes the number in each row and providing the opposite. Ask students to practice explaining their selections, using correct vocabulary and clear language. Then challenge students to add to this list with their own numbers. Have pairs exchange lists and complete their classmates' charts. Ask students to check one another's work and explain their classification processes.

Number	Integer	Whole	Positive	Negative	Opposite
−3	X			X	3
5	X	X	X		−5
2	X	X	X		−2
−4	X			X	4
−6	X			X	6

Math Coach Notes

Negative Numbers Using a number line to teach whole numbers and their reflections across 0, students will be able to grasp the concepts of opposites or mirror images. Focusing on this relationship to 0 will help students as they begin to use integer operations and properties.

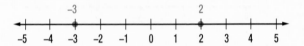

Practice

Using Manipulatives

Number Line When presenting Examples 1 and 2, use concrete materials such as number lines to model positive and negative integers.

```
        -3                    2
 +--+---+---+---+---+---+---+---+---+---+--
 -5  -4  -3  -2  -1   0   1   2   3   4   5
```

Ruler Use a ruler as a number line to demonstrate moving left and right to model lesser and greater positive integers.

Algebra Tiles Use red and yellow algebra tiles to represent negative and positive integers.

On-Hand Manipulatives Use two types of everyday objects as counters, such as beans and coins. Beans could represent negative integers, while coins represent positive integers.

Math Coach Notes

Strategies

1. Begin this lesson by discussing the different kinds of numbers using the vocabulary terms *integers*, *positive*, *negative*, *whole numbers*, and *opposites*. Ask volunteers to give examples of each kind of number. Use nonexamples in the discussion to reinforce correct vocabulary usage and clear language.

2. Discuss real-world examples of integers in students' everyday lives. Ask students to brainstorm examples of when they would use each kind of number in their everyday routines.

Who is Correct?

Write −8, 7, 6, and −5 in order from least to greatest.

Circle correct answers. Cross out incorrect answers.

▶ Guided Practice

Write <, =, or > in each circle to make a true statement.

1. 3 ⊝ 4   3 < 4
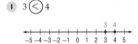

2. −6 ⊝ −7   −6 > −7

3. −1 ⊝ 0   −1 < 0
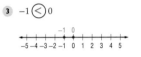

4. −3 ⊝ 1 ⊝ 3   −3 < 1 < 3

Step by Step Practice

5. Use a number line to compare the integers 6, −3, 10, −8, 1. Write the integers from least to greatest.

Step 1 Graph the numbers on the number line.

Step 2 What number is farthest to the left? __−8__

Step 3 Write the numbers in order.

__−8, −3, 1, 6, 10__

Who is Correct?
Diagnostic Teaching

- Omari's work is incorrect. She wrote the numbers in order from least to greatest, not considering the negative signs.

- Marisol's work is correct. The numbers are ordered correctly.

- Renée's work is incorrect. −8 is less than −5.

Remind students that the numbers that are farther left on the number line are less in value.

Graph the integers on a number line. Then write them in order from least to greatest.

6 5, −2, 1, 4, −4

_____−4, −2, 1, 4, 5_____

7 3, −5, 2, −2, 4

_____−5, −2, 2, 3, 4_____

8 2, −5, 0, 1, −3

_____−5, −3, 0, 1, 2_____

9 4, −2, 0, 2, −4

_____−4, −2, 0, 2, 4_____

Step by Step Problem-Solving Practice

Solve.

10 **WEATHER**   The temperature in Butte, Montana one morning was 7°F (Fahrenheit). The temperature at noon was 19°F. By evening, the temperature was −8°F. What was the lowest temperature that day?

Problem-Solving Strategies
☑ Draw a diagram.
☐ Use logical reasoning.
☐ Make a table.
☐ Solve a simpler problem.
☐ Work backward.

Understand	Read the problem. Write what you know. The temperature began at __7°F__. Then it was __19°F__. By evening, the temperature was __−8°F__.
Plan	Pick a strategy. One strategy is to draw a diagram. Make a line to represent a thermometer. Mark the 0. Then mark it in 2-degree increments.
Solve	Begin at 7°F. Then mark 19°F and −8°F. The lowest temperature that day was __−8°F__.
Check	Does the answer make sense? Look over your solution. Did you answer the question?

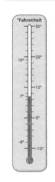

  GO ON

English Learner Strategy

Guiding Questions   Write −3, 4, 0, −1, and 2 on the board. Then ask the following questions.

- Which numbers are less than zero? What is the name of the symbol that tells you these numbers are less?

- Read the numbers out loud. Find each one on a number line.

- Explain how to compare two of the numbers. Which one is greater?

- Use appropriate terms such as *positive number*, *negative number*, *zero*, *whole number*, and *integer* to identify each of the numbers.

- Explain how to write the numbers in order from least to greatest. Use the correct vocabulary terms and clear language in your explanation.

Intervention Strategy   Visual Learners

Thermometers   Have students discuss the concept of temperature and how to compare two temperatures to determine which is colder. Ask students whether 5°F or 10°F is colder. Ask students whether −4°F or 2°F is colder. Have them explain their reasoning. Then have students tell whether −12°F or −8°F is colder. Include some Celsius temperatures for students that relate better to Celsius. Show students these temperatures on a drawing of a thermometer. Relate the drawing to a number line.

Are They Getting It? ?

Check students' understanding of integers by writing these problems on the board. Ask students to point out wrong answers and explain why they are wrong.

1. −5 is greater than −3. This is incorrect. −5 is farther left than −3 on a number line, so −3 is greater than −5.

2. Nick climbed 12 feet down the mountain. This means he was −12 feet from where he began. This is correct.

3. Positive numbers include 2, 8, −4, 6, and −10. This is incorrect. Positive numbers are numbers greater than 0, so −4 and −10 are not positive numbers.

Odd/Even Assignments

Exercises 14–40 are structured so that students practice the same concepts whether they are assigned the odd or even problems.

In-Class Assignment

Have students complete Exercises 14, 20, 23, 28, 32, 36, and 44 to ensure that they understand the concept.

---

11 **SCUBA DIVING**   When Isaac went scuba diving he saw a clown fish at 42 feet below the surface. What integer represents this depth?

Check off each step.

✔ Understand: I underlined key words.

✔ Plan: To solve the problem, I will __draw a diagram__.

✔ Solve: The answer is __Isaac was 42 feet below sea level, or –42.__

✔ Check: I checked my answer by __reviewing the solution__.

12 **BUDGETS**   Martha's Moving, Inc. is $274 below their budget for this month. What integer represents this amount of money?
__–$274__

13 **Reflect**   How does the scale on a thermometer help you understand positive and negative integers?

__The scale on a thermometer is often a vertical version of a number line.__

__Temperatures above 0° represent positive integers, and temperatures below 0°__

__represent negative integers.__

▶ Skills, Concepts, and Problem Solving

Use <, =, or > to compare each pair of numbers.

14 13 and 0

__13 > 0__

15 0 and –4

__0 > –4__

16 25 and –25

__25 > –25__

17 –9 and –7

__–9 < –7__

18 14 and –160

__14 > –160__

19 –981 and 992

__–981 < 992__

20 9 ⟩ 0 ⟩ –3

21 –40 ⟨ 40 ⟩ –4

Intervention Strategy   Linguistic/Auditory

Write Integer Examples   Ask students to write five sentences that represent integers. Model two examples on the board such as, *I borrowed 8 dollars from my brother* or *He ran 63 yards to make the touchdown.* Have students include the integer that each sentence represents. Collect their examples and read a few throughout the class period. Invite student volunteers to the board to write the integer represented in the sentence. Ask volunteers to show how the integer matches the situation. Challenge more proficient students to use several integers in one sentence.

Graph the integers on a number line. Then write them in order from least to greatest.

22 −3, −1, 5, 0, −5

−5, −3, −1, 0, 5

23 8, −4, 5, −1, 9

−4, −1, 5, 8, 9

24 10, −3, −2, 4, −6

−6, −3, −2, 4, 10

25 −9, 8, −5, 2, 1

−9, −5, 1, 2, 8

26 3, −4, −5, 7, −2

−5, −4, −2, 3, 7

27 9, −4, −7, −9, 1

−9, −7, −4, 1, 9

Write the integers from least to greatest.

28 64, −52, 18, −53, −16

−53, −52, −16, 18, 64

29 −55, 91, −102, 87, 78

−102, −55, 78, 87, 91

30 −47, 41, 74, 17, −71

−71, −47, 17, 41, 74

31 109, −901, 91, −19, 0

−901, −19, 0, 91, 109

Write the integers from greatest to least.

32 −256, −24, 182, −346, 265

265, 182, −24, −256, −346

33 −802, 805, −806, −808, 809

809, 805, −802, −806, −808

34 1,024; −565; 4,506; −5,656

4,506; 1,024; −565; −5,656

35 2,262; −262; −2,062; 6,262

6,262; 2,262; −262; −2,062

GO ON

Visual/ Naturalist/ Interpersonal Learners

Intervention Strategy

Integer Models   Divide students into small groups. Assign each group a different integer. Have each group create as many examples of their integer as possible. Encourage students to use concrete materials, drawings, sentences, and anything in their environment to demonstrate their numbers. Have students share their representations with the class. Ask that each member of each group explain at least one of their models.

Math Coach Notes

Study Tip   Encourage students to draw or use a number line to visualize integers' relationships to zero, especially when comparing two negative numbers. Students will be more comfortable with positive integers, so reinforce using concrete materials when working with negative integers.

Math Challenge

Plot Points   Write the numbers 1–13 with a red marker on separate note cards. Then write the same numbers on different note cards with a black marker. The cards with red numbers will represent negative integers, and the cards with black numbers will represent positive integers. Have students draw a number line and use the note cards to practice plotting positive and negative numbers. Shuffle two sets of cards together. Have students draw a card and plot it on their number lines. Continue until all of the numbers are plotted. Challenge more proficient students to include numbers greater than 13.

Exercise 39 If students struggle with Exercise 39, encourage them to use concrete materials such as number lines or money manipulatives to visualize the concept of a negative dollar amount. Relate negative money to borrowing $10 from a friend and then repaying him when you get some money. Show these relationships on a number line, moving left to represent negative numbers and moving right to represent positive numbers.

(4) Assess

See It, Do It, Say It, Write It

Step 1 Write several integers on the board. Ask student volunteers to identify and classify each number using correct vocabulary terms and clear language.

Step 2 Ask students to model the problems using manipulatives or drawings.

Step 3 Write another set of integers on the board. Have students work in pairs. Tell them to write a sentence to represent each integer. It should include the integer and a model that represents the situation. Have students share their sentences in small groups or with the class.

Looking Ahead: Pre-teach

Add Integers In the next lesson, students will learn how to add integers. Use a number line to teach moving to the right as adding a positive and moving to the left as adding a negative.

Example

Find the sum of −2 and 3.

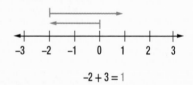

−2 + 3 = 1

Have students find the sum of each pair of integers using a number line.

1. −4 and 2 −2

2. 5 and −2 3

3. −3 and 3 0

Solve.

36 FOOTBALL In a football game, players on the offensive team are not allowed to move before the ball is snapped. If this happens the team is given a five-yard penalty. What integer represents this penalty when a team breaks the rules?

___−5___

37 AWARDS Carlos has worked for Louis Laboratories for 25 years. Last week, he received a service award for $250 dollars. What integer represents this award?

___250___

38 SCHOLARSHIPS Last year, Investment in Education, Inc. gave a $1,500 scholarship to a student in Chicago, Illinois. What integer represents the scholarship that Investment in Education provided?

___−1,500___

39 CHECKING ACCOUNTS Mr. Fuentes deposited $457 into his checking account on Saturday. What integer represents the deposit?

___457___

40 WEATHER The low temperature in Fairbanks, Alaska on February 1 was 13° below zero. What integer represents the temperature?

___−13___

Vocabulary Check **Write the vocabulary word that completes each sentence.**

41 ___Integers___ are the whole numbers and their opposites.

42 A(n) ___positive___ number is a number greater than 0.

43 Numbers that are the same distance from 0 on a number line are ___opposite___ integers.

44 Writing in Math Explain how to find the opposite of −6.

___Sample answer: First, find −6 on a number line. It is 6 places to the left of 0 on___
___the number line. To find the opposite, find the point that is 6 places to the right___
___(in the opposite direction) of 0 on the number line. The opposite of −6 is 6.___

STOP

Ticket Out the Door

Write the Order Write the following on the board: 24, −22, 15, 19, −16, 14. Ask students to write the numbers in order from least to greatest. Have them explain how they determined the order. Students will hand in their papers as they exit the classroom. −22, −16, 14, 15, 19, 24

KEY Concept

The answer to an addition problem is called the **sum**.

To add positive numbers on a number line, begin at the *first* number. Move right the *same* number of spaces as the *second* number.

To add negative numbers on a number line, begin at the *first* number. Move left the same number of spaces as the second number.

Example: $-4 + (-2)$

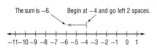

The sum is -6.   Begin at -4 and go left 2 spaces.

$-11\ -10\ -9\ -8\ -7\ -6\ -5\ -4\ -3\ -2\ -1\ \ 0\ \ 1$

The sum of an integer and its opposite is always zero. This is the **Inverse Property of Addition**.

$$17 + (-17) = 0 \text{ or } (-17) + 17 = 0$$

VOCABULARY

Commutative Property of Addition
the order in which two numbers are added does not change the sum
Example: $12 + 15 = 15 + 12$

Inverse Property of Addition
for any number, the sum of that number and its opposite is zero

The **Commutative Property of Addition** also applies when adding integers.

Example 1

What is the opposite of -6? Write an addition sentence to show the Inverse Property of Addition.

1. Graph the number. What number is the same distance from zero as -6? 6

$-10\ -8\ -6\ -4\ -2\ \ 0\ \ 2\ \ 4\ \ 6\ \ 8\ \ 10$

2. Write an example of the inverse property using the two numbers.

$-6 + 6 = 0$

YOUR TURN!

What is the opposite of 4? Write an addition sentence to show the Inverse Property of Addition.

1. Graph the number. What number is the same distance from zero as 4? __-4__

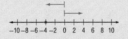

$-10\ -8\ -6\ -4\ -2\ \ 0\ \ 2\ \ 4\ \ 6\ \ 8\ \ 10$

2. Write an example of the inverse property using the two numbers.

$4 + \underline{(-4)} = 0$

Additional *Example 1*

What is the opposite of -5? Write an addition sentence to show the Inverse Property of Addition.

$-5\ -4\ -3\ -2\ -1\ \ 0\ \ 1\ \ 2\ \ 3\ \ 4\ \ 5$

1. Graph the number. What number is the same distance from zero as -5? 5

2. Write an example of the inverse property using the two numbers. $-5 + 5 = 0$

Lesson Notes

Lesson Planner

Objective   Find the sum of integers.

Vocabulary   Commutative Property of Addition , Inverse Property of Addition

Materials/Manipulatives   number lines, algebra tiles, counters, thermometers

Chapter Resource Masters

- CRM Vocabulary and English Language Development (p. A8)
- CRM Skills Practice (p. A9)
- CRM Problem-Solving Practice (p. A10)
- CRM Homework Practice (p. A11)

---

① Introduce

Vocabulary

Addition Properties   Write $-5 + 3 = ?$ on the board. Ask students to determine the *sum* and *property* represented by the sentence. Model this sentence on a number line. Have students discuss and decide if this is an example of *opposites*. Ask a volunteer to explain why this is not an example of the Inverse Property of Addition. Follow this process with several more addition expressions.

---

② Teach

Key Concept

Foundational Skills and Concepts   After students have read through the Key Concept box, have them try these exercises.

1. Which property does $-4 + 4 = 0$ demonstrate?
   Inverse Property of Addition

2. When adding two negative integers with a number line, which direction should you move? left

Find the sum of −7 and 3. Use algebra tiles.

I. Use 7 negative tiles to represent the first number.

2. Use 3 positive tiles to represent the second number.

3. A zero pair is made up of 1 positive tile and 1 negative tile. You can make 3 zero pairs.

4. There are 4 negative tiles left.

5. −7 + 3 = −4

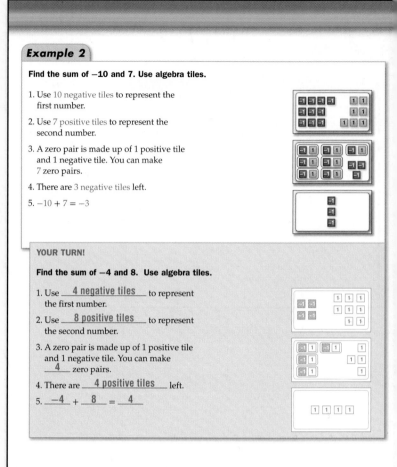

Example 2

Find the sum of −10 and 7. Use algebra tiles.

1. Use 10 negative tiles to represent the first number.

2. Use 7 positive tiles to represent the second number.

3. A zero pair is made up of 1 positive tile and 1 negative tile. You can make 7 zero pairs.

4. There are 3 negative tiles left.

5. −10 + 7 = −3

YOUR TURN!

Find the sum of −4 and 8. Use algebra tiles.

1. Use ___4 negative tiles___ to represent the first number.

2. Use ___8 positive tiles___ to represent the second number.

3. A zero pair is made up of 1 positive tile and 1 negative tile. You can make ___4___ zero pairs.

4. There are ___4 positive tiles___ left.

5. ___−4___ + ___8___ = ___4___

Math Coach Notes

Signs   As students work through Example 2, remind them that the sign of the answer will be the sign of the tiles of which you have the most.

Example: −5 + 3

You have five negative (red) tiles and three positive (yellow) tiles. You have more negative tiles. The answer will have a negative sign.

Number Properties   Reteaching and reinforcing the Associative, Commutative, and Distributive properties will enable students to extend and apply arithmetic processes for counting numbers to integers. If students are familiar and comfortable with these properties and processes for counting numbers, applying them to integers, fractions, and decimals will be a smoother transition.

Intervention Strategy

Visual/Kinesthetic/ Naturalist Learners

Visual Integers   Dedicate one bulletin board or area for students to create visual references for integers. Ask students to work in groups to develop visual examples of positive and negative integers. Encourage students to create displays such as an elevator that moves to floors above and below ground inside a tall building, a score sheet for a golf game that shows the putts per hole above and below par, a diagram of football plays illustrating yardage losses and gains, and so on. Tell students to use real-world situations that model addition situations with integers. Have each group write an explanation for their displays and present them. Keep the displays up for students to reference throughout the chapter.

Example 3

Find the sum of −8 and 6. Use a number line.

1. Graph the first number.

2. From the first number, go right on the number line.

$$-10\ -8\ -6\ -4\ -2\ \ 0\ \ 2\ \ 4\ \ 6\ \ 8\ \ 10$$

3. You are at −2 on the number line.

4. Write the sum. $-8 + 6 = -2$

YOUR TURN!

Find the sum of −4 and 10. Use the number line.

1. Graph the first number.

2. From the first number, go __right__ on the number line.

$$-10\ -8\ -6\ -4\ -2\ \ 0\ \ 2\ \ 4\ \ 6\ \ 8\ \ 10$$

3. You are at __6__ on the number line.

4. Write the sum. $-4 + 10 =$ __6__

Who is Correct?

Find the sum of 9 and −2.

Michael
$9 + (-2) = -7$

Sareeta
$9 + (-2) = 7$

Bianca
$9 + (-2) = -11$

Circle correct answer(s). Cross out incorrect answer(s).

 Guided Practice

What is the opposite of each number? Write an addition sentence to show the Inverse Property of Addition.

1. −3 ___ $3; -3 + 3 = 0$

2. 11 ___ $-11; 11 + (-11) = 0$

3. 25 ___ $-25; 25 + (-25) = 0$

4. −62 ___ $62; -62 + 62 = 0$

5. 97 ___ $-97; 97 + (-97) = 0$

6. 201 ___ $-201; 201 + (-201) = 0$

 GO ON

Who is Correct?
Diagnostic Teaching

• Michael's work is incorrect. He moved in the opposite direction for negative and positive numbers.

• Sareeta's work is correct. She added correctly.

• Bianca's work is incorrect. She added the digits without regard to the signs.

Remind students to look carefully at the signs of both numbers.

 Additional **Example 3**

Find the sum of −3 and 5. Use a number line.

1. Graph the first number.

$$-4\ -3\ -2\ -1\ \ 0\ \ 1\ \ 2\ \ 3\ \ 4$$

2. From the first number, go right on the number line.

3. You are at 2 on the number line.

4. Write the sum. $-3 + 5 = 2$

---

③ Practice

Using Manipulatives

Algebra Tiles When presenting the addition of integers, use concrete materials such as algebra tiles to model positive and negative integers.

On-Hand Manipulatives Use two types of everyday objects as counters, such as beans and coins. Beans could represent negative integers, while coins represent positive integers.

Thermometer Use a thermometer that shows only one measurement scale, such as Fahrenheit, to help students visualize positive and negative temperatures and temperature changes during the day.

Common Error *Alert*

Add Integers with Visual Aids   If students are having difficulty understanding how to add integers, use concrete models to represent the relationships.

Number Line

$$-2 + (-3) = -5$$

Integers Chart

−25	−24	−23	−22	−21	−20	−19	−18	−17	−16
−15	−14	−13	−12	−11	−10	−9	−8	−7	−6
−5	−4	−3	−2	−1	0	1	2	3	4
5	6	7	8	9	10	11	12	13	14
15	16	17	18	19	20	21	22	23	24
25									

$$-6 + 10 = 4$$

Thermometer

$$-5 + 25 = 20$$

Math Coach Notes

Strategies

1. Begin this lesson by reviewing the Inverse and Commutative Properties of Addition using counting numbers. Use nonexamples in the discussion to reinforce correct vocabulary usage and clear language. Slowly progress to include negative integers in the examples.

2. Discuss real-world examples of when students would add positive and negative integers in their everyday lives. Brainstorm situations as a whole group, providing models whenever possible.

Common Error *Alert*

Add Two Negative Numbers   If students have difficulty with adding two negative numbers, they might be confused about which way to move on the number line. Reinforce that negative numbers always move left on a number line, even during addition. Use concrete materials such as a number line to model examples.

Find each sum. Use algebra tiles.

7 $8 + (-1) = $ _____7_____

8 $7 + (-4) = $ _____3_____

9 $-7 + 9 = $ _____2_____

10 $-3 + (-6) = $ _____−9_____

Step *by* Step **Practice**

11 Find the sum of 0 and −6. Use the number line.

Step 1 Graph the first number.

Step 2 From the first number, move _____left_____.

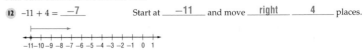

Step 3 Where are you on the number line?
_____−6_____

Step 4 Write the sum. ___$0 + (-6) = -6$___

Find each sum. Use the number line.

12 $-11 + 4 = $ ___−7___   Start at ___−11___ and move ___right___ ___4___ places.

13 $-3 + (-6) = $ ___−9___

14 $-2 + (-3) = $ ___−5___

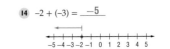

Are They Getting It? **?**

Check students' understanding of adding integers by writing these problems on the board. Have students state which are correct and which are not correct. Encourage them to use drawings or examples in their explanations.

1. $-10 + 3 = 7$ This is incorrect. $-10 + 3 = -7$

2. The number line shows $4 + (-5) = -9$. This is incorrect. The number line shows $4 + (-5) = -1$.

3. The sum of −8 and −4 is −12. This is correct.

Find each sum.

15 $-4 + (-5) = $ ___−9___ **16** $10 + (-3) = $ ___7___

17 $-7 + (-1) = $ ___−8___ **18** $15 + (-5) = $ ___10___

19 $-17 + (-11) = $ ___−28___ **20** $25 + (-15) = $ ___10___

Step by Step *Problem-Solving Practice*

Solve.

Problem-Solving Strategies
- ☑ Draw a picture.
- ☐ Use logical reasoning.
- ☐ Make a table.
- ☐ Solve a simpler problem.
- ☐ Work backward.

21 ELEVATION Osceola County has the highest point of elevation in the state of Iowa. This point is approximately 500 meters above sea level. One point in Lee County, Iowa has the lowest elevation in the state. There is approximately 350 meters difference between the two points. What is the elevation of the lowest point in Iowa?

Understand Read the problem. Write what you know.

The highest point is at an elevation of ___500 meters___.

The difference between the points is ___350 meters___.

Plan Pick a strategy. One strategy is to draw a picture.

Solve Begin at 500 meters and go down 350 meters.
___$500 + (-350) = 150$ meters___

Check Does the answer make sense? Look over your solution. Did you answer the question?

22 VENDING MACHINES Hanako puts 12 quarters into a vending machine. She uses $2.25 of her credit. How much credit does she have left?

Check off each step.

___✔___ Understand: I underlined key words.

___✔___ Plan: To solve the problem I will ___draw a diagram___

___✔___ Solve: The answer is ___$3.00 + (-$2.25) = $0.75___

___✔___ Check: I checked my answer by ___rereading the question___

GO ON ➡

Intervention Strategy — Kinesthetic/Visual Learners

Student Integers Write several addition sentences on the board. Divide students randomly into two groups. Give each student a blank index card. One group should label their cards with a positive (+) sign to represent the positive numbers. The second group should label their cards with a negative (−) sign. Ask a student volunteer to choose a sentence from the board to model using the other students as the manipulatives. For example, a volunteer gathers 6 positive students and 3 negative students. He or she pairs each positive student with a negative student and shows the remaining students as the sum. The class would have to decide which sentence from the board is being modeled. After the sentences on the board have all been modeled, ask students to create their own examples and have their classmates determine the addition problems from the models the class creates.

⚠ Common Error *Alert*

Multi-Step Problems If students struggle with Exercises 21–23, encourage them to make a drawing of, or act out, the situations. When a word problem presents multiple pieces of data, students may become overwhelmed by the information. Encourage them to break the information down into smaller parts and focus on one part at a time. Ask students to act out the situation or draw a diagram, verbally explaining each piece of the problem. Have students determine how each new piece of information changes the status of the situation and brings them to the solution. Once they have an answer, have them reread the problem to evaluate the reasonableness and completeness of their answer.

Intervention Strategy — Auditory/Logical Learners

Explanations Ask students to practice explaining how to model adding integers to one another. Working in pairs, have each student use correct terms and clear language to model an addition problem and find its sum. Students can use any concrete materials for the models, including algebra tiles, number lines, integer charts, thermometers, or drawings. For proficient learners, challenge the pairs to make errors during the explanations to see if the listeners can catch the mistakes.

Odd/Even Assignments

Exercises 25–42 are structured so that students practice the same concepts whether they are assigned the odd or even problems.

In-Class Assignment

Have students complete Exercises 25, 29, 31, 35, 41, and 44 to ensure that they understand the concept.

Math Coach Notes

Study Tip   Encourage students to mark negative numbers in a way that will alert them to the negative sign. One example is to place parentheses around the negative number in an addition sentence so the negative sign is not overlooked during calculations.

---

23 STOCKS   Reynaldo has stock in the Capital Calendar Company. At the beginning of the day the price per share was $42.50. At the end of the day, the price per share had gone down by $5.00. What was the price per share at the end of the day?

$$\underline{\$42.50 + (-\$5.00) = \$37.50}$$

24 Reflect   Write and solve two addition sentences using positive and negative integers to show the Inverse Property of Addition. Explain your answer.

Sample answer: $5 + (-2) = 3$ and $-2 + 5 = 3$; The order of the addends

5 and –2 is not important. The sum is 3 using either order.

 Skills, Concepts, and Problem Solving

What is the opposite of each number? Write an addition sentence to show the Inverse Property of Addition.

25 -9 $9; -9 + 9 = 0$

26 16 $-16; 16 + (-16) = 0$

27 59 $-59; 59 + (-59) = 0$

28 -73 $73; -73 + 73 = 0$

Find each sum. Use algebra tiles.

29 $3 + (-6) = \underline{-3}$

30 $-4 + 6 = \underline{2}$

Find each sum. Use the number line.

31 $-2 + 3 = \underline{1}$

32 $3 + (-3) = \underline{0}$

33 $4 + (-10) = \underline{-6}$

34 $-6 + (-2) = \underline{-8}$

Math Challenge

Card Addition   Challenge students to use cards to practice adding integers. Write ten numbers between 1 and 100 in red marker on separate note cards. Then write the same numbers in black marker on a separate set of note cards. Tell students the cards with red numbers represent negative numbers and the cards with black numbers represent positive numbers. Have students shuffle cards and draw two cards to add together. Ask students to write the addition sentence and find the sum. Play until all the cards have been drawn from the deck. For more proficient students, challenge them to add cards to the deck with numbers greater than 100, and include them in the deck for their addition sentences.

Find each sum.

35 $28 + (-12) =$ ___16___

36 $-46 + (-35) =$ ___-81___

37 $-42 + 41 =$ ___-1___

38 $-37 + (-7) =$ ___-44___

39 $-52 + 12 =$ ___-40___

40 $-105 + 80 =$ ___-25___

41 TRAVEL An airplane has 66 passengers traveling from Columbus, Ohio to Atlanta, Georgia. There are 6 first-class passengers. The first-class passengers exit the airplane first. How many people remain on the airplane?

$66 + (-6) = 60$; 60 passengers remain on the airplane.

42 SPORTING EVENTS Christopher is attending a basketball game. He walked up to row 32 to buy a bag of peanuts for his sister. Christopher walked down 15 rows to arrive at his seat. In what row is Christopher's seat?

$32 + (-15) = 17$; His seat is in row 17.

Vocabulary Check **Write the vocabulary word that completes the sentence.**

43 The property that states that the order in which numbers are added does not affect the sum is the _Commutative Property of Addition_.

44 Writing in Math Explain how to use the number line to find the sum of −7 and −3.

$-10\ -9\ -8\ -7\ -6\ -5\ -4\ -3\ -2\ -1\ \ 0$

Start at −7. Go to the left 3 spaces to add −3. The answer is −10.

 Spiral Review

Write the integers from least to greatest. (Lesson 1-1, p. 4)

45 −18, −10, 20, 14, −13 _−18, −13, −10, 14, 20_

46 68, −42, 91, −19, 35 _−42, −19, 35, 68, 91_

47 FINANCES You spend $37. What integer represents your money? _−37_

Ticket Out the Door

Solve and Explain Write the following on the board.

1. $-32 + 48 =$ ____ 16

2. $67 + -59 =$ ____ 8

3. $-81 + -29 =$ ____ −110

Ask students to solve each problem and provide an explanation proving that their answers are correct. Students will hand in their papers as they exit the classroom.

Assess

See It, Do It, Say It, Write It

Step 1 Write several integers on the board. Ask students to write three addition sentences using numbers from the list. Tell them to determine the sum for each of their sentences.

Step 2 Ask students to model the problems using manipulatives or drawings.

Step 3 Write an addition sentence using negative integers on the board. Have students work in pairs. Tell them to write a word problem to represent the addition sentence. Include the solution and a model that represents the situation. Have students share their word problems in small groups or with the class.

Looking Ahead: Pre-teach

Subtract Integers In the next lesson, students will learn how to subtract integers. Subtraction can be defined as adding the opposite.

Example

Find the difference of 4 and 6.

4 − 6 is the same as 4 + (−6). Find the sum.

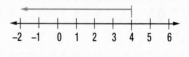
−2 −1 0 1 2 3 4 5 6

$4 + (-6) = -2$

Have students find the difference of each pair of integers. Write each as a sentence showing an addition of the opposite.

1. −4 and 2 $-4 - 2 = -4 + (-2) = -6$

2. 3 and −5 $3 - (-5) = 3 + (5) = 8$

3. −8 and −7 $-8 - (-7) = -8 + (7) = -1$

Progress Check 1

Formative Assessment

Use the Progress Check to assess students' mastery of the previous lessons. Have students review the lesson indicated for the problems they answered incorrectly.

Odd/Even Assignments

Exercises are structured so that students practice the same concepts whether they are assigned the odd or even problems.

⚠ Common Error *Alert*

Use Diagrams   Students should try to make a transition between using a diagram to solve the problems to solving the problems abstractly.

Exercise 4   If students look at Exercise 4 and see the 15 and the 10 (not taking into account the negative signs) and select −15 as the greater of the two numbers, they can refer to a number line to visualize the answer.

Exercises 12 and 13   Encourage the students to break down the information in Exercise 12 into pieces. Ask: Does the word "burn" indicate negative or positive? Encourage students to draw a diagram for Exercise 13.

Chapter 1   **Progress Check 1** (Lessons 1-1 and 1-2)

Graph the integers on a number line. Then write them in order from least to greatest.

1   −13, −2, 3, −3 __−13, −3, −2, 3__

2   −2, 6, 2, −5, 0 __−5, −2, 0, 2, 6__

Write <, =, or > in each circle to make a true statement.

3   −6 (<) 0

4   10 (>) −15

5   2 (>) −12

What is the opposite of each number? Use it to show the Inverse Property of Addition.

6   3 __(−3); 3 + (−3) = 0__

7   −18 __18; (−18) + 18 = 0__

Find each sum. Use algebra tiles.

8   −5 + (−3) = __−8__

9   6 + (−9) = __−3__

Find each sum. Use the number line.

10   −6 + (−5) = __−11__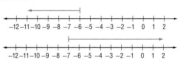

11   −7 + 9 = __2__

Solve.

12   **CALORIES**   Every 10 steps burns 5 Calories. Every taco adds 185 Calories. If Beth ate 1 taco and took 100 steps, how many calories would she have gained or lost?
__gained 135 Calories or lost −135 calories__

13   **FOOTBALL**   Matthew's team was at their own 35-yard line during a football game. They lost 15 yards. What yard line were they on for the next play?
__20-yard line__

Data-Driven Decision Making

Students missing Exercises . . .	Have trouble with . . .	Should review and practice . . .
1–2	graphing integers on a number line, then writing them in order from least to greatest.	SSG Lesson 1-1, p. 4 CRM Skills Practice, p. A5
3–5	comparing pairs of integers.	SSG Lesson 1-1, p. 4 CRM Skills Practice, p. A5
6–7	stating opposites and showing the Inverse Property of Addition.	SSG Lesson 1-2, p. 11 CRM Skills Practice, p. A9
8–11	using models to find sums.	SSG Lesson 1-2, p. 11 CRM Skills Practice, p. A9
12–13	solving word problems involving sums of integers.	CRM Problem Solving Practice, pp. A6 and A10

Subtract Integers

KEY Concept

Subtraction can be defined as adding the **opposite** of a number.

$3 - 7$ can be written as the addition expression $3 + (-7)$.

You can use the number line to show the sum.

$$-5\;-4\;-3\;-2\;-1\quad 0\quad 1\quad 2\quad 3\quad 4\quad 5$$

Start at the first number. Since the next number is negative, move to the *left* 7 places. The sum is –4.

The **absolute value** of a number is the distance the number is from zero. The symbol for absolute value of the number x is $|x|$.

$$-5\;-4\;-3\;-2\;-1\quad 0\quad 1\quad 2\quad 3\quad 4\quad 5$$

$|-4| = 4$ and $|4| = 4$

Finding the absolute value of numbers can help you when adding and subtracting integers.

Subtracting Integers			
Subtraction	Rewritten as Addition	Signs	Answer
$-2 - 6$	$-2 + (-6)$	same	-8
$2 - 6$	$2 + (-6)$	different	-4
$-2 - (-6)$	$-2 + 6$	different	4
$2 - (-6)$	$2 + 6$	same	8

Rewrite subtraction problems as adding the opposite. The rules given above for determining the sign of an answer are used for both addition and subtraction problems.

VOCABULARY

absolute value
the distance between a number and 0 on a number line

opposites
numbers that are the same distance from zero in opposite directions

GO ON

Intervention Strategy

Logical/Linguistic/ Interpersonal

Subtraction Cards   Have students work in pairs or small groups. Write the numbers 1–10 in red marker on separate note cards. Write the same numbers in black marker on a set of different note cards. Tell students the cards with red numbers represent negative numbers and the cards with black numbers represent positive numbers. Have students shuffle the cards, draw two cards, and find their difference. Ask students to write the subtraction sentence and practice explaining how to find the difference. For more proficient students, challenge them to draw three cards and do the subtraction from left to right, adding the opposites as they go.

Lesson Notes

Lesson Planner

Objective   Find the difference of two or more integers.

Vocabulary   absolute value , opposites

Materials/Manipulatives   number lines, algebra tiles, money, thermometers, counters, pattern blocks

Chapter Resource Masters

- CRM Vocabulary and English Language Development (p. A12)
- CRM Skills Practice (p. A13)
- CRM Problem-Solving Practice (p. A14)
- CRM Homework Practice (p. A15)

1 Introduce

Vocabulary

Absolute Value   Draw a number line on the board. Plot two points at –4 and 5. Ask for a student volunteer to determine which *integer* has the greater *absolute value*. Have the volunteer explain why an absolute value is never negative.

2 Teach

Key Concept

Foundational Skills and Concepts   After students have read through the Key Concept box, have them try these exercises.

1. Rewrite $3 - 8$ as an addition expression. $3 + (-8)$

2. Use a number line to show which integer has the greater absolute value: $|-6|$ or $|3|$. $|-6| = 6$ and $|3| = 3$, so -6 has the greater absolute value.

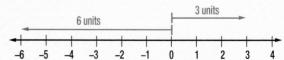

6 units

3 units

$$-6\quad -5\quad -4\quad -3\quad -2\quad -1\quad 0\quad 1\quad 2\quad 3\quad 4$$

Additional *Example 1*

Find the difference of –2 and –5. Use algebra tiles.

1. Write the subtraction expression. $-2 - (-5)$

2. Add the opposite.
Write the addition expression. $-2 + (+5)$

3. Use 2 negative tiles and 5 positive tiles to represent the numbers.

4. You can make 2 zero pairs.

5. There are 3 positive tiles left.

6. Write the difference. $-2 - (-5) = 3$

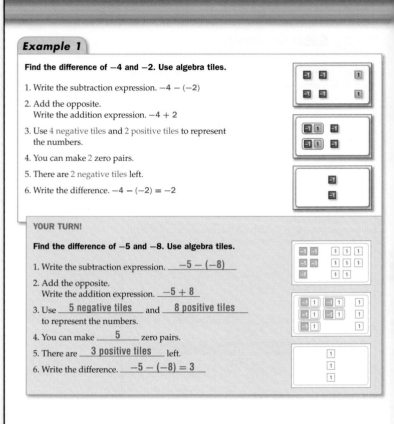

Example 1

Find the difference of –4 and –2. Use algebra tiles.

1. Write the subtraction expression. $-4 - (-2)$

2. Add the opposite.
Write the addition expression. $-4 + 2$

3. Use 4 negative tiles and 2 positive tiles to represent the numbers.

4. You can make 2 zero pairs.

5. There are 2 negative tiles left.

6. Write the difference. $-4 - (-2) = -2$

YOUR TURN!

Find the difference of –5 and –8. Use algebra tiles.

1. Write the subtraction expression. $\underline{-5 - (-8)}$

2. Add the opposite.
Write the addition expression. $\underline{-5 + 8}$

3. Use <u>5 negative tiles</u> and <u>8 positive tiles</u> to represent the numbers.

4. You can make <u>5</u> zero pairs.

5. There are <u>3 positive tiles</u> left.

6. Write the difference. $\underline{-5 - (-8) = 3}$

English Learner Strategy

Guiding Questions Write –8 and 3 on a sheet of paper. Then ask the following questions to ensure that students understand the concept.

- Read these two numbers out loud. Find them on a number line.

- What is the opposite of –8? What is the opposite of 3?

- Which has a greater distance from zero: –8 or 3?

- Use a number line and the absolute value symbol to explain your answer.

- Explain how to find the difference of –8 and 3.

Example 2

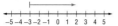

Find the difference of −3 and −5. Use the number line.

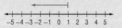

1. Write the subtraction expression.

   −3 − (−5)

2. To subtract integers, add the opposite.
   Write the addition expression.

   −3 + 5

3. Graph the first number.

4. The sign of the second integer is positive.
   Move right on the number line.

5. You are at 2 on the number line.

6. Write the difference. −3 − (−5) = 2

YOUR TURN!

Find the difference of 1 and 4. Use the number line.

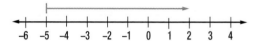

1. Write the subtraction expression.
   <u>   1 − 4   </u>

2. To subtract integers, add the opposite.
   Write the addition expression.
   <u>   1 + (− 4)   </u>

3. Graph the first number.

4. The sign of the second integer is <u>   negative   </u>.
   Move <u> left </u> on the number line.

5. You are at <u> −3 </u> on the number line.

6. Write the difference. <u>   1 − 4 = −3   </u>

GO ON

Find the difference of −5 and −7. Use a number line.

1. Write the subtraction expression. −5 − (−7)

2. To subtract integers, add the opposite.
   Write the addition expression. −5 + 7

3. Graph the first number.

4. The sign of the second integer is positive.
   Move right on the number line.

5. You are at 2 on the number line.

6. Write the difference. −5 − (−7) = 2

Math Coach Notes

Addition in Disguise   Teaching absolute value and opposites with the subtraction of integers helps students recognize subtraction as another form of addition. Modeling 5 − 7 as 5 + (−7) gives students another avenue on which to build connections and gain a broader perspective of number relationships.

⚠ Common Error *Alert*

Absolute Value

If students are having difficulty understanding subtraction and absolute value, use concrete models to represent the relationships.

Show students that subtracting is the same as adding the opposite. Draw or show students the two number lines below.

 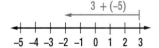

So, 3 − 5 = 3 + (−5).

Additional *Example 3*

Does −9 or 7 have a greater absolute value?

1. −9 is 9 units from 0. So, $|-9| = 9$.

2. 7 is 7 units from 0. So, $|7| = 7$.

3. Which integer has the greater absolute value?
−9

7 units

9 units

$-9\ -8\ -7\ -6\ -5\ -4\ -3\ -2\ -1\ \ 0\ \ 1\ \ 2\ \ 3\ \ 4\ \ 5\ \ 6\ \ 7$

Example 3

Does −5 or 3 have a greater absolute value?

1. −5 is 5 units from 0. So, $|-5| = 5$.

2. 3 is 3 units from 0. So, $|3| = 3$.

3. Which integer has the greater absolute value?
−5

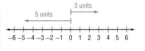

3 units

5 units

$-6\ -5\ -4\ -3\ -2\ -1\ \ 0\ \ 1\ \ 2\ \ 3\ \ 4\ \ 5\ \ 6$

YOUR TURN!

Does 5 or −6 have a greater absolute value?

1. How far is 5 from 0? __5 units__
   So, $|5| =$ __5__.

2. How far is −6 from 0? __6 units__
   So, $|-6| =$ __6__.

3. Which integer has the greater absolute value?
   __−6__

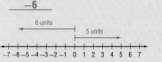

6 units

5 units

$-7\ -6\ -5\ -4\ -3\ -2\ -1\ \ 0\ \ 1\ \ 2\ \ 3\ \ 4\ \ 5\ \ 6\ \ 7$

Who is Correct?

Find the difference of −3 and 5. Use algebra tiles.

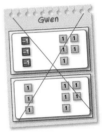

Gwen

Reina

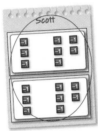

Scott

Circle correct answer(s). Cross out incorrect answer(s).

Who *is Correct?*
Diagnostic Teaching

• Gwen's work is incorrect. She used her algebra tiles incorrectly. She flipped the −3 tiles instead of the +5 tiles.

• Reina's work is incorrect. She set up her algebra tiles incorrectly. She also incorrectly made zero pairs.

• Scott's work is correct.

Remind students to add the opposite of the number after the minus sign.

Guided Practice

Find each difference. Use algebra tiles.

1. $4 - 2 =$ ___2___

2. $-6 - (-4) =$ ___−2___

Step by Step Practice

3. Find the difference of −3 and −6. Use the number line.

   Step 1 Write the subtraction expression. ___$-3 - (-6)$___

   Step 2 To subtract integers, add the opposite.
   Write the addition expression. ___$-3 + 6$___
   This is the new expression.

   Step 3 Graph the first number.

   Step 4 The sign of the second integer is ___positive___.
   Which direction will you go on the
   number line? ___right___

   Step 5 Where are you on the number
   line? ___3___

   Step 6 Write the difference. ___$-3 + 6 = 3$___

Find each difference. Use the number line.

4. $3 - (-5)$ addition sentence: $\dfrac{3}{3} + \dfrac{5}{5}$
   sum: $\dfrac{3}{3} + \dfrac{5}{5} =$ ___8___

5. $4 - (-9) =$ ___13___

6. $-5 - (-7) =$ ___2___

 GO ON

Are They Getting It?

Check students' understanding of subtracting integers by writing these problems on the board. Ask students to point out wrong answers and explain why they are wrong.

1. $-18 - (-6) = -24$

   This is incorrect. $-18 - (-6) = -18 + 6 = -12$

2. $|5|$ has a greater absolute value than $|-7|$.

   This is incorrect. -7 is farther away from 0 than 5, so $|-7|$ has a greater absolute value.

3. The difference of −35 and 15 is −50.

   This is correct.

Using Manipulatives

Algebra Tiles   When presenting the subtraction of integers, use concrete materials such as algebra tiles to model positive and negative integers.

Pattern Blocks   Use different pattern blocks to represent positive and negative numbers in subtraction sentences.

On-Hand Manipulatives   Use two types of everyday objects as counters, such as beans and coins. Beans could represent negative integers, while coins represent positive integers.

Thermometer   Use a thermometer to model subtraction sentences and find differences.

Money   Use money to model subtraction. Owing someone money is the same as subtracting or adding a negative number.

Kinesthetic/
Visual/
Naturalist
Learners

Intervention Strategy

Create Subtraction Models   Write $15 - (-20)$ on the board. Ask students to work in small groups. Challenge them to write a word problem or create a model to represent this subtraction sentence. Encourage students to use objects or ideas from their environment. Models can include physical demonstrations, oral presentations, or displays students build. Ask students to provide a written explanation of how their creation matches the sentence. Give groups time to share their models with their classmates.

Multi-Step Problem   If students have difficulty with Exercises 14–16, check if students are writing the correct integers for each piece of information. Ask students to restate each fact in their own words and write the integer it represents. Then have them explain step-by-step the process of changing the subtraction sentence into an addition sentence by writing the opposite of the second number in the problem. Model how to use inverse operations to check the reasonableness of their answers.

Math Coach Notes

Study Tip   Explain to students that absolute value expresses the distance between an integer and zero. Distance is always positive. Whether the integer inside the absolute value bars is positive or negative, that distance is always expressed as a positive number.

Find each difference. Use algebra tiles.

7 $-12 - 7 = \underline{-19}$

8 $-20 - 11 = \underline{-31}$

9 $15 - (-16) = \underline{31}$

10 $-23 - (-21) = \underline{-2}$

Which number has the greater absolute value?

11 3 or -5 $\underline{-5}$

12 15 or -15 $\underline{same}$

13 10 or -7 $\underline{10}$

Step *by* **Step** *Problem-Solving Practice*

Solve.

Problem-Solving Strategies
☐ Draw a diagram.
☐ Use logical reasoning.
☑ Make a table.
☐ Solve a simpler problem.
☐ Act it out.

14 **GAS PRICES**   Josephina used estimates to compare the cost of 10 gallons of gas. In February 2006, the cost was $22. During 2007, the cost was about $1 lower. In February 2008, the cost was $8 higher than 2007. What was the cost of 10 gallons of gas in February 2008?

Understand	Read the problem. Write what you know.
	Ten gallons of gas cost about $\underline{\$22}$ in 2006.
	Ten gallons of gas cost $\underline{\$1}$ less in 2007.
	The price rose by $\underline{\$8}$ in 2008.
Plan	Pick a strategy. One strategy is to make a table.
Solve	Follow the changes in gas prices by using the table.
	$\underline{\$22} - \underline{\$1} + \underline{\$8} = \underline{\$29}$
Check	Use algebra tiles to check your answer.

Change ($)	Cost
	$22
−1	$21
+8	$29

15 **SPORTS**   Dion took a vacation in North Carolina. He went scuba diving to a depth of <u>240 feet below sea level</u>. Later that week, he hiked to the peak of Mount Mitchell at <u>6,700 feet above sea level</u>. What is the <u>difference in altitudes</u> between the two locations?

Check off each step.

✔ Understand: I underlined key words.

✔ Plan: To solve the problem, I will __write an equation__

✔ Solve: The answer is __−240 + 6,700 = 6,460 feet__

✔ Check: I checked my answer by __using a related addition sentence__

24 **Chapter 1** Integers

Intervention Strategy   Linguistic/Interpersonal Learners

Subtract and Compare   Write the following sentences on the board.

$-13 - (-22)$ ☐ $|-7|$ $-18 - 7$ ☐ $15 - (-10)$

Ask students to work in pairs to determine which sign (>, <, or =) goes in each box to make the statements true. Have students practice reading the sentences out loud and explaining how to find the value of each side. After groups are finished, invite student volunteers to the board to write the symbols and explain their thought processes.

16 **WEATHER** Evelina was comparing the record temperatures for January in Fairbanks, Alaska. The highest recorded temperature was 50°F in 1981. The lowest recorded temperature was −66°F in 1934. What is the difference between these two records?

$50 − (−66) = 50 + 66 = 116$; there is 116 degree difference.

17 **Reflect** Explain how to determine the absolute value of −12.

−12−11−10 −9 −8 −7 −6 −5 −4 −3 −2 −1 0

The absolute value of a number is the number's distance from 0 on a number line.

The distance between −12 and 0 is 12 units. The absolute value of −12 is 12.

▶ Skills, Concepts, and Problem Solving

Find each difference. Use algebra tiles.

18 $2 − 6 =$ ___−4___

19 $−3 − 4 =$ ___−7___

Find each difference. Use the number line.

20 $−4 − 7 =$ ___−11___

−12−11−10 −9 −8 −7 −6 −5 −4 −3 −2 −1 0 1 2

21 $−9 − (−10) =$ ___1___

−12−11−10 −9 −8 −7 −6 −5 −4 −3 −2 −1 0 1 2

Which number has the greater absolute value?

22 −5 or 5 ___same___   **23** −2 or −12 ___−12___   **24** 5 or −3 ___5___

Find each difference.

25 $−4 − (−2) =$ ___−2___   **26** $−16 − 60 =$ ___−76___

27 $−5 − 48 =$ ___−53___   **28** $−96 − (−56) =$ ___−40___

 GO ON

Lesson 1-3 Subtract Integers **25**

Odd/Even Assignments

Exercises 18–30 are structured so that students practice the same concepts whether they are assigned the odd or even problems.

In-Class Assignment

Have students complete Exercises 18, 20, 22, 25, 29, and 32 to ensure that they understand the concept.

⚠ Common Error *Alert*

Exercises 25–28 If students struggle with Exercises 25–28, they might be confused about subtracting two negatives or the concept of adding the opposite. Have students isolate the second number in the subtraction sentence by placing a finger or marker over the first number and the subtraction sign. Ask students to determine the opposite of the second number and place an addition sign in front of it before considering the first number. Breaking down the subtraction sentence into two parts can help eliminate some of the confusion over the signs.

Math Challenge

Logical Statements Have students determine if each sentence is *true* or *false*. For each false sentence, write an example that proves the falsehood.

1. A negative number minus a negative number will always yield a positive number. false; $−8 − (−6) = −2$

2. A positive number minus a negative number will always yield a positive number. true

3. A negative number minus a positive number will always yield a negative number. true

4. A positive number minus a positive number will always yield a positive number. false; $7 − 10 = −3$

See It, Do It, Say It, Write It

Step 1 Write several subtraction sentences on the board using negative integers. Ask students to find the difference for each sentence.

Step 2 Ask students to model the problems using a number line or counters.

Step 3 Have students work in pairs. Tell them to write a word problem to represent a subtraction sentence. Include the solution and a model that represents the situation. Have students share their word problems in small groups or with the class.

Looking Ahead: Pre-teach

Multiply Integers   In the next lesson, students will learn about multiplying integers. All of the multiplication properties for whole numbers apply to integers.

Example

The Commutative Property of Multiplication states that the order in which two numbers are multiplied does not change the product.

$9 \cdot (-3) = -27$
$-3 \cdot 9 = -27$
So, $9 \cdot (-3) = -3 \cdot 9$.

Have students find the product of each pair of integers.

1. Using the Identity Property of Multiplication,
$-8 \cdot 1 =$ _____. -8

2. Using the Zero Property of Multiplication,
$0 \cdot (-12) =$ _____. 0

Have students name an equivalent equation using the same factors.

3. Using the Commutative Property of Multiplication,
$4 \cdot (-6) =$ _____. $-6 \cdot 4$

---

29 NUTRITION For breakfast, Grace ate a bagel and cream cheese. Her breakfast had 390 Calories. Later that morning Grace ran for 45 minutes and burned 460 Calories. What is her net gain of Calories?

_____−70 Calories_____

30 SPORTS Brandon went to watch his little brother's football game on Saturday. During one play, his brother ran the wrong direction for 7 yards. He later turned around and ran in the correct direction for 42 yards. What is the net gain of yards?

_____35 yards_____

Vocabulary Check   **Write the vocabulary word that completes the sentence.**

31 The _____absolute value_____ of a number is the distance the number is from zero.

32 Writing in Math Sadzi lives 400 miles east of Albuquerque, New Mexico. Her friend Khadijah lives 1,750 miles west of Albuquerque, New Mexico. What is the difference in distance between the friends' homes? Explain how to find the distance using a number line.

Using a number line, place Albuquerque, New Mexico at 0. Place Sadzi's house

at 400, and Khadijah's house at −1,750. Subtract the two numbers.

$400 - (-1,750) = 2,150$ miles

 Spiral Review

What is the opposite of each number? Use it to show the Inverse Property of Addition. (Lesson 1-2, p. 11)

33 8 _____−8; 8 + (−8) = 0_____

34 −19 _____19; −19 + 19 = 0_____

35 −47 _____47; −47 + 47 = 0_____

36 241 _____−241; 241 + (−241) = 0_____

37 FINANCES Emma borrowed $15 from her sister last Monday. This Monday, Emma borrowed another $17. How much money does Emma have? Use integers to write an equation.

_____−15 + (−17) = −32; Emma has −$32._____

Ticket Out the Door

Weather Report   Write the following on the board.

The temperature in the early morning was −15°F. By afternoon, the temperature was 29°F. What was the difference in temperatures for this day? 44°F

Ask students to write a subtraction sentence for this problem and find the difference. Students will hand in their papers as they exit the classroom.

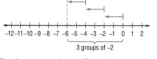
KEY Concept

To find the **product** of two integers, multiply the absolute values of the **factors** and then determine the correct sign of the answer.

If the signs are the same, then the sign of the product is positive.

$$4 \cdot 4 = 16 \text{ and } -4 \cdot (-4) = 16$$

If the signs are different, then the sign of the product is negative.

$$3 \cdot (-2) = -6 \text{ and } -3 \cdot 2 = -6$$

Multiplication of integers can be shown on a number line as repeated addition.

$$-2 \cdot 3 \text{ is } (-2) + (-2) + (-2) \text{ or } -6$$

3 groups of –2

The multiplication properties apply to integers.

Properties of Multiplication

Property	States that...	Example
Zero	any number times zero equals zero.	$-3 \cdot 0 = 0$
Identity	any number times 1 equals that number.	$-2 \cdot 1 = -2$
Commutative	the order in which numbers are multiplied does not change the product.	$-4 \cdot 2 = 2 \cdot (-4)$
Associative	the manner in which factors are grouped does not change the product.	$3 \cdot (-4 \cdot 4) = 4 \cdot [(-4) \cdot 3]$

You can use the Distributive Property to simplify addition and multiplication problems.

$$8(10 + (-2)) = (8 \cdot 10) + (8 \cdot (-2))$$

GO ON

Lesson 1-4 Multiply Integers **27**

VOCABULARY

Associative Properties
the way in which numbers are grouped does not change the sum or product

Commutative Properties
the order in which numbers are added or multiplied does not change the sum or product

Distributive Property
to multiply a sum by a number, multiply each addend by the number outside the parentheses

factor
a number that divides into a whole number with a remainder of zero; also a number that is multiplied by another number

product
the answer or result to a multiplication problem; it also refers to expressing a number as the product of its factors

Intervention Strategy
Logical/Interpersonal Learners

Multiplication Cards Have students work in pairs or small groups. Have students write the integers 1 to 13 in red marker on separate note cards. Then write the same numbers in black marker on a different set of note cards. Tell students that the cards with red numbers represent negative numbers and the cards with black numbers represent positive numbers. Have students shuffle the cards and draw two cards to multiply. Ask students to write each multiplication sentence and practice explaining how to find the product. For more proficient students, challenge them to include numbers greater than 10.

Lesson Notes

Lesson Planner

Objective Find the product of two integers.

Vocabulary Associative Properties, Commutative Properties, Distributive Property, factor, product

Materials/Manipulatives number lines, algebra tiles, geoboards, multiplication tables, hundreds chart

Chapter Resource Masters

CRM Vocabulary and English Language Development (p. A16)

CRM Skills Practice (p. A17)

CRM Problem-Solving Practice (p. A18)

CRM Homework Practice (p. A19)

1 Introduce

Vocabulary

Multiplication Terms Write a multiplication sentence that can be modeled with a number line, such as $-5 \cdot 3$. Ask volunteers to determine the *factors*, the *product*, and how to write this expression as a *repeated addition* sentence. Model this sentence on the number line. Then review the *properties of multiplication*.

2 Teach

Key Concept

Foundational Skills and Concepts After students have read through the Key Concept box, have them try these exercises.

1. Which property is modeled by:
   $4(7 + (-6)) = (4 \cdot 7) + (4 \cdot -6)$
   Distributive Property

2. Explain how to find the product of −9 and −6.
   Multiply the absolute values of each factor and then determine the correct sign. When the signs of both factors are the same, the product will be positive, so $-9 \cdot -6 = 54$.

Lesson 1-4 Multiply Integers **27**

Find 2 · (−7). Use a number line.

1. Identify the first number in the expression. 2
    This is the number of times the group is repeated.

2. Identify the second number in the expression. −7
    This is the group size.

3. Draw a number line. Mark off 2 groups of −7.

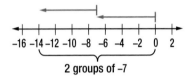

    2 groups of −7

4. The signs are different, so the product is negative.

5. Write the product. −14

Additional *Example 2*

Find 6 · (−8) by multiplying absolute values.

1. Find the absolute value of each.
    $|6| = 6$ $|-8| = 8$

2. Multiply the absolute values of the numbers.
    $6 · 8 = 48$

3. The signs are different, so the product is negative.

4. Write the product with the sign. −48

Math Coach Notes

Multiply Negative Integers   By presenting the justification for $(-x)(-y) = xy$ if x and y are rational numbers, students will understand why they can multiply the absolute values of integers to determine their products.

Example 1

Find 2 · (−4). Use a number line.

1. Identify the first number in the expression. 2
   This is the number of times the group is repeated.

2. Identify the second number in the expression. −4
   This is the group size.

3. Draw a number line. Mark off 2 groups of −4.

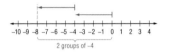

   2 groups of −4

4. The signs are different, so the product is negative.

5. Write the product.
   −8

YOUR TURN!

Find 3 · (−2). Use a number line.

1. What is the first number in the expression? 3
   This is the number of times the group is repeated.

2. Identify the second number in the expression. −2
   This is the group size.

3. Draw a number line. Mark off 3 groups of −2 .

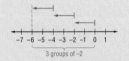

   3 groups of −2

4. Are the signs the same or different? different Will the product be positive or negative? negative

5. Write the product.
   −6

Example 2

Find 6 · (−3) by multiplying absolute values.

1. Find the absolute value of each.
   $|6| = 6$ and $|-3| = 3$

2. Multiply the absolute values of the numbers.
   $6 · 3 = 18$

3. The signs are different, so the product is negative.

4. Write the product with the sign.
   −18

YOUR TURN!

Find 7 · (−5) by multiplying absolute values.

1. Find the absolute value of each.
   $|7| = 7$ and $|-5| = 5$

2. Multiply the absolute values of the numbers.
   $7 · 5 = 35$

3. Are the signs the same or different? different Will the product be positive or negative? negative

4. Write the product with the sign.
   −35

English Learner Strategy

Develop Multiplication Skills   Use algebra tiles or other similar manipulatives to show multiplying integers as repeated addition. Initially, use only positive numbers for factors. Model how to arrange groups of tiles to represent a written multiplication expression. Label the groups and numbers of tiles per group as factors. Write the term *factor* on an index card. Show the numeric and pictorial form of the model on this index card for the student's reference. Ask the student to mimic you with other multiplication expressions, using the terms *factor, product, multiplication,* and *repeated addition.* Encourage correct vocabulary and clear language. Progress to using negative factors in the expressions. Explain how to determine the correct sign for the product and have the student repeat the explanation in his or her own words.

Example 3

Simplify. Name the multiplication properties that are used in each step.

$(3 \cdot (-8)) \cdot 1 = 3 \cdot (-8 \cdot 1)$ Associative Property

$= 3 \cdot (-8)$ Identity Property

$= -24$

YOUR TURN!

Simplify. Name the multiplication properties that are used in each step.

$(-12 \cdot 0) = (0 \cdot (-12))$ <u>Commutative Property</u>

$= 0$ <u>Zero Property</u>

Who is Correct?

Find $7 \cdot (-10)$.

Alejandro
$7 \cdot (-10) = -3$

Heather
$7 \cdot (-10) = -70$

Kendrick
$7 \cdot (-10) = 70$

Circle correct answer(s). Cross out incorrect answer(s).

Guided Practice

Find each product. Use a number line.

1 $-1 \cdot 7 = \underline{-7}$

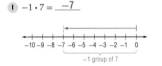

$-10\ -9\ -8\ -7\ -6\ -5\ -4\ -3\ -2\ -1\ \ 0$
−1 group of 7

2 $4 \cdot (-3) = \underline{-12}$

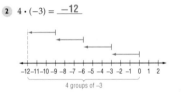

$-12\,-11\,-10\,-9\ -8\ -7\ -6\ -5\ -4\ -3\ -2\ -1\ \ 0\ \ 1\ \ 2$
4 groups of −3

GO ON

Simplify. Name the multiplication properties that are used in each step.

$1 \cdot 12 \cdot -3 = 12 \cdot 1 \cdot -3$ Commutative Property

$= 12 \cdot -3$ Identity Property

$= -36$

 3 Practice

Using Manipulatives

Geoboards   When presenting Examples 1 and 2, use concrete materials such as geoboards to determine the products. Determine the correct sign for the product based on the signs of the factors.

Algebra Tiles   Use algebra tiles to form arrays for multiplication sentences. Use yellow tiles if the factors have like signs. Use red tiles if the factors have unlike signs.

On-Hand Manipulatives   Use a hundreds chart to practice and solve multiplication sentences. Students will need to determine the correct sign for the product based on the signs of the factors.

Who is Correct?
Diagnostic Teaching

• Alejandro's work is incorrect. He added instead of multiplied.

• Heather's work is correct. She multiplied and used the sign correctly.

• Kendrick's work is incorrect. He multiplied correctly, but has the incorrect sign.

Remind students that when multiplying integers, the signs have to be different for the product to be negative.

Math Coach Notes

Study Tip   Review with students that absolute value expresses the distance between an integer and zero. Distance is always positive. Tell students as they are multiplying integers to focus on the multiplication first and then follow the rules for determining the correct sign on the product.

Strategies

1. Begin this lesson by using concrete materials. Model some multiplication sentences with only positive factors using a number line or algebra tiles. Have students write the numeric forms of these models on paper. Then include multiplication sentences with one negative factor.

2. Write several multiplication expressions on the board. Vary the expressions to include factors with the same sign and those with mixed factors. Ask students to practice explaining to one another how to determine the correct sign of a product. Encourage correct vocabulary and clear language.

Intervention Strategy

Linguistic/ Visual Learners

Create Word Problems   Ask students to work in small groups. Challenge them to create word problems that require the multiplication of integers. Have students write or draw their word problems, including the solutions and a written explanation. Allow time for students to share their word problems in small groups or with the class.

Step by Step Practice

3 Find $-8 \cdot (-7)$.

Step 1   Find the absolute value of each. $|-8| = 8$ and $|-7| = 7$

Step 2   Multiply the absolute values of the numbers.
$\underline{8} \cdot \underline{7} = \underline{56}$

Step 3   Are the signs the same or different? __same__

Step 4   Will the product be positive or negative? __positive__

Step 5   Write the product with the sign. __56__

Step 6   Check the sign to make sure it is correct.
$(-) \cdot (-) = (+)$
__Same signs mean the product will be positive.__

Find each product.

4 $-8 \cdot (-6)$ absolute value: $\underline{8} \cdot \underline{6} = \underline{48}$
product: __48__   sign: __positive__

5 $7 \cdot (-9) = \underline{-63}$ **6** $5 \cdot 7 = \underline{35}$ **7** $-4 \cdot 8 = \underline{-32}$ **8** $-9 \cdot (-6) = \underline{54}$

Step by Step Problem-Solving Practice

Problem-Solving Strategies
☑ Draw a diagram.
☐ Use logical reasoning.
☐ Guess and check.
☐ Solve a simpler problem.
☐ Work backwards.

Solve.

9   EVAPORATION   The height of the water in Fernando's swimming pool decreases 2 centimeters per week due to evaporation. What is the change in the height of the water over a six-week period, due to evaporation?

Understand   Read the problem. Write what you know.
The height of the pool water changed by __-2__ cm each week for __6__ weeks.

Plan   Pick a strategy. One strategy is to draw a number line to represent the height of the pool water.

Solve   Use the number line to find the change in value.

Draw a number line.
Mark off __6__ groups of __-2__.
The change in the height of the water is __-12__ cm.

Check   Use the Commutative Property to multiply the factors in a different order. Your product should be the same.

Are They Getting It?

Check students' understanding of multiplying integers by writing these problems on the board. Ask students to point out wrong answers and explain why they are incorrect.

1. $-6 \cdot 5 = 30$
This is incorrect. The signs are different, so the answer is negative.

2. $-7 \cdot (-4) = 28$
This is correct.

3. $8 \cdot (-9) = -72$
This is correct.

10 HIKING Hayden and his friend went hiking in the Rocky Mountains. They descended the mountain at a rate of 7 feet per minute. What is the change in elevation of the hikers after 15 minutes?

Check off each step.

   ✔   Understand: I underlined key words.

   ✔   Plan: To solve the problem I will __solve an equation__.

   ✔   Solve: The answer is __$-7 \cdot 15 = -105$ feet__.

   ✔   Check: I checked my answer by __using the Commutative Property.__

11 WEATHER During a certain week, the temperature in Pensacola, Florida dropped 3°F each day. What is the change in temperature in Pensacola over 5 days?

   __−15°F__

12 Reflect Explain how to use a number line to multiply $3 \cdot (-4)$.

   __Draw a number line. Begin at 0 on the number line. Move 3 units left of zero__

   __4 times. Mark the ending point at −12.__

 Skills, Concepts, and Problem Solving

Find each product. Use a number line.

13 $2 \cdot (-5) =$ __−10__

14 $3 \cdot (-6) =$ __−18__

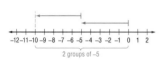
2 groups of −5   3 groups of −6

Find each product.

15 $3 \cdot (-4) =$ __−12__

16 $-9 \cdot 2 =$ __−18__

17 $-8 \cdot (-10) =$ __80__

18 $4 \cdot (-7) =$ __−28__

19 $6 \cdot (-8) =$ __−48__

20 $-12 \cdot (-5) =$ __60__

Find the missing number. Name the multiplication property.

21 $-84 \cdot$ __1__ $= -84$ __Identity Property__

22 $(4 \cdot 7) \cdot (-8) = 4 \cdot [$ __7__ $\cdot (-8)]$ __Associative Property__

 GO ON

Odd/Even Assignments

Exercises 13–24 are structured so that students practice the same concepts whether they are assigned the odd or even problems.

In-Class Assignment

Have students complete Exercises 14, 16, 21, 23, and 27 to ensure that they understand the concept.

Intervention Strategy

Naturalist/ Intrapersonal Learners

Real-World Examples Ask students to find examples of when they multiply integers in their everyday lives. Challenge them to especially look for situations in which they use negative integers. Encourage students to use their environment for inspiration. Have them write a list of examples collected from their daily routines, both at school and at home. Ask volunteers to share their examples with the class.

Math Challenge

Expressions of 64 Write the number 64 on the board. Challenge students to write a list of multiplication expressions that have a product of 64. Ask students to include negative factors in their lists of expressions. When students are finished, have them compare their work and compile a complete list to post in the classroom.

Common Error *Alert*

Multi-Step Problem If students struggle with Exercises 23 and 24, they might not comprehend the reading clues that indicate the signs for the integers represented in the situation. Have students read the problems aloud and translate the given integers using their own words. Encourage students to draw a diagram, create a chart or table, or act out the situations to aid comprehension. When students find a solution, ask them to reread the problem to check the answer for reasonableness and completeness.

See It, Do It, Say It, Write It

Step 1 Write several multiplication expressions on the board using positive and negative integers. Ask students to find the product for each expression.

Step 2 Ask students to explain in pairs how to model the sentences using a number line or algebra tiles.

Step 3 Have students work in pairs to write a word problem to represent one of the multiplication sentences on the board. Include the solution and a model that represents the situation. Have students share their word problems in small groups or with the class.

Looking Ahead: Pre-teach

Divide Integers In the next lesson, students will learn about dividing integers. Division is the inverse operation for multiplication. The rules for dividing integers are the same as the rules for multiplying integers.

Example

Find $-24 \div 6$.
Divide the absolute values of the numbers.
$24 \div 6 = 4$
The signs are different so the quotient will be negative.
The quotient is -4.

Have students find each quotient.

1. $-18 \div (-3)$ 6

2. $-81 \div 9$ -9

3. $100 \div (-25)$ -4

Solve.

23 POPULATION The population of Jefferson Middle School has decreased by 15 students every year for the past three years. What is the change in the population?

$\underline{-15 \cdot 3 = -45;\ \text{The population decreased by 45 students.}}$

24 FINANCES Jasmine bought a stock for $27 a share. The stock lost $3 for each of the next 5 months. How much did each share of stock lose in value?

$\underline{-3 \cdot 5 = -15;\ \text{The stock lost \$15.}}$

Vocabulary Check **Write the vocabulary word that completes each sentence.**

25 The ___Zero Property of Multiplication___ states that when you multiply a number by 0, the product is zero.

26 In the equation $-3 \cdot (-7) = 21$, the integers $\underline{-3}$ and $\underline{-7}$ are factors.

27 Writing in Math Audrey worked the following problem. What mistake did she make?

$\underline{\text{The mistake was made by using addition instead of multiplication. The product of}}$
$\underline{\text{the two absolute values is 45. The signs of the two numbers are different, so the}}$
$\underline{\text{product should have a negative value. } 5 \cdot (-9) = -45}$

 Spiral Review

Find each sum or difference. (Lesson 1-2, p. 11 and Lesson 1-3, p. 19)

28 $5 + (-7) = \underline{-2}$ **29** $-110 - (-60) = \underline{-50}$

30 $-44 - (-32) = \underline{-12}$ **31** $-81 + 100 = \underline{19}$

Solve. (Lesson 1-1, p. 4)

32 AIRPLANES An airplane was cruising at an altitude of 27,000 feet. The pilot descended 350 feet to avoid a thunderstorm. What integer describes the airplane's altitude?

$\underline{27,000 + (-350) = 26,650 \text{ feet}}$

Ticket Out the Door

Banking Money Write the following on the board.

Henri made three $20 withdrawals from his account per month for two months in a row. What is his net loss? $6 \times (-20) = -120$; net loss of $120; $(-20) + (-20) + (-20) + (-20) + (-20) + (-20) = -120$

Ask students to write a multiplication sentence for this problem and then find the product. Tell them to prove their answers are correct by showing a repeated addition sentence yielding the same result. Students will hand in their papers as they exit the classroom.

Lesson 1-5 Divide Integers

KEY Concept

Division is the inverse operation for multiplication. You use the multiplication facts whenever you divide integers.

If the signs are the same, then the **quotient** is positive.

$72 \div 8 = 9$
$(-72) \div (-8) = 9$

If the signs are different, then the quotient is negative.

$(-72) \div 8 = -9$
$72 \div (-8) = -9$

VOCABULARY

dividend
the number that is being divided

$$\text{divisor} \rightarrow 4\overline{)8} \begin{array}{l} \leftarrow \text{quotient} \\ \leftarrow \text{dividend} \end{array}$$

divisor
the number by which the dividend is being divided

quotient
the answer or result of a division problem

You can find the quotient of two integers by using a related multiplication sentence, $-8 \cdot (-9) = 72$. So, $72 \div (-8) = -9$.

Example 1

Find $48 \div (-6)$.

1. The signs are different. The quotient will be negative.
2. Find the absolute value of each. $|48| = 48$ and $|-6| = 6$
3. Divide the absolute values of the numbers. $48 \div 6 = 8$
4. Write the quotient with a negative sign. -8

YOUR TURN!

Find $-88 \div 8$.

1. Are the signs the same or different? _____different_____
2. Find the absolute value of each. ___$|-88| = 88$ and $|8| = 8$___
3. Divide the absolute values of the numbers. __88__ $\div$ __8__ $=$ __11__
4. Write the quotient with the sign. __-11__

GO ON

Additional *Example 1*

Find $-64 \div (-8)$.

1. The signs are the same. The quotient will be positive.

2. Find the absolute value of each.
   $|-64| = 64$ $|-8| = 8$

3. Divide the absolute values of the numbers. $64 \div 8 = 8$

4. Write the quotient with the sign. 8

Lesson Notes

Lesson Planner

Objective   Find the quotient of two integers.

Vocabulary   dividend, divisor, quotient

Materials/Manipulatives   algebra tiles, geoboards, number lines, hundreds chart

Chapter Resource Masters

- CRM Vocabulary and English Language Development (p. A20)
- CRM Skills Practice (p. A21)
- CRM Problem-Solving Practice (p. A22)
- CRM Homework Practice (p. A23)

 **1 Introduce**

Vocabulary

Divide Integers   Write several division expressions on the board, varying the formats and the signs on the dividends and divisors. Explain that the sign rules for dividing integers are the same as the rules for multiplying them. Ask volunteers to identify each part of the expressions, using the terms *dividend, divisor,* and *quotient.*

 2 Teach

Key Concept

Foundational Skills and Concepts   After students have read through the Key Concept box, have them try these exercises.

1. **Find the quotient of 42 and −6.** The signs are different, so the quotient will be negative. $42 \div 6 = 7$ so $42 \div (-6) = -7$

2. **Explain how to find $\dfrac{-32}{-8}$. Use inverse operations to prove your answer is correct.** 32 is the dividend and 8 is the divisor. The signs are the same so the quotient will be positive. $-32 \div (-8) = 4$ because $4 \cdot (-8) = -32$.

Find $\dfrac{-64}{4}$.

1. The signs are different.

2. The quotient will be negative.

3. Divide the absolute values of the numbers.
   $64 \div 4 = 16$

4. Write the quotient. -16

Math Coach Notes

Division as Multiplication in Disguise By teaching division as an alternate and equivalent form of expressing multiplication facts, students will be able to grasp division with more confidence. Reinforcing these fact families will enable students to extend these relationships into fractions and decimals more easily.

Kinesthetic/ Logical/ Auditory Learners

Intervention Strategy

Integer Bingo Have students create their own board or placemat for an integer bingo game. Tell students to randomly fill the squares of their board with positive and negative integers between −12 and 12 but not to include 0. Play the game in small groups or as a whole class. Call out division expressions that include positive and negative integers. Students should determine each quotient and cover any spaces on their boards that have that number. Tell students they can write the recited expressions on a piece of scrap paper to help them determine the quotient, if necessary. Play until someone gets five covered spaces in a row.

Example 2

Find $\dfrac{-42}{-6}$.

1. The signs are the same.

2. The quotient will be positive.

3. Divide the absolute values of the numbers.
   $42 \div 6 = 7$

4. Write the quotient. 7

YOUR TURN!

Find $\dfrac{-35}{-5}$.

1. Are the signs the same or different?
   <u>same</u>

2. Will the quotient be positive or negative?
   <u>positive</u>

3. Divide the absolute values of the numbers.
   <u>35</u> ÷ <u>5</u> = <u>7</u>

4. Write the quotient. <u>7</u>

Who is Correct?

Simplify $-63 \div (-9)$.

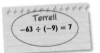

Circle correct answer(s). Cross out incorrect answer(s).

▶ Guided Practice

Find each quotient.

1. $12 \div 1 = \underline{12}$

2. $-42 \div 1 = \underline{-42}$

3. $-27 \div (-1) = \underline{27}$

4. $93 \div (-1) = \underline{-93}$

5. $72 \div (-12) = \underline{-6}$

6. $-64 \div (-4) = \underline{16}$

7. $-60 \div 5 = \underline{-12}$

8. $44 \div 2 = \underline{22}$

Who *is Correct?*
Diagnostic Teaching

- Grayson's work is incorrect. He added instead of divided.

- Pilar's work is incorrect. The signs are the same so the quotient should be positive.

- Terrell's work is correct. He divided and wrote the quotient correctly.

Remind students that when the signs of the dividend and divisor are the same, the quotient is positive.

Step by Step Practice

9 Find $-12 \div 2$.

Step 1 Are the signs the same or different? ___different___

Step 2 Will the quotient be positive or negative? ___negative___

Step 3 Divide the absolute values of the numbers.

$$\underline{12 \div 2 = 6}$$

Step 4 Write the quotient. __−6__

Check the number line. The integer -12 can be divided into 2 groups of -6.

Find each quotient.

10 $-9 \div 3$

signs: $\underline{(-)} \div \underline{(+)} = \underline{(-)}$

quotient: __−3__

11 $\dfrac{-8}{4}$

signs: $\underline{(-)} \div \underline{(+)} = \underline{(-)}$

quotient: __−2__

12 $-36 \div 3 = \underline{-12}$

13 $52 \div (-13) = \underline{-4}$

14 $-20 \div (-4) = \underline{5}$

15 $-50 \div (-5) = \underline{10}$

16 $\dfrac{-14}{2} = \underline{-7}$

17 $\dfrac{-23}{1} = \underline{-23}$

18 $\dfrac{56}{-4} = \underline{-14}$

19 $\dfrac{-36}{12} = \underline{-3}$

20 $\dfrac{-200}{-25} = \underline{8}$

21 $\dfrac{-72}{-12} = \underline{6}$

GO ON →

Lesson 1-5 Divide Integers **35**

Using Manipulatives

Geoboards When presenting Examples 1 and 2, use concrete materials such as geoboards to determine the quotients. Determine the correct sign for the quotient based on the signs of the dividend and divisor.

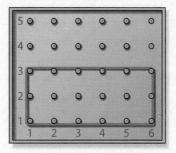

$$-18 \div 3 = -6$$

On-Hand Manipulatives Use a hundreds chart to practice and solve division sentences. Students will need to determine the correct sign for the product based on the signs of the factors.

Math Coach Notes

Strategy Begin this lesson by using concrete materials. Use manipulatives such as counters to model some division sentences. Have students write the numeric forms of these models on paper. Ask them to find the quotient and confirm it using inverse operations. Then have students create their own models of division sentences and ask their peers to find the quotients.

Are They Getting It? ?

Check students' understanding of dividing integers by writing these problems on the board. Ask students to point out wrong answers and explain why they are wrong.

1. $\dfrac{-28}{7}$ means $7 \div -28$. The quotient is -4, since $-4 \times 7 = -28$.

This is incorrect. $\dfrac{-28}{7}$ means $-28 \div 7$.

2. $-96 \div (-6) = 16$ This is correct.

3. $54 \div (-18) = 3$ This is incorrect. The signs are not the same so the quotient should be negative.
$54 \div (-18) = -3$

⚠ **Common Error** *Alert*

Exercises 12–21 If students have difficulty with Exercises 12–21, encourage them to review the fact families. Tell students to focus on the absolute values of the integers in the problems to identify the missing number. Practice basic multiplication and division facts using flashcards and identify the other members of the fact family. Then review the rules for determining the correct sign for the product or quotient.

English Learner Strategy

Division Language   Write the following words on index cards: *division, divide, quotient, dividend, divisor, multiplication, multiply, product, factor, fact family, positive number,* and *negative number.* Write several division expressions on a sheet of paper. Model how to read one of the expressions aloud. Point to the word *division* to describe what type of expression it is. Ask the student to mimic you. Continue this process while identifying each part of the division expression. Use concrete materials to build a model of one of the division sentences. Use the model to discuss its fact family. Repeatedly point to each term as you use it during the conversation. Use clear, consistent language.

Math Coach Notes

Study Tip   Encourage students to practice the basic multiplication and division facts on a regular basis. This continued practice will greatly increase automaticity and confidence, especially as students progress to fraction and decimal operations.

Step by Step *Problem-Solving Practice*

Solve.

Problem-Solving Strategies
- ☑ Use a model.
- ☐ Use logical reasoning.
- ☐ Make a table.
- ☐ Guess and check.
- ☐ Solve a simpler problem.

22   **FINANCES**   Mr. Sullivan withdrew $720 from his savings account over the last 6 months. If he withdrew the same amount each month, what was the amount of each monthly withdrawal?

Understand   Read the problem. Write what you know.

Mr. Sullivan withdrew a total of __$720__ over a period of __6__ months.

Plan   Pick a strategy. One strategy is to use a model.

Draw a fraction bar worth a total of $720. Divide it into 6 equal parts. How much is each part worth?

| $120 | $120 | $120 | $120 | $120 | $120 |

Solve   Divide. __$720__ ÷ __6__ = __$120__
Mr. Sullivan withdrew __$120__ per month.

Check   Multiply to check your answer.

__$120__ · 6 = __$720__

---

23   **EROSION**   One shoreline along the Gulf of Mexico has <u>receded</u> by <u>42 feet</u> over the past <u>7 years</u>. If the beach has eroded at the <u>same rate</u> each year, what is the <u>average yearly rate of erosion</u>?

Check off each step.

____✔____ Understand: I underlined key words.

____✔____ Plan: To solve the problem I will _____use a model_____.

____✔____ Solve: The answer is __−42 ÷ 7 = −6 feet; The beach has eroded an average of 6 feet per year.__

____✔____ Check: I checked my answer by __using multiplication__

Intervention Strategy
Linguistic/Naturalist/Visual Learners

Real-World Division   Have students work in pairs. Ask them to find examples of when they divide integers in their everyday lives. Challenge them to use their environment for inspiration. Have students gather ideas from their daily routines, both at school and at home. Encourage pairs to display their ideas in an innovative way. Students can create overhead transparencies, bulletin boards, displays, drawings or collages, songs or poems, and so on. Allow each group to present their discoveries to the class.

24 AVIATION   A plane descends from an altitude of 7,500 feet at a rate of 500 feet per minute. How long does it take for the plane to land?

__15 minutes__

25 SWIMMING POOLS   Mrs. Whitmore is draining the family pool for the winter. The pool holds 540 gallons of water. If the pool drains at a rate of 90 gallons per hour, how many hours will it be before the pool is empty?

__540 ÷ (−90) = −6; It will take 6 hours to empty.__

26 Reflect   Lorenzo completed the following equation. $-27 \div 3 = -9$
He plans to check his answer using the following
multiplication expression. $-3 \cdot (-9)$
Is Lorenzo's plan correct? Explain your answer.

__This multiplication expression will not be helpful. The factor 3 should be a positive__

__integer. The correct multiplication expression to use would be $3 \cdot (-9)$ -27.__

▶ **Skills, Concepts, and Problem Solving**

Find each quotient.

27 $-10 \div 5 =$ __−2__

signs: __(−)__ ÷ __(+)__ = __(−)__

quotient: __−2__

28 $\dfrac{-14}{7} =$ __−2__

signs: __(−)__ ÷ __(+)__ = __(−)__

quotient: __−2__

29 $-64 \div 8 =$ __−8__

30 $54 \div (-9) =$ __−6__

31 $-72 \div (-6) =$ __12__

32 $70 \div 14 =$ __5__

33 $\dfrac{-49}{7} =$ __−7__

34 $\dfrac{42}{-6} =$ __−7__

35 $\dfrac{-54}{-3} =$ __18__

36 $\dfrac{36}{6} =$ __6__

GO ON

Lesson 1-5 Divide Integers   **37**

Odd/Even Assignments

Exercises 27–38 are structured so that students practice the same concepts whether they are assigned the odd or even problems.

In-Class Assignment

Have students complete Exercises 27, 29, 33, 37, and 41 to ensure that they understand the concept.

Math Challenge

Dividend of −48   Write the number −48 on the board. Challenge students to write a list of division sentences with −48 as the dividend. Ask students to vary the formats in their lists of expressions. When students are finished, have them compare their work in small groups and then compile a complete list to post in the classroom.

Common Error Alert

Multi-Step Problem If students struggle with Exercise 38, they might not be able to organize the given information into useful parts. Have students start by reading the entire problem aloud, then reread for smaller pieces of information. For each piece of data, show students how to draw a diagram or model to make the information more tangible. Tell students to summarize each piece of information in their own words and identify what they need to know to answer the question. Encourage students to try a variety of strategies to solve for the answer. Then ask students to review the problem again to check their solution for reasonableness and completeness.

(4) Assess

See It, Do It, Say It, Write It

Step 1 Write several division expressions on the board using positive and negative integers. Vary the formats of the expressions. Ask students to find the quotient for each expression and then label each part of the division sentences.

Step 2 Ask students to explain in pairs how to model the sentences using concrete materials. Have students build a model for one of the sentences on the board.

Step 3 Write a new division expression on the board. Have students work in pairs to write a word problem to represent the expression. Ask students to include the quotient and a model that represents the situation. Have students share their word problems in small groups or with the class.

Solve.

37 INVESTMENTS Last year, Yolanda had a total of $675 deducted from her paycheck and sent into her individual retirement account (IRA). She made 3 payments to her individual retirement account. What integer represents the amount of money that was deducted for each IRA payment?

−$225; −$675 ÷ 3 = −$225; Each IRA payment deducted $225 from her paycheck.

38 WEATHER The temperature at the base of the mountain is 37°F. At the top of the mountain, which is 5,000 feet high, the temperature is −13°F. Khalid is driving up to the peak of the mountain. What integer describes the change in temperature for every 200 feet he travels?

−2; Every 200 feet that Khalid drives up the mountain, the temperature will decrease 2°F.

Vocabulary Check Write the vocabulary word that completes each sentence.

39 The _quotient_ is the result of a division problem.

40 A(n) _negative_ number is less than zero.

41 Writing in Math Celeste worked the problem on the right. What mistake did she make?

She used the wrong sign. The signs of the dividend and divisor are different, so the quotient is negative.

−28 ÷ 4 = 7

▶ Spiral Review

Find the missing number. Name the multiplication property. (Lesson 1–4, p. 27)

42 −84 · _0_ = 0 _____ Zero Property

43 4 · (−7) = _−7_ · 4 _____ Commutative Property

Solve. (Lesson 1–3, p. 19)

44 NUTRITION Elena ate a cereal and fruit bar and a glass of orange juice for breakfast. Her breakfast had 240 Calories. Later that morning Elena bicycled for 45 minutes and burned 354 Calories. What is her net gain of Calories? _−114 Calories_

38 Chapter 1 Integers

Ticket Out the Door

Solve and Confirm Write the following on the board.

1. 108 ÷ (−12) −9

2. −140 ÷ −10 14

3. $\frac{-49}{7}$ −7

Ask students to find each quotient and write a multiplication sentence that confirms their quotients are correct. Students will hand in their papers as they exit the classroom.

Find each difference. Use algebra tiles.

1   $-8 - (-2) = \underline{-6}$

2   $-3 - 2 = \underline{-5}$

Which number has the greater absolute value?

3   −16 or 3 $\underline{-16}$

4   −12 or 12 $\underline{same}$

5   4 or 7 $\underline{7}$

6   −8 or −6 $\underline{-8}$

Find each product.

7   $7 \cdot (-4) = \underline{-28}$

8   $-9 \cdot 5 = \underline{-45}$

9   $-9 \cdot (-12) = \underline{108}$

10   $8 \cdot (-7) = \underline{-56}$

11   $13 \cdot (-8) = \underline{-104}$

12   $-14 \cdot (-5) = \underline{70}$

Find each quotient.

13   $-36 \div (-4) = \underline{9}$

14   $-55 \div 5 = \underline{-11}$

15   $-72 \div (-12) = \underline{6}$

16   $\dfrac{56}{-8} = \underline{-7}$

17   $\dfrac{-64}{4} = \underline{-16}$

18   $\dfrac{-120}{-12} = \underline{10}$

Solve.

19   **FINANCES**   Mr. Wilkerson bought stock for $27 a share. Each share lost $3 for each of the next 4 months. How much has each share lost in value?

$\underline{-3 \cdot 4 = -12;\ \text{Each share lost } \$12.}$

20   **TRAVEL**   Casandra hiked The Big Tree Trail in the Oregon Caves National Monument. She hiked up the trail 1,100 feet. Then she began her descent back to the trailhead. So far, she has descended 550 feet. What integer describes her elevation?

$\underline{1,100 + (-550) = 550}$

Formative Assessment

Use the Progress Check to assess students' mastery of the previous lessons. Have students review the lesson indicated for the problems they answered incorrectly.

Odd/Even Assignments

Exercises are structured so that students practice the same concepts whether they are assigned the odd or even problems.

⚠ Common Error *Alert*

Watch the Signs!   Remind students to double-check their answer when computing with positive and negative integers. After finding the numerical part of their answer, they should look at the signs of the integers and ask themselves, "Should the answer be positive or negative?"

Exercise 20   Students should extract the information from the word problem and write a number sentence before solving the problem. They should verify their answers are reasonable.

Data-Driven Decision Making

Students missing Exercises . . .	Have trouble with . . .	Should review and practice . . .
1–2	finding differences using models.	SSG Lesson 1-3, p. 19 CRM Skills Practice, p. A13
3–6	comparing absolute values.	SSG Lesson 1-3, p. 19 CRM Skills Practice, p. A13
7–12	multiplying integers.	SSG Lesson 1-4, p. 27 CRM Skills Practice, p. A17
13–18	dividing integers.	SSG Lesson 1-5, p. 33 CRM Skills Practice, p. A21
19–20	solving word problems that involve operations with integers.	CRM Problem Solving Practice, pp. A14, A18, and A22

Study Guide
Formative Assessment

Vocabulary and Concept Check

If students have difficulty answering Exercises 1–8, remind them that they can use the page references to refresh their memories about the vocabulary terms.

Vocabulary Review Strategies

Vocabulary Table   Have students fold a sheet of notebook paper vertically. On the left side, they should list the vocabulary terms. On the right side, they should provide a definition or summary for each of the terms, including examples or models when appropriate.

Lesson Review

Each example walks the students through the main concepts of this chapter, which include the following:
- using inequality and/or equal signs to compare integers, with the use of number lines as models
- ordering integers, with the aid of number lines
- adding integers (demonstrated through the use of number lines)
- subtracting integers (demonstrated through the use of number lines)
- comparing absolute values (demonstrated through the use of number lines)
- multiplying integers (by multiplying absolute values)
- dividing integers (by dividing absolute values)

If the given examples are not sufficient to review the questions, remind students that the page references tell them where to review that topic in their textbooks.

Find **Extra Practice** for these concepts in the Practice Worksheets, pages A4–A23.

Chapter 1 Study Guide

Vocabulary and Concept Check

absolute value, *p. 19*
Commutative Property of Addition, *p. 11*
dividend, *p. 33*
divisor, *p. 33*
Identity Property of Multiplication, *p. 27*
integers, *p. 4*
Inverse Property of Addition, *p. 11*
negative number, *p. 4*
opposite, *p. 4*
positive number, *p. 4*
quotient, *p. 33*
whole number, *p. 4*
Zero Property of Multiplication, *p. 27*

Write the vocabulary word that completes each sentence. Not all vocabulary terms will be used.

1 0, 1, 2, 3, 4 … are __whole numbers__.

2 The __absolute value__ is the distance between a number and 0 on a number line.

3 A number less than zero is a(n) __negative number__.

4 …−3, −2, −1, 0, 1, 2, 3 … are __integers__.

5 Two different numbers that are the same distance from 0 on a number line are __opposite__ numbers.

Write the name of the property shown below.

6 $-5 \cdot 0 = 0$ __Zero Property of Multiplication__

7 $9 + (-9) = 0$ __Inverse Property of Addition__

8 $75 \cdot 1 = 75$ __Identity Property of Multiplication__

Lesson Review

1-1 **Model Integers** (pp. 4–10)

Write <, =, or > in each circle to make a true statement.

9 $2 \bigcirc -3$

10 $-6 \bigcirc 6$

Example 1

Use <, =, or > to compare −5 and 3.

1. Graph both numbers on the number line.

2. The number farthest to the right is 3, so it is the greater number.

3. Since −5 is less than 3, you need to use the "less than" symbol.
$-5 < 3$

Classroom Management

Pair and Share   Pair a student who has a good grasp of the material with another student who needs extra support. Have the student pairs take turns giving each other questions that they write (based upon the examples in the Study Guide). After answering the questions, if necessary, have the author of the questions explain the strategy and answer to the other student.

Chapter 1 Study Guide **41**

1-2 Add Integers (pp. 11-17)

Find each sum. Use algebra tiles.

11 $4 + (-3) = $ __1__

12 $-5 + (-2) = $ __-7__

13 $-7 + 5 = $ __-2__

Find each sum.

14 $-1 + 8 = $ __7__

15 $8 + (-7) = $ __1__

16 $-7 + (-5) = $ __-12__

17 $15 + (-4) = $ __11__

18 $9 + 23 = $ __32__

19 $-27 + (-10) = $ __-37__

Example 2

Find the sum of −6 and 2. Use algebra tiles.

1. Use six negative tiles and two positive tiles to represent the numbers.

2. You can make 2 zero pairs.

3. There are four negative tiles left.

4. The sum is 4.
$-6 + 2 = 4$

Example 3

Find the sum of 5 and −6. Use the number line.

1. Graph the first number.

2. From the first number, go left on the number line.

3. You are at −1 on the number line.

4. Write the sum.
$5 + (-6) = -1$

FOLDABLES Study Organizer — Dinah Zike's Foldables

Review Remind students to complete and refer to their Foldables as they progress through the Chapter 1 Study Guide. Have students share and compare their completed Foldables with a partner. You may also choose to have them use their Foldable as a study aid in preparing for the Chapter Test. (For complete instructions, see Chapter Resource Masters, p. A1.)

	Terms	Example(s)
Model Integers		
Add Integers		
Subtract Integers		
Multiply Integers		
Divide Integers		

Note This!

Create a Checklist Help students create a study checklist. The checklist should include all of the following items:

- Notes from class
- Sketches, drawings, or number lines in their notebooks
- Foldables
- Vocabulary terms and definitions
- Lesson Examples
- Written assignments and quizzes
- Chapter 1 Study Guide

Intervention Strategy — Visual Learners

Use of Number Lines Have students use number lines any time they need visualization of the various operations involving integers.

1-3 Subtract Integers (pp. 19–26)

Find each difference. Use algebra tiles.

20. $4 - (-3) = $ ___7___

21. $-6 - (-2) = $ ___−4___

22. $-4 - 5 = $ ___−9___

Find each difference.

23. $-5 - 8 = $ ___−13___

24. $14 - (-3) = $ ___17___

25. $6 - 18 = $ ___−12___

26. $-3 - (-8) = $ ___5___

Which number has the greater absolute value?

27. 2 or −9 ___−9___

28. −15 or −3 ___−15___

Example 4

Find the difference of −5 and −3. Use algebra tiles.

1. Write the subtraction expression. $-5 - (-3)$

2. Write the addition expression. $-5 + 3$

3. Use five negative tiles and three positive tiles to represent the numbers.

4. You can make 3 zero pairs.

5. There are 2 negative tiles left.

6. The difference is −2.
$$-5 - (-3) = -2$$

Example 5

Which number has the greater absolute value?

$|5|$ or $|-3|$

1. 5 is 5 units from 0.

2. −3 is 3 units from 0.

3. Which integer has the greater absolute value? 5

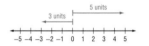

42 Chapter 1 Study Guide

Intervention Strategy **Kinesthetic Learners**

Use of Counters or Algebra Tiles For those students who benefit from "hands-on" mathematical techniques, provide them with the opportunity to use counters or algebra tiles for integer addition and subtraction exercises.

1-4 Multiply Integers (pp. 27-32)

Find each product.

29 $-8 \cdot (-3)$

absolute value: __8__ · __3__ = __24__

sign: __positive__   product: __24__

30 $-13 \cdot (5)$

absolute value: $|$__13__$| \cdot |$__5__$| = |$__65__$|$

sign: __negative__   product: __−65__

31 $8 \cdot (-6) =$

__−48__

32 $-9 \cdot (-12) =$

__108__

33 $-6 \cdot (-15) =$

__90__

Example 6

Find $-7 \cdot (-13)$ **by multiplying absolute values.**

1. Find the absolute value of each.
   $|-7| = 7$ and $|-13| = 13$

2. Multiply the absolute values of the numbers.
   $7 \cdot 13 = 91$

3. The signs are the same. The product is positive.

4. Write the product with the sign.
   91

1-5 Divide Integers (pp. 33-38)

Find each quotient.

34 $\dfrac{-48}{-6} =$

__8__

35 $-49 \div 7 =$

__−7__

36 $\dfrac{84}{-12} =$

__−7__

37 $-99 \div (-11) =$

__9__

Example 7

Find $36 \div (-3)$**.**

1. Find the absolute value of each.
   $|36| = 36$ and $|-3| = 3$

2. The signs are different.
   The quotient will be negative.

3. Divide the absolute values of the numbers.
   $36 \div 3 = 12$

4. Write the quotient with a negative sign.
   −12

Math Coach Notes

Test-Taking Tip   Have students define the various properties of multiplication. Have them demonstrate the properties by showing examples.

Ticket Out the Door

Write Word Problems   Divide the class into two groups. Have each student in the first group create a word problem that demonstrates a real-world application of the use of addition or subtraction of integers. Similarly, have each student in the second group create a word problem that demonstrates a real-world application of the use of multiplication or division of integers. Groups should exchange the problems and solve them before handing them to you as they exit the classroom.

Chapter Test

Chapter Resource Masters

Additional forms of the Chapter 1 Tests are available.

Test Format	Where to Find it
Chapter 1 Test	Math Online ▷ glencoe.com
Blackline Masters	Assessment Masters, p. A29

ExamView®
Assessment Suite

Customize and create multiple versions of your chapter test and their answer keys. All of these questions from the chapter tests are available on ExamView® Assessment Suite.

Advance TRACKER

Online Assessment and Reporting
glencoe.com

This online assessment tool allows teachers to track student progress with easily-accessible, comprehensive reports available for every student. Assess students using any internet-ready computer.

Alternative Assessment

Use Portfolios   Ask students to write examples of each type of problem from this chapter in their portfolios. Ask them to include a number line, a drawing of algebra tiles, or a sketch with the examples, where appropriate or needed. Also, have the students find the answer to each example in their portfolios. Emphasize that they show all of the work required to arrive at their answer.

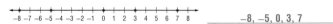

 Chapter Test

1 Graph $-8, 3, 0, -5, 7$. Then write the numbers in order from least to greatest.

$$\overset{\longleftrightarrow}{\underset{-8\ -7\ -6\ -5\ -4\ -3\ -2\ -1\ \ 0\ \ 1\ \ 2\ \ 3\ \ 4\ \ 5\ \ 6\ \ 7\ \ 8}{\vert\vert\vert\vert\vert\vert\vert\vert\vert\vert\vert\vert\vert\vert\vert\vert\vert}} \qquad \underline{-8, -5, 0, 3, 7}$$

Write <, =, or > in each circle to make a true statement.

2 $-7 \; \textcircled{>} \; -10$

3 $-12 \; \textcircled{<} \; 2$

4 $0 \; \textcircled{>} \; -17$

5 $|-3| \; \textcircled{=} \; |3|$

Find each sum.

6 $-5 + (-4) = \underline{-9}$

7 $(-3) + 12 = \underline{9}$

8 What is the opposite of 18? Use it to show the Inverse Property of Addition.

$\underline{\quad -18;\ 18 + (-18) = 0 \quad}$

Find each difference.

9 $-2 - (-4) = \underline{2}$

10 $-7 - (-1) = \underline{-6}$

11 $7 - (-2) = \underline{9}$

12 $6 - 9 = \underline{-3}$

Which number has the greater absolute value?

13 -12 or 9 $\underline{-12}$

14 -13 or 5 $\underline{-13}$

15 -7 or 7 $\underline{same}$

16 18 or -8 $\underline{18}$

Find each product.

17 $6 \cdot (-7) = \underline{-42}$

18 $-9 \cdot (-8) = \underline{72}$

19 $-12 \cdot 5 = \underline{-60}$

20 $10 \cdot (-11) = \underline{-110}$

44   Chapter 1 Test

English Learner Strategy

Assessment   Allow students time to look over the assessment. Have the students take a close look at all the problem directions and the word problems.

Most of the directions are not very complicated; however, be sure the students are aware of the *Inverse Property of Addition*, which is referred to in the test. If students are having trouble remembering the property, provide an opportunity for them to clarify the definition by referring them to the appropriate page in their text where it is stated and demonstrated.

Divide.

21 $-144 \div 12 =$ __−12__

22 $\dfrac{-66}{-11} =$ __6__

23 $-27 \div 1 =$ __−27__

24 $360 \div (-10) =$ __−36__

Solve.

25 **HEALTH** Collin went to the doctor. The cost was $164. His insurance was expected to pay $115. Collin paid $49. Later, Collin found out that his insurance actually paid $131. Assuming Collin had no prior balance, what is the balance after his insurance payment was received?

__He had an account balance of −$16. The doctor owed him $16.__

26 **FINANCES** Amelia had $146 in her checking account. She used her debit card to purchase dinner for $17 and a birthday present for her mother for $28. On Friday, she deposited $75. What is her checking account balance after her deposit?

__$146 + (−17) = 129 + (−28) = 101 + 75 = 176$;__

__Her balance is $176.__

Correct the mistakes.

27 **CHEMISTRY** The boiling point of neon is approximately −246°C. The melting point of neon is about −259°C. Trent says that the difference between these two temperatures is −505. What is wrong with Trent's answer?

__$-246 - (-259) = 13°C$; The difference is 13°C.__

__Trent added instead of subtracting.__

28 **WEATHER** The weather forecaster on the radio said, "It is currently five degrees below zero. We expect that the sun will warm up the temperatures this afternoon. The temperature should rise about thirty degrees during the day." Salvador told his friend that the high temperature that day would be 35°F. What is wrong with Salvador's answer?

__$-5 + 30 = 25$; The high temperature will be 25°F.__

Test-Taking Tip Have students circle or highlight the numbers in the word problems that are to be used in the calculation(s), and cross out any numbers that are insignificant to finding a solution.

Data-Driven Decision Making

Students missing Exercises . . .	Have trouble with . . .	Should review and practice . . .
1–5	graphing, ordering, and comparing integers.	SSG Lesson 1-1, p. 4 CRM Skills Practice, p. A5
6–8	finding sums of integers, demonstrating the Inverse Property.	SSG Lesson 1-2, p. 11 CRM Skills Practice, p. A9
9–12	finding differences of integers.	SSG Lesson 1-3, p. 19 CRM Skills Practice, p. A13
13–16	finding and comparing absolute values.	SSG Lesson 1-3, p. 19 CRM Skills Practice, p. A13
17–24	multiplying and dividing integers.	SSG Lessons 1-4 and 1-5, pp. 27 and 33 CRM Skills Practice, pp. A17 and A21
25–28	solving word problems involving integer operations.	CRM Problem Solving Practice, pp. A6, A10, A14, A18, and A22

Test Practice

⚠ Diagnose Student Errors

Survey student responses for each item. Class trends may indicate common errors and misconceptions.

1. Ⓐ correct
   B guess
   C misinterpreted operation
   D misinterpreted operation

2. Ⓐ correct
   B guess
   C misunderstood magnitude
   D misinterpreted concept of comparison

3. Ⓐ correct
   B division error, $-39 \div 3 = -13$
   C calculation error
   D guess

4. Ⓐ correct
   B misinterpreted operations, subtracted first two amounts
   C guess
   D misinterpreted operations, added the numbers together

5. A *A* represents −5
   Ⓑ correct
   C *C* represents 1
   D *D* represents 4

6. A misinterpreted change in direction
   Ⓑ correct
   C misinterpreted depth below sea level
   D misinterpreted change in direction

7. Ⓐ correct
   B subtracted integers
   C added integers
   D incorrect sign

8. A incorrect sign
   B misinterpreted product as difference
   C misinterpreted product as sum
   Ⓓ correct

9. A incorrectly thought of opening price as negative
   Ⓑ correct
   C added values, thought answer was the sum
   D multiplied values, thought answer was the product

10. A misrepresented quotient as sum
    B misrepresented quotient as difference
    C incorrect sign
    Ⓓ correct

11. Ⓐ correct
    B guess
    C misrepresented opposite as reciprocal
    D guess

12. Ⓐ correct
    B added values and used opposite for descent, thought answer was the sum
    C added values, thought answer was the sum
    D incorrect sign

Choose the best answer and fill in the corresponding circle on the sheet at right.

1 Due to a construction project, a small electronics store loses $3,000 per day in business. If this pattern continues for the next 4 days, how much money will this store have compared to its normal sales?

  Ⓐ −$12,000   C −$8,000

  B −$10,000   D −$4,000

2 Which symbol makes this math sentence true?

$$-500 - 27 \bigcirc -500 - (-27)$$

  Ⓐ <   C >

  B =   D −

3 A football team lost 39 yards on 3 plays. If the team lost the same number of yards on each play, which integer shows the yards lost per play?

  Ⓐ −13 yards   C −10 yards

  B −12 yards   D −8 yards

4 Alex owed his sister $15. He also owed his father $22. If he earns $65 next week, how much money will he have left after he pays what he owes?

  Ⓐ $28   C $72

  B $58   D $102

5 Which letter on the number line represents −3?

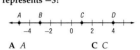

  A *A*   C *C*

  Ⓑ *B*   D *D*

6 Toshiro went scuba diving. He dove to 75 feet below sea level to explore a cave in Manatee Springs. Then he climbed 39 feet to take pictures of jellyfish. Where is Toshiro in relation to sea level?

  A −74 feet   C 36 feet

  Ⓑ −36 feet   D 74 feet

7 Find the product of −12 and −8.

  Ⓐ 96   C −20

  B −4   D −96

8 What is the product of −108 and 4?

  A 432   C −104

  B −112   Ⓓ −432

9 Esmerelda has stock in the Capital Calendar Company. At the beginning of the day the price per share was $37.00. At the end of the day, the price per share had gone down by $3.00. What was the price per share at the end of the day?

A −$40   C $40

B $34   D $111

---

10 Find the quotient of −56 and −8.

A −64   C −7

B −48   D 7

---

11 What is the opposite of 8?

A −8   C $\frac{1}{8}$

B 0   D 1

---

12 Tamara and her family went hiking in the Appalachian Mountains. They descended the mountain at a rate of 6 feet per minute. What is their change in elevation after 15 minutes?

A −90   C 21

B −21   D 90

ANSWER SHEET

Directions: Fill in the circle of each correct answer.

1   Ⓐ Ⓑ Ⓒ Ⓓ
2   Ⓐ Ⓑ Ⓒ Ⓓ
3   Ⓐ Ⓑ Ⓒ Ⓓ
4   Ⓐ Ⓑ Ⓒ Ⓓ
5   Ⓐ Ⓑ Ⓒ Ⓓ
6   Ⓐ Ⓑ Ⓒ Ⓓ
7   Ⓐ Ⓑ Ⓒ Ⓓ
8   Ⓐ Ⓑ Ⓒ Ⓓ
9   Ⓐ Ⓑ Ⓒ Ⓓ
10 Ⓐ Ⓑ Ⓒ Ⓓ
11 Ⓐ Ⓑ Ⓒ Ⓓ
12 Ⓐ Ⓑ Ⓒ Ⓓ

Success Strategy

When checking your answers, do not change your mind on your answer choice unless you misread the question. Your first choice is often the right one.

Diagnosing Student Errors and Misconceptions

Corrections   When working on the Test Practice problems, have students show their work on a separate sheet of notebook paper that can be used later as a reference as needed. After the class has completed the Test Practice problems, have them trade papers (without their names showing). Go over all the correct responses and have the students score each other's responses. Collect the papers and redistribute them to their owners. Have students correct missed problems.

Polls   Take an informal poll of how many students missed each question. Tell them to refer to their work and try to find and correct any mistakes made. You should explain any questions that are continuing to confuse a number of students at this point.

⚠ Common Error *Alert*

Eliminate Wrong Answers   If students are not able to successfully eliminate wrong answer choices, it would be helpful for you to point out the following:

Exercise 4 Have students put themselves in the place of Alex. They should picture getting a paycheck and paying family members.

Exercise 9 Students should ask themselves, "At the end of the day, is the price higher or lower than the beginning of the day?"

Exercise 12 Encourage students to make a table of values. Each row should represent one minute and there should be 15 rows. Corresponding to each row should be the change in elevation after each minute.

Chapter Overview

Chapter-at-a-Glance

Lesson	Math Objective	State/Local Standards
2-1 Number Relationships (pp. 50-56)	Solve simple problems involving functional relationships.	
2-2 Introduction to Functions (pp. 57-62)	Use a function table to identify ordered pairs.	
Progress Check 1 (p. 63)		
2-3 Ordered Pairs (pp. 64-70)	Identify and graph ordered pairs on a coordinate grid.	
2-4 Coordinate Grids (pp. 71-78)	Graph linear relationships on a coordinate grid.	
2-5 Linear and Nonlinear Functions (pp. 79-86)	Graph linear and nonlinear relationships.	
Progress Check 2 (p. 87)		

Content-at-a-Glance

The diagram below summarizes and unpacks Chapter 2 content.

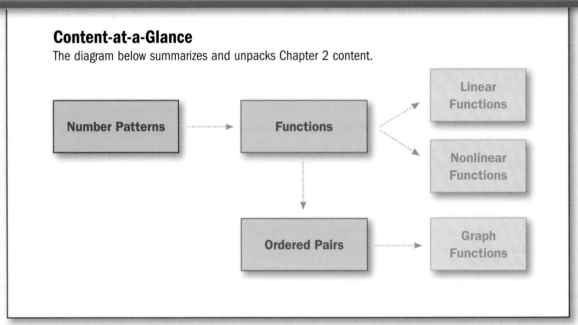

Chapter Assessment Manager

Diagnostic Diagnose students' readiness.

	Student/Teacher Editions	Assessment Masters	Technology
Course Placement Test		1	ExamView® Assessment Suite
Book 1 Pretest		23	ExamView® Assessment Suite
Chapter 2 Pretest		37	ExamView® Assessment Suite
Quiz/Preview	SSG 49		Math Online glencoe.com StudentWorks™ Plus

Formative Identify students' misconceptions of content knowledge.

	Student/Teacher Editions	Assessment Masters	Technology
Progress Checks	SSG 63, 87		Math Online glencoe.com StudentWorks™ Plus
Vocabulary Review	SSG 88		Math Online glencoe.com
Lesson Assessments			ExamView® Assessment Suite
Are They Getting It?	TE 53, 59, 67, 75, 84		Math Online glencoe.com

Summative Determine student success in learning the concepts in the lesson, chapter, or book.

	Student/Teacher Editions	Assessment Masters	Technology
Chapter 2 Test	SSG 92	40	ExamView® Assessment Suite
Test Practice	SSG 94	43	
Alternative Assessment	TE 92	46	ExamView® Assessment Suite
See It, Do It, Say It, Write It	TE 56, 62, 70, 78, 86		
Book 1 Test		59	ExamView® Assessment Suite

Backmapping and Vertical Alignment McGraw-Hill's *Math Triumphs* intervention program was conceived and developed with the final result in mind: student success in grade-level mathematics, including Algebra 1 and beyond. The authors, using the **NCTM Focal Points and Focal Connections** as their guide, developed this brand-new series by backmapping from grade-level and Algebra 1 concepts, and vertically aligning the topics so that they build upon prior skills and concepts and serve as a foundation for future topics.

	Lesson 2-1	Lesson 2-2	Lesson 2-3	Lesson 2-4
Concept	Number Relationships	Introduction to Functions	Ordered Pairs	Coordinate Grids
Objective	Solve simple problems involving functional relationships.	Use a function table to identify ordered pairs.	Identify and graph ordered pairs on a coordinate grid.	Graph linear relationships on a coordinate grid.
Math Vocabulary	pattern rule term	equation function function table variable	coordinate grid ordered pair origin x-axis y-axis	coordinate grid ordered pair
Lesson Resources	**Materials** • number lines • colored pencils **Manipulatives** • number lines • unit cubes **Other Resources** CRM Vocabulary and English Language Development CRM Skills Practice CRM Problem-Solving Practice CRM Homework Practice	**Materials** • beans • construction paper • index cards **Manipulatives** • algebra tiles **Other Resources** CRM Vocabulary and English Language Development CRM Skills Practice CRM Problem-Solving Practice CRM Homework Practice	**Materials** • grid paper • dry erase marker • plastic page covers **Manipulatives** • geoboards • coordinate grids **Other Resources** CRM Vocabulary and English Language Development CRM Skills Practice CRM Problem-Solving Practice CRM Homework Practice	**Materials** • grid paper **Manipulatives** • coordinate grids **Other Resources** CRM Vocabulary and English Language Development CRM Skills Practice CRM Problem-Solving Practice CRM Homework Practice
Technology	**Math Online** ▷ glencoe.com StudentWorks™ Plus ⊙ ExamView® Assessment Suite	**Math Online** ▷ glencoe.com StudentWorks™ Plus ⊙ ExamView® Assessment Suite	**Math Online** ▷ glencoe.com StudentWorks™ Plus ⊙ ExamView® Assessment Suite	**Math Online** ▷ glencoe.com StudentWorks™ Plus ⊙ ExamView® Assessment Suite

Lesson 2-5

Linear and Nonlinear Functions	**Concept**
Graph linear and nonlinear relationships.	**Objective**
function function table linear function nonlinear function	**Math Vocabulary**
Materials • grid paper	**Lesson Resources**
Manipulatives • algebra tiles • coordinate grids	
Other Resources **CRM** Vocabulary and English Language Development **CRM** Skills Practice **CRM** Problem-Solving Practice **CRM** Homework Practice	
Math Online > glencoe.com StudentWorks™ Plus 💿 ExamView® Assessment Suite	**Technology**

Intervention Strategy

Does the Machine Function?

Arrange the students into two teams. This activity consists of two phases, one preparing for a competition and the other participating in the competition.

The goal of the competition is to correctly identify which pattern rules describe a function, while trying to stump the opposing team.

Phase 1: As a team, write five pattern rules. Use different input values to determine if your pattern describes a function or not. Seek ways to write challenging pattern rules that may cause the opponents' function machine to malfunction.

Examples of pattern rules for functions

$$y = 2x - 5 \qquad y = -10 \qquad y = |x|$$

Examples of pattern rules for non-functions

$$x = 6 \qquad x = |y|$$

Examples of pattern rules for functions that may confuse the opponents

$$y = 0 \qquad y = -x^2 \qquad y = \frac{5}{x}$$

Phase 2: Select three team members to role play the actions of a function machine. One person has the job of input operator. Another person has the job of output operator. The third person has the job of the function machine. The rest of the team will sit behind the machine and act as its processor, feeding the correct answers to the person role playing the machine. The team should establish sound effects for

- Feeding input into the machine.
- Processing the rule.
- Producing output from a function.
- Malfunction (failure to produce output because it is not a function).

The team that processes the most pattern rules correctly is the winner.

Chapter Notes

Real-World Applications

RECIPES The table below shows how many cups of pecans Janice needs when she makes spinach salad. Do you see the pattern? If Janice wants to make spinach salad to serve 40 people, how many cups of pecans will she need? 5

Number of Servings	4	8	12	16	20	24	28
Number of Cups of Pecans Needed	$\frac{1}{2}$	1	$1\frac{1}{2}$	2	$2\frac{1}{2}$	3	$3\frac{1}{2}$

Intervention Strategy
Everyday Patterns

Step 1 Separate students into small groups. Assign each group a place or setting, such as home, school, and after school.

Step 2 Each group collects and presents examples of patterns they see in the assigned setting. Example: In the lunch line, 1 student gets 1 drink, 2 students get 2 drinks, and so on.

Chapter 2
Patterns and Graphs

Have you ever calculated driving distance?

The length of one lap on a certain race track is 2.5 miles. If a car is driving 125 miles per hour, how many laps will the driver complete in 15 minutes?

48 Chapter 2 Patterns

Key Vocabulary

Find interactive definitions in 13 languages in the **eGlossary** at glencoe.com.

English   Español *Introduce the most important vocabulary terms from Chapter 2.*

coordinate grid   cuadriculado de coordenadas

a grid in which a horizontal number line and a vertical number line intersect at their zero points (p. 64)

function   función

a relationship in which one quantity depends upon another quantity (for every *x*-value, there is exactly one *y*-value) (p. 57)

ordered pair   por ordenado

a pair of numbers that are the coordinates of a point in a coordinate grid written in the order (horizontal coordinate, vertical coordinate) (p. 64)

pattern   modelo

a sequence of numbers, figures, or symbols that follows a rule or design (p. 50)

$$\underline{2},\ \underline{4},\ \underline{6},\ \underline{8},\ \underline{10},\ \underline{12},\ \ldots$$
terms

rule   regla

tells how numbers are related to each other (p. 50)

term   término

each number in a sequence (p. 50)

variable   variable

a symbol, usually a letter, used to represent a number (p. 57)

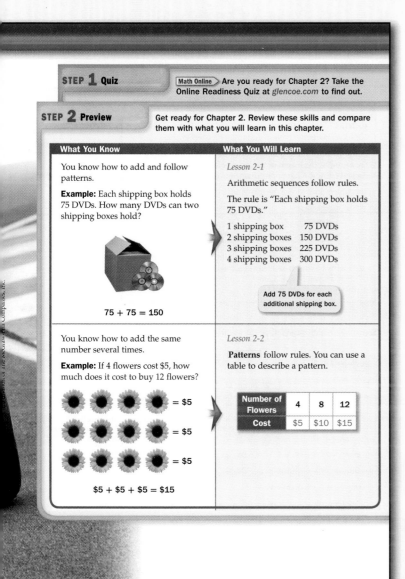

STEP **1** Quiz

Math Online ▷ Are you ready for Chapter 2? Take the Online Readiness Quiz at *glencoe.com* to find out.

STEP **2** Preview

Get ready for Chapter 2. Review these skills and compare them with what you will learn in this chapter.

What You Know	What You Will Learn
You know how to add and follow patterns. **Example:** Each shipping box holds 75 DVDs. How many DVDs can two shipping boxes hold? $75 + 75 = 150$	*Lesson 2-1* Arithmetic sequences follow rules. The rule is "Each shipping box holds 75 DVDs." 1 shipping box — 75 DVDs; 2 shipping boxes — 150 DVDs; 3 shipping boxes — 225 DVDs; 4 shipping boxes — 300 DVDs. Add 75 DVDs for each additional shipping box.
You know how to add the same number several times. **Example:** If 4 flowers cost $5, how much does it cost to buy 12 flowers? = $5, = $5, = $5. $\$5 + \$5 + \$5 = \$15$	*Lesson 2-2* **Patterns** follow rules. You can use a table to describe a pattern.

Number of Flowers	4	8	12
Cost	$5	$10	$15

Vocabulary Preview

- As students complete the Chapter Preview, have them make a list of important terms throughout the chapter.

- Divide students into pairs. Have each pair compare their lists of terms to make one list. Key words should be included in the list.

- Once the list is final, the pair should prepare to give an oral definition of each term.

- When all groups are finished, they should present the terms to the class. An option is to have pairs define the terms for another pair to guess.

Step 1 Quiz

Pretest/Prescribe Students can take the Online Readiness Quiz online or the Diagnostic Pretest in the Assessment Masters.

Step 2 Preview

Use this pre-chapter activity to activate students' prior knowledge, build confidence, and help students preview the lessons.

 **Dinah Zike's Foldables®**

Guide students through the directions on p. A24 in the Chapter Resource Masters to create their own Foldable graphic organizer for use with this chapter.

Home Connections

- Choose three foods that have a certain number of pieces in each container. Make a table for each food showing the total number of pieces when 1, 2, 3, 4, and 5 containers are purchased.

Professional Development

Targeted professional development has been articulated throughout **McGraw-Hill's** *Math Triumphs* intervention program. **The McGraw-Hill Professional Development Video Library** provides short videos that support the **NCTM Focal Points and Focal Connections**. For more information, visit glencoe.com.

Model Lessons | Instructional Strategies

Lesson Planner

Objective Solve simple problems involving functional relationships.

Vocabulary pattern, rule, term

Materials/Manipulatives number lines, unit cubes, colored pencils

Chapter Resource Masters

[CRM] Vocabulary and English Language Development (p. A27)

[CRM] Skills Practice (p. A28)

[CRM] Problem-Solving Practice (p. A29)

[CRM] Homework Practice (p. A30)

 **Introduce**

Vocabulary

Arithmetic Sequences After you teach students the meaning of an arithmetic sequence, have each student write an arithmetic sequence that contains four terms. On a separate piece of paper, students should write the next three terms in their sequences, and explain their reasoning.

 **Teach**

Key Concept

Foundational Skills and Concepts After students have read through the Key Concept box, have them try these exercises.

1. What is the radius of a circle with a 13-inch diameter? 6.5 in.

2. Describe the pattern in the table below.

Perimeter of square (in.)	40	32	24	16
Length of side (in.)	10	8	6	4

To find the length, divide the perimeter by 4.

KEY Concept

Patterns follow a rule. You can use a **rule** to answer questions about the pattern and to predict **terms**.

Rules define relationships between numbers. For example, the length of the radius of a circle is half the length of its diameter.

The table below shows the relationship between the numbers.

Radius	$\frac{1}{2}$ in.	1 in.	$1\frac{1}{2}$ in.	2 in.	$2\frac{1}{2}$ in.
Diameter	1 in.	2 in.	3 in.	4 in.	5 in.

You can use number patterns to find the next three terms. A circle with a 6-inch diameter has a 3-inch radius. A circle with a 7-inch diameter has a $3\frac{1}{2}$-inch radius. A circle with an 8-inch diameter has a 4-inch radius.

VOCABULARY

pattern
a sequence of numbers, figures, or symbols that follows a rule or design

rule
tells how numbers are related to each other

term
each number in a sequence

Sometimes patterns can follow rules with more than one operation.

Example 1

Esther had a balance of $25 in her checking account. Each day she withdrew $8 for lunch. What is the balance of her checking account after 5 days? Use two rules to find the answer.

1. One rule is add −$8 each day. Start with her account balance of $25.

> Remember that adding −8 is equal to subtracting 8.

Day 1 $25 + (-8) = 17$ Day 2 $17 + (-8) = 9$

Day 3 $9 + (-8) = 1$ Day 4 $1 + (-8) = -7$

Day 5 $-7 + (-8) = -15$

2. Another rule is multiply the number of days by $8, and then subtract.

$5 \cdot 8 = 40$ $25 - 40 = -15$

3. Esther has a balance of –$15 in her account.

Additional *Example 1*

Randy adds three nickels to his coin bank each school day. On Sunday, the bank had $6.40. How much money is in his bank on the next Saturday? Use two rules to find the answer.

1. The bank has $6.40.

2. One rule is "Add 0.15 each day, Monday through Friday."

$6.40 + 0.15 = 6.55$ $6.55 + 0.15 = 6.70$
$6.70 + 0.15 = 6.85$ $6.85 + 0.15 = 7.00$
$7.00 + 0.15 = 7.15$

3. Another rule is "Multiply the number of days by $0.15 and then add to $6.40."

YOUR TURN!

A workbook has 159 pages. Each lesson is 7 pages. If Dominick tears out 4 lessons, how many pages are left? Use two rules to find the answer.

1. One rule is subtract 7 pages for each lesson

$159 - \underline{7} = \underline{152}$ $152 - \underline{7} = \underline{145}$

$\underline{145} - \underline{7} = 138$ $138 - \underline{7} = \underline{131}$

2. Another rule is multiply the number of lessons by 7, and then subtract

$\underline{7} \cdot \underline{4} = \underline{28}$ $159 - \underline{28} = \underline{131}$

3. There are $\underline{131}$ pages left in the book.

Example 2

Find a rule. Then write the next three terms.

0.75; 1.50; 2.25; 3.00; 3.75

1. One rule is add 0.75.

$0.75 + 0.75 = 1.50$
$1.50 + 0.75 = 2.25$
$2.25 + 0.75 = 3.00$
$3.00 + 0.75 = 3.75$

2. Continue the pattern.

$3.75 + 0.75 = 4.50$
$4.50 + 0.75 = 5.25$
$5.25 + 0.75 = 6.00$

3. The next three terms are 4.50; 5.25; and 6.00.

YOUR TURN!

Find a rule. Then write the next three terms.

$$\frac{1}{12}, \frac{3}{12}, \frac{5}{12}, \frac{7}{12}, \frac{9}{12}$$

1. One rule is add $\frac{2}{12}$

$\frac{1}{12} + \frac{2}{12} = \frac{3}{12}$

$\frac{3}{12} + \frac{2}{12} = \frac{5}{12}$

$\frac{5}{12} + \frac{2}{12} = \frac{7}{12}$

$\frac{7}{12} + \frac{2}{12} = \frac{9}{12}$

2. Continue the pattern.

$\frac{9}{12} + \frac{2}{12} = \frac{11}{12}$

$\frac{11}{12} + \frac{2}{12} = \frac{13}{12}$

$\frac{13}{12} + \frac{2}{12} = \frac{15}{12}$

3. The next three terms are $\frac{11}{12}$, $\frac{13}{12}$, and $\frac{15}{12}$

GO ON

Additional *Example 2*

Find a rule. Then write the next three terms.

10.50; 9.05; 7.60; 6.15; 4.70

1. One rule is "Subtract 1.45."

$10.50 - 1.45 = 9.05$
$9.05 - 1.45 = 7.60$
$7.60 - 1.45 = 6.15$
$6.15 - 1.45 = 4.70$

2. Find the next three terms by following the rule.

$4.70 - 1.45 = 3.25$
$3.25 - 1.45 = 1.80$
$1.80 - 1.45 = 0.35$

3. The next three terms are 3.25, 1.80, and 0.35.

Math Coach Notes

Verifying the Rule   Remind students that not all sequences are arithmetic sequences. Stress to students that they need to find the difference between each pair of terms, not just the first two terms. If the sequence is an arithmetic sequence, the difference will be common among all of the pairs of terms. If the difference is not common, then the sequence is not an arithmetic sequence.

Intervention Strategy   Interpersonal Learners

All Operations   Have the students work in groups of four. Each group needs to write four sequences, one with each of the four basic operations. A different member of the group should be the leader for each operation. The leader should decide the operation, the starting term, and the rule. All group members should write the sequence and then compare their answers. Groups should not move on to the next operation and sequences until all group members agree on the described sequence.

Find a rule. Then write the next three terms.

1, 2, 5, 14

I. One rule is multiply by 3, and then subtract 1.

$1 \cdot 3 - 1 = 2$
$2 \cdot 3 - 1 = 5$
$5 \cdot 3 - 1 = 14$

2. Continue the pattern.

$14 \cdot 3 - 1 = 41$
$41 \cdot 3 - 1 = 122$
$122 \cdot 3 - 1 = 365$

3. The next three terms are 41, 122, and 365.

③ Practice

Using Manipulatives

Unit Cubes For arithmetic sequences, students can use cubes to build prisms using the number indicated by each term. This will provide a physical and visual representation of the common number added to each term.

On-Hand Manipulatives Have students use colored pencils or markers to keep track of the repeated computations when finding the next terms in a sequence.

Example 3

Find a rule. Then write the next three terms.

1, 6, 31, 156

1. One rule is multiply by 5, and then add 1.

$1 \cdot 5 = 5 + 1 \quad\quad = 6$
$6 \cdot 5 = 30 + 1 \quad\quad = 31$
$31 \cdot 5 = 155 + 1 = 156$

2. Continue the pattern.

$156 \cdot 5 = 780 + 1 \quad\quad = 781$
$781 \cdot 5 = 3,905 + 1 \quad = 3,906$
$3,906 \cdot 5 = 19,530 + 1 = 19,531$

The next three terms are 781; 3,906; 19,531.

YOUR TURN!

Find a rule. Then write the next three terms.

4; 34; 334; 3,334

1. One rule is __multiply by 10, and then__ __subtract 6.__

$\quad 4 \cdot 10 = 40 - 6 = 34$
$\quad 34 \cdot 10 = 340 - 6 = 334$
$\quad 334 \cdot 10 = 3,340 - 6 = 3,334$

2. Continue the pattern.

$\quad 3,334 \cdot 10 = 33,340 - 6 = 33,334$
$\quad 33,334 \cdot 10 = 333,340 - 6 = 333,334$
$\quad 333,334 \cdot 10 = 3,333,340 - 6 = 3,333,334$

The next three terms are __33,334__; __333,334__; __3,333,334__.

Who is Correct?

How many ounces are in 5 quarts?

Number of Quarts	1	2	3	4	5
Number of Ounces	32	64	96	128	160

Javier 96   Rojen 160   Roxanne 150

Circle correct answer(s). Cross out incorrect answer(s).

▶ Guided Practice

Find a rule for each pattern.

① 207, 202, 197, 192 __subtract 5__

② 124, 141, 158, 175 __add 17__

③ 117,649; 16,807; 2,401; 343 __divide by 7__

④ 39; 117; 351; 1,053 __multiply by 3__

Who **is Correct?**
Diagnostic Teaching

• Javier is incorrect. He wrote the number of ounces for 3 quarts.

• Rojen is correct. He read the correct column from the chart, or he multiplied 5 · 32.

• Roxanne is incorrect. She incorrectly multiplied 5 and 32.

Step by Step Practice

5 There are 48 apples in each crate. Find a rule. Then write the next three terms in the pattern.

Step 1 One rule is multiply by __48__.

Step 2 Multiply the number of crates by __48__ to continue the pattern.

2 · __48__ = __96__   3 · __48__ = __144__   4 · __48__ = __192__

Step 3 The next three terms are __96__, __144__, and __192__.

In each sequence, find a rule. Then write the next three terms.

6 479, 456, 433, 410, _____, _____, _____

Rule: __subtract 23__

410 − __23__ = __387__

__387__ − __23__ = __364__

__364__ − __23__ = __341__

The next three terms are __387__, __364__, and __341__.

7 12,672; 6,336; 3,168; 1,584; _____; _____; _____

Rule: __divide by 2__

1,584 ÷ __2__ = __792__

__792__ ÷ __2__ = __396__

__396__ ÷ __2__ = __198__

The next three terms are __14,592__; __396__; and __198__.

8 57; 228; 912; 3,648; _____; _____; _____

Rule: __multiply by 4__

The next three terms are __14,592__; __58,368__; and __233,472__.

9 153; 384; 846; 1,770; _____; _____; _____

Rule: __add 39 then multiply by 2__

The next three terms are __3,618__; __7,314__; and __14,706__.

 GO ON

Math Coach Notes

Choosing the Operation   When students are trying to identify the rule of a sequence, have them use logical reasoning to get started.

- If the terms of the sequence increase,
  - **think:** addition or multiplication.
  - **ask:** constant increase or quick increase?
  - **test:** choose a rule and test it from term to term. If it does not work for all terms, it is not the rule.

- If the terms of the sequence decrease,
  - **think:** subtraction or division.
  - **ask:** constant decrease or quick decrease?
  - **test:** choose a rule and test it from term to term. If it does not work for all terms, it is not the rule.

- If a single operation does not pass a test, try a combination of operations; one multiplication or division, and the other addition or subtraction.

 Common Error *Alert*

Exercises 7–9   Remind students that rules can include multiplication, division, or a combination of any of the four operations.

Are They Getting It?

Check students' understanding of number relationships by writing these problems on the board. Have students explain the rule for each sequence.

I. 12; 11.92; 11.84; 11.76; 11.68 Subtract 0.08.

2. 1.2; 3.6; 10.8; 32.4; 97.2 Multiply by 3.

3. 2, 27, 52, 77, 102 Add 25.

4. 1,000; 200; 40; 8; 1.6; 0.32 Divide by 5.

Identify Each Rule   Tell students not to give up before identifying a rule. Encourage students to ask questions. Explain that incorrect responses could be caused by a miscalculation. Have students review their work several times. If they cannot find their own mistakes, encourage them to ask for assistance. Tell students that other classmates may have missed the same rule or made the same miscalculation. Asking questions will benefit the entire class and help students understand common errors.

Math Coach Notes

SQ3R Method   When students read their text, they can make the most of their time by using the **SQ3R** method. This acronym means to first **survey** by reading the introduction, the highlights, and the boldface lettering. Next, purposefully **pose questions** about the survey. Then, **read** the text, looking for answers to the questions that were created from the survey. **Recite** the answers to the questions, covering up the text to help memorize the answers. Finally, **review** the highlights, the questions, and the answers to aid in reading comprehension and concept retention.

Write the next three conversions in each pattern.

10

Number of Yards	1	2	3	4
Number of Inches	36	72	108	144

11

Number of Miles	1	2	3	4
Number of Yards	1,760	3,520	5,280	7,040

Step by Step Problem-Solving Practice

Solve.

12 FASHION   Marcella bought 7 sweaters. The first sweater cost $36.75. Each additional sweater cost $28.25. How much did she spend in all?

Problem-Solving Strategies
- ☑ Make a table.
- ☐ Guess and check.
- ☐ Act it out.
- ☐ Solve a simpler problem.
- ☐ Work backward.

Understand   Read the problem. Write what you know.

The first sweater cost _$36.75_.

Each additional sweater cost _$28.25_.

Plan   Pick a strategy. One strategy is to make a table. Label the rows of the table "Sweater" and "Cost."

Solve   One sweater cost _$36.75_. Each additional sweater costs _$28.25_.

The rule is _add $28.25_.

To find the total cost, complete the table.

Sweater	1	2	3	4	5	6	7
Cost	36.75	65.00	93.25	121.50	149.75	178.00	206.25

Marcella spent _$206.25_ on sweaters.

Check   Use a different rule to check your answer. Start with your answer and work backward.

Math Challenge

Fractions in Sequences   This is a good opportunity to give students some review on operating with fractions. Have students find the rule for each sequence below and write the next three terms. Then ask students to write a sequence that involves fractions to give to a partner to add the next three terms.

1. $1, 2\frac{1}{3}, 3\frac{2}{3}, 5, 6\frac{1}{3}, \ldots$ Rule: Add $1\frac{1}{3}$;

The next three terms are: $7\frac{2}{3}, 9, 10\frac{1}{3}$

2. $\frac{3}{4}, \frac{1}{2}, \frac{1}{3}, \frac{2}{9}, \frac{4}{27}, \ldots$ Rule: Multiply by $\frac{2}{3}$;

The next three terms are: $\frac{8}{81}, \frac{16}{243}, \frac{32}{729}$

13 PETS Manuel is buying an aquarium. The store will charge $579.95 for the aquarium and an additional $30.75 for each fish. What is the price for the aquarium and 8 fish? Check off each step.

✔ Understand: I underlined key words.

✔ Plan: To solve the problem I will ___make a table___.

✔ Solve: The answer is ___$825.95___.

✔ Check: I checked my answer by ___working backward___.

14 ZOOS The zookeeper ordered 300 kilograms of feeding fish. Each day, Sarah the sea lion eats 17.4 kilograms of fish. After 14 days, how many kilograms of fish will remain?

The zookeeper's supply will have 56.4 kilograms of feed

fish left over.

15 Reflect Explain a rule for the terms 32, 69, 143, 291.

Sample answer: One rule is to multiply by 2 and add 5 to

continue this sequence of terms.

▶ **Skills, Concepts, and Problem Solving**

Find a rule for each pattern.

16 248,832; 20,736; 1,728; 144 ___divide by 12___

17 845.6; 837.7; 829.8; 821.9 ___subtract 7.9 or add −7.9___

18 $\frac{9}{12}$; $1\frac{2}{12}$; $1\frac{7}{12}$; 2 ___add $\frac{5}{12}$___

19 2; 13; 46; 145 ___multiply by 3, add 7___

In each sequence, find a rule. Then write the next three terms.

20 2, −4, 8, −16, 32

Rule: ___multiply by −2___

Next terms: ___−64___ ; ___128___ ; ___−256___

21 781,250; 156,250; 31,250; 6,250

Rule: ___divide by 5___

Next terms: ___1,250___; ___250___ ; ___50___

22 641.72; 650.00; 658.28; 666.56

Rule: ___add 8.28___

Next terms: ___674.84___; ___683.12___; ___691.40___

23 3, 12, 30, 66

Rule: ___add 3 and multiply by 2___

Next terms: ___138___ ; ___282___ ; ___570___ GO ON

Intervention Strategy Interpersonal Learners

Exercises 19 and 23 Some students will struggle to identify rules that use more than one operation. Use Exercise 15 to evaluate students' abilities. Pair those students who struggled with Exercise 15 with a partner who was successful. Allow students to discuss the process used in determining the answers for Exercises 19 and 23.

Odd/Even Assignments

Exercises 16–27 are structured so that students practice the same concepts whether they are assigned the odd or even problems.

In-Class Assignment

Have students complete Exercises 16, 20, 25, 26, and 30 to ensure that they understand the concept.

⚠ **Common Error Alert**

Exercise 14 Caution students to read the question carefully. If the student chooses not to make a table and solve the problem as other pattern problems in the lesson, the answer he or she will get is likely 43.6 kg. Many students will think about multiplying 17.4 by 14, but then not subtract from 300.

Exercise 15 Many students will struggle identifying a rule for sequences that are not single operation rules. Guide students to find a rule for this sequence by asking the following questions:

1. What do you add to 32 to get 69? 37

2. What do you add to 69 to get to 143? 74

3. What do you add to 143 to get 291? 148

4. What is the relationship between 37 and 74? Multiply 37 times 2.

5. What is the relationship between 74 and 148? Multiply 74 times 2.

6. If you multiply 32 by 2, what do you need to do to get to 69? Add 5.

7. If you multiply 69 by 2, what do you need to do to get to 143. Add 5.

Now students should know the rule and be able to test it.

(4) Assess

See It, Do It, Say It, Write It

Step 1 Choose any sequence or pattern given in this lesson. Identify how many terms are in the sequence.

Step 2 Find the rule to the sequence used in Step 1. Extend the sequence to list ten terms.

Step 3 Arrange students into small groups. Have each student show their group members the sequences they selected; point out the terms that they added and name the rule. The group members can check the rule and the added terms.

Step 4 Have students work alone to write how they found the rule and show the calculations that test the rule for each term, including the newly added terms.

Looking Ahead: Pre-teach

Introduction to Functions   In the next lesson, students will learn about relationships in which one quantity depends on another quantity.

Example

Jalesa has one roll of 14 breath mints. How many mints does Jalesa have if she has three rolls of mints?

1 roll has 14 mints.

2 rolls have 14 · 2 = 28 mints.

3 rolls have 14 · 3 = 42 mints.

How many mints are there in 6 rolls of mints?

14 · 6 = 84

Write the next three conversions in each pattern.

24

Fluid Ounces	1	2	3	4	5
Gallons	128	256	384	512	640

25

Days	1	2	3	4	5
Minutes	1,440	2,880	4,320	5,760	7,200

Solve.

26 FINANCE   Sergei opened his savings account with $467. Each week he withdrew $62. What is the balance in his savings account after 7 weeks?

467 + [7 · (−62)] = 33; The balance is $33.

27 THEATERS   A new stadium-style movie theater just opened in town. The first row has 16 seats. Each row after has two additional seats. How many seats are 8 rows of the theater?

Rows	1	2	3	4	5	6	7	8
Total Number of Seats	16	34	54	76	100	126	154	184

Vocabulary Check   **Write the vocabulary word that completes each sentence.**

28 The number 396 is a(n) _term_ in the sequence 300, 396, 492, 588.

29 A _pattern_ is a sequence of numbers, figures, or symbols that follows a rule or design.

30 Writing in Math   Compare and contrast the differences between these two sequences.

Sequence A: 1, −3, 9, −27, 81
Sequence B: 1, 3, 9, 27, 81

Sample answer: Each term in Sequence A (1, −3, 9, −27, 81) can be found by multiplying the previous term by −3. Every other term in this sequence is negative.

Each term in Sequence B (1, 3, 9, 27, 81) can be found by multiplying the previous term by 3. All terms in this sequence are positive.

Ticket Out the Door

Terms 6, 7, and 8   Write the following sequence on the board. Tell students to find the rule and calculate the next three terms. As students approach the classroom door to exit, alternate asking them to name the sixth, seventh, and eighth terms in the sequence.

18, 78, 168, 288, 438, ...

Multiply the number of the preceeding term by 30 and add the product to the previous term.
The sixth term is 618.
The seventh term is 828.
The eight term is 1,068.

Introduction to Functions

KEY Concept

A **function** is a relationship in which one quantity depends upon another quantity. The function assigns exactly one output value to each input value using a rule.

A **function table** uses the function, or rule, to show the relationship between the values. The function is written in an equation.

Imagine that a coral reef grows 2 millimeters each year. The value y shows the amount of change in reef size each year.

growth of the coral reef — **Function:** $y = 2x$ — number of years

Function Table		
Input	Function	Output
x	$2x$	y
0	$2 \cdot 0$	0
1	$2 \cdot 1$	2
2	$2 \cdot 2$	4
3	$2 \cdot 3$	6

The function table above shows the growth of the coral reef, y, based on the number of years, x.

VOCABULARY

equation
a mathematical sentence that contains an equal sign

function
a relationship in which one quantity depends upon another quantity (for every x-value there is exactly one y-value)

function table
a table of ordered pairs that is based on a rule

variable
a symbol, usually a letter, used to represent a number

Example 1

Write a function to represent the situation.

Jodi is 6 years older than Max.

1. Let x = Max's age and y = Jodi's age.
2. The function is $y = x + 6$.

YOUR TURN!

Write a function to represent the situation.

Every triangle has 3 sides.

1. Let __x__ = the number of triangles and __y__ = the number of sides.
2. The function is __$y = 3x$__ .

GO ON

Copyright © Glencoe/McGraw-Hill, a division of The McGraw-Hill Companies, Inc.

Additional **Example 1**

Write a function to represent the situation.

AGES Ben is 4 years older than Akira.

1. The function to describe the situation is $y = x + 4$, when x = Akira's age and y = Ben's age.
2. Make a function table using the rule $y = x + 4$. Start with $x = 4$.

Akira's Age, x	$x + 4$	Ben's Age, y
4	$4 + 4$	8
5	$5 + 4$	9
6	$6 + 4$	10
7	$7 + 4$	11

3. How old will Akira be when Ben is 11?
   Akira will be 7 when Ben is 11.

Lesson Notes

Lesson Planner

Objective Use a function table to identify ordered pairs.

Vocabulary equation, function, function table, variable

Materials/Manipulatives algebra tiles, beans, construction paper, index cards

Chapter Resource Masters

- CRM Vocabulary and English Language Development (p. A31)
- CRM Skills Practice (p. A32)
- CRM Problem-Solving Practice (p. A33)
- CRM Homework Practice (p. A34)

1 Introduce

Vocabulary

Access Vocabulary Use the table in the Key Concept box to discuss the requirements for a function table. Students should understand that the input values can be selected, but the output values are determined by the function.

2 Teach

Key Concept

Foundational Skills and Concepts After students have read through the Key Concept box, have them try these exercises.

1. What is the pattern in the function table? The pattern is that every x-value is multiplied by 2.
2. How much does the reef grow after 3 years? 6 mm

Additional *Example 2*

Make a function table for the equation y = 3x + 2.

1. Substitute each value of *x* in the function.

2. Solve the equation to find *y*.

x	3x + 2	y
−2	3(−2) + 2	−4
−1	3(−1) + 2	−1
0	3(0) + 2	2
1	3(1) + 2	5
2	3(2) + 2	8

Math Coach Notes

Strategies

1. Write a relevant and interesting function by using classroom data. For instance, how many thumbs does each student have? Draw a function table on the board and survey the class.

2. Ask students if they see a pattern in the table and if so, what the pattern is.

Example 2

Make a function table for the equation y = −2x + 2.

1. Substitute each value of *x* in the function.

2. Solve the equation to find *y*.

x	−2	−1	0	1	2
y = −2x + 2	(−2) (−2) + 2	(−2) (−1) + 2	(−2) (0) + 2	(−2) (1) + 2	(−2) (2) + 2
y	6	4	2	0	−2

YOUR TURN!

Make a function table for the equation y = 2x + 1.

1. Substitute each value of *x* in the function.

2. Solve the equation to find *y*.

x	−2	−1	0	1	2
y = 2x + 1	2(−2) + 1	2(−1) + 1	2(0) + 1	2(1) + 1	(2)(2) + 1
y	−3	−1	1	3	5

Who is Correct?

Make a function table for the equation y = x − 5.

x	y
−2	−3
0	−5
2	3

Dennis

x	y
−2	−7
0	5
2	3

Quinton

x	y
−2	−7
0	−5
2	−3

Polly

Circle correct answer(s). Cross out incorrect answer(s).

Who *is Correct?*
Diagnostic Teaching

- Dennis is incorrect. Two *y*-values are incorrect.

- Quinton is incorrect. His *y*-values for *x* = 0 and *x* = 2 are incorrect.

- Polly is correct.

Guided Practice

Write a function to represent each situation.

1. Mike walks 2 miles fewer than Darrell every day. $y = x - 2$

2. Jarrod feeds 4 times as many fish as Patricia. $y = 4x$

Step by Step Practice

Write a function and make a function table.

3. MUSIC   A music club charges $3 for membership and $2 for every downloaded song. How much will Alonso pay for joining the music club and downloading 6 songs?

   Step 1   Write a function to describe the cost of membership and x downloads. Let x = the number of downloaded songs and y = cost.

   $y = \underline{2x + 3}$

   Step 2   Make a function table using the rule $y = \underline{2x + 3}$.

Number of Downloads, x	1	2	3	4	5	6
$2x + 3$	$2(1) + 3$	$2(2) + 3$	$2(3) + 3$	$2(4) + 3$	$2(5) + 3$	$2(6) + 3$
Total Cost, y	5	7	9	11	13	15

   Step 3   Alonso will pay $\$\underline{15}$ for joining the music club and downloading 6 songs.

Write a function and make a function table.

4. SCHOOL   Each book Jackie carries weighs 3 pounds. Her backpack weighs 1 pound. Write a function to show the weight of her backpack if she is carrying x books.

   $y = \underline{3x + 1}$

Number of Books, x	1	2	3	4
Weight, y	4	7	10	13

   If Jackie carries 3 books, her backpack weighs $\underline{10}$ pounds.

GO ON

 Practice

Using Manipulatives

Algebra Tiles   When presenting function tables for equations, use algebra tiles to give students a visual concept of functions. Use the algebra tiles to show the equation, and then show the value of y for every x-value. Modeling this will show students a pattern to the function, which will allow them to predict the next values.

On-Hand Manipulatives   Use objects, beans, marked index cards, or squares of construction paper as you would algebra tiles.

Intervention Strategy

Logical Learners

Relay Functions   Divide students into groups of three. One student will state a function rule. Another student chooses an input. The third student states the output. Students should exchange roles until all have played each role.

Are They Getting It?

Check students' understanding of functions by writing these problems on the board. Have students identify and explain the incorrect information in each problem. Encourage students to use a table in their explanation.

Write a function to represent each situation.

1. Serena earns $4 more than Tatiana.
   $y = x + 4$
   This is correct.

2. Alberto can ride his bike 2 times faster than Quinn.
   $y = x + 2$
   This is not correct. The correct function is $y = 2x$.

3. The state fair charges $5 for entry and $3 for every ride.
   $y = 3x + 5$
   This is correct.

English Learner Strategy

Invite students to share with the class a dependent relationship that might be unique to their country. Have the class members determine which quantity depends on the other while the ESL student plays the role of the teacher. Repeat this activity for any ESL students that want to share with the class.

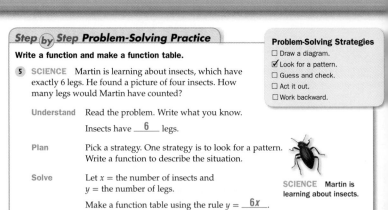

Step by Step Problem-Solving Practice

Write a function and make a function table.

Problem-Solving Strategies
☐ Draw a diagram.
☑ Look for a pattern.
☐ Guess and check.
☐ Act it out.
☐ Work backward.

5 SCIENCE Martin is learning about insects, which have exactly 6 legs. He found a picture of four insects. How many legs would Martin have counted?

Understand Read the problem. Write what you know.

Insects have __6__ legs.

Plan Pick a strategy. One strategy is to look for a pattern. Write a function to describe the situation.

Solve Let x = the number of insects and y = the number of legs.

Make a function table using the rule $y = $ __6x__.

Number of insects, x	1	2	3	4
6x	6(1)	6(2)	6(3)	6(4)
Legs, y	6	12	18	24

Martin counted __24__ insect legs.

Check Substitute __4__ for x in the function.

SCIENCE Martin is learning about insects.

6 CELEBRATIONS A high-school reunion is celebrated every 5 years. Keanu was 18 years old when he graduated. How old will he be at his third high-school reunion? Check off each step.

✔ Understand: I underlined key words.

✔ Plan: To solve this problem, I will __look for a pattern__.

✔ Solve: The function is __$y = 18 + 5x$__.

✔ Check: I checked my answer by __substituting for x__.

Reunion, x	1	2	3	4
18 + 5x	18 + 5(1)	18 + 5(2)	18 + 5(3)	18 + 5(4)
Keanu's age, y	23	28	33	38

Keanu will be __33__ years old.

Intervention Strategy
Auditory/Naturalists Learners

Describe each situation below. Have students discuss among themselves two quantities related to the situation and determine which quantity depends on the other. After the class has reached agreement on these situations, invite students to share a situation for the class to analyze the relationship of the quantities.

• Books in a backpack number of books; weight of the backpack; weight depends on number of books

• Getting a haircut number of inches to cut off; number of weeks since the last haircut; inches to cut off depends on number of weeks since last haircut

Copyright © Glencoe/McGraw-Hill, a division of The McGraw-Hill Companies, Inc.

7 **Reflect** Does $y = 4x - 3$ match the data in the table? Explain.

x	-2	-1	0	1	2
$4x - 3$	$4(-2) - 3$	$4(-1) - 3$	$4(0) - 3$	$4(1) - 3$	$4(2) - 3$
y	-11	-7	-3	1	5

Yes; Substitute each x value in the table for x in the function $y = 4x - 3$ to verify.

▶ **Skills, Concepts, and Problem Solving**

Write a function to represent each situation.

8 Linda writes 3 fewer e-mails than Suja each day. $\underline{y = x - 3}$

9 Bruce works 5 times as many hours as Ronnie. $\underline{y = 5x}$

Write a function and make a function table.

10 TRAVEL   Kala drove from Detroit to New York City. She drove 45 miles every hour. If it took Kala 15 hours to drive from Detroit to New York City, how many miles did Kala drive?

$y = \underline{45x}$

Number of Hours, x	3	6	9	12	15
$45x$	$45(3)$	$45(6)$	$45(9)$	$45(12)$	$45(15)$
Number of Miles, y	135	270	405	540	675

Kala drove $\underline{675}$ miles to get to New York City.

11 FAMILY   Keenan is 3 years older than his sister Tracey. How old will Keenan be when Tracey is 4?

$y = \underline{x + 3}$

Tracey's Age, x	$x + 3$	Keenan's Age, y
1	$1 + 3$	4
2	$2 + 3$	5
3	$3 + 3$	6
4	$4 + 3$	7

Keenan will be $\underline{7}$ when Tracey is 4.

GO ON ▶

Odd/Even Assignments

Exercises 8–12 are structured so that students practice the same concepts whether they are assigned the odd or even problems.

In-Class Assignment

Have students complete Exercises 8, 10, 11 and 15 to ensure that they understand the concept.

Math Challenge

Mileage Chart   Choose two cities. Rewrite Exercise 10 with data to match the two cities you selected. If the driving is mostly on an interstate, use 60 or 65 miles per hour. If the driving is a combination of city streets and interstate driving, use 40 or 45 miles per hour. Then create a function table to solve a similar problem.

④ Assess

See It, Do It, Say It, Write It

Step 1 Write a word problem on the board.

Step 2 Have students make a function table that results from the problem.

Step 3 Arrange students in pairs and have them explain to each other how they found the function that fits the given situation.

Looking Ahead: Pre-teach

Ordered Pairs   In the next lesson, students will learn about ordered pairs. An ordered pair, (x, y), tells the position of a point on a coordinate grid.

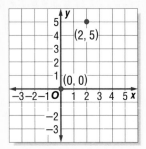

Example

There are two ordered pairs on the graph. What are they? $(0, 0)$ and $(2, 5)$

1. The first point is on the origin. To move from the origin $(0, 0)$ to the other point, how many squares to the right should you go? 2
2. How many squares up should you go? 5

Write a function and make a function table.

12 **CHEMISTRY**   In a lab experiment, a scientist used 2.5 liters of solution for every milliliter of water. If the scientist had to mix 8 milliliters of water, how many liters of solution will the scientist need?

$y = \underline{2.5x}$

Milliliters of Water, x	2	4	6	8
$2.5x$	2.5(2)	2.5(4)	2.5(6)	2.5(8)
Liters of Solution, y	5	10	15	20

The scientist needs __20__ liters of solution.

Vocabulary Check   Write the vocabulary word that completes each sentence.

13 A(n) ___function table___ is a table of ordered pairs that is based on a rule.

14 A(n) ___function___ is a relationship in which one quantity depends upon another quantity.

15 **Writing in Math**   Explain how to make a function table.

Make a function table using the rule of a function. Substitute each value of x in the function. Solve the equation to find y.

▶ Spiral Review

16 **FITNESS**   Courtney practices soccer for 45 minutes each day except for Sundays. After 2 weeks, how much time will Courtney have practiced? (Lesson 2-1, p. 50)

After 2 weeks, Courtney will have spent 540 minutes or 9 hours practicing.

STOP

Ticket Out the Door

Measure Heights   Arrange students in pairs and have them measure their heights in inches. Have students line up at the door. As students approach the door, they should write a function that represents their heights compared to the height of the person in front of them. Continue until all students have exited the classroom.

Chapter 2 Progress Check 1 (Lessons 2-1 and 2-2)

In each sequence, find a rule. Then write the next three terms.

1 4, −12, 36, −108, 324

Rule: **multiply by −3**

Next terms: **−972** ; **2,916** ; **−8,748**

2 250; 247.7; 245.4; 243.1

Rule: **subtract 2.3**

Next terms: **240.8** ; **238.5** ; **236.2**

Write a function to represent each situation.

3 Hannah earns $8 an hour more than Russ. **$y = x + 8$**

4 A quilting club charges $50 for membership and $100 for every quilt purchased.

$y = 50 + 100x$

Write a function and make a function table.

5 **CRAFTS** Aurelia knits approximately 5 new scarves each week. In 6 weeks, about how many scarves would Aurelia make?

$y =$ **$5x$**

Number of Weeks, x	1	2	3	4	5	6
Number of Scarves, y	5	10	15	20	25	30

Aurelia would make about **30** scarves in 6 weeks.

6 Juan counted the number of cars that pass his house each hour. How many cars have passed after 4 hours?

$y =$ **$3x$**

Hours, x	1	2	3	4
Cars Passed, y	3	6	9	12

After 4 hours, **12** cars have passed.

Progress Check **63**

Progress Check 1

Formative Assessment

Use the Progress Check to assess students' mastery of the previous lessons. Have students review the lesson indicated for the problems they answered incorrectly.

Odd/Even Assignments

Exercises are structured so that students practice the same concepts whether they are assigned the odd or even problems.

Common Error Alert

Label Variables   It may be good for students to get in the habit of stating or labeling the variables as to what they represent. As problems become more complex, it will help students keep the information in the problem organized.

Apply the technique described above as follows:
Exercise 3 Let $x =$ the amount Russ earns.
Exercise 4 Let $x =$ number of quilts purchased.

Math Coach Notes

More Practice with Functions   If students need more practice making function tables, use the functions from Exercises 1-4 with the direction line from Exercises 5 and 6. Before students make tables for these problems, check to be certain that they have written the correct functions for Exercises 1-4.

Data-Driven Decision Making

Students missing Exercises . . .	Have trouble with . . .	Should review and practice . . .
1–2	finding a rule for a given sequence.	SSG Lesson 2-1, p. 50 CRM Skills Practice p. A28
3–4	writing functions to represent given situations.	SSG Lesson 2-2, p. 57 CRM Skills Practice p. A32
5–6	writing functions, making function tables.	SSG Lesson 2-2, p. 57 CRM Skills Practice p. A32

Lesson Planner

Objective Identify and graph ordered pairs on a coordinate grid.

Vocabulary coordinate grid, ordered pair, origin, *x*-axis, *y*-axis

Materials/Manipulatives grid paper, geoboards, coordinate grids, dry erase markers, plastic page covers

Chapter Resource Masters

- CRM Vocabulary and English Language Development (p. A35)
- CRM Skills Practice (p. A36)
- CRM Problem-Solving Practice (p. A37)
- CRM Homework Practice (p. A38)

① Introduce

Vocabulary

Use Vocabulary Project a *coordinate grid* on the board. Point out the *x*- and *y*-axes. Plot a point. What is the *ordered pair*? Practice plotting points. Where is (0, 0)? This is the *origin*.

② Teach

Key Concept

Foundational Skills and Concepts After students have read through the Key Concept box, have them try these exercises.

1. Which axis is the *x*-axis? horizontal

2. What is an ordered pair? the *x*- and *y*-coordinates of a point on a coordinate grid

3. Where do you always start when you are graphing an ordered pair? the origin

---

Lesson 2-3 Ordered Pairs

KEY Concept

Follow these steps to graph the **ordered pair** (4, 5) on a **coordinate grid**.

> The *x*-coordinate is the first part of an ordered pair. It indicates how far to the left or to the right of the *y*-axis the corresponding point is located.

> The *y*-coordinate is the second part of an ordered pair. It indicates how far above or below the *x*-axis the corresponding point is located.

1. Start at the origin, (0, 0).
2. Move 4 units to the right, along the *x*-axis.
3. Then move 5 units up, along a line parallel to the *y*-axis.
4. Plot a point.

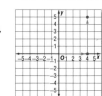

Start at the origin, (0, 0). If the *x*-coordinate is positive, move to the *right*. If it is negative, move to the *left*. If the *y*-coordinate is positive, move *up*. If it is negative, move *down*.

Example 1

Name the ordered pair for point *R*.

1. Start at the origin, (0, 0).
2. Move to the right, along the *x*-axis, until you are above point *R*. You moved right 5 units, so the *x*-coordinate is 5.
3. Then move 3 units down, along a line parallel to the *y*-axis, until you reach point *R*. You moved down 3 units, so the *y*-coordinate is −3.
4. The ordered pair for point *R* is (5, −3).

64 Chapter 2 Patterns and Graphs

Additional *Example 1*

Name the ordered pair for point *S*.

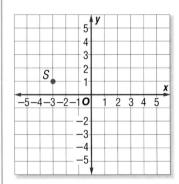

I. Start at the origin, (0, 0).

2. Move to the left, along the *x*-axis, until you are under point *S*. You moved left 3 units, so the *x*-coordinate is −3.

3. Then move 1 unit up, along a line parallel to the *y*-axis, until you reach point *S*. You moved 1 unit up, so the *y*-coordinate is 1.

4. The ordered pair for point *S* is (−3, 1).

YOUR TURN!

Name the ordered pair for point *T*.

1. Start at the origin, (0, 0).

2. Move to the __left__, along the *x*-axis, until you are under point *T*. You moved __left__ __2__ units, so the *x*-coordinate is __−2__.

3. Then move __4__ units __up__ along a line parallel to the *y*-axis, until you reach point *T*. You moved __up__ __4__ units, so the *y*-coordinate is __4__.

4. The ordered pair for point *T* is __(−2, 4)__.

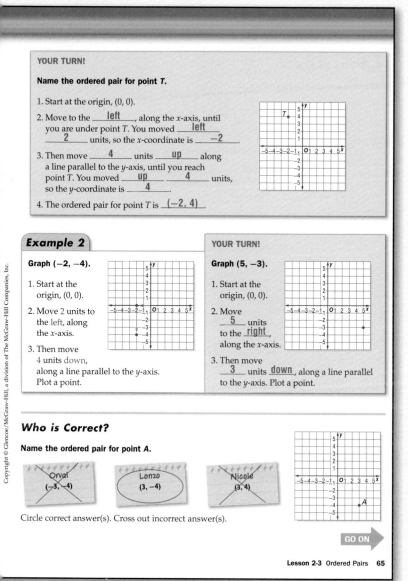

Example 2

Graph (−2, −4).

1. Start at the origin, (0, 0).

2. Move 2 units to the left, along the *x*-axis.

3. Then move 4 units down, along a line parallel to the *y*-axis. Plot a point.

YOUR TURN!

Graph (5, −3).

1. Start at the origin, (0, 0).

2. Move __5__ units to the __right__, along the *x*-axis.

3. Then move __3__ units __down__, along a line parallel to the *y*-axis. Plot a point.

Who is Correct?

Name the ordered pair for point *A*.

Orval (−3, −4)

Lonzo (3, −4)

Nicole (3, 4)

Circle correct answer(s). Cross out incorrect answer(s).

GO ON

Graph (−5, −2).

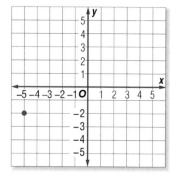

1. Start at the origin, (0, 0).

2. Move 5 units to the left, along the *x*-axis.

3. Then move 2 units down, along a line parallel to the *y*-axis. Plot a point.

Intervention Strategy
Visual Learners

Graph Ordered Pairs Draw or distribute a coordinate graph. Have students plot the following points: (1, 3), and (4, −3).

Have students connect the points. Ask students to name the two ordered pairs on the graph. Now have students plot (−2, −3) and connect the points. What shape is formed? triangle

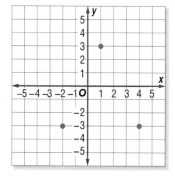

Who *is Correct?*
Diagnostic Teaching

• Orval wrote (−3, −4). This is not correct because the x-coordinate should be positive, not negative.

• Lonzo wrote (3, −4). This is correct.

• Nicole wrote (3, 4). This is not correct because the y-coordinate should be negative, not positive.

Remind students to begin at the origin. Then first move along the x-axis, and then the y-axis.

Practice

Using Manipulatives

Grid Paper Enlarge a coordinate grid that can be placed into a page cover. Students can use a dry erase marker to plot points. Then they can erase the points and reuse it.

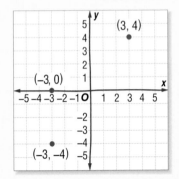

Geoboards Use bands to make shapes on a geoboard. Initially, use the board as Quadrant I. Eventually use it as other quadrants.

 On-Hand Manipulatives Have students draw light vertical lines on lined notebook paper to represent coordinate grids. Make sure they label the origin.

⚠ Common Error *Alert*

Ordered Pairs When naming the ordered pairs in Exercises 1 through 3, students may have a tendency to reverse the order of the coordinates. One way to help students remember the correct order is that x comes before y in the alphabet. This is also true for ordered pairs.

▶ Guided Practice

Name the ordered pair for each point.

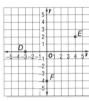

1. D __(−3, 0)__
2. E __(4, 2)__
3. F __(0, −4)__

Step by **Step Practice**

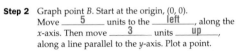

4. Graph the ordered pairs A(4, 3) and B(−5, 3). Then connect the points. What do you notice?

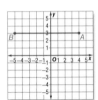

Step 1 Graph point A. Start at the origin, (0, 0). Move __4__ units to the __right__, along the x-axis. Then move __3__ units __up__, along a line parallel to the y-axis. Plot a point.

Step 2 Graph point B. Start at the origin, (0, 0). Move __5__ units to the __left__, along the x-axis. Then move __3__ units __up__, along a line parallel to the y-axis. Plot a point.

Step 3 Connect the points with a line. (4, 3) and (−5, 3) are on a line parallel to the x-axis because they have the same __y__-coordinate.

Graph the ordered pairs.

5. Graph the ordered pairs M(−5, 2) and N(−5, −4).

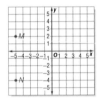

Graph point M. Start at the origin, (0, 0).
Move __5__ units to the __left__. Then move __2__ units __up__. Plot a point.

Graph point N. Start at the origin, (0, 0). Move __5__ units to the __left__. Then move __4__ units __down__. Plot a point.

Intervention Strategy **Kinesthetic Learners**

Classroom Coordinate Grid Students can measure the classroom and make a coordinate grid using masking tape. Students can work in small groups to make a map of the classroom by plotting points for the locations of objects in the classroom.

6 Graph the ordered pairs $S(-1, -4)$ and $T(5, -4)$. Then connect the points. What do you notice?

$(-1, -4)$ and $(5, -4)$ have the same ___*y*___-coordinate.

Step by Step Problem-Solving Practice

Solve.

7 **TRAVEL** Rina has a map of historical sites in her city. How many miles separate the museum from the town square? Each unit on the *x*- or *y*-axis represents one mile.

Problem-Solving Strategies
☐ Look for a pattern.
☐ Guess and check.
☐ Act it out.
☑ Use a graph.
☐ Work backward.

Understand Read the problem. Write what you know. You must find the distance between the

___town square___ and the ___museum___.

Plan Pick a strategy. One strategy is to use a graph. Find the ordered pairs for the town square and the museum. Then find the distance from one to the other.

Solve The town square is located at ___$(-1, 4)$___.

The museum is located at ___$(5, 4)$___.

The town square and the museum are on a line parallel to the *x*-axis. Count the number of units between the town square and the museum.

There are ___6___ units between the town square and the museum.

The museum is ___6___ miles from the town square.

Remember:
The absolute value is the distance between a number and 0 on a number line.

Check Use the absolute value of the ___*x*___ -coordinates to verify the distance.
$|-1| + |5| =$ ___6___

GO ON

Math Coach Notes

Study Tip Suggest that when students are preparing for a test that they take a practice test. This can be a test that they make up themselves. It should be a compilation of problems from homework or past quizzes. It can also be a review at the end of the chapter in the book. The important thing is that they study the correct information. If they have a question about the answer to a problem, tell them to ask you.

Write the Steps Have students make a coordinate graph on poster board. Tell them to label the origin and both axes. Then have them write the steps for plotting a point and reading a point on the graph.

Are They Getting It?

Check students' understanding of ordered pairs by drawing a coordinate grid and writing these problems on the board. Ask students to point out the wrong answers and explain why they are wrong.

I. The ordered pair for point *B* is (5, 4). This is incorrect. The ordered pair for point *B* is (−5, −4).

2. To get to point *C* from the origin, you move to the right. This is incorrect. You move to the left.

3. The ordered pair (3, 4) is point *A*. This is not correct. The coordinates are reversed.

4. Points *B* and *D* are 3 units from each other. This is correct.

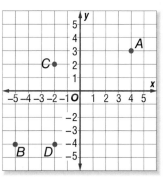

Common Error *Alert*

Plot a Picture   If students are having difficulty plotting ordered pairs, a good practice is to have them plot the points of a picture. If, after plotting these points, any of the points are graphed incorrectly, it is very easy to recognize.

CITIES   Reagan has a map of a city. Each unit on the *x*- or *y*-axis represents one block. Use the map to answer Exercises 8 and 9.

8   How many blocks separate the park from the grocery store? Check off each step.

  ✔___ Understand: I underlined key words.

  ✔___ Plan: To solve this problem, I will ___use a graph___.

  ✔___ Solve: The answer is ___6 blocks___.

  ✔___ Check: I checked my answer by ___using the absolute___

  value of the *x*-coordinates___.

9   How many blocks separate the grocery store from the fire station?

  ___7 blocks___

10   Make a map of Satinka's school. Graph the ordered pairs.

  Cafeteria   (3, 4)
  Classroom   (3, −2)
  Library   (−4, 4)

  What is the distance between the cafeteria and the library?

  $|3| + |-4| = 7$ The distance is 7 units.

11   **Reflect**   How can you find the distance between two points on a coordinate graph with the same *x*- or *y*-coordinates?

  ___You can graph the points and count the number of units___

  ___between them, or you can use the absolute value of the___

  ___different coordinates.___

Math Challenge

Partner Pictures   Give each student a coordinate grid. Tell students to draw a simple shape on their grid and plot the points. Then have them write ordered pairs on paper and give the ordered pairs to their partner. Their partners will use the ordered pairs to recreate the shape on a blank coordinate grid.

▶ Skills, Concepts, and Problem Solving

Name the ordered pair for each point.

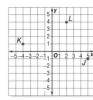

12. J __(5, −1)__

13. K __(−4, 1)__

14. L __(2, 4)__

Graph the ordered pairs.

15. Q(5, 4)

16. R(0, −3)

17. S(−4, 2)

Solve.

TOWNS Morena has a map of a town. Each unit on the *x*- or *y*-axis represents one mile. Use the map to answer Exercises 18 and 19.

18. How many miles separate the fountain from the flag?

    __5__

19. How many miles separate the fountain from the post office?

    __8__

20. Make a map of Starrtown. Graph the ordered pairs.

Post Office	(2, 1)
School	(2, −3)
Grocery Store	(−1, 1)

What is the distance between the post office and the school?

__|1| + |−3| = 4; The distance is 4 units.__

GO ON

⚠ Common Error *Alert*

Exercise 18 If students count the units instead of adding the absolute values, they may find the distance to be 6 units. Encourage students to use the addition method because then they do not have to remember if they are to count the units between the points or if they are to include the units where the points are located.

Remind students that to find the distance of two points on the same vertical line, they use *y*-coordinates of the ordered pairs. The *y*-coordinates are different numbers.

Math Coach Notes

Quadrants Point out the four quadrants to students.

- Ask several students to name ordered pairs in Quadrant I (upper right). Write these ordered pairs on the board grouped together with the label of Quadrant I.

- Ask several students to name ordered pairs in Quadrant II (upper left). Write these ordered pairs on the board grouped together with the label of Quadrant II.

- Ask several students to name ordered pairs in Quadrant III (lower left). Write these ordered pairs on the board grouped together with the label of Quadrant III.

- Ask several students to name ordered pairs in Quadrant IV (lower right). Write these ordered pairs on the board grouped together with the label of Quadrant IV.

- Have students analyze the relationship of the points written for each quadrant. Ask students to make a general statement about the ordered pairs in each quadrant. Guide students to see that all of the points in each quadrant follow these rules for signs.

Quadrant II	Quadrant I
(−, +)	(+, +)
Quadrant III	Quadrant IV
(−, −)	(+, −)

Odd/Even Assignments

Exercises 12–20 are structured so that students practice the same concepts whether they are assigned the odd or even problems.

In-Class Assignment

Have students complete Exercises 12, 16, 19, and 23 to ensure that they understand the concept.

See It, Do It, Say It, Write It

Step 1 Project a coordinate grid on the board. Ask students to guide you to graph several points such as, (5, 7), (−2, 5), and (−8, −2). Then ask them to name the ordered pairs of other points that you plot.

Step 2 Write five points on the board that include at least one point in each quadrant. Tell students to graph these points. Have students share their work and discuss their strategies.

Step 3 Tell students to draw a coordinate grid on paper. Ask them to plot any two points of their choosing, making certain to label the points. Tell them to write their method for naming the points.

Looking Ahead: Pre-teach

Coordinate Grids   In the next lesson, students will learn about graphing equations on a coordinate grid.

Example

Name three ordered pairs for y and x that can make this equation true.
$y = 2x$ (0, 0), (2, 4), (1, 2), and (3, 6)

Have students complete the following exercises.

1. Plot the ordered pairs on a coordinate grid.

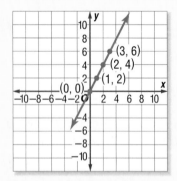

2. Connect the points. What did you make?
a straight line

3. Use the line to find the value of y, if $x = 4$.
8

Vocabulary Check   Write the vocabulary word that completes each sentence.

21 A(n) ___ordered pair___ is a pair of numbers that gives the location of a point on a map or coordinate grid.

22 The ___origin___ is the point (0, 0) on a coordinate grid where the x-axis and y-axis intersect.

23 **Writing in Math**   Explain how to graph the point (−3, −2) in two different ways.

Start at the origin, (0, 0). Move 3 units to the left and 2 units down.

Plot a point. Or, move 2 units down and 3 units to the left. Plot a point.

Spiral Review

Write a function to represent each situation. (Lesson 2-2, p. 57)

24 Dalila walks 3 more miles a day than Basilio.

$y = x + 3$

25 Aidia watches 2 times as many movies each week as Bob.

$y = 2x$

26 Make a function table for the equation $y = 3x - 1$.

x	−2	−1	0	1	2
$y = 3x - 1$	$3(-2) - 1$	$3(-1) - 1$	$3(0) - 1$	$3(1) - 1$	$3(2) - 1$
y	−7	−4	−1	2	5

Write a function and make a function table. (Lesson 2-2, p. 57)

27 **COMMUTING**   Every day Victor travels 27.4 miles to and from work. In a five-day work week, how many miles does Victor travel?

$y =$ ___27.4x___

Number of Days, x	1	2	3	4	5
27.4x	27.4(1)	27.4(2)	27.4(3)	27.4(4)	27.4(5)
Number of Miles, y	27.4	54.8	82.2	109.6	137

Victor drives ___137___ miles.

70 Chapter 2 Patterns and Graphs

Ticket Out the Door

Team Ordered Pairs   Two students each get a number cube. One student is the x-coordinate and the other is the y-coordinate. Students will roll their cubes together six times and write down the ordered pairs for each roll. Have them plot these ordered pairs together. Students can turn in their work as they exit the classroom.

Coordinate Grids

KEY Concept

To graph an equation, substitute different x-values into the equation. Evaluate the equation to find the y-values.

The x and y values form an ordered pair. Graph the ordered pairs on a coordinate grid.

Equation

$$y = -x - 1$$

> The x values can be selected at random.

Table

x	$-x - 1$	y	Ordered Pair (x, y)
2	$-2 - 1$	-3	$(2, -3)$
1	$-1 - 1$	-2	$(1, -2)$
0	$0 - 1$	-1	$(0, -1)$
-1	$-(-1) - 1$	0	$(-1, 0)$
-2	$-(-2) - 1$	1	$(-2, 1)$

After you graph the ordered pairs, connect the points with a line.

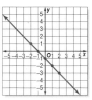

The ordered pair for each point on the line is a solution to the equation. This shows that the equation has an infinite number of solutions.

VOCABULARY

coordinate grid
a grid in which a horizontal number line and a vertical number line intersect at their zero points

ordered pair
a pair of numbers that are the coordinates of a point in a coordinate grid written in the order (horizontal coordinate, vertical coordinate)

GO ON

Intervention Strategy

Logical/Visual Learners

Graph an Equation   Ask students:

How do you graph an equation? Use a table. Use the values for x to find values of y. Graph each ordered pair. Connect the points to make a line.

Graph the equation, $y = x + 2$. Sample points: $(0, 2)$, $(1, 3)$, $(2, 4)$, $(-1, 1)$

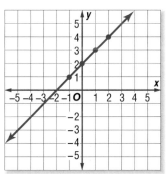

Lesson Notes

Lesson Planner

Objective   Graph linear relationships on a coordinate grid.

Vocabulary   coordinate grid , ordered pair

Materials/Manipulatives   grid paper, coordinate grids

Chapter Resource Masters

CRM Vocabulary and English Language Development (p. A39)

CRM Skills Practice (p. A40)

CRM Problem-Solving Practice (p. A41)

CRM Homework Practice (p. A42)

① Introduce

Vocabulary

Function Vocabulary   Draw a table. Show students how to pick a value for x, the input, to find a value for y, the output. Write the solutions as *ordered pairs* and plot them on a *coordinate grid*. Ask students what they notice about the points. Connect the points and make a line. Without using a table, show students how to find other *ordered pairs* that satisfy the equation.

Graphing Functions   Students should understand that the graph of an equation is all the ordered pairs that are solutions to the equation.

② Teach

Key Concept

Foundational Skills and Concepts   After students have read through the Key Concept box, have them try this exercise.

What is the relationship between x and y? The output (y) is a direct result of the input (x).

Additional *Example 1*

Graph the equation $y = 2x + 1$.

1. Make a table. Substitute $-2, -1, 0, 1,$ and $2,$ for x. Solve for y.

x	2x + 1	y	Ordered Pair
-2	2(-2) + 1	-3	(-2, -3)
-1	2(-1) + 1	-1	(-1, -1)
0	2(0) + 1	1	(0, 1)
1	2(1) + 1	3	(1, 3)
2	2(2) + 1	5	(2, 5)

2. Graph the ordered pairs. Connect the points with a line.

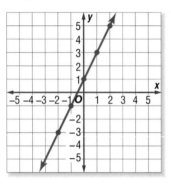

Math Coach Notes

Graphing Tip Tell students to pick zero for the x value when choosing points for the table. This is the intersection of the line with the y-axis. It is easy to evaluate an equation when the value of x is 0. The point located on the y-axis will have an x-coordinate of 0.

Example 1

Graph the equation $y = x + 3$.

1. Make a table. Substitute $-2, -1, 0, 1,$ and 2 for x. Solve for y.

x	x + 3	y	Ordered Pair
-2	-2 + 3	1	(-2, 1)
-1	-1 + 3	2	(-1, 2)
0	0 + 3	3	(0, 3)
1	1 + 3	4	(1, 4)
2	2 + 3	5	(2, 5)

2. Graph the ordered pairs. Connect the points with a line.

YOUR TURN!

Graph the equation $y = -2x - 3$.

1. Make a table. Substitute $-3, -2, -1, 0,$ and 1 for x. Solve for y.

x	-2x - 3	y	Ordered Pair
-3	-2(-3) - 3	3	(-3, 3)
-2	-2(-2) - 3	1	(-2, 1)
-1	-2(-1) - 3	-1	(-1, -1)
0	-2(0) - 3	-3	(0, -3)
1	-2(1) - 3	-5	(1, -5)

2. Graph the ordered pairs. Connect the points with a line.

Example 2

There are 3 feet in 1 yard. Show the relationship between the number of feet and the number of yards on a coordinate grid. How many feet are in 4 yards?

Let x = number of yards and y = number of feet.

feet	equals	3	times	yards
y	=	3	·	x

1. The equation is $y = 3x$.

2. Make a table. Substitute 0, 1, 2, 3, and 4 for x. Solve for y.

x	$3x$	y	Ordered Pair
0	3(0)	0	(0, 0)
1	3(1)	3	(1, 3)
2	3(2)	6	(2, 6)
3	3(3)	9	(3, 9)
4	3(4)	12	(4, 12)

3. Graph the ordered pairs. Connect the points with a line.

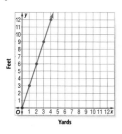

The ordered pair (4, 12) means that 4 yards have 12 feet.

YOUR TURN!

Maria earns 2 points for each layup she makes in the basketball game. Show the relationship between the number of layups she makes and the number of points she earns on a coordinate grid. How many points will Maria earn for making 5 layups?

Let x = number of layups made and y = number of points earned.

points earned	equals	2	times	layups
y	=	2	·	x

1. The equation is $y = 2x$.

2. Make a table. Substitute 1, 2, 3, 4, and 5 for x. Solve for y.

x	$2x$	y	Ordered Pair
1	2(1)	2	(1, 2)
2	2(2)	4	(2, 4)
3	2(3)	6	(3, 6)
4	2(4)	8	(4, 8)
5	2(5)	10	(5, 10)

3. Graph the ordered pairs. Connect the points with a line.

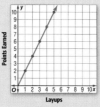

The ordered pair __(5, 10)__ means that Maria earned __10__ points for making 5 layups.

GO ON

Additional Example 2

There are 4 quarts in 1 gallon. Show the relationship between the number of quarts and the number of gallons on a coordinate grid. How many quarts are in 5 gallons?

Let x = number of gallons and y = number of quarts.

quarts	equals	4	times	gallons
y	=	4	·	x

The equation is $y = 4x$.

1. Make a table. Substitute 0, 1, 2, 3, 4, and 5 for x.

x	$4x$	y	Ordered Pair
0	4(0)	0	(0, 0)
1	4(1)	4	(1, 4)
2	4(2)	8	(2, 8)
3	4(3)	12	(3, 12)
4	4(4)	16	(4, 16)
5	4(5)	20	(5, 20)

2. Graph the ordered pairs. Connect the points with a line.

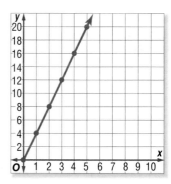

The ordered pair (5, 20) means that 5 gallons have 20 quarts.

Intervention Strategy

Interpersonal/Logical Learners

Conversion Equations Have students work in pairs. Give each pair a measurement conversion, such as 1 meter = 10 decimeters, that can be written as an equation and graphed. Tell students to make the left side of the conversion equation the y and the right side the x, multiplied by the integer. In this example, the equation is $y = 10x$. Check students' work. Then tell them to graph the equation. Each pair can present their work and answer conversion questions from the class.

Using Manipulatives

Grid Paper   Enlarge a coordinate grid that can be placed into a page protector. Students can use a dry erase marker to plot points and sketch lines. They can erase the marker and use the grid again.

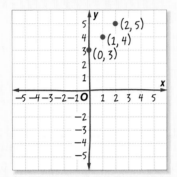

 On-Hand Manipulatives   Have students draw light vertical lines on lined notebook paper to represent coordinate grids. Make sure they label the origin.

Common Error *Alert*

Exercises 1 and 2   When completing the tables for Exercises 1 and 2, students may have difficulty remembering which coordinate is the *x*-value and which coordinate is the *y*-value. Tell students that just as *x* comes before *y* in the alphabet, i (for input) comes before o (for output).

Intervention Strategy
Logical Learners

Function Machine   Draw a function machine on the board. Using Examples 1 or 2, illustrate how a function machine can help students find the output, or *y* values, of an equation. Ask students to look around the classroom or in printed material to make a function using the function machine.

Who is Correct?

Make a table for three ordered pairs for the equation $y = 3x - 7$.

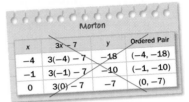

Morton

x	3x − 7	y	Ordered Pair
−4	3(−4) − 7	−18	(−4, −18)
−1	3(−1) − 7	−10	(−1, −10)
0	3(0) − 7	−7	(0, −7)

Kiele

x	3x − 7	y	Ordered Pair
1	3(1) − 7	−4	(1, −4)
3	3(3) − 7	2	(3, 2)
4	3(4) − 7	5	(4, 5)

Ernesto

x	3x − 7	y	Ordered Pair
−2	3(−2) − 7	−13	(−2, −13)
0	3(0) − 7	−7	(0, −7)
2	3(2) − 7	−1	(2, −1)

Circle correct answer(s). Cross out incorrect answer(s).

Guided Practice

Make a table for each equation.

1 $y = 9x - 4$

x	9x − 4	y	Ordered Pair
−2	9(−2) − 4	−22	(−2, −22)
−1	9(−1) − 4	−13	(−1, −13)
0	9(0) − 4	−4	(0, −4)
1	9(1) − 4	5	(1, 5)
2	9(2) − 4	14	(2, 14)

2 $y = \frac{x}{2} + 6$

x	$\frac{x}{2}$ + 6	y	Ordered Pair
−4	$\frac{-4}{2}$ + 6	4	(−4, 4)
−2	$\frac{-2}{2}$ + 6	5	(−2, 5)
0	$\frac{0}{2}$ + 6	6	(0, 6)
2	$\frac{2}{2}$ + 6	7	(2, 7)
4	$\frac{4}{2}$ + 6	8	(4, 8)

Who *is Correct?*
Diagnostic Teaching

- Morton's table is not correct because $3(-4) - 7 = -19$, not −18.

- Kiele's table is correct.

- Ernesto's table is correct.

Remind students to substitute the input (*x*) value into the equation to get the output (*y*) value.

3 Make a table for the equation.
$y = -x + 3$

x	−x + 3	y	Ordered Pair
−1	−(−1) + 3	4	(−1, 4)
1	−(1) + 3	2	(1, 2)
2	−(2) + 3	1	(2, 1)
0	−(0) + 3	3	(0, 3)

4 Graph the equation from Exercise 3.

Step by Step Practice

5 Kyle pays $4d - 2$ dollars a week to join an exercise class at his health club, where d is the number of days he attends. Show the relationship between the number of days Kyle exercises at the health club, and the amount of money he will pay each week, on the coordinate grid. How much money, m, will Kyle pay if he attends the class 3 days this week?

Step 1 Make a table. Substitute 1, 2, and 3 for d. Solve for m.

Step 2 Graph the ordered pairs. Connect the points with a line.

d	4d − 2	m	Ordered Pair
1	4(1) − 2	2	(1, 2)
2	4(2) − 2	6	(2, 6)
3	4(3) − 2	10	(3, 10)

The ordered pair __(3, 10)__ means that Kyle will pay $__10__ to attend the exercise class 3 days this week.

GO ON

Intervention Strategy

Input/Output Table To help students who struggle finding values for x and y, give them a template for the input/output table. The table can be enlarged and placed into a page protector so students can write directly on it using a dry-erase marker. As these students become more proficient, have them copy the table onto paper so they will have practice labeling the columns.

Math Coach Notes

Practice Tip Tell students that when they study to make certain that they find 4 or 5 points to graph the equation. Although 2 points are enough, it is always better to do multiple points to ensure accuracy.

Are They Getting It?

Check students' understanding of coordinate grids by writing these problems on the board. Ask students to point out wrong answers and explain why they are wrong.

1. The table for $y = -2x + 3$ looks like this.

x	−2x + 3	y	Ordered Pair
0	−2(0) + 3	3	(0, 3)
1	−2(1) + 3	5	(1, 5)
2	−2(2) + 3	7	(2, 7)
3	−2(3) + 3	9	(3, 9)

This is incorrect. The ordered pairs are (0, 3), (1, 1), (2, −1) and (3, −3).

2. Graph the equation $y = 3x - 1$. This is correct.

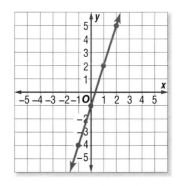

3. The ordered pairs in a table represent all the solutions for an equation. This is not correct. The line represents all the solutions.

Math Coach Notes

Connect Concepts

1. Begin this lesson by connecting it to the last lesson. Plot some points in a straight line. Demonstrate how the line can be extended to gather points on the line.

2. Make certain that students remember how to calculate with integers. You might need to review these concepts (see Book 1, Chapter 1).

Intervention Strategy

Logical/
Visual
Learners

Input/Output   Give each pair of students an item, such as a box of crayons, an eraser with the price of $0.50 on it, or a ruler. Already have an equation written on the item that students can use to graph. For instance, the box of 8 crayons would have the equation $y = 8x$, while the eraser would have $y = 0.50x$. Tell students to make a table and graph the equation. Ask them to present their findings. Use the opportunity to discuss the input (number of items) and the output further. Ensure that students create equal scales for both axes. For example, when graphing $y = 0.50x$, both the x-axis and y-axis should increase in increments of 0.5.

Step by Step Problem-Solving Practice

Solve.

Problem-Solving Strategies
- ☑ Make a graph.
- ☐ Look for a pattern.
- ☐ Guess and check.
- ☐ Act it out.
- ☐ Solve a simpler problem.

6 VIDEO GAMES   It costs $3 to rent new video games and $1 to rent older games. Sabrina has $10 to rent video games. Substitute three values in the equation $3x + y = 10$ to show how many new, x, and older games, y, Sabrina can rent for $10.

Understand   Read the problem. Write what you know. Let ___x___ represent the number of new video games and ___y___ represent the older games. Sabrina can spend __$10__. The values that you substitute for x and y must fit the equation $3x + y = 10$.

Plan   Pick a strategy. One strategy is to make a graph.

Solve   Rewrite the equation by solving for y.

$$3x + y = 10$$
$$3x + y - 3x = 10 - 3x$$
$$y = 10 - 3x$$

Then make a table. Substitute 1, 2, and 3 for x. Solve for y.

x	10 − 3x	y	Ordered Pair
1	10 − 3(1)	7	(1, 7)
2	10 − 3(2)	4	(2, 4)
3	10 − 3(3)	1	(3, 1)

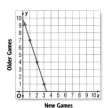

Graph the ordered pairs. Explain the solutions.

Sabrina can rent 1 new and __7__ older games for $10.
Sabrina can rent 2 new and __4__ older games for $10.
Sabrina can rent __3__ new and __1__ older game for $10.

Check   Use multiplication to check your answers.

7 NATURE Julio wants to have a picnic with his friends at a state park. The <u>cost of admission</u> to the park is <u>$2 per person, plus $1 for parking</u>. <u>Write an equation</u> to represent the situation. Then <u>substitute four values</u> to find out how much Julio will have to pay. <u>Make a table</u> and then <u>graph the ordered pairs</u>. Check off each step.

✔ Understand: I underlined key words.

✔ Plan: To solve the problem I will ___make a graph___.

✔ Solve: The answer is found below.

✔ Check: I checked my answer by ___using multiplication___.

x	2x + 1	y	Ordered Pair
1	2(1) + 1	3	(1, 3)
2	2(2) + 1	5	(2, 5)
3	2(3) + 1	7	(3, 7)
4	2(4) + 1	9	(4, 9)

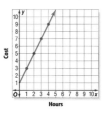

8 Reflect Explain how to graph the equation $y = 5x + 8$.

Substitute values for x into the equation and solve

for y. Graph the ordered pairs.

Skills, Concepts, and Problem Solving

9 Make a table for the equation.
$y = -3x + 4$

x	-3x + 4	y	Ordered Pair
-2	-3(-2) + 4	10	(-2, 10)
-1	-3(-1) + 4	7	(-1, 7)
0	-3(0) + 4	4	(0, 4)
1	-3(1) + 4	1	(1, 1)
2	-3(2) + 4	-2	(2, -2)

10 Graph the equation from Exercise 9.

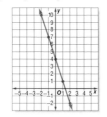

GO ON

Assignments

Assign exercises 9–11 so that students practice all the concepts presented in this lesson.

In-Class Assignment

Have students complete Exercises 9, 11, and 14 to ensure that they understand the concept.

⚠ Common Error *Alert*

Exercise 7 If students struggle with Exercise 7, it may be because they are having difficulty visualizing the situation. Suggest these students make a list to represent the situation. The list can be as follows:

1 person = $2.00
2 people = $2.00 + $2.00   } + $1.00
3 people = $2.00 + $2.00 + $2.00

Math Challenge

Intersect Lines Give students two equations whose lines will intersect. For instance, $y = x + 4$, and $y = -2x$. Tell students to make a table and graph each equation on the same coordinate grid. Ask students to write what they observe. What conclusions can they draw about the point of intersection of the two lines? Elicit the response that at the point of intersection, the ordered pair is a solution to both equations.

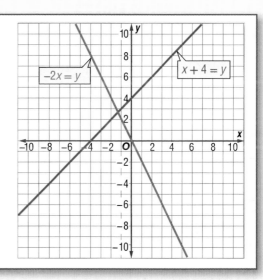

See It, Do It, Say It, Write It

Step 1 Write the equation $y = 4x - 2$ on the board. Make a table and have students help fill it in. Project or draw a grid and plot one or two points. Then have students guide you to complete the graph.

Step 2 Write the equation $y = 2x + 1$ on the board. Discuss with students how they would graph the equation. Then tell them to make a table and graph it.

Step 3 Write $y = -x - 1$ on the board. Tell students to graph the equation. Discuss the results.

Step 4 Tell students to make a graph that shows an equation for converting feet to inches. What is the input? The output? Write the equation $y = 12x$ on the board. Tell students to write about the meanings of *input* and *output*. Ask them to describe the relationship between an equation and its graph.

Looking Ahead: Pre-teach

Graph Linear and Nonlinear Functions   In the next lesson, students will learn how to graph linear and nonlinear functions.

Example

Make a function table and graph for the function $y = x^2 + 4$.

x	1	2	3	4	5
$x^2 + 4$	$1^2 + 4$	$2^2 + 4$	$3^2 + 4$	$4^2 + 4$	$5^2 + 4$
y	5	8	13	20	29

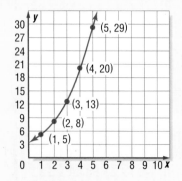

Solve.

11 JOGGING   Ronald walks 3 miles in 1 hour. Write an equation to represent the situation. Then substitute four values to find how far Ronald can walk in each situation. Make a table and then graph the ordered pairs to find the solutions.

h	$3h$	m	Ordered Pair
0	3(0)	0	(0, 0)
1	3(1)	3	(1, 3)
2	3(2)	6	(2, 6)
3	3(3)	9	(3, 9)

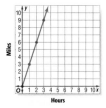

How many miles can Ronald walk in 3 hours?

The ordered pair (3, 9) means that in 3 hours Ronald can walk 9 miles.

Vocabulary Check   **Write the vocabulary word that completes each sentence.**

12 A(n) ___coordinate grid___ is a grid in which a horizontal number line and a vertical number line intersect at their zero points.

13 A(n) ___ordered pair___ is a pair of numbers that are the coordinates of a point in a coordinate grid.

14 Writing in Math   Explain how to make a table for the equation $y = -x + 7$.

Substitute $-2, -1, 0, 1,$ and 2 for x in the equation $y = -x + 7$. Solve the equation to find the values for y. $-(-2) + 7 = 9$; $-(-1) + 7 = 8$; $-(0) + 7 = 7$; $-(1) + 7 = 6$; $-(2) + 7 = 5$. The ordered pairs to graph are: $(-2, 9), (-1, 8), (0, 7), (1, 6),$ and $(2, 5)$.

 **Spiral Review**

15 SHAPES   Dylan wants to draw a square. The first three points are plotted on the coordinate grid. Where should the fourth point be plotted to make a square? Plot the point. (Lesson 2-3, p. 64)   (5, 5)

Ticket Out the Door

Write and Graph   Instruct students to write an equation, set up an input/output table, and graph the equation. Have them hand in their work as they exit the classroom.

Lesson 2-5 Linear and Nonlinear Functions

KEY Concept

A **nonlinear function** is a set of ordered pairs that are related to each other by a non-constant rate. A **function table** can be used to create ordered pairs.

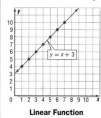

Linear Function

The **function** $y = x + 3$ is a straight line when graphed. The distance between each point along the x-axis is constant (the same). The distance between each point along the y-axis is constant.

Linear functions show a constant rate of change when graphed. So, $y = x + 3$ is a linear function.

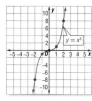

Nonlinear Function

The function $y = x^3$ is not a straight line when graphed. The distance between each point along the x-axis is constant. The distance between each corresponding point along the y-axis is not constant.

Nonlinear functions show a rate of change that is not constant when graphed. So, $y = x^3$ is a nonlinear function.

The graph of a nonlinear function is not a straight line.

GO ON

Lesson 2-5 Linear and Nonlinear Functions 79

VOCABULARY

function
a relationship in which one quantity depends upon another quantity

function table
a table of ordered pairs that is based on a rule

linear function
a function whose graph is a straight line

nonlinear function
a function whose graph is not a straight line

Lesson Planner

Objective Graph linear and nonlinear relationships.

Vocabulary function, function table, linear function, nonlinear function

Materials/Manipulatives grid paper, algebra tiles, coordinate grids

Chapter Resource Masters

- CRM Vocabulary and English Language Development (p. A43)
- CRM Skills Practice (p. A44)
- CRM Problem-Solving Practice (p. A45)
- CRM Homework Practice (p. A46)

1 Introduce

Vocabulary

Access Vocabulary Ask student volunteers to define, using their own words, what *linear* means. Challenge students to think of situations in everyday life that are *linear* and *nonlinear*.

2 Teach

Key Concept

Foundational Skills and Concepts After students have read through the Key Concept box, have them try this exercise.

How can you identify whether the function is linear or nonlinear from the graph? If the graph is a straight line, then the function is linear. If the graph is a curved line, it is a nonlinear function.

Intervention Strategy Logical/Visual Learners

Compare Linear and Nonlinear Functions

1. Write a linear function on the board with its graph, such as $x + 4$. Point out that the x-value does not have an exponent.

2. Write two nonlinear functions on the board with their graphs. Make sure that one x-value is squared and the other is cubed. Point out that the x-values have exponents.

3. Ask students if they see a connection between the x-value exponent and the graph. Have each student make a conjecture about the x-value and its graph.

Match $y = -x^2 + 2$ with its function table and its graph.

A.

x	−2	−1	0	1	2
y	2	−1	−2	−1	2

B.

x	−2	−1	0	1	2
y	−2	1	2	1	−2

I.

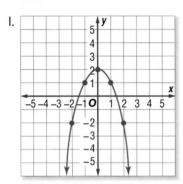

II.

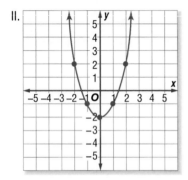

Example 1

Match $y = -3x^2 - 1$ with its function table and its graph.

A.

x	−2	−1	0	1	2
y	13	4	0	4	13

B.

x	−2	−1	0	1	2
y	−13	−4	−1	−4	−13

I.

II.

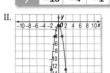

1. Use a table to check the output values.

x	−2	−1	0	1	2
$-3x^2 - 1$	$-3(-2)^2 - 1$	$-3(-1)^2 - 1$	$-3(0)^2 - 1$	$-3(1)^2 - 1$	$-3(2)^2 - 1$
y	−13	−4	−1	−4	−13

2. Table B is the function table for $y = -3x^2 - 1$. Graph II is the graph of $y = -3x^2 - 1$.

YOUR TURN!

Match $y = 4x + 3$ with its function table and its graph.

A.

x	−2	−1	0	1	2
y	−5	−1	3	7	11

B.

x	−2	−1	0	1	2
y	−11	−7	3	7	11

I.

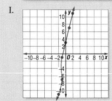

II.

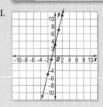

1. Use a table to check the output values.

x	−2	−1	0	1	2
$4x + 3$	$4(-2) + 3$	$4(-1) + 3$	$4(0) + 3$	$4(1) + 3$	$4(2) + 3$
y	−5	−1	3	7	11

2. Table ___A___ is the function table for $y = 4x + 3$.
   Graph ___II___ is the graph of $y = 4x + 3$.

80   **Chapter 2** Patterns and Graphs

I. Use a table to check the output values.

x	−2	−1	0	1	2
$y = -x^2 + 2$	$-(-2)^2 + 2$	$-(-1)^2 + 2$	$-(0)^2 + 2$	$-(1)^2 + 2$	$-(2)^2 + 2$
y	−2	1	2	1	−2

2. Table B is the function table for $y = -x^2 + 2$. The graph of $y = -x^2 + 2$ is Graph I.

Example 2

Make a function table and a graph for the function $y = x^2$. Is the function linear or nonlinear?

1. Make a function table using the rule $y = x^2$.

x	1	2	3	4	5
x^2	1^2	2^2	3^2	4^2	5^2
y	1	4	9	16	25

2. Graph the ordered pairs.
3. Evaluate the rate of change.

   If the rate of change is constant, draw a straight line.

   If the rate of change is not constant, draw a smooth curve to connect the points.

4. The function is nonlinear. The graph should show a smooth curve.

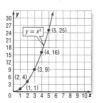

YOUR TURN!

Make a function table and a graph for the function $y = 2x^2$. Is the function linear or nonlinear?

1. Make a function table using the rule $y = \underline{2x^2}$.

x	1	2	3	4	5	6
$2x^2$	$2 \cdot 1^2$	$2 \cdot 2^2$	$2 \cdot 3^2$	$2 \cdot 4^2$	$2 \cdot 5^2$	$2 \cdot 6^2$
y	2	8	18	32	50	72

2. Graph the ordered pairs.
3. The rate of change is __not constant__.
4. The function is __nonlinear__.

   The graph should show a __smooth curve__.

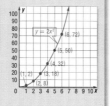

GO ON

Intervention Strategy Logical Learners

Solve Problems   Have students work to create function tables and graph the functions.

4 more than the square of a number $y = x^2 + 4$

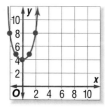

fifteen more than a number $y = x + 15$

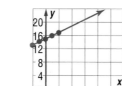

Additional *Example 2*

Make a function table and a graph for the function $y = 3x^2$. Is the function linear or nonlinear?

1. Make a function table using the rule $y = 3x^2$.

x	1	2	3	4	5
$3x^2$	$3 \cdot 1^2$	$3 \cdot 2^2$	$3 \cdot 3^2$	$3 \cdot 4^2$	$3 \cdot 5^2$
y	3	12	27	48	75

2. Graph the ordered pairs.

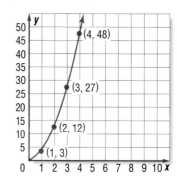

3. Evaluate the rate of change. If the rate of change is constant, draw a line. If the rate of change is not constant, draw a smooth curve to connect the points.

4. The function is nonlinear. The graph should show a smooth curve.

Math Coach Notes

Neatness and Graph Paper   Be sure that all students have graph paper. Recommend that students not only use the graph paper to graph the functions, but also to create the function table. The grid system makes it easier for students to create neat tables.

3 Practice

Using Manipulatives

Algebra Tiles Use algebra tiles to give students a visual concept of functions. Use the algebra tiles to show the equation, and then show the value of y for every x value. Modeling this will show students a pattern to the function, which will allow them to predict the next values.

On-Hand Manipulatives Use objects, beans, marked index cards, or squares of construction paper as you would algebra tiles.

Grid Paper Give grid paper to students to help them graph linear and nonlinear functions. Show students how to create a coordinate grid on graph paper. This will provide a visual concept of graphing linear and nonlinear functions. Students can then visually predict whether the function is linear or nonlinear.

⚠ Common Error *Alert*

Who is Correct Tell students that the coefficient of -2 is not part of the base of the power. Cube the value substituted for x and then multiply by -2.

Intervention Strategy | Kinesthetic Learners

Model Graphs Arrange students into pairs and have each pair create a graph using a piece of string for nonlinear functions and a piece of spaghetti for linear functions. They should then make a function table that represents each type and glue their object to the graph to show the rest of the class.

Who is Correct?

Make a function table for $y = -2x^3$.

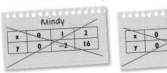 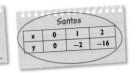

Circle correct answer(s). Cross out incorrect answer(s).

▶ Guided Practice

Complete each function table.

1 $y = x^3 - 5$

x	−2	−1	0	1	2
y	−13	−6	−5	−4	3

2 $y = 5x + 10$

x	−2	−1	0	1	2
y	0	5	10	15	20

Match each function with its function table and its graph.

3 $y = 5x - 2$
Function table ___B___
Graph ___II___

4 $y = 2x^2 + 1$
Function table ___A___
Graph ___III___

A.

x	−2	−1	0	1	2
y	9	3	1	3	9

B.

x	−2	−1	0	1	2
y	−12	−7	−2	3	8

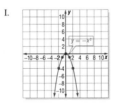 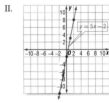 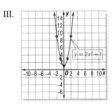

Who *is Correct?*
Diagnostic Teaching

- Mindy is not correct. She made an error computing the sign of $y = -2(2)^3$.

- RJ is incorrect. He made a computational error when simplifying $y = -2(2)^3$.

- Santos is correct.

Remind students to choose input values and calculate the output values. Have them show all the steps for simplifying to avoid careless errors.

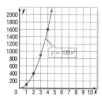

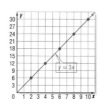

5 Make a function table and a graph for the function $y = 100x^2$. Is the function linear or nonlinear?

Step 1 Make a function table using the rule $y =$ ___100x²___.

x	1	2	3	4
y	100	400	900	1,600

Step 2 Graph the ordered pairs.

Step 3 The rate of change is ___not constant___.

Step 4 Connect the points. The function is ___nonlinear___.

The graph should show a ___smooth curve___.

6 Make a function table and a graph for $y = 3x$. Is the function linear or nonlinear?

x	2	4	6	8	10
y	6	12	18	24	30

The function is ___linear___.

GO ON

Lesson 2-5 Linear and Nonlinear Functions   **83**

English Learner Strategy

Teaching in Native Language Place students who share the same native language in a study team so that they can explain the concepts to each other using their native language. Retention increases when students are given the opportunity to teach what they have learned. By allowing the teaching to occur in the more familiar language, you will enhance understanding and retention.

Step by Step Problem-Solving Practice

Problem-Solving Strategies
- ☑ Make a table.
- ☐ Look for a pattern.
- ☐ Guess and check.
- ☐ Act it out.
- ☐ Solve a simpler problem.

7   INVESTING   Jada invested in a new company. The amount of money she earned is one dollar less than the cube of the number of years she has invested. How much money did Jada earn in the third year?

Understand   Read the problem. Write what you know.

Write a function. Let x = the number of years and y = the number of dollars Jada earned.

Plan   Pick a strategy. One strategy is to make a table.

Solve   Make a function table using the rule $y = \underline{x^3 - 1}$.

Number of Years, x	1	2	3
Number of Dollars, y	0	7	26

Graph the ordered pairs. Evaluate the rate of change. Connect the points.

In the third year, Jada earned $\underline{\$26}$.

Check   Substitute $\underline{3}$ for x in the function.

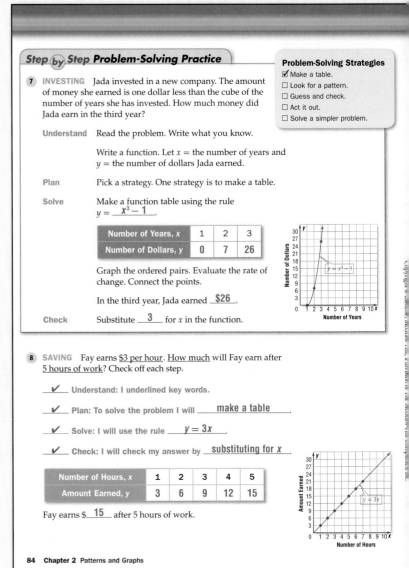

8   SAVING   Fay earns <u>$3 per hour</u>. <u>How much</u> will Fay earn after <u>5 hours of work</u>? Check off each step.

✔ Understand: I underlined key words.

✔ Plan: To solve the problem I will __make a table__.

✔ Solve: I will use the rule __$y = 3x$__.

✔ Check: I will check my answer by __substituting for x__.

Number of Hours, x	1	2	3	4	5
Amount Earned, y	3	6	9	12	15

Fay earns $ __15__ after 5 hours of work.

Are They Getting It? ?

Check students' understanding of linear and nonlinear functions by writing these problems on the board. Have students explain the incorrect information in each problem. Encourage students to use a table or a graph in their explanation.

Write a function to represent each situation.

1. This is the area of a rectangle with a length that is 11 centimeters longer than its width.

$y = x(x + 11)$ This is correct.

2. Ian gives 2 times the square of the number of hours worked to a charity.

$y = x \times 2$ This is not correct. The correct function is $y = 2x^2$.

3. At a fundraiser drawing, the number of tickets picked was 6 less than 3 times the cube of the players.

$y = 3x^3 - 6$ This is correct.

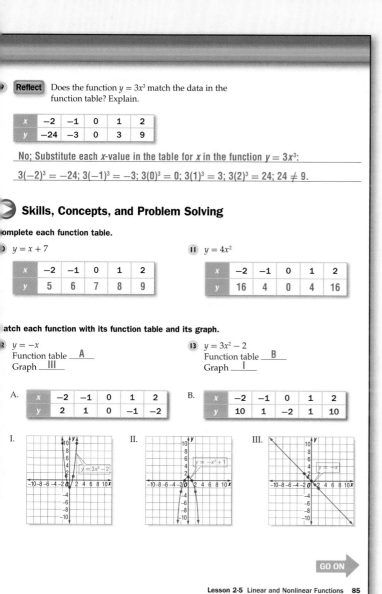

Reflect Does the function $y = 3x^3$ match the data in the function table? Explain.

x	−2	−1	0	1	2
y	−24	−3	0	3	9

No; Substitute each x-value in the table for x in the function $y = 3x^3$:

$3(−2)^3 = −24; 3(−1)^3 = −3; 3(0)^3 = 0; 3(1)^3 = 3; 3(2)^3 = 24; 24 \neq 9.$

Skills, Concepts, and Problem Solving

Complete each function table.

10. $y = x + 7$

x	−2	−1	0	1	2
y	5	6	7	8	9

11. $y = 4x^2$

x	−2	−1	0	1	2
y	16	4	0	4	16

Match each function with its function table and its graph.

12. $y = −x$
Function table __A__
Graph __III__

13. $y = 3x^2 − 2$
Function table __B__
Graph __I__

A.
x	−2	−1	0	1	2
y	2	1	0	−1	−2

B.
x	−2	−1	0	1	2
y	10	1	−2	1	10

GO ON

Lesson 2-5 Linear and Nonlinear Functions 85

Common Error *Alert*

More with Exponents If students are having difficulty graphing functions of the type $y = 3x^2 − 2$, have them practice computing with exponents. Make sure that students practice simplifying negative base numbers and numbers cubed.

Odd/Even Assignments

Exercises 10–15 are structured so that students practice the same concepts whether they are assigned the odd or even problems.

In-Class Assignment

Have students complete Exercises 10, 13, 14, and 17, to ensure that they understand the concept.

Intervention Strategy   Visual Learners

Vertical Line Test A test used to determine if a relation is a function graphically is the vertical line test. It states that a relation is a function if there are no vertical lines that intersect the graph at more than one point. Have students try the vertical line test on examples that are and are not functions.

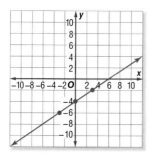

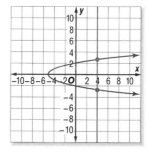

This graph is the graph of a function because there are no vertical lines that intersect the graph at more than one point.

This graph is not the graph of a function because there are many vertical lines that could intersect the graph more than once.

Lesson 2-5 Linear and Nonlinear Functions **85**

See It, Do It, Say It, Write It

Step 1 Write multiple linear pattern word problems on the board.

Step 2 Have students make a function table (showing the relationship between the *x* and *y* values).

Step 3 Arrange students into pairs and have them explain to each other how they found the pattern that fits the given situation.

Step 4 Have students write in their own words the definitions of each of the vocabulary words. They should also solve a linear pattern in their math journals.

Math Challenge

Graphing Calculators Provide students with graphing calculators to verify that their graphs are accurate. They must enter the functions at the $y =$ screen and then graph in an appropriate viewing window.

Make a function table and a graph for each function. Is the function linear or nonlinear?

14 $y = x(x + 8)$

x	1	2	3	4	5
y	9	20	33	48	65

The function is _nonlinear_.

15 $y = x^3 - 5$

x	2	3	4	5
y	3	22	59	120

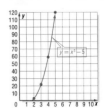

The function is _nonlinear_.

Vocabulary Check **Write the vocabulary word that completes each sentence.**

16 A(n) _____function_____ is a relationship in which one quantity depends upon another quantity.

17 **Writing in Math** Explain how to graph a nonlinear function.

Make a function table using the rule of a function. Then graph the

ordered pairs. Draw a smooth curve to connect the ordered pairs.

 Spiral Review

18 Make a table for the equation $y = 4x + 2$. (Lesson 2-4, p. 71)

x	4x + 2	y	Ordered Pair
−2	4(−2) + 2	−6	(−2, −6)
−1	4(−1) + 2	−2	(−1, −2)
0	4(0) + 2	2	(0, 2)
1	4(1) + 2	6	(1, 6)
2	4(2) + 2	10	(2, 10)

Ticket Out the Door

Mental Math Write the function $y = -\left(\dfrac{x}{2}\right)^2$ on the board. As each student approaches the door, give him or her an input value. The student should compute the output value. Continue until all students have exited the classroom.

Progress Check 2 (Lessons 2-3, 2-4, and 2-5)

Name the ordered pair for each point.

1. A (−7, −6)
2. B (−3, 8)
3. C (6, 3)
4. D (4, −8)

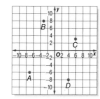

Write a function, make a function table, and make a graph. Is the function linear or nonlinear?

5. **CRAFTS** Carlita makes bracelets at Jade's Jewelry. She makes approximately 5 new bracelets to sell each day.

y = 5x

Number of Days, x	1	2	3	4	5	6
Number of Bracelets, y	5	10	15	20	25	30

In 6 days, about how many bracelets would Carlita make to sell at the jewelry store?

Carlita would make about **30** bracelets in 6 days. The function is **linear**.

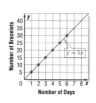

6. Jae measured how many cups of water drip from a broken sink faucet each hour.

y = 2x

Hours Passed, x	1	2	3	4
Cups of Water, y	2	4	6	8

How many cups of water have dripped after 4 hours?

After 4 hours, **8** cups of water have dripped. The function is **linear**.

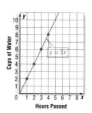

Progress Check 87

Progress Check 2

Formative Assessment

Use the Progress Check to assess students' mastery of the previous lessons. Have students review the lesson indicated for the problems they answered incorrectly.

Odd/Even Assignments

Exercises are structured so that students practice the same concepts whether they are assigned the odd or even problems.

Math Coach Notes

Notice the Graphs Point out the axes labels on the graphs to students. Emphasize that the horizontal axis is labeled *x*, and the vertical axis is labeled *y*. Be sure students understand that they will eventually have to supply the labels and mark the increments of the graphs themselves.

Data-Driven Decision Making

Students missing Exercises . . .	Have trouble with . . .	Should review and practice . . .
1–4	identifying ordered pairs.	SSG Lesson 2-3, p. 64 CRM Skills Practice, p. A36
5–6	writing functions, making function tables, making a graph from the data on the table, then stating whether the graph is linear or nonlinear.	SSG Lessons 2-4 and 2-5, pp. 71 and 79 CRM Skills Practice, pp. A40 and A44

Study Guide
Formative Assessment

Vocabulary and Concept Check

If students have difficulty answering Exercises 1–10, remind them that they can use the page references to refresh their memories about the vocabulary terms.

Vocabulary Review Strategies

Vocabulary Frames   Have students create vocabulary frames for the words. On the set of cards, state the definition, and on the other side write the vocabulary term. If a vocabulary term can be better expressed in the form of a picture, then draw a picture in place of the definition for those words. The students can use the frames to study by themselves or with partners.

Lesson Review

The examples walk the students through solving problems involving writing rules for patterns, making function tables, graphing ordered pairs, determining whether a graph is linear or nonlinear, and graphing a line given its equation. If additional examples are needed to review the topics, have students design their own example(s) from a particular section of the chapter. When finished, have them trade their examples with other students.

Find **Extra Practice** for these concepts in the Practice Worksheets, pages A27–A46.

Classroom Management

Group Practice   For additional practice with all the steps of functions, divide the class into groups and give each group a different "situation" for which they have to write a function, make a function table, and create a graph. Then after a few minutes, have the groups present their "situation" to the class.

Vocabulary and Concept Check

equation, *p. 57*
function, *p. 57*
function table, *p. 57*
linear function, *p. 79*
nonlinear function, *p. 79*
ordered pair, *p. 64*
origin, *p. 64*
pattern, *p. 50*
rule, *p. 50*
term, *p. 50*
variable, *p. 57*
x-axis, *p. 64*
y-axis, *p. 64*

Write the vocabulary word that completes each sentence.

1 A(n) ____function____ is a relationship in which one quantity depends upon another quantity.

2 A(n) ____function table____ is a table of ordered pairs that is based on a rule.

3 A(n) ____linear function____ is a function whose graph is a line.

4 Each number in a sequence is called a(n) ____term____.

5 A mathematical sentence that contains an equal sign is called a(n) ____equation____.

Label each diagram below. Write the correct vocabulary term in each blank.

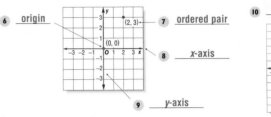

6 ____origin____

7 ____ordered pair____

8 ____x-axis____

9 ____y-axis____

10 ____nonlinear function____

Lesson Review

2-1   Number Relationships (pp. 50–56)

Find a rule for each pattern.

11 185, 179, 173, 167 ____subtract 6____

12 −4, 8, −16, 32 ____multiply by −2____

13 SHAPES   An octagon has 8 sides. How many sides do 7 octagons have?

____56 sides____

Example 1

How many toes are on 6 owl feet?

1. Each foot has 4 toes. The rule is multiply the number of feet by 4.

2. There are 24 toes on 6 feet.

2-2 Introduction to Functions (pp. 57–63)

Write a function and make a function table.

14 Mary is 3 years younger than Rae.

Let x = Rae's age and y = Mary's age.
$y = \underline{\quad x - 3 \quad}$

Rae's Age, x	14	15	16	17	18	19
Mary's Age, y	11	12	13	14	15	16

How old will Mary be when Rae is 19?

Mary will be 16 years old.

Example 2

Write a function and make a function table.

1. Every quadrilateral has 4 sides. What is the total number of sides in x quadrilaterals?

2. Use the function $y = 4x$ where x = the number of quadrilaterals and y = the number of sides.

3. Make a function table using the rule $y = 4x$.

Number of Quadrilaterals, x	1	2	3	4	5
Number of Sides, y	4	8	12	16	20

4. How many sides do 5 quadrilaterals have?
Five quadrilaterals have a total of 20 sides.

2-3 Ordered Pairs (pp. 64–70)

Graph each ordered pair.

15 $A\,(-4, -4)$

16 $B\,(2, 4)$

17 $C\,(-3, 5)$

18 $D\,(5, 0)$

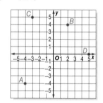

Example 3

Graph the ordered pair (5, −3).

1. Start at the origin, $(0, 0)$.
Move 5 units to the right, along the x-axis.
Then move 3 units down, along a line parallel to the y-axis.

2. Plot a point.

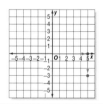

 **Dinah Zike's Foldables**

Review   Remind students to complete and refer to their Foldables as they progress through the Chapter 2 Study Guide. Have students share and compare their completed Foldables with a partner. You may also choose to have them use their Foldable as a study aid in preparing for the Chapter Test. (For complete instructions, see Chapter Resource Masters, p. A24.)

Number Relationships

Note This!

Functions   Ask students to look at the equations they have worked with that have been linear and those that have been nonlinear. Ask them if they notice anything consistently different between the two types. *They should mention the squared or cubed power of the variable.*

Common Error *Alert*

Use Self-Guided Questioning   If students are having trouble with word problems involving writing an equation given a scenario, making an input/output table based upon the equation, then graphing the data in the input/output table, perhaps they need to ask themselves some or all of the following questions.

- *What am I trying to find?*

- *What is the dependent variable?*

- *What is the independent variable?*

- *What is my equation?*

- *What are some good examples of x-coordinates I should use in my input/output table? Will I graph this on a coordinate grid with all four quadrants, or will it be in only one (such as Quadrant I)?*

2-4 **Coordinate Grids** (pp. 71–78)

19 Graph the equation $y = -3x - 1$.

x	−3x − 1	y	Ordered Pair
−2	−3(−2) − 1	5	(−2, 5)
−1	−3(−1) − 1	2	(−1, 2)
0	−3(0) − 1	−1	(0, −1)
1	−3(1) − 1	−4	(1, −4)

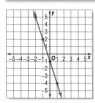

20 Tony has $3 in his savings account. He wants to save $2 more each week. Show the relationship between the number of dollars he saves each week and the total amount of money in his savings account, without interest.

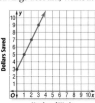

How much money will Tony have in his savings account after 3 more weeks?

Tony will have $ __9__ .

Example 4

There are 2 pints in a quart. Write an equation to represent the situation. Then substitute five values to show the relationship between pints and quarts on a coordinate grid. How many pints are in 4 quarts?

1. Let x = number of pints and y = number of quarts.

quarts	equals	0.5	times	pints
y	=	0.5	·	x

2. Write the equation: $y = 0.5x$.

3. Make a table. Substitute 0, 2, 6, 8, and 10 for x. Solve for y.

x	0.5x	y	Ordered Pair
0	0.5(0)	0	(0, 0)
2	0.5(2)	1	(2, 1)
6	0.5(6)	3	(6, 3)
8	0.5(8)	4	(8, 4)
10	0.5(10)	5	(10, 5)

4. Graph the ordered pairs. Connect the points with a line.

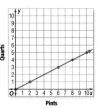

5. The ordered pair (10, 5) means that there are 10 pints in 5 quarts.

2-5 Linear and Nonlinear Functions (pp. 79–86)

Write a function, make a function table, and make a graph. Is the function linear or nonlinear?

21 **VIDEOS** It will cost Peyton $15 to join the video game club. Then the club will charge him $4 for each video game rental.

$y =$ $\underline{4x + 15}$

Number of Video Games, x	1	2	3	4
Amount (in dollars), y	19	23	27	31

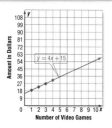

How much does Peyton pay if he joins the club and then rents 3 games?

Peyton pays $\underline{\quad 27 \quad}$ for a membership plus $4 per video game rental.

The function is $\underline{\quad \text{linear} \quad}$.

Example 5

Write a function, make a function table, and make a graph. Is the function linear or nonlinear?

GRADES For every A Jase earns on his report card, he receives three times the square of the number of A's in quarters from his grandfather. How many quarters does Jase receive if he earns 6 A's on his report card?

1. Use the function $y = 3x^2$ where $x =$ the number of A's on Jase's report card and $y =$ the amount received (in quarters).

2. Make a function table using the rule $y = 3x^2$.

Number of A's, x	1	2	3	4	5	6
Amount (in quarters), y	3	12	27	48	75	108

3. Graph the ordered pairs. Draw a smooth curve to connect the ordered pairs.

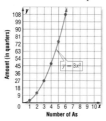

4. Jase will receive 108 quarters, or $27, from his grandfather if he earns 6 A's on his report card. The function is nonlinear.

Math Coach Notes

Study Tips Give students the following study tips.

- Review material right after class when the concepts are fresh in your mind.

- Start out by studying the most important information.

- Study in a quiet place with few or no distractions.

- Summarize your notes by including the most important concepts.

- Break down the steps to solving each problem. Write them down.

- Space out your studying. Do not try to learn everything all in one night.

Ticket Out the Door

Do These Problems Write a situation on the board. Have students write a function for the situation and find three ordered pair solutions. Have the students graph the ordered pairs and connect them with a line. They should turn in their graphs as they exit the classroom.

Chapter Test

Chapter Resource Masters

Additional forms of the Chapter 2 Tests are available.

Test Format	Where to Find it
Chapter 2 Test	**Math Online** glencoe.com
Blackline Masters	Assessment Masters, p. 40

ExamView®
Assessment Suite

Customize and create multiple versions of your chapter tests and their answer keys. All of these questions from the chapter tests are available on ExamView® Assessment Suite.

Advance TRACKER

Online Assessment and Reporting
glencoe.com

This online assessment tool allows teachers to track student progress with easily-accessible, comprehensive reports available for every student. Assess students using any internet-ready computer.

Alternative Assessment

Use Portfolios Ask students to summarize the methods for all of the following: writing functions, making function tables, and recognizing linear and nonlinear graphs. They should organize the information in the way that best suits them, such as in a portfolio with examples (including tables and diagrams, as needed), on a Foldable, in a list, or in a paragraph.

Chapter
2 **Chapter Test**

In each sequence, find a rule. Then write the next three terms.

1 $4, -12, 36, -108, 324$

Rule: _____ multiply by -3 _____
Next terms:
_____ $-972; 2,916; -8,748$ _____

2 $641.72; 627.50; 613.28; 599.06$

Rule: _____ subtract 14.22 _____
Next terms:
_____ $584.84; 570.62; 556.40$ _____

Write a function to represent each situation.

3 Tanner is 4 years older than Justice. _____ $y = x + 4$ _____

4 Zita spent \$10 more than twice the amount Virginia spent.
_____ $y = 2x + 10$ _____

Name the ordered pair for each point.

5 A _____ $(-3, 4)$ _____

6 B _____ $(5, 2)$ _____

7 C _____ $(4, -2)$ _____

8 D _____ $(-1, 0)$ _____

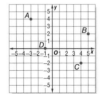

9 Make a table for the equation.
$y = 3x - 2$

x	y
−1	−5
0	−2
1	1
2	4

10 Graph the equation from Exercise 9.

English Learner Strategy

Assessment Provide students with time to look over the assessment. Have them take a close look at all of the section directions, as well as any terms in the word problems. Be sure students understand what is being asked of them in each problem. If necessary, provide them with clarification. Also have students look for math vocabulary terms used throughout the assessment. Go over the terms with the class, and review all of the meanings of the essential math vocabulary.

Write a function, make a function table, and graph the ordered pairs.

11 COOKING   Diana is baking some cookies for her annual cookie exchange. She is going to make 4 batches of her cookies, and each batch requires 3 large eggs. How many eggs does she need to make x batches of cookies?

$y = \underline{\ 3x\ }$

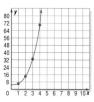

Number of Cookie Batches, x	1	2	3	4
Number of Eggs, y	3	6	9	12

How many eggs would Diana use to make all 4 batches of her cookies? $\underline{\ 12\ }$

Make a function table and graph for the function. Is the function linear or nonlinear?

12 $y = x^3 + 6$

x	1	2	3	4
y	7	14	33	70

The function is $\underline{\quad nonlinear \quad}$.

Solve.

13 TRAVEL   During each day of her one-week vacation on Mackinac Island, Monica biked a distance of 15 miles. Over the entire vacation, how many miles did Monica bike?

$\underline{\text{Monica biked a total of 105 miles.}}$

Correct the mistakes.

14 On Nikki's math quiz, the problem stated: "For every mile you bicycle, you burn 35 Calories. Write the function."

What is the mistake Nikki made?

$\underline{\text{Nikki added instead of multiplying. The answer}}$

$\underline{\text{should be } y = 35x.}$

Nikki
$y = x + 35$

STOP

Chapter 2 Test   93

Data-Driven Decision Making

Students missing Exercises . . .	Have trouble with . . .	Should review and practice . . .
1–2	finding the rule of a pattern.	SSG Lesson 2-1, p. 50 CRM Skills Practice, p. A28
3–4	writing a function to represent a situation.	SSG Lesson 2-2, p. 57 CRM Skills Practice, p. A32
5–8	identifying ordered pairs.	SSG Lesson 2-3, p. 64 CRM Skills Practice, p. A36
9–12	writing a function, making a function table, and making a graph.	SSG Lessons 2-4 and 2-5, pp. 71 and 79 CRM Skills Practice, pp. A40 and A44
13–14	solving word problems involving functions, equations, and graphs.	CRM Problem-Solving Practice, pp. A29, A33, A37, A41 and A45

Test Practice

⚠ Diagnose Student Errors

Survey student responses for each item. Class trends may indicate common errors and misconceptions.

1. A reversed *x*- and *y*-coordinates
    Ⓑ correct
    C guess
    D guess

2. A opposite sides are not parallel
    B opposite sides are not parallel
    C opposite sides are not parallel
    Ⓓ correct

3. A miscalculated, 4 T-shirts × $9 = $36
    B miscalculated, 5 T-shirts × $9 = $45
    C miscalculated, 6 T-shirts × $9 = $54
    Ⓓ correct

4. A pattern not consistent
    B pattern increasing, not decreasing
    Ⓒ correct
    D pattern not consistent

5. Ⓐ correct
    B miscalculated pattern
    C skipped a number
    D skipped two numbers

6. A guess
    B misinterpreted pattern
    C guess
    Ⓓ correct

7. Ⓐ correct
    B point falls on the line
    C point falls on the line
    D point falls on the line

8. A misinterpreted pattern
    Ⓑ correct
    C misinterpreted next number
    D misinterpreted pattern

Choose the best answer and fill in the corresponding circle on the sheet at right.

1 Which point on the grid corresponds to the ordered pair (4, 6)?

A *A*
Ⓑ *B*
C *C*
D *D*

---

2 Which shape is made by plotting and connecting the following points on the coordinate grid: (3, 1), (7, 4), (7, 6), (3, 9)?

A parallelogram
B rectangle
C square
Ⓓ trapezoid

---

3 Molly is selling T-shirts for a school fund-raiser. Use her chart to make a line graph that shows the data. If her goal is to raise at least $60, how many T-shirts does Molly need to sell?

T-Shirts Sold, *x*	Money Raised, *y*
1	$9
2	$18
3	$27

A 4 T-shirts
B 5 T-shirts
C 6 T-shirts
Ⓓ 7 T-shirts

---

4 What is a rule for this pattern?

    30, 60, 120, 240, 480, 960

A add 30
B subtract 30
Ⓒ multiply by 2
D add 60

5 What is the next number in the sequence?

12, 17, 22, 27, 32, _____

(A) 37   C 42

B 40   D 47

---

6 Find the missing number.

x	5	8	9	12
y	10	16	18	?

A 27   C 25

B 26   (D) 24

---

7 Which ordered pair does *not* fall on the line for the equation $y = x + 3$?

(A) (3, 7)   C (5, 8)

B (2, 5)   D (6, 9)

---

8 What is the next number in the sequence?

9, 18, 27, 36, 45, _____

A 50

(B) 54

C 58

D 60

ANSWER SHEET

Directions: Fill in the circle of each correct answer.

1 (A) (●B) (C) (D)
2 (A) (B) (C) (●D)
3 (A) (B) (C) (●D)
4 (A) (B) (●C) (D)
5 (●A) (B) (C) (D)
6 (A) (B) (C) (●D)
7 (●A) (B) (C) (D)
8 (A) (●B) (C) (D)

Diagnosing Student Errors and Misconceptions

Polls When working on the Test Practice problems, have students show their work on a separate sheet of notebook paper that can be used later as a reference as needed. After the class has completed the Test Practice problems, randomly solicit answers to each question. After each question, take an informal poll of how many students answered the question correctly. If you notice that a significant number of students missed a particular question or questions, then review the method or strategy behind the question with the entire class.

Chapter Overview

Chapter-at-a-Glance

Lesson	Math Objective	State/Local Standards
3-1 Order of Operations (pp. 98–104)	Use the order of operations to evaluate expressions.	
3-2 Evaluate Algebraic Expressions (pp. 105–111)	Write, simplify, and evaluate expressions.	
Progress Check 1 (p. 112)		
3-3 Solve Algebraic Equations (pp. 113–118)	Solve simple linear equations.	
3-4 Relate Algebraic Equations and Formulas (pp. 119–125)	Solve simple linear equations for one variable in terms of another.	
Progress Check 2 (p. 126)		

Content-at-a-Glance

The diagram below summarizes and unpacks Chapter 3 content.

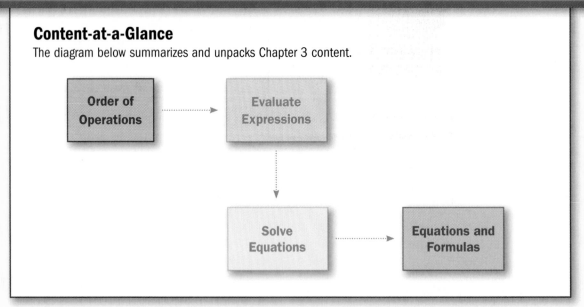

Diagnostic   Diagnose students' readiness.

	Student/Teacher Editions	Assessment Masters	Technology
Course Placement Test		1	⊙ ExamView® Assessment Suite
Book 1 Pretest		23	⊙ ExamView® Assessment Suite
Chapter 3 Pretest		48	⊙ ExamView® Assessment Suite
Quiz/Preview	SSG 97		Math Online ⟩ glencoe.com StudentWorks™ Plus

Formative   Identify students' misconceptions of content knowledge.

	Student/Teacher Editions	Assessment Masters	Technology
Progress Checks	SSG 112, 126		Math Online ⟩ glencoe.com StudentWorks™ Plus
Vocabulary Review	SSG 127		Math Online ⟩ glencoe.com
Lesson Assessments			⊙ ExamView® Assessment Suite
Are They Getting It?	TE 101, 107, 115, 122		Math Online ⟩ glencoe.com

Summative   Determine student success in learning the concepts in the lesson, chapter, or book.

	Student/Teacher Editions	Assessment Masters	Technology
Chapter 3 Test	SSG 132	51	⊙ ExamView® Assessment Suite
Test Practice	SSG 134	54	⊙ ExamView® Assessment Suite
Alternative Assessment	TE 132	57	
See It, Do It, Say It, Write It	TE 104, 111, 118, 125		
Book 1 Test		59	⊙ ExamView® Assessment Suite

Backmapping and Vertical Alignment **McGraw-Hill's** *Math Triumphs* intervention program was conceived and developed with the final results in mind: student success in grade-level mathematics, including Algebra 1 and beyond. The authors, using the **NCTM Focal Points and Focal Connections** as their guide, developed this brand-new series by backmapping from grade-level and Algebra 1 concepts, and vertically aligning the topics so that they build upon prior skills and concepts and serve as a foundation for future topics.

	Lesson 3-1	Lesson 3-2	Lesson 3-3	Lesson 3-4
Concept	Order of Operations	Evaluate Algebraic Expressions	Solve Algebraic Equations	Relate Algebraic Equations and Formulas
Objective	Use the order of operations to evaluate expressions.	Write, simplify, and evaluate expressions.	Solve simple linear equations.	Solve simple linear equations for one variable in terms of another.
Math Vocabulary	base exponent order of operations	algebraic expression evaluate order of operations	algebraic expression equation inverse operations variable	area equation formula variable
Lesson Resources	**Materials** • Poster board • Index cards **Manipulatives** • Algebra tiles • Balance scale **Other Resources** CRM Vocabulary and English Language Development CRM Skills Practice CRM Problem-Solving Practice CRM Homework Practice	**Materials** • Everyday objects • Index cards **Manipulatives** • Two-color counters **Other Resources** CRM Vocabulary and English Language Development CRM Skills Practice CRM Problem-Solving Practice CRM Homework Practice	**Materials** • Stamper markers **Manipulatives** • Algebra tiles • Two-color counters • Balance scale **Other Resources** CRM Vocabulary and English Language Development CRM Skills Practice CRM Problem-Solving Practice CRM Homework Practice	**Materials** • Grid paper **Manipulatives** • Balance scale • Unit cubes • Geoboards **Other Resources** CRM Vocabulary and English Language Development CRM Skills Practice CRM Problem-Solving Practice CRM Homework Practice
Technology	**Math Online** glencoe.com StudentWorks™ Plus ⊙ ExamView® Assessment Suite	**Math Online** glencoe.com StudentWorks™ Plus ⊙ ExamView® Assessment Suite	**Math Online** glencoe.com StudentWorks™ Plus ⊙ ExamView® Assessment Suite	**Math Online** glencoe.com StudentWorks™ Plus ⊙ ExamView® Assessment Suite

Intervention Strategy

Words to Numbers

Students translate verbal problems to equations to connect mathematics to their everyday life. Then solve the equations in an interactive environment.

Step 1

Have students work in pairs. Write a word problem on the board such as "Terry has 7 more pencils than Jim. Together they have 13 pencils."

Step 2

Have one student pair come to the board and identify and circle the known and unknown values in the sentence.

Step 3

A different student pair comes to the board and identifies the operation the problem indicates. The students will choose a variable for the unknown and write an equation to represent the situation. Discuss the accuracy of the equation.

Step 4

All pairs can solve the equation. One pair comes to the board and explains the steps involved. Explain how the Property of Equality was used and remind students to substitute to check their answers.

Step 5

Repeat with word problems that require subtraction, multiplication, and division to solve.

Step 6

Have students write verbal sentences that connect to their world. These sentences can refer to music, food, homework, friends, and so on. Students can share their word problems on the board. An alternative is to have each student pair 'play teacher' and lead the class to identify the known and unknown values, write the equation, and solve the equation for their situation.

Real-World Applications

Popcorn and Peanuts You and four friends are at a baseball game. Three of you each want a box of popcorn and the others each want a bag of peanuts. If you are going to buy all the snacks, how much money should you take if the popcorn is $1.75 per box and the peanuts are $2.50 per bag? $10.25

Intervention Strategy
Concession Stand Sales

Step 1 Arrange students into groups of 3. Explain that each group will act out the situation of working in a concession stand. Have students choose 3 or 4 items that they would like to sell in their concession stand.

Step 2 Students should agree on a per item price for each item sold in the concession stand. Prices should not be whole dollar amounts, but rather rounded to the nearest dime.

Step 3 Have students write an equation for each item that calculates the total amount to charge when more than one of each item is purchased. Discuss with students that solving the equation each time a customer comes to the counter is not efficient. Have students make tables showing the prices for buying 1 to 10 of each item.

Chapter 3

Expressions and Equations

You solve equations all the time.

One night a weather forecaster says an additional 3 inches of snow fell, bringing the total snowfall for the year to 9 inches. You can solve the linear equation $x + 3 = 9$ to find the snowfall before the additional 3 inches fell.

The snowfall was 6 inches.

96   Chapter 3 Expressions and Equations

Key Vocabulary

Find interactive definitions in 13 languages in the **eGlossary** at glencoe.com

English   Español *Introduce the most important vocabulary terms from Chapter 3.*

algebraic expression
expresión algebraica

 a combination of numbers, variables, and at least one operation (p. 105)

equation   ecuación

 a mathematical sentence that contains an equal sign, = (p. 113)

evaluate   evaluar

 to find the value of an algebraic expression by replacing variables with numbers (p. 105)

formula   fórmula

 an equation that shows a relationship among certain quantities (p. 119)

order of operations   la orden de operaciones

 the rules that tell which operation to perform first when more than one operation is used (p. 98)

variable   variable

 a symbol, usually a letter, used to represent a number (p. 113)

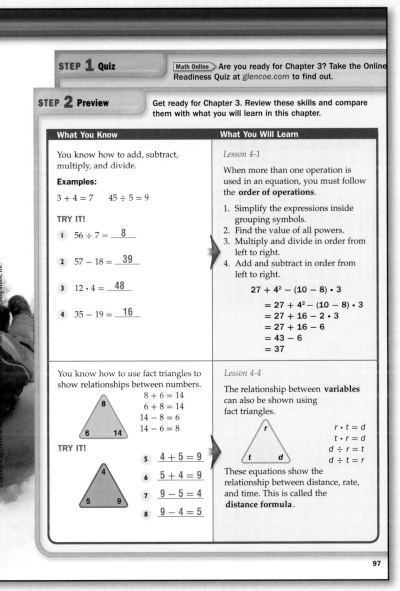

STEP 1 Quiz

Math Online ▸ Are you ready for Chapter 3? Take the Online Readiness Quiz at *glencoe.com* to find out.

STEP 2 Preview

Get ready for Chapter 3. Review these skills and compare them with what you will learn in this chapter.

What You Know	**What You Will Learn**
You know how to add, subtract, multiply, and divide. **Examples:** $3 + 4 = 7$ $45 \div 5 = 9$	*Lesson 4-1* When more than one operation is used in an equation, you must follow the **order of operations**.

TRY IT!

1. $56 \div 7 = \underline{8}$
2. $57 - 18 = \underline{39}$
3. $12 \cdot 4 = \underline{48}$
4. $35 - 19 = \underline{16}$

1. Simplify the expressions inside grouping symbols.
2. Find the value of all powers.
3. Multiply and divide in order from left to right.
4. Add and subtract in order from left to right.

$$27 + 4^2 - (10 - 8) \cdot 3$$
$$= 27 + 4^2 - (10 - 8) \cdot 3$$
$$= 27 + 16 - 2 \cdot 3$$
$$= 27 + 16 - 6$$
$$= 43 - 6$$
$$= 37$$

You know how to use fact triangles to show relationships between numbers.

$8 + 6 = 14$
$6 + 8 = 14$
$14 - 8 = 6$
$14 - 6 = 8$

Lesson 4-4

The relationship between **variables** can also be shown using fact triangles.

$r \cdot t = d$
$t \cdot r = d$
$d \div r = t$
$d \div t = r$

These equations show the relationship between distance, rate, and time. This is called the **distance formula**.

TRY IT!

5. $4 + 5 = 9$
6. $5 + 4 = 9$
7. $9 - 5 = 4$
8. $9 - 4 = 5$

97

Vocabulary Preview

- As students complete the Chapter Preview, have them make a list of important terms throughout the chapter.

- Divide students into pairs. Have the pairs compare their lists of terms to make one list. Key words should be included.

- Once the list is final, the pair should prepare a skit to act out each term. Pairs can also write an example of each term.

- When all groups are finished, they should act out the terms for the class, or present their examples to the class. An option is to have pairs act out the terms for another pair to guess the term.

Step 1 Quiz

Pretest/Prescribe Students can take the Online Readiness Quiz online or the Diagnostic Pretest in the Assessment Masters.

Step 2 Preview

Use this pre-chapter activity to activate students' prior knowledge, build confidence, and help students preview the lessons.

Dinah Zike's Foldables

Guide students through the directions on p. A47 in the Chapter Resource Masters to create their own Foldable graphic organizer for use with this chapter.

Home Connections

- Have students make a list of five sets of common, everyday variables that do not have a linear relationship. For example, age and height.

McGraw Hill Professional Development

Targeted professional development has been articulated throughout **McGraw-Hill's *Math Triumphs*** intervention program. **The McGraw-Hill Professional Development Video Library** provides short videos that support the **NCTM Focal Points and Focal Connections**. For more information, visit glencoe.com.

Model Lessons   Instructional Strategies

Lesson Notes

Lesson Planner

Objective Use the order of operations to evaluate expressions.

Vocabulary base, exponent, order of operations

Materials/Manipulatives poster board, algebra tiles, balance scale, index cards

Chapter Resource Masters

- **CRM** Vocabulary and English Language Development (p. A50)
- **CRM** Skills Practice (p. A51)
- **CRM** Problem-Solving Practice (p. A52)
- **CRM** Homework Practice (p. A53)

1 Introduce

Vocabulary

From Left to Right Explain that *multiply and divide from left to right* means that multiplication and division are the same level. These operations must be performed from left to right, not multiply and then divide. Addition and subtraction are the same level and must be performed from left to right, as well.

2 Teach

Key Concept

Foundational Skills and Concepts After students have read through the Key Concept box, have them try these exercises.

1. Is multiplication always done before division? No, when there are multiplication and division operations, the order is done left to right, or according to grouping symbols.

2. List the order of operations. grouping symbols, powers, multiplication/division from left to right, addition/subtraction from left to right

---

Lesson 3-1 Order of Operations

KEY Concept

You must follow the **order of operations** to evaluate mathematical expressions correctly.

Order of Operations	Symbol
1. Simplify grouping symbols.	(parentheses) [brackets] $\frac{2-1}{b-3}$ fraction bar
2. Find the values of all powers.	base → 2^5 ← exponent
3. Multiply and divide in order from left to right.	× • ÷ /
4. Add and subtract in order from left to right.	+ −

VOCABULARY

base
In a power, the number used as a factor; in 10^3, the base is 10. That is, $10^3 = 10 \times 10 \times 10$.

exponent
In a power, the number of times the base is used as a factor; in 5^3, the exponent is 3. That is, $5^3 = 5 \times 5 \times 5$.

order of operations
the rules that tell which operation to perform first when more than one operation is used

Sometimes parentheses are used to set a number apart from other operations. If there is no operation to be performed inside the parentheses, check for **exponents**.

Example 1

Find the value of $4 - 2 + 16 \div 4$.

Use the order of operations. There are no grouping symbols or exponents.

$$
\begin{aligned}
4 - 2 + 16 \div 4 &= 4 - 2 + 4 \quad \text{Multiply and divide from left to right.} \\
&= 2 + 4 \quad \text{Add and subtract from left to right.} \\
&= 6
\end{aligned}
$$

> From left to right, subtraction comes first in this expression.

YOUR TURN!

Find the value of $10 - 5 + 6 \cdot 3$.

Use the order of operations. There are no grouping symbols or exponents.

$$
\begin{aligned}
10 - 5 + 6 \cdot 3 &= 10 - 5 + \underline{18} \\
&= \underline{5} + \underline{18} \\
&= \underline{23}
\end{aligned}
$$

Additional *Example 1*

Find the value of $6 \div 2 \cdot 5 - 3$.

Use the order of operations. There are no grouping symbols or exponents.

$$
\begin{aligned}
6 \div 2 \cdot 5 - 3 &= 3 \cdot 5 - 3 \quad \text{Multiply and divide from left to right.} \\
&= 15 - 3 \quad \text{Add and subtract from left to right.} \\
&= 12
\end{aligned}
$$

Example 2

Find the value of $71 - \dfrac{36 - 12}{6 + 2} \cdot 4^2$.

$71 - \dfrac{36 - 12}{6 + 2} \cdot 4^2 = 71 - \dfrac{24}{8} \cdot 4^2$ Simplify grouping symbols.

$= 71 - \dfrac{24}{8} \cdot 16$ Simplify exponents.

$= 71 - 3 \cdot 16$ Divide.

$= 71 - 48$ Multiply.

$= 23$ Subtract.

YOUR TURN!

Find the value of
$56 \div 14 + (1 + 4)^2 \cdot 2 - 4$.

$56 \div 14 + (1 + 4)^2 \cdot 2 - 4$

$= 56 \div 14 + \underline{(5)^2} \cdot 2 - 4$

$= 56 \div 14 + \underline{25} \cdot 2 - 4$

$= \underline{4} + \underline{50} - 4$

$= \underline{54} - 4$

$= \underline{50}$

Example 3

Write and simplify an expression to answer the question.

Seth arranged 24 chairs in rows of 6. He took 1 chair out of each row. Then, he placed 10 more chairs on the stage. How many chairs did Seth leave on the stage?

1. Translate each phrase.

Word Phrase	Math Meaning
4 rows	4
24 chairs in rows of 6	$24 \div 6$
1 chair from each row	$- 1$
Ten more	$+ 10$

2. Write the expression.

$[4 \cdot (24 \div 6 - 1)] + 10$

3. Simplify the expression.

$[4 \cdot (4 - 1)] + 10 = 12 + 10 = 22$

Seth arranged 22 chairs.

YOUR TURN!

Write and simplify an expression to answer the question.

Susana bought 2 packs of 8 fruit bars. She gave 13 fruit bars away to her friends. Then she purchased 3 packs of granola bars with 6 bars in each pack. How many snacks does Susana have now?

1. Translate each phrase.

Word Phrase	Math Meaning
2 packs of 8	$2 \cdot 8$
Gave away 13	$- 13$
Then she purchased	$+$
3 packs of 6	$3 \cdot 6$

2. Write the expression.

$\underline{(2 \cdot 8 - 13) + 3 \cdot 6}$

3. Simplify the expression.

$(\underline{16} - \underline{13}) + \underline{18} = \underline{3} + \underline{18} = \underline{21}$

Susana has $\underline{21}$ snack bars.

GO ON

Additional Example 2

Find the value of $4 \cdot 9 + (7 - 5)^2 \div 4 - 3$.

$4 \cdot 9 + (7 - 5)^2 \div 4 - 3$

$= 4 \cdot 9 + 2^2 \div 4 - 3$ Simplify within grouping symbols.

$= 4 \cdot 9 + 4 \div 4 - 3$ Simplify the exponent.

$= 36 + 4 \div 4 - 3$ Multiply.

$= 36 + 1 - 3$ Divide.

$= 37 - 3$ Add.

$= 34$ Subtract.

Additional Example 3

Write and simplify an expression to answer the question.

Marika planted 36 petunias in rows of 9. She then decided to add 2 more to each row. She also planted 16 petunias under the tree. How many petunias did Marika plant in all?

1. Translate each phrase.

Word Phrase	Math Meaning
4 rows	4
36 petunias in rows of 9	$36 \div 9$
2 more in each of the rows	$+ 2$
sixteen more	$+ 16$

2. Write the expression.
$[4 \cdot (36 \div 9 + 2)] + 16$

3. Simplify the expression.
$[4 \cdot (36 \div 9 + 2)] + 16 =$
$[4 \cdot (4 + 2)] + 16 = 4 \cdot 6 + 16 = 40$

Marika planted 60 petunias in all.

③ Practice

Using Manipulatives

Algebra Tiles   Use unit blocks to give students a visual concept of the order of operations. First show the problem using the unit cubes.

$$3 + (4 - 2)^2 \div 2$$

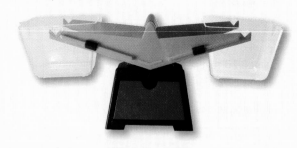

Next show the simplified answer after each operation until the expression is simplified.

Balance Scale   Use a balance scale to give students another visual concept of equality after performing the order of operations. Show the scale balanced after each operation to reflect the equality of the simplified value.

Who is Correct?

Find the value of $25 \div 5 + (8 - 4)^2 \cdot 2$.

Circle correct answer(s). Cross out incorrect answer(s).

▶ Guided Practice

Name the step that should be performed first in each expression.

1. $8 \cdot 3 + (30 - 3) \div 6^2$ ___subtraction___

2. $17 \div 1 - (12 + 2) \cdot 2$ ___addition___

3. $18 + 5^2 \div 5 + 4 \cdot 3$ ___exponent___

4. $8 + 17 \div 7 \cdot 5 - 6$ ___division___

Step by Step Practice

5. Find the value of $17 - 6 \cdot (3 - 2)^2 - 5 + 2$.

Step 1   Use the order of operations. Simplify the grouping symbols.

$17 - 6 \cdot (3 - 2)^2 - 5 + 2 = 17 - 6 \cdot (\underline{\ 1\ })^2 - 5 + 2$

Step 2   Simplify the exponent.

$17 - 6 \cdot 1^2 - 5 + 2 = 17 - 6 \cdot \underline{\ 1\ } - 5 + 2$

Step 3   Multiply and divide.

$17 - 6 \cdot 1 - 5 + 2 = 17 - \underline{\ 6\ } - 5 + 2$

Step 4   Add and subtract.

$17 - 6 - 5 + 2 = \underline{\ 11\ } - 5 + 2$
$= \underline{\ 6\ } + 2$
$= \underline{\ 8\ }$

Who *is Correct?*
Diagnostic Teaching

- Cedric's answer is incorrect. He did not follow the order of operations. He added prior to multiplying.

- Gracia's answer is incorrect. She did not follow the order of operations. She simplified from left to right.

- Hannah's answer is correct. She followed the order of operations.

Find the value of each expression.

6 $64 \div 16 + (5 \cdot 2)^2 - 23 = 64 \div 16 + (\underline{\,10\,})^2 - 23$

$\qquad\qquad\qquad\qquad = 64 \div 16 + \underline{\,100\,} - 23$

$\qquad\qquad\qquad\qquad = \underline{\,4\,} + \underline{\,100\,} - 23$

$\qquad\qquad\qquad\qquad = \underline{\,104\,} - 23$

$\qquad\qquad\qquad\qquad = \underline{\,81\,}$

7 $50 \div (9 + 1) \cdot 4 \div 2 = \underline{\,10\,}$

8 $30 \div \frac{43 - 8}{3 + 4} \div 2 \cdot 12 = \underline{\,36\,}$

9 $20 - 4^2 \div 4 \cdot 2 + (20 - 17) = \underline{\,15\,}$

10 $(21 - 20)^2 \cdot 50 \div 5 - (72 \div 8) = \underline{\,1\,}$

Step **Step** *Practice*

11 **TRANSPORTATION** McArthur Community Center has 2 vans that hold 12 passengers each. They own 6 more minibuses that will hold 20 passengers each. How many passengers can the community center transport in all?

Problem-Solving Strategies
☐ Draw a diagram.
☐ Guess and check.
☐ Act it out.
☑ Write an expression.
☐ Work backward.

Understand Read the problem. Write what you know.

There are __2__ vans with __12__ passengers each

and __6__ minibuses with __20__ passengers each.

Plan Pick a strategy. One strategy is to write and simplify an expression.

Solve Translate each phrase.

Word Phrase	2 vans of 12	More	6 buses of 20
Math Meaning	2 · 12	+	6 · 20

Write and simplify the expression using the order of operations.

$= \underline{\,2 \cdot 12\,} + \underline{\,6 \cdot 20\,}$

$= \underline{\,24\,} + \underline{\,120\,}$

$= \underline{\,144\,}$

The community center can transport __144__ passengers.

Check You can draw a picture to check your answer.

GO ON ▶

Math Coach Notes

Evaluate Expressions To emphasize the importance of the order of operations, illustrate how one problem could be solved several different ways to arrive at different answers.

Show students the expression.

$6 + 4 \cdot 3$

Illustrate that without an order of operations, one student may find the answer $6 + 4 \cdot 3 = 10 \cdot 3 = 30$ instead of $6 + 4 \cdot 3 = 6 + 12 = 18$. The order of operations ensures that there is only one correct answer.

Are They Getting It? ❓

Check students' understanding of the order of operations by writing these problems on the board. Have students point out wrong answers and explain why they are wrong. Encourage students to use a diagram in their explanations.

1. $7 + (18 \div 3) - (5 \cdot 2) = 7 + 6 - 10 = 13 - 10 = 3$

This is correct. The operations performed first were the operations in parentheses.

2. $8 \cdot 5 + (3 + 1)^2 \div 4 = 40 + (4)^2 \div 4 = 56 \div 4 = 14$

This is incorrect. The operations were performed from left to right. The division operation should have been performed before addition.

3. $9 + 2 + 8^2 \div 4 \cdot 2 = 9 + 2 + 64 \div 4 \cdot 2 =$

$\qquad\qquad\qquad\qquad\qquad 9 + 2 + 16 \cdot 2 =$

$\qquad\qquad\qquad\qquad\qquad\quad 9 + 2 + 32 =$

$\qquad\qquad\qquad\qquad\qquad\quad\quad 11 + 32 =$

$\qquad\qquad\qquad\qquad\qquad\qquad\quad 43$

This is correct.

Common Error *Alert*

Circle and Check   If students are having difficulty with the order of operations, give the class the following problem. Ask them to solve it individually. Have students circle the operation and write the step number above the circle.

$$21 + 4 \cdot 5 - \overset{1}{(5-3)^2} + 18 \div 3$$

Have the students circle the next step and write the step number above the circle. After simplifying the expression, have another student check each step and verify the step number.

English Learner Strategy

Reference Material   Provide students with 8.5" × 11" poster board. Turn the board to landscape orientation. On the right side of the board, students should write the order of operations in English. On the left side, students should write the order of operations in their native languages (aligned with the steps in English). In between the lists, include an expression that is simplified at each step in the order.

Write and simplify an expression to solve each problem.

12 GARDENS   Cierra likes to plant flowers. She planted <u>2</u> daffodils. She also planted <u>3 rows of 4 tulips</u>. <u>Five of the flowers were eaten</u> by squirrels. <u>How many flowers were left</u>? Check off each step.

✔ Understand: I underlined key words.

✔ Plan: To solve the problem, I will ___solve a simpler problem___.

✔ Solve: The answer is ___$2 + 3 \cdot 4 - 5 = 9$; 9 flowers___.

✔ Check: I checked my answer by ___drawing a picture___.

13 SUPPLIES   Caine bought 3 packs of markers. Each pack had 5 markers. He gave 7 markers to his brother. Then he bought 2 more packs with 18 markers in each. How many markers does Caine have now?

Word Phrase	3 packs of 5	Gave away 7	More	2 packs of 18
Math Meaning	$3 \cdot 5$	-7	$+$	$2 \cdot 18$

$3 \cdot 5 - 7 + 2 \cdot 18 = 15 - 7 + 36 = 8 + 36 = 44$; 44 markers

14 PHOTOGRAPHY   Marcos was using his new digital camera at a family reunion. He took 6 pictures of each of his four aunts. He deleted 2 of the photos. Then he took 10 pictures of each of his 8 cousins. Finally, he took 4 photos that included his grandfather. How many photos are left on his camera?

Word Phrase	Math Meaning
6 pictures of 4 aunts	$6 \cdot 4$
deleted 2	-2
10 pictures of each of his 8 cousins	$10 \cdot 8$
4 photos of grandfather	$+4$

$6 \cdot 4 - 2 + 10 \cdot 8 + 4 = 24 - 2 + 80 + 4 = 22 + 80 + 4 =$

$102 + 4 = 106$; 106 photos

15 **Reflect**   Explain why $40 \div 4 + 6$ has a different value than $40 \div (4 + 6)$.

Answers will vary. Sample answer: $40 \div 4 + 6 = 16$ and $40 \div (4 + 6) = 4$

The parentheses change the order of operations.

Intervention Strategy   Linguistic Learners

Mnemonic Device   Many have learned to remember the order of operations using the mnemonic device of the phrase *Please Excuse My Dear Aunt Sally,* where the initial letter of each word starts with the same letter as the key words in the order of operations. P for parentheses, E for exponents, M for multiplication, D for division, A for addition, and S for subtraction. Encourage students to learn the phrase *Please Excuse My Dear Aunt Sally,* or make up one that has a personal meaning for them.

Skills, Concepts, and Problem Solving

Name the step that should be performed first in each expression.

16 $5 \cdot 2 + (17 \div 1) - 22$ _____division_____

17 $4 \cdot (2 - 6)^2 + 12 \div 3$ _____subtraction_____

18 $(6 - 2^2 \cdot 4) - 16 \div 2$ _____exponent_____

19 $9 + (6 - 1 \cdot 14) \div 2^2$ _____multiplication_____

20 $3[(75 + 75) \cdot 3] - 25$ _____addition_____

21 $\dfrac{18 + 66}{35 - 14} \cdot 3 + 2$ _____fraction bar_____

Find the value of each expression.

22 $14 - (7 + 5) + 7 \cdot 4^2 = 14 - \underline{12} + 7 \cdot 4^2$

$= 14 - \underline{12} + 7 \cdot \underline{16}$

$= 14 - \underline{12} + \underline{112}$

$= \underline{2} + \underline{112}$

$= \underline{114}$

23 $48 \div \dfrac{(37 + 3)}{(9 - 4)} - 4 \div 2 \cdot 7^2 = 48 \div \dfrac{40}{5} - 4 \div 2 \cdot 7^2$

$= 48 \div \underline{8} - 4 \div 2 \cdot 7^2$

$= 48 \div \underline{8} - 4 \div 2 \cdot \underline{49}$

$= \underline{6} - \underline{2} \cdot \underline{49}$

$= \underline{6} - \underline{98}$

$= \underline{-92}$

24 $50 \div 5 + 3 \cdot 2^2 - (15 - 9) = \underline{16}$

25 $3^2 + 8 \div 2 - (10 + 2) = \underline{1}$

26 $18 - 5^2 \cdot 0 + 16 - 15 = \underline{19}$

27 $(9 - 6)^2 + 8 \div 4 + 5 \cdot 6 = \underline{41}$

28 $\dfrac{27 + 23}{16 + 9} \cdot 5 = \underline{10}$

29 $\dfrac{4^2}{2 + (27 \cdot 0)} = \underline{8}$

30 $10[8(2^2 + 2) - (2 \cdot 6)] = \underline{360}$

31 $5[(17 \cdot 1) - 3(25 \div 5)] = \underline{10}$

GO ON

Odd/Even Assignments

Exercises 16–33 are structured so that students practice the same concepts whether they are assigned the odd or even problems.

In-Class Assignment

Have students complete Exercises 16, 20, 22, 27, 32, and 36 to ensure that they understand the concept.

Math Challenge

Creating Mistakes, Correcting Mistakes Have each student write two problems that include multiple operations. On a separate piece of paper, have them simplify their problems using the proper order of operations. Then have students return to their original paper and use the order of operations incorrectly to get a simplified answer. Students should trade papers with each other and correct the mistakes made using the order of operations. Once corrected, students can check one another's work by using their papers with the correct order of operations.

4 Assess

See It, Do It, Say It, Write It

Step 1 Write the following problem on the board:
$5^2 + 14 \div 7 - (2 \cdot 6)$

Step 2 Have students circle each operation as they simplify and then write the step number above the circle.

Step 3 Arrange students in pairs and have them explain to each other how they used the order of operations to simplify.

Step 4 Have students write the order of operations in their math journals using their own words.

Looking Ahead: Pre-teach

Evaluate Algebraic Expressions In the next lesson, students will learn how to evaluate algebraic expressions.

Example

1. Simplify the expression $7d - 6 + 3d$.
   $10d - 6$

2. Evaluate $3b + 11 - b$ when $b = 6$.
   $3 \cdot 6 + 11 - 6 = 18 + 11 - 6 = 29 - 6 = 23$

3. Evaluate when $x = -3, -1$, and 4.
   $x - 2$
   $x - 2 = -3 - 2 = -5$
   $x - 2 = -1 - 2 = -3$
   $x - 2 = 4 - 2 = 2$

Write and simplify an expression to solve each problem.

32 COLLECTIONS Evan had 100 bobble heads. He sold 5 sets of 10 bobble heads. He then bought 3 sets of 12 bobble heads. Then Evan sold 25 bobble heads. How many bobble heads does Evan have left?

Word Phrase	Math Meaning
had 100	100
sold	−
5 sets of 10	5 · 10
bought	+
3 sets of 12	3 · 12
sold 25	− 25

$100 - 5 \cdot 10 + 3 \cdot 12 - 25 = 100 - 50 + 36 - 25 = 50 + 36 - 25 =$

$86 - 25$ or 61; 61 bobble heads

33 BOOKS Each week Serena uses her library card. On her first visit she borrowed 2 stacks of 8 books. She returned 9 books on the second week. On the third week, Serena borrowed 2 stacks of 5 books. How many books does Serena have now?

Word Phrase	2 stacks of 8	returned 9	2 stacks of 5
Math Meaning	2 · 8	− 9	2 · 5

$2 \cdot 8 - 9 + 2 \cdot 5 = 16 - 9 + 10 = 7 + 10$ or 17; 17 books

Vocabulary Check Write the vocabulary word that completes each sentence.

34 The _order of operations_ is a set of rules that tells what order to follow when evaluating an expression.

35 A(n) _exponent_ is the number of times a base is multiplied by itself.

36 Writing in Math Does $40 - (7 - 5)$ equal $(40 - 7) - 5$? Explain.

No; $40 - (7 - 5) = 38$ and $(40 - 7) - 5 = 28$; The parentheses change the order in which the expressions are simplified.

Ticket Out the Door

Say the Order Have students line up at the door in single file. As each student approaches the door, instruct them to say the next operation in the correct order. Continue through the order of operations (repeating them several times) until all students have exited the classroom.

Lesson **3-2** Evaluate Algebraic Expressions

KEY Concept

To **evaluate** an **algebraic expression**, substitute a value for a variable. Then perform the operations.

$n = 2$ $p = -3$

$$4n + 5p = 4(2) + 5(-3)$$
$$= 8 + (-15)$$
$$= -7$$

Remember to use the **order of operations** after substituting, or replacing, the variables with numbers.

VOCABULARY

algebraic expression
a combination of numbers, variables, and at least one operation

evaluate
to find the *value* of an *algebraic expression* by replacing variables with numbers

order of operations
the rules that tell which operation to perform first when more than one operation is used
1. Simplify the expressions inside grouping symbols, like parentheses.
2. Find the value of all powers.
3. Multiply and divide in order from left to right.
4. Add and subtract in order from left to right.

Example 1

Evaluate ▲ + (9 − 2) + □ when ▲ = 3 and □ = 1.

1. Replace ▲ with 3 in the expression.

   ▲ + (9 − 2) + □ = 3 + (9 − 2) + □

2. Replace □ with 1 in the expression.

   3 + (9 − 2) + 1

3. Simplify. Follow the order of operations.

   3 + (9 − 2) + 1 = 3 + 7 + 1
   = 11

YOUR TURN!

Evaluate 2 ●² + 4 ♥ when ● = 2 and ♥ = 3.

1. Replace ● with 2 in the expression.

   2(2)² + 4♥

2. Replace ♥ with 3 in the expression.

   2(2)² + 4(3)

3. Simplify. Follow the order of operations.

   2(4) + 4(3) = 8 + 12 = 20

GO ON →

Additional *Example 1*

Evaluate 6 ◯ + ★² when ★ = 7 and ◯ = 5.

I. Replace ★ with 7 in the expression.

   6 ◯ + 7²

2. Replace ◯ with 5 in the expression.

   6(5) + 7²

3. Simplify. Follow the order of operations.

   6(5) + 7² = 6(5) + 49
   = 30 + 49
   = 79

Lesson Notes

Lesson Planner

Objective   Write, simplify, and evaluate expressions.

Vocabulary   algebraic expression, evaluate, order of operations

Materials/Manipulatives   everyday objects, index cards, two-color counters

Chapter Resource Masters

CRM Vocabulary and English Language Development (p. A54)

CRM Skills Practice (p. A55)

CRM Problem-Solving Practice (p. A56)

CRM Homework Practice (p. A57)

1 Introduce

Vocabulary

Access Vocabulary   Have students recall the definitions for the words *value, expression,* and *order of operations* from previous lessons. Write the word *evaluate* on the board and ask students to explain the meaning in their own words using the other vocabulary words. Compare students' definitions as a class until an agreed-upon definition is the result. Have students compare the class definition with the definition found in the text.

2 Teach

Key Concept

Foundational Skills and Concepts   After students have read through the Key Concept box, have them try these exercises.

I. What operation does 4*n* represent?   multiplication

2. When you multiply a positive number with a negative number, what sign is the product? negative

Evaluate $x \div 2 + 3y - 4 \cdot 2$ when $x = 8$ and $y = 3$.

I. Replace x with 8 and y with 3 in the expression.

$x \div 2 + 3y - 4 \cdot 2 = 8 \div 2 + 3(3) - 4 \cdot 2$

2. Simplify using the order of operations.

$= 4 + 3(3) - 4 \cdot 2$	Divide.
$= 4 + 9 - 4 \cdot 2$	Multiply.
$= 4 + 9 - 8$	Multiply.
$= 13 - 8$	Add.
$= 5$	Subtract.

 **3** **Practice**

Using Manipulatives

Two-Colored Counters When evaluating Additional Example 2, use two-colored counters to give students a visual representation of the variables. A two-colored counter will work with expressions that have 2 or less variables.

$$x \div 2 + 3y - 4 \cdot 2$$

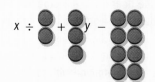

On-Hand Manipulatives Demonstrate evaluating expressions using two-colored counters. Use classroom objects in a similar manner as the two-colored counters.

Example 2

Evaluate $4 \div y + x \cdot 3 - 7$ when $x = 5$ and $y = 2$.

1. Replace x with 5 and y with 2 in the expression.

$4 \div y + x \cdot 3 - 7 = 4 \div 2 + 5 \cdot 3 - 7$

2. Simplify using the order of operations.

$4 \div 2 + 5 \cdot 3 - 7$	
$= 2 + 5 \cdot 3 - 7$	Divide.
$= 2 + 15 - 7$	Multiply.
$= 17 - 7$	Add.
$= 10$	Subtract.

YOUR TURN!

Evaluate $3y^2 + x \cdot 3 - 2$ when $x = 4$ and $y = 2$.

1. Replace y with 2 and x with 4. Write the expression.

$\underline{3(2)^2 + 4 \cdot 3 - 2}$

2. Simplify using the order of operations.
$3(2)^2 + 4 \cdot 3 - 2$

$= \underline{3(4) + 4 \cdot 3 - 2}$	Exponent
$= \underline{12 + 12 - 2}$	Multiply.
$= \underline{24 - 2}$	Add.
$= \underline{22}$	Subtract.

Who is Correct?

Evaluate the expression $12x - 5 + 4y \cdot 2$ when $x = 4$ and $y = 2$.

Ines

$12x - 5 + 4y \cdot 2$

$= 12(4) - 5 + 4(2) \cdot 2$

$= 48 - 5 + 8 \cdot 2$

$= 43 + 8 \cdot 2$

$= 56 \cdot 2$

$= 112$

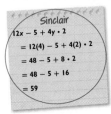

Sinclair

$12x - 5 + 4y \cdot 2$

$= 12(4) - 5 + 4(2) \cdot 2$

$= 48 - 5 + 8 \cdot 2$

$= 48 - 5 + 16$

$= 59$

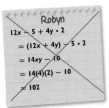

Robyn

$12x - 5 + 4y \cdot 2$

$= (12x + 4y) - 5 \cdot 2$

$= 14xy - 10$

$= 14(4)(2) - 10$

$= 102$

Circle correct answer(s). Cross out incorrect answer(s).

▶ **Guided Practice**

Evaluate each expression when ☆ = 6.

1 $9 \cdot$ ☆ $\underline{\qquad 9 \cdot 6 = 54 \qquad}$

2 $72 \div$ ☆ $\underline{\qquad 72 \div 6 = 12 \qquad}$

3 $4 +$ ☆ $- 5 \cdot 3 \div 3$
$\underline{\qquad 4 + 6 - 5 \cdot 3 \div 3 = 5 \qquad}$

4 $8 \cdot 4 +$ ☆ $+ 7$
$\underline{\qquad 8 \cdot 4 + 6 + 7 = 45 \qquad}$

106 Chapter 3 Expressions and Equations

Who *is Correct?*
Diagnostic Teaching

• Ines' answer is incorrect. She did not follow the order of operations in the fourth step. She needed to multiply, then add.

• Sinclair's answer is correct.

• Robyn's answer is incorrect. She used the Commutative Property to reorder terms. However, the Commutative Property does not apply to subtraction. These terms cannot be reordered using this property.

Evaluate each expression when ☺ = 8 and ♣ = 6.

5 $☺^2 + 9 - 7 + ♣ \cdot 10$

Replace symbols with values: __$8^2 + 9 - 7 + 6 \cdot 10$__

Value of the expression: __126__

6 $10^2 \div 20 - (-6 + ♣) \cdot ☺$

Replace symbols with values: __$10^2 \div 20 - (-6 + 6) \cdot 8$__

Value of the expression: __5__

7 $(27 - 18)^2 + ☺ - 12 \div 4 + ♣ \cdot 2$

Replace symbols with values:

__$(27 - 18)^2 + 8 - 12 \div 4 + 6 \cdot 2$__

Value of the expression: __98__

8 $16 \div 4 \cdot ♣ - 2 + (☺ - 5)$

Replace symbols with values:

__$16 \div 4 \cdot 6 - 2 + (8 - 5)$__

Value of the expression: __25__

Step by Step Practice

9 Evaluate the expression $5y + 2z - 4$ when $y = 7$ and $z = 10$.

Step 1 $5y$ means 5 __times__ y. Replace y with __7__ in the expression.

Step 2 $2z$ means 2 __times__ z. Replace z with __10__ in the expression.

Step 3 Write the expression with all substitutions made. Simplify using the order of operations.

$5 \cdot 7 + 2 \cdot 10 - 4 =$ __35__ + __20__ − __4__

$=$ __55__ − __4__

$=$ __51__

The value of the expression is __51__.

GO ON

Math Coach Notes

Analogies   Help students relate to substituting values for variables by discussing substitution in everyday activities. Substitutions are made in sporting events. A point guard may enter a basketball game when another point guard leaves the game. The game goes on, just with a different player. Turkey may be substituted into a casserole recipe that calls for chicken. The dish is still a casserole, but with turkey meat instead of chicken meat. Invite students to share their own ideas about everyday activities in which substitutions are made.

 Common Error *Alert*

Substitute Values for Variables   When students are substituting values for variables, they may get confused about what to do next. Show an example.

$3m$ means $3 \cdot m$.

Replace the variable with the value and multiply.

$3m$ can also be shown as $3(m)$.

Are They Getting It?

Check students' understanding of evaluating expressions by writing these problems on the board. Ask students to point out the wrong answers and explain why they are wrong.

Evaluate each expression when $x = 5$, $y = 4$, and $z = 1$.

1. $\dfrac{4x}{y} - z \div y = \dfrac{4(5)}{4} - 1 \div 4$

$= 5 - 1 \div 4$

$= 4 \div 4$

$= 1$

This is incorrect. The division should have been done before the subtraction.

2. $60(z + 2) - y(2x - 4)^2 = 60(1 + 2) - 4(2 \cdot 5 - 4)^2$

$= 60(3) - 4(10 - 4)^2$

$= 180 - 4(6)^2$

$= 180 - 4(36)$

$= 180 - 144$

$= 36$

This is correct.

English Learner Strategy

Reference Cards   Write the problem-solving strategies on index cards. On the front side write a description in English. On the reverse side, have students write a description in their native languages. When students are choosing a problem-solving strategy, display the card when using the strategy. Encourage the students to keep the problem-solving strategies index cards handy for reference.

Note This!

Study Strategies   When students are asked to evaluate variable expressions, encourage students to combine like terms before evaluating the expression, while following the order of operations. For example, instead of evaluating $4x + 3x$ for $x = 2$ as $4(2) + 3(2) = 8 + 6 = 14$, combine the like terms first and then evaluate, $4x + 3x = 7x = 7(2) = 14$.

Evaluate each expression when $x = 2$ and $y = 5$.

10 $7y - (5 + 1) \div 2 \cdot x^2 = 7(\underline{5}) - (5 + 1) \div 2 \cdot (\underline{2})^2$

$= 7(\underline{5}) - \underline{6} \div 2 \cdot 2^2$

$= 7(\underline{5}) - \underline{6} \div 2 \cdot \underline{4}$

$= \underline{35} - \underline{3} \cdot \underline{4}$

$= \underline{35} - \underline{12}$

$= \underline{23}$

11 $5 - x \div 2 + (3 \cdot 2)^2 - 5 \cdot 0 = 5 - \underline{2} \div 2 + (3 \cdot 2)^2 - 5 \cdot 0$

$= 5 - \underline{2} \div 2 + \underline{6}\,^2 - 5 \cdot 0$

$= 5 - \underline{2} \div 2 + \underline{36} - 5 \cdot 0$

$= 5 - \underline{1} + \underline{36} - \underline{0}$

$= \underline{40}$

12 $16 + 4^2 \cdot x - 5 + (8 - y) - 0$

Replace variables with values:

$\underline{16 + 4^2 \cdot 2 - 5 + (8 - 5) - 0}$

Value of the expression: $\underline{46}$

13 $5y^2 - 10 \div 5 + 3 \cdot 5x$

Replace variables with values:

$\underline{5(5^2) - 10 \div 5 + 3 \cdot 5(2)}$

Value of the expression: $\underline{153}$

14 $(x^2 - 1) + 3 \cdot 4 \div (7 - 1) + y$

Replace variables with values:

$\underline{(2^2 - 1) + 3 \cdot 4 \div (7 - 1) + 5}$

Value of the expression: $\underline{10}$

15 $100 \div y^2 + (x + 7)^2$

Replace variables with values:

$\underline{100 \div 5^2 + (2 + 7)^2}$

Value of the expression: $\underline{85}$

Intervention Strategy   Visual Learners

Use Color-Coding   When evaluating variable expressions, use a specific color for each variable. Use the same color for like variables. Rewrite the expression with the number substituted as the same color as the variable.

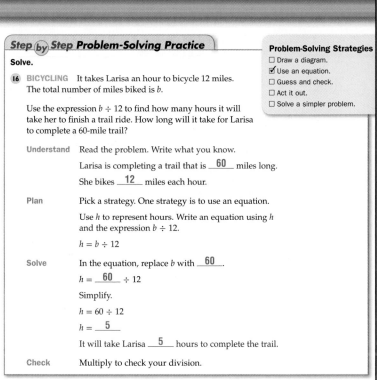

Showing Work Explain to students that it is important for them to show each step, and not to take shortcuts. With every step written, it is easier to look back over your work for mistakes or for someone else to find a mistake.

Step by Step Problem-Solving Practice

Solve.

16 BICYCLING It takes Larisa an hour to bicycle 12 miles. The total number of miles biked is b.

Use the expression $b \div 12$ to find how many hours it will take her to finish a trail ride. How long will it take for Larisa to complete a 60-mile trail?

Problem-Solving Strategies
- ☐ Draw a diagram.
- ☑ Use an equation.
- ☐ Guess and check.
- ☐ Act it out.
- ☐ Solve a simpler problem.

Understand Read the problem. Write what you know.

Larisa is completing a trail that is __60__ miles long.

She bikes __12__ miles each hour.

Plan Pick a strategy. One strategy is to use an equation.

Use h to represent hours. Write an equation using h and the expression $b \div 12$.

$h = b \div 12$

Solve In the equation, replace b with __60__.

$h = \underline{60} \div 12$

Simplify.

$h = 60 \div 12$

$h = \underline{5}$

It will take Larisa __5__ hours to complete the trail.

Check Multiply to check your division.

Note This!
Identify the Variable Part of your solution to a word problem needs to be a statement for the variable. Tell what letter you will use and what the variable represents.

17 CLOTHES Shawnell wants to buy an $8 T-shirt and 3 sweaters. Use the variable expression $8 + 3s$ to find the total cost, where s represents the cost per sweater. Evaluate the expression for sweaters that cost $18 each. Check off each step.

✔ Understand: I underlined key words.

✔ Plan: To solve the problem, I will ___use an equation___.

✔ Solve: The answer is ___$62___.

✔ Check: I checked my answer by ___using inverse operations___

GO ON

Odd/Even Assignments

Exercises 20–31 are structured so that students practice the same concepts whether they are assigned the odd or even problems.

In-Class Assignment

Have students complete Exercises 20, 24, 30, and 34 to ensure that they understand the concept.

---

18 **FOOD** Gabe's Grocery pays $26 per case for oranges. Write an expression for the cost of c cases. Find the cost of 8 cases. ___ $26c, \$208$ ___

19 **Reflect** Does the expression $50 \div k - 2$ have a greater value when $k = 5$ or $k = 10$? Explain.

The value of the expression is greater when $k = 5$. When $k = 5$, $50 \div k - 2 = 8$.

When $k = 10$, $50 \div k - 2 = 3$.

▶ **Skills, Concepts, and Problem Solving**

Evaluate each expression when ◆ = 5 and ● = 3.

20 $4 + ● - ◆$ ___ $4 + 3 - 5 = 2$ ___

21 $16 \cdot ● + ◆$ ___ $16 \cdot 3 + 5 = 53$ ___

22 $2^2 - 6 + ◆ \cdot ●^2$

___ $2^2 - 6 + 5 \cdot 3^2 = 43$ ___

23 $15 \div ● \cdot ◆ - 11 + 7$

___ $15 \div 3 \cdot 5 - 11 + 7 = 21$ ___

Evaluate each expression when $x = 9$ and $y = 3$.

24 $18 \div x \cdot (10 + y - x)$ ___ 8 ___

25 $90 - x^2 + 6 \div y \cdot 2$ ___ 13 ___

26 $x^2 \div y + 7 \cdot 2 - (6 \cdot 1)$ ___ 35 ___

27 $(8 \cdot 1) + 17 \cdot (4y - x)$ ___ 59 ___

28 $y^2 \div y + (x + y) \cdot 1$ ___ 15 ___

29 $(2x - 1) + x^2$ ___ 98 ___

Solve.

30 **GEOMETRY** The area of a rectangle equals the expression $\ell \cdot w$, where ℓ represents the length and w represents the width. Evaluate the expression to find the area of the rectangle at the right. ___ 24 square units ___

$w = 4$

$\ell = 6$

31 **RECREATION** Lamar plays a math game in which whole numbers are worth 10 points, decimals are worth 15 points, and fractions are worth 20 points. The total score equals the expression $10w + 15d + 20f$, when w represents the number of whole numbers, d represents the number of decimals, and f represents the number of fractions. Find Lamar's score when $w = 7, f = 11$, and $d = 15$.

___ 515 points ___

Math Challenge

From 1 to 10 by the Year Have students number their papers from 1 to 10. Instruct students to find an expression that simplifies to each number 1 to 10 using only the numerals in their birth year in the correct order. Each expression must be simplified using the order of operations. An example: Jamie was born in 1996. For the number 4, she can use the expression $1^9 + 9 - 6 = 4$. For the number 6, she can use the expression $1 \cdot 9 - 9 + 6 = 6$. Some numbers might require the use of negative numbers and other operations such as absolute value. For the number 2, Jamie could use the following: $| 1^9 - 9 + 6 |$.

Vocabulary Check Write the vocabulary word that completes each sentence.

32 The amount of a number is its ___value___.

33 Finding the value of an algebraic expression by replacing variables with numbers is called ___evaluating___ the expression.

34 **Writing in Math** Explain how to evaluate $r - 8 \cdot 2$ when $r = 30$.

  Sample answer: Replace r with 30 in the expression.

  Then simplify the expression using the order of operations. $30 - 8 \cdot 2 = 14$

 **Spiral Review**

Find the value of each expression. (Lesson 3-1, p. 98)

35 $56 \div \dfrac{(24 + 16)}{(21 - 16)} \cdot 6^2 \div 9 = 56 \div \dfrac{40}{5} \cdot 6^2 \div 9$

$$= 56 \div \underline{\ 8\ } \cdot 6^2 \div 9$$
$$= 56 \div \underline{\ 8\ } \cdot \underline{\ 36\ } \div 9$$
$$= \underline{\ 7\ } \cdot \underline{\ 36\ } \div 9$$
$$= \underline{\ 252\ } \div 9$$
$$= \underline{\ 28\ }$$

36 $27 - (16 + 5) + 7 \cdot 3^2 = 27 - \underline{\ 21\ } + 7 \cdot 3^2$

$$= 27 - \underline{\ 21\ } + 7 \cdot \underline{\ 9\ }$$
$$= 27 - \underline{\ 21\ } + \underline{\ 63\ }$$
$$= \underline{\ 6\ } + \underline{\ 63\ }$$
$$= \underline{\ 69\ }$$

Solve.

37 **FOOD** Imani was grocery shopping for the week. She bought 3 packs of each of 6 snack crackers. Then she bought 2 pieces of each of 4 different fruits. At the checkout counter, she returned one pack of snack crackers. How many items did Imani purchase?

Word Phrase	Math Meaning
3 packs of 6 crackers	$3 \cdot 6$
2 pieces of 4 kinds of fruit	$2 \cdot 4$
returned one pack of crackers	1

  $3 \cdot 6 + 2 \cdot 4 - 1 = 25$; 25 items

Lesson 3-2 Evaluate Algebraic Expressions **111**

Ticket Out the Door

What Comes After As each student approaches the doorway to exit, ask them to name one of the following:

What comes after simplifying the grouping symbols?
simplify exponents

What comes after simplifying exponents? multiply and divide from left to right

What comes after multiplication and division from left to right? addition and subtraction from left to right

See It, Do It, Say It, Write It

Step 1 Write a variable expression on the board. Show how to represent the expression with a drawing or model. Do this several times with different variable expressions. Ask students to use shapes to represent the variable in the expression.

Step 2 Make a list of variable expressions on the board. Repeat the process used in Step 1, with students using items to represent the variables. Share solutions in a class discussion.

Step 3 Have students work in pairs. Have one student create a variable expression and the other substitute shapes for the variables. Have students share their work with the class. Repeat several times.

Step 4 Have students work alone. Tell them to write and evaluate a variable expression. Encourage them to include a picture or a model.

Looking Ahead: Pre-teach

Solve Algebraic Equations In the next lesson, students will learn about equations with unknown quantities. Multiplication and division are *inverse operations*. Addition and subtraction are *inverse operations*. This means these operations undo each other.

Example

What number belongs in the blank to make the equation true? Check your answer using the inverse operation. $6 \cdot$ ____ $= 24$ 4; $24 \div 4 = 6$

Find the value of the variable.

1. $3 \cdot x = 18$ $x = 6$

2. $13 + z = 20$ $z = 7$

3. $\dfrac{y}{9} = 3$ $y = 27$

Formative Assessment

Use the Progress Check to assess students' mastery of the previous lessons. Have students review the lesson indicated for the problems they answered incorrectly.

Odd/Even Assignments

Exercises are structured so that students practice the same concepts whether they are assigned the odd or even problems.

⚠ **Common Error** *Alert*

One Step at a Time   If students are having difficulties with the order of operations, insist that they show all steps. Each time a step is performed, they should rewrite the entire expression in its entirety with only the substituted value of the operation they performed in that step. They should re-analyze the next step that should be done according to the order of operations.

Exercise 3 If a student simplified the expression as 23.5, they added 18 to 4 instead of adding 18 to 3, which is the value of $2^2 \div 4 \cdot 3$.

Exercise 11 Some students may read the problem quickly looking for numbers only. They may miss the written words that express numbers, such as six and two. Have them highlight key words in each problem.

Chapter
3

Progress Check 1 (Lessons 3-1 and 3-2)

Name each operation that should be performed first.

1 $8 - 4 \cdot (7 + 4)^2 \div 2$ __addition__

2 $3^2 \cdot 2 - (12 \div 4) + 6$ __division__

Find the value of each expression.

3 $18 + 2^2 \div 4 \cdot (5 - 2) + 7 =$ __28__

4 $10 - (2 - 1)^2 + 16 \div 2 \cdot (1 + 1) =$ __25__

5 $28 \div 2^2 \cdot 8 + 4 \div 2 =$ __58__

6 $64 \div 4^2 \cdot 25 - (30 - 18) \div 4 =$ __97__

Evaluate each expression when ■ = 3 and ▲ = 5.

7 $8 + 9 \cdot ■ - ▲$

$\underline{8 + 9 \cdot 3 - 5 = 30}$

8 $6 \div ■ + ▲ \cdot 3 - 2$

$\underline{6 \div 3 + 5 \cdot 3 - 2 = 15}$

Evaluate each expression when y = 8 and x = 2.

9 $19 - 2^2 - (6 + 2y) + 3y \div 2$

$\underline{19 - 2^2 - (6 + 2 \cdot 8) + 3(8) \div 2 = 5}$

10 $3y + x^2 - 32 \div 4 + (4 + 2 \cdot 3)$

$\underline{3(8) + 2^2 - 32 \div 4 + (4 + 2 \cdot 3) = 30}$

Solve.

11 **BASKETBALL**   Tama made six 2-point shots and two 3-point shots. How many points did Tama score?

$\underline{18 \text{ points}; 6 \cdot 2 + 2 \cdot 3 = 12 + 6 = 18}$

12 **SHOPPING**   Payton had 50 pencils. He sold 3 bags of pencils with 5 pencils each. He then bought 2 packs of pencils with 10 pencils each. Then Payton gave 20 pencils to his sister. How many pencils does Payton have left?

$\underline{35 \text{ pencils}; 50 - 3 \cdot 5 + 2 \cdot 10 - 20 = 50 - 15 + 20 - 20 =}$

$\underline{35 + 20 - 20 = 55 - 20 = 35}$

13 **UNIFORMS**   The school band bought uniforms. See the cost of the uniform at right. Write an expression for the cost of u uniforms. Find the cost of 12 uniforms.

$\underline{80u, \$960}$

MHS
$80

Data-Driven Decision Making

Students missing Exercises . . .	Have trouble with . . .	Should review and practice . . .
1–2	deciding what to do first in the order of operations.	SSG Lesson 3-1, p. 98 CRM Skills Practice, p. A51
3–10	using the order of operations to simplify and evaluate expressions.	SSG Lesson 3-2, p. 105 CRM Skills Practice, p. A55
11–13	solving word problems in which the order of operations are used.	CRM Problem-Solving Practice, pp. A52 and A56

Lesson 3-3 Solve Algebraic Equations

KEY Concept

Variables can be used in **algebraic expressions** and **equations**.

Expressions	Equations
$5 + \square$	$10 \cdot \square = 20$
$8 - a$	$16 \div d = 4$

Inverse operations are opposite operations. They are used to undo each other. Addition and subtraction are inverse operations. Multiplication and division are also inverse operations.

You can use inverse operations to solve for x.

$$3 + x = 8, \text{ so } 8 - 3 = x \qquad x = 5$$

You can also think about a fact triangle to help you solve simple equations.

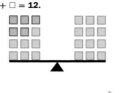

$3 + 5 = 8$	$5 + 3 = 8$
$8 - 3 = 5$	$8 - 5 = 3$

If you know that $3 + 5 = 8$, you can solve the equation $3 + x = 8$.

Fact triangles can help you find the unknown number. The equation shows the numbers 3 and 8. The number 5 is missing from the equation, so the value of x is 5.

VOCABULARY

algebraic expression
a combination of variables, numbers, and at least one operation

equation
a mathematical sentence that contains an equals sign

inverse operations
operations that undo each other

variable
a symbol, usually a letter, used to represent a number

Example 1

Find the value of the variable by modeling the equation $7 + \square = 12$.

1. Use the inverse operations of addition and subtraction.

   $7 + \square = 12$, so $12 - 7 = \square$ $12 - 7 = 5$, so $\square = 5$

2. Use a model to check your answer.
   Think: What number added to 7 equals 12?

   $7 + 5 = 12$ The value of $\square = 5$.

GO ON

Lesson 3-3 Solve Algebraic Equations   **113**

Additional Example 1

Find the value of the variable by modeling the equation $\square + 3 = 10$.

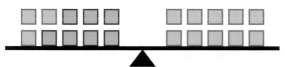

1. Use the inverse operations of addition and subtraction.

   $\square + 3 = 10$, so $10 - 3 = \square$ $10 - 3 = 7$, so $\square = 7$

2. Use a model to check your answer.
   Think: What number added to 3 equals 10?

   $3 + 7 = 10$ The value of $\square = 7$.

Lesson Notes

Lesson 3-3

Lesson Planner

Objective   Solve simple linear equations.

Vocabulary   algebraic expression, equation, inverse operations, variable

Materials/Manipulatives   two-color counters, algebra tiles, bingo markers, balance scale

Chapter Resource Masters

- CRM Vocabulary and English Language Development (p. A58)
- CRM Skills Practice (p. A59)
- CRM Problem-Solving Practice (p. A60)
- CRM Homework Practice (p. A61)

1 Introduce

Vocabulary

Inverse Actions   Explain to students that to fully understand the idea of inverse operations, the class will do an exercise that identifies opposite actions or actions that undo each other. Say each of the words given below to elicit the paired word.

go–stop; up–down; forward–backward; add–subtract; multiply–divide

2 Teach

Key Concept

Foundational Skills and Concepts   After students have read through the Key Concept box, have them try these exercises.

1. What inverse operation do you use to solve the equation $y + 5 = 11$? subtract 5

2. What fact can you use to solve the equation above? $6 + 5 = 11$

Find the value of d in the equation $8 \cdot d = 72$.

1. Use the inverse operations of multiplication and division.
$8 \cdot d = 72$, so $d = 72 \div 8$
$72 \div 8 = 9$, so $d = 9$

2. Check your answer by substituting 9 for d.
$8 \cdot d = 72$
$8 \cdot 9 = 72$
$72 = 72$ ✓

English Learner Strategy

Explain the Process   With a partner, have students read a problem. One partner should then explain to the other student the steps necessary to get the variable alone. After one partner has explained the process aloud, the partners should switch roles and repeat the process with a new problem.

YOUR TURN!

Find the value of the variable by modeling the equation $7 + \square = 15$.

1. Use the inverse operations of addition and __subtraction__.

2. Use a model to check your answer.
Think: What number added to 7 equals 15?

$7 + \boxed{8} = 15$

The value of $\square = $ ___8___.

Example 2

Find the value of c in the equation $7 \cdot c = 56$.

1. Use the inverse operations of multiplication and division.
$7 \cdot c = 56$, so $c = 56 \div 7$
$56 \div 7 = 8$, so $c = 8$

2. Check your answer by substituting 8 for c.
$7 \cdot c = 56$
$7 \cdot 8 = 56$
$56 = 56$ ✔

YOUR TURN!

Find the value of r in the equation $r \cdot 12 = 60$.

1. Use the inverse operations of multiplication and division.
$r \cdot 12 = 60$, so ___r___ $= 60 \div 12$
$60 \div 12 = $ ___5___, so ___5___ $= r$

2. Check your answer by substituting ___5___ for r.
$r \cdot 12 = 60$
___5___ $\cdot 12 = 60$
___60___ $= 60$

Who is Correct?

Find the value of the variable in the equation $24 \div t = 3$.

Dario
$24 \div t = 3$
$24 \div 3 = t$
$t = 8$

Pearl
$24 \div t = 3$
$24 \cdot 3 = t$
$t = 72$

Yoshiko
$24 \div t = 3$
$24 - 3 = t$
$t = 19$

Circle correct answer(s). Cross out incorrect answer(s).

Who *is Correct?*
Diagnostic Teaching

- Dario wrote $t = 8$. This is correct. He used the fact family to divide 24 by 3.

- Pearl wrote $t = 72$. This is incorrect. She multiplied 24 by 3.

- Yoshiko wrote $t = 19$. This is incorrect. He subtracted 3 from 24.

Guided Practice

Find the value of each variable by modeling the equation.

1 $5 + \square = 11$

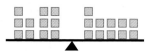

$\square = \underline{\quad 6 \quad}$

2 $7 - q = 3$

$q = \underline{\quad 4 \quad}$

Step by Step Practice

3 Find the value of f in the equation $\frac{f}{11} = 10$.

Step 1 $\frac{f}{11}$ means $f \div 11$. Use the inverse operations of multiplication and division.

$f \div 11 = \underline{\quad 10 \quad}$, so $f = 11 \cdot \underline{\quad 10 \quad}$

$11 \cdot \underline{\quad 10 \quad} = \underline{\quad 110 \quad}$, so $f = \underline{\quad 110 \quad}$

Step 2 Check your answer by substituting $\underline{\quad 110 \quad}$ for f.

$$\frac{f}{11} = 10$$

$$\frac{\boxed{110}}{11} = 10$$

$$\underline{\quad 10 \quad} = 10 \checkmark$$

Find the value of the variable in each equation.

4 $\square - 79 = 8$

$\square - 79 = 8$, so $\square = 8 + \underline{\quad 79 \quad}$

$8 + \underline{\quad 79 \quad} = \underline{\quad 87 \quad}$, so $\underline{\quad 87 \quad} = \square$

5 $13 \cdot m = 52$

$13 \cdot m = 52$, so $m = 52 \div \underline{\quad 13 \quad}$

$52 \div \underline{\quad 13 \quad} = \underline{\quad 4 \quad}$, so $\underline{\quad 4 \quad} = m$

6 $\frac{s}{6} = 7$

$s = \underline{\quad 42 \quad}$

7 $100 + p = 143$

$p = \underline{\quad 43 \quad}$

GO ON

Lesson 3-3 Solve Algebraic Equations **115**

Practice

Using Manipulatives

Counters Two-color counters can be used to represent known and unknown quantities in an equation.

Algebra Tiles Students can use algebra tiles to perform inverse operations and find the value of unknown quantities.

 On-Hand Manipulatives Use stamper markers of different colors in place of algebra tiles or counters.

Math Coach Notes
Strategies

1. Remind students that the values on either side of an equals sign are the same. To find the value of a variable, use inverse operations so that the variable is alone on one side of the equals sign.

2. Question students on what operations are in an equation, and what the inverse operation is. As algebraic equations increase in difficulty, students will need to know how to isolate the variable. Start with simple equations and then increase their complexity.

Are They Getting It?

Check students' understanding of solving equations to find the unknown quantity. Have them draw diagrams or models to explain. Ask students to point out which answers are wrong and explain the errors.

1. To find the value of x in $27 - x = 25$, use the inverse operation of subtraction.

This is incorrect.
The inverse operation of subtraction is addition.

2. If $9 + z = 12$, then $12 - 9 = z$.

This is correct because subtraction is the inverse operation of addition.

3. The value of y in $3 \cdot y = 39$ is 13.

This is correct because $3 \cdot 13 = 39$.

Lesson 3-3 Solve Algebraic Equations **115**

English Learner Strategy

Oral Explanations Put 3 blocks or tiles on the right side of a scale. Put 7 blocks on the left side. Working aloud with students, say:

- Add blocks to one side of the scale to make both sides equal.

- What is the value of x in $3 + x = 7$?

- What operation can be used in the equation $3 + x = 7$ so the variable will be alone on one side of the equation?

- Explain how to find the value of t in the equation $t \div 4 = 7$.

- Describe how to use inverse operations to find the value of an unknown quantity.

Step by Step Problem-Solving Practice

Problem-Solving Strategies
- ☐ Draw a diagram.
- ☐ Guess and check.
- ☐ Use a model.
- ☐ Solve a simpler problem.
- ☑ Write an equation.

Solve.

8 **FINANCE** Ms. Cartright had $47 in her wallet. She bought a birthday present for her best friend. Now she has $29 in her wallet.

How much money did she spend on the gift?

Understand Read the problem. Write what you know.

Ms. Cartright had __$47__.

She has __$29__ left.

Plan Pick a strategy. One strategy is to write and solve an equation.

Solve Let p represent the amount of money spent on the present. Write and solve the equation.

$$\underbrace{\$47}_{\text{money in wallet}} - \underbrace{p}_{\text{cost of present}} = \underbrace{\$29}_{\text{money left}}$$

To solve the equation, use another subtraction sentence from the same fact family.

If __47__ − __p__ = __29__ ,

then __47 − 29 = p__ .

$p =$ __18__

Ms. Cartright spent __$18__.

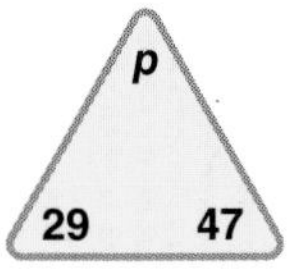

Check Substitute __$18__ for p in the equation.

$47 -$ __18__ $=$ __29__

__29__ $=$ __29__ ✔

(fact triangle: p at top, 29 and 47 at bottom)

Intervention Strategy Kinesthetic/Logical Learners

Fact Triangles Provide students with a triangle template that they can use to make a stack of fact triangles. Students should take an 8.5- by 14-inch piece of paper and fold it accordion-style along its longest side. Trace the triangle on the upper half and again on the lower half of the folded paper placing one vertex along one of the folded edges. When the triangles are cut, the stack will be like an accordion as long as the vertex on the fold is not cut. Use one accordion triangle for addition fact families (as shown in the Key Concept box) and the second accordion triangle for multiplication fact families. An example is shown below.

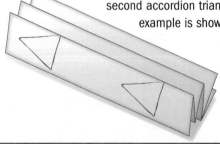

Solve.

9 SHIPPING   Dustin is packaging stuffed animals for a toy company. The shipping boxes will hold 14 toys each. How many boxes will he need to package 154 toys? Write an equation and solve for the variable. Check off each step.

✔ Understand: I underlined key words.

✔ Plan: To solve this problem, I will _write an equation_ .

✔ Solve: The answer is _14 • x = 154, x = 11_ .

✔ Check: To checked my answer by _substituting a value for the variable_ .

10 EXERCISE   Mr. Castillo jogs 3 miles every day. How many days will it take him to jog 42 miles? Write an equation and solve for the variable.

42 ÷ x = 3; x = 14; It will take him 14 days.

11 Reflect   Explain how to use the fact triangle to solve the equation $x + 4 = 7$.

Sample answer: The fact triangle can show the relationship

between the numbers. The equation $x + 4 = 7$ is related

_to $7 - 4 = x$. So, $x = 3$._

▶ Skills, Concepts, and Problem Solving

Find the value of each variable by modeling the equation.

12 $3 \cdot j = 15$

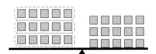

$j = \underline{5}$

13 $4 + \square = 11$

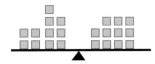

$\square = \underline{7}$

GO ON

David Young-Wolff/PhotoEdit

Odd/Even Assignments

Exercises 12–19 are structured so that students practice the same concepts whether they are assigned the odd or even problems.

In-Class Assignment

Have students complete Exercises 12, 16, 18, and 21 to ensure that they understand the concept.

Math Challenge

Working Backward   Students can generate equations by starting with a solution and working backward. Give students a solution and have them write at least five different equations that have the given solution. An example follows for $n = 3$.

$n = 3$	$n = 3$	$n = 3$	$n = 3$	$n = 3$
$n + 5 = 3 + 5$	$n + 10 = 3 + 10$	$n - 7 = 3 - 7$	$n \cdot 2 = 3 \cdot 2$	$n \div 9 = 3 \div 9$
$n + 5 = 8$	$n + 10 = 13$	$n - 7 = -4$	$2n = 6$	$n \div 9 = \frac{1}{3}$

Assess

See It, Do It, Say It, Write It

Step 1 Write four algebraic equations on the board using each of the four operations.

Step 2 Students can work in pairs or alone with algebra tiles and equation mats. Have them model several equations. Have students use the models to find the unknown quantities.

Step 3 Ask students to describe the inverse operations that are used to solve each equation, and then solve.

Step 4 Ask students to define the term variable. Have them write the steps they would take to solve two equations that you have written on the board.

Looking Ahead: Pre-teach

Relate Algebraic Equations and Formulas
In the next lesson, students will substitute known values into formulas and simplify to solve for an unknown. For example, the formula for area of a rectangle is $A = \ell \cdot w$.

Example

A rectangle has a length of 4 m and a width of 3 m. What is its area? $4 \cdot 3 = 12$, or 12 m²

Have students try these examples.

1. A rectangle has a length of 12 in. and a width of 4 in. What is its area? 48 in²

2. A rectangle has a length of 10 ft and a width of 2 ft. What is its area? 20 ft²

3. A square has a length of 5 cm and a width of 5 cm. What is its area? 25 cm²

Find the value of the variable in each equation.

14 $13 + n = 21$

$n = \underline{\quad 8 \quad}$

15 $126 - \square = 106$

$\square = \underline{\quad 20 \quad}$

16 $14 \cdot \square = 112$

$\square = \underline{\quad 8 \quad}$

17 $\frac{240}{t} = 12$

$t = \underline{\quad 20 \quad}$

Solve.

18 ADVERTISING   Mr. Michaels is opening a new coffee shop. He printed 375 flyers to advertise his new shop. He has distributed 254 of the flyers. How many does he have left? Write an equation and solve for the variable

$\underline{375 - x = 254;\ x = 121;\ \text{He has 121 flyers left.}}$

19 FINANCE   Juan Carlos earns $15 an hour. Last week he earned $330. How many hours did Juan Carlos work last week? Write an equation and solve for the variable.

$\underline{15 \cdot x = 330;\ x = 22;\ \text{He worked 22 hours last week.}}$

Vocabulary Check   Write the vocabulary word that completes each sentence.

20 A $\underline{\quad \text{variable} \quad}$ is a letter or symbol used to represent an unknown quantity.

21 **Writing in Math**   Explain the difference between an algebraic expression and an equation.

$\underline{\text{Sample answer: Algebraic expressions do not use an equals sign.}}$

$\underline{\text{Equations compare two equal expressions by using an equals sign.}}$

 Spiral Review

Evaluate the expression when ◌ **= 4 and** ◆ **= 3.** (Lesson 3-2, p. 105)

22 $◌^2 + 5 - 2 + ◆ \cdot 8$

Replace symbols with values: $\underline{4^2 + 5 - 2 + 3 \cdot 8}$

Value of the expression: $\underline{\quad 43 \quad}$

STOP

Ticket Out the Door

Solve the Equation   Give each student an equation to solve. Students should solve the equation and show you the solution as they exit the classroom.

Relate Algebraic Equations and Formulas

KEY Concept

Like other algebraic equations, many **formulas** use **variables** to show the relationships between values. Consider the algebraic equation $p + q = r$. The equation can be solved if the value of two variables is known. If $p = 3$ and $q = 2$, the value of r is 5.

$$p + q = r$$
$$3 + 2 = 5$$

Formulas often use more than one variable. For instance, distance, time, and rate are related values shown by the formula $d = r \cdot t$.

You can rewrite the formula to find the value of the unknown variable. Consider the following fact family.

$$d = r \cdot t \quad d = t \cdot r$$
$$r = d \div t \quad t = d \div r$$

Tanya traveled 50 miles in 2 hours. Substitute values for the variables to solve the equation.

$d = 50$ miles $t = 2$ hours $r = ?$

$r = d \div t$	Use the formula.
$r = 50 \div 2$	Substitute values.
$r = 25$	Solve.

The rate is 25 miles per hour.

VOCABULARY

area
the number of square units needed to cover the surface enclosed by a geometric figure

equation
a mathematical sentence that contains an equals sign

formula
an equation that shows a relationship among certain quantities

variable
a symbol, usually a letter, used to represent a number

Example 1

Use the formula $A = \ell \cdot w$ to solve for ℓ, length.

The area of the rectangle is 48 square centimeters. Its width is 8 centimeters. What is the length of the rectangle?

1. Substitute the values. $48 = \ell \cdot 8$
2. Use the inverse operation. $\dfrac{48}{8} = \dfrac{\ell \cdot 8}{8}$
3. What is the value of ℓ? $6 = \ell$
4. The length of the rectangle is 6 centimeters.

GO ON

Additional *Example 1*

Use the formula $A = \ell \cdot w$ to solve for ℓ, length.

The area of the rectangle is 72 square yards. Its width is 9 yards. What is the length of the rectangle?

1. Substitute the values. $72 = \ell \cdot 9$
2. Use the inverse operation. $\dfrac{72}{9} = \dfrac{\ell \cdot 9}{9}$
3. What is the value of ℓ? $8 = \ell$
4. The length of the rectangle is 8 yards.

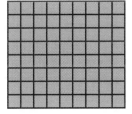

Lesson Planner

Objective   Solve simple linear equations for one variable in terms of another.

Vocabulary   area , equation , formula , variable

Materials/Manipulatives   balance scale, unit cubes, grid paper, geoboards

Chapter Resource Masters

- CRM Vocabulary and English Language Development (p. A62)
- CRM Skills Practice (p. A63)
- CRM Problem-Solving Practice (p. A64)
- CRM Homework Practice (p. A65)

① Introduce

Vocabulary

Variables   Use a fact family to reinforce how a variable can represent a number in an equation. When two of the three members of a fact family are known, the variable can be isolated to determine its value.

② Teach

Key Concept

Foundational Skills and Concepts   After students have read through the Key Concept box, have them try these exercises.

1. In the formula $d = r \cdot t$, what does the r represent? rate

2. Jalyn traveled 105 miles in 3 hours. What was her rate of speed? $105 = r \cdot 3, r = 35$; she traveled at 35 mph.

3. A plane traveling at 350 miles per hour flies a distance of 2,450 miles. How many hours does this trip take? $2,450 = 350 \cdot t, t = 7$; the trip takes 7 hours.

Additional *Example 2*

Use the formula $d = r \cdot t$ to solve for t, time.

Henry drove 264 miles at 48 miles per hour. How many hours did Henry drive?

1. Substitute the values.

$$d = r \cdot t \qquad 264 = 48 \cdot t$$

2. Use the inverse operation.

$$\frac{264}{48} = \frac{48 \cdot t}{48}$$

3. What is the value of t?

$$5.5 = t$$

4. Henry drove for 5.5 hours.

YOUR TURN!

Use the formula $A = \ell \cdot w$ to solve for w, width.

The area of the rectangle is 35 square yards. Its length is 5 yards. What is the width of the rectangle?

1. Substitute the values.

$$\underline{\quad 35 \quad} = \underline{\quad 5 \quad} \cdot w$$

2. Use the inverse operation.

$$\frac{\boxed{35}}{\boxed{5}} = \frac{\boxed{5}}{\boxed{5}} \cdot w$$

3. What is the value of w?

$$\underline{\quad 7 \quad} = w$$

Example 2

Use the formula $d = r \cdot t$ to solve for r, rate.

Shannon bicycled 36 miles in 3 hours. What was her rate of speed?

1. Substitute the values.

$$36 = r \cdot 3$$

2. Use the inverse operation.

$$\frac{36}{3} = \frac{r \cdot 3}{3}$$

3. What is the value of r?

$$12 = r$$

4. Shannon bicycled 12 miles per hour.

YOUR TURN!

Use the formula $d = r \cdot t$ to solve for t, time.

The Santa Lucia traveled 340 miles at 34 miles per hour. How many hours did the boat travel?

1. Substitute the values.

$$d = r \cdot t \qquad \underline{340} = \underline{34} \cdot t$$

2. Use the inverse operation.

$$\frac{\boxed{340}}{\boxed{34}} = \frac{\boxed{34} \cdot \boxed{t}}{\boxed{34}}$$

3. What is the value of t?

$$\underline{\quad 10 = t \quad}$$

4. The boat traveled for $\underline{\quad 10 \quad}$ hours.

English Learner Strategy

Terminology Confusion Review the terms *distance*, *rate*, and *time* with students. Explain what each term means and how to look for clues in a word problem. Practice reading a problem and labeling each piece of information. Reinforce the distance formula by writing out its fact family in words as well as their corresponding variables. Then model how to substitute values for the variables. Have students practice explaining the steps to one another using the terms and variables.

Who is Correct?

Find the value of f in the equation $a = c + f$, when $a = 47$ and $c = 38$.

Circle correct answer(s). Cross out incorrect answer(s).

 Guided Practice

Find the value of h, when $b = 24$ and $e = 2$.

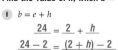

1 $b = e + h$

$\underline{24} = \underline{2} + \underline{h}$

$24 - 2 = (2 + h) - 2$

$h = \underline{22}$

2 $b = h - e$

$\underline{24} = h - \underline{2}$

$24 + 2 = (h - 2) + 2$

$h = \underline{26}$

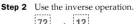 **Practice**

Use the formula $A = \ell \cdot w$ to solve for ℓ, length.

3 The area of the rectangle is 72 square meters. Its width is 12 centimeters. What is the length of the rectangle?

Step 1 Substitute the values.

$\underline{72} = \ell \cdot \underline{12}$

Step 2 Use the inverse operation.

$\dfrac{\boxed{72}}{\boxed{12}} = \dfrac{\ell \cdot \boxed{12}}{\boxed{12}}$

Step 3 What is the value of ℓ?

$\underline{6} = \ell$

Step 4 The length of the rectangle is __6__ centimeters.

GO ON

Who is Correct?
Diagnostic Teaching

- Chenoa is incorrect. The values for the variables were substituted correctly, but she did not isolate f correctly.

- Shristi is correct. The values for the variables were substituted correctly and the value of f is 9.

- Damian is incorrect. He substituted the wrong values for the variables.

---

③ Practice

Using Manipulatives

Balance Scale Use a balance scale to model equations. Have students use counters or unit cubes to determine missing values in equations. Remind students that the scale is balanced when both sides are equal.

 On-Hand Manipulatives Practice finding the area of a rectangle with unit cubes. Have students use the cubes to create a rectangle. From their models, students can write an equation with a variable for other students to solve.

Math Coach Notes

Inverse Operations To help students understand formulas, review the concept of inverse operations. Practice writing fact families. Include examples that use variables. Discuss how to isolate the variable using inverse operations. Reinforce that whatever operation is done to one side must be done to the other to maintain balance.

⚠ Common Error *Alert*

Exercises 1–2 Remind students to watch the operation signs carefully when isolating the variable. Students may make an error by not performing the same operation on each side of the equation. Model how to check the answer by inserting it in the original equation to test its accuracy.

Math Coach Notes

Substituting Values Have students practice inserting values and solving for variables by writing their own equations. Model the process by writing an equation, $a = b - c$. Then demonstrate how to assign two values: Find the value of b, when $a = 9$ and $c = 7$. Show how to insert the values into the equation and then isolate the variable to determine the missing value. Have students write three equations and assign variables. Tell them to create an answer key so they can check their classmates' work when students exchange equations.

Use the formula $A = \ell \cdot w$ to solve for ℓ, length.

4 The area of the rectangle is 24 square meters. Its width is 6 meters. What is the length of the rectangle?

$\underline{24} = \ell \cdot 6$, so $\ell = \underline{4}$ m

5 The area of the rectangle is 32 square feet. Its width is 4 feet. What is the length of the rectangle?

$\underline{32} = \ell \cdot 4$, so $\ell = \underline{8}$ ft

Use the formula $A = \ell \cdot w$ to solve for w, width.

6 The area of the rectangle is 21 square inches. Its length is 3 inches. What is the width of the rectangle?

$\underline{21} = 3 \cdot w$, so $w = \underline{7}$ in.

7 The area of the rectangle is 25 square miles. Its length is 5 miles. What is the width of the rectangle?

$\underline{25} = 5 \cdot w$, so $w = \underline{5}$ mi

Step by Step Problem-Solving Practice

Use the formula $d = r \cdot t$ to solve for r, rate.

8 Tiffany traveled 34 miles in 2 hours. What was her rate of speed?

Understand	Read the problem. Write what you know.
	The distance, or d is $\underline{34}$ miles.
	The time, or t, is $\underline{2}$ hours.
Plan	Pick a strategy. One strategy is to use a formula.
	Use the formula $d = r \cdot t$.
Solve	$\underline{34} = r \cdot \underline{2}$ Substitute the variables for values.
	$\dfrac{\boxed{34}}{\boxed{2}} = \dfrac{r \cdot \boxed{2}}{\boxed{2}}$ Use inverse operations.
	$\underline{17} = r$ Solve.
	Tiffany's rate of speed is $\underline{17}$ miles per hour.
Check	Substitute the values of r and t into the formula and solve for d.

Problem-Solving Strategies
- ☐ Draw a diagram.
- ☐ Use logical reasoning.
- ☐ Solve a simpler problem.
- ☐ Work backward.
- ☑ Use a formula.

Are They Getting It?

Check students' understanding of algebraic equations and formulas by writing these problems on the board. Ask them to point out incorrect answers and explain why they are incorrect.

I. Consider $h = m - r$. If $h = 41$ and $r = 27$, then $m = 14$. This is incorrect. $41 = m - 27$, so $m = 68$.

2. The area of a rectangle is 80 square yards. If its width is 16 yards, then its length is 8 yards. This is incorrect. $80 = \ell \cdot 16$, so $\ell = 5$; The length is 5 yards.

3. Cara drove 330 miles in 6 hours. So, her rate of speed is 55 miles per hour. This is correct.

Use the formula $d = r \cdot t$ to solve for the missing variable.

9 EXERCISE Lazaro ran <u>15 miles</u> at a rate of <u>5 miles per hour</u>. <u>How long</u> did it take Lazaro to complete his run? Check off each step.

✔ Understand: I underlined key words.

✔ Plan: To solve this problem I will ___ <u>use the formula $d = r \cdot t$</u> .

✔ Solve: The answer is ___ <u>$15 = 5 \cdot t$, $t = 3$; It took him 3 hours</u> .

✔ Check: I checked my answer by <u>substituting the values of r and t to solve for d</u>

10 SPACE TRAVEL The space shuttle Atlantis travels at a rate of 17,500 miles per hour while in orbit. It has traveled 70,000 miles in orbit. How long has the shuttle been in orbit?

<u>$70,000 = 17,500 \cdot t$, $t = 4$; The shuttle has been in orbit for 4 hours.</u>

11 Reflect Use the fact triangle to write four related multiplication and division equations for the formula of the area of a rectangle.

$A = \ell \cdot w$; $A = w \cdot \ell$; $\ell = A \div w$; $w = A \div \ell$

 Skills, Concepts, and Problem Solving

Find the value of q, when $r = 37$ and $s = 19$.

12 $r = s + q$

$\underline{37} = \underline{19} + q$

$\underline{37 - 19} = (19 + q) - 19$

$q = \underline{18}$

13 $s = q - r$

$\underline{19} = q - \underline{37}$

$\underline{19 + 37} = (q - 37) + 37$

$q = \underline{56}$

Use the formula $A = \ell \cdot w$ to solve for ℓ, length.

14 The area of the rectangle is 15 square kilometers. Its width is 5 kilometers. What is the length of the rectangle?

$15 = \ell \cdot 5$, so $\ell = 3$ km

15 The area of the rectangle is 36 square millimeters. Its width is 6 millimeters. What is the length of the rectangle?

$36 = \ell \cdot 6$, so $\ell = 6$ mm   GO ON

Lesson 3-4 Relate Algebraic Equations and Formulas **123**

 Common Error Alert

Exercise 12–13 Sometimes students switch variable values and solve incorrectly. Remind students to be careful to substitute the correct values for corresponding variables. Reinforce the importance of checking the answer by inserting all the values into the original equation to test for accuracy.

Odd/Even Assignments

Exercises 12–22 are structured so that students practice the same concepts whether they are assigned the odd or even problems.

In-Class Assignment

Have students complete Exercises 12, 15, 16, 18, 20, and 26 to ensure that they understand the concept.

Intervention Strategy **Kinesthetic Learners**

Geoboard Exercise Have students work in small groups. Give each student in the group a geoboard and several rubber bands. Ask students to create rectangles on the geoboard with the rubber bands. For each rectangle, students should determine the area and write an equation with a variable for either length or width. Have students write a word problem for each of their rectangles and exchange the word problems with other members of their group. Students should write equations and solutions to their classmates' problems and support them with a model on the geoboards.

Use the formula $A = \ell \cdot w$ to solve for w, width.

16 The area of the rectangle is 72 square meters. Its length is 9 meters. What is the width of the rectangle?

$\underline{72 = 9 \cdot w, \text{ so } w = 8 \text{ m}}$

17 The area of the rectangle is 28 square millimeters. Its length is 4 millimeters. What is the width of the rectangle?

$\underline{28 = 4 \cdot w, \text{ so } w = 7 \text{ mm}}$

18 The area of the rectangle is 49 square meters. Its length is 7 meters. What is the width of the rectangle?

$\underline{49 = 7 \cdot w, \text{ so } w = 7 \text{ m}}$

19 The area of the rectangle is 30 square feet. Its length is 5 feet. What is the width of the rectangle?

$\underline{30 = 5 \cdot w, \text{ so } w = 6 \text{ ft}}$

Use the formula $d = r \cdot t$ to solve for the missing variable.

20 **JETS**   The F-16 Fighting Falcon can travel 300 miles in 12 minutes. What is the jet's rate of speed?

$\underline{300 = 25 \cdot r, r = 25; \text{ The jet can travel at a rate of}}$
$\underline{25 \text{ miles per minute.}}$

21 **HELICOPTERS**   The Apache helicopter can travel 284 kilometers per hour. How long would it take the Apache to travel a distance of 1,420 kilometers at this rate of speed?

$\underline{1{,}420 = 284 \cdot t, t = 5; \text{ The Apache would travel for 5 hours.}}$

22 **EXERCISE**   Maribelle entered a cross-country skiing race. She skiied at a rate of 8 miles per hour. If the race is 16 miles long, how long will it take Maribelle to complete the race?

$\underline{16 = 8 \cdot t, t = 2; \text{ It would take Maribelle 2 hours.}}$

Math Challenge

Rectangle Dilemma   Have students solve the following problem. Tell them to provide proof and support for their answers.

The area of a large rectangle is 48 square inches. Its length is 3 inches. The area of a small rectangle is 28 square inches, and its length is 4 inches. How much wider is the larger rectangle?

The large rectangle is 9 inches wider.
large rectangle: $48 = 3 \cdot w, w = 16$
small rectangle: $28 = 4 \cdot w, w = 7$
$16 - 7 = 9$

Vocabulary Check **Write the vocabulary word that completes each sentence.**

23 A(n) _____equation_____ is a mathematical sentence that contains an equals sign.

24 An equation that shows a relationship among certain quantities is called a(n) _____formula_____.

25 _____Area_____ is the number of square units needed to cover the surface enclosed by a geometric figure.

26 **Writing in Math** The area of the rectangle to the right is 12 square units. Its width is 3 units. Find the length of the rectangle and explain how to use the diagram to check your answer.

$12 = \ell \cdot 3$, so $\ell = 4$; The diagram has a total of 12 square units. The

diagram shows 3 rows of 4 square units.

▶ **Spiral Review**

Find the value of each variable by modeling the equation. (Lesson 3-3, p. 113)

27 $5 + h = 12$

28 $2 \cdot r = 18$

$h = \underline{\quad 7 \quad}$

$r = \underline{\quad 9 \quad}$

Find the value of the variable in each equation. (Lesson 3-3, p. 113)

29 $\square - 18 = 35$

$\square - 18 = 35$, so $\square = 35 + \underline{\ 18\ }$

$35 + \underline{\ 18\ } = \square$, so $\underline{\ 53\ } = \square$

30 $8 \cdot g = 64$

$8 \cdot g = 64$, so $g = 64 \div \underline{\ 8\ }$

$64 \div \underline{\ 8\ } = \underline{\ 8\ }$, so $\underline{\ 8\ } = g$

Solve. (Lesson 3-3, p. 113)

31 **ENTERTAINMENT** Marina and Dylan went to a baseball game. They bought snacks that cost $9.50. The total cost of the game tickets and the snacks was $27.50. How much did they pay for the tickets?

Sample answer: $t + 9.50 = 27.50$; $t = \$18.00$

STOP

Copyright © Glencoe/McGraw-Hill, a division of The McGraw-Hill Companies, Inc.

④ Assess

See It, Do It, Say It, Write It

Step 1 Write the following problem on the board. "Solve the equation $f = g - h$, when $f = 62$ and $h = 39$."

Step 2 Have students solve for the missing variable.

Step 3 Ask students to work in pairs. Tell students to explain the steps they took to solve the equation.

Step 4 Have students work alone to write an explanation of how to solve the equation on the board. Encourage students to use vocabulary from the lesson.

Ticket Out the Door

Distance Formula Review Write the following problem on the board. Tell students to write an equation that represents the situation, and then solve for the variable. As students approach the classroom door to exit, alternate asking them to cite the equation for or give the solution to the problem.

A trained marathoner can run 19 kilometers per hour. How long would it take the marathoner to travel a distance of 57 kilometers at this rate of speed?

$57 = 19 \cdot t$, $t = 3$; It would take a marathoner 3 hours to travel 57 kilometers.

Formative Assessment

Use the Progress Check to assess students' mastery of the previous lessons. Have students review the lesson indicated for the problems they answered incorrectly.

Odd/Even Assignments

Exercises are structured so that students practice the same concepts whether they are assigned the odd or even problems.

⚠ Common Error *Alert*

Use Models   If students cannot visualize how to use the equation balance models, provide students with hands-on manipulatives that they can use to model the equations. You can give them tiles and an equation mat and have them physically add tiles to both sides or remove tiles from both sides.

Exercises 9–10   Ensure students write an equation before trying to find each solution. Remind them that the process of solving is more important than the solution. They can use their mental math skills to check their work.

Progress Check 2 (Lessons 3-3 and 3-4)

Find the value of each variable by modeling the equation.

1 $9 - n = 4$ $n = \underline{5}$

2 $2 + \square = 10$ $\square = \underline{8}$

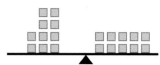

Find the value of the variable in each equation.

3 $15 + \square = 34$ $\square = \underline{19}$

4 $50 - \square = 13$ $\square = \underline{37}$

5 $9x = 108$ $x = \underline{12}$

6 $\frac{m}{4} = 7$ $m = \underline{28}$

Use the formula $A = \ell \cdot w$ to solve for w, width.

7 The area of the rectangle is 54 square inches. Its length is 6 inches. What is the width of the rectangle?

$\underline{54 = 6 \cdot w}$, so $w = 9$ in.

8 The area of the rectangle is 49 square miles. Its length is 7 miles. What is the width of the rectangle?

$\underline{49 = 7 \cdot w}$, so $w = 7$ mi

Write an equation to represent each situation. Then answer the question.

9 **MONEY**   Jade earned $10 per hour last week. Her total earnings were $250. How many hours did Jade work last week?

$\underline{10h = 250; \ 25 \ hours}$

Use the formula $d = r \cdot t$ to solve for the missing variable.

10 **EXERCISE**   Lydia entered a walk for charity with her family. She walked an 8-mile course in 2 hours. If Lydia walked at the same rate for all 8 miles, what was her rate of speed?

$\underline{8 = r \cdot 2, \ r = 4; \ She \ walked \ 4 \ miles \ per \ hour.}$

126   Chapter 3 Expressions and Equations

Data-Driven Decision Making

Students missing Exercises . . .	Have trouble with . . .	Should review and practice . . .
1–2	solving an equation by using a model.	SSG Lesson 3-3, p. 113 CRM Skills Practice, p. A59
3–6	solving an equation.	SSG Lesson 3-3, p. 113 CRM Skills Practice p. A59
7–8	using a formula.	SSG Lesson 3-4, p. 119 CRM Skills Practice, p. A63
9–10	solving a word problem that uses an equation.	CRM Problem-Solving Practice, pp. A60 and A64

Chapter 3 Study Guide

Vocabulary and Concept Check

algebraic expression, *p. 105*

area, *p. 119*

base, *p. 98*

equation, *p. 113*

evaluate, *p. 105*

exponent, *p. 98*

formula, *p. 119*

inverse operations, *p. 113*

order of operations, *p. 98*

variable, *p. 113*

Write the vocabulary word that completes each sentence.

1 To find the value of an algebraic expression by replacing variables with numbers is to ___evaluate___ the expression.

2 $7x + 9 - 3y$ is an example of a(n) ___algebraic expression___.

3 A symbol, usually a letter, used to represent a number is called a(n) ___variable___.

4 Addition and subtraction are ___inverse operations___ because they undo each other.

5 ___equation___

$$3x = 4 + 20$$

6 The formula for ___area___ is $A = \ell \cdot w$.

7 In the ___formula___, $d = r \cdot t$, the variable r represents the rate.

Write the correct vocabulary term in each blank.

8 ___base (of a power)___

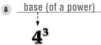

9 ___exponent___

10 ___order of operations___

1. Simplify within parentheses.

2. Simplify exponents.

3. Multiply and divide from left to right.

4. Add and subtract from left to right.

Chapter 3 Study Guide **127**

Study Guide
Formative Assessment

Vocabulary and Concept Check

If students have difficulty answering Exercises 1–10, remind them that they can use the page references to refresh their memories about the vocabulary terms.

Vocabulary Review Strategies

Color Code   Have students use a color-coding system to write expressions. They can use one color for each variable. When they associate the color with the variable, the more apt they are to substitute correctly.

Lesson Review

Each example walks the students through the parts of mathematical expressions and equations. When students are asked to simplify the expressions, ensure they simplify completely.

Find **Extra Practice** for these concepts in the Practice Worksheets, pages A50–A65.

Classroom Management

Early Finishers   Have students who finish the exercises before others create new exercises for each example. They can trade their exercises with other early finishers and check each other's work.

Dinah Zike's Foldables

Review Remind students to complete and refer to their Foldables as they progress through the Chapter 3 Study Guide. Have students share and compare their completed Foldables with a partner. You may also choose to have them use their Foldable as a study aid in preparing for the Chapter Test. (For complete instructions, see Chapter Resource Masters, p. A47.)

1. Simplify grouping symbols	2. Find the values of all powers.
3. Multiply and divide in order from left to right	4. Add and subtract in order from left to right

Common Error *Alert*

Simplifying Steps If students are not simplifying the expressions in Exercise 11–18 correctly, ensure they are showing each step as they simplify each expression. Students often have trouble identifying which sign (positive or negative) goes with the terms they are combining. It may help students to write each subtraction expression as an addition expression in which the opposite of the term is added.

3-1 Order of Operations (pp. 98–104)

Find the value of each expression.

11. $10 + 28 \div 7 - 3 \cdot 1 =$ __11__

12. $13 - 9 + 12 \cdot 2 =$ __28__

13. $5^2 + 20 \div 2 =$ __35__

14. $172 + 12 \div 4 - 6^2 =$ __139__

Find the value of each expression.

15. $6 \cdot 2 - (2^2 \cdot 2) + 21 \div 7 =$ __7__

16. $4^2 \div (3 + 1) - 0 =$ __4__

17. $(12 - 6)^2 + 3 \cdot 7 =$ __57__

18. $(14 \div 2)^2 + 70 \div 10 =$ __56__

> **Example 1**
>
> **Find the value of $8 - 4 + 35 \div 7 \cdot 4$.**
>
> 1. Use the order of operations.
> 2. There are no grouping symbols or exponents.
> 3. Multiply and divide.
> $$8 - 4 + 35 \div 7 \cdot 4 = 8 - 4 + 5 \cdot 4$$
> $$= 8 - 4 + 20$$
> 4. Add and subtract.
> $$8 - 4 + 20 = 4 + 20$$
> $$= 24$$

> **Example 2**
>
> **Find the value of $18 \div 3 + (2 + 1)^2 \cdot 4 - 5$.**
>
> 1. Use the order of operations.
> 2. Simplify the grouping symbols.
> $$18 \div 3 + (2 + 1)^2 \cdot 4 - 5 = 18 \div 3 + 3^2 \cdot 4 - 5$$
> 3. Simplify the exponent.
> $$18 \div 3 + 3^2 \cdot 4 - 5 = 18 \div 3 + 9 \cdot 4 - 5$$
> 4. Multiply and divide.
> $$18 \div 3 + 9 \cdot 4 - 5 = 6 + 36 - 5$$
> 5. Add and subtract.
> $$6 + 36 - 5 = 42 - 5$$
> $$= 37$$

3-2 Evaluate Variable Expressions (pp. 105–111)

Evaluate each expression when $\odot = 12$.

19 $7 \cdot \odot$

$7 \cdot 12 = 84$

20 $120 \div \odot$

$120 \div 12 = 10$

21 $14 + \odot \div 3 \cdot 5 - 1$

$14 + 12 \div 3 \cdot 5 - 1 = 33$

22 $8 \cdot 4 - 3^2 + \odot + 7$

$8 \cdot 4 - 3^2 + 12 + 7 = 42$

Evaluate each expression when $x = 4$ and $y = 0$.

23 $15 + 3^2 \cdot 4 - (x - 1) + 7y$

48

24 $(2x^2 - 2) \div 5 + 4xy$

6

25 $(5y + 10) \div (x - 2) + (3 \cdot 4)$

17

26 $(x - 3)^2 + (15 - 4y)$

16

27 $x \cdot y \cdot 3 + x \cdot 3 \div 6$

2

Example 3

Evaluate $37 - \blacklozenge$ when $\blacklozenge = 24$.

1. Replace $\blacklozenge$ with 24 in the expression.

$37 - \blacklozenge = 37 - 24$

2. Simplify. Follow the order of operations.

$37 - 24 = 13$

Example 4

Evaluate $16 \div 8 + y \cdot x - 7$ when $x = 2$ and $y = 7$.

1. Replace x with 2 and y with 7 in the expression.

$16 \div 8 + y \cdot x - 7 = 16 \div 8 + 7 \cdot 2 - 7$

2. Simplify using the order of operations.

Divide.	$= 16 \div 8 + 7 \cdot 2 - 7$
Multiply.	$= 2 + 7 \cdot 2 - 7$
Add.	$= 2 + 14 - 7$
Subtract.	$= 16 - 7$
	$= 9$

Chapter 3 Study Guide **129**

Common Error *Alert*

Substitute Correctly If students are not simplifying the expressions in Exercises 23–27 correctly, have them check to make sure they substituted the correct value for the variables. Ensure they are showing each step when simplifying the expressions and are following the order of operations.

Note This!

Create a Checklist Help students create a study checklist. The checklist should include all of the following:

- Notes from class
- Drawings from class
- Foldable
- Vocabulary terms and concepts
- Lesson examples
- All assignments and quizzes
- Chapter 3 Study Guide

Intervention Strategy

Interpersonal/Auditory Learners

Tic-Tac-Toe To practice solving equations, draw a tic-tac-toe game on the front board. Write a variety of equations on index cards, along with a value for x. Number the cards sequentially and place them number-side up on the board. Have students work in two teams, taking turns calling out a number. Students have 15 seconds (or whatever time is appropriate for the level of the class) to solve the problem. When a team solves the equation correctly, place an "X" or "O" in that spot. Whoever has three Xs or Os in a row, diagonally, or vertically, wins.

3-3 Operations with Unknown Quantities (pp. 113-118)

Find the value of the variable in each equation.

28 $27 + x = 35$

$x = \underline{\ 8\ }$

29 $42 - b = 8$

$b = \underline{\ 34\ }$

30 $y + 32 = 72$

$y = \underline{\ 40\ }$

31 $m - 17 = 28$

$m = \underline{\ 45\ }$

Find the value of the variable in each equation.

32 $\dfrac{y}{7} = 8$

$y = \underline{\ 56\ }$

33 $f \cdot 7 = 63$

$f = \underline{\ 9\ }$

34 $\dfrac{t}{6} = 12$

$t = \underline{\ 72\ }$

35 $b \cdot 8 = 64$

$b = \underline{\ 8\ }$

Example 5

Find the value of *a* in the equation $a - 3 = 5$.

1. Use the fact that addition and subtraction are inverse operations.

   $a - 3 = 5$, so $a = 3 + 5$

   $3 + 5 = 8$, so $8 = a$

2. Use a model to check your answer.

3. Think: What number minus 3 equals 5?

   $8 - 3 = 5$

4. The value of a must be 8.

Example 6

Find the value of *d* in the equation $7 \cdot d = 35$.

1. Think: What number times 7 equals 35?

2. Use the fact that multiplication and division are inverse operations.

   $7 \cdot d = 35$, so $d = 35 \div 7$

   $35 \div 7 = 5$, so $5 = d$

3. Check your answer by substituting 5 for d.

   $7 \cdot d = 35$

   $7 \cdot 5 = 35$

   $35 = 35$

4. $35 = 35$ is a true statement, so 5 is correct.

3-4 Relate Algebraic Equations and Formulas (pp. 119–126)

Use the formula $A = \ell \cdot w$ to solve for the missing variable.

36 The area of the rectangle is 16 square meters. Its width is 4 meters. What is the length of the rectangle?

$16 = \ell \cdot 4$, so $\ell = 4$ m

37 The area of the rectangle is 27 square meters. Its width is 3 meters. What is the length of the rectangle?

$27 = \ell \cdot 3$, so $\ell = 9$ m

Use the formula $d = r \cdot t$ to solve for the missing variable.

38 Jajuan can bicycle 14 miles per hour. How long would it take Jajuan to bicycle 42 miles at this rate?

$42 = 14 \cdot t$, $t = 3$; It would

take Jajuan 3 hours.

39 A certain cargo plane traveled 1,000 miles in 5 hours. If the airplane traveled at the same rate for 5 hours, what was its rate of speed?

$1{,}000 = r \cdot 5$, $r = 200$;

The cargo plane traveled 200

miles per hour.

Example 7

Use the formula $A = \ell \cdot w$ to solve for ℓ, length.

The area of the rectangle is 30 square feet. Its width is 6 feet. What is the length of the rectangle?

1. Substitute the values.

$A = \ell \cdot w \quad 30 = \ell \cdot 6$

2. Use the inverse operation.

$\dfrac{30}{6} = \ell \cdot \dfrac{6}{6}$

$5 = \ell$

3. The length of the rectangle is 5 feet.

Example 8

Use the formula $d = r \cdot t$ to solve for t, time.

Janet's remote control car can travel 88 feet in one minute. How long would it take the car to travel 352 feet?

1. Substitute the values.

$d = r \cdot t \qquad 352 = 88 \cdot t$

2. Use the inverse operation.

$\dfrac{352}{88} = \dfrac{88 \cdot t}{88}$

3. The value of t is 4.

4. The car would travel for 4 minutes.

Ticket Out the Door

A Variety of Problems   Have students solve four types of problems.

- simplify an expression

- solve an addition or subtraction equation

- solve a multiplication or division equation

- evaluate a formula

Chapter Test

Chapter Resource Masters

Additional forms of the Chapter 3 Tests are available.

Test Format	Where to Find it
Chapter 3 Test	Math Online › glencoe.com
Blackline Masters	Assessment Masters, p. 51

ExamView® Assessment Suite

Customize and create multiple versions of your chapter test and their answer keys. All of these questions from the chapter tests are available on ExamView® Assessment Suite.

Advance TRACKER

Online Assessment and Reporting
glencoe.com

This online assessment tool allows teachers to track student progress with easily-accessible, comprehensive reports available for every student. Assess students using any internet-ready computer.

Alternative Assessment

Use Portfolios Have students write three equations in their portfolios. Each equation should contain a unique operation. Have students solve their equations.

Chapter 3 **Chapter Test**

Find the value of each expression.

1. $16 + 4^2 \div 8 \cdot 5 - (16 - 10) =$ __20__

2. $27 - 6^2 \div 9 + 5 - (5 \cdot 2) =$ __18__

3. $(7 - 3)^2 \cdot 3 \div 4 + 11 + 8 =$ __31__

4. $(5 - 2)^2 + 8 \cdot 5 - (27 \div 9) =$ __46__

Evaluate each expression when $b = 4$ and $f = 2$.

5. $11 \cdot 3 + (b - f)^2 - 7 =$ __30__

6. $b \div 2 + 7^2 + 5 - (5 \cdot f) =$ __46__

7. $b^2 \cdot 3 \div b + 17 - f =$ __27__

8. $7 + 4b \div f + (f + 3) - b^2 =$ __4__

Find the value of the variable in each equation.

9. $27 + \square = 41$

$\square =$ __14__

10. $56 \cdot z = 8$

$z =$ __7__

11. $\frac{27}{n} = 3$

$n =$ __9__

12. $p - 15 = 71$

$p =$ __86__

Find the value of q, when $r = 37$ and $s = 19$.

13. $s = r + q$

$\underline{19} = 37 + \underline{q}$

$\underline{19 - 37} = (37 + q) - 37$

$q = \underline{-18}$

14. $r = q - s$

$\underline{37} = q - \underline{19}$

$\underline{37 + 19} = (q - 19) + 19$

$q = \underline{56}$

Use the formula $A = \ell \cdot w$ to solve for w, width.

15. The area of the rectangle is 44 square inches. Its length is 11 inches. What is the width of the rectangle?

$\underline{44 = 11 \cdot w}$, so $w = $ **4 in.**

16. The area of the rectangle is 81 square miles. Its length is 9 miles. What is the width of the rectangle?

$\underline{81 = 9 \cdot w}$, so $w = $ **9 mi**

English Learner Strategy

Assessment Encourage students to highlight key words in each of the word problems on the chapter test. They should find words that identify operations and rewrite the words in their native languages. Translating these words may help them identify the correct operation.

Math Coach Notes

Reasonable Answers Have students check their work by making sure their answers are reasonable. If students finish early, encourage them to simplify each expression again to ensure they arrive at the same answer.

Solve. Explain your reasoning.

17 POPULATION An apartment complex has 4 units. Five people lived in each unit. Then 8 people moved away. The next month 2 families of 5 moved into the complex. What is the total number of people living in the apartment complex now?

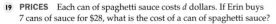

$4 \cdot 5 - 8 + (2 \cdot 5) = 22$; 22 people

18 AGES Paulo is y years old. His aunt Serena is 17 years older. If his aunt is 34 years old, how old is Paulo?

$y + 17 = 34$; Paulo is 17 years old.

19 PRICES Each can of spaghetti sauce costs d dollars. If Erin buys 7 cans of sauce for $28, what is the cost of a can of spaghetti sauce?

$d \cdot 7 = 28$; The cost of one can is $4.

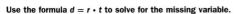

Use the formula $d = r \cdot t$ to solve for the missing variable.

20 EXERCISE Barkley went inline skating with his friends. If he travels 18 miles in 2 hours, what was his rate of speed?

$18 = r \cdot 2$, $r = 9$; He traveled 9 miles per hour.

21 CARS During a 450-mile race, a certain car traveled at a rate of 150 miles per hour. How long did it take the car to finish the race?

$450 = 150 \cdot t$, $t = 3$; The car finished the race in 3 hours.

Correct the mistakes.

22 PHOTOGRAPHY Angelina's teacher asked, "If you have shipping boxes that will each hold 175 picture frames, then how many picture frames will x shipping boxes hold?" Angelina's answer is shown. What mistake did she make?

175 ÷ x

She should have used multiplication instead of division.

The number of frames that x boxes can hold is actually $175 \cdot x$, or $175x$.

STOP

Data-Driven Decision Making

Students missing Exercises . . .	Have trouble with . . .	Should review and practice . . .
1–4	using the order of operations.	SSG Lesson 3-1, p. 98 CRM Skills Practice, p. A51
5–8, 13–14	evaluating an expression or equation.	SSG Lesson 3-2, p. 105 CRM Skills Practice, p. A55
9–12	solving an equation.	SSG Lesson 3-3, p. 113 CRM Skills Practice, p. A59
15–16	using formulas.	SSG Lesson 3-4, p. 119 CRM Skills Practice, p. A63
17–22	simplifying and solving expressions and equations from word problems.	CRM Problem-Solving Practice, pp. A52, A56, A60, and A64

Chapter 3 **Test Practice**

⚠ Diagnose Student Errors

Survey student responses for each item. Class trends may indicate common errors and misconceptions.

1. Ⓐ correct
   B did not follow order of operations
   C guess
   D multiplied before divison in second to last step

2. A miscalculation
   Ⓑ correct
   C went left to right without order of operations after parentheses
   D went left to right without order of operations and ignored parentheses

3. Ⓐ correct
   B did not find the exponent or divide the quantity in parentheses by 4
   C incorrect order of operations
   D miscalculation

4. A ignored exponent
   B did not apply exponent correctly, added
   Ⓒ correct
   D incorrect order of operations

5. A incorrect order of operations
   B incorrect sign
   Ⓒ correct
   D guess

6. A used correct numbers, misinterpreted operation
   Ⓑ correct
   C assumed division rather than writing a multiplication equation
   D guess

7. Ⓐ correct
   B used correct numbers, misinterpreted operation
   C guess
   D misinterpreted operation

8. A used incorrect inverse operation (multiplied)
   B used incorrect inverse operation (added)
   C used incorrect inverse operation (subtracted)
   Ⓓ correct

Select the best answer and fill in the corresponding circle on the sheet at right.

1. $234 \div 3 \cdot [5^2 - (4 \cdot 3)] =$
   Ⓐ 1,014
   B 954
   C 27
   D 6

2. What is the value of the expression?
   $20 \div 5 + 17 \cdot (7 - 5)$
   A 36
   Ⓑ 38
   C 42
   D 142

3. Evaluate $(5p - 2^2) \div 4$, if $p = 8$.
   Ⓐ 9   C 144
   B 38   D 361

4. Evaluate $x^2 - 5y$, if $x = 15$ and $y = 9$.
   A −30   Ⓒ 180
   B 75   D 1,980

5. What is the value of the expression?
   $25 \cdot (5 - 2) \div 5 - 12$
   A −285   Ⓒ 3
   B −3   D 62

6. Sasha's dad gave her $40 to take some friends to the movies. If movie tickets cost $8 per student, which equation will help Sasha figure out how many friends she can take? Let n equal the number of students going to the movies.
   A $8 − n = 40   C $8 \div n = 40
   Ⓑ $8 \cdot n = 40   D $40 − n = $8

7. Laura and Eric baked 10 pies. Laura baked 3 pies. Which equation is used to find the number of pies Eric baked?
   Ⓐ 3 + e = 10   C e − 3 = 10
   B 3 \cdot e = 10   D 10 \div e = 3

8. Solve for m in the equation.
   $\frac{48}{m} = 4$
   A 192   C 44
   B 52   Ⓓ 12

9. Solve for ● in the equation.
   $27 + ● = 52$
   Ⓐ 25   C 1,404
   B 79   D 4,104

9. Ⓐ correct
   B used incorrect inverse operation (added)
   C used incorrect inverse operation (multiplied)
   D guess

10. A this is miles traveled
    Ⓑ correct
    C estimated
    D this is the time the trip took

11. A multiplied given dimensions
    B added given dimensions
    C subtracted given dimensions
    Ⓓ correct

12. Ⓐ correct
    B miscalculated
    C used incorrect inverse operation (subtracted)
    D used incorrect inverse operation (added)

10 Use the formula $d = r \cdot t$, to solve for r, rate.

Frank traveled 212 miles in 4 hours. What was his rate of speed?

   A 212   C 50

   Ⓑ 53   D 4

---

11 The area of the rectangle is 42 square yards. Its width is 6 yards. What is the length of the rectangle?

     $A = \ell \cdot w$

   A 252 yd   C 36 yd

   B 48 yd   Ⓓ 7 yd

---

12 Solve for q in the equation.

$12 \cdot q = 60$

   Ⓐ 5   C 48

   B 6   D 72

ANSWER SHEET

Directions: Fill in the circle of each correct answer.

	A	B	C	D
1	●	Ⓑ	Ⓒ	Ⓓ
2	Ⓐ	●	Ⓒ	Ⓓ
3	●	Ⓑ	Ⓒ	Ⓓ
4	Ⓐ	Ⓑ	●	Ⓓ
5	Ⓐ	Ⓑ	●	Ⓓ
6	Ⓐ	●	Ⓒ	Ⓓ
7	●	Ⓑ	Ⓒ	Ⓓ
8	Ⓐ	Ⓑ	Ⓒ	●
9	●	Ⓑ	Ⓒ	Ⓓ
10	Ⓐ	●	Ⓒ	Ⓓ
11	Ⓐ	Ⓑ	Ⓒ	●
12	●	Ⓑ	Ⓒ	Ⓓ

Success Strategy

Read each problem carefully and look at each answer choice. Eliminate answers you know are wrong. This narrows your choices before solving the problem.

Diagnosing Student Errors and Misconceptions

Common Errors There are two common errors that students may encounter during the Test Practice.

1. They may not remember or use the order of operations correctly. Supervise the student when simplifying until you are sure the student knows the correct order of operations.

2. Students may not be able to determine which inverse operation to use when solving an equation. To remedy this, have students rewrite all operations with the inverse, or opposite of the operation.

Chapter Overview

Chapter-at-a-Glance

Lesson	Math Objective	State/Local Standards
4-1 Angles (pp. 138–144)	Measure, identify, and draw angles.	
4-2 Triangles (pp. 145–151)	Identify and draw triangles.	
Progress Check 1 (p. 152)		
4-3 Add Angles (pp. 153–160)	Add measures of angles and know the sum of complementary angles, supplementary angles, and the angles in a triangle.	
4-4 Transversals (pp. 161–167)	Identify the measure of an angle using knowledge about transversals and parallel lines.	
Progress Check 2 (p. 168)		

Content-at-a-Glance
The diagram below summarizes and unpacks Chapter 4 content.

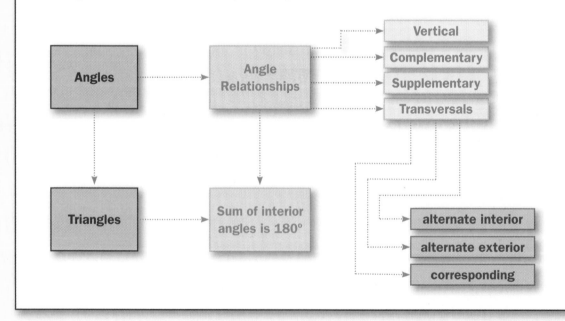

Chapter Assessment Manager

Diagnostic   Diagnose students' readiness.

	Student/Teacher Editions	Assessment Masters	Technology
Course Placement Test		1	ExamView® Assessment Suite
Book 2 Pretest		62	ExamView® Assessment Suite
Chapter 4 Pretest		65	ExamView® Assessment Suite
Quiz/Preview	SSG 137		Math Online glencoe.com StudentWorks™ Plus

Formative   Identify students' misconceptions of content knowledge.

	Student/Teacher Editions	Assessment Masters	Technology
Progress Checks	SSG 152, 168		Math Online glencoe.com StudentWorks™ Plus
Vocabulary Review	SSG 169		Math Online glencoe.com
Lesson Assessments			ExamView® Assessment Suite
Are They Getting It?	TE 141, 148, 156, 164		Math Online glencoe.com

Summative   Determine student success in learning the concepts in the lesson, chapter, or book.

	Student/Teacher Editions	Assessment Masters	Technology
Chapter 4 Test	SSG 174	68	ExamView® Assessment Suite
Test Practice	SSG 176	71	ExamView® Assessment Suite
Alternative Assessment	TE 174	74	
See It, Do It, Say It, Write It	TE 144, 151, 160, 167		
Book 2 Test		98	ExamView® Assessment Suite

Backmapping and Vertical Alignment **McGraw-Hill's** *Math Triumphs* intervention program was conceived and developed with the final results in mind: student success in grade-level mathematics, including Algebra 1 and beyond. The authors, using the **NCTM Focal Points and Focal Connections** as their guide, developed this brand-new series by backmapping from grade-level and Algebra 1 concepts, and vertically aligning the topics so that they build upon prior skills and concepts and serve as a foundation for future topics.

Teacher Works™ *Plus*
All-In-One Planner and Resource Center

	Lesson 4-1	**Lesson 4-2**	**Lesson 4-3**	**Lesson 4-4**
Concept	Angles	Triangles	Add Angles	Transversals
Objective	Measure, identify, and draw angles.	Identify and draw triangles.	Add measures of angles and know the sum of complementary angles, supplementary angles, and angles in a triangle.	Identify the measure of an angle using knowledge about transversals and parallel lines.
Math Vocabulary	angle degree protractor ray vertex	acute angle congruent obtuse angle right angle side triangle	complementary angles right angle straight angle supplementary angles	alternate exterior angles alternate interior angles congruent angles corresponding angles parallel lines transversal vertical angles
Lesson Resources	**Materials** • Protractors • Patty paper • Index cards **Manipulatives** • Card stock • Brass brads **Other Resources** CRM Vocabulary and English Language Development CRM Skills Practice CRM Problem-Solving Practice CRM Homework Practice	**Materials** • Protractors • Rulers • Index cards **Manipulatives** • Pattern blocks • Geoboard **Other Resources** CRM Vocabulary and English Language Development CRM Skills Practice CRM Problem-Solving Practice CRM Homework Practice	**Materials** • Protractors • Rulers • Drinking straws • Index cards **Other Resources** CRM Vocabulary and English Language Development CRM Skills Practice CRM Problem-Solving Practice CRM Homework Practice	**Materials** • Protractors • Straightedge • Pipe cleaners • Colored pencils **Other Resources** CRM Vocabulary and English Language Development CRM Skills Practice CRM Problem-Solving Practice CRM Homework Practice
Technology	**Math Online** ▷ glencoe.com StudentWorks™ Plus 💿 ExamView® Assessment Suite	**Math Online** ▷ glencoe.com StudentWorks™ Plus 💿 ExamView® Assessment Suite	**Math Online** ▷ glencoe.com StudentWorks™ Plus 💿 ExamView® Assessment Suite	**Math Online** ▷ glencoe.com StudentWorks™ Plus 💿 ExamView® Assessment Suite

Intervention Strategy

Terms and Definitions

Playing a memory game requires students to think about the relationships between angles and correct terminology.

Step 1

Use index cards and write vocabulary words that describe line and angle relationships such as complementary angles, alternative interior angles, vertical angles, and parallel lines on one side of the card. Include triangle classifications as well.

Step 2

Write the definition of the term, or a drawing representing the term, on a different index card. Then lay all the cards face down in random order and number the backs of the cards consecutively beginning with 1. The game can be faster if different colored index cards are used for the terms and definitions.

Step 3

Tape the cards in consecutive order with number sides up in even rows on the front board.

Step 4

Students can work alone, in pairs, or in groups. Students will take turns picking two numbers. Turn both cards term/definition side up. If the term matches the definition, keep them face side up. If they do not match, allow students a moment to memorize their placement, and then turn the cards number side (back side) up again.

Step 5

Students earn a point for each correct match. One alternative to the activity is to draw a picture instead of writing a definition on the back of the cards. An easier version is to have the cards face up instead of face down depending on the skill of your students. A third alternative is to have students make up the cards. To do this, assign each student or group vocabulary words.

Chapter Notes

Real-World Applications

Architecture Different classifications of triangles have various purposes in architecture. When triangles are used in blueprint designs, some serve the purpose of support, some serve the purpose of visual appeal and others serve the purpose of balance. Have students conduct research to find out why certain triangular-shaped objects are used in real-world designs.

Intervention Strategy

Human Triangle

Step 1 Arrange students into groups of 4.

Step 2 Have students stand at three different locations (not all along one line). Their positions will form the vertices of a triangle.

Step 3 Instruct the fourth group member to measure and record the distances between each of the three points. Using addition, have the group compare the lengths of the sides of the triangle.

Step 4 Have students experiment with other positions to try to find a triangle where the distance from one vertex to another vertex is the same as the distance from the first vertex to the third vertex, through the second vertex. Students will discover that it cannot be done.

Chapter 4 Angle Measures

Angle measures are important in building and design.

We must understand and measure angles to build planes, buildings, maps, rockets, cars, and bicycles.

Key Vocabulary

Find interactive definitions in 13 languages in the **eGlossary** at glencoe.com.

English **Español** *Introduce the most important vocabulary terms from Chapter 4.*

angle ángulo

two rays with a common endpoint form an angle (p. 138)

acute angle ángulo agudo

an angle with a measure greater than 0° and less than 90° (p. 145)

complementary angles ángulos complementarios

two angles are complementary if the sum of their measures is 90° (p. 153)

obtuse angle ángulo obtuso

an angle with a measure greater than 90° but less than 180° (p. 145)

right angle ángulo recto

an angle that measures 90° (p. 145)

supplementary angles ángulos suplementarios

two angles are supplementary if the sum of their measures is 180° (p. 153)

transversal transversal

a line that intersects two or more lines to form eight angles (p. 161)

triangle triángulo

a polygon with three sides and three angles (p. 145)

vertex vértice

the common endpoint of the two rays that form an angle (p. 138)

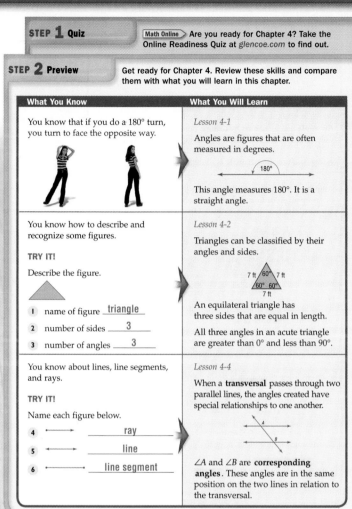

STEP **1** Quiz

 Are you ready for Chapter 4? Take the Online Readiness Quiz at *glencoe.com* to find out.

STEP **2** Preview

Get ready for Chapter 4. Review these skills and compare them with what you will learn in this chapter.

What You Know	What You Will Learn
You know that if you do a 180° turn, you turn to face the opposite way.	**Lesson 4-1** Angles are figures that are often measured in degrees. This angle measures 180°. It is a straight angle.
You know how to describe and recognize some figures. **TRY IT!** Describe the figure. 1 name of figure _triangle_ 2 number of sides _3_ 3 number of angles _3_	**Lesson 4-2** Triangles can be classified by their angles and sides. An equilateral triangle has three sides that are equal in length. All three angles in an acute triangle are greater than 0° and less than 90°.
You know about lines, line segments, and rays. **TRY IT!** Name each figure below. 4 _ray_ 5 _line_ 6 _line segment_	**Lesson 4-4** When a **transversal** passes through two parallel lines, the angles created have special relationships to one another. ∠*A* and ∠*B* are **corresponding angles**. These angles are in the same position on the two lines in relation to the transversal.

137

Step 1 Quiz

Pretest/Prescribe Students can take the Online Readiness Quiz or the Diagnostic Pretest in the Assessment Masters.

Step 2 Preview

Use this pre-chapter activity to activate students' prior knowledge, build confidence, and help students preview the lessons.

 **Dinah Zike's Foldables**

Guide students through the directions on p. A66 in the Chapter Resource Masters to create their own Foldable graphic organizer for use with this chapter.

Home Connections

Have students find examples of real-world triangles around their houses. Have them classify each triangle found.

Vocabulary Preview

- As students complete the Chapter Preview, have them make a three-column chart. The vocabulary word or key concept should be written in the first column. In the second column, students write the definition or describe the term or phrase. Students draw a picture of the item in the third column.

Term or Key Concept	Definition/ Description	Picture

- Call on student volunteers to share their terms, definitions, and pictures with the rest of the class.

Lesson Notes

Lesson Planner

Objective   Measure, identify, and draw angles.

Vocabulary   angle , degree , protractor , ray , vertex

Materials/Manipulatives   protractors, patty paper, index cards, card stock, brass brads

Chapter Resource Masters

CRM Vocabulary and English Language Development (p. A69)

CRM Skills Practice (p. A70)

CRM Problem-Solving Practice (p. A71)

CRM Homework Practice (p. A72)

1 Introduce

Vocabulary

Model Vocabulary   Draw the following example on the board. Identify the labels and discuss naming techniques.

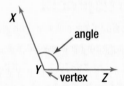

Point out that angles are measured with a *protractor*. The units are written in *degrees*.

2 Teach

Key Concept

Foundational Skills and Concepts   After students have read through the Key Concept box, have them try these exercises.

1. Can an angle be acute and obtuse? Explain.
   Possible answer: No; an angle less than 90° is acute, and an angle greater than 90° is obtuse.

2. Can an angle be acute and right? Explain.
   Possible answer: No; an angle less than 90° is acute, and an angle that is 90° is a right angle.

KEY Concept

An **angle** can be named by using a point on one ray, the vertex, and then a point on the other ray, such as ∠*ABC* or ∠*CBA*. An angle can also be named using the letter of the vertex, such as ∠*B*. An angle is sometimes named by a number, such as ∠1.

Angles are often measured in **degrees**. They can be classified, or grouped, according to their measures. You can use a **protractor** to measure an angle.

The pink square inside ∠*DEF* indicates that it is a right angle.

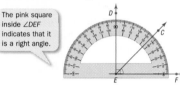

Acute angles measure between 0° and 90°. ∠*CEF* is an acute angle with a measure of 45°.

Right angles measure exactly 90°. ∠*DEF* is a right angle with a measure of exactly 90°.

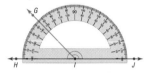

Obtuse angles measure between 90° and 180°. ∠*GIJ* is an obtuse angle with a measure of 135°.

Straight angles measure exactly 180°. ∠*HIJ* is a straight angle with a measure of exactly 180°.

Classify an angle as acute or obtuse to help you decide which scale of the protractor, the inner or outer, gives the angle's measurement.

VOCABULARY

angle
   two rays with a common endpoint form an angle

degree
   the most common unit of measure for angles

protractor
   an instrument marked in degrees, used for measuring or drawing angles

ray
   a part of a line that has one endpoint and extends indefinitely in one direction

vertex
   the common endpoint of the two rays that form an angle (the plural is vertices)

Intervention Strategy   Visual Learners

Why Protractors Work   To help students understand why protractors are used to measure angles, show them a 360° protractor to compare to the "half circle" protractor. You measure an angle with the center of the circle as the vertex. If your angle is $\frac{1}{8}$ of the circle, it would measure $\frac{360}{8}$ or 45°.

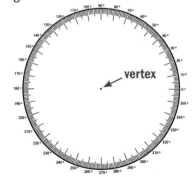

Example 1

Draw ∠DEF that measures 135°.

1. Draw $\overrightarrow{EF}$.

2. Place the center of the protractor at point E. Line up $\overrightarrow{EF}$ with the 0° mark on the protractor.

3. Use the inner scale. Draw a point D at 135°.

4. Draw $\overrightarrow{ED}$.

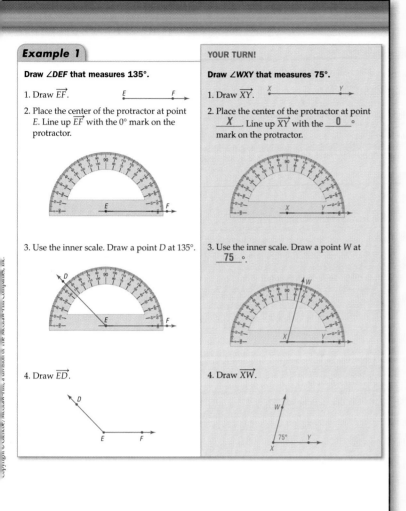

YOUR TURN!

Draw ∠WXY that measures 75°.

1. Draw $\overrightarrow{XY}$.

2. Place the center of the protractor at point ___X___. Line up $\overrightarrow{XY}$ with the ___0___° mark on the protractor.

3. Use the inner scale. Draw a point W at ___75___°.

4. Draw $\overrightarrow{XW}$.

GO ON

Lesson 4-1 Angles **139**

Additional *Example 1*

Draw ∠XYZ that measures 35°.

1. Draw $\overrightarrow{YZ}$.

2. Place the center of the protractor at point Y. Line up $\overrightarrow{YZ}$ with the 0° mark on the protractor.

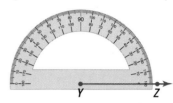

3. Use the inner scale. Draw a point X at 35°.

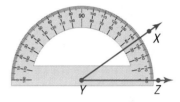

4. Draw $\overrightarrow{YX}$.

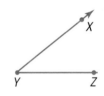

Intervention Strategy   Visual/Auditory Learners

Quick Check   Fasten two strips of cardstock with a brass brad to form an angle. Distribute an angle to each student. Verbally suggest an angle type to the students. In response, the students should use their cardstock angle to form the appropriately-sized angle. Have students hold up their angles so that you can quickly scan the classroom for students with incorrect responses. Have students estimate the measure of their angles.

Additional *Example 2*

Measure and identify the angle.

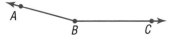

1. Place the center (hole or ⊥ symbol) of the protractor at the vertex, point *B*.

2. Line up $\overrightarrow{BC}$ with the line that extends from 0° to 180° on the protractor.

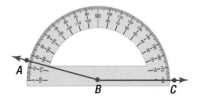

3. Look at point *A*. Use the 0° reading to know whether to read the inner scale or the outer scale on the protractor. Read the measure of the angle where $\overrightarrow{BA}$ passes through the inner scale.

∠*ABC* measures 165°. ∠*ABC* is a(n) obtuse angle.

 Common Error *Alert*

Read the Protractor A protractor has two rows of measures. Because there are many protractors that have two numbers listed for each mark, students sometimes choose the incorrect measure. Have students analyze whether the angle they are measuring is acute, right, obtuse, or straight. After they measure their angles, have them compare their angle measure in degrees to the classification they chose for the angle.

Math Coach Notes

Real-World Connections Have students name five letters of the alphabet that have at least one acute angle. Name five letters of the alphabet that have at least one right angle. Name three letters of the alphabet that have an obtuse angle.

Example 2

Measure and identify the angle.

1. Place the center (hole or ⊥ symbol) of the protractor at the vertex, point *Y*.

2. Line up $\overrightarrow{YZ}$ with the line that extends from 0° to 180° on the protractor.

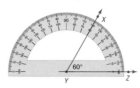

3. Look at point *X*. Use the 0° reading to know whether to read the inner scale or the outer scale on the protractor. Read the measure of the angle where $\overrightarrow{YX}$ passes through the inner scale.

∠*XYZ* measures 60°.

∠*XYZ* is an acute angle.

YOUR TURN!

Measure and identify the angle.

1. Place the center of the protractor at the vertex.

2. Line up $\overrightarrow{BC}$ with the line that extends from 0° to 180° on the protractor.

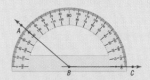

3. Look at point *A*. Use the 0° reading to know whether to read the inner scale or the outer scale on the protractor. Read the measure of the angle where $\overrightarrow{BA}$ passes through the inner scale.

∠*ABC* measures ___140°___.

∠*ABC* is a(n) ___obtuse___ angle.

Who is Correct?

What is the measure of ∠*B*?

Circle correct answer(s). Cross out incorrect answer(s).

Who *is Correct?*
Diagnostic Teaching

• Hannah is incorrect. The measure of ∠*B* is less than 90°.

• Tom is correct.

• Lamar is incorrect. The measure of ∠*B* is less than 70°.

Remind students that a 90°-angle forms a right angle, which looks like a square corner.

▶ Guided Practice

Draw an angle with the given measurement.

1 90°

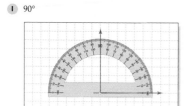

2 130°

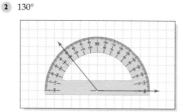

Step by Step Practice

3 Measure and identify the angle.

Step 1 Place the center of the protractor at point _____G_____.

Step 2 Line up the vertex and the line on the protractor that extends from 0° to 180° with _____$\overrightarrow{GH}$_____.

Step 3 Read from the _____outer_____ scale.

Step 4 Read the measure of the angle where _____$\overrightarrow{GF}$_____ passes through the outer scale.

∠FGH measures _____30°_____.

∠FGH is a(n) _____acute_____ angle.

Measure and identify each angle.

4 ∠MNO measures _____90°_____.

∠MNO is a(n) _____right_____ angle.

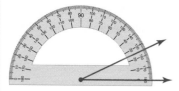

5 ∠TUV measures _____85°_____.

∠TUV is a(n) _____acute_____ angle.

GO ON

Are They Getting It? ?

Check students' understanding of angles by writing these problems on the board. Ask students to point out wrong answers and explain why they are wrong. Tell them to use a protractor to show why the answers are correct or incorrect.

Draw an angle with the given measurement.

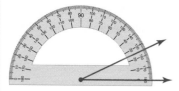

1. 155° This is incorrect. The angle shown is 25°.

2. 145° This is correct.

Using Manipulatives

Protractors   Give each student a protractor to measure the angles.

On-Hand Manipulatives   Show students that there are many real-world items that can make a 90° angle. Point out that when drawing a 90° angle, students can use the corner of a sheet of computer paper to make the angle.

Note This!
Angles   Encourage students to create their own definition for each angle type in their notes. Students can use words or pictures depending on their preferred learning style.

Math Coach Notes

Strategies

1. Start this lesson by modeling in great detail to the students on how to measure an angle accurately. Emphasize that students may need to extend the rays of the angle to get an accurate reading. Point out that they need to place the center of the protractor at the vertex.

2. Arrange students into pairs. Give a protractor to each student. Have each group measure different angles. Each group needs to write down the measures of the angles in degrees.

3. As a class, compare the angle measures and discuss any common mistakes.

Common Error *Alert*

Sizes of Angles Draw two angles of the same size on the board, but draw one using rays that are longer than the rays of the other angle. Students have the misconception that angles made with longer rays have a greater measure than angles made with shorter rays. Demonstrate that the measures of both angles are the same. Discuss that the length of the rays used to draw angles does not affect the measurement of the angles.

Step by Step *Problem-Solving Practice*

Solve.

Problem-Solving Strategies
- ☑ Use a diagram.
- ☐ Look for a pattern.
- ☐ Guess and check.
- ☐ Solve a simpler problem.
- ☐ Work backward.

6 KITES On a windy April afternoon, Karl is flying kites with his younger brother. He notices that the corners of his kite form angles. What types of angles are formed by the corners of his kite?

Understand Read the problem. Write what you know.

Karl is looking at the angles formed

by __the corners__ of his kite.

Plan Pick a strategy. One strategy is to use a diagram.

Solve Place the center of the protractor on the vertex labeled *A*. Line up the vertex and the line of the protractor that extends from 0° to 180°.

Read the measure of each angle.

Angle *A* = __60°__   Angle *B* = __120°__

Angle *C* = __60°__   Angle *D* = __120°__

The kite has __2 acute__ angles and __2 obtuse__ angles.

Check Review the definitions of acute and obtuse angles.

7 ROAD SIGNS Brenda's older brother is learning to drive. He must review the road signs for his driver's test. Describe the <u>angles of the stop sign</u>.

Check off each step.

__✔__ Understand: I underlined key words.

__✔__ Plan: To solve this problem, I will __use a diagram__

__✔__ Solve: The answer is __eight obtuse angles__

__✔__ Check: I checked my answer by __reviewing the definition of an obtuse angle__

Intervention Strategy   Kinesthetic Learners

Use Patty Paper Distribute a sheet of patty paper to each student. (Patty paper is 6 in. x 6 in. translucent squares of paper. Restaurants use patty paper to separate hamburger patties. It can be purchased from food service suppliers.) Inform students that the patty paper is a square. Instruct students to fold the patty paper from opposite corners to create a line that bisects each right angle. Have students guess what the measures are for those bisected angles. Repeat the process with other folds and estimate the measures. Have students check their estimates with a protractor.

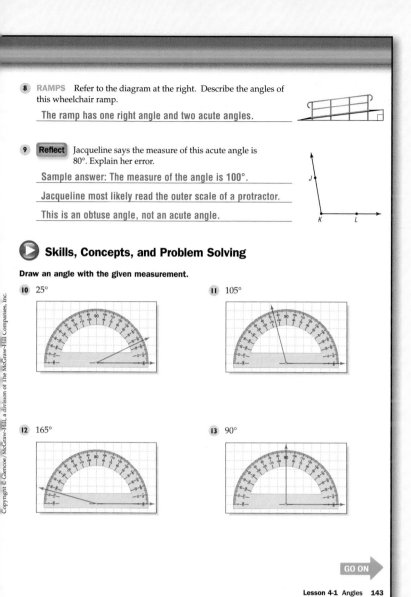

8   RAMPS   Refer to the diagram at the right.   Describe the angles of this wheelchair ramp.

The ramp has one right angle and two acute angles.

9   Reflect   Jacqueline says the measure of this acute angle is 80°. Explain her error.

Sample answer: The measure of the angle is 100°.

Jacqueline most likely read the outer scale of a protractor.

This is an obtuse angle, not an acute angle.

▶ Skills, Concepts, and Problem Solving

Draw an angle with the given measurement.

10   25°

11   105°

12   165°

13   90°

GO ON

Odd/Even Assignments

Exercises 10–17 are structured so that students practice the same concepts whether they are assigned the odd or even problems.

In-Class Assignment

Have students complete Exercises 10, 15, 16, and 22 to ensure that they understand the concept.

Math Challenge

Have students write step-by-step instructions on how to draw a 42-degree angle using a protractor. The steps should be illustrated and clear so that any person who has not had a lesson on drawing angles could successfully create the angle. Choose the work of a few students and have them present their instructions to the class. Save the best instructions to use in your classes when students need refresher skills or are absent on the day the lesson on drawing angles is taught.

See It, Do It, Say It, Write It

Step 1 Show students how to measure an angle using a protractor. Draw an angle on the board.

Step 2 Ask for a student volunteer to come to the board and measure the angle. Guide students to the correct answer, using this and other angles.

Step 3 Arrange students in pairs and have them explain to each other how they measure angles.

Step 4 Have students write in their own words the definitions of each word from the opening page. They should also explain how to measure an angle in their math journals.

Looking Ahead: Pre-Teach

Triangles   In the next lesson, students will learn about triangles.

Example

Classify the figure.

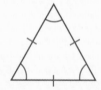

Three sides are equal in length. The figure is an equilateral triangle. Equilateral triangles also have three angles that are congruent.

Measure and identify each angle.

14 ∠WXY measures ___180°___.
∠WXY is a(n) ___straight___ angle.

15 ∠PQR measures ___170°___.
∠PQR is a(n) ___obtuse___ angle.

Solve.

16 CLOCKS   Val's soccer practice starts at 4:45 P.M. What type of angle is formed by the hands of the clock at 4:45?

___obtuse___

17 INTERIOR DESIGN   Garrett measured the angle of two walls in his living room. The angle measured 90°. What type of angle is this?

___right angle___

Vocabulary Check   **Write the vocabulary word that completes each sentence.**

18 A(n) ___angle___ is formed by two rays with a common endpoint.

19 A(n) ___protractor___ is an instrument, marked in degrees, used for measuring or drawing angles.

20 A(n) ___obtuse___ angle is an angle that measures greater than 90° but less than 180°.

21 A(n) ___acute___ angle is an angle that measures greater than 0° but less than 90°.

22 Writing in Math   Explain how to draw ∠XYZ measuring 125°.

Draw $\overrightarrow{YZ}$. Place the center of the protractor at point Y. Line up $\overrightarrow{YZ}$ with the 0° mark on the protractor. Use the correct scale. Draw a point X at 125°. Draw $\overrightarrow{YX}$.

Ticket Out the Door

Instruct students to draw two angles, each measuring 85°, but oriented differently. Students can draw each angle on a separate half sheet of paper. Then instruct students to hold their angles up to a light and place them on top of each other, and line them up to see that they are both the same size. Students can staple their papers together and hand them in as they exit the classroom.

Lesson 4-2 Triangles

KEY Concept

Triangles have three **sides** and three angles. Triangles can be classified by the lengths of their sides and by the measures of their angles.

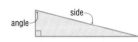

angle — side

Classify Triangles by Sides

Example	Type	Number of Congruent Sides
	scalene triangle	0
	isosceles triangle	2
	equilateral triangle	3

Classify Triangles by Angles

Example	Type	Measure of Angles
	acute triangle	all three angles measure less than 90°
	right triangle	one angle measures 90°
	obtuse triangle	one angle measures greater than 90°

Figures often have symbols that indicate congruence or right angles.

congruent sides   congruent angles   right angle

GO ON

Lesson 4-2 Triangles **145**

VOCABULARY

acute angle
an angle with a measure greater than 0° and less than 90°

congruent
line segments that have the same length, or angles that have the same measure

obtuse angle
an angle with a measure greater than 90°, but less than 180°

right angle
an angle that measures 90°

side
a ray that is part of an angle

triangle
a polygon with three sides and three angles

Lesson Notes

Lesson Planner

Objective   Identify and draw triangles.

Vocabulary   acute angle , congruent , obtuse angle , right angle , side , triangle

Materials/Manipulatives   protractor, index cards, ruler, pattern blocks, geoboard

Chapter Resource Masters

- CRM Vocabulary and English Language Development (p. A73)
- CRM Skills Practice (p. A74)
- CRM Problem-Solving Practice (p. A75)
- CRM Homework Practice (p. A76)

1 Introduce

Vocabulary

Prefix   The prefix of the word triangle is *tri*. *Tri* means three. Triangle means *three angles*. There are specific names for triangles with specific characteristics. You can use prefixes to help you remember what is special about specific types of triangles. One such example is the prefix *equi*, which means equal. Equilateral triangles have three equal sides.

2 Teach

Key Concept

Fundamental Skills and Concepts   After students have read through the Key Concept box, have them try these activities.

1. Draw two right triangles with different orientations. What do the triangles have in common besides having three angles and three sides? one 90°-angle
2. Draw two acute triangles with different orientations. What do the triangles have in common besides having three angles and three sides? All three angles are less than 90°.

English Learner Strategy

Triangle Sort   Arrange students into groups of three. It is ideal for each group to have only one ESL learner. Have students make an index card for each cell of the tables in the Key Concept box. When all the cards are finished, put them in one pile and shuffle them. Pass out three cards to each group member and place the rest in the center of the table. Students should play a game similar to *Go Fish* to form triples of the cards that name, illustrate, and describe each type of triangle.

Additional *Example 1*

Classify triangle *MNP* by the lengths of its sides.

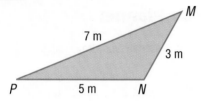

1. Find the measure of each side.

$\overline{MN} = 3$ m

$\overline{NP} = 5$ m

$\overline{MP} = 7$ m

2. Triangle *MNP* has 0 congruent sides.

3. Triangle *MNP* is a scalene triangle.

Additional *Example 2*

Classify triangle *QRS* by the measures of its angles.

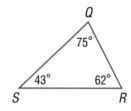

1. Find the measure of each angle.

$\angle Q = 75°$

$\angle R = 62°$

$\angle S = 43°$

2. Describe each angle.

$\angle Q$ is an acute angle.

$\angle R$ is an acute angle.

$\angle S$ is an acute angle.

3. Triangle *QRS* is an acute triangle.

Example 1

Classify triangle *ABC* by the lengths of its sides.

1. Find the measure of each side.

$\overline{AB} = 4$ cm

$\overline{BC} = 4$ cm

$\overline{CA} = 6$ cm

2. Triangle *ABC* has 2 congruent sides.

3. Triangle *ABC* is an isosceles triangle.

YOUR TURN!

Classify triangle *DEF* by the lengths of its sides.

1. Find the measure of each side.

$\overline{DE} = $ **17 in.**

$\overline{EF} = $ **17 in.**

$\overline{FD} = $ **17 in.**

2. Triangle *DEF* has **3** congruent sides.

3. Triangle *DEF* is a(n) **equilateral** triangle.

Example 2

Classify triangle *GHI* by the measures of its angles.

1. Find the measure of each angle.

$m\angle G = 43°$

$m\angle H = 110°$

$m\angle I = 27°$

> The abbreviation *m* means "The measure of."

2. Describe each angle.

$\angle G$ is an acute angle.

$\angle H$ is an obtuse angle.

$\angle I$ is an acute angle.

3. Triangle *GHI* is an obtuse triangle.

YOUR TURN!

Classify triangle *JKL* by the measures of its angles.

1. Find the measure of each angle.

$m\angle J = $ **90°**

$m\angle K = $ **45°**

$m\angle L = $ **45°**

2. Describe each angle.

$\angle J$ is **a right** angle.

$\angle K$ is **an acute** angle.

$\angle L$ is **an acute** angle.

3. Triangle *JKL* is a(n) **right** triangle.

Intervention Strategy — Visual Learners

Concept Map   List the different types of triangles. Have students make a concept map listing the different types of triangles. Also have them describe the steps they use in creating the different triangles.

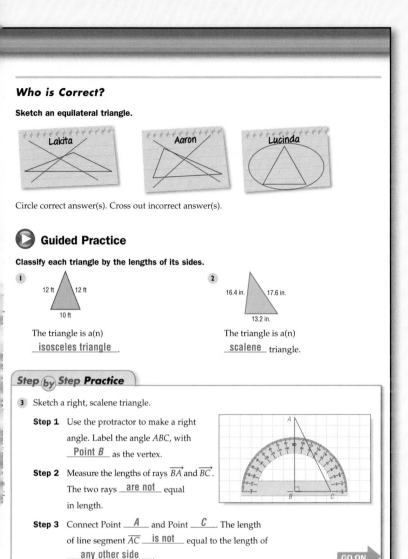

Who is Correct?

Sketch an equilateral triangle.

Circle correct answer(s). Cross out incorrect answer(s).

▶ **Guided Practice**

Classify each triangle by the lengths of its sides.

1. 12 ft   12 ft
   10 ft

   The triangle is a(n)
   isosceles triangle.

2. 16.4 in.   17.6 in.
   13.2 in.

   The triangle is a(n)
   scalene triangle.

Step (by) **Step Practice**

3. Sketch a right, scalene triangle.

   Step 1 Use the protractor to make a right angle. Label the angle *ABC*, with _Point B_ as the vertex.

   Step 2 Measure the lengths of rays $\overrightarrow{BA}$ and $\overrightarrow{BC}$. The two rays _are not_ equal in length.

   Step 3 Connect Point _A_ and Point _C_. The length of line segment $\overline{AC}$ _is not_ equal to the length of _any other side_.

   GO ON

Lesson 4-2 Triangles **147**

Using Manipulatives

Ruler When sketching figures, have students use a ruler to draw the figures accurately in their notes. Point out that when drawing a model, students should make sure that they accurately meet the classifications.

Protractor Have students use a protractor to draw the figures accurately in their notes. Point out that when drawing a model, students should make sure that they accurately meet the classifications.

On-Hand Manipulatives Show students that there are many real-world items that are triangles. Have students use pen and paper to draw all the types of triangles in this lesson to help them classify and remember the figures.

Who *is Correct?*
Diagnostic Teaching

• Lakita is incorrect. She has drawn a scalene triangle.

• Aaron is incorrect. He has drawn an acute triangle, but the sides are not congruent.

• Lucinda is correct.

Remind students that all equilateral triangles are acute. An equilateral triangle has three 60°-angles.

Labeling Triangles When making sketches of triangles in their notebooks, students need to carefully mark congruent angles and congruent side lengths. In geometry, it is not acceptable to think *"They look like they are equal."* Notation is needed to indicate the congruent parts.

Classify each triangle by the measures of its angles.

4

Angle	Measure	Type
∠P	60°	acute
∠Q	60°	acute
∠R	60°	acute

Triangle *PQR* is a(n) __acute__ triangle.

5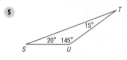

Angle	Measure	Type
∠S	20°	acute
∠T	15°	acute
∠U	145°	obtuse

Triangle *STU* is a(n) __obtuse__ triangle.

Step by Step Problem-Solving Practice

Problem-Solving Strategies
- ☑ Use a diagram.
- ☐ Look for a pattern.
- ☐ Guess and check.
- ☐ Act it out.
- ☐ Work backward.

Solve.

6 **CONSTRUCTION** Mr. Richardson is constructing the frame for the roof of a building. The triangle below shows the lengths of the sides and the measures of the angles. Classify this triangle by its sides and its angles.

Understand   Read the problem. Write what you know.

The frame of the roof is a __triangle__.

Plan   Pick a strategy. One strategy is to use a diagram.

Solve   List the lengths of the sides and the measures of the angles.

$\overline{VW}$ = __15 ft__ $m\angle V$ = __120°__

$\overline{WX}$ = __33 ft__ $m\angle W$ = __37°__

$\overline{XV}$ = __22.8 ft__ $m\angle X$ = __23°__

This triangle has __0__ congruent sides.

This triangle has __1 obtuse angle and 2 acute__ angles.

This triangle is a(n) __scalene__ and a(n) __obtuse__ triangle.

Check   Review the definitions of the figure that you named.

Are They Getting It?

Check students' understanding of triangles by writing these problems on the board. Have students explain the incorrect information in each problem. Tell them to use a protractor and a ruler to show why the answers are correct or are not correct.

Identify the figure.

1.   5 cm   13 cm   12 cm

The figure is an isosceles triangle. This is incorrect. The figure does not have any congruent sides so it is a scalene triangle.

2.

The figure is an obtuse scalene triangle. This is correct.

Solve.

7 **FLAGS** <u>The flag of the Philippines is shown at the right.</u>
<u>Classify the triangle</u> portion by the <u>length</u> of its sides
and the measure of its <u>angles</u>.

Check off each step.

✔ Understand: I underlined key words.

✔ Plan: To solve this problem, I will <u>use a diagram</u>

✔ Solve: The answer is <u>equilateral, acute triangle</u>

✔ Check: I checked my answer by <u>reviewing the definitions</u>

8 **TILES** Mrs. Jennings is tiling her bathroom. She needs to cut a
square tile in half. Classify the triangle that will be created by the
length of its sides and the measure of its angles.

<u>The tile will be a right, isosceles triangle.</u>

9 **Reflect** Can an equilateral triangle be classified as a right
triangle? Explain.

<u>No, an equilateral triangle is a triangle with three congruent sides and three</u>

<u>angles. The 3 angles are congruent and there are 180° in a triangle.</u>

<u>180° ÷ 3 = 60°. Each angle must be 60°.</u>

Sketch a figure with the description given.

10 obtuse, isosceles triangle

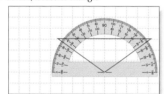

11 acute, equilateral triangle

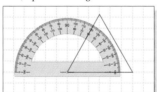

GO ON

Math Coach Notes

Practice Tip Exercises may require students to
classify triangles by their sides and/or angles.
Encourage students to study exercises carefully to avoid
incorrectly categorizing triangles.

Note This!
Review Materials Suggest that
students refer to their notes within 24 hours
after taking them. Have students edit their
notes for words and phrases that are
illegible or do not make sense. Instruct them
to edit with a different-colored pen to
distinguish between what they wrote in class
and what they filled in later.

Intervention Strategy — Visual Learners

Real-World Triangles Provide students with pictures of
architecture from around the world. Have students find examples of
triangles in the buildings. Students should trace the triangles onto a
sheet of paper. Prompt students to classify the triangles by their sides
and angles.

Odd/Even Assignments

Exercises 12–19 are structured so that students practice the same concepts whether they are assigned the odd or even problems.

In-Class Assignment

Have students complete Exercises 13, 15, 16, 18, and 22 to ensure that they understand the concept.

▶ **Skills, Concepts, and Problem Solving**

Classify each figure by the lengths of its sides and the measures of its angles.

12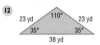

The figure is a(n)
     obtuse, isosceles triangle

13

The figure is a(n)
     right, scalene triangle

14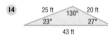

The figure is a(n)
     obtuse, scalene triangle

15

The figure is a(n)
     acute, isosceles triangle

Sketch a figure with the description given.

16   right, isosceles triangle

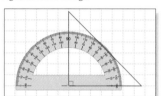

17   scalene, obtuse triangle

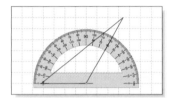

Solve.

18   **ART**   Gustavo made a model of the Great Pyramid in Egypt. Each triangle that made his pyramid had sides of length 30 centimeters, 26 centimeters, and 30 centimeters. Classify the triangle according to the measures of its sides.

          isosceles

Math Challenge

Double Classifications   Have students make a table with the following headings. Have students place an X in each cell where each classification can occur in the same triangle. Have students ask each other questions, such as *Can you draw an obtuse right triangle?*, or *Can you draw a scalene acute triangle?* Have students look back at the examples in their notes and in the exercise sets to test their conjectures.

	Acute	Right	Obtuse
Scalene	X	X	X
Isosceles	X	X	X
Equilateral	X		

19 LOGOS Trifecta Insurance Company uses the logo on the right. Classify the triangle in the logo by the length of its sides and the measure of its angles.

The triangle is an equilateral, acute triangle.

Vocabulary Check **Write the vocabulary word that completes each sentence.**

20 A(n) isosceles triangle is a triangle with at least two sides of the same length.

21 A(n) obtuse triangle is a triangle with one angle greater than 90° and less than 180°.

22 Writing in Math Explain how to classify a triangle.

Compare the lengths of the sides and degrees of the

angles so that you can classify the triangle.

 Spiral Review

Measure and identify each angle. (Lesson 4-1, p. 138)

23

∠RST measures 180° .

∠RST is a(n) straight angle.

24

∠UVW measures 100° .

∠UVW is a(n) obtuse angle.

25 ARCHITECTURE Presently, the famed Tower of Pisa in Italy is leaning at about a 6° angle. This makes the angle of the leaning side to the ground measure about 84°. What type of an angle is the angle of the leaning side to the ground? (Lesson 4-1, p. 138)

acute

ARCHITECTURE
Tower of Pisa

STOP

Lesson 4-2 Triangles **151**

Ticket Out the Door

Pick a Drawing Write the six classifications of triangles on the board. Have students sketch a drawing of each triangle on a separate small piece of paper. As a student approaches to exit the classroom, ask for a particular triangle. The student should choose the sketch of that triangle to turn in.

See It, Do It, Say It, Write It

Step 1 Draw the following figure on the board.

Step 2 Have students classify the figure by angles and by sides. acute isosceles triangle

Step 3 Arrange students into pairs and have them explain to each other how they classified the figure.

Step 4 Have students write in their own words how to classify triangles.

Looking Ahead: Pre-teach

Add Angles In the next lesson, students will learn about adding angles.

Example

The sum of the angles of a triangle is 180°. What is the measure of the missing angle?

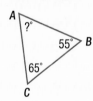

1. Find the sum of the measures of the known angles. $55° + 65° = 120°$

2. Subtract the sum of the known measures from 180°. $180° - 120° = 60°$

3. The measure of the missing angle is 60°.

Formative Assessment

Use the Progress Check to assess students' mastery of the previous lessons. Have students review the lesson indicated for the problems they answered incorrectly.

Odd/Even Assignments

Exercises are structured so that students practice the same concepts whether they are assigned the odd or even problems.

Common Error *Alert*

Exercises 1 and 2 Be sure students know how to use a protractor. They should line one of the sides of the protractor with one of the rays in the angle. They should also ensure the vertex on the angle is where it should be on the protractor and that the correct scale on the protractor is used.

 Progress Check 1 (Lessons 4-1 and 4-2)

Draw an angle with the given measurement.

1 150°

2 40°

Measure and identify each angle.

3

4

∠DEF measures __50°__.

∠DEF is a(n) __acute__ angle.

∠QRS measures __90°__.

∠QRS is a(n) __right__ angle.

Classify each figure by the lengths of its sides and the measures of its angles.

5

6

__right, scalene triangle__

__acute, equilateral triangle__

Sketch a figure with the description given.

7 acute, scalene triangle

8 obtuse, equilateral triangle

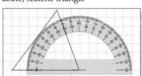

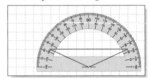

Solve.

9 TIME What type of angle is formed by the hands of the clock at 3:40?

__The angle is obtuse.__

152 Chapter 4 Angle Measures

Data-Driven Decision Making

Students missing Exercises . . .	Have trouble with . . .	Should review and practice . . .
1–2	drawing angles.	SSG Lesson 4-1, p. 138 CRM Skills Practice, p. A70
3–4	measuring and classifying angles.	SSG Lesson 4-1, p. 138 CRM Skills Practice, p. A70
5–6	classifying triangles.	SSG Lesson 4-2, p. 145 CRM Skills Practice, p. A74
7–8	drawing triangles.	SSG Lesson 4-2, p. 145 CRM Skills Practice, p. A74
9	solving word problems that involve angle classification.	SSG Lesson 4-1, p. 138 CRM Problem-Solving Practice, pp. A71 and A75

KEY Concept

Angles can be described as complementary or supplementary, according to their sums.

Complementary Angles

$\angle ABC$ and $\angle DBA$ are complementary.			
measure of the angles	40°	50°	90°
equation	40°	+ 50°	= 90°

Complementary angles with a common ray form a right angle.

Supplementary Angles

$\angle XYZ$ and $\angle RYX$ are supplementary.			
measure of the angles	115°	65°	180°
equation	115°	+ 65°	= 180°

Supplementary angles with a common ray form a straight angle.

Angles in Figures

The sum of the measures of the angles of a triangle is 180°.		95° + 50° + 35° = 180°
The sum of the measures of the angles of a quadrilateral is 360°.		180° + 180° = 360°

VOCABULARY

complementary angles
two angles are complementary if the sum of their measures is 90°

right angle
an angle that measures 90°

straight angle
an angle that measures exactly 180°

supplementary angles
two angles are supplementary if the sum of their measures is 180°

Lesson Planner

Objective   Add measures of angles and know the sum of complementary angles, supplementary angles, and angles in a triangle.

Vocabulary   complementary angles, right angle, straight angle, supplementary angles

Materials/Manipulatives   protractors, rulers, index cards, drinking straws

Chapter Resource Masters

- CRM Vocabulary and English Language Development (p. A77)
- CRM Skills Practice (p. A78)
- CRM Problem-Solving Practice (p. A79)
- CRM Homework Practice (p. A80)

1 Introduce

Vocabulary

Explore Vocabulary   Draw four angles on the board. Two angles should form a right angle and have measures with a sum of 90°, and two angles should form a straight angle and have measures with a sum of 180°. Identify the angles that add up to 90° as *complementary*. The angles that add up to 180° are *supplementary*.

2 Teach

Key Concept

Foundational Skills And Concepts   After students have read through the Key Concept box, have them complete these exercises.

1. Are two angles with measures of 85° and 95°, complementary or supplementary angles?
   supplementary angles

2. Are two angles with measures of 22° and 68°, complementary or supplementary angles?
   complementary angles

Intervention Strategy   Visual Learners

Shade Angles   Have students create two drawings of a protractor by tracing the object on a sheet of paper. Instruct them to label 0°, 90°, and 180° on each drawing. Now have them shade the region of the protractor that is a right angle with one color. Have students label this drawing "Complementary angles make right angles." On the second drawing, have them shade the region that is a straight angle with another color. Have students label this drawing, "Supplementary angles make straight angles."

Additional *Example 1*

Find the measure of the missing angle.

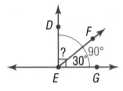

1. The measure of ∠DEG equals 90°.

2. ∠DEF and ∠FEG are complementary angles.

3. Find m∠DEF.

$$m∠DEF + m∠FEG = 90°$$
$$?° + 30° = 90°$$
$$?° = 60°$$

4. m∠DEF = 60°

Additional *Example 2*

Find the measure of the missing angle.

1. Find the sum of the measures of the known angles.

$$m∠L + m∠K = 90° + 42°$$
$$= 132°$$

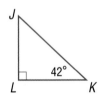

2. The sum of the measures of the angles of a triangle is 180°. Subtract the sum of the known measures from 180°.

$$180° − 132° = 48°$$

The measure of the missing angle is 48°.

A protractor can be used to measure and sketch angles.

Example 1

Find the measure of the missing angle.

1. The measure of ∠FHJ equals 180°.

2. ∠FHG and ∠GHJ are supplementary angles.

3. Find m∠GHJ.

$$m∠FHG + m∠GHJ = 180°$$
$$100° + ?° = 180°$$
$$?° = 80°$$

4. m∠GHJ = 80°

YOUR TURN!

Find the measure of the missing angle.

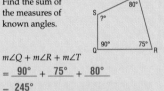

1. The measure of ∠ACD equals __90°__.

2. ∠ACB and ∠BCD are complementary angles.

3. Find m∠ACB.

$$m∠BCD + m∠ACB = \underline{90°}$$
$$\underline{25°} + ?° = \underline{90°}$$
$$?° = \underline{65°}$$

4. m∠ACB = __65°__

Example 2

Find the measure of the missing angle.

1. Find the sum of the measures of the known angles.

$$m∠G + m∠H$$
$$= 75° + 50°$$
$$= 125°$$

2. The sum of the measures of the angles of a triangle is 180°. Subtract the sum of the known measures from 180°.

$$180° − 125° = 55°$$

The measure of the missing angle is 55°.

YOUR TURN!

Find the measure of the missing angle.

1. Find the sum of the measures of known angles.

$$m∠Q + m∠R + m∠T$$
$$= \underline{90°} + \underline{75°} + \underline{80°}$$
$$= \underline{245°}$$

2. The sum of the measures of the angles of a quadrilateral is __360°__. Subtract the sum of the known measures from __360°__.

$$\underline{360°} − \underline{245°} = \underline{115°}$$

The measure of the missing angle is __115°__.

Intervention Strategy   Kinesthetic Learners

Prove It   When students are finding an unknown measure of a triangle, they can prove that all three angles equal 180°. Have students draw the triangle on a sheet of paper with the appropriate angle measures. Then have students cut out the triangle with scissors. On another sheet of paper, have students draw a straight line with a ruler and place a point on the line. Finally, have students tear each vertex off the triangle and place each vertex on the drawn line at the point. The torn angles should fill exactly either the top or the bottom of the straight line.

Example 3

Sketch supplementary angles when one angle's measure is 45°.

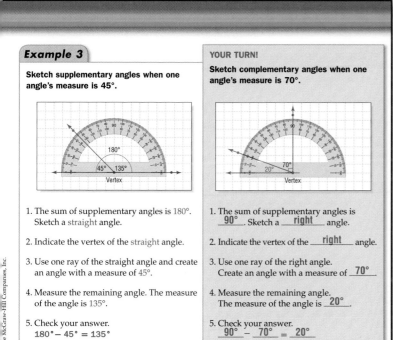

1. The sum of supplementary angles is 180°. Sketch a straight angle.

2. Indicate the vertex of the straight angle.

3. Use one ray of the straight angle and create an angle with a measure of 45°.

4. Measure the remaining angle. The measure of the angle is 135°.

5. Check your answer.
   180° − 45° = 135°

YOUR TURN!

Sketch complementary angles when one angle's measure is 70°.

1. The sum of supplementary angles is __90°__. Sketch a __right__ angle.

2. Indicate the vertex of the __right__ angle.

3. Use one ray of the right angle. Create an angle with a measure of __70°__.

4. Measure the remaining angle. The measure of the angle is __20°__.

5. Check your answer.
   __90°__ − __70°__ = __20°__

Who is Correct?

∠MNO and ∠PNQ are supplementary angles. The measure of ∠MNO is 67°. What is the measure of ∠PNQ?

Diego
90° − 67° = 23°

Tionne
180° − 67° = 123°

Malia
180° − 67° = 113°

Circle correct answer(s). Cross out incorrect answer(s).

Lesson 4-3 Add Angles **155**

Additional *Example 3*

Sketch complementary angles when one angle's measure is 32°.

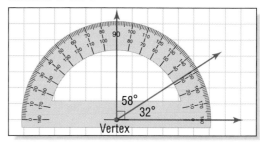

1. The sum of complementary angles is 90°. Sketch a right angle.

2. Indicate the vertex of the right angle.

3. Use one ray of the right angle and create an angle with a measure of 32°.

4. Measure the remaining angle. The measure of the angle is 58°.

5. Check your answer.
   90° − 32° = 58°

Intervention Strategy
Visual Learners

Addition Exercises   On a sheet of paper, draw five noncongruent angles and label them 1 through 5. On the bottom of the paper, list several addition problems involving the angles. Distribute a protractor and a copy of the paper to each student. Have students use the protractor to measure the angles and then solve the addition exercises.

Who *is Correct?*
Diagnostic Teaching

• Diego is incorrect. He found the angle measure that would make the angles complementary.

• Tionne is incorrect. She made a computational error.

• Malia is correct.

Remind students that supplementary angles have a sum of 180°. Encourage them to double-check their computation by using the inverse operation to ensure that their differences are what was intended.

Lesson 4-3 Add Angles **155**

Practice

Using Manipulatives

Protractor Have students use a protractor to draw figures accurately in their notes. As a good review of using a protractor, encourage students to measure the angles in the drawings, even though the measure is given. This provides an opportunity for students to practice and get immediate feedback about the accuracy of their readings.

On-Hand Manipulatives Straws are a good manipulatives for modeling angles. One straw can model a straight angle. Two straws can be set to model any angle degree. If a straw is a "bendy" straw, a single straw can be used to model an acute, a right, an obtuse, or a straight angle. Have students use two straws to model angles of different degrees, and choose students to identify their straw angles by name.

Math Coach Notes

Strategies

1. Start this lesson by relating angle measurement to triangle classification. When explaining how to classify figures, emphasize that a triangle can be classified by either the sides or the angles or both.

2. Arrange students into pairs. Give each student a ruler and a protractor. Have each group use their protractors and rulers to classify figures. Each group needs to write down their classifications.

3. As a class, compare the classifications and discuss any common mistakes.

> **Note This!**
> **Add Angles** When adding angles, it may be beneficial to explore the different types of angles (acute, right, obtuse, and straight). Encourage students to add a variety of angles together and describe the solution. For example, have students add an acute angle and a right angle. The result must be an obtuse angle.

> **Guided Practice**
>
> Find the measure of the missing angle.
>
> ① 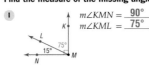 $m\angle KMN = \underline{90°}$
> $m\angle KML = \underline{75°}$
>
> ② 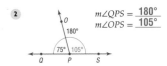 $m\angle QPS = \underline{180°}$
> $m\angle OPS = \underline{105°}$
>
> ### Step by Step Practice
>
> ③ Find the measure of the missing angle.
>
> **Step 1** Find the sum of the measures of known angles.
>
> $m\angle D + m\angle E = \underline{49°} + \underline{63°} = \underline{112°}$
>
> **Step 2** The sum of the measures of the angles of a triangle is $\underline{180°}$. Subtract the sum of measures of the known angles from $\underline{180°}$.
>
> $\underline{180°} - \underline{112°} = \underline{68°}$
>
> The measure of the missing angle is $\underline{68°}$.
>
> Find the measure of each missing angle.
>
> ④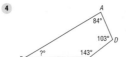
>
> $m\angle A + m\angle C + m\angle D =$
> $\underline{84°} + \underline{143°} + \underline{103°} = \underline{330°}$
> $\underline{360°} - \underline{330°} = \underline{30°}$
>
> The measure of the missing angle is $\underline{30°}$.
>
> ⑤ 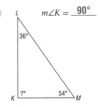 $m\angle K = \underline{90°}$

Are They Getting It?

Check students' understanding of adding angles by writing these problems on the board. Have students explain the incorrect information in each problem. Tell them to use a protractor and a ruler to show why the answers are correct or incorrect.

1. The measure of the missing angle is 230°. This is incorrect. The sum of the measures of the angles of a triangle is 180°. The missing angle is 50°.

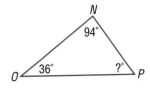

2. The measure of the missing angle is 120°. This is incorrect. The sum of the measures of the angles of a quadrilateral is 360° not 380°. The missing angle is 100°.

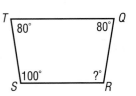

Sketch each type of angle given.

6 Sketch supplementary angles when one angle's measure is 85°.

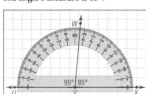

7 Sketch complementary angles when one angle's measure is 41°.

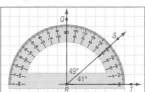

Step by Step Problem-Solving Practice

Solve.

8 **ART** Samir drew a version of a pine tree in the shape of a triangle. It had a 36° angle and a 70° angle. What was the measure of the third angle of Samir's pine tree?

Problem-Solving Strategies
☐ Draw a diagram.
☐ Look for a pattern.
☐ Guess and check.
☐ Act it out.
☑ Solve a simpler problem.

Understand Read the problem. Write what you know.

The measures of the known angles are __36°__ and __70°__.

Plan Pick a strategy. One strategy is to solve a simpler problem.

Solve Subtract the sum of the known angles from 180°.

$$\underline{36°} + \underline{70°} = \underline{106°}$$

$$180° - \underline{106°} = \underline{74°}$$

The measure of the third angle is __74°__.

Check The sum of the three angle measures must equal __180°__.

$$36° + 70° + \underline{74°} = \underline{180°}$$

GO ON ▶

Note This!

Cornell Method Tell students that one researched method of notetaking is the Cornell Method. Draw the diagram below on the board or describe it to students.

• Use the note-taking area to record your notes from class.

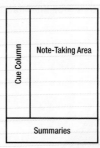

• Use the cue column to jot phrases, sketches, or other clues to understanding the concepts.
• After class, summarize the main idea of that day's lesson in the summaries area.

⚠ Common Error *Alert*

Exercise 8 When students pick the strategy *draw a diagram*, emphasize that they need to understand what the question is asking and draw a diagram that accurately reflects the situation.

Odd/Even Assignments

Exercises 12–23 are structured so that students practice the same concepts whether they are assigned the odd or even problems.

In-Class Assignment

Have students complete Exercises 13, 14, 16, 18, 21, and 26 to ensure that they understand the concept.

---

9 AGRICULTURE A cow pasture is shaped like a <u>parallelogram</u>. <u>Three</u> of the <u>angles measure 68°, 68°, and 112°</u>. What is the <u>measure of the fourth angle</u>?

Check off each step.

✔ Understand: I underlined key words.

✔ Plan: To solve this problem, I will <u>solve a simpler problem</u>.

✔ Solve: The answer is <u>112°</u>.

✔ Check: I checked my answer by <u>adding to 360°</u>.

10 SPORTS Hughes Hardware engraves trophies. The trophies have sides in the shape of isosceles triangles. The two base angles each measure 73°. What is the measure of the top angle?

<u>34°</u>

11 **Reflect** Explain how you can find the sum of the angle measures in a pentagon.

<u>Divide the pentagon into triangles. Since the sum of the</u>
<u>angles of each triangle equals 180°, the sum of the angle</u>
<u>measures of a pentagon must equal 3(180), or 540°.</u>

▶ Skills, Concepts, and Problem Solving

Find the measure of the missing angle.

12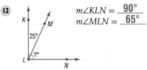
$m\angle KLN = $ <u>90°</u>
$m\angle MLN = $ <u>65°</u>

13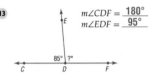
$m\angle CDF = $ <u>180°</u>
$m\angle EDF = $ <u>95°</u>

Find the measure of each missing angle.

14
$m\angle U = $ <u>113°</u>

15
$m\angle S = $ <u>105°</u>

158 Chapter 4 Angle Measures

Math Challenge

Sums of Angles in Figures Instruct students to create a table that reflects the sum of the measures of the angles of figures with three or more sides. Have students make a table with three columns that are labeled *figure, sides,* and *angle measures.* Advise them to start with a triangle and then add one side down each row. Point out that they will see a pattern. Have them write what pattern they see.

Find the measure of the missing angle.

16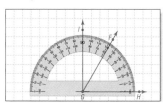

$m\angle K = \underline{110°}$

17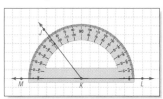

$m\angle X = \underline{50°}$

Sketch each type of angle given.

18 Sketch complementary angles when one angle's measure is 58°.

19 Sketch supplementary angles when one angle's measure is 52°.

Solve.

20 GARDENING   The butterfly garden at Sweet Valley Academy is placed in the corner of the courtyard. It is in the shape of a triangle. The butterfly garden has angles that measure 62° and 47°. What is the measure of the third angle? $\underline{71°}$

21 SCULPTURE   The geometric sculpture that sits at the entrance of Ugo Park has a triangle for its base. It has angles that measure 38° and 104°. What is the measure of the third angle? $\underline{38°}$

22 PETS   The play area at Pooch Paradise is in the shape of a quadrilateral. Three angles of the area measure 25°, 112°, and 82°. What is the measure of the fourth angle? $\underline{141°}$

23 CROSS-COUNTRY   A cross-country team ran on a path near the school that was in the shape of a quadrilateral. Three angles of the path measured 42°, 85°, and 102°. What is the measure of the fourth angle? $\underline{131°}$

Lesson 4-3 Add Angles   **159**

English Learner Strategy

Word Problems   Encourage students to create a diagram or sketch for each word problem. This will help clarify what information is given in the problem and which information is required to solve the problem.

Intervention Strategy   Interpersonal Learners

Write, Exchange, and Solve   Distribute 3 to 4 index cards to each student. On one side of each index card, have students create an angle addition problem. On the reverse side, have students draw a picture representing the problem and write the answer to the problem. Exchange index cards with another student. Have students study their partner's index cards and solve the problems. Then have students compare their answer to their partner's answers.

See It, Do It, Say It, Write It

Step 1 Draw the following figure on the board.

54°

?°   72°

Step 2 Have students find the measure of the missing angle. 54°

Step 3 Arrange students into pairs and have them explain to each other how they found the sum of the angle measures and the missing angle measure.

Step 4 Have students write in their own words how they determine the sum of the angle measures.

Looking Ahead: Pre-Teach

Transversals In the next lesson, students will learn about angles formed by transversals.

Draw two parallel lines intersected by a transversal on the board, as shown below.

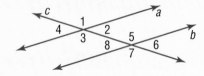

Have students answer these questions.

1. Which lines appear to be parallel? *a and b*

2. Which angles are between the parallel lines? ∠2, ∠3, ∠5, ∠8

3. Which angles are outside of the parallel lines? ∠1, ∠4, ∠6 and ∠7

Vocabulary Check Write the vocabulary word that completes each sentence.

24 __Complementary__ angles are two angles that have measures with a sum of 90°.

25 __Supplementary__ angles are two angles that have measures with a sum of 180°.

26 Writing in Math Explain how to find the missing angle of a quadrilateral when the measures of three angles are given.

Sample answer: Find the sum of the known angle measures. The sum of the measures of the angles of a quadrilateral is 360°. Subtract the sum of the known angle measures from 360°.

▶ Spiral Review

Classify each triangle by the lengths of its sides and the measures of its angles. (Lesson 4-2, p. 145)

27

55°
27 mi   34 mi
75°   50°
30 mi

__acute, scalene__ triangle

28

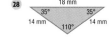

18 mm
35°   35°
14 mm   14 mm
110°

__obtuse, isosceles__ triangle

Sketch a figure with the description given. (Lesson 4-2, p. 145)

29 acute, isosceles triangle

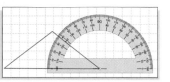

30 right, scalene triangle

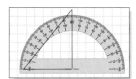

160 Chapter 4 Angle Measures

Ticket Out the Door

Drawings to Dismiss Arrange students into groups of four. Instruct two students to draw an example of complementary angles, while two students draw an example of supplementary angles. Have students explain their examples as they exit the classroom.

KEY Concept

In the diagram below, the ray creates supplementary angles A and B.

A similar relationship occurs when two lines intersect. When line ℓ intersects line m four angles are created.

$\angle A$ and $\angle D$ are **vertical angles**. They are opposite angles that were formed when the two lines intersected. $\angle B$ and $\angle C$ are also vertical angles. Each pair of vertical angles are congruent.

$$\angle A \cong \angle D$$
$$\angle B \cong \angle C$$

Other angle relationships occur when a transversal passes through two parallel lines. The table below lists these relationships.

Angle Relationships	
alternate interior	$\angle C$ and $\angle F$ $\angle D$ and $\angle E$
alternate exterior	$\angle A$ and $\angle H$ $\angle B$ and $\angle G$
corresponding	$\angle A$ and $\angle E$ $\angle B$ and $\angle F$ $\angle C$ and $\angle G$ $\angle D$ and $\angle H$
vertical	$\angle A$ and $\angle D$ $\angle B$ and $\angle C$ $\angle E$ and $\angle H$ $\angle F$ and $\angle G$

GO ON

VOCABULARY

alternate exterior angles
exterior angles that lie on opposite sides of the transversal

alternate interior angles
interior angles that lie on opposite sides of the transversal

congruent angles
angles with the same measure

corresponding angles
angles that have the same position on two different parallel lines cut by a transversal

parallel lines
lines that do not intersect

transversal
a line that intersects two or more lines to form eight angles

vertical angles
nonadjacent angles formed by a pair of lines that intersect

Intervention Strategy — Interpersonal Learners

Classifying Angle Relationships On the board, draw two parallel lines with a transversal passing through them. Label each angle with a letter. Have the students work in pairs to explain how to identify the corresponding and vertical angle relationships in the diagram. Tell each group to write a sentence labeling each pair of angles. For more proficient students, ask them to identify the alternate interior and alternate exterior angles. Encourage them to write their sentences using the congruency symbol.

Lesson Notes

Lesson Planner

Objective Identify the measure of an angle using knowledge about transversals and parallel lines.

Vocabulary **alternate exterior angles**, **alternate interior angles**, **congruent angles**, **corresponding angles**, **parallel lines**, **transversal**, **vertical angles**

Materials/Manipulatives protractors, straightedge, pipe cleaners, colored pencils

Chapter Resource Masters

CRM Vocabulary and English Language Development (p. A81)

CRM Skills Practice (p. A82)

CRM Problem-Solving Practice (p. A83)

CRM Homework Practice (p. A84)

 Introduce

Vocabulary

Interior and Exterior Compare the terms *interior* and *exterior* to *inside* and *outside*. Highlight the parallel lines in a different color and discuss the angles *inside* and *outside* of the highlighted area. Also show students the congruency symbol ($\cong$) and explain its meaning.

 Teach

Key Concept

Foundational Skills and Concepts After students have read through the Key Concept box, have them try these exercises.

1. What does congruent mean? same size and shape with equal angle measures

2. List all the angles that are congruent to $\angle F$. $\angle B, \angle C, \angle G$

3. If $\angle E$ measures 145°, what is the measure of $\angle H$? They are congruent, so $m\angle H$ is 145°.

Additional *Example 1*

Identify the measure of ∠Q if the measure of ∠R is 32°.

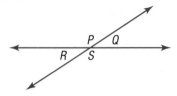

1. Identify two pairs of vertical angles.

∠R and ∠Q

∠P and ∠S

2. To find the measure of the missing angle, find the measure of the opposite angle.

∠Q ≅ ∠R

3. The measure of ∠Q is 32°.

Additional *Example 2*

Name the alternate interior angles.

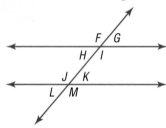

1. Name the angles that are between the two parallel lines.

∠H, ∠I, ∠J, and ∠K

2. Identify two sets of alternate angles.

∠H and ∠K

∠I and ∠J

Example 1

Identify the measure of ∠K if the measure of ∠H is 100°.

1. Identify two pairs of vertical angles.

∠H and ∠K

∠I and ∠J

2. To find the measure of the missing angle, find the measure of the opposite angle.

∠H ≅ ∠K

3. The measure of ∠K is 100°.

YOUR TURN!

Identify the measure of ∠N if the measure of ∠M is 15°.

1. Identify two pairs of vertical angles.

__∠L__ and __∠O__

__∠N__ and __∠M__

2. To find the measure of the missing angle, find the measure of the opposite angle.

∠ __M__ ≅ ∠N

3. The measure of ∠N is __15°__.

Example 2

Name the alternate interior angles.

1. Name the angles that are between the two parallel lines.

∠Q, ∠T, ∠S, and ∠V

2. Identify two sets of alternate angles.

∠Q and ∠V

∠S and ∠T

YOUR TURN!

Name the alternate exterior angles.

1. Name the angles that are on the outside of the two parallel lines.

__∠X__ , __∠Y__ , __∠D__ and __∠E__

2. Identify two sets of alternate angles.

__∠X__ and __∠E__

__∠Y__ and __∠D__

English Learner Strategy

Angle Vocabulary On a piece of paper, draw a straight line with a ray that creates supplementary angles A and B. Remind students that the measure of a straight line is 180°, so ∠A + ∠B = 180°. Then draw two intersecting lines and label each angle. Ask students to identify each pair of supplementary angles in the diagram. Have them write a sentence for each pair, indicating the sum is 180°.

Repeat the exercise with a new diagram, this time including one angle measurement. Model how to find the missing angle measure for each pair of supplementary angles. Demonstrate how to start with the known angle and work with angle relationships to find the other angle measures in the diagram.

Example 3

Find the value of *x* if the given angle equals 125°.

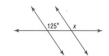

1. Identify the relationship between the given angle and angle *x*.

   The given angle and ∠*x* are corresponding angles.

2. The measures of these two angles are equal.

3. The value of *x* is 125°.

YOUR TURN!

Find the value of *x* if the given angle equals 20°.

1. Identify the relationship between the given angle and angle *x*.

   The given angle and ∠*x* are <u>alternate exterior angles</u>

2. The measures of these two angles <u>are equal</u>

3. The value of *x* is <u>20°</u>.

Who is Correct?

Name the alternate exterior angles.

Circle correct answer(s). Cross out incorrect answer(s).

 Guided Practice

Identify the measure of each indicated angle.

$m\angle J = 10°$, so $m\angle K = $ <u>10°</u>.

$m\angle M = 117°$, so $m\angle P = $ <u>117°</u>.

> GO ON

Lesson 4-4 Transversals **163**

Additional *Example 3*

Find the value of *x* if the given angle equals 115°.

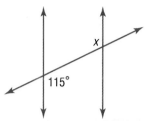

I. Identify the relationship between the given angle and angle *x*.

The given angle and ∠*x* are alternate interior angles.

2. The measures of these two angles are equal.

3. The value of *x* is 115°.

Math Coach Notes

Isolating Angles To help students focus on specific angles, have them cover up the other angles. Ask students to identify the alternate interior angles in a diagram. Cover the exterior angles to focus their attention to the angles between the parallel lines. Do the same to help differentiate alternate exterior angles.

③ Practice

Using Manipulatives

Pipe Cleaners Use a pair of pipe cleaners to create two intersecting lines. Give the measure of one of the angles, and have students determine the measures of the remaining angles.

On-Hand Manipulatives To create angles and a transversal, students can use three rulers. Have students then identify and classify the angle relationships the intersecting rulers produce.

Who *is Correct?*
Diagnostic Teaching

• Jermaine is correct. He named both pairs of alternate exterior angles.

• Allison is incorrect. She named both pairs of alternate interior angles.

• Dasan is incorrect. He named two pairs of supplementary angles.

Lesson 4-4 Transversals **163**

Copyright © Glencoe/McGraw-Hill, a division of The McGraw-Hill Companies, Inc.

Math Coach Notes

Partner Practice   Ask students to practice explaining to one another how to determine angle relationships created by a transversal. Have students identify each part of a diagram, and prove which angles are congruent using lesson vocabulary and clear language. Invite partners to model their explanations for the class.

Common Error *Alert*

Exercise 6–9   Students may confuse the terms interior and exterior. Differentiate interior versus exterior by relating the terms to the interior and exterior of a building. Emphasize to students that interior angles are *inside* the two parallel lines, while exterior angles are *outside* the parallel lines.

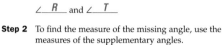

3 Identify the measure of ∠T if ∠R equals 85°.

> **Step 1**   Identify two pairs of supplementary angles.
>
> ∠ __Q__ and ∠ __S__
>
> ∠ __R__ and ∠ __T__
>
> **Step 2**   To find the measure of the missing angle, use the measures of the supplementary angles.
>
> $m∠$ __R__ $+ m∠$ __T__ $= $ __180°__
>
> __180__ $-$ __85__ $= $ __95__
>
> **Step 3**   The measure of ∠ __T__ is __95°__.

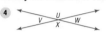

Identify the measure of each angle indicated.

4

$m∠V = 26°$, so $m∠W = $ __26°__.

5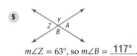

$m∠Z = 63°$, so $m∠B = $ __117°__.

Name the alternate interior angles.

6

∠ __C__ and ∠ __F__   ∠ __D__ and ∠ __E__

7

∠ __J__ and ∠ __O__   ∠ __L__ and ∠ __M__

Name the alternate exterior angles.

8

∠ __A__ and ∠ __H__   ∠ __B__ and ∠ __G__

9

∠ __I__ and ∠ __P__   ∠ __K__ and ∠ __N__

164   Chapter 4   Angle Measures

Are They Getting It?

Check students' understanding of angle relationships by drawing the lines and statements below on the board. Ask them to point out incorrect answers and explain their reasoning.

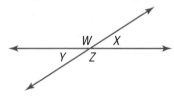

1. ∠W and ∠X are congruent.
   This is incorrect. They are supplementary.

2. If $m∠X = 32°$, then $m∠Y = 148°$.
   This is incorrect. ∠X and ∠Y are vertical, so they are congruent.

3. ∠Z and ∠W are vertical angles.   This is correct.

Step by Step Problem-Solving Practice

Solve.

Problem-Solving Strategies
- ☐ Draw a diagram.
- ☐ Use logical reasoning.
- ☐ Solve a simpler problem.
- ☐ Work backward.
- ☑ Look for a pattern.

10 **STAIRS** Mr. Hataro is building a staircase in a new home. The rails are parallel. He checks the rails by measuring the angles. If the measure of $\angle Q$ is 85°, what is the value of x?

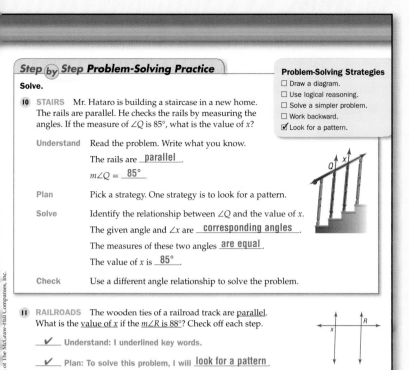

Understand Read the problem. Write what you know.

The rails are **parallel**.

$m\angle Q =$ **85°**

Plan Pick a strategy. One strategy is to look for a pattern.

Solve Identify the relationship between $\angle Q$ and the value of x.

The given angle and $\angle x$ are **corresponding angles**.

The measures of these two angles **are equal**.

The value of x is **85°**.

Check Use a different angle relationship to solve the problem.

11 **RAILROADS** The wooden ties of a railroad track are <u>parallel</u>. What is the <u>value of x</u> if the <u>$m\angle R$ is 88°</u>? Check off each step.

✔ Understand: I underlined key words.

✔ Plan: To solve this problem, I will **look for a pattern**.

✔ Solve: The answer is _____ **$x = 88°$** _____.

✔ Check: I checked my answer by **using a different angle relationship**.

12 **QUILTS** Mrs. Hawkins is making a quilt. The lines shown on the quilt are parallel. What is the value of x if the measure of $\angle S$ is 30°?

The value of x is 30°.

13 **Reflect** If you know one of the angle measures in the quilt sample, can you find the measures of the remaining angles without using a protractor?

Yes; Angle relationships, such as supplementary angles
vertical angles, and corresponding angles could be used.

GO ON

Note This!

Reviewing Congruency Use colored pencils to reinforce vocabulary and concepts. Have students draw two parallel lines with a transversal intersecting both lines. Ask students to use one colored pencil to label the corresponding angles of equal measure, and a second color to label the corresponding angles of the supplementary measure. Use lesson vocabulary to identify the angle relationships in the diagram. Encourage students to use the term *congruent* when describing equal angle measures.

Intervention Strategy   Visual/Logical Learners

Find the Missing Angle Reinforce to students that the sum of the angles in a triangle equals 180 degrees. Draw the diagram below on the board.

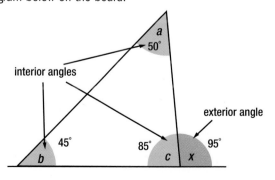

Explain to students that $\angle x$ is called an *exterior angle*. Fill in the measures of the angles as $\angle a = 50°$ and $\angle b = 45°$.

Have students find the measures of $\angle c$ and $\angle x$. Then say, "The exterior angle of a triangle is equal to the sum of the interior angles at the other two vertices of the triangle." Write the following on the board: $x = a + b$. Ask students to help you prove this theorem. Tell them:

The angles in the triangle add up to 180 degrees. So, $a + b + c = 180°$. ($m\angle c = 85°$)

The angles on a straight line add up to 180 degrees. So, $c + x = 180°$. Therefore, $c = 180 - x$.

Putting this into the first equation gives us: $a + b + 180 - x = 180$. Therefore, $a + b = x$ after simplifying the equation.

$50° + 45° = 95°$ $x = 95°$ and $c = 85°$

Odd/Even Assignments

Exercises 14–23 are structured so that students practice the same concepts whether they are assigned the odd or even problems.

In-Class Assignment

Have students complete Exercises 14, 18, 21, 23, and 26 to ensure that they understand the concept.

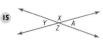

Skills, Concepts, and Problem Solving

Identify the measure of each missing angle.

14.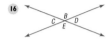

$m\angle U = 23°$, so $m\angle V = $ ___23°___ .

15.

$m\angle X = 146°$, so $m\angle Z = $ ___146°___ .

16.

$m\angle D = 42°$, so $m\angle E = $ ___138°___ .

17.

$m\angle I = 121°$, so $m\angle G = $ ___59°___ .

Name the alternate interior angles.

18.

___$\angle B$___ and ___$\angle G$___   ___$\angle D$___ and ___$\angle E$___

19.

___$\angle K$___ and ___$\angle N$___   ___$\angle L$___ and ___$\angle M$___

Name the alternate exterior angles.

20.

___$\angle A$___ and ___$\angle H$___   ___$\angle C$___ and ___$\angle F$___

21.

___$\angle I$___ and ___$\angle P$___   ___$\angle J$___ and ___$\angle O$___

Solve.

22. **MAPS**   First Street and Second Street run parallel to one another. Main Street intersects both of them. What is the value of x if the measure of $\angle Q$ is 84°?

___The value of *x* is 96°.___

Math Challenge

Applying Angle Relationships   Have students classify the angle relationships in the diagram. Then ask them to find the measure of each angle from the one given.

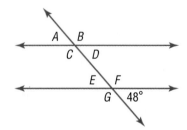

23 BRIDGES   The top beam and the floor of the bridge are parallel. What is the value of *x* if the measure of ∠*S* is 45°?

The value of *x* is 45°.

Vocabulary Check   Write the vocabulary word that completes each sentence.

24 ____Congruent____ angles are angles with the same measure.

25 A(n) ____transversal____ is a line that intersects two or more lines to form eight angles.

26 Writing in Math   If two parallel lines are cut by a transversal, what relationship exists between alternate exterior angles? Explain.

Alternate exterior angles have angles of equal measure. They are congruent.

▶ **Spiral Review**

Sketch supplementary angles when one angle's measure is 65°.
(Lesson 4-3, p. 153)

27

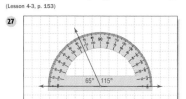

Find the measure of each missing angle.   (Lesson 4-2, p. 145)

28

35°

29

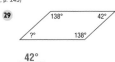

42°

Solve.   (Lesson 4-2, p. 145)

30 TENTS   The doorway to Claudio's new tent is in the shape of a quadrilateral. Three angles of the doorway measure 123°, 123°, and 57°. What is the measure of the missing angle?

The missing angle measures 57°.

See It, Do It, Say It, Write It

Step 1   Draw two parallel lines with a transversal intersecting both lines on the board. Label each angle with a letter.

Step 2   Have students classify all of the angle relationships in the diagram.

Step 3   Ask students to work in pairs or small groups. Have students discuss and identify each part of the diagram, including the transversal, parallel lines, and angle relationships.

Step 4   Have students work alone to write their evaluations of the diagram. Encourage students to use the correct vocabulary terms in their explanations, including the term *congruent*.

Ticket Out the Door

Angles and Transversals   Draw the following diagram on the board. Tell students to classify the angle relationships and identify the congruent angles. As students approach the classroom door to exit, alternate asking them to name the congruent angles and various angle relationships from the diagram.

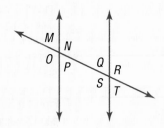

Formative Assessment

Use the Progress Check to assess students' mastery of the previous lessons. Have students review the lesson indicated for the problems they answered incorrectly.

Odd/Even Assignments

Exercises are structured so that students practice the same concepts whether they are assigned the odd or even problems.

Common Error *Alert*

Students will often have a hard time remembering the difference between complementary and supplementary. They remember that the sum of the angle measures is 90° or 180°, but struggle with keeping them straight.

Have students think of the names in alphabetical order, complementary, then supplementary. Have students think of the measures in numerical order, 90, then 180. Explain that they can remember the meanings if they think of the words and numbers in alphabetic and numeric order.

Draw each type of angle given.

1. Draw supplementary angles when one angle's measure is 120°.

2. Draw complementary angles when one angle's measure is 45°.

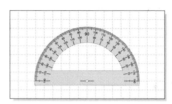
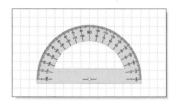

Find the measure of each missing angle.

3. $m\angle H =$ _____

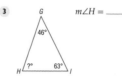

4. $m\angle L =$ _____

Identify the measure of each angle indicated.

5.

$m\angle N = 126°$, so $m\angle O =$ _____.

6.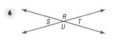

$m\angle R = 149°$, so $m\angle T =$ _____.

Solve.

7. **REPAIRS** A school bus was placed on a lift so that repair workers could see under the bus. The vertical lift bars are parallel to one another, and the horizontal bars are parallel to one another. If the measure of $\angle B$ is 113°, what is the value of x?

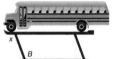

_____

_____

Data-Driven Decision Making

Students missing Exercises . . .	Have trouble with . . .	Should review and practice . . .
1–2	drawing angles.	SSG Lesson 4-3, p. 153 CRM Skills Practice, p. A78
3–4	finding missing angle measures in triangles and quadrilaterals.	SSG Lesson 4-3, p. 153 CRM Skills Practice, p. A78
5–6	identifying angle measures using the relationships of angles.	SSG Lesson 4-4, p. 161 CRM Skills Practice, p. A82
7	solving word problems involving angle measures.	CRM Problem-Solving Practice, pp. A79 and A83

Study Guide

Vocabulary and Concept Check

acute angle, *p. 145*

angle, *p. 138*

complementary angles, *p. 153*

congruent, *p. 145*

degree, *p. 138*

obtuse angle, *p. 145*

parallel lines, *p. 161*

protractor, *p. 138*

right angle, *p. 145*

side, *p. 145*

straight angle, *p. 153*

supplementary angles, *p. 153*

triangle, *p. 145*

vertex, *p. 138*

Write the vocabulary word that completes each sentence.

1 A(n) _____protractor_____ is an instrument marked in degrees, used for measuring or drawing angles.

2 A(n) _____degree_____ is a unit for measuring angles.

3 Two angles are <u>supplementary angles</u> if the sum of their measures is 180°.

4 Two rays with a common endpoint form an _____angle_____.

5 A(n) _____obtuse_____ angle measures greater than 90°, but less than 180°.

Label each diagram below. Write the correct vocabulary term in each blank.

6 _____parallel lines_____
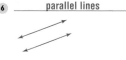

7 _____right angle_____

8 _____equilateral triangle_____
4 cm   4 cm
4 cm

9 _____vertex_____

10 _____straight angle_____
G   H   I

11 _____complementary angles_____
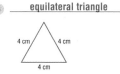

Study Guide

Formative Assessment

Chapter **4**

Vocabulary and Concept Check

If students have difficulty answering Exercises 1–11, remind them that they can use the page references to refresh their memories about the vocabulary terms.

Vocabulary Review Strategies

Games   Have the class divide into small groups. Have each group design a game that they can use to review their vocabulary words. They should provide the answer to a question. Other students ask the question. For example, the answer might be: "Between 0° and 90°." Then the proper question response would be, "What is the measure of an acute angle?"

Lesson Review

Each example walks the students through the main concepts of this chapter. If the given examples are not sufficient to review the questions, remind students that the page references tell them where to review that topic in their textbooks.

Find **Extra Practice** for these concepts in the Practice Worksheets, pages A69–A84.

Classroom Management

Early Finishers   Have those students with extra time design a lab for their classmates. You could supply them with some real-world examples of angles and triangles that they can use, classify, and/or measure.

For example: Bring in a photograph of an image with two lines cut by a transversal. Have students measure one angle, and use that measure to find the other angle measures.

Dinah Zike's Foldables®

Review Remind students to complete and refer to their Foldables as they progress through the Chapter 4 Study Guide. Have students share and compare their completed Foldables with a partner. You may also choose to have them use their Foldable as a study aid in preparing for the Chapter Test. (For complete instructions, see Chapter Resource Masters, p. A66.)

Note This!

Create a Checklist Help students create a study checklist. The checklist should include the following items:

- Measuring and classifying angles
- Classifying triangles
- Recognizing supplementary and complementary angles
- Finding missing angle measures

Students should put a check mark next to each topic when they feel they have a good grasp of the process.

Lesson Review

4-1 Angles (pp. 138–144)

12 Draw ∠MNO that measures 135°.

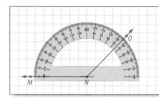

13 Draw ∠PQR that measures 40°.

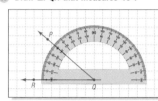

Measure and identify the angle.

14

∠NOP measures ___105°___.
∠NOP is a(n) ___obtuse___ angle.

15

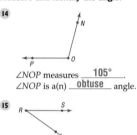

∠QRS measures ___35°___.
∠QRS is a(n) ___acute___ angle.

Example 1

Draw ∠JKL that measures 55°.

1. Draw $\overrightarrow{KL}$.
2. Place point K as the vertex.
3. Use the inner scale and draw point J at 55°.
4. Draw $\overrightarrow{KJ}$.

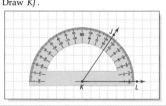

Example 2

Measure and identify the angle.

1. Place the center of the protractor at point B. Line up $\overrightarrow{BC}$ with the line that extends from 0° to 180° on the protractor.

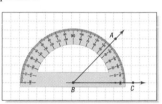

2. Look at point A. Read the measure of the angle where $\overrightarrow{BA}$ passes through the inner scale. ∠ABC measures 45°.

Intervention Strategy   Auditory Learners

Review Game Play a game with students during the last few minutes of class to reinforce some of the topics in the chapter. For example, use the phrase, "We are two angles that total 90°." Elicit the correct student response of "You are complementary angles."

4-2 Triangles (pp. 145–151)

Classify each triangle by the lengths of its sides.

16

The figure is a(n)
<u>scalene triangle</u>.

17

The figure is a(n)
<u>isosceles triangle</u>.

Classify each triangle by the measure of its angles.

18

The figure is a(n)
<u>obtuse triangle</u>.

19

The figure is a(n)
<u>acute triangle</u>.

Example 3

Classify the triangle by the lengths of its sides.

1. The side lengths are 21 feet, 42 feet, and 33 feet.

2. None of the sides of the triangle are equal in length. The figure is a scalene triangle.

Example 4

Classify triangle MNO by the measure of its angles.

1. $m\angle O = 65°$ $\angle O$ is an acute angle.
2. $m\angle M = 90°$ $\angle M$ is a right angle.
3. $m\angle N = 25°$ $\angle N$ is an acute angle.
4. The figure is a right triangle.

Note This!

Create a Chart   Help students create a chart of words that correspond with each of the chapter's topics. The chart should include words that have a reference to *angles,* (acute, obtuse, right, supplementary, and complementary). You could do the same for all of the topics found in the chapter.

Intervention Strategy   Kinesthetic Learners

Classify Shapes and Angles   Break the students into pairs or small groups and give the students some shape and angle cutouts, a ruler, and a protractor. Have them take measurements and classify their shapes and angles based upon their findings.

Math Coach Notes

Study Tips   Encourage students to study out loud. As they read over their notes, have them talk through the notes, describe examples and sketches, and create their own examples. Students can "teach" their notes to themselves. This will help them remember the facts.

4-3 Add Angles (pp. 153–160)

Find the measure of each missing angle.

20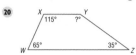

The measure of the missing angle is __145°__.

21

The measure of the missing angle is __30°__.

Find the measure of the missing angle.

22

$m\angle DEF =$ __180°__

$m\angle GED =$ __97°__

23

$m\angle HIJ =$ __90°__

$m\angle KIJ =$ __73°__

Example 5

What is the measure of the missing angle?

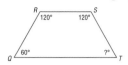

1. Find the sum of the measures of known angles.

   $m\angle Q + m\angle R + m\angle S = 300°$

2. The sum of the measures of the angles of a quadrilateral is 360°. Subtract the sum of the known measures from 360°.

   $360° - 300° = 60°$

Example 6

Find the measure of the missing angle.

1. The measure of $\angle ABC$ equals 180°.

2. Find $m\angle ABD$.

   $m\angle ABD + m\angle DBC = 180°$

   $?° \ + \ 148° = 180°$

   $?° \ \ = 32°$

3. $m\angle ABD = 32°$

4-4 Transversals (pp. 161–167)

Identify the measure of each indicated angle.

24 $m\angle E = 86°$, so $m\angle H = \underline{86°}$.

25 $m\angle E = 86°$, so $m\angle F = \underline{94°}$.

26 $m\angle K = 64°$, so $m\angle J = \underline{64°}$.

27 $m\angle K = 64°$, so $m\angle L = \underline{116°}$.

28 Name the alternate exterior angles.

$\underline{\angle I}$ and $\underline{\angle Q}$

$\underline{\angle K}$ and $\underline{\angle P}$

29 Name the alternate interior angles.

$\underline{\angle L}$ and $\underline{\angle O}$

$\underline{\angle M}$ and $\underline{\angle N}$

Example 7

Identify the measure of $\angle D$ if the measure of $\angle A$ is 97°.

1. $\angle A$ and $\angle D$ are vertical angles.
   $\angle B$ and $\angle C$ are vertical angles.

2. Find the measure of the opposite angle.

   $\angle A \cong \angle D$

3. The measure of $\angle D$ is 97°.

Example 8

Name the alternate interior angles.

1. Name the angles that are between the two parallel lines.

   $\angle B$, $\angle E$, $\angle D$, and $\angle G$

2. Identify two sets of alternate angles.

   $\angle B$ and $\angle G$
   $\angle D$ and $\angle E$

Three Questions Have students answer a total of three questions that you give them on a half-sheet of paper. Ask questions covering each of the following: (1) measure a given angle and classify it, (2) find the missing angle measure of a triangle (given the other two angle measures), (3) classify a triangle given its angle and side measures.

Chapter Resource Masters

Additional forms of the Chapter 4 Tests are available.

Test Format	Where to Find it
Chapter 4 Test	**Math Online** glencoe.com
Blackline Masters	Assessment Masters, p. 68

Customize and create multiple versions of your chapter test and their answer keys. All of these questions from the leveled chapter tests are available on ExamView® Assessment Suite.

Online Assessment and Reporting

glencoe.com

This online assessment tool allows teachers to track student progress with easily-accessible, comprehensive reports available for every student. Assess students using any internet-ready computer.

Alternative Assessment

Use Portfolios Ask students to write examples of each type of problem from this chapter in their portfolios. Require them to include a diagram or picture with each example. Have students find the answer to each example in their portfolio and describe the steps they took to solve or simplify each one.

 Chapter 4 **Chapter Test**

Measure and identify each angle.

1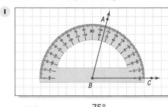

∠ABC measures ___75°___.

∠ABC is a(n) ___acute angle___.

2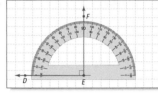

∠DEF measures ___90°___.

∠DEF is a(n) ___right angle___.

Draw each type of angle given.

3 complementary angles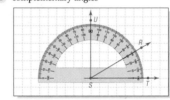

4 supplementary angles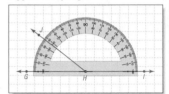

Find the measure of the missing angle.

5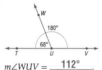

$m\angle WUV =$ ___112°___.

6

$m\angle XYA =$ ___18°___.

7

$m\angle J =$ ___51°___.

8

$m\angle P =$ ___77°___.

English Learner Strategy

Assessment Allow students time to look over the assessment. Have students take a close look at all the problem directions, as well as any terms in the word problems. Provide an opportunity for students to clarify any words they think they do not understand by conducting a brief question-and-answer period, or provide a dictionary or a translation manual for those who have a primary or native language other than English.

Identify the measure of each missing angle.

9

$m\angle U = 32°$, so $m\angle V = \underline{\quad 32° \quad}$.

10

$m\angle A = 157°$, so $m\angle B = \underline{\quad 157° \quad}$.

Solve.

11 CONSTRUCTION Angela had to fit two pieces of crown molding together at a 125° angle. What type of angle did the molding form?

  <u>   obtuse   </u>

12 COOKING Jada made some fried corn tortillas like the one pictured at the right. What type of triangle do Jada's tortillas represent?

  <u>   equilateral triangles   </u>

3 in.   3 in.
3 in.

13 LABELS Ms. Saracino is designing a label for a lotion bottle. The label has four sides. Three angles have measures 72°, 72°, and 90°. What is the measure of the missing angle?

  <u>$72 + 72 + 90 = 234$, $360 - 234 = 126$,   The missing angle is 126°.</u>

14 DOORS The door of Emilio's room makes a right angle with the wall. His door will open at a 73° angle. What is the angle between his door and the wall?

  <u>The angle between his door and the wall is 17°.</u>

Correct the mistakes.

15 Saba says that $\angle P$ and $\angle Q$ are congruent angles. Is she correct? Why or why not?

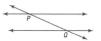
P
Q

  <u>Yes, she is correct. Congruent angles are angles</u>

  <u>with equal measures. The two angles are</u>

  <u>corresponding angles. The measures of</u>

  <u>corresponding angles are equal, or congruent.</u>

STOP

Learning from Mistakes

Review Review commonly missed questions as a small group or class. Ask students to share their methods of answering each question. Try to point out when any errors occur and take corrective measures.

Data-Driven Decision Making

Students missing Exercises . . .	Have trouble with . . .	Should review and practice . . .
1–4	drawing and classifying angles.	**SSG** Lesson 4-1, p. 138 **CRM** Skills Practice, p. A70
5–10	finding the measure of missing angles.	**SSG** Lessons 4-2, 4-3, and 4-4, pp. 145, 153, and 161 **CRM** Skills Practice, pp. A74, A78, and A82
11–15	solving word problems involving angle measures.	**SSG** Lessons 4-1, 4-2, 4-3, and 4-4, pp. 138, 145, 153, and 161 **CRM** Problem Solving Practice, pp. A71, A75, A79, and A83

Test Practice

![warning icon] **Diagnose Student Errors**

Survey student responses for each item. Class trends may indicate common errors and misconceptions.

1. A   guess
     B   guess
     C   guess
     Ⓓ   correct

2. A   angle greater than 90°
     B   angle greater than 90°
     Ⓒ   correct
     D   angle smaller than 175°

3. A   incorrectly assumed angles were congruent
     B   miscalculation
     Ⓒ   correct
     D   did not include right angle as a known angle

4. Ⓐ   correct
     B   chose wrong angle, parallelograms have opposite angles congruent
     C   added the two known angle measures
     D   this is the sum of all 4 angles

5. A   guess
     Ⓑ   correct
     C   guess
     D   confused acute and obtuse

6. Ⓐ   correct
     B   guess
     C   confused right and straight
     D   guess

7. A   guess
     B   chose degrees in a right angle
     Ⓒ   correct
     D   chose degrees in a quadrilateral

8. A   subtracted from 90°
     B   thought angles were vertical angles
     Ⓒ   correct
     D   did not subtract 53°

9. A   confused complementary and supplementary
     B   incorrect term
     C   classifies ∠GFH
     Ⓓ   correct

Choose the best answer and fill in the corresponding circle on the sheet at right.

1   Which best describes these lines?

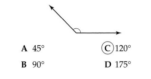

     A   perpendicular   C   bisecting
     B   intersecting   Ⓓ parallel

2   What is the approximate measure of this angle?

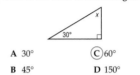

     A   45°   Ⓒ 120°
     B   90°   D   175°

3   What is the value of x in the figure?

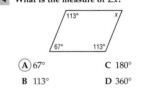

     A   30°   Ⓒ 60°
     B   45°   D   150°

4   What is the measure of ∠x?

     Ⓐ 67°   C   180°
     B   113°   D   360°

5   What type of angle is ∠ABC?

     A   right   C   congruent
     Ⓑ obtuse   D   acute

6   What is the approximate measure of angle ∠QRS?

     Ⓐ 180°   C   90°
     B   165°   D   45°

7   What is the sum of the measures of the angles of a triangle?

     A   45°   Ⓒ 180°
     B   90°   D   360°

176   Chapter 4 Test Practice

---

10. A   figure has 3 sides
      Ⓑ   correct
      C   figure has 2 congruent sides
      D   figure has 3 acute angles

11. Ⓐ   correct
      B   miscalculated
      C   angles are supplementary, not complementary
      D   guess

8 What is the value of *x*?

A 37°   C 127°

B 53°   D 180°

---

9 What term describes angles *EFG* and *GFH*?

A complementary   C obtuse

B congruent   D supplementary

---

10 What term does NOT describe the figure below?

A triangle   C isosceles

B obtuse   D acute

---

11 What is the measure of ∠*A* and ∠*B*?

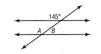

A 145°, 35°   C 55°, 35°

B 145°, 65°   D 140°, 40°

ANSWER SHEET

Directions: Fill in the circle of each correct answer.

1 (A) (B) (C) (●D)
2 (A) (B) (●C) (D)
3 (A) (B) (●C) (D)
4 (●A) (B) (C) (D)
5 (A) (●B) (C) (D)
6 (●A) (B) (C) (D)
7 (A) (B) (●C) (D)
8 (A) (B) (●C) (D)
9 (A) (B) (C) (●D)
10 (A) (●B) (C) (D)
11 (●A) (B) (C) (D)

Success Strategy

If you do not know the answer to a question, go on to the next question. Come back to the problem, if you have time. You might find another question later in the test that will help you figure out the skipped problem.

STOP

Diagnosing Student Errors and Misconceptions

Review   When working on the Test Practice problems, have the students show their work on a separate sheet of notebook paper that can be used later as a reference as needed. After the class has completed the Test Practice problems, go over all the correct responses and have the students score their own responses.

Have students try to find and correct their mistakes. If they are still having trouble, try to determine whether or not the mistake was due to a basic computational error or whether they just performed the wrong operation altogether. If the majority of errors are computational, then try to determine if the mistakes are minor and careless. If they are not simply the result of working too quickly or carelessly, then review some of the algorithms required in these exercises.

Chapter Overview

Chapter-at-a-Glance

Lesson	Math Objective	State/Local Standards
5-1 Ratios (pp. 180–186)	Interpret and use ratios.	
5-2 Rates and Unit Costs (pp. 187–192)	Determine unit costs and understand rates.	
Progress Check 1 (p. 193)		
5-3 Proportions (pp. 194–200)	Use proportions to compare sets of different sizes.	
5-4 Solve Problems Using Proportions (pp. 201–207)	Use proportions to compare figures and solve problems.	
Progress Check 2 (p. 208)		

Content-at-a-Glance

The diagram below summarizes and unpacks Chapter 5 content.

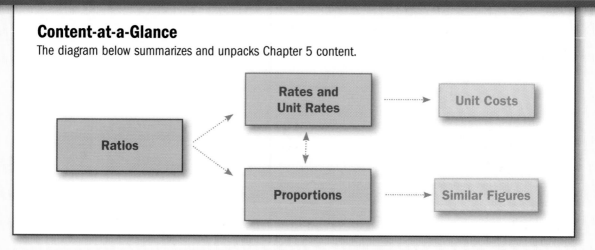

Chapter Assessment Manager

Diagnostic   Diagnose students' readiness.

	Student/Teacher Editions	Assessment Masters	Technology
Course Placement Test		1	ExamView® Assessment Suite
Book 2 Pretest		62	ExamView® Assessment Suite
Chapter 5 Pretest		76	ExamView® Assessment Suite
Quiz/Preview	SSG 179		Math Online glencoe.com StudentWorks™ Plus

Formative   Identify students' misconceptions of content knowledge.

	Student/Teacher Editions	Assessment Masters	Technology
Progress Checks	SSG 193, 208		Math Online glencoe.com StudentWorks™ Plus
Vocabulary Review	SSG 209		Math Online glencoe.com
Lesson Assessments			ExamView® Assessment Suite
Are They Getting It?	TE 183, 190, 197, 204		Math Online glencoe.com

Summative   Determine student success in learning the concepts in the lesson, chapter, or book.

	Student/Teacher Editions	Assessment Masters	Technology
Chapter 5 Test	SSG 212	79	ExamView® Assessment Suite
Test Practice	SSG 214	82	
Alternative Assessment	TE 212	85	ExamView® Assessment Suite
See It, Do It, Say It, Write It	TE 186, 192, 200, 207		
Book 2 Test		98	ExamView® Assessment Suite

Backmapping and Vertical Alignment **McGraw-Hill's** *Math Triumphs* intervention program was conceived and developed with the final result in mind: student success in grade-level mathematics, including Algebra 1 and beyond. The authors, using the **NCTM Focal Points and Focal Connections** as their guide, developed this brand-new series by backmapping from grade-level and Algebra 1 concepts, and vertically aligning the topics so that they build upon prior skills and concepts and serve as a foundation for future topics.

Chapter Resource Manager

	Lesson 5-1	Lesson 5-2	Lesson 5-3	Lesson 5-4
Concept	Ratios	Rates and Unit Costs	Proportions	Solve Problems Using Proportions
Objective	Interpret and use ratios.	Determine unit costs and understand rates.	Use proportions to compare sets of different sizes.	Use proportions to compare figures and solve problems.
Math Vocabulary	greatest common factor (GCF) ratio simplest form	rate ratio unit cost unit rate	cross product proportion ratio	proportion similar figures
Lesson Resources	**Materials** • Money • Colored pencils • Index cards **Manipulatives** • Pattern blocks • Connecting cubes • Tangrams • Counters **Other Resources** CRM Vocabulary and English Language Development CRM Skills Practice CRM Problem-Solving Practice CRM Homework Practice	**Materials** • Household objects that have a price per unit **Other Resources** CRM Vocabulary and English Language Development CRM Skills Practice CRM Problem-Solving Practice CRM Homework Practice	**Materials** • Colored pencils **Manipulatives** • Tiles or cubes • Counters **Other Resources** CRM Vocabulary and English Language Development CRM Skills Practice CRM Problem-Solving Practice CRM Homework Practice	**Materials** • Grid paper • Colored pencils **Manipulatives** • Geoboards **Other Resources** CRM Vocabulary and English Language Development CRM Skills Practice CRM Problem-Solving Practice CRM Homework Practice
Technology	Math Online glencoe.com StudentWorks™ Plus ExamView® Assessment Suite	Math Online glencoe.com StudentWorks™ Plus ExamView® Assessment Suite	Math Online glencoe.com StudentWorks™ Plus ExamView® Assessment Suite	Math Online glencoe.com StudentWorks™ Plus ExamView® Assessment Suite

Intervention Strategy

Solving Proportions

Students use a map to explore proportions and connect mathematics to a real-life situation.

Step 1

Provide each student pair with a state map that has a scale. Tell students that they have a visitor coming and they are to plan a tour of the state that has 4 or 5 stops. These stops can include other cities, natural destinations such as rivers or mountain peaks, or state parks. The trip will begin and end in their town. The activity can be adapted for city, country, or world maps.

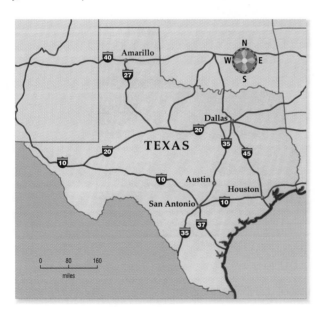

Step 2

Tell students to plan their itinerary using the map. Then have them measure each distance from stop to stop on the map with a ruler. Have them use the key and proportions to calculate the actual distance between each stop. Students must use proportions and show their work.

For example, if the distance between two cities is 3 inches and the key indicates that an inch equals 50 miles, the student would set up this proportion and solve for x:

$$\frac{1 \text{ in.}}{50 \text{ mi}} = \frac{3 \text{ in.}}{x \text{ mi}}$$

Step 3

Have student pairs present their itineraries to the class, as well as their actual distances.

Real-World Applications

Investment Ratios Investors use ratios to determine the profitability of businesses. A common ratio used in investing is a P/E ratio, or a ratio of price to earnings. It is a ratio of the company's stock market value to its earnings per share of stock. A high P/E ratio suggests that investors of the company are expecting a higher earnings growth in the future. The P/E ratio plus other information can help an investor pick which company to invest in.

Intervention Strategy

Better Buy

Step 1 Divide the class into two to four teams.

Step 2 List two options for each student team to buy. For example, a 10-ounce can of sauce for $2.49 or a 5-ounce can for $1.79. Have student teams select which item is the better buy.

Step 3 Award teams that select the better buy with a point or with play money.

Step 4 Continue until teams acquire 5 points, or 5 bills of the play money. Reward winning teams with a token prize.

Key Vocabulary

Find interactive definitions in 13 languages in the **eGlossary** at glencoe.com

English   Español *Introduce the most important vocabulary terms from Chapter 5.*

greatest common factor (GCF)
máximo común divisor

the greatest of the common factors of two or more numbers (p. 180)

proportion   proporción

an equation stating that two ratios are equivalent (p. 194)

$$\frac{5}{6} = \frac{25}{30}$$

rate   tasa

a ratio comparing two quantities with different kinds of units (p. 187)

100 miles in 2 hours

ratio   razón

a comparison of two numbers by division (p. 180)

The ratio of 2 to 3 can be stated as 2 out of 3, 2 to 3, 2:3, or $\frac{2}{3}$.

similar figures   figuras semejantes

figures that have the same shape but may have different sizes (p. 201)

unit cost   costo unitario

the cost of a single item or unit (p. 187)

21 cents per ounce

unit rate   tasa unitaria

a rate that has a denominator of 1 (p. 187)

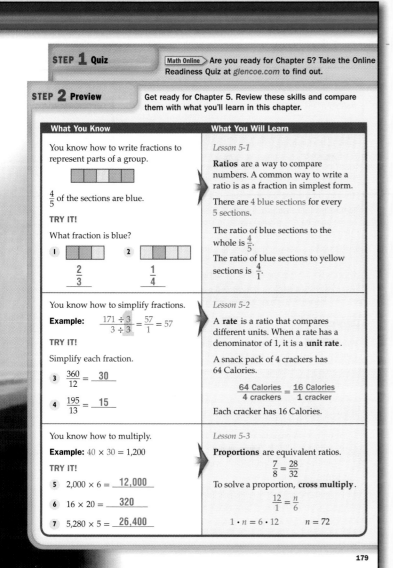

STEP 1 Quiz Math Online ▷ Are you ready for Chapter 5? Take the Online Readiness Quiz at *glencoe.com* to find out.

STEP 2 Preview Get ready for Chapter 5. Review these skills and compare them with what you'll learn in this chapter.

What You Know	What You Will Learn
You know how to write fractions to represent parts of a group.	*Lesson 5-1*
	Ratios are a way to compare numbers. A common way to write a ratio is as a fraction in simplest form.
$\frac{4}{5}$ of the sections are blue.	There are 4 blue sections for every 5 sections.
TRY IT!	The ratio of blue sections to the whole is $\frac{4}{5}$.
What fraction is blue?	The ratio of blue sections to yellow sections is $\frac{4}{1}$.
1 **2** $\frac{2}{3}$ $\frac{1}{4}$	
You know how to simplify fractions.	*Lesson 5-2*
Example: $\frac{171 \div 3}{3 \div 3} = \frac{57}{1} = 57$	A **rate** is a ratio that compares different units. When a rate has a denominator of 1, it is a **unit rate**.
TRY IT!	A snack pack of 4 crackers has 64 Calories.
Simplify each fraction.	$\frac{64 \text{ Calories}}{4 \text{ crackers}} = \frac{16 \text{ Calories}}{1 \text{ cracker}}$
3 $\frac{360}{12} = \underline{\ 30\ }$	Each cracker has 16 Calories.
4 $\frac{195}{13} = \underline{\ 15\ }$	
You know how to multiply.	*Lesson 5-3*
Example: $40 \times 30 = 1,200$	**Proportions** are equivalent ratios.
TRY IT!	$\frac{7}{8} = \frac{28}{32}$
5 $2,000 \times 6 = \underline{\ 12,000\ }$	To solve a proportion, **cross multiply**.
6 $16 \times 20 = \underline{\ 320\ }$	$\frac{12}{1} = \frac{n}{6}$
7 $5,280 \times 5 = \underline{\ 26,400\ }$	$1 \cdot n = 6 \cdot 12 \qquad n = 72$

179

Vocabulary Preview

- As students complete the Chapter Preview, have them make a list of important terms throughout the chapter.

- Using graph paper, have students create a word search of at least 10 important terms throughout the chapter, including the key vocabulary terms.

- Instead of giving a list of the terms to search for, have students make a list of the definitions of each term. The seeker will then have to search for the terms described by the definitions.

- Once students are finished with creating their word searches, have them trade with a partner to complete the challenge.

Step 1 Quiz

Pretest/Prescribe Students can take the Online Readiness Quiz or the Diagnostic Pretest in the Assessment Masters.

Step 2 Preview

Use this pre-chapter activity to activate students' prior knowledge, build confidence, and help students preview the lessons.

FOLDABLES Study Organizer

Dinah Zike's Foldables

Guide students through the directions on p. A85 in the Chapter Resource Masters to create their own Foldable graphic organizer for use with this chapter.

Home Connections

- Type or write for three minutes to find your keyboarding or handwriting rate. Calculate the unit rate. Then have a family member do the same and compare your unit rates.

McGraw Hill

Professional Development

Targeted professional development has been articulated throughout **McGraw-Hill's *Math Triumphs*** intervention program. **The McGraw-Hill Professional Development Video Library** provides short videos that support the **NCTM Focal Points and Focal Connections**. For more information, visit glencoe.com.

Model Lessons   Instructional Strategies

Lesson Planner

Objective Interpret and use ratios.

Vocabulary greatest common factor (GCF), ratio, simplest form

Materials/Manipulatives pattern blocks, connecting cubes, money, tangrams, counters, colored pencils, index cards

Chapter Resource Masters

- CRM Vocabulary and English Language Development (p. A88)
- CRM Skills Practice (p. A89)
- CRM Problem-Solving Practice (p. A90)
- CRM Homework Practice (p. A91)

① Introduce

Vocabulary

Intro Vocabulary Show students 16 two-colored counters that are yellow. Turn four counters over to red. Ask: How many are red? Guide students to say "4 out of 16 are red." Explain the *ratio* of red to total counters is 4 out of 16, or 1 out of 4 if the numbers are written in simplest form.

Ratios Students need to know that in a ratio of A to B, B is the divisor. Therefore, a ratio is another way to talk about division. If A and B have different units, then it is called a rate.

② Teach

Key Concept

Foundational Skills and Concepts After students have read through the Key Concept box, have them try these exercises.

1. What type of operation is a ratio? division

2. What are three ways to write, 7 vowels out of 11 letters? 7 to 11, 7 out of 11, $\frac{7}{11}$, 7:11

3. What is the simplest form of $\frac{12}{15}$? $\frac{4}{5}$

180 Chapter 5 Ratios, Rates, and Similarity

KEY Concept

Ratios are a way to compare numbers. A **ratio** is a comparison of two quantities by division. Ratios can compare a part to a part, a part to a whole, or a whole to a part.

Look at the following pattern.

The pattern shows 6 triangles out of 10 figures.

The ratio of triangles to figures is $\frac{6}{10}$.

Ratios are often written in **simplest form**. To find the simplest form you need the **greatest common factor**. The greatest common factor of 6 and 10 is 2.

$$\frac{6}{10} = \frac{6}{10} \div \frac{2}{2} = \frac{3}{5}$$

Other ways to write the ratio of triangles to figures are:

3 to 5   3 out of 5   3:5

VOCABULARY

greatest common factor (GCF)
the greatest of the common factors of two or more numbers; the GCF of 24 and 30 is 6

ratio
a comparison of two numbers by division; the ratio of 2 to 3 can be stated as 2 out of 3, 2 to 3, 2:3, or $\frac{2}{3}$

simplest form
the form of a fraction when the GCF of the numerator and the denominator is 1

Example 1

Write the ratio that compares the number of dimes to the number of pennies. Explain the meaning of the ratio.

1. Write the ratio with the number of dimes in the numerator and the number of pennies in the denominator.
$\frac{3}{5}$ ← dimes
   ← pennies

2. The only common factor of 3 and 5 is 1. The ratio is in simplest form.

3. The ratio of the number of dimes to the number of pennies is written as $\frac{3}{5}$, 3 to 5, or 3:5.

4. The ratio means *for every 3 dimes, there are 5 pennies.*

180   Chapter 5 Ratio, Rates, and Similarity

Additional **Example 1**

Write the ratio that compares the number of triangles to the number of squares. Explain the meaning of the ratio.

1. Write the ratio with the number of triangles in the numerator and the number of squares in the denominator. $\frac{3 \text{ triangles}}{4 \text{ squares}}$

2. The only common factor of 3 and 4 is 1. The ratio is in simplest form.

3. The ratio of the number of triangles to the number of squares can be written as: $\frac{3}{4}$, 3 to 4, or 3:4.

4. The ratio means *for every 3 triangles there are 4 squares.*

YOUR TURN!

Write the ratio that compares the number of pennies to the total number of coins. Explain the meaning of the ratio.

1. Write the ratio.

   $\dfrac{5}{10}$ ← pennies
   ← total coins

2. The numerator and denominator have a common factor of __5__. Write the fraction in simplest form.

   $\dfrac{5}{10} = \dfrac{5 \div 5}{10 \div 5} = \dfrac{1}{2}$

3. Write the ratio of the number of pennies to the number of coins.

   $\dfrac{1}{2}$, 1 to 2, 1:2

4. What does the ratio mean? __1 out of every 2 coins is a penny.__

Write the ratio as a fraction in simplest form.

7 goldfish out of 21 total pets

I. Write the ratio with the number of goldfish in the numerator and the total number of pets in the denominator.

$$\dfrac{7}{21}$$

2. The greatest common factor of 7 and 21 is 7. Divide each by 7 to write the fraction in simplest form.

$$\dfrac{7}{21} = \dfrac{7 \div 7}{21 \div 7} = \dfrac{1}{3}$$

Example 2

Write the ratio as a fraction in simplest form.

4 boys out of 12 children

1. Write the ratio with the number of boys in the numerator and the total number of children in the denominator.

   $\dfrac{4}{12}$

2. The greatest common factor of 4 and 12 is 4. Divide by 4 to write the fraction in simplest form.

   $\dfrac{4}{12} = \dfrac{4 \div 4}{12 \div 4} = \dfrac{1}{3}$

YOUR TURN!

Write the ratio as a fraction in simplest form.

12 children to 18 adults

1. Write the ratio.

   $\dfrac{12}{18}$

2. The greatest common factor of 12 and 18 is __6__. Write the fraction in simplest form.

   $\dfrac{12}{18} = \dfrac{12 \div 6}{18 \div 6} = \dfrac{2}{3}$

GO ON

English Learner Strategy

Understand Ratios   Begin with a set of 10 yellow counters. Turn 3 over. Ask: What ratio is represented? Represent a variety of ratios. Have students say the ratio "3 out of 10 counters are red" and "for every 10 counters, 3 are red." Also have them write the ratio in different forms. Next, use classroom objects to demonstrate ratios. Ask: How many of the 6 textbooks are green? Finally, have students write their own examples of ratios. Students should use either classroom or real-world examples.

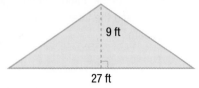

Additional *Example 3*

Write the ratio of the height of the triangle to the length of the base as a fraction in simplest form.

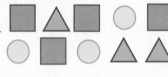

9 ft

27 ft

1. Write the ratio as a fraction with the height over the base. $\frac{9}{27}$

2. The greatest common factor of 9 and 27 is 9. Divide by 9 to write the fraction in simplest form.

$$\frac{9}{27} = \frac{9 \div 9}{27 \div 9} = \frac{1}{3}$$

③ Practice

Using Manipulatives

Pattern Blocks
Represent Example 1 using pattern blocks to give students a visual representation of the ratio.

Connecting Cubes   Connect different-colored cubes to represent ratios.

Money   Use coins to represent items in a ratio.

Tangrams   Compare the different pieces to explore ratios.

On-Hand Manipulatives   Use classroom objects to represent the objects in a ratio.

Example 3

Write the ratio of the length of the base to the height of the triangle as a fraction in simplest form.

height = 3 cm
base = 18 cm

1. Write the ratio as a fraction with the base over the height.
$$\frac{18}{3}$$

2. The greatest common factor of 3 and 18 is 3. Divide by 3 to write the fraction in simplest form.

$$\frac{18}{3} = \frac{18 \div 3}{3 \div 3} = \frac{6}{1}$$

YOUR TURN!

Write the ratio of the length of the base to the height of the triangle as a fraction in simplest form.

height = 8 cm
base = 22 cm

1. Write the ratio. $\frac{\Box}{\Box}$

2. The greatest common factor of 22 and 8 is _____. Write the fraction in simplest form.

$$\frac{\Box}{\Box} = \frac{\Box \div \Box}{\Box \div \Box} = \frac{\Box}{\Box}$$

Who is Correct?

Write the ratio as a fraction in simplest form.
96 boys to 8 girls

Pamela
$\frac{96}{8} = \frac{24}{4}$

Mateo
$\frac{96}{8} = \frac{12}{2}$

Rodrigo
$\frac{96}{8} = \frac{12}{1}$

Circle correct answer(s). Cross out incorrect answer(s).

▶ Guided Practice

Use the diagram to write each ratio as a fraction in simplest form.

1. The number of triangles to the number of circles is _____.

2. The number of triangles to the total number of figures is _____.

3. The number of circles to the total number of figures is _____.

Who *is Correct?*
Diagnostic Teaching

• Pamela is incorrect. She wrote a ratio of 96 boys to 8 girls, but did not simplify completely.

• Mateo is incorrect. He wrote a ratio of 96 boys to 8 girls, but did not simplify completely.

• Rodrigo is correct.

Review the different ways that ratios can be written: 12 to 1, $\frac{12}{1}$, 12:1.

Step by Step Practice

4 **ANIMALS** A petting zoo has 8 rabbits, 3 goats, 6 ducks, and 7 sheep. Write the ratio of each type of animal to the total number of animals in the zoo. Write each as a fraction in simplest form.

Step 1 The total number of animals is __24__. This will be the __denominator__ in each fraction.

Step 2 Write a ratio for the number of rabbits to the total number of animals. _____ $\dfrac{8}{24}$

What is the common factor of the numerator and denominator? __8__

Write the fraction in simplest form. $\dfrac{8}{24} = \dfrac{8 \div 8}{24 \div 8} = \dfrac{1}{3}$

Step 3 Write a ratio for the number of goats to the total number of animals. _____ $\dfrac{3}{24}$

What is the common factor of the numerator and denominator? __3__

Write the fraction in simplest form. $\dfrac{3}{24} = \dfrac{3 \div 3}{24 \div 3} = \dfrac{1}{8}$

Step 4 Write a ratio for the number of ducks to the total number of animals. _____ $\dfrac{6}{24}$

What is the common factor of the numerator and denominator? __6__

Write the fraction in simplest form. $\dfrac{6 \div 6}{24 \div 6} = \dfrac{1}{4}$

Step 5 Write a ratio for the number of sheep to the total number of animals. _____ $\dfrac{7}{24}$

What is the common factor of the numerator and denominator? __1__

Write the fraction in simplest form. $\dfrac{7}{24}$

Write each ratio as a fraction in simplest form.

5 **FLOWERS** In a vase of flowers, there are 6 tulips and 9 roses. Write the ratio of tulips to roses.

tulips → $\dfrac{6}{9} = \dfrac{6 \div 3}{9 \div 3} = \dfrac{2}{3}$ ← roses

GO ON

Are They Getting It?

Check students' understanding of ratios by writing these problems on the board. Ask students to point out the wrong answers and explain why they are wrong.

1. This figure shows the ratio $\dfrac{4}{5}$. This is correct.

2. The ratio of the width to the length is 7 to 1. This is incorrect because the ratio was not simplified correctly. It should be 5 to 1.

15 mm

3 mm

3. Five out of 20 is another way to write the ratio $\dfrac{25}{100}$. This is correct.

Math Coach Notes

Strategies

1. You might want to begin this lesson by reviewing equivalent fractions. Then have students work in pairs and represent ratios using pattern blocks or counters. You may even want to use classroom items or real-world examples of ratios so students will find the material more relevant.

2. Make certain that students do not learn ratios just one way. They should be able to read, write, and recognize ratios under a variety of circumstances.

3. Students can use ratio tables to find equivalent ratios.

$\times 2$ $\times 3$ $\times 4$

Numerator	3	6	9	12
Denominator	5	10	15	20

$\times 2$ $\times 3$ $\times 4$

The ratios $\dfrac{3}{5}$, $\dfrac{6}{10}$, $\dfrac{9}{15}$, and $\dfrac{12}{20}$ are equivalent.

---

6 **COMPUTERS** In a classroom, there are 32 students and 6 computers. Write the ratio of students to computers.

$$\frac{16}{3}$$

7 **BASKETS** In a shipment of 18 baskets, there are 16 that are not white. Write the ratio of white baskets to nonwhite baskets.

$$\frac{1}{8}$$

8 **SPORTS** In a sports equipment closet, there are 6 baseballs, 4 basketballs, 4 footballs, and 7 soccer balls. Write the ratio of soccer balls to the total number of balls.

$$\frac{1}{3}$$

Step by Step Problem-Solving Practice

Solve.

9 **MUSIC** Freeman has 30 CDs, and his sister Iesha has 18 CDs. If they both buy two more CDs, what will be the ratio of Freeman's CDs to Iesha's CDs?

Problem-Solving Strategies
- ☐ Draw a diagram.
- ☐ Use logical reasoning.
- ☐ Solve a simpler problem.
- ☑ Make a list.
- ☐ Work backward.

Understand Read the problem. Write what you know.

Freeman has __30__ CDs.

Iesha has __18__ CDs.

If they both buy two more, Freeman will have __32__ CDs, and Iesha will have __20__ CDs.

Plan Pick a strategy. One strategy is to make a list.

Solve List the factors of each number.

__32__ : __1, 2, 4, 8, 16, 32__

__20__ : __1, 2, 4, 5, 10, 20__

The greatest common factor is __4__.

$$\frac{32}{20} = \frac{32 \div 4}{20 \div 4} = \frac{8}{5}$$

The ratio of Freeman's CDs to Iesha's CDs is $\dfrac{8}{5}$.

Check Look over your solution. Did you answer the question?

Intervention Strategy
Kinesthetic/Interpersonal Learner

Ratio Match Up Distribute an index card to each student with one of these numbers: 1, 2, 3, 4, 5, 6, and 8. Give each student another index card with one of these numbers: 10, 12, 15, 18, 20, 24, 30, 36, 40, 48, and 50. Have two students volunteer to come to the front of the class. These students need to use their single-digit index cards to form a ratio and write it on the board. Have the other students use their double-digit index cards to try to form as many ratios that are equivalent to the ratio on the board. Verify all ratios are equivalent. Repeat the activity multiple times with different students.

Odd/Even Assignments

Exercises 13–22 are structured so that students practice the same concepts whether they are assigned the odd or even problems.

In-Class Assignment

Have students complete Exercises 14, 17, 18, 20, and 25 to ensure that they understand the concept.

10 **FOOTBALL** In the high school playoffs, the Creekville Cougars played the Southtown Sharks. The Cougars' season record was 12 wins and 4 losses. The Sharks' season record was 16 wins and 0 losses. What was the ratio of wins for the Cougars to wins for the Sharks? Check off each step.

✔ Understand: I underlined key words.

✔ Plan: To solve this problem, I will __make a list__.

✔ Solve: The answer is __$\frac{3}{4}$__.

✔ Check: I checked my answer by __multiplying by the GCF, 4__.

11 **CHESS** Jena and Niles played 10 games of chess. Jena won 6 of them. Write a ratio of Jena's wins to the total number of games in simplest form. __$\frac{3}{5}$__

12 **Reflect** What is a greatest common factor? Explain using examples.

__Sample answer: It is the greatest of the common factors of__
__two or more numbers. The numbers 24 and 36 have common__
__factors of 1, 2, 4, 6, and 12. The GCF of 24 and 36 is 12.__

▶ Skills, Concepts, and Problem Solving

Use the diagram to write each ratio as a fraction in simplest form.

13 circles and triangles to squares and pentagons __$\frac{7}{5}$__

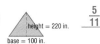

14 figures that are *not* triangles to total figures __$\frac{3}{4}$__

15 triangles to circles and squares __$\frac{1}{2}$__

Write the ratio of the length of the base to the height of the triangle as a fraction in simplest form.

16  height = 4 m; base = 16 m __$\frac{4}{1}$, or 4__

17 height = 220 in.; base = 100 in. __$\frac{5}{11}$__

GO ON

Lesson 5-1 Ratios **185**

Math Challenge

Rectangle Ratios Have students use graph paper to draw a rectangle that has side lengths in a ratio of 2:5. Compare the rectangles drawn by students and show all of the different rectangles to the class. Ask students to increase the length of each side by 2 units. Ask students if the new rectangle has side lengths in a ratio of 2:5. Guide students to see that the new rectangle is not similar to the original rectangle. Discuss how to adjust the lengths of the sides so that any new rectangles created have side lengths in a ratio of 2:5. Guide students to realize the lengths of the sides have to be multiplied or divided by the same number to maintain the ratio of the original rectangle.

See It, Do It, Say It, Write It

Step 1 Draw 6 triangles on the board and shade 2. Ask: What is the ratio of shaded triangles to unshaded triangles? How do we put it in simplest form? Model several ratios using both drawings and items from the class. Have students name the ratio. Ask them how to represent other ratios.

Step 2 Give each student pair a ratio written on an index card. Tell them to model the ratio with a model or drawing and then write the ratio in three different forms on the other side of the index card. Discuss the results with the class. Compare different representations of the same ratio.

Step 3 Tell students to write the definition of *ratio* in their own words.

Looking Ahead: Pre-teach

Rates and Unit Costs In the next lesson, students will learn about rates and unit costs. *Unit cost* is the cost of a single item.

Example

Twelve CDs cost $108. How much is one CD? $9.00

Have students answer the following questions.

1. Clyde runs 160 yards in 20 seconds. How far does he go in 1 second? 8 yards

2. If a wheel turns 60 times in 4 minutes, how many times does it turn in 1 minute? 15

3. A 16-oz can of soup is $0.96. How much is 1-oz of soup? $0.06

Write the ratio of the length of the base to the height of each triangle as a fraction in simplest form.

18  $\dfrac{25}{6}$

19 $\dfrac{7}{11}$

GRADES The quiz average is the ratio of the number of correct answers to the total number of exercises. Refer to the table to answer Exercises 20–22.

20 Which students had the same quiz average?
Tabitha, Geoff, and Adelfo
What is that quiz average?
$\dfrac{3}{4}$

Quiz Results		
Name	Correct Answers	Number of Exercises
Tabitha	27	36
Elvin	30	48
Adelfo	54	72
Emil	32	40
Geoff	33	44

21 Did the student with the most correct answers have the highest quiz average? Explain.
No. Adelfo had the most correct answers, but Emil had the highest quiz average at $\dfrac{4}{5}$.

22 Explain the meaning of Adelfo's quiz average.
Answers will vary. Adelfo answered 3 out of every 4 questions correctly.

Vocabulary Check **Write the vocabulary word that completes each sentence.**

23 A(n) __ratio__ compares two quantities.

24 The __greatest common factor__ of 30 and 42 is 6.

25 **Writing in Math** Write the ratio of *5 pens out of a total of 6 pens* four different ways.
$\dfrac{5}{6}$, 5 out of 6, 5 to 6, 5:6

Solve.

26 **GAMES** Nadia and Brock played 8 games of checkers. Nadia won 6 of them. Write a ratio of Nadia's wins to the total number of games in simplest form. $\dfrac{3}{4}$

Ticket Out the Door

Shoe Ratios Count the number of students in class out loud. Then have those wearing gym shoes raise their hands. Tell students to write a ratio of the number wearing gym shoes to the total number of students. Have students write the ratio in at least three different ways. They can turn their papers in as they exit the classroom.

Rates and Unit Costs

KEY Concept

The table shows the distance Marcus drove each day. A **rate** is a **ratio** of two measurements having different units.

Day	Monday	Tuesday	Wednesday	Thursday	Friday
Distance	60 mi	60 mi	60 mi	60 mi	60 mi

The rate $\frac{300 \text{ miles}}{5 \text{ days}}$ describes both the units of distance and time.

To show the **unit rate**, simplify the rate so that it has a denominator of 1 unit.

$$\frac{300 \text{ miles} \div 5}{5 \text{ days} \div 5} = \frac{60 \text{ miles}}{1 \text{ day}}$$ The unit rate is $\frac{60 \text{ miles}}{1 \text{ day}}$.

Unit cost is the cost of a single item or unit of measure. The cost of a 20-ounce bottle of water is $1.60.

$$\frac{\$1.60}{20 \text{ ounces}} = \frac{160 \text{ cents}}{20 \text{ ounces}} \rightarrow 20\overline{)160}\,^{8} \rightarrow \frac{8 \text{ cents}}{1 \text{ ounce}}$$

One ounce costs $0.08.

VOCABULARY

rate
a ratio comparing two quantities with different kinds of units

ratio
a comparison of two numbers by division

unit cost
the cost of a single item or unit

unit rate
a rate that has a denominator of 1

Rates are often written using abbreviations, such as 300 mi/5 days, 60 mi/h, or $0.21/oz.

Example 1

Andrés bought a pack of trading cards for $6.65. The pack contains 15 cards. Find the unit cost to the nearest cent.

1. Write the rate as a fraction.
$$\frac{\$6.65}{15 \text{ cards}}$$

2. Divide the numerator by the denominator.
$$15\overline{)6.65}\,^{0.44}$$
$$-60$$
$$65$$
$$-60$$
$$5$$

3. Round to the nearest cent.

Each card costs about $0.44.

YOUR TURN!

Elise bought a bouquet of flowers for $26.95. The bouquet contains 12 flowers. Find the unit cost to the nearest cent.

1. Write the rate as a fraction.
$$\frac{\$26.95}{12 \text{ flowers}}$$
$$12\overline{)26.95}\,^{2.24}$$
$$-24$$
$$29$$
$$-24$$
$$55$$
$$-48$$
$$7$$

2. Divide the numerator by the denominator.

3. Round to the nearest cent.

Each flower costs about $2.25.

GO ON

Additional *Example 1*

A box of markers costs $6.00. The box contains 12 pens. Find the unit cost to the nearest cent.

1. Write the rate as a fraction. $\dfrac{\$6.00}{12 \text{ pens}}$

2. Divide the numerator by the denominator.

$$12\overline{)6.00}\,^{0.50}$$
$$-6\,00$$
$$0$$

3. Provide your answer to the nearest cent.

Each pen costs $0.50.

Lesson Planner

Objective Determine unit costs and understand rates.

Vocabulary rate, ratio, unit cost, unit rate

Materials/Manipulatives household objects that have a price per unit

Chapter Resource Masters

- CRM Vocabulary and English Language Development (p. A92)
- CRM Skills Practice (p. A93)
- CRM Problem-Solving Practice (p. A94)
- CRM Homework Practice (p. A95)

Vocabulary

Unit Cost Invite students to tell about something that they recently purchased that came in a package with more than one of the item, such as a bag of apples or a carton of soft drinks. Ask them to tell the number of items in the package and its total price. Take each package described by a student and ask the class how much just one of the items would cost. Explain that this is a unit cost. Unit cost can refer to the price per item, the price per pound, the price per foot, and so on.

Key Concept

Foundational Skills and Concepts After students have read through the Key Concept box, have them try these exercises.

1. What is the difference between *unit rate* and *unit cost*? They are both rates with a 1 in their denominators, but unit cost always uses units of money in the numerator.

2. If a 10-pound bag of potatoes costs $3.95, what is the unit cost to the nearest cent? $0.40 per pound

Additional *Example 2*

Find the unit rate for driving 168 miles in 4 hours. Use the unit rate to find the distance that could be driven in 7 hours.

1. Write the rate as a fraction.

$$\frac{168 \text{ miles}}{4 \text{ hours}}$$

2. Find an equivalent rate with a denominator of 1.
Divide the numerator and denominator by 4.

$$\frac{168 \div 4}{4 \div 4} = \frac{42}{1}$$

3. The unit rate is 42 miles per hour.

4. To find how many miles could be driven in 7 hours, multiply the numerator and denominator by 7.

$$\frac{42 \text{ miles} \cdot 7}{1 \text{ hour} \cdot 7} = \frac{294 \text{ miles}}{7 \text{ hours}}$$

5. At this rate, 294 miles could be driven in 7 hours.

Example 2

Find the unit rate for swimming 300 meters in 6 minutes. Use the unit rate to find the number of meters swam in 5 minutes.

1. Write the rate as a fraction.
$$\frac{300 \text{ meters}}{6 \text{ minutes}}$$

2. Find an equivalent rate with a denominator of 1.

   Divide the numerator and denominator by 6.
   $$\frac{300 \div 6}{6 \div 6} = \frac{50}{1}$$

3. The unit rate is 50 meters/minute.

4. To find how many meters will be swam at this rate in 5 minutes, multiply the numerator and denominator by 5.

   $$\frac{50 \text{ meters} \cdot 5}{1 \text{ minute} \cdot 5} = \frac{250 \text{ meters}}{5 \text{ minutes}}$$

At this rate, 250 meters will be swam in 5 minutes.

YOUR TURN!

Find the unit rate for traveling 616 feet in 7 seconds. Use the unit rate to find the number of feet traveled in 12 seconds.

1. Write the rate as a fraction.
$$\frac{\boxed{616} \text{ ft}}{\boxed{7} \text{ s}}$$

2. Divide the numerator and denominator by ___7___.
$$\frac{\boxed{616} \text{ ft} \div \boxed{7}}{\boxed{7} \text{ s} \div \boxed{7}} = \frac{\boxed{88} \text{ ft}}{\boxed{1} \text{ s}}$$

3. The unit rate is __88 ft__ / ___ s___.

4. Multiply the numerator and denominator by ___12___.
$$\frac{\boxed{88} \text{ ft} \cdot \boxed{12}}{\boxed{1} \text{ s} \cdot \boxed{12}} = \frac{\boxed{1,056} \text{ ft}}{\boxed{12} \text{ s}}$$

At this rate, __1,056__ feet will be traveled in 12 seconds.

Who is Correct?

Keli spent $2.00 to purchase 8 oranges. Find the unit rate.

Ashima
$$\frac{8 \div 2}{2 \div 2} = 4$$
Unit rate = $0.40/orange

Alana
$$\frac{2 \div 2}{8 \div 2} = \frac{1}{4}$$
$\frac{1}{4}$ of $1 is $0.25.
Unit rate = $0.25/orange

Cole
0.25
8)2.00
−16
40
−40
0
Unit rate = $0.25/orange

Circle correct answer(s). Cross out incorrect answer(s).

Who *is Correct?*
Diagnostic Teaching

- Ashima is incorrect. She wrote the number of oranges in the numerator and the cost in the denominator and did not find the cost per orange.

- Alana is correct. She wrote the ratio as a fraction and simplified it.

- Cole is correct. He used long division.

Write each rate as a fraction. Find each unit rate.

1 140 words in 4 minutes

$$\frac{140}{4} \; ; \; 35 \text{ words/min}$$

2 12 books in 5 days

$$\frac{12}{5} \; ; \; 2.4 \text{ books/day}$$

Find each unit rate. Use the unit rate to find the unknown amount.

3 150 feet in 8 seconds; ☐ feet in 14 seconds

18.75 ft/s; 262.5

4 $5 for 4 books; ☐ dollars for 15 books

$1.25/book; $18.75

Step by Step Practice

5 Use the table to find which box of pens has the lowest unit cost.

Step 1 Find the unit cost of a 12-count package.

$$\frac{5.76}{12} \rightarrow 12\overline{)5.76} \rightarrow \$ \underline{0.48}/\text{pen}$$

Box Size	Price
12-count	$5.76
16-count	$6.72
32-count	$11.84

Step 2 Find the unit cost of a 16-count package.

$$\frac{6.72}{16} \rightarrow 16\overline{)6.72} \rightarrow \$ \underline{0.42}/\text{pen}$$

Step 3 Find the unit cost of a 32-count package.

$$\frac{11.84}{32} \rightarrow 32\overline{)11.84} \rightarrow \$ \underline{0.37}/\text{pen}$$

Step 4 Which package costs the least per pen? __32-count package__

Which product has the lowest unit cost?

6 a 12-oz water bottle for $0.72 or a 24-oz water bottle for $1.92

12-oz bottle: $$\frac{0.72}{12} \rightarrow 12\overline{)0.72} \rightarrow \$ \underline{0.06}/\text{oz}$$

24-oz bottle: $$\frac{1.92}{24} \rightarrow 24\overline{)1.92} \rightarrow \$ \underline{0.08}/\text{oz}$$

The __12-oz__ water bottle costs less per ounce.

GO ON →

Intervention Strategy

Interpersonal/Naturalist Learners

Unit Cost Have each student bring sale flyers from local grocery stores or discount stores. Instruct students to select three items that are sold in a package with more than one item or in a container that holds multiple units. Students should find the unit cost of each of their selected items and write the names of the items and unit costs on the board. Then have students check their flyers trying to find a better unit cost for each of the items listed on the board.

③ Practice

Using Manipulatives

On-Hand Manipulatives Have students choose items in their homes and note the price paid for the item and the number of units in the item. Students should look for different types of items so as to see the many different units used to package items.

JUICE

6.75 FL. OZ
(200 mL)

Math Coach Notes

Connecting to Previously Learned Material
Make the connection between a function table and a unit cost. Explain that the total cost of an item is its unit cost multiplied by the number of units being purchased. The first row of a table can be the number of items, and the second row can be the total cost. The first column in a function table will list the price for 1 item, and each column to the right will give the price for that number of items. An example is shown.

$$y = 0.15x$$

Number of Apples, x	1	2	3	4	5
Total Price, y	$0.15	$0.30	$0.45	$0.60	$0.75

Denominators   Students may continue to forget what to divide to find the unit cost or unit rate. Tell them to ask themselves, what word is after the "per"? That unit is the denominator, the one to divide *by*. So, to find miles *per* gallon, divide the total miles *by* the number of gallons. To find the cost *per* ounce, divide the total cost *by* the number of ounces. Tell students to multiply once they have an answer to check to see if they have calculated correctly.

Note This!
Label Units   Encourage students to always write the units being used for unit rate and unit cost. For example, instead of writing 7/1, tell them to write $7 per 1 pound or $7/lb. This will avoid confusion later when they are reviewing their notes.

Which product has the lowest unit cost?

7 a 6-pack of fruit bar for $1.98 or a 12-pack of fruit bar for $3.48
    __12-pack__

8 a 16-oz box of rice for $3.04, a 32-oz box of rice for $3.84, or a 48-oz box of rice for $5.28
    __48-oz bag__

9 50-count vitamins for $5.50, 100-count vitamins for $9.00, or 150-count vitamins for $15.00
    __100-count package__

Step *by* Step *Problem-Solving Practice*

Solve.

Problem-Solving Strategies
☐ Draw a diagram.
☐ Look for a pattern.
☐ Guess and check.
☐ Make a table.
☑ Solve a simpler problem.

10 NATURE   A gray wolf can travel at speeds up to 27 kilometers in 25 minutes. A certain gazelle can travel at speeds up to 20 kilometers in 15 minutes. Which animal can travel at a faster rate?

Understand   Read the problem. Write what you know.

A gray wolf can travel

__27__ kilometers in __25__ minutes.

A gazelle can travel

__20__ kilometers in __15__ minutes.

Plan   Pick a strategy. One strategy is to solve a simpler problem. Find each unit rate.

Solve   Write each unit rate as a fraction. Find an equivalent rate with a denominator of 1.

Wolf: $\dfrac{27 \div 25}{25 \div 25} = \dfrac{1.08\text{km}}{1\text{ min}}$

Gazelle: $\dfrac{20 \div 15}{15 \div 15} = \dfrac{1.33\text{km}}{1\text{ min}}$

Compare the unit rates.

__1.08__ km/min < __1.33__ km/min

The __gazelle__ travels at a faster rate.

Check   Look over your answer. Did you answer the question?

Are They Getting It?   ?

Check students' understanding of rates and unit costs by writing these problems on the board. Ask students to point out wrong answers and explain why they are wrong.

1. Rita paid $2.65 for a package of 5 combs. Tina paid $0.55 for a single comb. The unit cost for one of Rita's combs was five cents less than the cost of Tina's comb. This is incorrect. The unit cost of Rita's combs was 2 cents less than Rita's cost.

2. Tony runs 4 miles in 56 minutes. Tammy runs 6 miles in 1 hour 21 minutes. Tammy says she runs faster than Tony. This is correct.

3. Ken and Emily are reading the same 230-page book. Emily reads on average 6 pages every 10 minutes. Ken reads on average 20 pages every 18 minutes. Ken says it will take him one hour less to read the book than Emily. This is correct. Ken needs about 76 fewer minutes to read the book than Emily.

11 BUSINESS   Mitch worked at a landscaping company for the summer. He earned $753 in 12 weeks. Justine worked for a grocery store for the summer. She earned $632.50 in 10 weeks. Find the unit rates to describe their weekly wages. Whose weekly wages were higher? Check off each step.

✔ Understand: I underlined key words.

✔ Plan: To solve the problem I will _____ will solve a simpler problem _____.

✔ Solve: The answer is _Mitch's rate is $62.75/week and Justine's_ _rate is $63.25/week. Justine's weekly wages were higher_.

✔ Check: I checked my answer by _____ multiplying to check _____.

12 POPULATION   The population of Pennsylvania is about 12.4 million people. Its land area is approximately 44,817 square miles. Find the population per square mile. _277 people/sq mi_

13 Reflect   Explain the difference between a rate and ratio. What is the difference between unit rate and unit cost?

See TE margin.

▶ Skills, Concepts, and Problem Solving

Write each rate as a fraction. Find each unit rate.

14 33 hits out of 40 at-bats
$\frac{33}{40}$; 0.825 hits/at bat (batting average)

15 12 bars of soap for $9
$\frac{9}{12}$ or $\frac{3}{4}$; $0.75/bar

Find each unit rate. Use the unit rate to find the unknown amount.

16 75 meters in 4 seconds; ☐ meters in 14 seconds _____ 18.75 m/s; 262.5

17 50 fence posts every 8 yards; ☐ fence posts in 20 yards _____ 6.25 fence posts/yd; 125

18 $15 for 8 pounds; ☐ dollars for 6 pounds _____ $1.88/lb; $11.28

Which product has the lower unit cost? Round to the nearest cent.

19 4 cards for $3 or 10 cards for $8.50 _____ 4 cards

20 16 oz of glass cleaner for $3 or 8 oz of glass cleaner for $1.75 _____ 16-oz bottle   **GO ON** ▶

Additional Answers

Exercise 13   A ratio is a comparison of two quantities by division. A rate is a special ratio that compares different units. A unit rate reduces the rate so the denominator is one. Unit cost refers specifically to the cost (in dollars or cents) to one item.

Odd/Even Assignments

Exercises 14–22 are structured so that students practice the same concepts whether they are assigned the odd or even problems.

In-Class Assignment

Have students complete Exercises 14, 17, 19, 22, and 25 to ensure that they understand the concept.

Math Challenge

Price Check   Have students design a single-page advertisement sale flyer that shows five school supply items that are sold in packages of 3, 4, and 5 items. Students should price each of the items so that the unit costs are between $0.75 and $0.99 each.

See It, Do It, Say It, Write It

Step 1 Tell students to work in pairs and write their names as many times as they can while you time them for 2 or 3 minutes. When time is up, have them count how many times they wrote their names. Have them work with their partners to find the unit rates.

Step 2 Make a table on the board. Write different costs of different amounts of gasoline for students to use to find the unit costs. Model how to find the first unit cost.

Step 3 Tell students to write about the differences between unit rate and unit cost. Ask them to provide an example of each.

Looking Ahead: Pre-teach

Proportions   In the next lesson, students will determine whether two ratios are proportional, or equivalent.

Example

Are the two ratios below proportional?

$\frac{3}{5}$ and $\frac{9}{15}$ yes; $\frac{3}{5} \cdot \frac{3}{3} = \frac{9}{15}$

Have students determine whether the following pairs of ratios are proportional.

1. $\frac{13}{25}$ and $\frac{65}{100}$ no

2. $\frac{4}{10}$ and $\frac{1}{5}$ no

3. $\frac{18}{21}$ and $\frac{6}{7}$ yes; $\frac{18}{21} \div \frac{3}{3} = \frac{6}{7}$

Solve.

21 SALES   Amanda sold 225 DVDs in 6 days, while Hayden sold 181 DVDs in 4 days. Who sold DVDs at a faster rate? Explain.

Hayden; Amanda sold 37.5 DVDs/day. Hayden sold 45.25 DVDs/day. 45.25 > 37.5

22 POPULATION   Which state has the lower population per square mile?

State	Population	Area in Square Miles
Montana	944,632	145,552
North Dakota	635,867	68,976

Montana; Montana's population is about 6.49 people per square mile.

North Dakota's population is about 9.22 people per square mile. 6.49 < 9.22

Vocabulary Check   **Write the vocabulary word that completes each sentence.**

23 A ratio of two measurements or amounts of different units, where the denominator is 1 is a(n) unit rate .

24 The cost of a single item or unit is the unit cost .

25 Writing in Math   Explain how to find the unit cost for a box of 8 granola bars for $3.36. Then determine the cost of buying 11 granola bars with the same unit cost.

To find the unit cost divide 3.36 by 8. $3.36 ÷ 8 = $0.42. Next, multiply

the unit cost ($0.42) by the number of granola bars (11). $0.42 × 11 = $4.62

 Spiral Review

Use the diagram shown at the right to write each ratio as a fraction in simplest form.   (Lesson 5-1, p. 180)

26 The number of red tiles to the number of yellow tiles is _____. $\frac{1}{2}$

27 The number of red tiles to the total number of tiles is ___ $\frac{1}{3}$

28 The number of yellow tiles to the total number of tiles is ___ . $\frac{2}{3}$

Ticket Out the Door

Timed Marching   Tell students when you say "Start," they should march in place and count their steps until you say "Stop." Have students march in place for 12 seconds. Instruct students to determine their per-minute rates of marching using their counts knowing that the time was 12 seconds. Students can turn in their calculations showing the unit rate as they exit the classroom.

Progress Check 1 (Lessons 5-1 and 5-2)

Use the diagrams to write each ratio as a fraction in simplest form.

1

2

blue to yellow squares $\dfrac{3}{6} = \dfrac{1}{2}$

green parts to total parts $\dfrac{2}{8} = \dfrac{1}{4}$

Write the ratio of the height to the length of the base of the triangle as a fraction in simplest form.

3 $\dfrac{4}{5}$

height = 4 km

base = 5 km

4 $\dfrac{5}{1}$

height = 10 in.

base = 2 in.

Write each rate as a fraction. Find each unit rate.

5 90 meters in 18 minutes $\dfrac{90}{18}$; 5 m/min

6 6 people in 150 miles $\dfrac{6}{150}$; 0.04 people/mi

Write each ratio as a fraction in simplest form.

7 21 out of 147 boys wore glasses $\dfrac{1}{7}$

8 15 black dogs out of 36 dogs $\dfrac{5}{12}$

Which product has the lowest unit cost?

9 12-oz can for $1.56, a 16-oz can for $2.40, or a 32-oz can for $3.84
32-oz can

10 9 lemons for $1.35, 14 lemons for $2.25, or 20 lemons for $3.80
9 lemons

Solve.

11 SPELLING Write a fraction in simplest form for the ratio of the number of vowels in *Math Triumphs* to the total number of letters. $\dfrac{1}{4}$

12 SPORTS Nick jumped rope 72 times in 48 seconds. What is his unit rate?
1.5 jumps/second

Chapter 5 Progress Check **193**

Progress Check 1

Formative Assessment

Use the Progress Check to assess students' mastery of the previous lessons. Have students review the lesson indicated for the problems they answered incorrectly.

Odd/Even Assignments

Exercises are structured so that students practice the same concepts whether they are assigned the odd or even problems.

⚠ Common Error *Alert*

Key Words Students may have trouble with terms such as *rate*, *unit rate*, *ratio*, and *simplest form*. Remind them that to be a unit rate, the rate has to be in terms of one.

Exercises 7–8 Students may have difficulty reducing fractions to simplest form. They may have to reduce the fractions more than once if they do not use the greatest common factor the first time.

Exercises 9–10 Ensure that students realize they have to complete three division problems in order to find three different unit costs. Then they can make their comparisons.

Data-Driven Decision Making

Students missing Exercises . . .	Have trouble with . . .	Should review and practice . . .
1–2	using a diagram to write a ratio.	SSG Lesson 5-1, p. 180 CRM Skills Practice, p. A89
3–4, 7–8	writing ratios as fractions in simplest form.	SSG Lesson 5-1, p. 180 CRM Skills Practice, p. A89
5–6	writing rates as a fraction, then writing the unit rates.	SSG Lesson 5-2, p. 187 CRM Skills Practice, p. A93
9–10	finding the lowest unit cost.	SSG Lesson 5-2, p. 187 CRM Skills Practice, p. A93
11–12	solving word problems involving writing a fraction in simplest form and finding a unit rate.	CRM Problem Solving Practice, pp. A90 and A94

Lesson Planner

Objective   Use proportions to compare sets of different sizes.

Vocabulary   cross product , proportion , ratio

Materials/Manipulatives   tiles or cubes, colored pencils, counters

Chapter Resource Masters

- [CRM] Vocabulary and English Language Development (p. A96)
- [CRM] Skills Practice (p. A97)
- [CRM] Problem-Solving Practice (p. A98)
- [CRM] Homework Practice (p. A99)

1 Introduce

Vocabulary

Proportion Vocabulary   Write $\frac{3}{5}$ and $\frac{6}{10}$ on the board. Demonstrate with a model how each is an equivalent ratio. Draw arrows to demonstrate cross products. Because the cross products are $3 \cdot 10 = 30$ and $6 \cdot 5 = 30$, these ratios are proportional.

2 Teach

Key Concept

Foundational Skills and Concepts   After students have read through the Key Concept box, have them try these exercises.

1. How do you know if two ratios are proportional? The cross products are equal.

2. When should you use cross products in a proportion? when one value is not known

---

KEY Concept

An equation stating that two **ratios** are equivalent is a **proportion**. For two ratios to form a proportion, their cross products must be equal.

$1 \cdot 6$ is one cross product.

$\begin{array}{cc} 1 & 3 \\ 2 & 6 \end{array}$

$2 \cdot 3$ is the other cross product.

$$1 \cdot 6 = 2 \cdot 3$$
$$6 = 6 \qquad \text{The } \textbf{cross products} \text{ are equal.}$$

Cross multiplying works because a common denominator of the two fractions is $6 \cdot 2$ or 12. Multiply both sides of the proportion by $6 \cdot 2$.

On the left side cancel the 2s. On the right side cancel the 6s.

$$(2 \cdot 6) \frac{1}{2} = \frac{3}{6} (2 \cdot 6)$$

This results in $1 \cdot 6 = 2 \cdot 3$. Notice that $1 \cdot 6$ and $2 \cdot 3$ are the same as the two cross products of the original proportion.

Cross multiply to solve proportions when one value in the proportion is not known. If two bagels cost $0.50, you can use a proportion to find the cost of 12 bagels.

$$\frac{0.50}{2} = \frac{y}{12} \qquad y = \text{the cost of 12 bagels}$$
$$0.50 \cdot 12 = 2 \cdot y \qquad \text{Cross multiply.}$$
$$\frac{6}{2} = \frac{2y}{2} \qquad \text{Divide by 2 to find the value of } y.$$
$$3 = y \qquad \text{12 bagels would cost \$3.}$$

VOCABULARY

cross product
   in a proportion, a cross product is the product of the numerator of one ratio and the denominator of the other ratio

proportion
   an equation stating that two ratios are equivalent

ratio
   a comparison of two quantities by division

Example 1

Determine whether the ratios are proportional. Write $=$ or $\neq$ in the circle.

$\frac{3}{4} \bigcirc \frac{7}{21}$

1. Find the cross products.
2. The cross products are not equal. Therefore, the ratios are not proportional.

$3 \cdot 21 \bigcirc 4 \cdot 7$
$63 \neq 28$

Additional *Example 1*

Determine whether the ratios are proportional. Write $=$ or $\neq$ in the circle.

$\frac{7}{8} \bigcirc \frac{42}{49}$

1. Find the cross products.

$7 \cdot 49 \bigcirc 8 \cdot 42$
$343 \neq 336$

2. The cross products are not equal; therefore, the ratios are not proportional.

YOUR TURN!

Determine whether the ratios are proportional. Write = or ≠ in the circle.

$\frac{2}{5}$ ◯ $\frac{4}{10}$

1. Find the cross products.

2. The cross products are __equal__. Therefore, the ratios __are__ proportional.

$2 \cdot 10$ ⊜ $4 \cdot 5$

$20 = 20$

Example 2

Solve for t.

$\frac{14}{t} = \frac{10}{11}$

1. Find the cross products.

2. Solve.

$14 \cdot 11 = t \cdot 10$

$154 = 10t$

$t = 15.4$

YOUR TURN!

Solve for w.

$\frac{w}{6} = \frac{2.8}{7}$

1. Find the cross products.

2. Solve.

$w \cdot 7 = $ __6__ $\cdot$ __2.8__

$7w = $ __16.8__

$w = $ __2.4__

Example 3

Wyley Auto Sales orders 8 cars to every 3 trucks ordered. How many cars are ordered when 15 trucks are ordered?

1. Write the ratio of cars to trucks. $\frac{8}{3}$

> Do you remember how to write a ratio?
> Example: There are 3 girls in every 5 students. The ratio of girls to students is $\frac{3}{5}$.

2. Write another ratio of cars to trucks using 15 for the number of trucks. $\frac{c}{15}$

3. Write these two ratios as a proportion.

4. Cross multiply and solve.

cars → $\frac{8}{3} = \frac{c}{15}$ ← cars
trucks → $\quad\quad\quad$ ← trucks

$\frac{8}{3} = \frac{c}{15}$

$8 \cdot 15 = 3c$

$\frac{120}{3} = \frac{3c}{3}$

$40 = c$

Forty cars are ordered when 15 trucks are ordered.

GO ON

Additional *Example 2*

Solve for y.

$\frac{5}{6} = \frac{y}{84}$

1. Find the cross products. $5 \cdot 84 = 6y$

2. Solve.

$420 = 6y$

$y = 70$

Additional *Example 3*

There are 6 girls for every 7 boys in a local sports league. How many girls are there if there are 133 boys in the league?

1. Write the ratio of girls to boys. $\frac{6}{7}$

2. Write another ratio of girls to boys using 133 for the number of boys. $\frac{g}{133}$

3. Write these two ratios as a proportion.

$\frac{g}{133} = \frac{6}{7}$

4. Cross multiply and solve.

$\frac{g}{133} = \frac{6}{7}$

$7g = 6 \cdot 133$

$\frac{7g}{7} = \frac{798}{7}$

$g = 114$

There are 114 girls if there are 133 boys in the league.

Math Coach Notes

Proportions Ensure that students are solid in their understanding of ratios before moving forward to proportional relationships. Students should have plenty of practice with proportions in their study with money. Use the connection with money to aid in students' understanding.

English Learner Strategy

Guiding Questions Write $\frac{2}{5} = \frac{4}{10}$ on the board. Point to the equal sign.

Write $2 \cdot 10 = 4 \cdot 5$ on the board.

- Point to the numbers in the ratios that are being multiplied. Ask: Are both sides equal?

- Write $\frac{3}{z} = \frac{21}{42}$. Write the multiplication equation. Ask: What is the value of z?

- Explain how to find the solution to $\frac{15}{300} = \frac{t}{210}$.

Math Coach Notes

Strategies

I. When writing proportions on the board, remind students that multiplication is the inverse operation of division. Use simple examples to demonstrate *why* cross multiplication works.

Example:

$$\frac{3}{4} = \frac{6}{8}$$ A common denominator of the two fractions is 32.

$$(4 \cdot 8)\frac{3}{4} = \frac{6}{8}(4 \cdot 8)$$ Multiply both sides of the proportion by 4 · 8. Cancel the 4s on the left side. Cancel the 8s on the right side.

The result is 8 · 3 = 6 · 4, which is the same as the two cross products of the original proportion.

2. Remind students that a proportion says that two ratios are equal. If the quotients of the ratios are not the same, then the ratios are *not* equal.

YOUR TURN!

A recipe that makes 3 dozen cookies calls for 7 cups of flour. How many dozens of cookies can be made with 28 cups of flour?

1. Write the ratio of dozens of cookies to cups of flour. $\dfrac{3}{7}$

2. Write another ratio of __dozens of cookies__ to __cups of flour__

   using __28__ for the number of cups of flour. $\dfrac{f}{28}$

   where __f__ is the number of dozens made with 28 cups of flour.

3. Write these two ratios as a proportion. $\begin{array}{l}\text{cookies} \rightarrow \\ \text{cups} \rightarrow\end{array}\dfrac{3}{7} = \dfrac{f}{28}\begin{array}{l}\leftarrow \text{cookies} \\ \leftarrow \text{cups}\end{array}$

4. Cross multiply and solve.

$$\frac{3}{7} = \frac{f}{28}$$

$$\frac{3 \quad \cdot \quad 28}{84} = \frac{7f}{7f}$$

$$\frac{84}{7} = \frac{7f}{7}$$

$$f = \underline{12}$$

__12__ dozen cookies can be made with 28 cups of flour.

Who is Correct?

Irina uses 4 inches of wire for every 3.6 feet of ribbon to make big bows. If she has 48 inches of wire, how many feet of ribbon does she need to use all the wire?

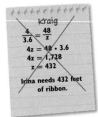

Kraig

$\dfrac{4}{3.6} = \dfrac{48}{z}$

$4z = 48 \cdot 3.6$

$4z = 1,728$

$z = 432$

Irina needs 432 feet of ribbon.

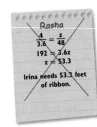

Rasha

$\dfrac{4}{3.6} = \dfrac{z}{48}$

$192 = 3.6z$

$z = 53.3$

Irina needs 53.3 feet of ribbon.

Frances

$\dfrac{4}{3.6} = \dfrac{48}{z}$

$4z = 48 \cdot 3.6$

$4z = 172.8$

$z = 43.2$

Irina needs 43.2 feet of ribbon.

Circle correct answer(s). Cross out incorrect answer(s).

Who *is Correct?*
Diagnostic Teaching

- Kraig wrote 432 feet. This is incorrect. He did not place the decimal point in the proper place when he cross multiplied. He multiplied incorrectly.

- Rasha wrote 53.3 feet. This is incorrect. Rasha put the wire over ribbon in the left ratio, but in the right ratio, placed the ribbon over the wire.

- Frances wrote 43.2 feet. This is correct.

Remind students that the numerators of each ratio must represent the same unit, and the denominators must represent the same unit.

Guided Practice

Determine whether each pair of ratios is proportional. Write = or ≠ in each circle.

1. $\dfrac{5}{9}$ ⊜ $\dfrac{10}{18}$ (=)

2. $\dfrac{2}{7}$ ⊜ $\dfrac{18}{42}$ (≠)

3. $\dfrac{36}{12}$ ⊜ $\dfrac{12}{4}$ (=)

4. $\dfrac{350}{1{,}750}$ ⊜ $\dfrac{2}{10}$ (=)

Step by Step Practice

5. Solve the proportion. $\dfrac{2}{12} = \dfrac{a}{36}$

   Step 1 Cross multiply.

$$2 \cdot 36 = 12 \cdot a$$

$$72 = 12a$$

   Step 2 Solve.

$$\dfrac{72}{12} = \dfrac{12a}{12}$$

   Step 3 The solution is ___6___.

$$a = 6$$

Solve each proportion.

6. $\dfrac{n}{8} = \dfrac{3}{4}$

$$= \dfrac{n}{3} \cdot \dfrac{4}{8}$$

$$n = 6$$

7. $\dfrac{w}{3} = \dfrac{34}{51}$

$$= \dfrac{w}{3} \cdot \dfrac{51}{34}$$

$$w = 2$$

8. $\dfrac{9}{15} = \dfrac{b}{10}$ ___6___

9. $\dfrac{3}{5} = \dfrac{0.2}{d}$ $\dfrac{1}{3}$ or $0.\overline{3}$

10. $\dfrac{2.5}{14.52} = \dfrac{7.5}{x}$ ___43.56___

11. $\dfrac{3}{n} = \dfrac{27}{18}$ ___2___

12. Two apples cost $0.58. How many apples could you buy for $2.32? ___8___

13. Refer to the price sticker on the books to the right. How many books cost $17.85? ___3___

14. Twenty bows make 8 centerpieces. How many bows make 30 centerpieces? ___75___

15. Thirty-two yards of cloth make 6 blankets. How many yards make 9 blankets? ___48___

GO ON

Are They Getting It?

Check students' understanding of proportions by writing these problems on the board. Ask students to point out the wrong answers and explain why they are wrong.

1. $\dfrac{24}{80} = \dfrac{6}{10}$ This is incorrect. $\dfrac{24}{80} = \dfrac{3}{10}$.

2. In $\dfrac{165}{x} = \dfrac{11}{15}$, $x = 225$. This is correct.

3. Janisha read 5 pages in 15 minutes, so it will take her 20 minutes to read 7 pages. This is incorrect. It will take her 21 minutes to read 7 pages.

4. It rained 3 inches in 24 hours. If the rate remained constant, it would rain 15 inches in 120 hours. This is correct.

---

③ Practice

Using Manipulatives

Two-Color Counters Students can model the ratios in the proportion using counters or other objects.

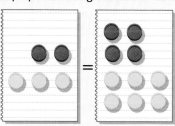

On-Hand Manipulatives Use colored construction paper or beans as counters to model proportions.

Note This!

Strategies Tell students to be flexible when taking notes. Sometimes the information will fit nicely into an outline. Other times, the material is familiar or presented in a big chunk, so a summary paragraph might be best. There may be times when several examples will be included in their notes and other times when there will be few, if any, examples. Whatever style they use that day, remind students to always leave ample white space to add more information later.

⚠ Common Error Alert

Multi-Step Problem If students are having difficulty with Exercises 12 through 15, they may not understand how to translate the words into ratios. Suggest that these students break the problem into pieces. Use the first sentence to write the first ratio, making certain to write in the units. Then tell students to identify what they know and what they need to know for the other ratio.

Lesson 5-3 Proportions   **197**

Intervention Strategy

Model Proportions Distribute colored tiles or cubes to each student. Using the tiles or cubes, have students set up a proportion to represent all or part of the tiles/cubes. For example, a student could divide the tiles by color into red and blue tiles. One group could contain 3 red and 4 blue tiles. Another group could contain 9 red and 12 blue tiles. Since 3:4 = 9:12, this would be an accurate proportion.

Math Coach Notes

Make Tables Students should practice using different strategies to solve problems. One strategy for students to solve proportions is to make a table like the one in Exercise 16.

If students have difficulty understanding the table, explain that the table shows equivalent ratios.

$$\frac{2}{1} = \frac{4}{2} = \frac{6}{3}$$

To complete this table, continue the pattern.

Step by Step Problem-Solving Practice

Problem-Solving Strategies
☑ Make a table.
☐ Look for a pattern.
☐ Guess and check.
☐ Solve a simpler problem.
☐ Work backward.

Solve.

16 PETS Cats drink about 2 milliliters of water for each gram of food they eat. If a cat eats about 9 grams of food, how much water will it drink?

Understand Read the problem. Write what you know.

Cats drink _____2_____ milliliters of water for every _____1_____ gram of food.

Plan Pick a strategy. One strategy is to make a table.

water (mL)	2	4	6	8	10	12	14	16	18
food (g)	1	2	3	4	5	6	7	8	9

Solve What pattern do you observe? Write the pattern as a ratio.

$$\frac{2 \text{ ml water}}{1 \text{ g food}}$$

Use the table or the ratio to find the solution.
_____18 mL_____

Check Use your answer to write a ratio. Is your ratio equivalent to the ratio in the table?

---

17 BIKING A group of bicyclers went on a bike ride. After 1 hour, they had traveled 16 miles. How long will it take for them to complete 60 miles?

Check off each step.

✔ Understand: I underlined key words.

✔ Plan: To solve this problem I will ___make a table___.

✔ Solve: The answer is $3\frac{3}{4}$ hours or 3 hours, 45 minutes.

✔ Check: I checked my answer by ___working backward___.

18 SCHOOL On a field trip there must be 3 adults for every 24 students. If there are 12 adults, how many students can go on the field trip? ___96 students___

Intervention Strategy

Student Proportions Use students from the class to represent proportions. Have five boys and two girls stand on one side of the classroom and write an equals sign on the board. Ask: How many boys and girls should be on the other side of the classroom to have a proportion? Represent different ratios this way. Next, have six boys and eight girls stand on one side while three boys stand on the other. How many girls should come up to make the ratios equal?

19 **Reflect** Describe a situation in which you might use a proportion.

<u>Sample answers may include descriptions of maps, scale models, unit rates,</u>

<u>or recipes (doubling or tripling ingredients).</u>

▶ Skills, Concepts, and Problem Solving

Determine whether each pair of ratios is proportional. Write = or ≠ in each circle.

20 $\frac{2}{9}$ ⊘ $\frac{4}{16}$

21 $\frac{5}{10}$ ⊜ $\frac{4}{8}$

22 $\frac{3}{4}$ ⊘ $\frac{12}{3}$

23 $\frac{72}{12}$ ⊜ $\frac{12}{2}$

Solve each proportion.

24 $\frac{2}{5} = \frac{8}{x}$ $x = $ __20__

25 $\frac{2}{7} = \frac{4}{y}$ $y = $ __14__

26 $\frac{3}{5} = \frac{b}{30}$ $b = $ __18__

27 $\frac{2}{9} = \frac{c}{36}$ $c = $ __8__

28 $\frac{4}{5} = \frac{d}{25}$ $d = $ __20__

29 $\frac{20}{4} = \frac{10}{f}$ $f = $ __2__

30 $\frac{d}{16} = \frac{3}{8}$ $d = $ __6__

31 $\frac{1.2}{9} = \frac{c}{1.5}$ $c = $ __0.2__

Solve.

32 READING   Pravat read 4 pages in 6 minutes. At this rate, how long would it take him to read 6 pages?

__9 minutes__

33 FOOD   How many Calories would you expect to find in 5 slices of the same kind of pizza? (See the photo at right.)

__1437.5 Calories__

2 slices = 575 Calories

34 BUSINESS   Jermaine can type 180 words in 3 minutes. How many words would you expect him to type in 10 minutes?

__600 words__

GO ON

Odd/Even Assignments

Exercises 20–34 are structured so that students practice the same concepts whether they are assigned the odd or even problems.

In-Class Assignment

Have students complete Exercises 20, 25, 33, and 37 to ensure that they understand the concept.

Math Coach Notes

Recite Key Information   One key to learning is recitation. Tell students that when they review their notes *that day* to recite the key concepts aloud. Tell them to first read the key concepts aloud, and then cover their notes and try to say the concepts aloud without looking.

Math Challenge

Rolled Ratios   Have students work in pairs or small groups. One student rolls a number cube, and then another student does the same. These two numbers make up the numerator and denominator in a ratio. Students write the ratio and put an equals sign after it. A student will roll another number cube. This number goes in the denominator of the other ratio. Students will now solve for the unknown quantity. Tell them to round to the tenths place.

For instance, two students roll a 5 and then a 6. Another student rolls a 3. The proportion will look like this: $\frac{5}{6} = \frac{x}{3}$. The student that gets the correct answer earns the point. The first student to 5 points wins.

See It, Do It, Say It, Write It

Step 1 Write $\frac{21}{90} = \frac{7}{45}$ on the board. Ask: Are the ratios proportional? Multiply 21 by 45 and 7 by 90 to show students the ratios are not equal. Write other ratios on the board. Have students determine if they are proportional or not. Now write $\frac{8}{9} = \frac{x}{54}$. Have students guide you to find the value for x. Repeat.

Step 2 Ask students to work in pairs and write four proportions, using a variable for one unknown quantity. Have student volunteers write some examples on the board for the class to solve.

Step 3 Discuss the steps for solving proportions with students. Ask them to offer their strategies for finding unknown quantities.

Step 4 Have students write a definition for *proportion*. Then tell them to write the steps for finding an unknown quantity in a proportion.

Looking Ahead: Pre-teach

Similarity In the next lesson, students will learn how to use proportions to solve problems. Proportions can be used to find the missing side length of a figure that is similar (the same shape, but a different size) to another figure.

Example

The two figures are similar. What is the value of x?

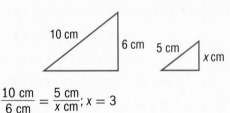

$\frac{10 \text{ cm}}{6 \text{ cm}} = \frac{5 \text{ cm}}{x \text{ cm}}$; $x = 3$

Vocabulary Check Write the vocabulary word that completes each sentence.

35 A(n) ____proportion____ is an equation stating that two ratios or rates are equivalent.

36 A(n) ____cross product____ is the product of a numerator of one ratio and the denominator of another ratio.

37 **Writing in Math** Describe the relationship between the two ratios in a proportion.

The two ratios in a proportion are equal. They have

a constant rate or ratio.

▶ Spiral Review

Use the diagram to write each ratio as a fraction in simplest form. (Lesson 5-1, p. 180)

38 apples and plums to pears and bananas ____ $\frac{8}{9}$

39 pieces of fruit that are not bananas to total fruit ____ $\frac{10}{17}$

40 apples to plums and bananas ____ $\frac{5}{10} = \frac{1}{2}$

Write each rate as a fraction. Find each unit rate. (Lesson 5-2, p. 187)

41 5 pounds of turkey for 8 people? ____ $\frac{5}{8}$; 0.625 pounds per person

42 168 miles in 3 hours ____ $\frac{168}{3}$; 56 miles per hour

Solve. (Lesson 5-2, p. 187)

43 **GAS MILEAGE** Jude can drive 330 miles on 12 gallons of gas. Find the unit rate. Use the unit rate to find the number of miles Jude can drive on 64 gallons of gas.

The unit rate is 27.5 miles/gallon of gas. Jude can drive

1,760 miles on 64 gallons of gas.

44 **POPULATION** The population of New Mexico is about 1,954,599. Its land area is about 121,356 square miles. Find the estimated population per square mile.

The population is about 16.11 people per square mile.

Ticket Out The Door

Write a Proportion Divide students into pairs. One student in each pair should write a ratio on an index card or half sheet of paper. The other student should write an equivalent ratio. Student pairs should explain to you why the ratios are proportional as they exit the classroom.

Solve Problems Using Proportions

KEY Concept

Similar figures have the same shape but may have different sizes. The corresponding angles of similar figures are congruent, or the same. The corresponding sides of similar figures are proportional.

The corresponding angles are
∠ B and ∠ E
∠ A and ∠ D
∠ C and ∠ F

The corresponding sides are
AB and DE
BC and EF
CA and FD

The corresponding angles of triangles *ABC* and *DEF* are congruent. The ratios of the corresponding sides are equivalent.

$$\frac{18}{6} = \frac{12}{4} = \frac{15}{5} = \frac{3}{1} = 3$$

If two figures are similar, the ratio of two sides of one figure is equal to the ratio of the corresponding two sides of the other figure. In triangles *ABC* and *DEF*, the ratio $\frac{AB}{AC}$, which is $\frac{5}{4}$, is equal to the ratio $\frac{DE}{DF}$, which is $\frac{15}{12}$.

VOCABULARY

proportion
an equation stating that two ratios or rates are equivalent

similar figures
figures that have the same shape but may have different sizes

Proportions can be used to find unknown measures in similar figures, in percent proportions, and for unit conversions.

Example 1

Find the value of *x*. Triangle *GHI* is similar to triangle *JKL*.

1. The ratio of corresponding sides $\overline{GH}$ and $\overline{JK}$ is $\frac{9}{21}$.

2. The ratio of corresponding sides $\overline{HI}$ and $\overline{KL}$ is $\frac{x}{14}$.

3. Since the two triangles are similar, these two ratios are equal. Write the proportion and solve for *x*.

4. The length of side $\overline{HI}$ is 6 meters.

> Be careful to write the ratios in the same order.

$$\frac{9}{21} = \frac{x}{14}$$
$$21x = 14(9) \quad \text{Find the cross products.}$$
$$\frac{21x}{21} = \frac{126}{21} \quad \text{Simplify. Divide by 21.}$$
$$x = 6$$

Additional *Example 1*

Find the value of *n*. Triangle *RST* is similar to triangle *XYZ*.

 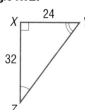

1. The ratio of corresponding sides $\overline{RS}$ and $\overline{XY}$ is $\frac{9}{24}$.

2. The ratio of corresponding sides $\overline{RT}$ and $\overline{XZ}$ is $\frac{n}{32}$.

3. Since the two triangles are similar, these two ratios are equal. Write the proportion and solve for *n*.

$$\frac{9}{24} = \frac{n}{32}$$
$$24n = 32(9) \quad \text{Find the cross products.}$$
$$\frac{24n}{24} = \frac{288}{24} \quad \text{Simplify. Divide by 24.}$$

4. The length of side $\overline{RT}$ is 12 units.

Lesson Planner

Objective   Use proportions to compare figures and solve problems.

Vocabulary   proportion , similar figures

Materials/Manipulatives   grid paper, geoboards, colored pencils

Chapter Resource Masters

- CRM Vocabulary and English Language Development (p. A100)
- CRM Skills Practice (p. A101)
- CRM Problem-Solving Practice (p. A102)
- CRM Homework Practice (p. A103)

① Introduce

Vocabulary

Review Vocabulary   Draw two rectangles on the board, one that is about twice the size of the other. Label the sides on the larger rectangle with measures that are twice the size of the smaller one. Tell students the figures are *similar*. Challenge them to define *similar*. Use nonexamples by drawing figures that are the same size and shape or figures that are different shapes but the same size.

② Teach

Key Concept

Foundational Skills and Concepts   After students have read through the Key Concept box, have them try this exercise.

Are the figures similar? Explain. No. They are not the same shape.

Additional *Example 2*

A caterpillar can travel 2 feet in 42 seconds. How long would it take the caterpillar to travel a total of 5 feet?

1. Write a ratio for feet to seconds.

$$\frac{2 \text{ ft}}{42 \text{ s}}$$

2. Set up a proportion to find the time it would take to travel 5 feet.

$$\frac{2 \text{ ft}}{42 \text{ s}} = \frac{5 \text{ ft}}{t}$$

3. Cross multiply and solve.

$$2t = 42 \cdot 5$$
$$2t = 210$$
$$t = 105$$

It will take 105 seconds for the caterpillar to travel 5 feet.

Math Coach Notes

Proportions   Always remember to instill in students that $\frac{A}{B}$ = a fixed number, k. In a proportion, $\frac{A_1}{B_1} = k = \frac{A_2}{B_2}$. Do not emphasize setting up the proportion correctly without emphasizing that the quotient of each corresponding ratio is a constant.

YOUR TURN!

Find the value of x. Triangle *MNO* is similar to triangle *PQR*.

1. The ratio of corresponding sides $\overline{MN}$ and $\overline{PQ}$ is _____. $\frac{5}{x}$

2. The ratio of corresponding sides $\overline{NO}$ and $\overline{QR}$ is _____. $\frac{4}{3}$

3. Since the two triangles are similar, these two ratios are equal.

   Write the proportion and solve for x.

$$\frac{5}{x} = \frac{4}{3}$$
$$5(3) = 4(x)$$
$$\frac{15}{4} = \frac{4x}{4}$$
$$x = 3.75$$

4. The length of side $\overline{PQ}$ is __3.75 cm__.

Example 2

An A-37 Dragonfly jet can travel 42 miles in 4 seconds. How long would it take the jet to travel a total of 105 miles?

1. Write a ratio for miles to seconds. $\frac{42 \text{ mi}}{4 \text{ s}}$

2. Set up a proportion to find the time it would take to travel 105 miles. $\frac{42 \text{ mi}}{4 \text{ s}} = \frac{105 \text{ mi}}{t}$

3. Cross multiply and solve. $42t = 4 \cdot 105$
   $42t = 420$

   $t = 10$

4. It will take 10 seconds for the jet to travel 105 miles.

Intervention Strategy   Visual Learners

Color Codes   When students are first learning to set up proportions, encourage them to use colors to match up the corresponding parts. For example, with the similar triangles below, use the same color to write 4 and 3, and a different color to write 7 and z. Use the colors in the proportion so that the numerators match colors, and the denominators match colors.

$$\frac{4}{7} = \frac{3}{z}$$

YOUR TURN!

A cargo airplane is traveling 987 miles. It has flown 282 miles in 1.5 hours. How long will it take the airplane to fly the entire trip if the plane travels at the same rate of speed?

1. Write a ratio for miles to hours.

$$\frac{282 \text{ mi}}{1.5 \text{ h}}$$

2. Set up a proportion to find the time it would take to travel 987 miles.

$$\frac{282 \text{ mi}}{1.5 \text{ h}} = \frac{987 \text{ mi}}{t}$$

3. Cross multiply and solve.

$$282t = 1.5 \cdot 987$$
$$282t = 1,480$$
$$t = 5.25$$

4. It will take __5.25__ hours for the airplane to complete its journey.

Who is Correct?

Edita bicycled for 25 minutes and burned 293 calories. Use a proportion to find how long it would take her to burn 704 calories at that rate.

Circle correct answer(s). Cross out incorrect answer(s).

 Guided Practice

Find the value of *x* in each pair of similar triangles.

① $x =$ __3.6__

② $x =$ __5.2__

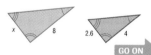

GO ON

 Practice

Using Manipulatives

Grid Paper   Students can learn about similar figures by drawing the figures on grid paper. The scale will vary depending on the problem.

2 cm

3 cm   4 cm   x

Geoboard   Students can experiment with similar figures using a geoboard. Tell them to make a figure with one color band and then make another figure that is similar, therefore proportional, using another color. They can calculate the ratios to verify the figures are similar.

On-Hand Manipulatives   Have students draw sketches of similar figures in their notebooks. Give them different colors of pens or pencils to outline the corresponding sides. This will aid them in setting up the correct proportion.

Math Coach Notes

Similar Figures   Make certain students realize that even if figures appear similar, they might not be. Unless students are told in the problem that the figures are similar, they should not assume that they are similar because they look similar.

Triangles   Explain to students that not all triangles have the same shape. Isosceles and equilateral triangles would be defined as different shapes, due to the lengths of their sides.

Who *is Correct?*
Diagnostic Teaching

• Marie wrote 60.07 minutes. This is correct.

• Liam wrote 10.40 minutes. This is incorrect. The 293 calories and 25 minutes should be in the same ratio.

• Alejandro wrote 8,250. This is incorrect. Calories should be in either the numerator or the denominator of both ratios.

Remind students to be sure that their ratios represent a rate described in the problem.

Intervention Strategy

Correct the Mistakes Provide each student pair or small group with a problem, the work shown for the problem, and the solution. Solve some of the problems correctly, but solve other problems incorrectly. You might want to use anonymous student work for these examples. Have students identify and describe the inaccuracies and then correct the mistakes. Students can present and discuss their findings.

Step by Step Practice

3 An Apache helicopter traveled 14.2 kilometers in 3 minutes. If the pilot maintains this rate of speed, how far will the Apache travel in 20 minutes?

Step 1 Write a ratio for kilometers to minutes.

$$\frac{14.2 \text{ km}}{3 \text{ min}}$$

Step 2 Set up a proportion to find the kilometers the Apache would travel in 20 minutes.

$$\frac{14.2 \text{ km}}{3 \text{ min}} = \frac{x \text{ km}}{20 \text{ min}}$$

Step 3 Cross multiply and solve.

$$3x = 14.2(20)$$

Step 4 The Apache could travel about __94.7__ kilometers in 20 minutes.

Solve.

4 WORK Carson earns $35 for working 5 hours. At that rate, how many hours would he need to work in order to earn $140?

$$\frac{\$35}{5} = \frac{\$140}{x}$$

$$\frac{\$35x}{35} = \frac{\$140(5)}{35}$$

$$x = 20$$

Carson needs to work __20__ hours.

5 Miranda wants to attend a class trip to the ballet. The trip will cost $65. She has already saved $25. She can earn $4 an hour cleaning the basement for her grandmother. How many hours will she need to clean in order to pay for the trip?

__10 hours__

6 Presta's mom drove for 2 hours at 30 miles per hour through city traffic. Then she drove 3 more hours at 55 miles per hour on the highway. How far did she drive?

__225 miles__

Are They Getting It? ?

Check students' understanding of solving problems using proportions by writing these problems on the board. Ask students to point out wrong answers and explain why they are wrong.

1. Similar figures are always the same size and the same shape. This is incorrect. Similar figures are the same shape, but could be different sizes. If they are the same size and shape, then they are called *congruent*.

2. If the value of *x* is 10 inches, then these figures are similar. This is incorrect. The sides are not proportional, if the value of *x* is 10 in.

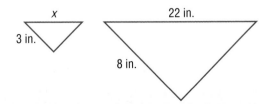

Step by Step Problem-Solving Practice

Solve.

Problem-Solving Strategies
- ☑ Use a table.
- ☐ Look for a pattern.
- ☐ Guess and check.
- ☐ Solve a simpler problem.
- ☐ Act it out.

7 GEOMETRY Each side of triangle *ABC* is $3\frac{1}{4}$ times as long as the corresponding side of triangle *FGH*. Find the perimeter of triangle *ABC*.

Understand Read the problem. Write what you know.

Each side of triangle *ABC* is $3\frac{1}{4}$ times as long as the corresponding side of triangle *FGH*.

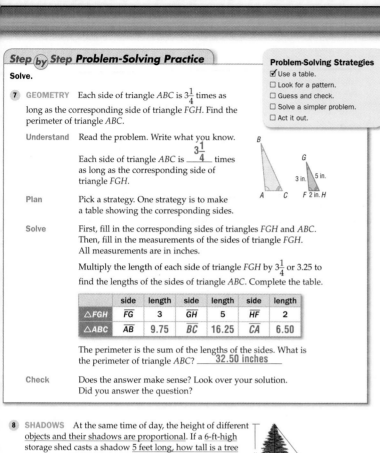

Plan Pick a strategy. One strategy is to make a table showing the corresponding sides.

Solve First, fill in the corresponding sides of triangles *FGH* and *ABC*. Then, fill in the measurements of the sides of triangle *FGH*. All measurements are in inches.

Multiply the length of each side of triangle *FGH* by $3\frac{1}{4}$ or 3.25 to find the lengths of the sides of triangle *ABC*. Complete the table.

	side	length	side	length	side	length
△FGH	$\overline{FG}$	3	$\overline{GH}$	5	$\overline{HF}$	2
△ABC	$\overline{AB}$	9.75	$\overline{BC}$	16.25	$\overline{CA}$	6.50

The perimeter is the sum of the lengths of the sides. What is the perimeter of triangle *ABC*? ___32.50 inches___

Check Does the answer make sense? Look over your solution. Did you answer the question?

Math Coach Notes

Exercise 7 After students have completed Exercise 7, ask, "Are the figures similar?" Have students explain why the figures in this exercise are or are not similar. The definition of *similar figures* is that the figures have the same shapes, but different sizes. Triangle *ABC* is the same shape, but 3.25 times larger. To check, verify that each ratio between the corresponding sides is the same.

8 SHADOWS At the same time of day, the height of different objects and their shadows are proportional. If a 6-ft-high storage shed casts a shadow 5 feet long, how tall is a tree that casts a 12.5-ft shadow? Check off each step.

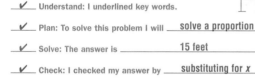

 ✔ **Understand:** I underlined key words.

✔ **Plan:** To solve this problem I will ___solve a proportion___.

✔ **Solve:** The answer is ___15 feet___.

✔ **Check:** I checked my answer by ___substituting for *x*___.

GO ON ▶

Common Error Alert

Exercise 7 Remind students that they are multiplying by the decimal 3.25. This number has two decimal places, so the lengths of the sides in the second row of the table will also have two decimal places.

Odd/Even Assignments

Exercises 11–20 are structured so that students practice the same concepts whether they are assigned the odd or even problems.

In-Class Assignment

Have students complete Exercises 11, 17, 20, and 23 to ensure that they understand the concept.

---

9 **EVENTS** Eloise sells pizza slices at a carnival. She sold 180 slices and then took a 5-minute break. She then sold another 60 slices to complete the event. It took her 6 hours to complete the sale from start to finish. About how many pizza slices did she sell each hour?

about 40 slices per hour

10 **Reflect** List the types of problems that proportions can be used to solve.

Sample answer: Proportions can be used to find missing lengths in similar figures, indirect measurement, percents, unit costs, and unit rates.

▶ Skills, Concepts, and Problem Solving

Find the value of x in each pair of similar figures.

11 $x =$ **39 ft**

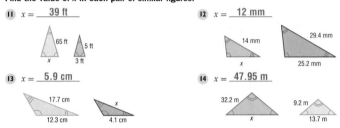

12 $x =$ **12 mm**

13 $x =$ **5.9 cm**

14 $x =$ **47.95 m**

Use a proportion to solve.

15 Dante's remote control car can travel 3 miles in 18 minutes. At this speed, how long will it take to travel 25 miles?
150 minutes or 2 hours and 30 minutes

16 Halona canoed 3 miles in 29 minutes. At this rate, how long would it take her to canoe 5 miles?
48.33 minutes

17 At 82°F, sound travels approximately 2,299 meters in 6.6 seconds through dry air. Find the speed of sound per second under these conditions.
348.33 meters per second

18 A Spine-tail swift can fly 31.5 miles in 18 minutes. How far would this bird fly if it continued at the same rate for 45 minutes?
78.75 miles

206 **Chapter 5** Ratios, Rates, and Similarity

Math Challenge

Similar Shapes In a computerized graphic art program, draw a polygon other than a triangle. Label the vertices of the shape and at least two of its dimensions. Use the copy and paste feature to duplicate the shape. Then use the scale capabilities to either enlarge or shrink the second shape. Label these vertices with different letters and one dimension that corresponds with a dimension marked in the original shape. Have students write a similarity statement to go with their drawings. Students can print the drawings and trade with a partner to solve each other's problems.

Solve.

19 SAFETY   Safe Child, Inc. produces 39 car seats every 2 days. How long will it take the company to produce 429 car seats?

_____**22 days**_____

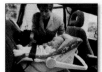

20 FITNESS   Winston bicycled 5 miles on Saturday morning at a rate of 12.5 miles per hour. How many minutes did he bicycle?

_____**24 minutes**_____

He bicycled 3 miles on Monday at a rate of 11.7 miles per hour. Did he bicycle for a longer amount of time on Saturday or Monday?

**He bicycled for a longer amount of time on Saturday.**

Vocabulary Check   **Write the vocabulary word that completes each sentence.**

21 Figures whose shapes are the same but may have different sizes are

_____**similar figures**_____.

22 A(n) _____**ratio**_____ is a comparison of two numbers by division.

23 Writing in Math   Ruth says that if two figures are similar, their corresponding sides are equal and their corresponding angles are proportional. Is she correct? Explain.

**Sample answer: No, Ruth is not correct. If two figures are similar, their**

**corrresponding angles are equal and their corresponding sides are proportional.**

 Spiral Review

Solve. (Lesson 5-3, p. 194)

24 If a turtle travels 7.5 feet in 15 minutes, what is its rate per minute?
**0.5 feet per minute**

25 If a motorcycle travels 30 miles per hour, what is the distance it travels in 5.5 hours? _____**165 miles**_____

26 ENTERTAINMENT   Catalina sold 330 tickets to the theater in 5 hours while working at the ticket booth. Later, Troy sold 480 tickets while working an 8-hour shift. Who sold tickets at a higher rate? Explain. (Lesson 5-2, p. 187)

Catalina's rate was $\frac{330}{5}$ = 66 tickets/h. Troy's rate was

$\frac{480}{8}$ = 60 tickets/h. Catalina; 66 > 60

 STOP

See It, Do It, Say It, Write It

Step 1 Draw two similar figures on the board. Label their measures so they are proportional. Have students guide you to find the ratios of the corresponding sides to verify. Draw other figures that look similar but are not according to their measures. Have students calculate and verify. Finally, draw similar figures with side lengths that must be determined.

Step 2 Tell students to work in pairs. Have them measure and draw a triangle of any type. Then tell them to draw another triangle that is similar to the first. Students will present their work and explain their methodology.

Step 3 Tell students to explain how to determine if figures are similar. Ask them to include an example.

Ticket Out the Door

Proportions Problems   Write the ratio 4:5 on the board. Instruct students to write an equivalent ratio with whole numbers. Students should show their work and explain their thinking. Then instruct students to write another equivalent ratio with decimal values. Students should show their work to prove the ratios are equivalent. As students exit the classroom, have them hand in their proportions.

Progress Check 2

Formative Assessment

Use the Progress Check to assess students' mastery of the previous lessons. Have students review the lesson indicated for the problems they answered incorrectly.

Odd/Even Assignments

Exercises are structured so that students practice the same concepts whether they are assigned the odd or even problems.

Common Error *Alert*

Exercise 11 Tell students to break the problem down into pieces and work backward. This problem gives them quite a bit of information to manipulate; students need to ask themselves what they need to find in order to answer this problem. (1) They must multiply the number of gallons the gas tank will hold by the cost per gallon. (2) They must compare the cost calculated with the $35 Nayla has in order to determine whether there is enough money to fill the tank.

 Chapter 5 **Progress Check 2** (Lessons 5-3 and 5-4)

Determine whether each pair of ratios is proportional. Write = or ≠ in each circle.

1. $\frac{5}{2}$ ⊘ $\frac{10}{5}$ (≠)

2. $\frac{15}{5}$ ⊜ 3   (=)

Solve each proportion.

3. $\frac{34}{15} = \frac{n}{5}$ $n = \underline{11\frac{1}{3}}$

4. $\frac{2}{3} = \frac{72}{d}$ $d = \underline{108}$

5. $\frac{0.75}{5} = \frac{n}{25}$ $n = \underline{3.75}$

6. $\frac{27}{3} = \frac{90}{c}$ $c = \underline{10}$

Find the value of x in each pair of similar figures.

7. $x = \underline{6\ in.}$

8. $x = \underline{9.6\ mm}$

Use a proportion to solve.

9. A child weighs about 27 kilograms. If 1 kilogram is about 2.2 pounds, how much does the child weigh in pounds?

   $\underline{about\ 59.4\ pounds}$

10. Two dozen books cost $26. How much do 3.5 dozen books cost?

    $\underline{\$45.50}$

Solve.

11. **TRAVEL** The gasoline tank of Nayla's car holds 14 gallons of gas. A gallon of gas costs $3.19. If Roxanna has $35, does she have enough money to fill the tank? Exactly how much will she spend if the tank is completely empty?

    $\underline{No.\ She\ would\ need\ \$44.66\ to\ fill\ the\ tank.}$

12. **EARTH SCIENCE** Surface waves from an earthquake travel about 3.7 miles per second through Earth's crust. How long would it take for a surface wave to travel 444 miles?

    $\underline{120\ seconds\ or\ 2\ minutes}$

Data-Driven Decision Making

Students missing Exercises . . .	Have trouble with . . .	Should review and practice . . .
1–2	determining whether pairs of ratios are proportional.	SSG Lesson 5-3, p. 194 CRM Practice Skills, p. A97
3–6	solving proportions.	SSG Lesson 5-3, p. 194 CRM Practice Skills, p. A97
7–8	using proportions with similar figures.	SSG Lesson 5-4, p. 201 CRM Practice Skills, p. A101
9–12	solving word problems involving proportions.	CRM Problem Solving Practice, pp. A98 and A102

Vocabulary and Concept Check

proportion, *p. 194*
rate, *p. 187*
ratio, *p. 180*
similar figures, *p. 201*
unit cost, *p. 187*
unit rate, *p. 187*

Write the vocabulary word that completes each sentence.

1 An equation stating that two ratios are equivalent is a(n) __proportion__ .

2 A(n) __rate__ is a ratio of two measurements or amounts made with different units, such as 2 miles in 5 minutes.

3 The corresponding sides of __similar figures__ are proportional.

4 A(n) __ratio__ is a comparison of two numbers by division.

Write the correct vocabulary term in each blank.

5 $4.19 per gallon __unit cost__

6 67 miles per hour __unit rate__

Lesson Review

5-1 Ratios (pp. 180–186)

Write each ratio as a fraction in simplest form.

7 16 people to 24 chairs __$\frac{2}{3}$__

8 10 pens to 30 pencils __$\frac{1}{3}$__

9 12 cell phones to 4 walkie talkies __$\frac{3}{1}$__

10 84 buttons to 21 pairs of jeans __$\frac{4}{1}$__

Example 1

Write the ratio as a fraction in simplest form.
6 math books out of 30 total books

1. Write the ratio with the number of math books in the numerator and the total number of books in the denominator.

$$\frac{6}{30}$$

2. Write the fraction in simplest form.

$$\frac{6 \div 6}{30 \div 6} = \frac{1}{5}$$

Chapter 5 Study Guide **209**

Vocabulary and Concept Check

If students have difficulty answering Exercises 1–6, remind them that they can use the page references to refresh their memories about the vocabulary terms.

Vocabulary Review Strategies

Vocabulary Flashcards Have students create flashcards for the vocabulary words. On one side of the card, state the definition, and on the other side, the vocabulary term. The students can study these cards by looking at the vocabulary term and stating its definition (flipping the card over to check and see if they got the definition correct). Students can also read the side with the definition and state its corresponding vocabulary term (flipping the card over to see if they got the correct term).

Lesson Review

The examples walk the students through writing ratios as fractions in simplest form, writing rates as fractions and finding the corresponding unit rates, solving proportions, and similar figure applications. If the given examples are not sufficient to review the questions, have students design their own example from a particular section of the chapter. When finished, have them share their example and its solution with a partner.

Find **Extra Practice** for these concepts in the Practice Worksheets, pages A88–A103.

Classroom Management

Early Finishers Have students who finish the review problems for each example create additional problems. They should create the problem and include an answer (with a labeled diagram as needed). When complete, have these students exchange their problems and double-check each other's work or share them with the class.

Review Remind students to complete and refer to their Foldables as they progress through the Chapter 5 Study Guide. Have students share and compare their completed Foldables with a partner. You may also choose to have them use their Foldable as a study aid in preparing for the Chapter Test. (For complete instructions, see Chapter Resource Masters, p. A85.)

Ratios	Proportions	Similiar Figures

Definition & Notes	Definition & Notes	Definition & Notes
Examples	Examples	Examples

Note This!

Create a Checklist Help students create a study checklist. The checklist should include all of the following:

- Notes from class/examples from each lesson
- Vocabulary terms and definitions
- Foldables
- Corrected homework assignments
- Quizzes and Progress Checks
- Chapter 5 Study Guide

5-2 Rates and Unit Costs (pp. 187–192)

Write each rate as a fraction. Find each unit rate.

11. 228 jumps in 4 minutes
$\frac{228}{4}$ or $\frac{57}{1}$; 57 jumps/min

12. 48 waves in 12 seconds
$\frac{48}{12}$ or $\frac{4}{1}$; 4 waves/s

13. 60 gallons in 5 minutes
$\frac{60}{5}$ $\frac{12}{1}$; 12 gal/min

Example 2

Write the rate 60 rotations per 10 seconds as a fraction. Find the unit rate.

1. Write the rate as a fraction.
$\frac{60 \text{ rotations}}{10 \text{ seconds}}$

2. Find an equivalent rate with a denominator of 1.
$\frac{60 \text{ rotations} \div 10}{10 \text{ seconds} \div 10} = \frac{6 \text{ rotations}}{1 \text{ second}}$

3. Name the unit rate.
6 rotations per second or 6 rotations/s

5-3 Proportions (pp. 194–200)

Determine whether each pair of ratios is proportional. Write = or ≠ in each circle.

14. $\frac{3}{4}$ ⊜ $\frac{21}{28}$

15. $\frac{1}{7}$ ⊘ $\frac{6}{56}$

16. $\frac{5}{7}$ ⊜ $\frac{60}{84}$

Solve each proportion.

17. $\frac{7}{9} = \frac{x}{45}$ $x = 35$

18. $\frac{p}{3} = \frac{12}{4.5}$ $p = 8$

19. $\frac{6}{7} = \frac{78}{m}$ $m = 91$

20. $\frac{2.2}{14} = \frac{t}{7}$ $t = 1.1$

Example 3

Determine whether the ratios are proportional. Write = or ≠ in the circle.
$\frac{2}{3}$ ◯ $\frac{26}{39}$

1. Find the cross products.
$2 \cdot 39$ ◯ $3 \cdot 26$
$78 = 78$

2. The cross products are equal. The ratios form a proportion.

Example 4

Solve for *n*. $\frac{7}{8} = \frac{n}{24}$

1. Find the cross products. $7 \cdot 24 = 8n$
$\frac{168}{8} = \frac{8n}{8}$

2. Solve. $21 = n$

Intervention Strategy Interpersonal Learners

Make a table on the board with the counts for males and females in the class, as well as counts for brown hair, blonde hair, black hair, red hair, and other colors of hair. Ask for a ratio that can be gathered from the data in the table, such as the ratio of the number of males to the number of all students, or the ratio of the number of students with brown hair to the number of students with blonde hair. Use a variety of ratios when asking the questions.

5-4 Solve Problems Using Proportions (pp. 201–207)

Find the value of x in each pair of similar figures.

21 $x =$ __9 ft__

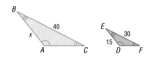

22 $x =$ __20__

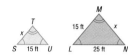

Use a proportion to solve.

23 A 12-oz package of beads contains 21 pieces. How many beads would you expect to find in a 16-oz package?

__28 beads__

24 Tyler jogged 6 miles in 36 minutes. How long will it take him to run 8 miles?

__48 minutes__

25 The Concorde jet can travel 133.2 miles in 6 minutes. How far can the jet travel in 9 minutes? __199.8 miles__

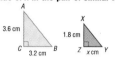

Example 5

Find the value of x in the pair of similar figures.

1. The ratio of sides AC to CB in triangle ABC is $\frac{3.6}{3.2}$.

2. The ratio of the corresponding side measures in triangle XYZ is $\frac{1.8}{x}$.

3. Set up a proportion and solve for x.

$$\frac{3.6}{3.2} = \frac{1.8}{x}$$
$$3.6x = 1.8(3.2)$$
$$\frac{3.6x}{3.6} = \frac{5.76}{3.6}$$

4. The length of $\overline{YZ}$ is 1.6 centimeters.

Example 6

Use a proportion to solve.

About 17 out of every 25 customers at The Craft Store purchase scrapbooking supplies. Sunday there were 75 customers. How many customers would purchase scrapbooking supplies at this rate?

1. Write a proportion. Use n to represent the number of scrapbooking customers.

$$\frac{17}{25} = \frac{n}{75}$$

2. Solve for n.

$$17(75) = 25n$$
$$1,275 = 25n$$

3. On Sunday, about 51 customers would purchase scrapbooking supplies.

$$\frac{1275}{25} = \frac{25n}{25}$$
$$51 = n$$

Math Coach Notes

Create a Checklist Give the students a short list of important ideas from the chapter that they need to understand:

- What is the significance of cross products?
- What is a proportion?
- Name some of the ways proportions were used in this chapter.
- What does it mean for two figures to be similar?

Ticket Out the Door

Proportion Applications Have students write and answer three proportion problems: one involving similar figures, one involving a rate, and one involving a cost. Because these directives are not giving a great deal of specifics, tell students to look back through their lessons and try to imitate what they have already written and solved.

Chapter Test

Chapter Resource Masters

Additional forms of the Chapter 5 Tests are available.

Test Format	Where to Find it
Chapter 5 Test	**Math Online** > glencoe.com
Blackline Masters	Assessment Masters, p. 79

ExamView®
Assessment Suite

Customize and create multiple versions of your chapter tests and their answer keys. All of these questions from the chapter tests are available on ExamView® Assessment Suite.

Advance

Online Assessment and Reporting
glencoe.com

This online assessment tool allows teachers to track student progress with easily accessible comprehensive reports available for every student. Assess students using any internet-ready computer.

Alternative Assessment

Use Portfolios   Ask students to write examples of all of the different types of problems from this chapter. These should include: writing a ratio as a fraction in simplest form, finding unit rate, finding unit cost, and using proportions to solve problems.

Chapter Test

Use the diagram to write each ratio as a fraction in simplest form.

1 blue figures to total figures
$\frac{3}{10}$

2 triangles to circles
$\frac{3}{2}$

Write the ratio of the length of the base to the height of each triangle as a fraction in simplest form.

3 $\frac{5}{7}$ height = 7 cm   base = 5 cm

4 $\frac{9}{17}$ height = 17 ft   base = 9 ft

Write each rate as a fraction. Find each unit rate.

5 180 pages in 3 books
$\frac{180}{3}$; 60 pages/book

6 12 ounces in 3 bottles
$\frac{12}{3}$; 4 oz/bottle

Write each ratio as a fraction in simplest form.

7 18 out of 144 were not wearing jeans ____ $\frac{1}{8}$

8 7 of the 25 children in the class play soccer ____ $\frac{7}{25}$

9 112 markers in 16 bags ____ $\frac{7}{1}$ or 7

Which product has the lowest unit cost? Round to the nearest cent.

10 8-oz bag of crackers for $1.99, a 12-oz bag of crackers for $2.49, or a 16-oz bag of crackers for $2.99
16-oz bag = $0.19/cracker

11 4 limes for $1, 10 limes for $2, or 24 limes for $6
10 limes = $0.20/lime

12 4 flower pots for $59.99, 6 flower pots for $74.99, or 10 flower pots for $99.99
10 flower pots = $10.00/flower pot

212   Chapter 5 Test

English Learner Strategy

Assessment   Allow students time to look over the assessment. Have the students take a close look at all the problem directions, as well as any terms in the word problems. Be sure that students understand what is being asked of them in each problem. If necessary, provide them with some form of clarification. For example, on Exercise 20 students may need to be reminded that there are 16 ounces in one pound.

Determine whether the ratios are proportional. Write $=$ or $\neq$ in each circle.

13. $\dfrac{3}{5}$ $\neq$ $\dfrac{2}{3}$

14. $\dfrac{5}{9}$ $=$ $\dfrac{15}{27}$

Solve each proportion.

15. $\dfrac{p}{18} = \dfrac{3}{2}$ $\quad p = \underline{\ \ 27\ \ }$

16. $\dfrac{9}{25} = \dfrac{36}{f}$ $\quad f = \underline{\ \ 100\ \ }$

Solve.

17. **WRITING** Keith was working on his lab journal for his science class. He completed 144 of the book's 200 pages. Write the pages Keith has completed to the total number of pages as a ratio in simplest form.

$\underline{\dfrac{144}{200} = \dfrac{18}{25}}$

18. **TRAVEL** Margo drove her van 186 miles in 3 hours. What was her unit rate?

$\underline{\ \ \text{62 miles per hour}\ \ }$

19. **ART** The two triangles shown are proportional. What is the length of the missing side?

$\underline{16\dfrac{2}{3}\ \text{inches}}$

20 in.　18 in.

x　15 in.

Correct the mistakes.

20. At the Johnson Family Market, a sign in the window read: "8-oz bag of peanuts for \$2.99. That's less than \$5 per pound!" Is the sign correct?

$\underline{\text{No. A pound is 16 ounces. It will take two bags of 8-oz peanuts}}$

$\underline{\text{to make one pound. } 2 \times 2.99 > \$5}$

21. Jeremy's mother needed $1\dfrac{1}{2}$ pounds of walnuts for a recipe. She looked at the store's ad and saw that walnuts were on sale for \$6.99 per pound. She gave Jeremy a 10-dollar bill to buy the walnuts. What mistake did she make?

$\underline{\text{He would need more than \$10 in order to purchase the amount his mother}}$

$\underline{\text{requested. He would need about \$0.50 more.}}$

Copyright © Glencoe/McGraw-Hill, a division of The McGraw-Hill Companies, Inc.

Learning from Mistakes

Review Review commonly missed questions or topics in small groups or as a class. Ask students to share their methods of answering each question. Try to point out when any errors occur and take corrective measures.

Data-Driven Decision Making

Students missing Exercises . . .	Have trouble with . . .	Should review and practice . . .
1–4 and 7–9	writing ratios as fractions in simplest form.	SSG Lesson 5-1, p. 180 CRM Skills Practice, p. A89
5–6	writing rates as fractions in simplest form and finding unit rates.	SSG Lesson 5-2, p. 187 CRM Skills Practice, p. A93
10–12	finding and comparing unit costs.	SSG Lesson 5-2, p. 187 CRM Skills Practice, p. A93
13–16	determining whether ratios are proportional and solving proportions.	SSG Lessons 5-3 and 5-4, pp. 194 and 201 CRM Skills Practice, pp. A97 and A101
17–21	solving word problems involving writing ratios in simplest form, finding a unit rate, and using proportions.	CRM Problem Solving Practice, pp. A90, A94, A98, and A102

Diagnose Student Errors

Survey student responses for each item. Class trends may indicate common errors and misconceptions.

1. Ⓐ correct
    B miscalculated
    C miscalculated
    D guess

2. Ⓐ correct
    B guess
    C divided quantity by cost instead of reverse
    D misinterpreted question

3. A ratio of science to biographies
    Ⓑ correct
    C ratio of nonfiction to science fiction
    D guess

4. A rate per day; forgot to multiply by 6
    B miscalculated
    Ⓒ correct
    D did not calculate rate

5. Ⓐ correct
    B did not include teacher in total number
    C miscalculated
    D guess

6. A misinterpreted question
    B misinterpreted question
    C miscalculated
    Ⓓ correct

7. A multiplied instead of divided
    B misinterpreted question
    Ⓒ correct
    D miscalculated rate

8. A did not count objects correctly
    Ⓑ correct
    C ratio was written in incorrect order
    D number of circles to total objects

9. A guess
    Ⓑ correct
    C guess
    D multiplied instead of divided

Chapter
5

Test Practice

Select the best answer and fill in the corresponding circle on the sheet at right.

1 Brianna finished reading a novel in 8 days. The book was 384 pages. About how many pages did she read per day?

Ⓐ 48 pages   C 96 pages

B 64 pages   D 112 pages

2 A store sells an 8-pack of juice for $4. What is the cost of one bottle of juice?

Ⓐ $0.50   C $2.00

B $1.00   D $4.00

3 In Allie's bookshelf, there are 32 science fiction books, 10 nonfiction titles, and 4 biographies. What is the ratio of science fiction to nonfiction books?

A $\frac{8}{1}$; 8:1, or 8 to 1

Ⓑ $\frac{16}{5}$; 16:5, or 16 to 5

C $\frac{5}{16}$; 5:16, or 5 to 16

D $\frac{16}{23}$; 16:23, or 16 to 23

4 Diego is an avid biker. He rides about 140 miles every 4 days. At this rate, how many miles does he ride in 6 days?

A 35 miles   Ⓒ 210 miles

B 175 miles   D 840 miles

5 Mrs. Delgado and her 26 students are going to the theater. Admission and lunch for everyone will cost $364.50. What is the price per person?

Ⓐ $13.50   C $14.50

B $14.02   D $15.00

6 Isabel is running in a 26.2-mile marathon. If she completes the marathon in 4 hours, what rate did she average?

A 26.2 miles   C 5.15 miles/hour

B 4 hours   Ⓓ 6.55 miles/hour

7 Cecil is driving to Chicago, Illinois. He makes the 275-mile trip in 5 hours. What is Cecil's average speed?

A 1,375 miles   Ⓒ 55 miles/hour

B 5 hours   D 65 miles/hour

8 Write a ratio that compares the number of circles to the number of squares.

A 1 to 1   C 4 to 1

Ⓑ 1 to 4   D 1 to 5

10. A doubled 13 miles; guess
    B multiplied 15 by 3; guess
    Ⓒ correct
    D multiplied 13 by 15; guess

11. A miscalculated ratio
    B guess
    C guess
    Ⓓ correct

12. A guess
    B used given number in ratio
    Ⓒ correct
    D used given number in ratio

9 One inch equals about 2.54 centimeters. About how many inches equal 12.7 centimeters?

   A 3 inches   C 8 inches

   Ⓑ 5 inches   D 32.258 inches

---

10 A horse galloped at 13 miles per hour for 2 hours. Then the horse galloped at 15 miles per hour for 3 hours. How far did the horse travel in all?

   A 26 miles   Ⓒ 71 miles

   B 45 miles   D 195 miles

---

11 Triangle *ABC* is similar to triangle *DEF*. Find the value of *x*.

   A 6   C 7.75

   B 7.5   Ⓓ 8

---

12 In Mr. Cameron's class, 5 out of 32 students play basketball. There are 128 students in the eighth grade. If the ratio is the same for the entire eighth grade, how many students play basketball?

   A 4   Ⓒ 20

   B 5   D 32

ANSWER SHEET

Directions: Fill in the circle of each correct answer.

1 Ⓐ Ⓑ Ⓒ Ⓓ
2 Ⓐ Ⓑ Ⓒ Ⓓ
3 Ⓐ Ⓑ Ⓒ Ⓓ
4 Ⓐ Ⓑ Ⓒ Ⓓ
5 Ⓐ Ⓑ Ⓒ Ⓓ
6 Ⓐ Ⓑ Ⓒ Ⓓ
7 Ⓐ Ⓑ Ⓒ Ⓓ
8 Ⓐ Ⓑ Ⓒ Ⓓ
9 Ⓐ Ⓑ Ⓒ Ⓓ
10 Ⓐ Ⓑ Ⓒ Ⓓ
11 Ⓐ Ⓑ Ⓒ Ⓓ
12 Ⓐ Ⓑ Ⓒ Ⓓ

Diagnosing Student Errors and Misconceptions

Polls   When working on the Test Practice problems, have students show their work on a separate sheet of notebook paper that can be used later as a reference as needed. After the class has completed the Test Practice problems, randomly solicit answers to each question. After each question, take an informal poll of how many students answered the question correctly. If you notice that a significant number of students missed a particular question or questions, then review the method or strategy behind the question with the entire class.

⚠ Common Error *Alert*

Eliminate Wrong Answers   If students are not able to successfully eliminate wrong answer choices, they may need the corresponding reminder.

Exercise 4 There are two ways to do this. Students can find the unit rate of miles per day and then multiply it by 6. They may also set up a proportion to find the unknown. A likely mistake here may be that students only find the unit rate for miles per day.

Chapter-at-a-Glance

Lesson	Math Objective	State/Local Standards
6-1 Squaring a Number (pp. 218–224)	Find square numbers of positive integers through 225.	
6-2 Square Roots (pp. 225–230)	Find positive roots of perfect squares.	
Progress Check 1 (p. 231)		
6-3 Approximate Square Roots (pp. 232–238)	Estimate positive square roots.	
6-4 Pythagorean Theorem (pp. 239–246)	Know and use the Pythagorean Theorem to find the lengths of unknown sides of a right triangle.	
Progress Check 2 (p. 247)		
6-5 Introduction to Slope (pp. 248–254)	Determine and graph slope of a line.	
6-6 Slope Formula (pp. 255–261)	Know and use the slope formula.	
Progress Check 3 (p. 262)		

Content-at-a-Glance

The diagram below summarizes and unpacks Chapter 6 content.

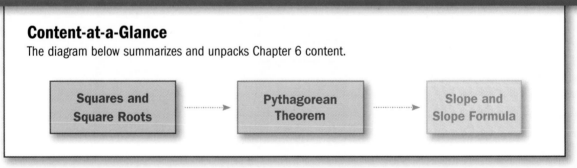

Chapter Assessment Manager

Diagnostic Diagnose students' readiness.

	Student/Teacher Editions	Assessment Masters	Technology
Course Placement Test		1	ExamView® Assessment Suite
Book 2 Pretest		62	ExamView® Assessment Suite
Chapter 6 Pretest		87	ExamView® Assessment Suite
Quiz/Preview	SSG 217		Math Online glencoe.com StudentWorks™ Plus

Formative Identify students' misconceptions of content knowledge.

	Student/Teacher Editions	Assessment Masters	Technology
Progress Checks	SSG 231, 247, 262		Math Online glencoe.com StudentWorks™ Plus
Vocabulary Review	SSG 263		Math Online glencoe.com
Lesson Assessments			ExamView® Assessment Suite
Are They Getting It?	TE 220, 228, 235, 243, 251, 258		Math Online glencoe.com

Summative Determine student success in learning the concepts in the lesson, chapter, or book.

	Student/Teacher Editions	Assessment Masters	Technology
Chapter 6 Test	SSG 268	90	ExamView® Assessment Suite
Test Practice	SSG 270	93	
Alternative Assessment	TE 268	96	ExamView® Assessment Suite
See It, Do It, Say It, Write It	TE 224, 230, 238, 246, 254, 261		
Book 2 Test		98	ExamView® Assessment Suite

Backmapping and Vertical Alignment McGraw-Hill's *Math Triumphs* intervention program was conceived and developed with the final result in mind: student success in grade-level mathematics, including Algebra 1 and beyond. The authors, using the **NCTM Focal Points and Focal Connections** as their guide, developed this brand-new series by backmapping from grade-level and Algebra 1 concepts, and vertically aligning the topics so that they build upon prior skills and concepts and serve as a foundation for future topics.

	Lesson 6-1	Lesson 6-2	Lesson 6-3	Lesson 6-4
Concept	Squaring a Number	Square Roots	Approximate Square Roots	Pythagorean Theorem
Objective	Find square numbers of positive integers through 225.	Find positive roots of perfect squares.	Estimate positive square roots.	Know and use the Pythagorean Theorem to find the lengths of unknown sides of a right triangle.
Math Vocabulary	base exponent factor square of a number	factors inverse operations radical sign square of a number square root	estimate square root	hypotenuse legs Pythagorean Theorem square of a number square root
Lesson Resources	**Materials** • Construction paper • Index cards • Number cubes **Manipulatives** • Algebra tiles • Base-ten blocks • Geoboards **Other Resources** [CRM] Vocabulary and English Language Development [CRM] Skills Practice [CRM] Problem-Solving Practice [CRM] Homework Practice	**Materials** • Multiplication facts chart • Rubber bands **Manipulatives** • Geoboards • Unit cubes **Other Resources** [CRM] Vocabulary and English Language Development [CRM] Skills Practice [CRM] Problem-Solving Practice [CRM] Homework Practice	**Materials** • Calculators • Index cards • Masking tape • Rulers **Other Resources** [CRM] Vocabulary and English Language Development [CRM] Skills Practice [CRM] Problem-Solving Practice [CRM] Homework Practice	**Materials** • Grid paper • Protractors • Rulers • Index cards **Other Resources** [CRM] Vocabulary and English Language Development [CRM] Skills Practice [CRM] Problem-Solving Practice [CRM] Homework Practice
Technology	**Math Online** glencoe.com StudentWorks™ Plus ⊙ ExamView® Assessment Suite	**Math Online** glencoe.com StudentWorks™ Plus ⊙ ExamView® Assessment Suite	**Math Online** glencoe.com StudentWorks™ Plus ⊙ ExamView® Assessment Suite	**Math Online** glencoe.com StudentWorks™ Plus ⊙ ExamView® Assessment Suite

	Lesson 6-5	Lesson 6-6	
Concept	Introduction to Slope	Slope Formula	
Objective	Determine and graph slope of a line.	Know and use the slope formula.	
Math Vocabulary	coordinate grid origin slope x-coordinate y-coordinate	linear function slope	
Lesson Resources	**Materials** • Bulletin board • Centimeter grid paper • Push pins • Rulers **Manipulatives** • Counters	**Materials** • Grid paper **Manipulatives** • Geoboards	
	Other Resources **CRM** Vocabulary and English Language Development **CRM** Skills Practice **CRM** Problem-Solving Practice **CRM** Homework Practice	**Other Resources** **CRM** Vocabulary and English Language Development **CRM** Skills Practice **CRM** Problem-Solving Practice **CRM** Homework Practice	
Technology	**Math Online** glencoe.com StudentWorks™ Plus ● ExamView® Assessment Suite	**Math Online** glencoe.com StudentWorks™ Plus ● ExamView® Assessment Suite	

Intervention Strategy

Pythagorean Proof

Using a hands-on activity to prove the Pythagorean Theorem will help students to remember the relationship between the three sides of a right triangle.

Step 1

Have students draw a right triangle using a protractor and a centimeter ruler. Tell them to draw each side length to a whole millimeter. Ask students to label the sides *a, b, c,* making sure that *c* is the hypotenuse or longest side length. Provide Pythagorean triples to students that have trouble drawing a right triangle.

Step 2

Now have students extend each of the 3 side lengths into a square.

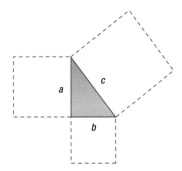

Step 3

Write the Pythagorean Theorem on the board.
$c^2 = a^2 + b^2$
Have students re-measure their triangle's side lengths to the nearest millimeter. Then have them calculate the area of each square and then substitute those areas into the equation to prove the theorem. Assist students whose measurements or calculations do not work out correctly.

Step 4

Discuss the results. Have students trade and measure each others' triangle lengths and prove the theorem.

Chapter Notes

Real-World Applications

Taking the Shortcut Brianna and George each live at the end of sidewalks that go around two sides of the community park. When Brianna meets George at his house, she rides her bike on the sidewalk to get to George's house. When George meets Brianna at her house, he walks and takes a shortcut. Describe a shortcut that George could take to get to Brianna's house.

Intervention Strategy
Perfect Squares to 15^2

Step 1 Provide each student with a piece of card stock paper.

Step 2 Students should cut a bookmark from the card stock paper and list all perfect squares from 1^2 to 15^2.

Step 3 When students have their bookmarks made, they should team up with a partner to compare bookmarks to be sure all 15 perfect squares listed are correct.

Step 4 Have students study their bookmarks for a few days in their spare time.

Step 5 One day, have students quiz each other to see how many of the perfect squares they have memorized.

Chapter 6

Squares, Square Roots, and the Pythagorean Theorem

You can use squared numbers and square roots to solve problems.

Malina's bedroom is in the shape of a square. She wants to cover the floor with tile. She will need to know how much area will be covered. If the length of the room equals 8 feet, what is the area of the room?

216 Chapter 6 Squares, Square Roots, and the Pythagorean Theorem

Key Vocabulary

Find interactive definitions in 13 languages in the **eGlossary** at glencoe.com

English   Español *Introduce the most important vocabulary terms from Chapter 6.*

base   base de una potencia

in a power, the number used as a factor (p. 218)

coordinate grid   cuadriculado de coordenadas

a grid in which a horizontal number line (*x*-axis) and a vertical number line (*y*-axis) intersect at their zero points (p. 248)

exponent   exponente

in a power, the number of times the base is used as a factor (p. 218)

hypotenuse   hipotenusa

the side opposite the right angle in a right triangle (p. 239)

origin   origen

the point of intersection of the *x*-axis and the *y*-axis in a coordinate system (p. 248)

Pythagorean Theorem   teorema de Pitágoras

in a right triangle, the square of the length of the hypotenuse, *c*, is equal to the sum of the squares of the lengths of the legs, *a* and *b* (p. 239)

Step 1 Quiz

Pretest/Prescribe Students can take the Online Readiness Quiz or the Diagnostic Pretest in the Assessment Masters.

Step 2 Preview

Use this pre-chapter activity to activate students' prior knowledge, build confidence, and help students preview the lessons.

 **Dinah Zike's Foldables®**

Guide students through the directions on p. A104 in the Chapter Resource Masters to create their own Foldable graphic organizer for use with this chapter.

Home Connections

- Make a list of all of the perfect squares between 1 and 225.

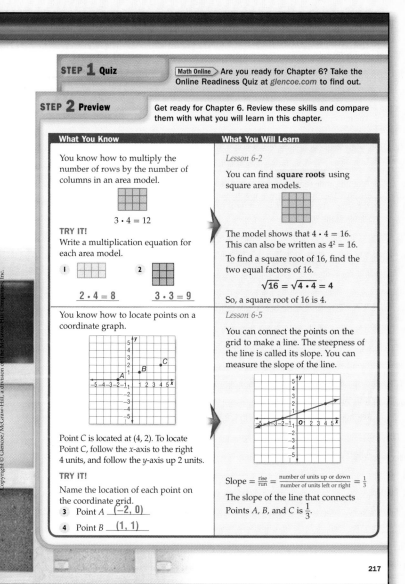

STEP 1 Quiz

Math Online ▷ Are you ready for Chapter 6? Take the Online Readiness Quiz at *glencoe.com* to find out.

STEP 2 Preview Get ready for Chapter 6. Review these skills and compare them with what you will learn in this chapter.

What You Know	What You Will Learn
You know how to multiply the number of rows by the number of columns in an area model. $3 \cdot 4 = 12$ **TRY IT!** Write a multiplication equation for each area model. **1** $2 \cdot 4 = 8$ **2** $3 \cdot 3 = 9$	**Lesson 6-2** You can find **square roots** using square area models. The model shows that $4 \cdot 4 = 16$. This can also be written as $4^2 = 16$. To find a square root of 16, find the two equal factors of 16. $\sqrt{16} = \sqrt{4 \cdot 4} = 4$ So, a square root of 16 is 4.
You know how to locate points on a coordinate graph. Point C is located at (4, 2). To locate Point C, follow the x-axis to the right 4 units, and follow the y-axis up 2 units. **TRY IT!** Name the location of each point on the coordinate grid. **3** Point A $(-2, 0)$ **4** Point B $(1, 1)$	**Lesson 6-5** You can connect the points on the grid to make a line. The steepness of the line is called its slope. You can measure the slope of the line. Slope $= \frac{\text{rise}}{\text{run}} = \frac{\text{number of units up or down}}{\text{number of units left or right}} = \frac{1}{3}$ The slope of the line that connects Points A, B, and C is $\frac{1}{3}$.

217

Vocabulary Preview

- As students complete the Chapter Preview, have each write down the key vocabulary words on a strip of paper.

- Students will then fold their strips of paper and place them into a jar called the "Word Jar."

- Walk around the classroom and have students pull strips from the Word Jar. The student should say the word aloud and explain its meaning. The class should correct any mistakes in defining the word.

- Continue the process until the terms become familiar to the students.

Professional Development

Targeted professional development has been articulated throughout **McGraw-Hill's** *Math Triumphs* intervention program. **The McGraw-Hill Professional Development Video Library** provides short videos that support the **NCTM Focal Points and Focal Connections**. For more information, visit glencoe.com.

Model Lessons   Instructional Strategies

Lesson Planner

Objective Find square numbers of positive integers through 225.

Vocabulary base, exponent, factor, square of a number

Materials/Manipulatives base-ten blocks, geoboards, algebra tiles, construction paper, number cubes, index cards

Chapter Resource Masters

CRM Vocabulary and English Language Development (p. A107)

CRM Skills Practice (p. A108)

CRM Problem-Solving Practice (p. A109)

CRM Homework Practice (p. A110)

① Introduce

Vocabulary

Connect Vocabulary What are the 3s called in the expression 3 • 3? *factors* When 3 • 3 is written as 3^2, what is the 3 called then? *base* What do we call the 2? *exponent* What does it tell you? How many times to multiply the *base* by itself. Now draw a 3 • 3 array. What can be said about the shape? It is a square. What is the product of 3^2? 9 Nine is called a *perfect square* because it is the product of two identical factors.

② Teach

Key Concept

Foundational Skills and Concepts After students have read through the Key Concept box, have them try these exercises.

1. What are 3 perfect squares under 20? 4, 9, 16

2. What is the product of 5^2? 25

3. True or false: 8 • 8 is a perfect square. False; the product of 8 • 8, which is 64, is a perfect square.

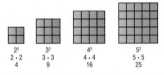

KEY Concept

The multiplication sentences below have two identical **factors**.

$1 \cdot 1 = 1$	$5 \cdot 5 = 25$	$9 \cdot 9 = 81$
$2 \cdot 2 = 4$	$6 \cdot 6 = 36$	$10 \cdot 10 = 100$
$3 \cdot 3 = 9$	$7 \cdot 7 = 49$	$11 \cdot 11 = 121$
$4 \cdot 4 = 16$	$8 \cdot 8 = 64$	$12 \cdot 12 = 144$

Multiplication sentences can be modeled using a square array because the number of rows and the number of columns are the same. The **square of a number** is the product of two identical factors.

2^2	3^2	4^2	5^2
$2 \cdot 2$	$3 \cdot 3$	$4 \cdot 4$	$5 \cdot 5$
4	9	16	25

The exponent 2 shows that the base is used as a factor 2 times. In the expression 5^2, 5 is the **base** and 2 is the **exponent**.

Example 1

Write an equation using exponents to represent the model.

1. How many rows in the array? 6

2. How many columns? 6

3. Label the array.

4. Write the expression and product. 6 • 6; 36

5. Write the equation using exponents. 6 is multiplied twice, so $6^2 = 36$.

6 • 6

Write an equation using exponents to represent the model.

7 • 7

I. How many rows are in the array? 7

2. How many columns? 7

3. Label the array.

4. Write the expression and product. 7 • 7; 49

5. Write the equation using exponents.
7 is multiplied twice, so $7^2 = 49$.

YOUR TURN!

Write an equation using exponents to represent the model.

1. How many rows in the array? ___8___

2. How many columns? ___8___

3. Label the array.

4. Write the expression and product.
   ___8___ · ___8___ ; ___64___

5. Write the equation using exponents.
   ___8^2___ = ___64___

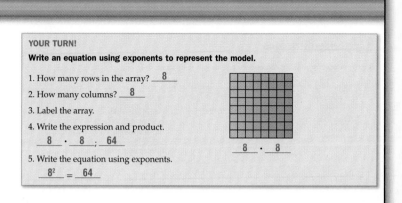

___8___ · ___8___

Example 2

Evaluate the expression 4^2.

1. What number is the base? 4

2. What number is the exponent? 2

3. Multiply to find the value of the expression.
   $4 \cdot 4 = 16$

YOUR TURN!

Evaluate the expression 5^2.

1. What number is the base? ___5___

2. What number is the exponent? ___2___

3. Multiply to find the value of the expression. ___5___ · ___5___ = ___25___

Who is Correct?

Evaluate the expression 7^2.

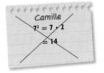
Camille
$7^2 = 7 \cdot 2$
= 14

Edward
$7^2 = 7 \cdot 7$
= 14

Robert
$7^2 = 7 \cdot 7$
= 49

Circle correct answer(s). Cross out incorrect answer(s).

GO ON

Evaluate the expression 9^2.

1. What number is the base? 9

2. What number is the exponent? 2

3. Multiply to find the value of the expression.
   $9 \cdot 9 = 81$

Who **is Correct?**
Diagnostic Teaching

• Camille is incorrect. The exponent tells how many times to multiply the base times itself, so $7^2 = 7 \cdot 7$, not $7 \cdot 2$.

• Edward is incorrect. He multiplied the exponent and the base, and should have multiplied the base times itself the number of the exponent.

• Robert wrote 49. This is correct.

③ Practice

Using Manipulatives

Base-Ten Blocks   Base-ten blocks can be used to represent square arrays. For Exercise 4, the model would look like this:

10 • 10

Geoboard

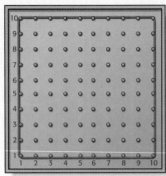

10 • 10

Algebra Tiles

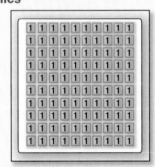

10 • 10

On-Hand Manipulatives   Use two different colors of construction paper. Cut out squares to use as counters.

Math Coach Notes

Label Arrays   Tell students to label the sides of their arrays if they are not using grid paper. It is important that students see that a perfect square is a perfectly square array. If they are not using grid paper, the array may not appear square, and that impression is crucial to understanding the concept.

▶ Guided Practice

Write an equation using exponents to represent each model.

1    $\underline{\ 5^2\ }$ = $\underline{\ 25\ }$

2    $\underline{\ 7^2\ }$ = $\underline{\ 49\ }$

Step by Step Practice

3   Evaluate the expression 9^2.

  Step 1   What is the base? ____9____

  Step 2   What is the exponent? ____2____

  The exponent tells you how many times the __base__ is used as a __factor__.

  Step 3   Multiply to find the value of the expression. $9^2 = 9 \cdot 9 = 81$

Evaluate each expression.

4   10^2 base: ____10____

      exponent: ____2____

      10^2 = __10__ • __10__ = __100__

5   12^2 __12 • 12 = 144__

6   8^2 __8 • 8 = 64__

7   6^2 __6 • 6 = 36__

8   3^2 __3 • 3 = 9__

9   5^2 __5 • 5 = 25__

10   11^2 __11 • 11 = 121__

11   1^2 __1 • 1 = 1__

12   4^2 __4 • 4 = 16__

220   **Chapter 6** Squares, Square Roots, and the Pythagorean Theorem

---

Are They Getting It?

Check students' understanding of perfect squares by writing these problems on the board. Have students explain the incorrect information in each problem. Tell them to use a drawing or another visual aid to show why the answers are correct or incorrect.

1. 46 is a perfect square. This is incorrect. There are no two identical whole number factors that can be multiplied to get a product of 46.

2. In the term 13^2, 2 is the base and 13 is the exponent. This is incorrect. The base is 13 and the exponent is 2.

3. A number that is a perfect square is a product. This is correct.

4. $11^2 = 11 \cdot 2 = 22$ This is incorrect. The exponent of 2 says how many times 11 is multiplied by itself. So, $11^2 = 11 \cdot 11 = 121$.

---

220 Chapter 6 Squares, Square Roots, and the Pythagorean Theorem

Step by Step Problem-Solving Practice

Solve.

13 **INTERIOR DESIGN**   Rajesh is buying new carpet for his room. His room is square and has lengths of 12 feet. How many square feet of carpet will he need?

Problem-Solving Strategies
- ☑ Draw a diagram.
- ☐ Use logical reasoning.
- ☐ Solve a simpler problem.
- ☐ Work backward.
- ☐ Make a table.

Understand   Read the problem. Write what you know.

The bedroom is a __square__ with lengths of __12__ feet.

Plan   Pick a strategy. One strategy is to draw a diagram.

You can make an array to represent his room.

Solve   Count the squares to find how many square feet fill the room.

The total number of squares is the same as the product of __12__ · __12__.

__12__ · __12__ = __144__

So, Rajesh will need __144__ square feet of carpet.

Check   Does your answer seem reasonable? Count each square unit in the diagram.

14 **HEALTH**   Jocelyn has been training for a marathon. The <u>first week</u> she trained <u>1 hour</u>, the <u>second week</u> she trained <u>4 hours</u>, and the <u>third week</u> she trained <u>9 hours</u>. If she <u>continues this pattern</u>, <u>how many hours</u> will she train for the marathon the <u>fourth week</u>? Check off each step.

___✔___ Understand: I underlined key words.

___✔___ Plan: To solve the problem, I will __draw a diagram__

___✔___ Solve: The answer is ____$4^2 = 16$ hours____

___✔___ Check: I checked my answer by __counting the square units in the diagram__

GO ON

Intervention Strategy

Kinesthetic/Intrapersonal Learners

Recognize Perfect Squares   Give each student a sheet of grid paper. Write 1^2 on the board. What does the array look like? Write the other square numbers on the board from 2^2 to 6^2 and have students make a square array for each. Now write 64 on the board. Is this a square number? How do we know? Move back and forth between exponents and perfect squares so students can gain automaticity in recognizing perfect squares.

Math Coach Notes

Flashcards   Tell students to make a set of flashcards with the base and exponent on one side, and the perfect square on the other. Students can quiz each other to develop automaticity.

Strategies

1. Begin this lesson with a hands-on anchoring experience. Tell students to make as many arrays for each number up to 20 as they can. Then go through the arrays. Notice patterns. Guide students to see that only a few numbers can form square arrays.

2. During this lesson connect square units to perfect squares in preparation for future lessons on area.

Common Error Alert

Multi-Step Problems   If students have difficulty finding the products in Exercise 15, use tiles. Have students make models to represent the expression. How many tiles make up the array? How do we write the length times the width of the array using an exponent? Have them complete the table as they proceed. Guide students to see the relationship between the terms and expressions on the table.

Odd/Even Assignments

Exercises 17–40 are structured so that students practice the same concepts whether they are assigned the odd or even problems.

In-Class Assignment

Have students complete Exercises 18, 21, 23, 35, 38, and 44 to ensure that they understand the concept.

15 SCIENCE   Derrick is conducting an experiment growing mold. He measures the area it covers daily. Complete the table showing the mold's growth.

Dimensions	1 · 1	2 · 2	3 · 3	4 · 4	5 · 5	6 · 6	7 · 7	8 · 8	9 · 9	10 · 10
Exponential Form	1^2	2^2	3^2	4^2	5^2	6^2	7^2	8^2	9^2	10^2
Area	1	4	9	16	25	36	49	64	81	100

16 Reflect   Define an exponent. Explain why you would use an exponent.

An exponent tells how many times a base is multiplied by itself.

It is a shortcut and saves space.

▶ Skills, Concepts, and Problem Solving

Write an equation using exponents to represent each model.

17 $4^2 = 16$

18 $8^2 = 64$

19 $6^2 = 36$

20 $9^2 = 81$

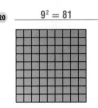

English Learner Strategy

Use a Number Line   Have students make a number line with the numbers from 1^2 to 12^2 evenly spaced above the line. Then have them write the squares of each number under the line. Students can use this number line as a reference to see if a number is a perfect square or what the perfect square of a square term is.

Write an equation using exponents to represent each model.

21 $11^2 = 121$

22 $10^2 = 100$

Evaluate each expression.

23 7^2 $\quad 7 \cdot 7 = 49$

24 12^2 $\quad 12 \cdot 12 = 144$

25 11^2 $\quad 11 \cdot 11 = 121$

26 9^2 $\quad 9 \cdot 9 = 81$

27 2^2 $\quad 2 \cdot 2 = 4$

28 8^2 $\quad 8 \cdot 8 = 64$

29 4^2 $\quad 4 \cdot 4 = 16$

30 6^2 $\quad 6 \cdot 6 = 36$

31 5^2 $\quad 5 \cdot 5 = 25$

32 10^2 $\quad 10 \cdot 10 = 100$

33 3^2 $\quad 3 \cdot 3 = 9$

34 1^2 $\quad 1 \cdot 1 = 1$

Solve.

35 PUZZLES Write a two-digit number the sum of whose digits is 10. The number is a squared number. __64__

36 PUZZLES Write a two-digit number the sum of whose digits is 7. The number is a squared even number. __16__

37 PUZZLES Write a two-digit number the sum of whose digits is 9. The number is a squared odd number. __81__

GO ON

Kinesthetic/
Visual/
Logical
Learners

Intervention Strategy

Real-World Objects Have students select items from home or the classroom that have square bases or are a square. These items could include a book, a tissue box, or a square pyramid. Tell students to measure the base side to the nearest whole number and then write the area of the base as an exponent. For instance, a tissue box with a side length of about 4 inches would have an area of 4^2 inches. Demonstrate to students how 4^2 inches is written as 16 square inches or 16 in². Have them write the area of their base in square units. Discuss the results.

Math Challenge

Make and Play Cards Students can play in pairs. Have them make two sets of cards on index cards. One set should be composed of five 0s, five 1s, and five 10s. The other set should be numbers from 0 to 20. Shuffle both and set them facedown. One student will draw a card from each pile. The student who finds the product first gets the point.

See It, Do It, Say It, Write It

Step 1 Write 3 • 3 on the board. Ask students how to write the expression in exponent form. What will the array look like? Repeat with other expressions.

Step 2 Give each student grid or dot paper. Tell them to draw five square arrays with side lengths of 12 or less. Then have them trade with a partner.

Step 3 Tell them to say the fact for each array, along with the product. What are these products called?

Step 4 Tell students to write the words *factor, perfect square, base,* and *exponent* on paper. Then tell them to write a definition for each word. Ask them to include one example or illustration.

Looking Ahead: Pre-Teach

Square Roots In the next lesson, students will learn about square roots.

Example

Find $\sqrt{25}$.

Name two equal factors that have a product of 25.
$5 \cdot 5 = 25$
$\sqrt{25} = 5$

Have students find each square root.

1. $\sqrt{16}$ 4

2. $\sqrt{100}$ 10

3. $\sqrt{1}$ 1

---

38 **FARMING** Darin planted 12 rows of 12 bean plants. Write an expression using an exponent to represent the number of bean plants. Find the value of the expression.

$12^2 = 12 \cdot 12 = 144$; 144 bean plants

39 **REUNION** The reunion committee has arranged name tags on the welcome table in 13 rows of 13. Write an expression using an exponent to represent the number of name tags placed on the table. Find the value of the expression.

$13^2 = 13 \cdot 13 = 169$; 169 name tags

40 **OFFICE SPACE** Sarasa is arranging cubicles for her company. She will use 10 rows of 10 cubicles. Make an array to represent the area.

Write an expression using an exponent to represent the number of cubicles Sarasa will arrange. Find the value of the expression.

$10^2 = 10 \cdot 10 = 100$; 100 cubicles

Vocabulary Check **Write the vocabulary word that completes each sentence.**

41 A(n) _____squared_____ number is a number multiplied by itself, such as 4 • 4.

42 The _____exponent_____ tells you how many times a base is multiplied by itself.

43 In the number 8^2, the _____base_____ is 8.

44 **Writing in Math** The expression $(-4)^2$ has a value of 16 because $-4 \cdot (-4) = 16$. What is the value of the expression $(-6)^2$? Explain your reasoning.

The value of the expression $(-6)^2$ is 36. $(-6)^2 = -6 \cdot (-6)$ When two negative integers are multiplied, the product is positive. $-6 \cdot (-6) = 36$

Ticket Out the Door

Square the Cube Have students work in pairs. Each student will roll a number cube. Students will then square the number of each cube and then find the difference of their values. Tell them to write down all their work. For example, if the two numbers rolled are 3 and 8, students would write $8^2 - 3^2$, and the difference will be $64 - 9 = 55$. Students will hand in their papers as they exit the classroom.

Lesson 6-2 Square Roots

KEY Concept

The **square of a number** is the product of two identical factors. For example, 5^2 means $5 \cdot 5$. The product of $5 \cdot 5$ is 25.

5 units

5 units

$5 \cdot 5 = 25$

Squaring a number and finding a **square root** are **inverse operations**. The square root of a number is one of its two equal factors.

The symbol for the positive square root is a **radical sign**, $\sqrt{\ }$.

The positive square root of 25 is written as $\sqrt{25}$. Since $5 \cdot 5 = 25$, we can rewrite $\sqrt{25}$ as $\sqrt{5 \cdot 5}$. So, 5 is the positive square root of 25.

$$\sqrt{25} = \sqrt{5 \cdot 5}$$
$$= 5$$

VOCABULARY

factor
a number that is multiplied by another number

inverse operations
operations which undo each other

radical sign
the symbol used to indicate a nonnegative square root, $\sqrt{\ }$

square of a number
the product of a number multiplied by itself; $4 \cdot 4$, or 4^2

square root
one of two equal factors of a number; if $a^2 = b$, then a is the square root of b

An area model represents a square number when the number of rows and the number of columns are equal. In the area model above there are 5 rows and 5 columns.

Example 1

Find the positive square root using an area model.

1. How many square units are shown? 16
2. How many columns are shown? 4
3. How many rows are shown? 4
4. Are the number of rows and columns equal? yes

So, $\sqrt{16} = 4$.

GO ON

Lesson 6-2 Square Roots **225**

Additional *Example 1*

Find the positive square root using an area model.

1. How many square units are shown? 36
2. How many columns are shown? 6
3. How many rows are shown? 6
4. Are the number of rows and columns equal? yes

So, $\sqrt{36} = 6$.

Lesson Planner

Objective Find positive roots of perfect squares.

Vocabulary factors, inverse operations, radical sign, square of a number, square root

Materials/Manipulatives multiplication facts chart, unit cubes, geoboard, rubber bands

Chapter Resource Masters

- [CRM] Vocabulary and English Language Development (p. A111)
- [CRM] Skills Practice (p. A112)
- [CRM] Problem-Solving Practice (p. A113)
- [CRM] Homework Practice (p. A114)

① Introduce

Vocabulary

Exponents Review how to evaluate powers. Write 3^2 on the board. Ask what the base is. Then ask what the exponent is. Which is a factor, the base or the exponent?

② Teach

Key Concept

Foundational Skills and Concepts After students have read through the Key Concept box, have them try these exercises.

1. What does $\sqrt{16}$ mean? It means a factor multiplied by itself will equal 16, or $\sqrt{4 \cdot 4}$.

2. What square root simplifies to 6? the answer as a factor two times; $6 = \sqrt{6 \cdot 6} = \sqrt{36}$

3. Evaluate 7^2. 7^2 means 7 multiplied by itself 2 times; $7 \cdot 7 = 49$

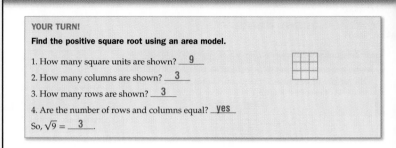

Additional *Example 2*

Find the positive square root of 144.

1. Write the expression. $\sqrt{144}$

2. Name the factor pairs of 144.
$1 \cdot 144, 2 \cdot 72, 3 \cdot 48, 4 \cdot 36, 6 \cdot 24,$
$8 \cdot 18, 9 \cdot 16, 12 \cdot 12$

3. Replace 144 with the set of identical factors.
$\sqrt{12 \cdot 12}$

So, $\sqrt{144} = 12.$

Math Coach Notes

Fluency Encourage students to practice finding positive square roots until fluency is attained. When students master automatic recognition of positive square roots, more complex computation can be done using mental math. Have students practice by creating and using flash cards.

YOUR TURN!

Find the positive square root using an area model.

1. How many square units are shown? __9__
2. How many columns are shown? __3__
3. How many rows are shown? __3__
4. Are the number of rows and columns equal? __yes__

So, $\sqrt{9} = $ __3__.

Example 2

Find the positive square root of 49.

1. Write the expression.
$\sqrt{49}$

2. Name the factor pairs of 49.
$1 \cdot 49, 7 \cdot 7$

3. Replace 49 with the set of identical factors.
$\sqrt{7 \cdot 7}$

So, $\sqrt{49} = 7.$

YOUR TURN!

Find the positive square root of 64.

1. Write the expression.
$\sqrt{64}$

2. Name the factor pairs of 64.
$1 \cdot 64, 2 \cdot 32, 4 \cdot 16, 8 \cdot 8$

3. Replace 64 with the set of identical factors.
$\sqrt{8 \cdot 8}$

So, $\sqrt{64} = 8$.

Who is Correct?

Find the positive square root of 16.

Circle the correct answer(s). Cross out incorrect answer(s).

Who *is Correct?*
Diagnostic Teaching

- Rondell is correct. He found identical factors to determine the square root.

- Kenyon is incorrect. He used identical addends of 16 under the radical sign instead of factors.

- Orenda is incorrect. Her factors under the radical sign are not identical.

Remind students that a square root of a number is the product of identical factors.

Guided Practice

Find the positive square root using an area model.

1

$\sqrt{4} = \underline{\quad 2 \quad}$

2

$\sqrt{1} = \underline{\quad 1 \quad}$

Step by Step **Practice**

3 Find the positive square root of 121.

Step 1 Write the expression. $\underline{\quad \sqrt{121} \quad}$

Step 2 Name the factor pairs of 121. $\underline{\quad 1 \cdot 121, \ 11 \cdot 11 \quad}$

Step 3 Replace 121 with the set of identical factors. $\underline{\quad \sqrt{11 \cdot 11} \quad}$

Step 4 $\underline{\quad \sqrt{121} = 11 \quad}$

Find the positive square root of each number.

4 169

Write the expression. $\underline{\quad \sqrt{169} \quad}$

Name the factor pairs. $\underline{\quad 1 \cdot 169, \ 13 \cdot 13 \quad}$

Replace 169 with the set of identical factors. $\underline{\quad \sqrt{13 \cdot 13} \quad}$

$\sqrt{169} = \underline{\quad 13 \quad}$

5 36

Write the expression. $\underline{\quad \sqrt{36} \quad}$

Name the factor pairs. $\underline{\quad 1 \cdot 36, \ 2 \cdot 18, \ 3 \cdot 12, \ 4 \cdot 9, \ 6 \cdot 6 \quad}$

Replace 36 with the set of identical factors. $\underline{\quad \sqrt{6 \cdot 6} \quad}$

$\sqrt{36} = \underline{\quad 6 \quad}$

6 144

Write the expression. $\underline{\quad \sqrt{144} \quad}$

Name the factor pairs. $\underline{\quad 1 \cdot 144, \ 2 \cdot 72, \ 3 \cdot 48, \ 4 \cdot 36, \ 6 \cdot 24, \ 8 \cdot 18, \ 9 \cdot 16, \ 12 \cdot 12 \quad}$

Replace 144 with the set of identical factors. $\underline{\quad \sqrt{12 \cdot 12} \quad}$

$\sqrt{144} = \underline{\quad 12 \quad}$

GO ON

Lesson 6-2 Square Roots   **227**

---

3 Practice

Using Manipulatives

Geoboards   Model how to make an area model using a geoboard and a rubber band. Have students create models and write square root expressions for their models.

On-Hand Manipulatives   Have students use unit cubes to create area models. Ask students to write and evaluate fact families and square roots based on the models. Students can also use the unit cubes to model inverse operations.

⚠️ **Common Error** *Alert*

Square Root of 1   In Exercise 2, the area model shows one unit. This may be confusing to students. Explain that the model indicates 1 row of 1 column. Point out the family of $1 \cdot 1 = 1$ and remind students that $\sqrt{1}$ is the same as $\sqrt{1 \cdot 1}$.

English Learner Strategy

Background Knowledge   In Exercise 8, explain what a mosaic is. Encourage students to discuss when and where they have seen mosaics or whether they have ever made one. Include details about what kinds of materials could be used to make mosaics, the different shapes and sizes of the pieces, and how the smaller pieces are used to create a whole. Then relate the composition of mosaics to area models.

Note This!

Square Root Expressions   When evaluating square roots, the only operation under the radical sign is multiplication. The factors must be identical to extract a square root.

Step by Step Problem-Solving Practice

Solve.

7   **GARDENS**   Mrs. Ramano's garden has an area of 144 square feet. The length of the garden and the width of the garden are the same. Use the positive square root of 144 to find the length of the garden.

Problem-Solving Strategies
- ☐ Draw a diagram.
- ☐ Use logical reasoning.
- ☐ Solve a simpler problem.
- ☐ Work backward.
- ☑ Use a model.

Understand	Read the problem. Write what you know.

The garden has an area of __144__ square feet.

The length and the width are __equal__.

Plan   Pick a strategy. One strategy is to use an area model.

Solve   Use the square to create an area model. Divide the square into equal rows and columns until 144 square units are shown.

There are __12__ rows and __12__ columns.

$\sqrt{144} = \sqrt{12 \cdot 12} = 12$

The length of the garden is __12__ feet.

Check   Use the inverse operation. __12^2__ $= 144$

8   **TILES**   Margarette is making a mosaic for her aunt's birthday present. She wants the mosaic to be <u>square</u>. She plans to use <u>81 tiles</u>. Use the <u>positive square root of 81</u> to determine <u>how many rows and columns</u> she will create.

Check off each step.

__✔__ Understand: I underlined key words.

__✔__ Plan: To solve the problem, I will __use an area model__.

__✔__ Solve: The answer is __$\sqrt{81} = 9$; 9 columns and 9 rows__.

__✔__ Check: I checked my answer by using __the inverse__ operation; $9^2 = 81$

228   **Chapter 6** Squares, Square Roots, and the Pythagorean Theorem

---

Are They Getting It?

Check students' understanding of square roots by writing these problems on the board. Ask them to point out incorrect answers and explain their reasoning.

1. $6^2 = 6 \cdot 2$. This is incorrect. The exponent tells how many times to multiply the base times itself. $6^2 = 6 \cdot 6$, or 36

2. If $x^2 = y$, then $\sqrt{x} = y$. This is incorrect. If $x^2 = y$, then $x = \sqrt{y}$.

3. The positive square root of 225 is 15. This is correct.

9 **Reflect** Explain how knowing the factors of a number helps you find the number's positive square root.

Listing the factor pairs will help you find the identical factors. For instance,
the factors of 9 are 1 · 9 and 3 · 3. Since 3 · 3 shows identical factors of 3,
the positive square root of 9 is 3.

▶ Skills, Concepts, and Problem Solving

Find the positive square root using an area model.

10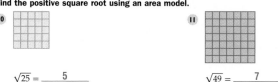

$\sqrt{25} =$ ___5___

11

$\sqrt{49} =$ ___7___

Find the positive square root of each number.

12 81

Write the expression. ___$\sqrt{81}$___

Name the factor pairs. ___1 · 81, 3 · 27, 9 · 9___

Replace 81 with the set of identical factors. ___$\sqrt{9 \cdot 9}$___

$\sqrt{81} =$ ___9___

13 100

Write the expression. ___$\sqrt{100}$___

Name the factor pairs. ___1 · 100, 2 · 50, 4 · 25, 5 · 20, 10 · 10___

Replace 100 with the set of identical factors. ___$\sqrt{10 \cdot 10}$___

$\sqrt{100} =$ ___10___

14 196

Write the expression. ___$\sqrt{196}$___

Name the factor pairs. ___1 · 196, 2 · 98, 7 · 28, 4 · 49, 14 · 14___

Replace 196 with the set of identical factors. ___$\sqrt{14 \cdot 14}$___

$\sqrt{196} =$ ___14___

GO ON

Odd/Even Assignments

Exercises 10–16 are structured so that students practice the same concepts whether they are assigned the odd or even problems.

In-Class Assignment

Have students complete Exercises 10, 12, 15, and 19 to ensure that they understand the concept.

⚠ **Common Error** _Alert_

Exercises 12–14 Use these practice problems to remind students to find identical factors when solving for square roots. They may not extend the list of factors long enough to find the identical pair. Encourage students to name all of the factors first before looking at the pairs.

Math Challenge

Area Max and Tyrell each have square bedrooms. The square root of Max's bedroom is 10 feet. The square root of Tyrell's bedroom is 2 feet less. How many total square feet is Tyrell's bedroom?

64 square feet

See It, Do It, Say It, Write It

Step 1 Draw an 11 • 11 area model on the board.

Step 2 Ask students to write the square root expression modeled on the board. Then have them name the factors of the expression and find the square root.

Step 3 Have students work in pairs. Tell them to discuss how they determined the expression, found the identical factors, and decided on the square root.

Step 4 Students should work alone to write their evaluations of the area model on the board. Encourage clear and correct vocabulary in their explanations.

Looking Ahead: Pre-teach

Approximate Square Roots   In the next lesson, students will learn to approximate square roots.

Example

Estimate $\sqrt{20}$ to the nearest whole number.

Write an inequality using common square roots.
$$\sqrt{16} < \sqrt{20} < \sqrt{25}$$
$$\sqrt{4 \cdot 4} < \sqrt{20} < \sqrt{5 \cdot 5}$$
$$4 < \sqrt{20} < 5$$
$\sqrt{20}$ is closer to $\sqrt{16}$, so $\sqrt{20}$ is closer to 4.

Have students approximate each square root.

1. $\sqrt{5}$ 2
2. $\sqrt{30}$ 5
3. $\sqrt{18}$ 4

Solve.

15. **CLASS SUPPLIES**   Mr. Orta wants to order a set of cubbie boxes with 169 small squares. The cubbie box has the same number of rows and columns. Use the positive square root of 169 to find the number of columns on the cubbie box.

$\sqrt{169} = \sqrt{13 \cdot 13} = 13.$ There are 13 columns on the cubbie box.

16. **CHESS**   A chessboard has 64 small squares that create a larger square. The number of rows is equal to the number of columns. Use the positive square root of 64 to find the number of rows on a chessboard.

$\sqrt{64} = \sqrt{8 \cdot 8} = 8.$ There are 8 rows on a chessboard.

Vocabulary Check   Write the vocabulary word that completes each sentence.

17. Squaring a number and finding a square root are <u>inverse operations</u>.

18. The <u>square root</u> of a number is one of two equal factors of the number.

19. **Writing in Math**   Explain how an area model can help you find the positive square root of a number.

To find the positive square root, count the number of rows and columns. If the number of rows is equal to the number of columns, this is the positive square root of the number.

 **Spiral Review**

Solve. (Lesson 6–1, p. 218)

20. **GAMES**   Mariska wants to arrange 8 rows of 8 game cards for her memory game. How many cards will she need? Write an expression using exponents to represent the number of cards. Find the value of the expression.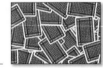

$8^2 = 8 \cdot 8 = 64;$ 64 cards

Evaluate each expression. (Lesson 6–1, p. 218)

21. 5^2 $5 \cdot 5 = 25$

22. 7^2 $7 \cdot 7 = 49$

23. 9^2 $9 \cdot 9 = 81$

24. 6^2 $6 \cdot 6 = 36$

Ticket Out the Door

Evaluating Square Roots   Draw an 8 • 8 area model on the board. As students approach the classroom door to exit, alternate asking them to name the square root expression the model represents, list a factor pair of the expression, or identify the square root.

Progress Check 1 (Lessons 6-1 and 6-2)

Write an equation using exponents to represent each model.

1 $6^2 = 36$

2 $3^2 = 9$

Evaluate each expression.

3 1^2 $1 \cdot 1 = 1$

4 7^2 $7 \cdot 7 = 49$

5 9^2 $9 \cdot 9 = 81$

6 11^2 $11 \cdot 11 = 121$

Find the positive square root of each number.

7 64

Name the factor pairs. $1 \cdot 64, 2 \cdot 32, 4 \cdot 16, 8 \cdot 8$

Replace 64 with the set of identical factors. $\sqrt{8 \cdot 8}$

$\sqrt{64} =$ 8

8 225

Name the factor pairs. $1 \cdot 225, 3 \cdot 75, 5 \cdot 45, 9 \cdot 25, 15 \cdot 15$

Replace 225 with the set of identical factors. $\sqrt{15 \cdot 15}$

$\sqrt{225} =$ 15

9 169

Name the factor pairs. $1 \cdot 169, 13 \cdot 13$

Replace 169 with the set of identical factors. $\sqrt{13 \cdot 13}$

$\sqrt{169} =$ 13

Solve.

10 **PUZZLES** Write a two-digit number the sum of whose digits is 13. The number is a squared number. 49

11 **CHAIRS** A small concert hall has 144 seats. The number of rows is equal to the number of columns. Use the positive square root of 144 to find the number of seats in each row.

$\sqrt{144} = \sqrt{12 \cdot 12} = 12$; There are 12 seats in each row.

Progress Check **231**

Progress Check 1

Formative Assessment

Use the Progress Check to assess students' mastery of the previous lessons. Have students review the lesson indicated for the problems they answered incorrectly.

Odd/Even Assignments

Exercises are structured so that students practice the same concepts whether they are assigned the odd or even problems.

 Common Error *Alert*

Exercise 8 For numbers greater than 100, many students will not recognize perfect squares. If they list all the sets of factors and do not find an identical pair, encourage them to make a factor tree and then group the factors into identical groups of factors. The square root is the product of the group of factors. For Exercise 8, the factor tree might be

$225 = 5 \cdot 45$
$= 5 \cdot 5 \cdot 9$
$= 5 \cdot 5 \cdot 3 \cdot 3$

Arrange into identical groups.

$5 \cdot 3 \quad 5 \cdot 3$
$\sqrt{225} = 15$

Data-Driven Decision Making

Students missing Exercises . . .	Have trouble with . . .	Should review and practice . . .
1–2	using models to find perfect squares.	SSG Lesson 6-1, p. 218 CRM Skills Practice, p. A108
3–6	finding perfect squares.	SSG Lesson 6-1, p. 218 CRM Skills Practice, p. A108
7–9	finding square roots.	SSG Lesson 6-2, p. 225 CRM Skills Practice, p. A112
10–11	solving word problems involving squares and square roots.	CRM Problem-Solving Practice, pp. A109 and A113

Lesson Notes

Lesson Planner

Objective   Estimate positive square roots.

Vocabulary   estimate , square root

Materials/Manipulatives   rulers, masking tape, index cards, calculators

Chapter Resource Masters

- CRM Vocabulary and English Language Development (p. A115)
- CRM Skills Practice (p. A116)
- CRM Problem-Solving Practice (p. A117)
- CRM Homework Practice (p. A118)

1 Introduce

Vocabulary

Whole Numbers   Review the set of whole numbers. Use a number line to plot and compare these numbers. Review inequality symbols. Write inequalities and encourage students to state math sentences using whole numbers.

2 Teach

Key Concept

Foundational Skills and Concepts   After students have read through the Key Concept box, have them try these exercises.

1. If $6 < 7$, write an inequality using their positive square roots.
   $$\sqrt{6} < \sqrt{7}$$

2. Compare the positive square root of 18 to the positive square root of 25.
   $18 < 25$, so $\sqrt{18} < \sqrt{25}$.

3. Use the positive square root of 9 to estimate the positive square root of 11.
   You know that $9 < 11$, so $\sqrt{9} < \sqrt{11}$.
   The positive square root of 9 is 3, so the positive square root of 11 is greater than 3.

Approximate Square Roots

KEY Concept

If you know how to determine the square root of a positive whole number, you can **estimate** square roots.

The table below shows some common **square roots**.

Common Square Roots		
$\sqrt{1} = 1$	$\sqrt{36} = 6$	$\sqrt{121} = 11$
$\sqrt{4} = 2$	$\sqrt{49} = 7$	$\sqrt{144} = 12$
$\sqrt{9} = 3$	$\sqrt{64} = 8$	$\sqrt{169} = 13$
$\sqrt{16} = 4$	$\sqrt{81} = 9$	$\sqrt{196} = 14$
$\sqrt{25} = 5$	$\sqrt{100} = 10$	$\sqrt{225} = 15$

You can use these square roots to estimate other square roots.

You know that the number 5 is between 4 and 9. The number line below shows this relationship.

Since 5 is between 4 and 9, $\sqrt{5}$ must be between $\sqrt{4}$ and $\sqrt{9}$.

The number line above shows the relationship between the square roots.

$$\sqrt{4} = 2.00 \qquad \sqrt{5} \approx 2.23 \qquad \sqrt{9} = 3.00$$

This relationship can be shown as an inequality.

$$\sqrt{4} < \sqrt{5} < \sqrt{9}$$

VOCABULARY

estimate
a number close to an exact value; an estimate indicates *about* how much

square root
one of two equal factors of a number; if $a^2 = b$, then a is the square root of b

Memorizing the common square roots in the table will help you estimate square roots through 225.

Intervention Strategy

Kinesthetic Learners

Big Number Line   Use masking tape to create a number line in equal increments on the classroom floor. Split a package of index cards among groups of students. Have one group write the numbers 1 through 15, one number per card. With the remaining cards, other groups should write one square root per card ($\sqrt{1}, \sqrt{2}, \sqrt{3}, \sqrt{4}$, etc.) up to $\sqrt{225}$.

Have students use the cards to create visual inequalities. Invite a group of three students to the number line. One student draws a card from the square root pile. The group decides between which two whole numbers that square root is located. The three students find the two whole number cards and stand on the number line, each holding an index card to model where the square root would be between these two whole numbers. Have the class write the inequalities shown by each group's cards.

Example 1

Estimate $\sqrt{14}$ to the nearest whole number.

1. Write an inequality using common square roots.

$\sqrt{9} < \sqrt{14} < \sqrt{16}$

2. Find the values of the common square roots.

$\sqrt{9} = \sqrt{3 \cdot 3} = 3 \qquad \sqrt{16} = \sqrt{4 \cdot 4} = 4$

3. Plot the values of each square root on the number line.

So, $\sqrt{14}$ is between 3 and 4.

4. Since $\sqrt{14}$ is closer to $\sqrt{16}$ than $\sqrt{9}$, $\sqrt{14}$ is closer to the whole number 4.

YOUR TURN!

Estimate $\sqrt{8}$ to the nearest whole number.

1. Write an inequality using common square roots.

$\underline{\sqrt{4}} < \underline{\sqrt{8}} < \underline{\sqrt{9}}$

2. Find the values of the common square roots.

$\sqrt{4} = \dfrac{\sqrt{2 \cdot 2}}{2} = \underline{2} \qquad \sqrt{9} = \dfrac{\sqrt{3 \cdot 3}}{3} = \underline{3}$

3. Plot the values of each square root on the number line.

So, $\sqrt{8}$ is between $\underline{2}$ and $\underline{3}$.

4. Since $\sqrt{8}$ is closer to $\underline{\sqrt{9}}$ than $\underline{\sqrt{4}}$, $\sqrt{8}$ is closer to the whole number $\underline{3}$.

GO ON

Additional *Example 1*

Estimate $\sqrt{21}$ to the nearest whole number.

1. Write an inequality using common square roots.

$\sqrt{16} < \sqrt{21} < \sqrt{25}$

2. Find the values of the common square roots.

$\sqrt{16} = \sqrt{4 \cdot 4} = 4$
$\sqrt{25} = \sqrt{5 \cdot 5} = 5$

3. Plot the values of each square root on the number line.

So, $\sqrt{21}$ is between 4 and 5.

4. Since $\sqrt{21}$ is closer to $\sqrt{25}$ than $\sqrt{16}$, $\sqrt{21}$ is closer to the whole number 5.

Note This!

Multiplication Facts Students will be better able to recognize square roots if they have mastered their multiplication facts. Have students practice squaring whole numbers up to 15. The more times they see these products, the more quickly they will be able to estimate and compare square roots of uncommon whole numbers.

English Learner Strategy

Connections Have students discuss when they would use estimation in their daily lives. Tell students to brainstorm real-life situations in which an exact answer is not necessary and estimating is enough. Give examples such as deciding if you had enough money to purchase an item, whether an object will fit into a container, deciding what to wear based on the temperature, or if you have enough time to complete a task. Encourage students to use clear vocabulary and to give enough details for their examples.

Choose a reasonable estimate for $\sqrt{130}$.

1. Write an inequality using common square roots.

$$\sqrt{121} < \sqrt{130} < \sqrt{144}$$

2. Find the values of the common square roots.

$$\sqrt{121} = \sqrt{11 \cdot 11} = 11$$
$$\sqrt{144} = \sqrt{12 \cdot 12} = 12$$

3. So, $\sqrt{130}$ is between 11 and 12.

4. Since $\sqrt{130}$ is closer to $\sqrt{121}$ than $\sqrt{144}$, $\sqrt{130}$ is closer to the whole number 11.

5. Circle the reasonable estimate.

    12.3   11.8   (11.4)

Example 2

Choose a reasonable estimate for $\sqrt{109}$.

1. Write an inequality using common square roots.

$\sqrt{100} < \sqrt{109} < \sqrt{121}$

2. Find the values of the common square roots.

$\sqrt{100} = \sqrt{10 \cdot 10} = 10 \qquad \sqrt{121} = \sqrt{11 \cdot 11} = 11$

So, $\sqrt{109}$ is between 10 and 11.

4. Since $\sqrt{109}$ is closer to $\sqrt{100}$ than $\sqrt{121}$, $\sqrt{109}$ is closer to the whole number 10.

5. Circle the reasonable estimate.

(10.4)   10.8   11.2

YOUR TURN!

Choose a reasonable estimate for $\sqrt{50}$.

1. Write an inequality using common square roots.

$\sqrt{\underline{49}} < \sqrt{50} < \sqrt{\underline{64}}$

2. Find the values of the common square roots.

$\sqrt{\underline{49}} = \sqrt{\underline{7 \cdot 7}} = \underline{7} \qquad \sqrt{\underline{64}} = \sqrt{\underline{8 \cdot 8}} = \underline{8}$

So, $\sqrt{50}$ is between $\underline{7}$ and $\underline{8}$.

4. Since $\sqrt{50}$ is closer to $\sqrt{\underline{49}}$ than $\sqrt{\underline{64}}$, $\sqrt{50}$ is closer to the whole number $\underline{7}$.

5. Circle the reasonable estimate.

6.8   (7.1)   7.6

Who is Correct?

Estimate $\sqrt{18}$ to the nearest whole number.

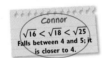
Connor
$\sqrt{16} < \sqrt{18} < \sqrt{25}$
Falls between 4 and 5; it is closer to 4.

Rachelle
$\sqrt{16} < \sqrt{18} < \sqrt{20}$
Falls between 9 and 10; it is closer to 9.

Masao
$\sqrt{16} < \sqrt{18} < \sqrt{25}$
Falls between 4 and 5; it is closer to 5.

Circle correct answer(s). Cross out incorrect answer(s).

Who **is Correct?**
Diagnostic Teaching

- Connor is correct. He used the closest common square roots and estimated correctly.

- Rachelle is incorrect. She did not choose the closest common square roots. 20 is not a perfect square.

- Masao is incorrect. He used the closest common square roots, but did not name the closer number correctly.

Guided Practice

Write an inequality using common square roots.

1. $\sqrt{81} < \sqrt{84} < \sqrt{100}$

2. $\sqrt{121} < \sqrt{136} < \sqrt{144}$

3. $\sqrt{16} < \sqrt{21} < \sqrt{25}$

4. $\sqrt{36} < \sqrt{47} < \sqrt{49}$

5. $\sqrt{9} < \sqrt{13} < \sqrt{16}$

6. $\sqrt{196} < \sqrt{200} < \sqrt{225}$

Step by Step Practice

7. Estimate $\sqrt{92}$ to the nearest whole number.

Step 1 Write an inequality using common square roots.

$\sqrt{81} < \sqrt{92} < \sqrt{100}$

Step 2 Find the values of the common square roots.

$\sqrt{81} = \sqrt{9 \cdot 9} = \underline{9}$ $\sqrt{100} = \sqrt{10 \cdot 10} = \underline{10}$

Step 3 Plot the values of each square root on the number line.

So, $\sqrt{92}$ is between __9__ and __10__.

Step 4 Since $\sqrt{92}$ is closer to $\sqrt{100}$ than $\sqrt{81}$, $\sqrt{92}$ is closer to the whole number __10__.

Estimate each square root to the nearest whole number. Plot each value on a number line.

8. $\sqrt{7}$ is close to the whole number ___3___.

9. $\sqrt{68}$ is close to the whole number ___8___.

$\sqrt{64}$ $\sqrt{68}$ $\sqrt{81}$
8   9

GO ON

Practice

Using Manipulatives

Calculator   Use a calculator to practice finding the squares and square roots of numbers.

On-Hand Manipulatives   Use a ruler as a number line for comparisons. Have students identify where square roots would fall between the marked whole numbers.

Math Coach Notes

Number Lines   Help students practice interpreting number lines set up in increments of tenths. This will make it easier to compare square root values and determine which whole number makes a more accurate estimate for an uncommon square root. Remind students that 0.5 and larger rounds up to the next whole number.

Are They Getting It? ?

Check students' understanding of estimating square roots by writing these problems on the board. Ask them to point out incorrect answers and explain their reasoning.

1. A reasonable estimate for $\sqrt{8}$ is 3. This is correct.

2. $\sqrt{32}$ is between 6 and 7. This is incorrect.
   $\sqrt{25} < \sqrt{32} < \sqrt{36}$, so $\sqrt{32}$ is between 5 and 6.

3. $\sqrt{109}$ is between 9 and 10. This is incorrect.
   $\sqrt{100} < \sqrt{109} < \sqrt{121}$, so $\sqrt{109}$ is between 10 and 11.

Common Error *Alert*

Exercises 10 and 11 In determining a reasonable estimate for each square root, students may be able to quickly eliminate one of the three answer choices but struggle with deciding between the remaining two. Remind students to draw a number line divided into increments of tenths. Having a visual reference will help them decide on the more accurate estimate.

Choose a reasonable estimate for each square root.

10 $\sqrt{22}$

$\sqrt{16} < \sqrt{22} < \sqrt{25}$

$\sqrt{16} = \underline{4}$ $\sqrt{25} = \underline{5}$

4.2 (4.7) 5.1

11 $\sqrt{139}$

$\sqrt{121} < \sqrt{139} < \sqrt{144}$

$\sqrt{121} = \underline{11}$ $\sqrt{144} = \underline{12}$

(11.8) 12.1 12.6

Step *by* Step *Problem-Solving Practice*

Solve.

12 PATIOS   Troy has a square patio in his backyard. The patio has an area of 172 square feet. Estimate the length and width of the patio.

Understand   Read the problem. Write what you know.

The patio is the shape of a __square__.

The length and width of squares are __equal__.

The total area is __172__ square feet.

Plan   Pick a strategy. One strategy is to use logical reasoning.

Solve   Find the common square roots that are close in value.

$\sqrt{169} < \sqrt{172} < \sqrt{196}$

So, $\sqrt{172}$ is between __13__ and __14__.

Since $\sqrt{172}$ is closer to $\sqrt{169}$ than $\sqrt{196}$, $\sqrt{172}$ is closer to the whole number __13__.

Check   Use a number line to check your answer.

$\sqrt{169}$ $\sqrt{172}$ $\sqrt{196}$

13   14

Problem-Solving Strategies
☐ Draw a diagram.
☑ Use logical reasoning.
☐ Work backward.
☐ Solve a simpler problem.
☐ Look for a pattern.

Intervention Strategy   Visual Learners

Write the following square root expressions on the board. Have students work in pairs. Tell them to estimate each square root to the nearest whole number. Pairs should draw a number line and plot each square root to prove their estimates are correct. Have pairs compare their conclusions and number lines with one another.

$\sqrt{6} \approx 2$

$\sqrt{45} \approx 7$

$\sqrt{117} \approx 11$

$\sqrt{154} \approx 12$

$\sqrt{185} \approx 14$

Odd/Even Assignments

Exercises 15–29 are structured so that students practice the same concepts whether they are assigned the odd or even problems

In-Class Assignment

Have students complete Exercises 16, 20, 23, 28, and 32 to ensure that they understand the concept.

13 GARDENS   Marlene is creating a garden in her yard. The garden will cover an <u>area of 15 square feet</u>. The garden will be <u>arranged as a square</u>. <u>Estimate the length and width</u> of the garden to the <u>nearest whole number</u>.
Check off each step.

✔ Understand: I underlined key words.

✔ Plan: To solve the problem, I will ___use logical reasoning___.

✔ Solve: The answer is ___the length and width will be___ ___between 3 and 4 feet; closer to 4 feet___.

✔ Check: I checked my answer by using ___a number line___.

14 Reflect   How is it helpful to estimate?

___Sample answer: Estimating answers can help you determine if exact answer___ ___responses are reasonable.___

Skills, Concepts, and Problem Solving

Write an inequality using common square roots.

15 $\sqrt{4} < \sqrt{5} < \sqrt{9}$

16 $\sqrt{25} < \sqrt{29} < \sqrt{36}$

17 $\sqrt{196} < \sqrt{217} < \sqrt{225}$

18 $\sqrt{169} < \sqrt{191} < \sqrt{196}$

Estimate each square root to the nearest whole number. Plot each value on a number line.

19 $\sqrt{11}$ is close to the whole number ___3___.

$\sqrt{9}$ $\sqrt{11}$ $\sqrt{16}$
3   4

20 $\sqrt{143}$ is close to the whole number ___12___.

$\sqrt{121}$ $\sqrt{143}\,\sqrt{144}$
11   12

21 $\sqrt{38}$ is close to the whole number ___6___.

$\sqrt{36}\,\sqrt{38}$ $\sqrt{49}$
6   7

GO ON

Lesson 6-3 Approximate Square Roots   **237**

Copyright © Glencoe/McGraw-Hill, a division of The McGraw-Hill Companies, Inc.

Math Challenge

Quilting   Michayla is making a square quilt. If the area is 198 square inches, about how many inches wide is the quilt?

about 14 inches

If she makes a second square quilt with a length about 2 inches shorter than her first quilt, what is its approximate area?

about 144 square inches

See It, Do It, Say It, Write It

Step 1 Write $\sqrt{68}$ on the board.

Step 2 Tell students to estimate this square root to the nearest whole number. Then have them choose a reasonable estimate: 7.9, 8.2, 8.5.

Step 3 Have students work with a partner. Students should discuss their whole number and decimal estimates. Tell students to prove their work using a number line.

Step 4 Ask students to work alone to write their evaluations of the square root on the board. Explanations should include proof of how they know their estimates are correct. Encourage clear language and correct vocabulary.

Looking Ahead: Pre-teach

Square Roots In the next lesson, students will learn about the Pythagorean Theorem.

Example

Find the length of the hypotenuse of the right triangle shown.

$a = 3$, $b = 4$, $c = $ hypotenuse

$$a^2 + b^2 = c^2$$
$$3^2 + 4^2 = c^2$$
$$9 + 16 = c^2$$
$$25 = c^2$$
$$\sqrt{25} = \sqrt{c^2}$$
$$5 = c$$

Have students find the length of each hypotenuse.

1. $a = 8$, $b = 6$ $c = 10$

2. $a = 1$, $b = 1$ $c = \sqrt{2}$

3. $a = 2$, $b = 6$ $c = \sqrt{40}$

Choose a reasonable estimate for each square root.

22 $\sqrt{88}$

　　8.8　　9.1　　(9.4)

23 $\sqrt{57}$

　　5.7　　(7.5)　　7.9

24 $\sqrt{71}$

　　(8.4)　　8.7　　9.2

25 $\sqrt{63}$

　　6.3　　7.4　　(7.9)

26 $\sqrt{14}$

　　3.2　　(3.7)　　4.1

27 $\sqrt{2}$

　　1.1　　(1.4)　　1.9

Solve.

28 **GAMES** A square game board had a total of 64 one-inch squares and a $\frac{1}{4}$-inch border. Estimate the length and width of the game board.

　　__about 8 inches__

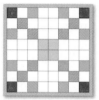

29 **AREA** Mr. Fox's bedroom is shaped like a square. The area is 120 square feet. Estimate the length and width of the room.

　　__about 11 feet__

Vocabulary Check **Write the vocabulary word that completes each sentence.**

30 A(n) _____estimate_____ indicates about how much.

31 The _____square root_____ of 169 is 13.

32 **Writing in Math** Explain how to find an estimate using a number line.

　　Write an inequality using common square roots. Then, find the values of the

　　common square roots. Compare the values of the square roots on the number line.

Spiral Review (Lesson 6-2, p. 225)

33 **VIDEO GAMES** Orlando is playing a dance video game. The game pad is made of 9 stepping squares. The number of rows and columns are the same. How many columns of stepping squares are on the game pad? Use the positive square root of 9 to determine the number of columns.

　　$\sqrt{9} = \sqrt{3 \cdot 3} = 3$; There are 3 columns on the game pad.

Ticket Out the Door

Estimating Square Roots Write $\sqrt{129}$ on the board. As students approach the classroom door to exit, alternate asking them to estimate this square root to the nearest whole number or state an inequality using this square root.

$\sqrt{129}$ is closest to 11. (11.36)

$\sqrt{121} < \sqrt{129} < \sqrt{144}$

$11 < \sqrt{129} < 12$

Lesson 6-4 Pythagorean Theorem

KEY Concept

You know that a triangle has three sides. A right triangle is a special triangle that has one right angle and two acute angles.

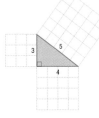

The sides of a right triangle have special names. A right triangle has two sides called **legs**. The legs in the triangle above are labeled a and b. The third side of the triangle is called the **hypotenuse**. It is labeled c.

The **Pythagorean Theorem** states that $a^2 + b^2 = c^2$. To prove the Pythagorean Theorem, count the number of squares beside each side of the triangle above.

You can also use the formula.

$a^2 + b^2 = c^2$	Use the formula.
$3^2 + 4^2 = 5^2$	Substitute the measures of each side.
$(3 \cdot 3) + (4 \cdot 4) = (5 \cdot 5)$	Simplify the exponents.
$9 + 16 = 25$	Multiply.
$25 = 25$	Add.

Given the measures of any two sides of a right triangle, you can use the Pythagorean Theorem to find the unknown length of the third side.

GO ON

VOCABULARY

hypotenuse
the side opposite the right angle in a right triangle

legs
the two sides of a right triangle that form the right angle

Pythagorean Theorem
in a right triangle, the square of the length of the hypotenuse, c, is equal to the sum of the squares of the lengths of the legs, a and b
$c^2 = a^2 + b^2$

square of a number
the product of a number multiplied by itself; $4 \cdot 4$, or 4^2

square root
one of two equal factors of a number; if $a^2 = b$, then a is the square root of b

Lesson 6-4 Pythagorean Theorem **239**

English Learner Strategy

Research Have students find information about Pythagoras on the Internet or in printed materials. Have them write a few sentences about Pythagoras on an index card with the theorem on the other side. Allow students to use the index card for reference.

Copyright © Glencoe/McGraw-Hill, a division of The McGraw-Hill Companies, Inc.

Lesson Notes

Lesson Planner

Objective Know and use the Pythagorean Theorem to find the lengths of unknown sides of a right triangle.

Vocabulary hypotenuse, legs, Pythagorean Theorem, square of a number, square root

Materials/Manipulatives rulers, protractors, grid paper, index cards

Chapter Resource Masters

- CRM Vocabulary and English Language Development (p. A119)
- CRM Skills Practice (p. A120)
- CRM Problem-Solving Practice (p. A121)
- CRM Homework Practice (p. A122)

1 Introduce

Vocabulary

Explore Vocabulary Draw a right triangle on the board with two leg measures. Have a student identify the right angle. Have a student volunteer come to the board and identify the *legs* and the *hypotenuse*. Explain that if the triangle is not a right triangle, then the Pythagorean Theorem cannot be used to find the length of a missing side.

2 Teach

Key Concept

Foundational Skills and Concepts After students have read through the Key Concept box, have them try these exercises.

1. What classification of a triangle applies to the Pythagorean Theorem? a right triangle

2. What is the name of the longest side in a right triangle? hypotenuse

3. How do you find a number to the second power? multiply it by itself

Lesson 6-4 Pythagorean Theorem **239**

Find the length of the hypotenuse of the
right triangle.

1. From the figure, you know that $a = 4$ and
   $b = 3$.

2. Substitute the values of a and b in the
   Pythagorean Theorem and solve for c.

   $$a^2 + b^2 = c^2 \quad \text{Use the formula.}$$
   $$4^2 + 3^2 = c^2 \quad \text{Substitute the measure of each side.}$$
   $$16 + 9 = c^2 \quad \text{Simplify the exponents.}$$
   $$25 = c^2 \quad \text{Add 16 and 9.}$$
   $$\sqrt{25} = \sqrt{c^2} \quad \text{Take the square root of both sides.}$$
   $$5 = c \quad \text{Simplify the square root.}$$

3. The length of the hypotenuse is 5 units.

Note This!

Sketch and Label Encourage students
to draw a picture of a right triangle with the
legs labeled a and b and the hypotenuse
labeled c. Underneath the picture, instruct
students to write the Pythagorean Theorem.
Suggest to students that they list instances
in which the Pythagorean Theorem is useful.

Example 1

Find the length of the hypotenuse of the right triangle.

1. From the figure, you know $a = 6$ and $b = 8$.

2. Substitute the values of a and b in the Pythagorean Theorem and
   solve for c.

   $$a^2 + b^2 = c^2 \quad \text{Use the formula.}$$
   $$6^2 + 8^2 = c^2 \quad \text{Substitute the measure of each side.}$$
   $$36 + 64 = c^2 \quad \text{Simplify the exponents.}$$
   $$100 = c^2 \quad \text{Add 36 and 64.}$$
   $$\sqrt{100} = \sqrt{c^2} \quad \text{Take the square root of both sides.}$$
   $$10 = c \quad \text{Simplify the square root.}$$

3. The length of the hypotenuse is 10 units.

YOUR TURN!

Find the length of the hypotenuse of the right triangle.

1. From the figure, you know
   $a = \underline{\;9\;}$ and $b = \underline{\;12\;}$.

2. Substitute the values of a and b in the Pythagorean Theorem and
   solve for c.

   $$a^2 + b^2 = c^2$$
   $$\underline{\;9\;}^2 + \underline{\;12\;}^2 = c^2$$
   $$\underline{\;81\;} + \underline{\;144\;} = c^2$$
   $$\underline{\;225\;} = c^2$$
   $$\sqrt{\underline{\;225\;}} = \sqrt{c^2}$$
   $$\underline{\;15\;} = c$$

3. The length of the hypotenuse is $\underline{\;15\;}$ units.

Intervention Strategy   **Logical Learners**

Answer Table   Present students with a set of various right
triangles in which the variable is either a leg or the hypotenuse. Label
each triangle with a number or letter. Have students make a table with
the values of the variable in the right column and the triangle number
or letter in the left column. Then ask the students to compare their
tables and values as a class.

Example 2

Find the length of the leg of the right triangle.

1. From the figure, you know $b = 60$ and $c = 75$.

2. Substitute the values of b and c in the Pythagorean Theorem and solve for a.

$a^2 + b^2 = c^2$	Use the formula.
$a^2 + 60^2 = 75^2$	Substitute the measure of each side.
$a^2 + 3{,}600 = 5{,}625$	Simplify the exponents.
$a^2 = 5{,}625 - 3{,}600$	Subtract 3,600 from 5,625.
$a^2 = 2{,}025$	Simplify.
$\sqrt{a^2} = \sqrt{2{,}025}$	Take the square root of both sides.
$a = 45$	Simplify the square root.

3. The length of the leg is 45 units.

YOUR TURN!

Find the length of the leg of the right triangle.

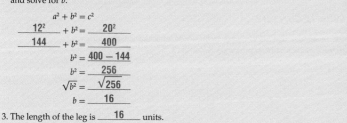

1. From the figure, you know

$a = \underline{\quad 12 \quad}$ and $c = \underline{\quad 20 \quad}$.

2. Substitute the values of a and c in the Pythagorean Theorem and solve for b.

$$a^2 + b^2 = c^2$$
$$\underline{12^2} + b^2 = \underline{20^2}$$
$$\underline{144} + b^2 = \underline{400}$$
$$b^2 = \underline{400 - 144}$$
$$b^2 = \underline{256}$$
$$\sqrt{b^2} = \underline{\sqrt{256}}$$
$$b = \underline{16}$$

3. The length of the leg is $\underline{\quad 16 \quad}$ units.

You can also do this in reverse. If the sum of the squares of the two smaller sides of a given triangle equals the square of the larger side, then the triangle is a right triangle.

GO ON

Intervention Strategy · Interpersonal Learners

Share-Pair Divide students into pairs. Using small chalkboards or dry-erase boards, have one member of the pair draw a triangle and label two of its sides. The other member should then solve to find the third side. Once the problem is complete, the students should reverse roles.

Additional *Example 2*

Find the length of the leg of the right triangle.

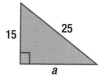

1. From the figure, you know that $b = 15$ and $c = 25$.

2. Substitute the values of b and c in the Pythagorean Theorem and solve for a.

$a^2 + b^2 = c^2$	Use the formula.
$a^2 + 15^2 = 25^2$	Substitute the measure of each side.
$a^2 + 225 = 625$	Simplify the exponents.
$a^2 = 625 - 225$	Subtract 225 from 625.
$a^2 = 400$	Simplify.
$\sqrt{a^2} = \sqrt{400}$	Take the square root of both sides.
$a = 20$	Simplify the square root.

3. The length of the leg is 20 units.

Math Coach Notes

Pythagorean Triples The examples and problems given in this lesson are Pythagorean triples. The sides of the legs and hypotenuse in these problems are whole numbers. As students become more familiar with right triangles, you can introduce lengths that will generate decimal answers. Students may benefit from using a calculator for problems with decimal answers.

Determine if the triangle is a right triangle, using the Pythagorean Theorem.

1. Determine which side is the longest. 12

2. Substitute the values into $a^2 + b^2 = c^2$, ensuring that the greatest number is c, and solve.

$a^2 + b^2 = c^2$	Use the formula.
$8^2 + 4^2 = 12^2$	Substitute the measure of each side.
$64 + 16 = 144$	Simplify the exponents.
$80 \neq 144$	Add 64 and 16.

3. Since this is a false statement, the triangle is not a right triangle.

Example 3

Determine if the triangle is a right triangle, using the Pythagorean Theorem.

1. Determine which side is the longest. 13

2. Substitute the values into $a^2 + b^2 = c^2$, ensuring that the largest number is c, and solve.

$a^2 + b^2 = a^2$	Use the formula.
$5^2 + 12^2 = 13^2$	Substitute the measure of each side.
$25 + 144 = 169$	Simplify the exponents.
$169 = 169$ ✓	Add 25 and 144.

3. Since this is a true statement, the triangle is a right triangle.

YOUR TURN!

Determine if the triangle is a right triangle, using the Pythagorean Theorem.

1. Determine which side is the longest. __15__

2. Substitute the values into $a^2 + b^2 = c^2$, ensuring that the largest number is c, and solve.

   $$a^2 + b^2 = c^2$$
   $$\underline{8^2} + \underline{12^2} = \underline{15^2}$$
   $$\underline{64} + \underline{144} = \underline{225}$$
   $$\underline{208} \neq \underline{225}$$

3. Since this is a __false__ statement, the triangle __is not__ a right triangle.

Who is Correct?

Mr. Fernandez told his students to draw and label the sides of a right triangle. Which student's triangle is correct?

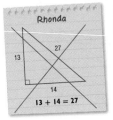
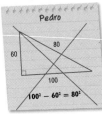
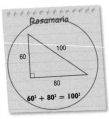

Circle correct answer(s). Cross out incorrect answer(s).

Who *is Correct?*
Diagnostic Teaching

- Rhonda is incorrect. She did not use the Pythagorean Theorem correctly. She did not square the sides according to the formula.

- Pedro is incorrect. The hypotenuse has to be the longest side of a right triangle.

- Rosamaria is correct.

Remind students that in a right triangle the side that is opposite the right angle has to be longer than the other sides.

Guided Practice

Find the length of the hypotenuse of the right triangle.

1

$c = $ _50 units_

2

$c = $ _30 units_

Step by Step Practice

3 Find the length of the leg of the right triangle.

Step 1 Find the lengths of sides a and c.

$a = $ _15_ and $c = $ _17_

Step 2 Substitute the values of a and c in the Pythagorean Theorem and solve for b.

$$a^2 + b^2 = c^2$$
$$\underline{15}^2 + b^2 = \underline{17}^2$$
$$\underline{225} + b^2 = \underline{289}$$
$$b^2 = \underline{64}$$
$$\sqrt{b^2} = \sqrt{64}$$
$$b = \underline{8}$$

The length of the leg is _8_ units.

Find the length of the leg of each right triangle.

4
$$a^2 + b^2 = c^2$$
$$a^2 + \underline{12}^2 = \underline{13}^2$$
$$a^2 + \underline{144} = \underline{169}$$
$$a^2 = \underline{25}$$
$$\sqrt{a^2} = \sqrt{25}$$
$$a = \underline{5} \text{ units}$$

5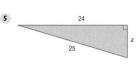

$a = $ _7_ units

GO ON

Are They Getting It? ?

Check students' understanding of the Pythagorean Theorem by writing these problems on the board. Ask students to point out wrong answers and explain why they are wrong.

Find the length of the leg or hypotenuse of each right triangle.

1. The length of the leg is 16 units. This is incorrect. The length of the leg is 12 units.

2. The length of the hypotenuse is 26 units. This is correct.

---

 ③ Practice

Using Manipulatives

Rulers and Protractors Have students use rulers and protractors to aid them when drawing right triangles.

On-Hand Manipulatives When presenting Examples 1 and 2, have students use grid paper to accurately draw the right triangles in their notes. Point out that when using the Pythagorean Theorem, students can visually square the length by making a square on each side of the triangle. Students can check their answers by adding the leg squares and setting it equal to the hypotenuse squared.

Math Coach Notes

Strategies

1. Start this lesson by showing right triangles in a wide range of orientations for recognition. When explaining the Pythagorean Theorem, emphasize that the triangles have to be right triangles with at least two side lengths given.

2. Arrange students into pairs and give each pair a right triangle. Have each pair write in different values for the lengths to get an idea of the numbers that are perfect squares.

3. As a class, compare the right triangles and discuss any common mistakes.

Math Coach Notes

Squares   While studying the Pythagorean Theorem, have students practice squaring a variety of numbers. Note the difference between the sum of two squares, and adding two numbers and then squaring. For example, $3^2 + 4^2$ is not the same as $(3 + 4)^2$.

Determine if each triangle is a right triangle, using the Pythagorean Theorem.

6

yes; $18^2 + 80^2 = 82^2$

7

no; $3^2 + 5^2 \neq 7^2$

Step by Step Problem-Solving Practice

Solve.

8 **HOME IMPROVEMENT**   Jerry's ladder is resting against a wall. The top of the ladder touches the wall at a height of 12 feet. The bottom of his ladder is 9 feet away from the base of the wall. How long is Jerry's ladder?

Understand	Read the problem. Write what you know.
	The ladder touches the wall at a height of ___12___ feet.
	The ladder is ___9___ feet away from the base of the wall.
Plan	Pick a strategy. One strategy is to draw a diagram. Then, use the Pythagorean Theorem to find the length of the ladder.
Solve	Substitute 9 for a and 12 for b in the Pythagorean Theorem and solve for c.

Problem-Solving Strategies

☑ Draw a diagram.
☐ Look for a pattern.
☐ Act it out.
☐ Solve a simpler problem.
☐ Work backward.

$$a^2 + b^2 = c^2$$
$$\underline{9}^2 + \underline{12}^2 = c^2$$
$$\underline{81} + \underline{144} = c^2$$
$$\underline{225} = c^2$$
$$\sqrt{\underline{225}} = \sqrt{c^2}$$
$$\underline{15} = c$$

The length of the ladder is ___15___ feet.

Check   Use a calculator to check your answer.

Intervention Strategy   Naturalist Learners

Real-World Examples   Have students explore the classroom for examples of right triangles. Using a ruler, have students measure two lengths of the triangle. Students then should use the Pythagorean Theorem to determine the third side. Students can check their work by measuring the third side with a ruler.

9 CONSTRUCTION A staircase to the attic in Cassandra's house has a length of 10 feet. The top of the stairs meets the wall at a height of 8 feet. How far away is the bottom of the staircase from the wall? Check off each step.

✔ Understand: I underlined key words.

✔ Plan: To solve the problem, I will ___draw a diagram___.

✔ Solve: The answer is ___6 feet___.

✔ Check: I checked my answer by ___using a calculator___.

10 ADVERTISING Splash Village advertised a water slide that is 20 yards long and shoots straight down to 12 yards from the base of the steps to the end of the slide. What is the height of the steps that reach the top of the slide?

___16 yards___

11 Reflect Can line segments with lengths 30 inches, 30 inches, and 50 inches form a right triangle? Explain.

No; substitute 30 for a, 30 for b, and 50 for c in the Pythagorean Theorem:

$30^2 + 30^2 \stackrel{?}{=} 50^2$; $900 + 900 \stackrel{?}{=} 2,500$; $1,800 \neq 2,500$.

▶ **Skills, Concepts, and Problem Solving**

Find the length of the leg or hypotenuse of each right triangle.

12

$a = $ ___12___ units

13

$c = $ ___13___ units

Determine if each triangle is a right triangle, using the Pythagorean Theorem.

14
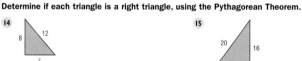

___no; $7^2 + 8^2 \neq 12^2$___

15

___yes; $12^2 + 16^2 = 20^2$___

GO ON

Odd/Even Assignments

Exercises 12–17 are structured so that students practice the same concepts whether they are assigned the odd or even problems.

In-Class Assignment

Have students complete Exercises 13, 14, 16, and 20 to ensure that they understand the concept.

Math Coach Notes

Cooperative Study Point out to students that studying in groups is helpful. Not only will other students be able to help one another with problems, but by helping one another, they will learn the material better. Students who do not know that topic very well will have greater difficulty explaining their thinking.

Math Challenge

Find the Measure Arrange students into pairs and give them various squares and rectangles with side measures. Instruct them to make a line segment from one vertex of the quadrilateral to the opposite vertex. Have them find the measure of the diagonal line that forms the hypotenuse of the two congruent triangles. Advise them to start with a square figure that has the same leg measures.

Assess

See It, Do It, Say It, Write It

Step 1 Draw the following figure on the board:

Step 2 Have students find the length of b to make the triangle a right triangle using the Pythagorean Theorem. $b = 12$

Step 3 Arrange students into pairs. Have them explain to each other how they found the side length using the Pythagorean Theorem.

Step 4 Have students write in their own words in their math journals how they determined the side length.

Looking Ahead: Pre-teach

Introduction to Slope   In the next lesson, students will learn about the slope of lines.

Example

Find the slope of the line shown.

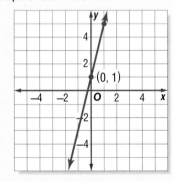

From the point (0, 1) to the point (1, 5), rise 4 units and run to the right 1 unit.

The slope of the line is $\dfrac{\text{rise}}{\text{run}} = \dfrac{4}{1}$.

Solve.

16 **TRAVEL**   Reggie left his house and drove 20 miles due east and then 15 miles due south. If Reggie follows a straight line to his house, how far is Reggie from his house?

<u>   25 miles   </u>

17 **DISTANCE**   A lighthouse on a cliff near Gina's house is 12 meters tall. Gina stood 9 meters away from the base of the lighthouse. How far away was Gina from the top of the lighthouse?

<u>   15 meters   </u>

Vocabulary Check   **Write the vocabulary word that completes each sentence.**

18 A(n) <u>   hypotenuse   </u> is the side opposite the right angle in a right triangle.

19 The <u>   Pythagorean Theorem   </u> states that the sum of the squares of the lengths of the legs in a right triangle is equal to the square of the length of the hypotenuse.

20 **Writing in Math**   Explain how to find the length of the hypotenuse of a right triangle when the lengths of the legs are known.

<u>Substitute the values of a and b in the Pythagorean Theorem ($a^2 + b^2 = c^2$)</u>

<u>and solve for c.</u>

 Spiral Review

Choose a reasonable estimate for each square root. (Lesson 6-3, p. 232)

21 $\sqrt{104}$

(10.2)   10.4   11.1

22 $\sqrt{46}$

4.6   6.2   (6.8)

23 $\sqrt{79}$

7.9   8.2   (8.9)

24 $\sqrt{128}$

11.0   (11.3)   12.1

STOP

Ticket Out the Door

Missing Side   Instruct each student to find the measure of one side of a right triangle using the Pythagorean Theorem. Have students show you their answers as they exit the classroom.

Find the length of the leg or hypotenuse of each right triangle.

1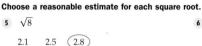

c = __15__ units

2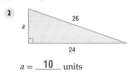

a = __10__ units

Estimate each square root to the nearest whole number. Plot each value on a number line.

3   $\sqrt{15}$ is close to the whole number __4__.

$\sqrt{9}$ $\sqrt{15}\sqrt{16}$
3   4

4   $\sqrt{165}$ is close to the whole number __13__.

$\sqrt{144}$ $\sqrt{165}\sqrt{169}$
12   13

Choose a reasonable estimate for each square root.

5   $\sqrt{8}$

2.1   2.5   (2.8)

6   $\sqrt{78}$

(8.8)   9.1   9.5

Solve.

7   **FLAGS** A flagpole stands in front of a city building. The base of the flagpole is 8 yards away from a spotlight that shines on the flag. The distance from the spotlight to the top of the flagpole is 10 yards. How tall is the flagpole?

__6 yards__

8   **RECTANGLES** What is the length of the diagonal of rectangle *MNOP*?

__13__

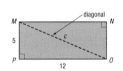

Progress Check 2

Formative Assessment

Use the Progress Check to assess students' mastery of the previous lessons. Have students review the lesson indicated for the problems they answered incorrectly.

Odd/Even Assignments

Exercises are structured so that students practice the same concepts whether they are assigned the odd or even problems.

Data-Driven Decision Making

Students missing Exercises . . .	Have trouble with . . .	Should review and practice . . .
1–2	using the Pythagorean Theorem.	SSG Lesson 6-4, p. 239 CRM Skills Practice, p. A120
3–4	using models to estimate square roots.	SSG Lesson 6-3, p. 232 CRM Skills Practice, p. A116
5–6	estimating square roots.	SSG Lesson 6-3, p. 232 CRM Skills Practice, p. A116
7–8	solving word problems that involve applying the Pythagorean Theorem.	CRM Problem-Solving Practice, pp. A117 and A121

Lesson Planner

Objective   Determine and graph slope of a line.

Vocabulary   coordinate grid , origin , slope , *x*-coordinate , *y*-coordinate

Materials/Manipulatives   centimeter grid paper, rulers, bulletin board, push pins, counters

Chapter Resource Masters

- CRM Vocabulary and English Language Development (p. A123)
- CRM Skills Practice (p. A124)
- CRM Problem-Solving Practice (p. A125)
- CRM Homework Practice (p. A126)

 Introduce

Vocabulary

Reviewing Direction   Review the terms vertical and horizontal. Relate horizontal lines to the horizon and draw examples of each kind of line on the board. While introducing the formula for slope, use hand gestures and the drawn lines for reference.

 Teach

Key Concept

Foundational Skills and Concepts   After students have read through the Key Concept box, have them try these exercises.

1. If a line has a positive rise and negative run, describe the direction of the line. The line has a negative slope; from left to right, it is "going down."

2. What is the formula to find the slope of a line? The formula is the vertical change divided by the horizontal change, or $\frac{rise}{run}$.

KEY Concept

When describing a line on a **coordinate grid**, you can describe the "steepness," or **slope**, of the line. Lines that move upward and to the right have a positive slope. Lines that move downward and to the left have a negative slope.

$$slope = \frac{\text{number of units up }(+)\text{ or down }(-)}{\text{number of units right }(+)\text{ or left }(-)} = \frac{rise}{run}$$

$\frac{rise}{run} = \frac{+2}{+3}$ = positive slope

$\frac{rise}{run} = \frac{-2}{+3}$ = negative slope

Look at each graph from left to right in order to determine if the slope is positive or negative. If the line goes up, the slope is positive. If the line goes down, the slope is negative.

VOCABULARY

coordinate grid
a grid in which a horizontal number line (*x*-axis) and a vertical number line (*y*-axis) intersect at their zero points

origin
the point of intersection of the *x*-axis and the *y*-axis in a coordinate system

slope
the rate of change between any two points on a line; the ratio of vertical change to horizontal change

x-coordinate
the first number of an ordered pair

y-coordinate
the second number of an ordered pair

A slope is negative if the value of the rise or the value of the run is negative.

Example 1

Find the slope of the line.

1. The rise is +4 units.

2. The run is +5 units.

3. The slope is positive.

4. $\frac{rise}{run} = \frac{+4}{+5} = \frac{4}{5}$

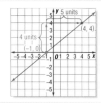

Additional *Example 1*

Find the slope of the line.

1. The rise is −1 units.

2. The run is +2 units.

3. The slope is negative.

4. $\frac{rise}{run} = \frac{-1}{+2} = -\frac{1}{2}$

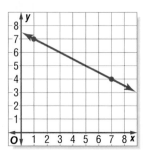

YOUR TURN!

Find the slope of the line.

1. The rise is __+5__ units.

2. The run is __−1__ units.

3. The slope is __negative__.

4. $\dfrac{\text{rise}}{\text{run}} = \dfrac{+5}{-1} = $ __−5__

Example 2

Graph another point on the line, given the point (3, 4) and the slope $\frac{1}{4}$.

1. Find the point (3, 4).

2. The "run" is +4. Add 4 to the x-coordinate.

   $3 + 4 = 7$
   $x = 7$

3. The "rise" is +1. Add 1 to the y-coordinate.

   $4 + 1 = 5$
   $y = 5$

4. Name and graph the new point.
   $(x, y) = (7, 5)$

YOUR TURN!

Graph another point on the line, given the point (5, 4) and the slope $-\frac{1}{3}$.

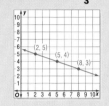

1. Find the point (__5__ , __4__).

2. The "run" is __+3__. __Add 3 to__ the x-coordinate.

   $5 \underline{+3} = \underline{8}$
   $x = \underline{8}$

3. The "rise" is __−1__ __Subtract 1 from__ the y-coordinate.

   $4 \underline{+(-1)} = \underline{3}$
   $y = \underline{3}$

4. Name and graph the new point.
   $(x, y) = (\underline{8} , \underline{3})$

GO ON

Graph another point on the line, given the point (1, 9) and the slope $-\dfrac{3}{5}$.

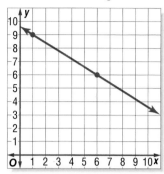

Sample answer:

1. Find the point (1, 9).

2. The "run" is +5. Add 5 to the x-coordinate.

   $1 + 5 = 6$

   $x = 6$

3. The "rise" is −3. Add −3 to the y-coordinate.

   $9 + (-3) = 6$

   $y = 6$

4. Name and graph the new point.

   $(x, y) = (6, 6)$

Intervention Strategy   Kinesthetic Learners

Lines and Slopes   Have students work in pairs. Distribute centimeter grid paper and a ruler to each student. Write the following list of points and slopes on the board. Tell students to create a coordinate grid for each line, with axes labeled. Have pairs plot the point and use the given slope to determine other points on the line. Ask students to use their rulers to connect the points and extend the lines. Students should list two other points on each line they create. Have pairs discuss how they found each of the other points. Allow time for pairs to share their graphs and additional plotted points with the class.

$(1, 8)$, slope: $-\dfrac{1}{4}$ $(-4, -5)$, slope: 2

$(2, -6)$, slope: $\dfrac{2}{3}$ $(-7, 9)$, slope: $-\dfrac{5}{3}$

Practice

Using Manipulatives

Counters   Use counters on grid paper to plot points and find the slope of a line. Students can draw a full-size coordinate grid on the paper and use this same grid for multiple problems.

On-Hand Manipulatives   Draw a large coordinate grid on a bulletin board. Have students use push pins to plot points and determine slope.

Math Coach Notes

Placing the Negative   Make sure students know that the negative sign can be placed on either the rise or run, depending on their starting point. However, one value should be positive and one value should be negative. Illustrate that $-\frac{1}{2}$, $\frac{-1}{2}$, and $\frac{1}{-2}$ are all equivalent.

Who is Correct?

Find the slope of the line.

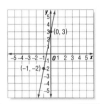

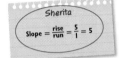

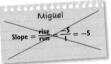

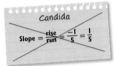

Circle the correct answer(s). Cross out incorrect answer(s).

▶ **Guided Practice**

Find the slope of each line.

1. The rise is $+3$ units.

   The run is -3 units.

   The slope is negative .

   $\dfrac{\text{rise}}{\text{run}} = \dfrac{+3}{-3} = \dfrac{3}{3} = -1$

2.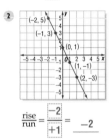

   $\dfrac{\text{rise}}{\text{run}} = \dfrac{-2}{+1} = -2$

3.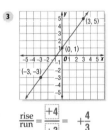

   $\dfrac{\text{rise}}{\text{run}} = \dfrac{+4}{+3} = +\dfrac{4}{3}$

250   Chapter 6 Squares, Square Roots, and the Pythagorean Theorem

---

Who *is Correct?*
Diagnostic Teaching

- Sherita is correct. She determined the correct rise and run ratio.

- Miguel is incorrect. He used an incorrect direction for the rise.

- Candida is incorrect. She wrote the rise and run in the opposite position and used the incorrect direction for the rise.

Remind students that a negative slope goes down from left to right and a positive slope goes up from left to right.

Math Coach Notes

Plotted Points   As students use a plotted point and slope to find other points on a line, remind students to find at least two additional points before drawing the line. Encourage them to make their plotted points large enough and use all of the points to make the line. This will increase accuracy and allow students to identify even more points that fall on this extended line.

Step (by) Step Practice

4 Graph another point on the line, given the point (8, 1) and the slope −3.

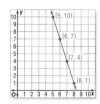

Hint: You can either consider the "rise" to be negative or the "run" to be negative.

Sample answer:

Step 1   Find the point (8, 1).

Step 2   The "run" is __−1__.

8 __−1__ = __7__ $x =$ __7__

Step 3   The "rise" is __+3__.

1 __+3__ = __4__ $y =$ __4__

Step 4   Name and graph the new point.

$(x, y) = ($ __7__ , __4__ $)$

Graph another point on each line, given one point on the line and the slope.

5

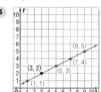

The slope is $\frac{1}{2}$.

6

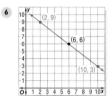

The slope is $-\frac{3}{4}$.

GO ON ▶

Are They Getting It?

Check students' understanding of slope by writing these problems on the board. Ask them to point out incorrect answers and explain their reasoning.

1. The graphed line has a negative slope.
This is incorrect. The slope is positive.

2. The slope of the line is $\frac{3}{2}$.
This is incorrect. The slope is $\frac{2}{3}$.

3. Another point on this line is (7, 6).
This is correct.

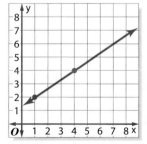

Math Coach Notes

Rising and Running   If students are writing the slope fraction incorrectly by putting the run number in the numerator, have them think of the following situation.

If a person is seated at one place in a room and wants to move to a different place, the person must rise from being seated before they run to the new place.

Solve.

Problem-Solving Strategies
- ☐ Draw a diagram.
- ☐ Use logical reasoning.
- ☑ Use a formula.
- ☐ Solve a simpler problem.
- ☐ Work backward.

7   RAMPS   Laura is learning how to do turns on a skateboard ramp. The ramp is 4 feet long and 2 feet tall. What is the slope of the ramp?

Understand   Read the problem. Write what you know.

The ramp length is __4 feet__.

The ramp height is __2 feet__.

Plan   Pick a strategy. One strategy is to use a formula. Use the formula for slope to solve the problem.

2 ft
4 ft

Solve   Find the rise and run and then simplify.

$$slope = \frac{2}{4} \div \frac{2}{2} = \frac{1}{2}$$

Check   Use a coordinate grid. Start at the origin and move 4 units to the right and 2 units upward. Graph that point and draw a line segment to connect the points. Use these two points to find the slope of the line segment.

8   SKIING   A ski lift transports people to the top of a hill. One support pole is 40 feet tall. The next support pole is 50 feet from the first and is 100 feet tall. Find the slope of the wire between the poles. Check off each step.

__✔__ Understand: I underlined key words.

__✔__ Plan: To solve this problem, I will __use a formula__

__✔__ Solve: The answer is $\frac{6}{5}$

__✔__ Check: I checked my answer by __referring back to__ __the diagram__.

100 ft
40 ft
50 ft

9   Reflect   How does viewing the line on the graph before looking at numeric values help you check your answers?

__Sample answer: Viewing the line can help you to determine if the slope is__

__positive or negative. It can also help to determine the values of the slope.__

252   Chapter 6 Squares, Square Roots, and the Pythagorean Theorem

English Learner Strategy

Ramps   Use Exercise 7 to discuss the topic of ramps. Ask students to share what kinds of ramps they see on a daily basis (freeway entrances and exits, near stairs in front of buildings, at curbs on corners of streets, on the backs of moving trucks or semis, etc.). Encourage students to use clear language in describing where they see ramps and what they are used for. Ask students to decide and explain if the degree of slope of these ramps makes a difference in each one's function.

Odd/Even Assignments

Exercises 10–18 are structured so that students practice the same concepts whether they are assigned the odd or even problems.

Skills, Concepts, and Problem Solving

Find the slope of each line.

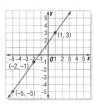

10 The rise is __+4__ units.

The run is __+3__ units.

The slope is __positive__.

$\dfrac{\text{rise}}{\text{run}} = \dfrac{+4}{+3} = \dfrac{4}{3}$

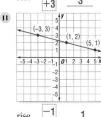

11

$\dfrac{\text{rise}}{\text{run}} = \dfrac{-1}{+4} = -\dfrac{1}{4}$

12

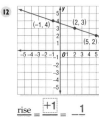

$\dfrac{\text{rise}}{\text{run}} = \dfrac{+1}{-3} = -\dfrac{1}{3}$

Graph another point on each line, given one point on the line and the slope.

13

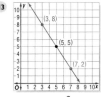

The slope is $-\dfrac{3}{2}$.

14

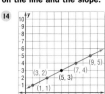

The slope is $\dfrac{1}{2}$.

15

The slope is $-\dfrac{1}{5}$.

16

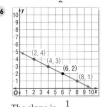

The slope is $-\dfrac{1}{2}$.

GO ON

In-Class Assignment

Have students complete Exercises 10, 13, 17, and 21 to ensure that they understand the concept.

Math Challenge

Design of Slopes   Draw a coordinate plane on a sheet of grid paper. Use a ruler to create a design made of only straight lines. Number each line in the design. Determine the slope of each numbered line. Share your design with a classmate and have them verify the slope of each of your lines.

See It, Do It, Say It, Write It

Step 1 Draw a coordinate grid on the board. Plot the points (2, 3) and (3, 6).

Step 2 Have students determine the slope of the line and find two additional points on this line.

Step 3 Ask students to work with a partner. Have them discuss how they found the slope and additional points. Tell them to explain whether the slope is positive.

Step 4 Have students work alone to write their evaluations of the graph. Students should write how they determined the slope and additional points, and provide support for their conclusion of the type of slope graphed.

Looking Ahead: Pre-Teach

Slope Formula In the next lesson, students will learn how to find the slope of a line using the slope formula.

Example

Determine the slope of a line that connects the points (3, 4) and (1, 0).

$$\text{slope} = \frac{y_2 - y_1}{x_2 - x_1} = \frac{4 - 0}{3 - 1} = \frac{4}{2} = 2$$

Have students determine the slope of a line that connects each pair of points.

1. (6, −1) and (5, 2) −3

2. (2, 2) and (−8, 8) $-\dfrac{3}{5}$

3. (0, 0) and (9, −3) $-\dfrac{1}{3}$

Solve.

17 **SAILS** A sail on a sailboat is 24 feet tall and 12 feet across the bottom. What is the slope of the sail?

$$\text{Slope} = \frac{\text{rise}}{\text{run}} = \frac{24}{12} = 2$$

18 **LADDERS** A ladder is leaning against a wall. It touches the wall 60 feet from the ground. The bottom of the ladder is 20 feet from the wall. What is the slope of the ladder?

$$\text{Slope} = \frac{\text{rise}}{\text{run}} = \frac{60}{20} = 3$$

Vocabulary Check **Write the vocabulary word that completes each sentence.**

19 The _slope_ of a line refers to the "steepness" of the line.

20 The _origin_ is the place where the x-axis and y-axis cross.

21 **Writing in Math** Explain what happens to the steepness of the line when the value of the slope increases.

Sample answer: The steeper the line is, the higher the absolute value of the slope.

 Spiral Review

Determine if each triangle is a right triangle using the Pythagorean Theorem. (Lesson 6-4, p. 239)

22

18   24
21

no; $18^2 + 21^2 \neq 24^2$

23

24
26   10

yes; $10^2 + 24^2 = 26^2$

Solve. (Lesson 6-4, p. 239)

24 **SHADOWS** The shadow of the locust tree in Quanah's backyard is 5 feet long. The distance from the end of the shadow to the top of the tree is 13 feet. How tall is the tree?

$13^2 - 5^2 = 12^2$; The tree is 12 feet tall.

Ticket Out the Door

Slope of a Line Draw a coordinate grid on the board and plot the segment (2, 6) to (5, 5). As students approach the classroom door to exit, alternate asking them to name the type of slope graphed, the slope of the line, or an additional point on the line.

negative slope; $-\dfrac{1}{3}$; (−1, 7), (8, 4) or (11, 3)

Lesson 6-6 Slope Formula

KEY Concept

The **slope** of a line illustrates the ratio of the number of units of rise to the number of units of run for a **linear function**. You can find the slope of a line from the graph of that line or by using the slope formula.

$$\text{slope} = m = \frac{\Delta y}{\Delta x} = \frac{\text{change in } y}{\text{change in } x}$$

A lowercase m represents slope.

$$m = \frac{y_2 - y_1}{x_2 - x_1}, \text{ where } x_2 \neq x_1$$

Look at the graph at the right. Choose two points on the line, such as $(-3, -2)$ and $(0, 0)$.

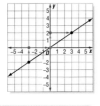

Find the slope by substituting the points $(0, 0)$ and $(3, 2)$ in the formula.

$$m = \frac{y_2 - y_2}{x_2 - x_2} = \frac{0 - 2}{0 - 3} = \frac{-2}{-3} = \frac{2}{3}$$

Remember that a negative number, divided by a negative number equals a positive quotient.

You can continue to move up 2 units and right 3 units because the slope of the line is constant.

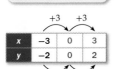

	+3	+3
x	−3	0	3
y	−2	0	2
	+2	+2

VOCABULARY

slope
the rate of change between any two points on a line; the ratio of vertical change to horizontal change

linear function
a function whose graph is a straight line

In the slope formula, the change in y-values is the numerator, and the change in x-values is the denominator.

GO ON

Intervention Strategy — Logical Learners

Introductory Activities Conduct the following activities to help students understand the concept.

1. Write two ordered pairs on the board. Have student volunteers use the slope formula to find the slope of the line.

2. Review how to subtract negative numbers using the additive inverse.

3. Have students use the slope formula to find the equation of the line from a graphed line.

Lesson Notes

Lesson Planner

Objective   Know and use the slope formula.

Vocabulary   linear function, slope

Materials/Manipulatives   geoboards, grid paper

Chapter Resource Masters

- CRM Vocabulary and English Language Development (p. A127)
- CRM Skills Practice (p. A128)
- CRM Problem-Solving Practice (p. A129)
- CRM Homework Practice (p. A130)

1 Introduce

Meaning of Δ   Point out to students the symbol Δ in the Key Concept box. Explain that this symbol is not a triangle symbol. Guide students to see that the segment that forms the right side of the triangular symbol is bolder than the other segments. This symbol is the Delta, a letter in the Greek alphabet. Its use in this case means "change in." For the slope formula, "change in" means to subtract the y elements of the order pairs, and subtract the x elements of the ordered pairs.

2 Teach

Key Concept

Foundational Skills and Concepts   After students have read through the Key Concept box, have them try these exercises.

1. Does it matter which ordered pairs are assigned to (x_1, y_1)? Explain.   No, as long as the ordered pairs are not switched.

2. Can you find the slope of a horizontal line? Explain.   Yes; because the numerator will be 0, the slope will be 0.

Determine the slope of the graph.

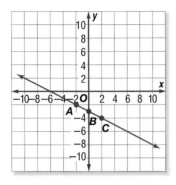

I. Complete a function table for the graph.

Point	A	B	C
x	−2	0	2
y	−2	−3	−4

2. Substitute the *x*- and *y*- values in the slope formula to find the slope of the line.

$$m = \frac{y_2 - y_1}{x_2 - x_1} = \frac{-3 - (-2)}{0 - (-2)} = \frac{-1}{2}$$

3. The slope is $-\frac{1}{2}$.

Math Coach Notes

Discussions   When the entire class is having a discussion, make sure students follow what everyone is saying. When something is said that the student feels should be noted or discussed more, they write it down. Emphasize that they should not be afraid to ask a question if they do not understand something or follow the line of the discussion.

Example 1

Determine the slope of the graph.

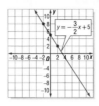

1. Complete a function table for the graph.

Point	A	B	C
x	2	0	−2
y	2	5	8

2. Substitute the *x* and *y* values in the slope formula to find the slope of the line.

$$m = \frac{y_2 - y_1}{x_2 - x_1} = \frac{5 - 2}{0 - 2}$$

$$= -\frac{3}{2}$$

3. The slope of the line is $-\frac{3}{2}$.

YOUR TURN!

Determine the slope of the graph.

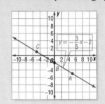

1. Complete a function table for the graph.

Point	A	B	C
x	5	0	−5
y	−5	−2	1

2. Substitute the *x* and *y* values in the slope formula to find the slope of the line.

$$m = \frac{y_2 - y_1}{x_2 - x_1} = \frac{-2 - (-5)}{0 - 5}$$

$$= \frac{\frac{3}{5}}{}$$

3. The slope of the line is $\frac{3}{5}$.

English Learner Strategy

Guiding Questions   Write $y = 2x - 2$ on the board. Then ask the following questions to ensure that students understand the concept.

- Point to the equals sign.
- What is the value of *m* in the formula $m = \frac{\triangle y}{\triangle x}$?
- Define *slope.*
- What is the formula to find slope?
- Explain how you can find the slope of a line from a graph.

Example 2

Graph $y = 2x + 3$ and determine the slope of the line.

1. Complete a function table for the equation.

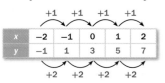

x	−2	−1	0	1	2
y	−1	1	3	5	7

2. Graph the ordered pairs and draw the line.

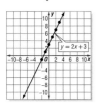

$y = 2x + 3$

3. Using two points on the graph, determine the slope.

$$m = \frac{1 - (-1)}{-1 - (-2)} = \frac{1 + 1}{-1 + 2} = \frac{2}{1} = 2$$

YOUR TURN!

Graph $y = \frac{1}{2}x - 8$ and determine the slope of the line.

1. Complete a function table for the equation.

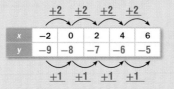

x	−2	0	2	4	6
y	−9	−8	−7	−6	−5

2. Graph the ordered pairs and draw the line.

$y = \frac{1}{2}x - 8$

3. Using two points on the graph, determine the slope.

$$m = \frac{\boxed{-8} - \boxed{(-9)}}{\boxed{0} - \boxed{(-2)}} = \frac{\boxed{-8 + 9}}{\boxed{0 + 2}} = \frac{1}{2}$$

Who is Correct?

What is the slope of the line on the graph?

Landon
Slope $= \frac{4 - 6}{0 - 7}$
$= \frac{-2}{-7} = \frac{2}{7}$

Jena
Slope $= \frac{4 - 2}{7 - 0}$
$= \frac{2}{-7} = \frac{2}{7}$

$y = \frac{2}{7}x + 4$

Circle correct answer(s). Cross out incorrect answer(s).

GO ON

Additional *Example 2*

Graph $y = 3x - 4$ and determine the slope of the line.

I. Complete a function table for the equation.

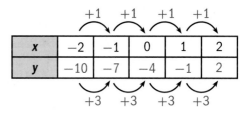

x	−2	−1	0	1	2
y	−10	−7	−4	−1	2

2. Graph the ordered pairs and draw a line.

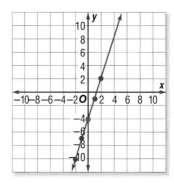

3. Using two points on the graph, determine the slope.

$$m = \frac{-10 - (-7)}{-2 - (-1)} = \frac{-10 + 7}{-2 + 1} = \frac{-3}{-1} = 3$$

Who *is Correct?*
Diagnostic Teaching

- Dale is incorrect. He substituted the *x*-values in the numerator and the *y*-values in the denominator.

- Landon is correct.

- Jena is incorrect. She used the incorrect coordinate for *y*.

Remind students to be mindful that slope is "rise" over "run."

Using Manipulatives

Geoboard When presenting Example 1, use a geoboard to give students a visual concept of the slope. The geoboard can mimic the line on the graph and the students can manipulate the angle to determine the correct slope.

On-Hand Manipulatives When presenting Example 2, have students use grid paper to draw a coordinate plane and graph the equation of a line. Model how to make and label a correct coordinate plane.

Math Coach Notes

Slope m Students might wonder why m is used for slope in the formula. Let them know that this question has been researched by math historians for many years; however, no definitive answers have been found. If students are interested, have them research the question and report their findings to the class.

Proficient Students Exercises 4 and 5 present an opportunity to challenge students to notice the formula for a line $y = mx + b$, where m is the slope, and b is the y-intercept. For students who are struggling to graph Exercise 4, have them begin with point $(0, -3)$, and work from there, or provide them with a function table and provide the x-values -4, 0, and 4.

▶ Guided Practice

Use the graph to answer each question.

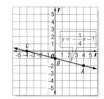

1. What is the location of Point A? __(4, −2)__

2. What is the location of Point B? __(0, −1)__

Step by Step Practice

3. **Determine the slope of the graph.**

   Step 1 Complete a function table for the graph.

x	0	1	2	3
y	−9	−6	−3	0

   Step 2 Substitute the x and y values in the slope formula to find the slope of the line.

   $$m = \frac{-6 - (-9)}{1 - 0} = \frac{-6 + 9}{1} = \frac{3}{1} \text{ or } \underline{3}$$

   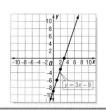

   Step 3 The slope of the line is __3__.

Graph each equation and determine its slope.

4. $y = -\dfrac{3}{4}x - 3$

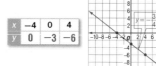

x	−4	0	4
y	0	−3	−6

   The slope is $-\dfrac{3}{4}$.

5. $y = 6x + 2$

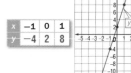

x	−1	0	1
y	−4	2	8

   The slope is __6__.

Are They Getting It?

Check students' understanding of slope by writing these problems on the board. Have students explain the incorrect information in each problem.

1. Graph $y = 4x - 3$. This is correct.

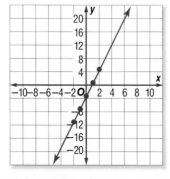

2. The slope of this line is $\dfrac{3}{5}$. This is incorrect.

The slope is $-\dfrac{3}{5}$.

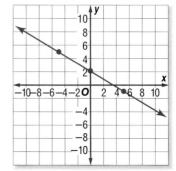

Step by Step Problem-Solving Practice

Solve.

6 **PRICES** Purified water costs $2 per gallon. Graph an equation to represent the cost of purchasing x gallons of water.

Understand Read the problem. Write what you know.
Purifed water costs ___$2 per gallon___.

Plan Pick a strategy. One strategy is to write an equation.

Let x represent the number of gallons and y represent the cost.
___$y = 2x$___

Solve Use the equation to make a function table.

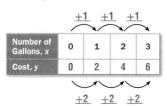

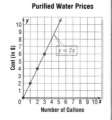

Purified Water Prices

Graph the ordered pairs from the table and draw the line on the graph.

Use the formula for slope.

$$m = \frac{y_2 - y_1}{x_2 - x_1} = \frac{\boxed{2} - \boxed{0}}{\boxed{1} - \boxed{0}} = \frac{2}{1}$$

Check slope $= \dfrac{\text{rise}}{\text{run}} = \dfrac{\boxed{2}}{\boxed{1}}$ or $\dfrac{2}{}$

To find the slope, move up ___2___ unit(s) and to the right ___1___ unit(s).

GO ON

Intervention Strategy

Find Slope Help students understand slope by drawing the following graphs on the board. The slope is the rise over the run, which is the change in y going up or down over the change in x going right or left.

Step 1

Graph three points. Connect them with a line.

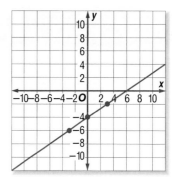

Step 2

Draw lines from the first point to the second point. (Form a triangle.)

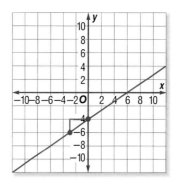

Step 3

Draw a line from the second point to the third point. (You form an identical triangle.)

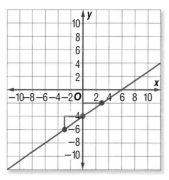

Step 4

If you draw lines from point to point on the line of a linear equation, you form identical triangles.

Assignments

Assign Exercises 9–11 so that students practice all the concepts presented in this lesson.

In-Class Assignment

Have the students complete Exercises 9, 11, and 13 to ensure that they understand the concept.

Common Error *Alert*

Correct Formula   When finding the slope of a line for a set of ordered pairs, students may use the formula incorrectly as the difference of the x-values divided by the difference of the y-values. Remind students that the proper formula is the difference of the y-values divided by the difference of the

Note This!
Discrete Data   In Exercise 7, a dashed line was used to indicate discrete data. Because only a whole number of cars can be washed, data does not exist between data points.

---

7 MONEY   Julián earns $4 for every car he washes. Graph an equation to represent the total amount Julián earns if he washes x cars. Include at least three points on the graph.

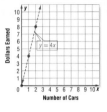

Check off each step.

✔ ___ Understand: I underlined key words.

✔ ___ Plan: To solve the problem I will ___write an equation___.

✔ ___ Solve: The equation is ___$y = 4x$___. The slope is ___4___.

✔ ___ Check: I checked my answer by ___using the formula___

8 Reflect   Draw two lines on the graph to the right. One line should have a slope of $\frac{1}{3}$. The second line should have a slope of $-\frac{1}{3}$. Describe the direction of the two lines.

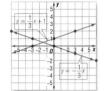

Sample answer: The line with the positive slope of $\frac{1}{3}$ moves up as you travel from left to right along the x-axis.

The line with the negative slope of $-\frac{1}{3}$ moves down as you travel from left to right along the x-axis.

▶ Skills, Concepts, and Problem Solving

Graph each equation and determine its slope.

9 $y = -6x + 4$

x	−1	0	1	2
y	10	4	−2	−8

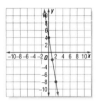

The slope is ___−6___.

Intervention Strategy   Visual Learners

Find Slope   Test students' understanding of the meaning of slope by asking student volunteers to draw parallel lines and perpendicular lines on the board. Ask: What is the slope of each line? How did you find the slope? Lead students to conclude that parallel lines have equal slopes, while perpendicular lines have negative reciprocal

10 CANOEING Ines can row a canoe 3 miles in 1 hour. Graph an equation to represent the number of miles Ines can row a canoe in x hours.

Write an equation. Let x represent the hours that Ines rows a canoe and y represent the number of miles.

$\underline{\quad y = 3x \quad}$

The slope is $\underline{\quad 3 \quad}$.

11 BOOK CLUB The Rosemill Book Club reads 2 books each month. Graph an equation to represent the total number of books read by the club for x months.

Write an equation. Let x represent the months and y represent the number of books.

$\underline{\quad y = 2x \quad}$

The slope is $\underline{\quad 2 \quad}$.

Vocabulary Check Write the vocabulary word that completes each sentence.

12 $\underline{\quad \text{Slope} \quad}$ is the ratio of the change in the y-value to the corresponding change in the x-value.

13 Writing in Math Explain how to find the slope for the equation $y = -2x + 7$.

To find the slope, first determine different points on the line.

Next, plot the points on a coordinate graph. Finally, find the change

in x-values and the change in y-values to determine the slope.

▶ **Spiral Review**

Graph another point on each line, given one point on the line and the slope. (Lesson 6-5, p. 248)

14

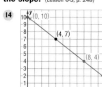

The slope is $-\dfrac{3}{4}$.

15

The slope is $\dfrac{3}{2}$.

STOP

④ Assess

See It, Do It, Say It, Write It

Step 1 Write multiple linear equations on the board.

Step 2 Have students graph the equations and find the slope using the slope formula.

Step 3 Arrange students in pairs and have them explain to each other how they found the information in Step 2.

Step 4 Have students write in their own words the definitions of each of the vocabulary words and how to find the slope in their math journals.

Ticket Out the Door

Find a Slope Have students line up at the door in single file. As each student approaches the door ask him or her to identify the slope of a graph. Continue until all students have exited the classroom.

Chapter 6 Progress Check 3

Formative Assessment

Use the Progress Check to assess students' mastery of the previous lessons. Have students review the lesson indicated for the problems they answered incorrectly.

Odd/Even Assignments

Exercises are structured so that students practice the same concepts whether they are assigned the odd or even problems.

Common Error *Alert*

Graph Lines If students are having difficulties with graphing an equation, remind them they can make a table of ordered pairs for the equation. Then they can plot these points on a coordinate plane and connect them with a line.

Slope Point out to students that if a line goes from the lower left to the upper right, then it has a positive slope. If a line goes from the upper left to the lower right, then it has a negative slope. Be sure to discuss *zero slope* and *no slope* situations.

Chapter 6 Progress Check 3 (Lessons 6-5 and 6-6)

Find the slope of the line.

1. What is the "rise" of the line? __3__

   What is the "run" of the line? __−2__

   What is the slope of the line? $-\dfrac{3}{2}$

Graph each equation.

2. Graph $y = 5x - 1$ and determine the slope of the line.

x	−1	0	1
y	−6	−1	4

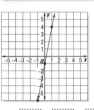

$$m = \frac{-1 - (-6)}{0 - (-1)} = \frac{-1 + 6}{1} = \frac{5}{1} = 5$$

3. Graph $y = 3x$ and determine the slope of the line.

x	−2	−1	0	1	2
y	−6	−3	0	3	6

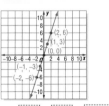

$$m = \frac{-3 - (-6)}{-1 - (-2)} = \frac{-3 + 6}{-1 + 2} = 3$$

4. **MOVIES** The cost of a movie ticket is $8. Graph an equation that shows the cost of x tickets. Write an equation. Let x represent the number of tickets y represent the cost.

   $y = 8x$

   The slope is __8__.

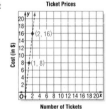

Data-Driven Decision Making

Students missing Exercises . . .	Have trouble with . . .	Should review and practice . . .
1	using the graph of a line to find the slope.	SSG Lesson 6-5, p. 248 CRM Skills Practice, p. A124
2–3	graphing equations.	SSG Lesson 6-6, p. 255 CRM Skills Practice, p. A128
4	solving a word problem that involves slope.	CRM Problem-Solving Practice, pp. A125 and A129

Study Guide

Vocabulary and Concept Check

base, *p. 218*	
coordinate grid, *p. 248*	
estimate, *p. 232*	
exponent, *p. 218*	
factor, *p. 218*	
hypotenuse, *p. 239*	
inverse operations, *p. 225*	
legs, *p. 239*	
origin, *p. 248*	
Pythagorean Theorem, *p. 239*	
radical sign, *p. 225*	
slope, *p. 248*	
square of a number, *p. 218*	
square root, *p. 225*	
x-coordinate, *p. 248*	
y-coordinate, *p. 248*	

Write the vocabulary word that completes each sentence.

1 In a power, the number used as a factor is the <u>base</u>.

2 <u>Slope</u> describes the rate of change between any two points on a line.

3 <u>Inverse operations</u> are operations which undo each other, such as squaring a number and finding its square root.

4 The product of a number multiplied by itself is called the <u>square of a number</u>.

5 The <u>radical sign</u> indicates a nonnegative square root.

6 The <u>Pythagorean Theorem</u> can be used to find the length of the hypotenuse of a right triangle.

7 The <u>hypotenuse</u> is the side of a right triangle that is opposite of the right angle.

8 A square number has a(n) <u>exponent</u> of 2.

Lesson Review

6-1 Squaring a Number (pp. 218–224)

Write an equation using exponents to represent the model.

9 3^2 = 9

Evaluate each expression.

10 2^2 $2 \cdot 2 = 4$

11 7^2 $7 \cdot 7 = 49$

12 4^2 $4 \cdot 4 = 16$

13 9^2 $9 \cdot 9 = 81$

Example 1

Evaluate the expression 8^2.

1. What number is the base? **8**

2. What number is the exponent? **2**

3. Write the base the number of times given by the exponent. **8 · 8**

4. What is the value of the expression? **64**

Chapter 6 Study Guide **263**

Study Guide
Formative Assessment

Vocabulary and Concept Check

If students have difficulty answering Exercises 1–8, remind them that they can use the page references to refresh their memories about the vocabulary terms.

Vocabulary Review Strategies

Vocabulary Frames   Have students create vocabulary frames for the words. On the set of cards, state the definition, and on the other side write the vocabulary term. If a vocabulary term can be expressed better in the form of a picture, then draw a picture in place of the definition for those words. The students can use the frames to study by themselves or with partners.

Lesson Review

The examples walk the students through finding squares and square roots, estimating square roots, using the Pythagorean Theorem, and determining slope. If additional examples are needed to review the topics, have students design their own example(s) from a particular section of the chapter. When finished, have them trade their examples with other students.

Find **Extra Practice** for these concepts in the Practice Worksheets, pages A107–A130.

Classroom Management

Group Practice   For additional practice with all the steps of functions, break the class into groups and give each group a different "situation" for which they have to write a function, make a function table, and create a graph. Then after a few minutes, have the groups present their "situation" to the class.

Review Remind students to complete and refer to their Foldables as they progress through the Chapter 6 Study Guide. Have students share and compare their completed Foldables with a partner. You may also choose to have them use their Foldable as a study aid in preparing for the Chapter Test. (For complete instructions, see Chapter Resource Masters, p. A104.)

Chapter 6:
Squares, Square Roots
and the Pythagorean
Theorem

6-2 Square Roots (pp. 225–230)

Find the positive square root using an area model.

14.

$\sqrt{25} = \underline{5}$

15.

$\sqrt{16} = \underline{4}$

16.

$\sqrt{49} = \underline{7}$

Find the positive square root of each number.

17. 169

$\sqrt{169} = \underline{13}$

18. 36

$\sqrt{36} = \underline{6}$

19. 81

$\sqrt{81} = \underline{9}$

20. 121

$\sqrt{121} = \underline{11}$

21. 196

$\sqrt{196} = \underline{14}$

264 Chapter 6 Study Guide

Example 2

Find the positive square root using an area model.

1. How many square units are shown? 4
2. Are the number of rows and columns equal? yes
3. How many columns are shown? 2
4. How many rows are shown? 2
5. $\sqrt{4} = 2$

Example 3

Find the positive square root of 49.

1. Write the expression.
   $\sqrt{49}$
2. Name the factors of 49.
   $1 \cdot 49, 7 \cdot 7$
3. Replace 49 with the set of identical factors.
   $\sqrt{7 \cdot 7}$
4. $\sqrt{49} = 7$

6-3 Approximate Square Roots (pp. 232–238)

Estimate each square root to the nearest whole number. Plot each value on a number line.

22. $\sqrt{10}$ is close to the whole number __3__.

23. $\sqrt{32}$ is close to the whole number __6__.

24. $\sqrt{119}$ is close to the whole number __11__.

Choose a reasonable estimate for each square root.

25. $\sqrt{102}$

    9.8   (10.1)   10.4

26. $\sqrt{167}$

    12.1   12.6   (12.9)

27. $\sqrt{198}$

    (14.1)   14.4   14.9

28. $\sqrt{213}$

    13.9   (14.6)   15.1

Example 4

Estimate $\sqrt{23}$ to the nearest whole number.

1. Write an inequality using common square roots.

$$\sqrt{16} < \sqrt{23} < \sqrt{25}$$

2. Find the values of the common square roots.

$$\sqrt{16} = \sqrt{4 \cdot 4} = 4 \qquad \sqrt{25} = \sqrt{5 \cdot 5} = 5$$

3. Plot the values of each square root on the number line.

4. So, $\sqrt{23}$ is between 4 and 5.
   Since $\sqrt{23}$ is closer to $\sqrt{25}$ than $\sqrt{16}$, $\sqrt{23}$ is closer to the whole number 5.

Example 5

Choose a reasonable estimate for $\sqrt{47}$.

1. Write an inequality using common square roots.

$$\sqrt{36} < \sqrt{47} < \sqrt{49}$$

2. So, $\sqrt{47}$ is between 6 and 7.

3. Circle the reasonable estimate.

    (6.9)   7.1   7.6

Math Coach Notes

Think Aloud Suggest that students say the steps out loud as they complete the exercises. "Thinking aloud" will help them remember the concepts.

Math Coach Notes

Study Tips   Give students the following study tips.

- Review material right after class when the concepts are fresh in your mind.

- Start out by studying the most important information.

- Study in a quiet place with few or no distractions.

- Summarize your notes by including the most important concepts.

- Break down the steps to solving each problem. Write them down.

- Space out your studying. Do not try to cram it all in one night.

Common Error *Alert*

Exercises 29 and 30   One of the common difficulties with questions like Exercises 29 and 30 is that when students are using the Pythagorean Theorem and find $b^2 = 100$, for instance, they leave this as the answer. They forget to take the square root of 100 to get the value of b. A good way to prevent this from happening is to ask the students to check their work.

6-4 Pythagorean Theorem (pp. 239–246)

Find the length of the leg of each right triangle.

29 $a = \underline{\ \ 8\ \ }$ units

30 $b = \underline{\ \ 5\ \ }$ units

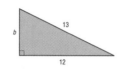

Example 6

Find the length of the leg of the right triangle.

1. From the figure, you know $a = 15$ and $c = 25$.

2. Substitute the values of a and c in the Pythagorean Theorem and solve for b.

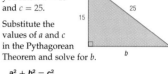

$$a^2 + b^2 = c^2$$
$$15^2 + b^2 = 25^2$$
$$225 + b^2 = 625$$
$$b^2 = 400$$
$$b = 20$$

3. The length of the leg is 20 units.

6-5 Introduction to Slope (pp. 248–254)

Find the slope of the line.

31
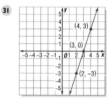

The rise is $\underline{\ +3\ }$ units.

The run is $\underline{\ +1\ }$ units.

The slope is $\underline{\ positive\ }$.

$$\dfrac{\text{rise}}{\text{run}} = \dfrac{+3}{+1} = \underline{\ \ 3\ \ }$$

Example 7

Find the slope of the line.

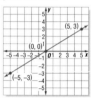

1. The rise is $+3$ units. The run is $+5$ units.

2. The slope is positive.

3. $\dfrac{\text{rise}}{\text{run}} = \dfrac{+3}{+5} = \dfrac{3}{5}$

266   Chapter 6 Study Guide

Intervention Strategy
Visual/Intrapersonal Learners

Graph Practice Cards   Give students a stack of "slope cards." For extra practice with graphing lines, have students randomly select one card from the stack and graph a line with that slope. The extra practice could prove beneficial prior to formal assessments.

6-6 Slope (pp. 255–261)

32 Graph $y = 3x - 1$ and determine the slope of the line.

1. Complete a function table for the equation.

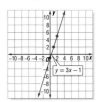

2. Plot the points and draw the line on the graph.

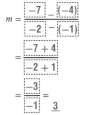

3. Using two points on the graph, determine the slope.

$$m = \frac{-7 - (-4)}{-2 - (-1)}$$

$$= \frac{-7 + 4}{-2 + 1}$$

$$= \frac{-3}{-1} = \underline{3}$$

Example 8

Graph $y = \frac{1}{4}x + 1$ and determine the slope of the line.

1. Complete a function table for the equation.

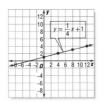

2. Plot the points and draw the line on the graph.

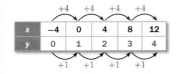

3. Using two points on the graph, determine the slope. 4

$$m = \frac{1 - 0}{0 - (-4)} = \frac{1}{0 + 4} = \frac{1}{4}$$

Ticket Out the Door

Do These Problems Have students answer four problems of the following types: (1) name a perfect square, (2) name the square root of a perfect square, (3) estimate the square root of a non-perfect square, (4) find the length of the hypotenuse of a right triangle, given the length of its legs, and (5) find the slope of a graph.

Chapter 6 — Chapter Test

Chapter Resource Masters

Additional forms of the Chapter 6 Tests are available.

Test Format	Where to Find it
Chapter 6 Test	Math Online ▸ glencoe.com
Blackline Masters	Assessment Masters, p. 90

ExamView® Assessment Suite

Customize and create multiple versions of your chapter test and their answer keys. All of these questions from the chapter tests are available on ExamView® Assessment Suite.

Advance TRACKER

Online Assessment and Reporting

glencoe.com

This online assessment tool allows teachers to track student progress with easily-accessible, comprehensive reports available for every student. Assess students using any internet-ready computer.

Alternative Assessment

Use Portfolios Ask students to summarize the methods for all of the following: finding squares and square roots, using the Pythagorean Theorem, using linear graphs to find the slope, and finding the slope using a formula. They should organize the information in the way that best suits them, such as in a portfolio with examples (including tables and diagrams, as needed), on a Foldable, in a list, or in a paragraph.

Chapter 6 — Chapter Test

Evaluate each expression.

1. 4^2 _____ 16 _____
2. 7^2 _____ 49 _____
3. 11^2 _____ 121 _____
4. $\sqrt{64}$ _____ 8 _____

Choose a reasonable estimate for each square root.

5. $\sqrt{161}$
   12.2   (12.7)   13.1

6. $\sqrt{227}$
   14.8   (15.1)   15.6

Find the length of the hypotenuse of the right triangle.

7.
   $c =$ _25_ units

8.
   $c =$ _15_ units

Determine the slope of the graph.

9. _____ $\dfrac{1}{2}$ _____

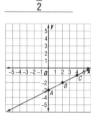

10. _____ $\dfrac{2}{3}$ _____

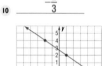

Estimate $\sqrt{96}$ to the nearest whole number. Plot each value on a number line.

11. $\sqrt{96}$ is close to the whole number _10_.

268   Chapter 6 Test

English Learner Strategy

Assessment Provide students with time to look over the assessment. Have them take a close look at all of the section directions, as well as any terms in the word problems. Be sure students understand what is being asked of them in each problem. If necessary, provide them with clarification. Also have students look for math vocabulary terms used throughout the assessment. Go over the terms with the class, and review all of the meanings of the essential math vocabulary.

Graph each equation and determine the slope of the line.

12 $y = x + 2$

slope = __1__

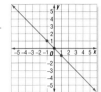

13 $y = -x$

slope = __−1__

Solve.

14 **ART** Mariah is mixing paint for an art project. She will make 4 gallons of green paint. Each gallon of green paint requires 3 quarts of yellow paint. How many quarts of yellow paint does she need to make x gallons of green paint?

$y = $ __3x__

Gallons of Green Paint, x	1	2	3	4
Quarts of Yellow Paint, y	3	6	9	12

How many quarts of yellow paint would Mariah use to make all 4 gallons of green paint? __12__

15 **PACKAGING** Each box at The Cardboard Warehouse can hold 6 glass jars. Graph an equation to represent the total number of jars contained in x boxes.

The equation is ___ $y = 6x$ ___.

The slope is ___ 6 ___.

Correct the mistakes.

16 On Nikki's math quiz, the problem stated: "For every mile you bicycle, you burn 35 Calories. Fill in the blanks."

Let $x = $ _____ ; let $y = $ _____.

Nikki
x = Calories
y = miles

What is the mistake Nikki made?

___$x = $ miles, $y = $ total Calories burned___

STOP

Math Coach Notes

Test-Taking Tip Ensure that students read each problem carefully. They should verify that their answers make sense in context.

Data-Driven Decision Making

Students missing Exercises . . .	Have trouble with . . .	Should review and practice . . .
1–4	finding squares and square roots.	SSG Lessons 6-1 and 6-2, pp. 218 and 225 CRM Skills Practice, pp. A108 and A112
5–6, 11	estimating square roots.	SSG Lesson 6-3, p. 232 CRM Skills Practice, p. A116
7–8	using the Pythagorean Theorem.	SSG Lesson 6-4, p. 239 CRM Skills Practice, p. A120
9–10, 12–13	determining the slope of a graph and graphing equations.	SSG Lessons 6-5 and 6-6, pp. 248 and 255 CRM Skills Practice, pp. A124 and A128
14–16	solving word problems.	CRM Problem-Solving Practice, pp. A109, A113, A117, A121, A125, and A129

⚠ Diagnose Student Errors

Survey student responses for each item. Class trends may indicate common errors and misconceptions.

I.

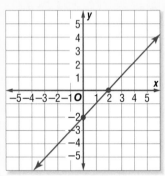

$$y = x - 2$$

- Ⓐ correct
- B point not on line
- C point not on line
- D point not on line

2. A miscounted rows and columns
- Ⓑ correct
- C guess
- D miscounted rows and columns

3.

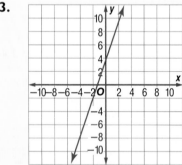

$$y = 3x + 4$$

- A point not on line
- B point not on line
- Ⓒ correct
- D point not on line

4. A guess
- Ⓑ correct
- C $9^2 + 12^2 \neq 17^2$
- D $9^2 + 12^2 \neq 18^2$

Chapter
6 **Test Practice**

Choose the best answer and fill in the corresponding circle on the sheet at right.

1 Which ordered pair falls on the line of the equation $y = x - 2$?
- Ⓐ $(-2, -4)$
- C $(-3, -2)$
- B $(0, -4)$
- D $(3, 2)$

---

2 Maribel is tiling her kitchen floor. She sets the square tiles in 7 rows and 7 columns. How many tiles will Maribel use?

- A 36
- C 52
- Ⓑ 49
- D 64

---

3 Which ordered pair falls on the line of the equation $y = 3x + 4$?
- A $(-1, -1)$
- Ⓒ $(-3, -5)$
- B $(3, 4)$
- D $(5, 9)$

---

4 Use the Pythagorean Theorem to find the triangle's missing side length.

- A 11 yd
- C 17 yd
- Ⓑ 15 yd
- D 18 yd

---

5 What is the slope of the line graphed below?

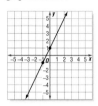

- A $-\frac{1}{2}$
- C 1
- B $\frac{1}{2}$
- Ⓓ 2

---

6 What is the approximate positive square root of 7?
- Ⓐ 2.6
- C 4.9
- B 3.1
- D 49

---

7 Jake is designing a square playground for his dog. It will cover an area of 64 square feet. What is the length and width of the playground?
- A 6 feet
- Ⓒ 8 feet
- B 7 feet
- D 9 feet

---

5. A guess; slope is positive, not negative
- B inverted x- and y-values
- C miscalculated
- Ⓓ correct

6. Ⓐ correct
- B guess; $3^2 = 9$, so answer is less than 3
- C squared 7 and divided by 10
- D squared 7

7. A miscalculated
- B miscalculated
- Ⓒ correct
- D miscalculated

8. A chose numbers from slope, used incorrect sign and inverted their places
- B chose numbers from slope ratio
- C chose numbers from slope, and inverted x- and y-value
- Ⓓ correct

8 Find another point on the line that has a slope of $\frac{3}{4}$ and includes the point (0, 1).

A (−4, −3) C (4, 3)

B (3, 4) (D) (4, 4)

---

9 What is the slope of the line graphed below?

A $-\frac{1}{4}$ C 1

B $\frac{1}{4}$ (D) −4

---

10 Which point on the number line below represents $\sqrt{47}$?

A Point A (C) Point C

B Point B D Point D

---

11 The length of the shadow of a light pole is 20 feet. The distance from the end of the shadow to the top of the light pole is 16 feet. How tall is the light pole?

(A) 12 feet C 14 feet

B 13 feet D 15 feet

ANSWER SHEET

Directions: Fill in the circle of each correct answer.

1 (●A) (B) (C) (D)
2 (A) (●B) (C) (D)
3 (A) (B) (●C) (D)
4 (A) (●B) (C) (D)
5 (A) (B) (C) (●D)
6 (●A) (B) (C) (D)
7 (A) (B) (●C) (D)
8 (A) (B) (C) (●D)
9 (A) (B) (C) (●D)
10 (A) (B) (●C) (D)
11 (●A) (B) (C) (D)

Success Strategy

If you do not know the answer to a question, go on to the next question. Come back to the problem, if you have time. You might find another question later in the test that will help you figure out the skipped problem.

STOP

Diagnosing Student Errors and Misconceptions

Scoring Guides Sharing a scoring guide can help students build test-taking skills. Students can benefit from scoring responses of other students, as well as from checking and revising their own work.

After students have scored their work, have them go back and take a look at the questions they missed. Ask them to try to find their mistakes, and once they do, have them try to make the appropriate corrections.

---

9. A inverted rise and run
B inverted rise and run, used incorrect sign
C guess
(D) correct

10. A guess
B guess
(C) correct
D chose whole number estimate

11. (A) correct
B miscalculated
C miscalculated
D miscalculated

Chapter Overview

Chapter-at-a-Glance

Lesson	Math Objective	State/Local Standards
7-1 Sort and Classify (pp. 274–280)	Sort and classify data.	
7-2 Mode, Median, and Range (pp. 281–288)	Find the mode, median, and range in a set of data.	
7-3 Mean (pp. 289–295)	Find the mean in a set of data.	
Progress Check 1 (p. 296)		
7-4 Interpret Bar Graphs (pp. 297–304)	Interpret data in bar graphs, including the measures of central tendency.	
7-5 Create Bar Graphs (pp. 305–313)	Display data in bar graphs.	
Progress Check 2 (p. 314)		
7-6 Interpret Line Graphs (pp. 315–322)	Interpret data in line graphs.	
7-7 Create Line Graphs (pp. 323–329)	Display data in line graphs.	
Progress Check 3 (p. 330)		

Content-at-a-Glance

The diagram below summarizes and unpacks Chapter 7 content.

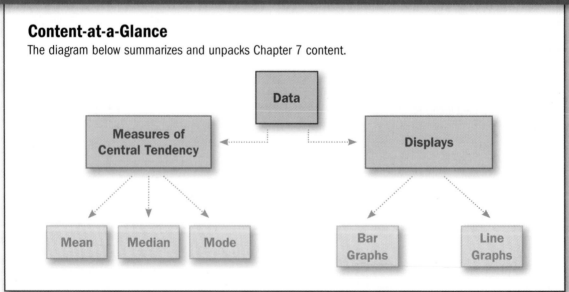

Chapter Assessment Manager

Diagnostic Diagnose students' readiness.

	Student/Teacher Editions	Assessment Masters	Technology
Course Placement Test		1	💿 ExamView® Assessment Suite
Book 3 Pretest		101	💿 ExamView® Assessment Suite
Chapter 7 Pretest		104	💿 ExamView® Assessment Suite
Quiz/Preview	SSG 273		Math Online > glencoe.com StudentWorks™ Plus

Formative Identify students' misconceptions of content knowledge.

	Student/Teacher Editions	Assessment Masters	Technology
Progress Checks	SSG 296, 314, 330		Math Online > glencoe.com StudentWorks™ Plus
Vocabulary Review	SSG 331		Math Online > glencoe.com
Lesson Assessments			💿 ExamView® Assessment Suite
Are They Getting It?	TE 277, 284, 293, 301, 309, 318, 327		Math Online > glencoe.com

Summative Determine student success in learning the concepts in the lesson, chapter, or book.

	Student/Teacher Editions	Assessment Masters	Technology
Chapter 7 Test	SSG 336	107	💿 ExamView® Assessment Suite
Test Practice	SSG 338	110	
Alternative Assessment	TE 336	113	💿 ExamView® Assessment Suite
See It, Do It, Say It, Write It	TE 280, 288, 295, 304, 313, 322, 329		
Book 3 Test		137	💿 ExamView® Assessment Suite

Backmapping and Vertical Alignment McGraw-Hill's *Math Triumphs* intervention program was conceived and developed with the final result in mind: student success in grade-level mathematics, including Algebra 1 and beyond. The authors, using the **NCTM Focal Points and Focal Connections** as their guide, developed this brand-new series by backmapping from grade-level and Algebra 1 concepts, and vertically aligning the topics so that they build upon prior skills and concepts and serve as a foundation for future topics.

Chapter Resource Manager

	Lesson 7-1	Lesson 7-2	Lesson 7-3	Lesson 7-4
Concept	Sort and Classify	Mode, Median, and Range	Mean	Interpret Bar Graphs
Objective	Sort and classify data.	Find the mode, median, and range in a set of data.	Find the mean in a set of data.	Interpret data in bar graphs, including the measures of central tendency.
Math Vocabulary	sort Venn diagram	data median mode range	average mean measures of central tendency outlier	bar graph horizontal axis interval scale vertical axis
Lesson Resources	**Materials** • Everyday objects to sort • Colored pencils **Manipulatives** • Pattern blocks • Counters **Other Resources** [CRM] Vocabulary and English Language Development [CRM] Skills Practice [CRM] Problem-Solving Practice [CRM] Homework Practice	**Materials** • Deck of playing cards • Dried beans **Manipulatives** • Unit cubes • Counters **Other Resources** [CRM] Vocabulary and English Language Development [CRM] Skills Practice [CRM] Problem-Solving Practice [CRM] Homework Practice	**Materials** • Calculator **Manipulatives** • Centimeter cubes • Counters **Other Resources** [CRM] Vocabulary and English Language Development [CRM] Skills Practice [CRM] Problem-Solving Practice [CRM] Homework Practice	**Materials** • Centimeter grid paper • Rulers **Manipulatives** • Centimeter unit cubes **Other Resources** [CRM] Vocabulary and English Language Development [CRM] Skills Practice [CRM] Problem-Solving Practice [CRM] Homework Practice
Technology	**Math Online** glencoe.com StudentWorks™ Plus ⊙ ExamView® Assessment Suite	**Math Online** glencoe.com StudentWorks™ Plus ⊙ ExamView® Assessment Suite	**Math Online** glencoe.com StudentWorks™ Plus ⊙ ExamView® Assessment Suite	**Math Online** glencoe.com StudentWorks™ Plus ⊙ ExamView® Assessment Suite

Lesson 7-5	Lesson 7-6	Lesson 7-7	
Create Bar Graphs	Interpret Line Graphs	Create Line Graphs	**Concept**
Display data in bar graphs.	Interpret data in line graphs.	Display data in line graphs.	**Objective**
bar graph horizontal axis interval scale vertical axis	horizontal axis interval line graph scale vertical axis	horizontal axis interval line graph scale vertical axis	**Math Vocabulary**
Materials • Centimeter grid paper • Rulers • Colored pencils • Index cards • Butcher paper **Manipulatives** • Unit cubes **Other Resources** CRM Vocabulary and English Language Development CRM Skills Practice CRM Problem-Solving Practice CRM Homework Practice	**Materials** • Centimeter grid paper **Manipulatives** • Centimeter cubes **Other Resources** CRM Vocabulary and English Language Development CRM Skills Practice CRM Problem-Solving Practice CRM Homework Practice	**Materials** • Centimeter grid paper • Rulers • Colored pencils • Index cards • Push pins • Yarn or string **Other Resources** CRM Vocabulary and English Language Development CRM Skills Practice CRM Problem-Solving Practice CRM Homework Practice	**Lesson Resources**

Math Online ⟩
glencoe.com
StudentWorks™ Plus
⊙ ExamView®
   Assessment Suite
	Math Online ⟩
	glencoe.com
	StudentWorks™ Plus
	⊙ ExamView®
	   Assessment Suite
		Math Online ⟩
		glencoe.com
		StudentWorks™ Plus
		⊙ ExamView®
		   Assessment Suite
			Technology

Chapter 7 Chapter Notes

Real-World Applications

TV Ratings Local news broadcasts compete for viewers to watch their stations over another station. Harold surveyed his neighbors and found that some people exclusively watch one channel, while other people watch two or three different channels. How can he summarize this data into a display that is easy to read? **By using a graph**

Intervention Strategy
Surveying

Step 1 Arrange students into groups of two. Allow each group to select a topic about which they want to conduct a survey. The group should then write a question that can be asked of people for the purpose of conducting a survey.

Step 2 Groups should conduct a survey using their questions. At least 10 people need to be surveyed. Groups should find a way to classify and sort the responses.

Step 3 Group members should agree on a style to display their survey results. The group should then create a display that can be showcased in the classroom.

Chapter 7 One-Variable Data

How are survey results displayed?

Roberta surveyed her friends to find out which animal was the most popular pet choice. Ten friends chose cats and twelve friends chose dogs. Three friends liked both cats and dogs equally. How could Roberta display this information?

She could display this information using a graph.

272 Chapter 7 One-Variable Data

Key Vocabulary

Find interactive definitions in 13 languages in the **eGlossary** at glencoe.com.

English   Español *Introduce the most important vocabulary terms from Chapter 7.*

bar graph   gráfica de barras

a graph using bars to compare quantities; the height or length of each bar represents a designated number (p. 297)

data   datos

information, often numerical, which is gathered for statistical purposes (p. 281)

line graph   gráfica lineal

a graph used to show how a set of data changes over a period of time (p. 315)

mean   media

the sum of the numbers in a set of data divided by the number of pieces of data (p. 289)

median   mediana

the middle numbers in a set of data when the data are arranged in numerical order; if the data has an even number, the median is the mean of the two middle numbers (p. 281)

mode   moda

the number(s) or item(s) that appear most often in a set of data (p. 281)

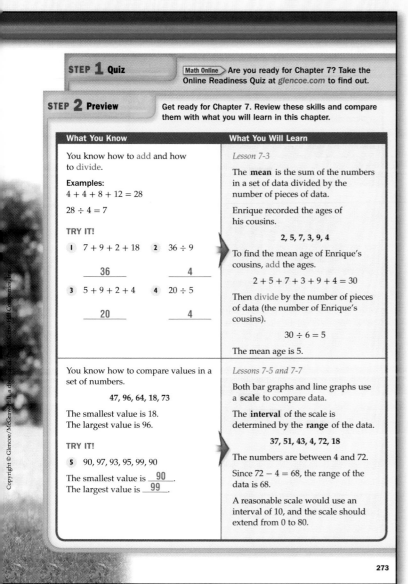

STEP 1 Quiz

Math Online ⟩ Are you ready for Chapter 7? Take the Online Readiness Quiz at glencoe.com to find out.

STEP 2 Preview

Get ready for Chapter 7. Review these skills and compare them with what you will learn in this chapter.

What You Know	What You Will Learn
You know how to add and how to divide. **Examples:** $4 + 4 + 8 + 12 = 28$ $28 \div 4 = 7$	*Lesson 7-3* The **mean** is the sum of the numbers in a set of data divided by the number of pieces of data. Enrique recorded the ages of his cousins. **2, 5, 7, 3, 9, 4** To find the mean age of Enrique's cousins, add the ages. $2 + 5 + 7 + 3 + 9 + 4 = 30$ Then divide by the number of pieces of data (the number of Enrique's cousins). $30 \div 6 = 5$ The mean age is 5.

TRY IT!

1 $7 + 9 + 2 + 18$ ____36____

2 $36 \div 9$ ____4____

3 $5 + 9 + 2 + 4$ ____20____

4 $20 \div 5$ ____4____

| You know how to compare values in a set of numbers. **47, 96, 64, 18, 73** The smallest value is 18. The largest value is 96. | *Lessons 7-5 and 7-7* Both bar graphs and line graphs use a **scale** to compare data. The **interval** of the scale is determined by the **range** of the data. **37, 51, 43, 4, 72, 18** The numbers are between 4 and 72. Since $72 - 4 = 68$, the range of the data is 68. A reasonable scale would use an interval of 10, and the scale should extend from 0 to 80. |

TRY IT!

5 90, 97, 93, 95, 99, 90

The smallest value is ____90____.
The largest value is ____99____.

273

Vocabulary Preview

- As students complete the Chapter Preview, have them make a list of important terms throughout the chapter.

- Divide students into pairs. Have each pair compare their lists of terms to make one list. Key words should be included in the list.

- Once the list is final, the pair should prepare to draw an illustration for each term.

- When all groups are finished, they should present their drawings to the class.

Step 1 Quiz

Pretest/Prescribe Students can take the Online Readiness Quiz or the Diagnostic Pretest in the Assessment Masters.

Step 2 Preview

Use this pre-chapter activity to activate students' prior knowledge, build confidence, and help students preview the lessons.

 **Dinah Zike's Foldables**

Guide students through the directions on p. A131 in the Chapter Resource Masters to create their own Foldable graphic organizer for use with this chapter.

Home Connections

- Look through current newspapers and magazines for graphic displays of data. Bring sample graphs to class. As a class, let students take turns showing their graphs so that the class can classify them as bar graphs, circle graphs, line graphs, and so on.

Professional Development

Targeted professional development has been articulated throughout **McGraw-Hill's *Math Triumphs*** intervention program. **The McGraw-Hill Professional Development Video Library** provides short videos that support the **NCTM Focal Points and Focal Connections**. For more information, visit glencoe.com.

Model Lessons   Instructional Strategies

Lesson Notes

Lesson Planner

Objective   Sort and classify data.

Vocabulary   sort , Venn diagram

Materials/Manipulatives   pattern blocks, everyday objects, counters, colored pencils

Chapter Resource Masters

CRM Vocabulary and English Language Development (p. A134)

CRM Skills Practice (p. A135)

CRM Problem-Solving Practice (p. A136)

CRM Homework Practice (p. A137)

1 Introduce

Vocabulary

Access Vocabulary   Draw a Venn diagram and write the names of students wearing blue in one circle, wearing red in another circle, and wearing both red and blue in the overlapping section. Before you label the diagram, challenge students to name the *attributes* that classify the students. Ask students for other examples they could *sort* in a *Venn diagram.*

2 Teach

Key Concept

Foundational Skills and Concepts   After students have read through the Key Concept box, have them try these exercises.

1. What are some common features of any apple?
Sample answer: red, solid, stem, round

2. What goes in a Venn diagram where the circles overlap? Objects that have both attributes.

3. How could you sort these shapes? Sample answer: Sort the striped shapes and the shaded shapes, group the circles and squares.

KEY Concept

A **Venn diagram** is one way to show how objects and numbers are sorted.

Follow these steps to sort and classify objects.
1. Sort objects by attribute.
2. Use a Venn diagram to show how the objects are sorted.

These objects are sorted by color and by shape.

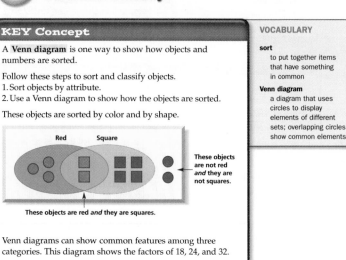

These objects are red *and* they are squares.

Venn diagrams can show common features among three categories. This diagram shows the factors of 18, 24, and 32.

These are common factors of 18, 24, and 32.

1 and 2 are common factors of 18, 24, and 32.

To sort and classify, think about how the objects are alike. Put the items that are alike in a group.

VOCABULARY

sort
to put together items that have something in common

Venn diagram
a diagram that uses circles to display elements of different sets; overlapping circles show common elements

Intervention Strategy   Visual Learners

Color Code   Have students make different-colored circles for each circle of the Venn diagram. For instance, the left circle and data are red, the right circle could be blue, and the overlap could be purple as shown on the models in the student text. Some students may find it helpful to write the head "Both" over the overlapping section.

Example 1

Create a Venn diagram to sort the numbers. Classify them as even numbers or as squares of whole numbers.

1, 2, 3, 4, 5, 6, 7, 8, 9

1. Sort and classify the numbers.

Even:	Squares of Whole Numbers:	Neither:
2, 4, 6, 8	4, 9	1, 3, 5, 7

2. Use a Venn diagram to show how the numbers are sorted. Identify the numbers in each group, in both groups, and in neither group.

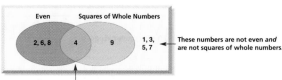

These numbers are even *and* squares of whole numbers.

YOUR TURN!

Create a Venn diagram to sort the numbers. Classify them as odd numbers or multiples of 3.

20, 21, 22, 23, 24, 25, 26, 27, 28, 29, 30

1. Sort and classify the numbers.

Odd:
 21 , 23 , 25 , 27 , 29
Multiples of 3:
 21 , 24 , 27 , 30
Neither:
 20 , 22 , 26 , 28

2. Use a Venn diagram to show how the numbers are sorted. Identify the numbers in each group, in both groups, and in neither group.

GO ON

Additional *Example 1*

Create a Venn diagram to sort the numbers. Classify them as odd numbers or as multiples of 7.

20, 21, 22, 23, 24, 25, 26, 27, 28, 29, 30

1. Sort and classify the numbers.

    Odd:
    21, 23, 25, 27, 29

    Multiples of 7:
    21, 28

    Neither:
    20, 22, 24, 26, 30

2. Use a Venn diagram to show how the numbers are sorted. Identify the numbers in each group, in both groups, and in neither group.

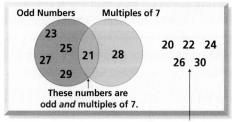

These numbers are odd *and* multiples of 7.

These numbers are not odd *and* not multiples of 7.

English Learner Strategy

Guiding Questions   Set out yellow and red counters, then ask students the following questions to ensure that they understand the concept.

- Separate the counters into red and yellow.

Add pattern blocks (yellow hexagons) and purple counters.

- How can you separate these shapes into "yellow shapes" and "shapes without edges"?

- Make a Venn diagram with string. Use it to sort and classify the shapes using different categories. How did you do it?

Note This!

Highlight Text   Hand out highlighters and let students practice highlighting text from their notes. Tell them to highlight key concepts and vocabulary words. Ask for student volunteers to share what they thought important enough to highlight. See if other students differed or were the same. Point out that students highlight differently. Encourage students to recognize that highlighting the majority of words is pointless.

Math Coach Notes

Sort Items

1. Give students ample opportunities to make Venn diagrams and then draw a picture that represents the model.

2. Have students create categories to sort and label different objects. Once they are proficient, they can begin sorting numbers by their attributes. Provide opportunities for students to sort objects and numbers according to specific classifications, as well as to distinguish attributes and decide upon their own classifications.

3 Practice

Using Manipulatives

Connecting Cubes Have students model a problem using connecting cubes. Students use pieces of string to make two overlapping circles, placing the cubes into the appropriate regions of the circles based on the relationship established with the categories.

Pattern Blocks Challenge students to make a list of different attributes of pattern blocks. Then they can sort them by these different attributes.

On-Hand Manipulatives Collect various classroom objects for students to sort and classify, such as pencils, pens, erasers, different-colored pieces of chalk, and so on.

Who is Correct?

What is the title for the category of numbers that contains 1 and 9?

Circle correct answer(s). Cross out incorrect answer(s).

▶ Guided Practice

Sort the numbers 1, 2, 3, 4, 5, 6, 7, 8, 9, and 10 into each category.

1. whole number factors of 12:
   1, 2, 3, 4, 6

2. even numbers:
   2, 4, 6, 8, 10

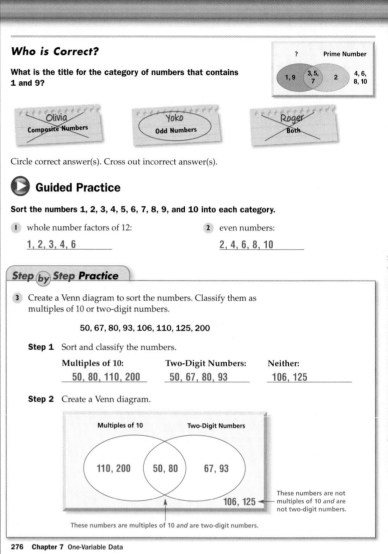

Step by Step Practice

3. Create a Venn diagram to sort the numbers. Classify them as multiples of 10 or two-digit numbers.

50, 67, 80, 93, 106, 110, 125, 200

Step 1 Sort and classify the numbers.

Multiples of 10:	Two-Digit Numbers:	Neither:
50, 80, 110, 200	50, 67, 80, 93	106, 125

Step 2 Create a Venn diagram.

These numbers are multiples of 10 *and* are two-digit numbers.

These numbers are not multiples of 10 *and* are not two-digit numbers.

Who *is Correct?*
Diagnostic Teaching

- Olivia is incorrect. The number 1 is not a composite number.

- Yoko noted that 1 and 9 are odd numbers; 2 is a prime number; and 3, 5, and 7 are both odd and prime numbers. Numbers 4, 6, 8, and 10 were neither odd nor prime numbers. This is correct.

- Roger did not read the diagram correctly. His answer is incorrect.

Remind students that prime and composite numbers are greater than 1. Therefore, 1 is not prime. Then they should review the information in each section to ensure that it matches the category title. If it does not, they need to revise the title.

4 Create a Venn diagram to sort the numbers **15, 25, 30, 45, 65, 80, 90** and **100**. Classify them as multiples of 15 or multiples of 10.

Multiples of 15:	Multiples of 10:	Neither:
15, 30, 45, 90	30, 80, 90, 100	25, 65

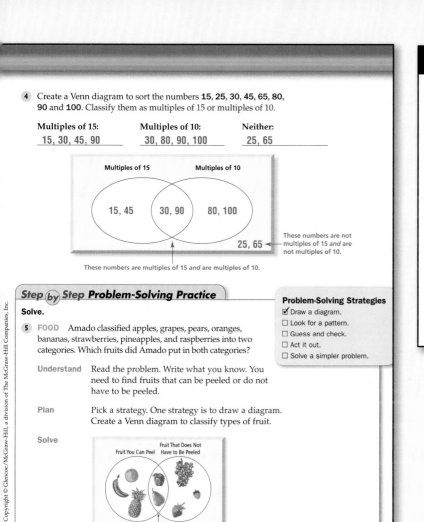

These numbers are not multiples of 15 *and* are not multiples of 10.

These numbers are multiples of 15 *and* are multiples of 10.

Step by Step Problem-Solving Practice

Solve.

5 FOOD Amado classified apples, grapes, pears, oranges, bananas, strawberries, pineapples, and raspberries into two categories. Which fruits did Amado put in both categories?

Problem-Solving Strategies
- ☑ Draw a diagram.
- ☐ Look for a pattern.
- ☐ Guess and check.
- ☐ Act it out.
- ☐ Solve a simpler problem.

Understand Read the problem. Write what you know. You need to find fruits that can be peeled or do not have to be peeled.

Plan Pick a strategy. One strategy is to draw a diagram. Create a Venn diagram to classify types of fruit.

Solve

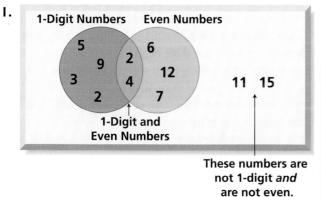

These fruits can be peeled or do not have to be peeled.

<u>Apples and pears</u> are in both categories.

Check Is your answer reasonable?

> GO ON

Lesson 7-1 Sort and Classify **277**

⚠ **Common Error** *Alert*

Exercise 4 If students write the numbers 25 and 65 as multiples of 15 in Exercise 4, it might be due to oversight. The 5 in the ones digit may cause students to think that the numbers are multiples of 15. Encourage students to think of the two circles of Venn diagrams as a way to sort numbers into as many as four categories. They should carefully go through each choice to see to which category it belongs.

Exercise 5 If students are struggling with Exercise 5, it might be because they are not familiar with each type of fruit. To avoid singling out any student, go around the class and have volunteers describe each type of fruit.

Are They Getting It? ❓

Check students' understanding of sorting and classifying by writing these problems on the board. Ask students to point out wrong answers and explain why they are wrong.

I.

1-Digit Numbers   **Even Numbers**

5 9 3 2   2 6 12 4 7   11 15

1-Digit and Even Numbers

These numbers are not 1-digit *and* are not even.

This is incorrect. 7 is not an even number, and 6 is a 1-digit and even number.

2. Use a Venn diagram to sort the objects.

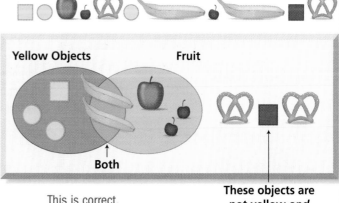

Yellow Objects   **Fruit**

Both

This is correct.

These objects are not yellow *and* are not fruit.

Lesson 7-1 Sort and Classify **277**

Sort Words   Make up a list of words that begin with a consonant, words that end with an "s," words that begin with a vowel, and words that begin with a consonant and end with an "s". Write these words on the board and have students sort and classify the words using a Venn diagram. Create other lists of words that students can sort and classify. Use categories such as different parts of speech, number of letters, or words with the same or different meanings. Alter this activity. Give students printed material so they can cut words out and use them to form their own Venn diagrams.

Odd/Even Assignments

Exercises 8–18 are structured so that students practice the same concepts whether they are assigned the odd or even problems.

In-Class Assignment

Have students complete Exercises 8–11, 16, 18, and 20 to ensure that they understand the concept.

---

6   NUMBER SENSE   Curt noticed that some <u>numbers</u> were made of <u>straight lines</u> and some had <u>curved lines</u>.

0 1 2 3 4 5 6 7 8 9

Which <u>two numbers</u> did Curt put in <u>both</u> categories? Check off each step.

_✔___ Understand: I underlined key words.

_✔___ Plan: To solve the problem, I will <u>draw a Venn diagram</u>

_✔___ Solve: The answers are _____2_____ and _____5_____.

_✔___ Check: I checked my answer by <u>reviewing the numbers in each category to see</u> <u>that they fit the specified category.</u>

7   Reflect   List three ways to classify the numbers 5, 10, 15, 20, 25, and 30.

<u>Sample answer: The numbers can be classified as multiples of 5, multiples of 10,</u> <u>and multiples of both.</u>

▶ **Skills, Concepts, and Problem Solving**

Sort each set of numbers into each category.

3, 7, 12, 14, 21, 32, 45, 50

8 multiples of 3: <u>3, 12, 21, 45</u>   **9** even numbers: <u>12, 14, 32, 50</u>

10 both: _____12_____   **11** neither: _____7_____

2, 3, 4, 17, 25, 50, 75, 90

12 factors of 100: <u>2, 4, 25, 50</u>   **13** odd numbers: <u>3, 17, 25, 75</u>

14 both: _____25_____   **15** neither: _____90_____

Partner Venn Diagrams   Have students work in pairs. One student will use connecting cubes to make cubes of different sizes and colors that can be sorted into three or four categories. The other student will use string to make a Venn diagram and sort the cubes. Then students can confer to see if the original classification was used. Students can do this activity using other objects, taking turns assembling the items and sorting them. Then have one student list numbers that can be classified into three or four categories. The diagrams can be drawn on paper.

16 Create a Venn diagram to sort the numbers. Classify them as multiples of 8 or multiples of 10.

16, 20, 32, 35, 40, 50, 75, 80, 92

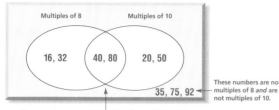

These numbers are not multiples of 8 *and* are not multiples of 10.

These numbers are multiples of 8 *and* are multiples of 10.

17 Create a Venn diagram to sort the numbers. Classify them as negative integers or even numbers.

−4, −3, −2, −1, 1, 2, 3, 4

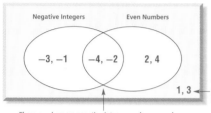

These numbers are not negative integers *and* are not even numbers.

These numbers are negative integers *and* even numbers.

Solve.

18 FOOD During lunch, Betsy wrote down how many students chose green beans, potatoes, or both. Betsy made the Venn diagram below.

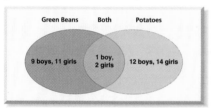

Out of 49 students, how many chose both vegetables? __3 students__   **GO ON**

Common Error *Alert*

Tables Some students will have a difficult time interpreting Venn diagrams. These students may benefit from transferring the information from the diagram to a table. Tell students to make a two-column table. They should label each column with the same classification as the circles of the Venn diagram. Ask them how they should represent the items that have both attributes. One way is it to erase the line that separates the columns and write the objects in between the two columns. The items that do not have any of the attributes go outside the table. When they are finished, have them count to ensure they have transferred all the information correctly.

Intervention Strategy   Interpersonal Learners

Classroom Sort Have students work in groups of three or four. Tell them to look around the class and find items that they can sort and then display using a Venn diagram. Have them draw a Venn diagram on poster board and present their project to the class. Make certain they label their diagrams.

Math Challenge

Matching Labels Draw Venn diagrams on index cards without labels. Lay the cards face down. Students will turn a card. Whoever is the first to figure out the correct labels gets the point. Have the cards numbered and have another set with corresponding numbers and the correct answers. The first student to earn 5 points wins.

See It, Do It, Say It, Write It

Step 1 Put a list of numbers on the board that can be sorted into multiples of 6, multiples of 7, both, or neither. Have students guide you to create a Venn diagram. Do this a number of times, letting students create the categories or list the numbers when given the categories.

Step 2 Have students work in pairs. Tell them to think of something that could be sorted in a Venn diagram.

Step 3 Students can share their completed work.

Step 4 Ask students to write the words *attribute* and *sort* on paper and define them. Then have them write a description of how they can use a Venn diagram to sort and classify.

Looking Ahead: Pre-Teach

Mode, Median, and Range   In the next lesson, students will learn about mode, median, and range.

Example

What is the mode, median, and range of the set?
{2, 5, 6, 12, 15, 22, 22, 29, 30}

The mode is the number that occurs in the data set most often. The mode is 22.

The median is the number in the middle position when the data are arranged in numerical order. The median is 15.

The range is the difference between the greatest number and the least number in the data set. The range is 30 − 2, or 28.

Name the mode, median, and range for each set.

1. {11, 16, 18, 18, 18, 21, 25} mode: 18; median: 18; range: 14

2. {67, 89, 95, 95, 101} mode: 95; median: 95; range: 34

3. {110, 111, 125, 125, 144, 159, 162, 162, 170} mode: 125, 162; median: 144; range: 60

Vocabulary Check   **Write the vocabulary word that completes each sentence.**

19 A(n) <u>Venn diagram</u> is a diagram that uses overlapping and separate circles or ellipses to organize and show data.

20 **Writing in Math**   Classify the numbers 3, 6, 7, 9, 12, 14, 21, and 28. Explain how to sort them.

<u>Sample answer: The numbers can be sorted into multiples of 3 (3, 6, 9, 12,</u>
<u>and 21), multiples of 7 (7, 14, 21, and 28), and multiples of both (21).</u>

21 Create a Venn diagram to sort the numbers. Classify them as even numbers or multiples of 5.

100, 101, 102, 103, 104, 105, 106, 107, 108, 109, 110

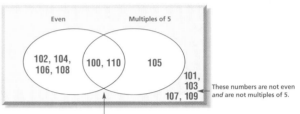

These numbers are even *and* are multiples of 5.

Solve.

22 **NUMBER SENSE**   Donald listed all the multiples of 4 up to 50. Lia listed all the multiples of 6 up to 50.

The students made a Venn diagram of the lists. Which multiples were in both categories? Explain your answer.

<u>The numbers 12, 24, 36, and 48 are in both categories.</u>

4 • 3 = 12; 6 • 2 = 12   4 • 6 = 24; 6 • 4 = 24

4 • 9 = 36; 6 • 6 = 36   4 • 12 = 48; 6 • 8 = 48

STOP

Ticket Out the Door

List to Diagram   Write a list of numbers on the board that can be sorted in a Venn diagram. Have the list contain multiples of 5 and even numbers. Tell students to draw a Venn diagram and sort the numbers. They should turn in their papers as they exit the classroom.

Mode, Median, and Range

KEY Concept

Data sets can be described by finding the mode, median, and range.

Five homerooms at Poncho Prairie Middle School collected quarters for hurricane relief. The coin jars are shown below.

Mr. D 117   Ms. M 125   Mrs. H 209   Mr. S 174   Ms. R 117

The **mode** is the number that appears most often in a set of data. In this set of data the number 117 appears twice, so it is the mode.

The **median** is the number that falls exactly in the middle of a set of data. In order to find the median, the terms must be arranged in order from least to greatest, or greatest to least.

$$117, \ 117, \ \widehat{125}, \ 174, \ 209$$

In a list of five terms, the third number will be the median. There are two numbers listed before the median and two numbers listed after the median. The median number of quarters collected is 125.

The **range** is the difference between the greatest and least number in a set of data. In this set of data, the greatest number of quarters collected is 209 and the least number of coins collected is 117. The range is 92.

$$209 - 117 = 92$$

Always put the data set in order from least to greatest before trying to describe the data set.

VOCABULARY

data
information, often numerical, which is gathered for statistical purposes

median
the middle numbers in a set of data when the data are arranged in numerical order; if the data has an even number, the median is the mean of the two middle numbers

mode
the number(s) or item(s) that appear most often in a set of data

range
the difference between the greatest number and the least number in a set of data

GO ON

Intervention Strategy   Kinesthetic Learners

Data Sets   Have students work in small groups. Distribute a deck of playing cards to each group, and have them remove the face cards. Tell students to randomly draw seven cards to create a data set. Students should manipulate the cards into ascending order and find the mode, median, and range for each set they draw. Ask students to practice explaining how to find each measure. Have groups record each data set and the measures on a piece of paper.

Lesson Notes

Lesson Planner

Objective   Find the mode, median, and range in a set of data.

Vocabulary   data , median , mode , range

Materials/Manipulatives   unit cubes, deck of playing cards, counters or dried beans

Chapter Resource Masters

CRM Vocabulary and English Language Development (p. A138)

CRM Skills Practice (p. A139)

CRM Problem-Solving Practice (p. A140)

CRM Homework Practice (p. A141)

1 Introduce

Vocabulary

Statistics   Explain the term *statistics* as math that involves the collection and analysis of data. Finding the mode, median, and range are ways to analyze or examine groups of numbers.

2 Teach

Key Concept

Foundational Skills and Concepts   After students have read through the Key Concept box, have them try these exercises.

28, 17, 9, 15, 22, 9, 8

1. What is the mode for this set of data? 9

2. Explain how to find the median of this data set.
Arrange the values from least to greatest. The median is the number that falls in the exact middle of the list, or the mean of the two middle numbers if the list has an even number of data. The median of this data set is 15.

3. What is the range for this set of data? 20

Additional *Example 1*

Find the mode for the given set of data.

Sophie asked nine classmates how many hours they spend on homework each week.

4, 10, 5, 8, 12, 8, 5, 7, 8

1. Arrange the numbers in order from least to greatest.

    4, 5, 5, 7, 8, 8, 8, 10, 12

2. The number(s) 5 and 8 appear more than once.

3. The mode is the number that appears most often. The number 8 appears three times.

4. The mode is 8.

Additional *Example 2*

Find the median for the given set of data.

Dominic surveyed the number of hours his friends worked last week.

9, 12, 8, 19, 16, 3, 9, 5, 11, 7, 4

1. Arrange the numbers in order from least to greatest.

    3, 4, 5, 7, 8, 9, 9, 11, 12, 16, 19

2. There are 11 numbers in the list. The sixth number, or the number in the middle, is the median.

3. The sixth number is 9.

    ⟶5 terms⟵ ⟶5 terms⟵
    3, 4, 5, 7, 8, ⑨ 9, 11, 12, 16, 19

Example 1

Find the mode for the given set of data.

Henry asked nine classmates how many DVDs they own.

4, 2, 0, 8, 6, 4, 5, 4, 0

1. Arrange the numbers in order from least to greatest.

    0, 0, 2, 4, 4, 4, 5, 6, 8

2. The number(s) 0 and 4 appear more than once.

3. The mode is the number that appears most often. The number 4 appears three times.

4. The mode is 4.

YOUR TURN!

Find the mode for the given set of data.

Ellis asked nine adults how many people they knew named Sarah.

3, 2, 6, 8, 6, 4, 6, 4, 1

1. Arrange the numbers in order from least to greatest.

    __1, 2, 3, 4, 4, 6, 6, 6, 8__

2. The number(s) __4 and 6__ appear more than once.

3. The mode is the number that __appears most often__. The number __6__ appears __three__ times.

4. The mode is __6__.

Example 2

Find the median for the given set of data.

Romana recorded the ages of her cousins at a family reunion.

3, 12, 4, 2, 14, 5, 7, 12, 18, 16, 1

1. Arrange the numbers in order from least to greatest.

    1, 2, 3, 4, 5, 7, 12, 12, 14, 16, 18

2. There are 11 numbers in the list. The sixth number, or the number in the middle, is the median.

3. The sixth number is 7.

    ⟶5 terms⟵ ⟶5 terms⟵
    1, 2, 3, 4, 5, ⑦ 12, 12, 14, 16, 18

YOUR TURN!

Find the median for the given set of data.

Wei-Ling recorded the number of coins she collected each day.

2, 10, 4, 3, 14, 5, 4, 12, 15,

1. Arrange the numbers in order from __least__ to __greatest__.

    __2, 3, 4, 4, 5, 10, 12, 14, 15__

2. There are __9__ numbers in the list. The __fifth__ number is the median.

3. The __fifth__ number is __5__.

English Language Learner Strategy

Questions Ask the following questions to help students understand the process of finding the mode, median, and range for a set of data.

5, 9, 7, 8, 5, 6, 9, 9, 7

- Are there any repeated numbers in the list? yes

- Which numbers appear more than one time? 5, 7, 9

- Which number appears the most? 9 This is the *mode*.

- Write the numbers in order from least to greatest. Which number is in the middle of the list? 7 This is the *median*, or middle number.

- What is the greatest number in the list? 9

- What is the least number in the list? 5

- What is the difference between the greatest and least numbers? 4 This is the *range*.

Example 3

Find the range for the given set of data.

Hesutu asked nine adults how many miles they live from their work place.

14, 1, 8, 3, 11, 3, 21, 9, 17

1. Arrange the numbers in order from least to greatest.

   1, 3, 3, 8, 9, 11, 14, 17, 21

2. The least number is 1.
   The greatest number is 21.

3. Subtract the greatest number and the least number.

   21 − 1 = 20

4. The range is 20.

YOUR TURN!

Find the range for the given set of data.

Tariq asked nine adults how many candles they have in their homes.

4, 8, 8, 22, 31, 3, 21, 17, 15

1. Arrange the numbers in order from __least__ to __greatest__.

   3, 4, 8, 8, 15, 17, 21, 22, 31

2. The __least__ number is __3__.
   The __greatest__ number is __31__.

3. Subtract the __greatest__ number and the __least__ number.

   __31__ − __3__ = __28__

4. The range is __28__.

Who is Correct?

Ava asked nine girls at what age they had their ears pierced. What is the mode of the data set?

7, 8, 4, 15, 15, 7, 3, 22, 5

Solidad
3, 4, 5, 7, 7, 8, 15, 15, 22
22 − 3 = 19
Mode = 19

Theo
3, 4, 5, 7, 7, 8, 15, 15, 22
Mode = 7

Takara
3, 4, 5, 7, 7, 8, 15, 15, 22
Mode = 7, 15

Circle the correct answer(s). Cross out incorrect answer(s).

 Guided Practice

Find the mode for each given set of data.

1. 1, 7, 8, 1, 9, 11, 2

   ___1___

2. 5, 4, 13, 9, 26, 14, 21, 33, 9

   ___9___

 GO ON

Additional *Example 3*

Find the range for the given set of data.

DaKara recorded the low temperatures for one week.

1, 15, 3, 6, 1, 5, 9

1. Arrange the numbers in order from least to greatest.

   1, 1, 3, 5, 6, 9, 15

2. The least number is 1.
   The greatest number is 15.

3. Subtract the least number from the greatest number.

   15 − 1 = 14

4. The range is 14.

 **3 Practice**

Using Manipulatives

Unit Cubes   Stack unit cubes to represent numbers in a data set. Have students manipulate the unit cubes to find the mode, median, and range for a given set.

On-Hand Manipulatives   Use counters or dried beans to model numbers in a data set. Students can manipulate the models to find the measures.

Who *is Correct?*
Diagnostic Teaching

• Solidad is incorrect. She found the range for the data set.

• Theo is incorrect. He found the median for the data set.

• Takara is correct. She correctly identified both modes.

Remind students that mode is the number that appears most often in a data set.

Math Coach Notes

Finding the Median Write a data set on the board. Model rewriting the numbers in ascending order. Then demonstrate how to find the median by counting in from both ends of the list to the middle. Place one hand on the least value and the other hand on the greatest value. Keep moving in one pair at a time until the middle number, the median, is isolated and identified. Students can mimic this process using their fingers to cover numbers in a data set on a piece of paper.

Common Error *Alert*

Exercise 3 Remind students to order the numbers before finding the median of a data set. It is much easier to identify the middle number when the data are in ascending order. Students may try to find the median by just looking at the list. Encourage them to rewrite the numbers to avoid mistakes.

Step *by* Step *Practice*

Find the median for the given set of data.

3 Jesse asked seven students in his class how many phone numbers they could name from memory.

$$5, 4, 13, 5, 9, 26, 21$$

Step 1 Arrange the data values in order from __least__ to __greatest__

__4, 5, 5, 9, 13, 21, 26__

Step 2 There are __7__ numbers in the list. The __fourth__ number, or the number in the middle, is the median.

Step 3 The __fourth__ number is __9__.

Find the median for each given set of data.

4 Grant asked seven adults how many plants they have in their home.

$$1, 7, 8, 1, 9, 11, 2$$

Arrange the numbers in order. __1__, __1__, __2__, __7__, __8__, __9__, __11__
The median is __7__.

5 Justin asked seven pet stores how many tropical fish they sold last week.

$$6, 7, 4, 5, 6, 13, 23$$

Arrange the numbers in order. __4__, __5__, __6__,
__6__, __7__, __13__, __23__
The median is __6__.

6 Kyle asked seven adults how many dollars they earned per hour.

$$18, 22, 20, 25, 31, 41, 20$$

The median is __22__.

7 The health teacher asked nine students to report how many times they flossed their teeth last month.

$$9, 4, 13, 5, 26, 14, 21, 33, 9$$

The median is __13__.

Are They Getting It?

Check students' understanding of mode, median, and range by writing these problems on the board. Ask them to point out incorrect answers and explain their reasoning.

$$6, 18, 12, 5, 9, 15, 12, 6, 8, 10, 12$$

1. The mode for this set of data is 12. This is correct.

2. The median for this data set is 9. This is incorrect. After writing the set in order, the sixth term or middle number is 10.

3. The range for this set of data is 11. This is incorrect. The greatest number in the set is 18. The least is 5. The difference of these two numbers, or the range, is 13.

Find the range for each given set of data.

8 1, 7, 8, 1, 9, 11, 2

The range of the number of plants in Exercise 4 is

__11__ – __1__ = __10__ .

9 6, 7, 4, 5, 6, 13, 23

The range of the number of tropical fish sold in Exercise 5 is

__23__ – __4__ = __19__ .

10 18, 22, 20, 25, 31, 41, 20

The range in the dollars earned per hour in Exercise 6 is __23__ .

11 9, 4, 13, 5, 26, 14, 21, 33, 9

The range in the number of times students flossed in Exercise 7 is __29__ .

Step by Step Problem-Solving Practice

Solve.

12 **HEIGHT** Each member of the girls' volleyball team at Westminster Middle School measured their heights in inches and recorded the results. Find the mode, median, and range of the heights of the girls on the team.

64, 70, 65, 64, 65, 71, 65, 62, 63, 68, 66

Problem-Solving Strategies
☐ Use a model.
☐ Use logical reasoning.
☐ Solve a simpler problem.
☐ Work backward.
☑ Look for a pattern.

Understand Read the problem. Write what you know.

There are __11__ numbers in the data set.

I want to find the __mode__ , __median__ , and __range__ .

Plan Pick a strategy. One strategy is to look for a pattern.

Solve Arrange the numbers in order from least to greatest.

The __mode__ , the number that appears most often,

is __65__ .

The __median__ , the number in the exact middle,

is __65__ .

The __range__ , the difference between the greatest number and the least number, is

__71__ – __62__ = __9__ .

Check Reverse the order of the numbers and list them from greatest to least. The mode, range, and median should remain the same.

GO ON

Note This!

Mnemonic Devices Help students remember how to find these measures using a mnemonic device for each word. Emphasize and exaggerate the long o sound in *mode* and *most* when reviewing that mōde is the number appearing mōst often. Reference a phrase such as "wide range of choices" or "on the open range" while using hand gestures indicating wide open space to reinforce that *range* describes the spread in data. For the term median, help students imagine a median in a road to remember median is the middle term in a data set.

Odd/Even Assignments

Exercises 15–27 are structured so that students practice the same concepts whether they are assigned the odd or even problems.

In-Class Assignment

Have students complete Exercises 15, 19, 22, 26, and 31 to ensure that they understand the concept.

---

13 CARNIVAL The middle school had a carnival. Each school club had a booth that charged tickets for each activity. The <u>data set</u> shows the <u>number of tickets each booth</u> collected at the end of the day. Find the <u>mode</u>, <u>median</u>, and <u>range</u> of the tickets collected. Check off each step.

234, 196, 145, 254, 196, 223, 176, 155, 231

✔ Understand: I underlined key words.

✔ Plan: To solve the problem, I will __look for a pattern__

✔ Solve: The answer is __mode = 196; median = 196; range = 109__.

✔ Check: I checked my answer by __listing the numbers from greatest to least__

14 Reflect How would adding the numbers 231 and 256 to the set of data below affect the median?

234, 196, 145, 254, 196, 223, 176, 155, 231

Sample answer: Often when two numbers are added to a data set and are greater than the median, the median will increase in value. The median of the original set of numbers was 196. The median of the new set of numbers is 223.

▶ Skills, Concepts, and Problem Solving

Find the mode for each given set of data.

15 4, 6, 7, 9, 7

__7__

16 32, 53, 23, 24, 31, 44, 23

__23__

17 6, 4, 7, 5, 19, 14, 19, 13, 8

__19__

18 7, 6, 3, 6, 4, 8, 9, 4, 6, 4, 7

__4 and 6__

Find the median for each given set of data.

19 Victoria asked seven adults how many dollars they spent in banking fees last year.

8, 6, 4, 8, 9, 3, 11

Arrange the numbers in order. __3__, __4__, __6__, __8__, __8__, __9__, __11__

The median is __8__.

Math Challenge

Changing Data How are the mode, median, and range affected if the numbers 47, 96, 124, and 128 are added to the following data set?

90, 53, 105, 72, 112, 53, 81

The mode does not change; it remains 53. The range of the original list is 59 and changes to 81 with the new numbers. The median of the original list is 81 and changes to 90 with the new numbers.

Find the median for each given set of data.

20 Gabriella kept a record of her team's score for the last five games.

52, 43, 26, 34, 29

The median is __34__.

21 Melisa asked seven students the ages of their oldest living relative.

65, 77, 87, 91, 96, 77, 73

The median is __77__.

Find the range for each given set of data.

22 16, 33, 17, 18, 22, 17, 21

__33__ – __16__ = __17__

The range is __17__.

23 8, 6, 4, 8, 9, 3, 11

__11__ – __3__ = __8__

The range is __8__.

24 52, 43, 26, 34, 29

The range is __26__.

25 65, 77, 87, 91, 96, 77, 73

The range is __31__.

Solve.

26 MOVIES A Hollywood movie company reported on the length, in minutes, of the last 13 movies they produced. The results are shown below. Find the mode, median, and range of the length of the movies.

83, 90, 121, 182, 122, 90, 97, 93, 122, 102, 99, 101, 92

The numbers in order are: 83, 90, 90, 92, 93, 97, 99, 101, 102, 121, 122, 122, 182.

The range = 99, mode = 90 and 122, and the median = 99.

27 VIDEO GAMES The newspaper surveyed middle school students and asked them how many video games they had at home. The results are shown below. Find the mode, median, and range of the data set.

11, 3, 2, 5, 13, 8, 9, 11, 5, 12, 4, 8, 6, 5, 7

The numbers in order are: 2, 3, 4, 5, 5, 5, 6, 7, 8, 8, 9, 11, 11, 12, 13.

The range = 11, mode = 5, and the median = 7.

GO ON

Note This!

Long Data Sets Model how to keep track of data when rewriting numbers in ascending order. Mark the numbers in the original list in some way, such as with a checkmark, underline, or circle, as you write the organized list. This will help prevent missing repeated numbers or dropping one of the data entirely. Show students how to count and compare the number of data after rewriting the list to make sure there are no missing numbers.

Intervention Strategy Auditory Learners

Explanations Write the following data sets on the board. Have students work in pairs. Ask students to practice explaining how to find the mode, median, and range for each set. As one student finds the measures, the listening partner should check the answers. Then switch roles for the next set. Have pairs write the measures down on a piece of paper. Groups can check their work with other pairs.

32, 35, 27, 32, 39 mode = 32, median = 32, range = 12

83, 97, 95, 64, 51, 95, 72 mode = 95, median = 83, range = 46

130, 106, 124, 159, 172, 118, 124, 119, 211 mode = 124, median = 124, range = 105

40, 26, 48, 18, 26, 48, 14, 30, 32, 48 mode = 48, median = 31, range = 34

Assess

See It, Do It, Say It, Write It

Step 1 Write the following data set on the board.

83, 97, 95, 64, 51, 95, 72

Step 2 Ask students to find the mode, median, and range for the data set. mode = 95, median = 83, range = 46

Step 3 Have students work in pairs to discuss the measures they found. Tell students to explain how they found each measure and compare their results.

Step 4 Tell students to work alone to write their evaluations of the data set on the board. Encourage students to use clear language in their explanations and provide reasoning for their measures.

Looking Ahead: Pre-Teach

Mean In the next lesson, students will learn about mean.

Example

Find the mean of the set 21, 34, 56, 78, 90, 105.

Find the sum of the numbers in the set.

$21 + 34 + 56 + 78 + 90 + 105 = 384$

Divide the sum by 6, the number of items in the data set. $\frac{384}{6} = 64$

Find the mean of each data set.

1. 44, 48, 68, 80 60
2. 1, 3, 5, 6, 6, 7, 9, 11, 11, 14, 15 8
3. 12, 10, 17, 18, 25 16.4

Vocabulary Check Write the vocabulary word that completes each sentence.

28 The _____median_____ is the value that falls exactly in the middle of a set of data.

29 The number that appears the most often in a data set is called the _____mode_____.

30 The difference between the greatest number and the least number in a data set is called _____range_____.

31 Writing in Math The data set below has an even number of data. How could you find the median, or the number in the middle?

2, 4, 8, 10, 12, 17

To find the median, find the number that falls between the two middle numbers. For example, the numbers 8 and 10 are in the middle of this set. The number that falls exactly in the middle between 8 and 10 is 9. The median is 9.

Spiral Review

32 Create a Venn diagram to sort the numbers. Classify them as factors of 24 or as prime numbers. (Lesson 7-1, p. 274)

2, 3, 4, 7, 8, 11, 12, 17, 20

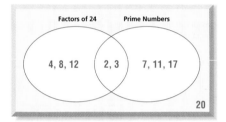

Ticket Out the Door

Mode, Median, and Range Write the following data set on the board. Tell students to find the mode, median, and range for this list. As students approach the classroom door to exit, alternate asking them to name one of the measures they found.

13, 18, 8, 10, 9, 12, 15, 9, 17

mode = 9, median = 12, range = 10

Lesson **7-3** Mean

KEY Concept

The **mean** is the sum of the numbers in a set of data divided by the number of pieces of data. Here are the award charts of four teams:

6   1   4   9

There are twenty ribbons in all. There are four teams. Redistribute the ribbons so that each team has the same number of ribbons.

5   5   5   5

If you redistribute the ribbons equally among the four teams, each team will have five ribbons. The mean of the number of ribbons for each team is five.

A set of data may contain an **outlier**, which is a value that is much higher or lower than the other values. Outliers can greatly affect the mean. Sometimes an outlier is dropped from the set of data in order to describe the data better.

VOCABULARY

average
the sum of two or more quantities divided by the number of quantities; the mean

mean
the sum of the numbers in a set of data divided by the number of pieces of data

measures of central tendency
numbers that are often used to describe the center of a set of data; these measures include the mean, median, and mode

outlier
a value that is much higher or much lower than the other values of a set of data

Example 1

Find the mean of 4, 9, 3, and 8.

1. Find the sum of the data. $4 + 9 + 3 + 8 = 24$
2. Count the items in the data set. There are 4 items in the data set.
3. Divide the sum by the number of items in the data set. $24 \div 4 = 6$
4. The mean of the data set is 6.

GO ON

Additional *Example 1*

Find the mean of 2, 9, 7, and 6.

1. Find the sum of the data.
   $2 + 9 + 7 + 6 = 24$

2. Count the items in the data set.
   There are 4 items in the data set.

3. Divide the sum by the number of items in the data set.
   $24 \div 4 = 6$

4. The mean of the data set is 6.

Lesson Notes

Lesson Planner

Objective   Find the mean in a set of data.

Vocabulary   average , mean , measures of central tendency , outlier

Materials/Manipulatives   counters, centimeter cubes, calculator

Chapter Resource Masters

CRM Vocabulary and English Language Development (p. A142)

CRM Skills Practice (p. A143)

CRM Problem-Solving Practice (p. A144)

CRM Homework Practice (p. A145)

1 Introduce

Vocabulary

Average   Explain that the terms *average* and *mean* are often used interchangeably. Both words refer to a single number used to describe all the numbers in a set of data.

2 Teach

Key Concept

Foundational Skills and Concepts   After students have read through the Key Concept box, have them try these exercises.

8, 10, 1, 9

1. What is the mean for this set of data? 7

2. Which number is the outlier for this data set? Explain. 1; It is much smaller than the other numbers in the set.

3. If the outlier is dropped from the set, how is the mean affected? The mean with the outlier is 7. Without the outlier, the mean is 9. This better represents the numbers in the data set.

Additional *Example 2*

Find the mean of 7, 10, 4, and 13. Convert the remainder into a fraction or a decimal.

1. Find the sum of the data.

$7 + 10 + 4 + 13 = 34$

2. Count the items in the data set.
There are 4 items in the data set.

3. Divide the sum by the number of items in the data set.

$34 \div 4 = 8.5$

4. Convert the remainder into a fraction or a decimal.

5. The mean of the data set is 8.5 or $8\frac{1}{2}$.

YOUR TURN!

Find the mean of 7, 2, 5, and 6.

1. Find the sum. __7__ + __2__ + __5__ + __6__ = __20__

2. Count the items in the data set. There are __4__ items in the data set.

3. Divide. __20__ ÷ __4__ = __5__

4. The mean of the data set is __5__.

Example 2

Find the mean of 5, 8, 4, and 1. Convert the remainder into a fraction or a decimal.

1. Find the sum of the data. $5 + 8 + 4 + 1 = 18$

2. Count the items in the data set.
There are 4 items in the data set.

3. Divide the sum by the number $4\overline{)18}$ 4 R2
of items in the data set.

4. Convert the remainder into a fraction $4 \text{ R2} = 4\frac{2}{4} = 4\frac{1}{2}$ or 4.5
or a decimal.

5. The mean of the data set is 4.5 or $4\frac{1}{2}$.

YOUR TURN!

Find the mean of 3, 6, 1, and 4. Convert the remainder into a fraction or a decimal.

1. Find the sum. __3__ + __6__ + __1__ + __4__ = __14__

2. Count the items in the data set.

There are __4__ items in the data set.

3. Divide. __14__ ÷ __4__ = __3.5__

4. Convert the remainder into a fraction or a __decimal__

5. The mean of the data set is __3.5 or $3\frac{1}{2}$__.

Intervention Strategy   Linguistic Learners

Talk, then write   Write the following data sets on the board. Have students work in pairs. Ask groups to verbally explain step-by-step to their partners how to find the mean of each set. Pairs should then write these directions including the answers on a piece of paper, using clear language and correct vocabulary. Tell pairs to exchange their directions with other groups and check explanations for clarity and accuracy.

29, 23, 17, 35   mean = 26

11, 34, 20, 16, 28, 26   mean = 22.5

Example 3

The mean of three numbers is 5. Two of the numbers are 7 and 5.
Find the missing number.

1. Find the total value of 3 numbers with a mean of 5. $3 \cdot 5 = 15$

2. Find the sum of the given numbers. $7 + 5 = 12$

3. Subtract the sum of the two numbers from the total sum. $15 - 12 = 3$

4. The missing number is 3.

> **YOUR TURN!**
>
> The mean of three numbers is 4. Two of the numbers are 1 and 5.
> Find the missing number.
>
> 1. Find the total value for 3 numbers with a mean of 4.
> $\underline{\ 3\ } \cdot \underline{\ 4\ } = \underline{\ 12\ }$
>
> 2. Find the sum of the given numbers.
> $\underline{\ 1\ } + \underline{\ 5\ } = \underline{\ 6\ }$
>
> 3. Subtract the sum of the two numbers from the total sum.
> $\underline{\ 12\ } - \underline{\ 6\ } = \underline{\ 6\ }$
>
> 4. The number missing from the data set is $\underline{\ 6\ }$.

Who is Correct?

Find the mean of 5, 6, 5, 1, and 13.

Greg
The mean is 5 because it occurs twice in the data set.

Dwayne
The mean is 6.
$5 + 6 + 5 + 1 + 13 = 30$
$30 \div 5 = 6$

Greta
The mean is 11, because the least number is 1 and the greatest number is 12.

Circle correct answer(s). Cross out incorrect answer(s).

GO ON

Additional *Example 3*

The mean of three numbers is 6. Two of the numbers are 3 and 8. Find the missing number.

1. Find the total value of 3 numbers with a mean of 6.

$3 \cdot 6 = 18$

2. Find the sum of the given numbers.

$3 + 8 = 11$

3. Subtract the sum of the two numbers from the total sum.

$18 - 11 = 7$

4. The missing number is 7.

Who *is Correct?*
Diagnostic Teaching

- Greg is incorrect. He identified the mode of the data set.

- Dwayne is correct. He found the mean of the list.

- Greta is incorrect. She identified the range of the data set.

Remind students that the mean of a data set is the average of all of the data.

③ Practice

Using Manipulatives

Counters   Use counters to represent numbers in a data set. Manipulate the counters into equal groups to model division and find the mean of the data set.

On-Hand Manipulatives   Model how to use a calculator to find the mean of a list of numbers.

Math Coach Notes

Measures of Central Tendency   Clarify that *range* is a measure of variation, or a number used to describe how spread out the values are in a data set. The other measures—mean, median, and mode—describe the center of the data. When there is a large outlier in the set, explain that the median is a better measure of central tendency than mean since the mean is skewed by the much larger or smaller number.

▶ Guided Practice

Find the mean of the data set. Convert the remainder into a fraction or a decimal.

1 9, 12, 7, 8

$$\underline{9} + \underline{12} + \underline{7} + \underline{8} = \underline{36}$$

$$\underline{36} \div \underline{4} = \underline{9}$$

The mean is __9__ .

2 7, 15, 12, 18

$$\underline{7} + \underline{15} + \underline{12} + \underline{18} = \underline{52}$$

$$\underline{52} \div \underline{4} = \underline{13}$$

The mean is __13__ .

3 10, 10, 10, 3, 5

$$\underline{10} + \underline{10} + \underline{10} + \underline{3} +$$
$$\underline{5} = \underline{38}$$

$$\underline{38} \div \underline{5} = \underline{7.6}$$

The mean is __7.6__ .

4 4, 8, 5, 7, 8

$$\underline{4} + \underline{8} + \underline{5} + \underline{7} +$$
$$\underline{8} = \underline{32}$$

$$\underline{32} \div \underline{5} = \underline{6.4}$$

The mean is __6.4__ .

Step by Step Practice

5 The mean of four numbers is 7. Three of the numbers are 9, 2, and 12. Find the missing number.

Step 1   Find the total value of 4 numbers with a mean of 7.

$$\underline{4} \cdot \underline{7} = \underline{28}$$

Step 2   Find the sum of the given numbers.

$$\underline{9} + \underline{2} + \underline{12} = \underline{23}$$

Step 3   Subtract the sum of the numbers from the total sum.

$$\underline{28} - \underline{23} = \underline{5}$$

Step 4   This missing number is __5__ .

Find one missing number from a data set when the mean is given.

6 Mean: 10   Data set: 8, 18, 6, __8__

7 Mean: 3   Data set: 1, 4, 3, __4__

8 Mean: 9   Data set: 4, 13, 9, __10__

9 Mean: 7   Data set: 7, 8, 9, __4__

Intervention Strategy   Kinesthetic Learners

Represent Data   During four cross-country practices, Mitch ran 7 miles, 3 miles, 4 miles, and 6 miles. Ask students to find the mean for this data set using unit cubes. Use the cubes to represent the number of miles completed during each practice. Have students then move the unit cubes until each stack has the same number of cubes.

Ask students to determine the mean number of miles Mitch ran during his practices. Students should explain their reasoning. Mitch ran an average of 5 miles per practice; there are 5 unit cubes in each of the four stacks.

Ask students: If Mitch runs 3 miles and 1 mile during his next two practices, how does the mean change? Have students use the unit cubes to provide support for their answers. The mean becomes 4 miles per practice. The stacks are now 6 groups of 4 unit cubes each.

Step by Step Problem-Solving Practice

Solve.

10 **NAMES** What is the mean number of letters in these students' names? CASSUNDRA, CARLY, KENT, and CARLOS.

Understand	Read the problem. Write what you know.
	There are __4__ students.
	The number of letters in each name is __9__, __5__, __4__, and __6__.
Plan	Pick a strategy. One strategy is to act it out.
Solve	Use counters to represent the letters in each student's name. Find the __sum__ of the letters by counting the counters.
	Divide the counters by the number of __names__.
	__24__ ÷ __4__ = __6__
	The mean number of letters is __6__.
Check	Use inverse operations and work backward.

11 **BASKETBALL** Five players on the girls' basketball team scored the following <u>number of points</u> in the first half of a game: <u>12, 4, 0, 8, and 5</u>. What was the <u>mean</u> of the points scored? Check off each step.

✔ Understand: I underlined key words.

✔ Plan: To solve the problem, I will _____use a model_____

✔ Solve: The answer is _____5.8_____

✔ Check: I checked my answer by ___inverse operations___

12 **TEST SCORES** Rochelle recorded the number of minutes she exercised over the last seven days. What is the mean of this data set?

64, 56, 60, 56, 68, 60, 63

The mean is 61. 64 + 56 + 60 + 56 + 68 + 60 + 63 = 427;

427 ÷ 7 = 61

GO ON

Math Coach Notes

Outliers Discuss how an outlier can affect the mean and skew a data set. Give the example of houses for sale in a neighborhood. If one house sells for much higher or lower than the others, it changes the average home value for the neighborhood. This could influence purchasing decisions. Another example could be a student's basketball record. If she shoots a record number of free-throws during one game but usually scores a lower number of these, her game statistics will be inaccurate. Sometimes the outliers are tossed out of a group of numbers to better reflect the entire data set.

Are They Getting It? ❓

Check students' understanding of finding the mean in a set of data by writing these problems on the board. Ask them to point out incorrect answers and explain their reasoning.

21, 8, 25, 26

1. The mean for this set of data is 23. This is incorrect. The sum of the numbers is 80. The mean is 80 ÷ 4, or 20.

2. The outlier for this data set is 8. This is correct.

3. If there are five numbers in this data set and 19 is the mean, then 18 is the missing number. This is incorrect. 5 × 19 = 95 and 95 − 80 (the sum of the given terms) is 15. The missing number in the data set is 15.

Odd/Even Assignments

Exercises 14–28 are structured so that students practice the same concepts whether they are assigned the odd or even problems.

In-Class Assignment

Have students complete Exercises 15, 18, 22, 26, 27, and 31 to ensure that they understand the concept.

---

13 **Reflect**   Otis earned scores of 97, 93, 92, and 84 on his last four math tests. On the next test Otis, earned a score of 61. How does this outlier affect his mean score?

The mean test score on four tests was 91.5. After the score of 61 is

used, Otis's mean test score drops to 85.4.

 Skills, Concepts, and Problem Solving

Find the mean of the data set.

14 97, 82, 71, 109, 91

90

15 14, 26, 21, 29, 12

20.4

16 4.6, 4.0, 3.6, 3.8, 4.9, 5.2, 6.1

4.6

17 5.9, 6.1, 6.0, 5.9, 6.1

6.0

Find the mean of the data set. Convert the remainder into a fraction or a decimal.

18 9, 4, 1, 8

5.5

19 15, 7, 10, 6

9.5

20 8, 12, 5, 6, 10

8.2

21 11, 7, 6, 10, 20

10.8

Find one missing number from a data set when the mean is given.

22 Mean: 10   Data set: 12, 15, __3__

23 Mean: 8   Data set: 4, 12, 7, __9__

24 Mean: 7   Data set: 11, 2, 8, __7__

25 Mean: 11   Data set: 11.6, 12.5, 8.1, __11.8__

26 The mean amount of money Jolene saved over the last six months was $52. She forgot to record the amount that she saved in April. What is the missing amount in the table at the right?

Jolene saved $44 in April.

Jolene's Savings Account	
Month	Dollars Saved ($)
March	46
April	44
May	52
June	64
July	50
August	56

Math Challenge

Math Scores   Manny earned the following scores on four math quizzes. What will he have to earn on the final quiz to have an average score of 85? Explain your reasoning.

90.5, 78.5, 83, 88.5

He must earn an 84.5. Five quizzes with an average of 85 is 5 × 85, or 425. The sum of his current scores is 340.5 and the difference between the two numbers is 84.5, the missing score in the data set.

Solve.

27 EXPERIMENT A group of students grabbed a handful of marbles for a scientific experiment. Stephanie picked up 5 marbles, Hector picked up 8, Drew picked up 7 marbles, and Heddy picked up 4. What was the mean number of marbles the students grabbed?

_____6 marbles_____

28 QUIZ SCORES Reyna scored 7, 8, 10, 6, and 8 on five weekly quizzes. What is the mean of her scores?

_____7.8_____

Vocabulary Check Write the vocabulary word that completes each sentence.

29 The sum of the numbers in a set of data divided by the number of pieces of data is called the _____mean_____.

30 The _____measures of central tendency_____ are numbers that are often used to describe the center of a set of data. This includes the mean, median, and mode.

31 Writing in Math Is it necessary to order the data from least to greatest before you find the mean of the data? Explain your answer.

_____No; The rule for finding the mean score of a set of data is to first find the sum of_____

_____the data pieces. The order of the data does not change that value, according to the_____

_____Commutative Property of Addition._____

 Spiral Review

Find the median and the range for each given set of data. (Lesson 7-2, p. 281)

32 Mariska recorded the ages of seven monkeys at the zoo.

8, 22, 15, 25, 36, 41, 30

The median is __25__.
The range is __33__.

33 The track coach asked nine students to report how many miles they ran last week.

9, 13, 15, 10, 16, 14, 21, 19, 9

The median is __14__.
The range is __12__.

 STOP

Ticket Out the Door

Outliers and Averages Write the following data set on the board. Tell students to find the mean, with and without the outlier. As students approach the classroom door to exit, alternate asking them to name the outlier, the mean for all the numbers, or the mean without the outlier.

4.5, 6, 17, 3.5, 6, 5

Outlier: 17
Mean with the outlier: 7
Mean without the outlier: 5

 **4 Assess**

See It, Do It, Say It, Write It

Step 1 Write the following data set on the board.

45, 53, 12, 38, 42

Step 2 Ask students to find the mean of the data set, with and without the outlier.

Step 3 Have students work in pairs to discuss the data set. Tell students to identify the outlier and explain how it affects the mean.

Step 4 Students should work alone to write their evaluations of the data set on the board. Ask students to explain if the mean is more accurate with or without the outlier.

Mean with the outlier: 38
Mean without the outlier: 44.5

Looking Ahead: Pre-Teach

Interpret Bar Graphs In the next lesson, students will learn to interpret bar graphs.

Example

How many seventh graders voted for the bear as the mascot?

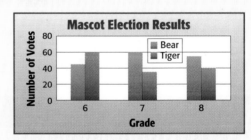

Read the scale that lines up with the red bar for seventh grade. 60 seventh graders voted for the bear.

Use the graph above to answer each question.

1. How many sixth graders voted? 105

2. How many votes did the tiger mascot receive in all? 135

Formative Assessment

Use the Progress Check to assess students' mastery of the previous lessons. Have students review the lesson indicated for the problems they answered incorrectly.

Odd/Even Assignments

Exercises are structured so that students practice the same concepts whether they are assigned the odd or even problems.

⚠️ **Common Error** *Alert*

Exercise 7 Ensure students multiply the given mean by the correct value. To solve this problem, students should multiply the given mean of 70 by 5, and then subtract the sum of the given numbers of volunteers. Some students will incorrectly multiply by 4 (because that is the number of values given).

Chapter
7 **Progress Check 1** (Lessons 7-1, 7-2, and 7-3)

Find the mode for each given set of data.

1 14, 26, 57, 39, 57

   57

2 26, 24, 27, 25, 39, 34, 39, 33, 28

   39

Find the median and the range for each given set of data.

3 Sarita asked seven adults how many cars they have owned in their lifetime.

         1, 5, 2, 3, 7, 2, 4

Arrange the numbers in order. _1_, _2_, _2_, _3_, _4_, _5_, _7_

The median is _3_.
The range is _6_.

Find the mean of the data set. Convert the remainder into a fraction or a decimal.

4 12, 5, 7, 8   _8_

5 18, 12, 15, 9, 10   _12.8_

6 **ANIMALS** Mr. Thomson listed these animals on the board: dog, lion, eagle, cat, elephant, and horse. He asked his class to sort these animals as pets or wild animals. Create a Venn diagram to sort these animals.

      Pets   **Wild Animals**

    dog   horse   lion
    cat   eagle
                 elephant

7 **SERVICE** Marco recorded the mean number of volunteers from the Nicolas Corporation for this year's charity events as 70 volunteers. However, he forgot to record the number of volunteers at the Children's Day event. Use the mean and the remaining data in the table to find the missing number.

   _61_

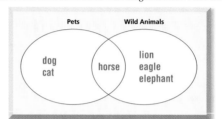

Nicolas Corporation Charity Events	
Event	Number of Volunteers
Children's Day	61
Health Fair	72
Golf Tournament	68
Jazz in the Park	52
Blankets for Babies	97

296 **Chapter 7** One-Variable Data

Data-Driven Decision Making

Students missing Exercises . . .	Have trouble with . . .	Should review and practice . . .
1–2	finding the mode of a data set.	**SSG** Lesson 7-2, p. 281 **CRM** Skills Practice, p. A139
3	finding the median and range of a data set.	**SSG** Lesson 7-2, p. 281 **CRM** Skills Practice, p. A139
4–5	finding the mean of a data set.	**SSG** Lesson 7-3, p. 289 **CRM** Skills Practice, p. A143
6–7	solving word problems involving categorizing objects or finding mean.	**CRM** Problem Solving Practice, pp. A136, A140, and A144

Lesson 7-4 — Interpret Bar Graphs

KEY Concept

A **bar graph** is commonly used to compare categories of data. The graph has several important features, such as the title, categories, and a scale.

The categories are commonly set on the **horizontal axis** of the graph. The categories used in this graph are "Grade 5," "Grade 6," "Grade 7," and "Grade 8."

 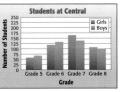

The **vertical axis** of the graph shows the scale of the numerical values. **Scales** use intervals to include data from larger value sets. Since the number of students at each grade ranges from 125 to 300 students, the **interval** used on the scale is 50.

Each bar represents a different grade. The bar height shows the number of students who are in each grade level.

The double-bar graph below shows the same set of data, but provides extra information about the number of boys and the number of girls in each grade level.

The interval on the scale has changed because the range of numbers is different.

The graphs above are vertical bar graphs. Horizontal bar graphs label the scales along the horizontal axis and the categories along the vertical axis.

GO ON

VOCABULARY

bar graph
a graph using bars to compare quantities; the height or length of each bar represents a designated number

horizontal axis
the axis on which the categories or values are shown in a bar and line graph

interval
the difference between successive values on a scale

scale
the set of all possible values in a given measurement, including the least and greatest numbers in the set, separated by the intervals used

vertical axis
the axis on which the scale and interval are shown in a bar or line graph

---

Lesson Notes

Lesson **7-4**

Lesson Planner

Objective Interpret data in bar graphs, including the measures of central tendency.

Vocabulary bar graph , horizontal axis , interval , scale , vertical axis

Materials/Manipulatives centimeter grid paper, centimeter unit cubes, rulers

Chapter Resource Masters

- CRM Vocabulary and English Language Development (p. A146)
- CRM Skills Practice (p. A147)
- CRM Problem-Solving Practice (p. A148)
- CRM Homework Practice (p. A149)

① Introduce

Vocabulary

Coordinate Plane Compare reading a bar graph to finding points on a coordinate plane. Using the axes, students will find a point where the two intersect to obtain information, similar to plotting a point on a coordinate grid.

② Teach

Key Concept

Foundational Skills and Concepts After students have read through the Key Concept box, have them try these exercises.

1. In the "Students at Central" bar graph, how many students are in Grade 6? 250

2. In the double-bar graph, how many boys are in Grade 8? 100

3. In the double-bar graph, how many more girls than boys are in Grade 7? 30

Intervention Strategy — Visual Learners

Interpret a Bar Graph Model how to interpret a bar graph by evaluating the following graph aloud. Ask students to help you evaluate each question using the information in the graph in Example 2 on page 298.

- What is the title of the graph? My Classmates' Favorite Pants

- What are the labels on the axes? Types of Pants and Votes

- What is the scale and interval of the graph? 0–20, 2s

- What are the categories on the horizontal axis? Sweats, Jeans, Khakis, Corduroys

- What was girls' favorite type of pants? sweats

- What type of pants, and from whom, got 8 votes? 8 girls voted for jeans; 8 boys voted for khakis

- What type of pants, and from who, got 5 votes? 5 boys voted for corduroys

Additional *Example 1*

Use the bar graph "Championship Series" to compare data.

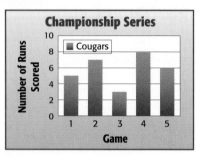

Championship Series

How many runs did the Cougars score in Games 4 and 5 combined?

1. How many runs did the Cougars score in Game 4? 8

2. How many runs did the Cougars score in Game 5? 6

3. To find how many runs were scored in both games, add.

$8 + 6 = 14$

4. The Cougars scored 14 runs in Games 4 and 5 combined.

Example 1

Use the bar graph "My Classmates' Favorite Pants" to compare data.

How many more students prefer sweats than khakis?

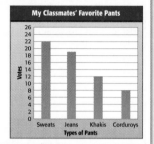

1. How many students chose sweats as their favorite pants? **22**

2. How many students chose khakis as their favorite pants? **12**

3. To find how many more chose sweats than khakis, subtract.

$22 - 12 = 10$

4. There are 10 more students who prefer sweats than khakis.

YOUR TURN!

Use the bar graph "My Classmates' Favorite Pants" to compare data.

How many students prefer jeans or corduroys?

1. How many students chose jeans as their favorite pants? __19__

2. How many students chose corduroys as their favorite pants? __8__

3. To find how many chose jeans or corduroys, __add__.

__19__ + __8__ = __27__

4. There are __27__ students who prefer jeans or corduroys.

Example 2

Use the double-bar graph "My Classmates' Favorite Pants" to compare data.

How many girls prefer jeans or corduroys?

1. How many girls chose jeans as their favorite pants? 8

2. How many girls chose corduroys as their favorite pants? 3

3. To find how many girls chose jeans or corduroys, add.

$8 + 3 = 11$

4. There are 11 girls who prefer jeans or corduroys.

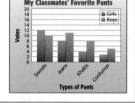

Additional *Example 2*

Use the double-bar graph "Championship Series" to compare data.

How many more runs were scored by the Cougars than the Eagles in Game 4?

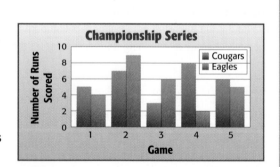

Championship Series

1. How many runs were scored by the Cougars in Game 4? 8

2. How many runs were scored by the Eagles in Game 4? 2

3. To find how many more runs were scored by the Cougars than the Eagles in Game 4, subtract.

$8 - 2 = 6$

4. There were 6 more runs scored by the Cougars than the Eagles in Game 4.

YOUR TURN!

Use the double-bar graph "My Classmates' Favorite Pants" on page 298 to compare data.

How many more boys than girls prefer khakis?

1. How many boys chose khakis as their favorite pants? __8__

2. How many girls chose khakis as their favorite pants? __4__

3. To find how many more boys chose khakis than girls, __subtract__ .

   __8__ – __4__ = __4__

4. There are __4__ more boys than girls who prefer khakis.

Who is Correct?

Use the double-bar graph "My Classmates' Favorite Pants" on page 298 to compare data.

Compare the number of boys who chose jeans, and the number of boys who chose sweats as their favorite pants.

Mallory
12 – 8 = 4
Four more boys chose jeans than sweats.

Tadeo
11 – 10 = 1
One more boy chose jeans than sweats.

Kei
11 – 8 = 3
Three more boys chose jeans than sweats.

Circle correct answer(s). Cross out incorrect answer(s).

 Guided Practice

Use the bar graph "Mary's Guitar Practice" to compare data.

1. What does the scale of the bar graph represent?

   __number of minutes__

2. What are the categories?

   __days of the week__

3. What interval is used for the scale? __5__

4. What does the height of each bar represent?

   __the number of minutes practiced each day of the week__

GO ON

Lesson 7-4 Interpret Bar Graphs **299**

Using Manipulatives

Unit Cubes   Use centimeter cubes and centimeter grid paper to create and manipulate bar graphs. Students can ask and answer questions based on their graphs. Remind students to label the axes and give their graphs a title.

On-Hand Manipulatives   Model how to use a ruler to read a bar graph. Show how to line up the ruler with the horizontal axis and follow the line over to the vertical axis to read each bar's value in a graph.

Who is Correct?
Diagnostic Teaching

- Mallory is incorrect. Only 11 boys chose jeans and 10 boys chose sweats.

- Tadeo is correct.

- Kei is incorrect. She compared the number of boys who chose jeans to the number of girls who chose jeans.

Remind students to be careful to focus on the correct bars when comparing information in a double-bar graph.

Math Coach Notes

Word Clues Model how to read questions for word or phrase clues to know which operation is needed. Explain how to associate clues such as *or, total,* or *altogether* with addition operations, and clues such as *more* or *compared to* with subtraction operations. Point out that some questions will require more than one operation.

English Learner Strategy

Connections Use Exercises 6–11 to discuss the graph of favorite types of TV shows. Encourage students to share which genre they prefer, including examples and reasons for their choices. Examine the graph and answer the questions together. After evaluating the exercise's graph, take a survey of the students' preferences and create a bar graph with the class's results. Ask the same questions from the exercises using the class graph.

Step by Step Practice

Use the bar graph "Mary's Guitar Practice" on page 299 to compare data.

5 How many more minutes did Mary practice on Tuesday than on Thursday?

    Step 1 How many minutes did Mary practice on Tuesday?
        <u>45 minutes</u>

    Step 2 How many minutes did Mary practice on Thursday?
        <u>30 minutes</u>

    Step 3 To find how many more minutes she practiced on Tuesday than on Thursday, <u>subtract</u>.

        <u>45</u> – <u>30</u> = <u>15</u>

    Step 4 Mary practiced <u>15</u> minutes more on <u>Tuesday</u>.

Use the bar graph "Favorite Type of TV Show" to compare data.

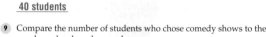

6 How many students chose horror shows as their favorite?

   <u>16 students</u>

7 What number of students chose action shows as their favorite?

   <u>20 students</u>

8 How many students chose comedy or animated shows as their favorite?

   <u>40 students</u>

9 Compare the number of students who chose comedy shows to the number who chose horror shows.

   <u>12 more students chose comedy shows</u>

10 Find the total number of students represented on the graph.

   <u>76 students</u>

11 Which type of TV show is preferred the most?

   <u>comedy</u>

300 Chapter 7 One-Variable Data

Intervention Strategy   Auditory Learners

Interactions Display the following graph. Have students work in small groups. Tell students to evaluate the bar graph together. Discussions should include identifying all the parts of the graph and explaining what the graph shows. Ask each group to share their evaluations as the class examines the graph together.

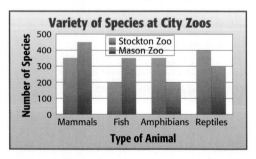

Step by Step Problem-Solving Practice

Solve.

12 **CAFETERIA** The cafeteria manager wanted to compare the favorite meals of the students at Madison Middle School. How many girls prefer pizza or spaghetti compared to the number of girls who prefer chicken nuggets or tacos?

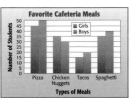

Favorite Cafeteria Meals

Understand	Read the problem and review the graph. Write what you know.

There are __45__ girls who prefer pizza.

There are __35__ girls who prefer chicken nuggets.

There are __15__ girls who prefer tacos.

There are __35__ girls who prefer spaghetti.

Plan Pick a strategy. One strategy is to solve a simpler problem.

Solve How many girls prefer pizza or spaghetti?

__45__ + __35__ = __80__

How many girls prefer chicken nuggets or tacos?

__35__ + __15__ = __50__

What is the difference between these two groups?

__80__ − __50__ = __30__

There are __30 more__ girls who prefer pizza or spaghetti compared to chicken nuggets or tacos.

Check Work backward and use inverse operations. Use addition to check subtraction, and subtraction to check addition.

 GO ON

Are They Getting It? ❓

Check students' understanding of interpreting bar graphs by writing these problems on the board. Ask them to point out incorrect answers and explain their reasoning.

1. The graph of "Mary's Guitar Practice" shows that she practiced a total of 185 minutes on the guitar during the week. This is incorrect. By adding the minutes from each of the 5 days, the total minutes equal 175.

2. The single-bar graph of "Students at Central" shows the number of seventh graders is 300. This is correct.

3. The double-bar graph of "My Classmates' Favorite Pants" shows that the same number of girls voted for jeans as boys voted for khakis. This is correct.

Odd/Even Assignments

Exercises 16–23 are structured so that students practice the same concepts whether they are assigned the odd or even problems.

In-Class Assignment

Have students complete Exercises 16, 18, 20, 22, and 26 to ensure that they understand the concept.

Intervention Strategy

Linguistic Learners

Questioning   Display the graph below. Have students work in pairs. Ask them to write questions about the graph with different difficulty levels—two easy, two medium, and two hard. Pairs should include answers to their questions on a separate piece of paper. Students can share their questions in a variety of ways, such as reading them aloud and challenging classmates to find the answers, or creating a class game with points awarded per question based on level of difficulty.

C07-03A-888224.ai

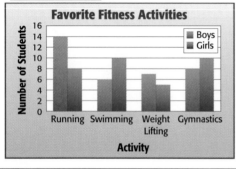

Favorite Fitness Activities

Use the double-bar graph "Favorite Cafeteria Meals" on page 301 to complete Exercises 13 and 14.

13   **FOOD**   The cafeteria manager wanted to compare the favorite meals of boys and girls. How many <u>girls</u> prefer <u>pizza or spaghetti</u> compared to the number of <u>boys</u> who prefer <u>pizza or spaghetti</u>? Check off each step.

✔   Understand: I underlined key words.

✔   Plan: I will solve this problem by _____ solving a simpler problem

✔   Solve: The answer is _____ 10 more boys than girls prefer pizza or spaghetti

✔   Check: To check my answer I will _____ work backward and use inverse operations

14   **PIZZA**   How many more students (boys and girls) preferred pizza compared to tacos?

60; $45 + 50 = 95$ preferred pizza, $15 + 20 = 35$ preferred tacos,

$95 - 35 = 60$ more students preferred pizza than tacos

15   **Reflect**   Other than comparing boys and girls, what other two groups could be compared using a double-bar graph?

Sample Answer: A double bar-graph could compare adults and children,

managers and employees, or residents of one state versus another state.

▶ Skills, Concepts, and Problem Solving

Use the bar graph "Favorite School Subject" to compare data.

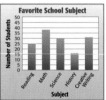

16   How many students chose math as their favorite subject?

38 students

17   How many students chose history as their favorite subject?

16 students

18   How many students chose reading or creative writing as their favorite subject?

56 students

Math Challenge

Analyze Graphs   Have students use the graph in the Intervention Strategy on page 302 to answer the following questions.

1. How many more students prefer running than swimming? 6

2. How many more boys voted than girls? 2

3. For boys, which two activities received the same number of votes together as running did for boys? swimming and gymnastics

4. For boys, which activity received half as many votes as another activity? Name both activities and write an expression to show the relationship. running, r; weight lifting, w; $r = 2w$ or $w = \frac{1}{2}r$

Use the bar graph "Favorite School Subject" on page 302 to compare data.

19 How many more students chose science than history as their favorite subject?

<u> 14 students </u>

20 How many students are represented on the graph?

<u> 140 students </u>

21 Which subject is preferred the least?

<u> history </u>

Use the double-bar graph "Favorite Sport" to complete Exercises 22 and 23.

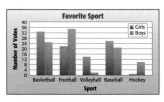

22 **SPORTS**   The physical education teacher wanted to compare the favorite sports of boys and girls. How many girls prefer basketball or baseball compared to the number of boys who prefer basketball or baseball?

<u> 13; 33 + 26 = 59 girls prefer basketball or baseball </u>

<u> 25 + 21 = 46 boys prefer basketball or baseball </u>

<u> 59 − 46 = 13 more girls than boys preferred basketball </u>

<u> or baseball </u>

23 **FOOTBALL**   How many more students (boys and girls) prefer football compared to hockey?

<u> 46 students; 22 + 35 = 57 prefer football; </u>

<u> 1 + 10 = 11 prefer hockey; 57 − 11 = 46 more students </u>

<u> prefer football than hockey </u>

GO ON

Note This!
Double-Bar Graph Questions   Explain how to differentiate when to use both bars per category in a double-bar graph and when to focus on one bar. Use Exercises 22–23 to compare the ways the questions are posed. Model breaking the problem into smaller pieces of information and restating the question in your own words. Point out that some questions ask for "students," meaning both bars, while others specifically ask for one bar.

4 Assess

See It, Do It, Say It, Write It

Step 1 Display the following graph.

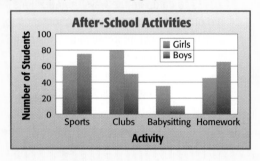

Step 2 Ask students to answer the following questions:

- How many girls are involved with sports? 60

- How many more girls are in clubs than boys? 30

- How many more boys and girls do homework than babysit? 65

Step 3 Have students work in pairs. Students should discuss their answers and explain how they found them.

Step 4 Tell students to independently write their evaluations of the double-bar graph. Students should include the answers to the questions and their reasoning.

Looking Ahead: Pre-Teach

Create Bar Graphs In the next lesson, students will learn to create bar graphs.

Example Determine an appropriate scale and interval to use to make a bar graph of the data in the table.

Pet	Dog	Cat	Fish	Bird
Number	12	16	8	3

The data ranges from 3 to 16, so the scale should be from 0 to 18 with intervals of 2.

Determine a scale and interval for each set of data.

Sample answers given.

1. 11, 20, 34, 41, 49   0 to 50 with an interval of 5

2. 16, 67, 35, 88, 91   0 to 100 with an interval of 10

Vocabulary Check **Write the vocabulary word that completes each sentence.**

24 A __bar graph__ is a graph using bars to compare quantities.

25 The __vertical axis__ is commonly the axis on which the scale and interval are shown in a bar or line graph.

26 **Writing in Math** Suppose you are creating a bar graph. Choose a scale for the following numbers. Include information about the interval you would use. Explain your answer.

56, 97, 125, 79, 205, 152

Sample answer: A scale from 0 to 250 could be used. None of the numbers are less than 0 or greater than 250. The scale could use intervals of 25 since most of the values are close to multiples of 25.

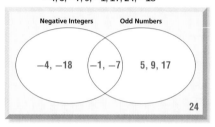 **Spiral Review**

Find one missing number from a data set when the mean is given.
(Lesson 7-3, p. 289)

27 Mean: 16

Data set: 18, 21, 19, __6__

28 Mean: 10

Data set: 7, 16, 9, __8__

29 Mean: 19

Data set: 24, 23, 27, __2__

30 Mean: 46

Data set: 47, 45, 46, __46__

31 Create a Venn diagram to sort the numbers. Classify them as negative integers or odd numbers. (Lesson 7-1, p. 274)

−4, 5, −7, 9, −1, 17, 24, −18

Negative Integers / Odd Numbers

−4, −18 | −1, −7 | 5, 9, 17

24

STOP

Ticket Out the Door

Double-Bar Graphs Refer to the Mascot Election Results double-bar graph on page 295 of the Teacher Edition. As students approach the classroom door to exit, alternate asking them to name the total number of students who voted, or how many more students voted for Bear than Tiger.

295 total students; 25 more students voted for Bear than Tiger

Lesson 7-5 Create Bar Graphs

KEY Concept

A **bar graph** can be created using information in a table. The final graph must show several important features, such as the title, categories, and a **scale**.

Pets Owned	
Pet	Number
Cat	10
Dog	12
Fish	5
Bird	2
Lizard	1
None	2

Notice that the title and the categories in the graph are similar to those shown in the table. The scale of the graph often starts at zero and extends to the largest value in the data set. The **interval** of the scale is determined by the range of the data. This graph uses an interval of 2.

A double-bar graph can also be created using the information in a table. This double-bar graph compares pet ownership of boys and girls.

Pets Owned		
Pet	Boys	Girls
Cat	2	8
Dog	6	6
Fish	3	2
Bird	0	2
Lizard	1	0
None	1	1

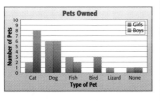

Double-bar graphs can compare categories other than boys and girls, such as two grade levels, adults and children, or other groups.

VOCABULARY

bar graph
a graph using bars to compare quantities; the height or length of each bar represents a designated number

horizontal axis
the axis on which the categories or values are shown in a bar and line graph

interval
the difference between successive values on a scale

scale
the set of all possible values in a given measurement, including the least and greatest numbers in the set, separated by the intervals used

vertical axis
the axis on which the scale and interval are shown in a bar or line graph

 GO ON

Intervention Strategy Visual Learners

Create Graphs Use butcher paper to cover a bulletin board or section of the classroom. Write the following table on the left side of the butcher paper. Construct a bar graph together from the information in the table on the right side. Have students write the title, label the axes, determine the interval, and complete the scale. Complete the graph by drawing bars to represent the data in the table. Use index cards to label parts of the graph with the correct vocabulary terms for students' reference.

Favorite Types of Fiction	
Genre	Number of Votes
Graphic Novel	16
Mystery	32
Romance	20
Fantasy	24

Lesson Planner

Objective Display data in bar graphs.

Vocabulary bar graph, horizontal axis, interval, scale, vertical axis

Materials/Manipulatives centimeter grid paper, ruler, colored pencils or markers, index cards, unit cubes, butcher paper

Chapter Resource Masters

- CRM Vocabulary and English Language Development (p. A150)
- CRM Skills Practice (p. A151)
- CRM Problem-Solving Practice (p. A152)
- CRM Homework Practice (p. A153)

① Introduce

Vocabulary

Interval Explore the concept of *interval*. Discuss how to determine an appropriate interval for a bar graph based on the numbers given in a table. Compare what happens to the bars when the intervals are increased or decreased.

② Teach

Key Concept

Foundational Skills and Concepts After students have read through the Key Concept box, have them try these exercises.

1. How are the table and single bar graph similar? Both share the same title, axes or column labels, and numeric information.

2. What is the benefit of displaying information in a bar graph? It allows assessments and conclusions to be drawn quickly, sometimes without calculations.

3. Describe what happens to the bars in a bar graph if the scale interval is increased. The bars appear shorter or smaller.

Use the data in the table to create a bar graph.

The table shows the number of pounds of vegetables sold during the month of June at a local Farmer's Market.

June Vegetable Sales	
Vegetable	**Number of Pounds Sold**
Zucchinis	32
Cucumbers	48
Peppers	23
Tomatoes	54
Green Beans	39

1. Write the title.

2. Label the horizontal and vertical axes.

3. Choose the interval and complete the scale.

4. Draw the bars to represent the number of pounds.

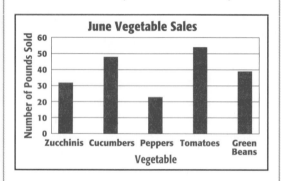

Example 1

Use the data in the table to create a bar graph.

The table shows the number of points scored last week by the top four players on the Carlson Middle School boys' basketball team.

Number of Points Scored	
Name	**Points**
Tai	24
Jordan	12
Gregorio	17
Chandler	14

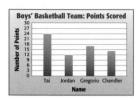

1. Write the title.
2. Label the horizontal and vertical axes.
3. Choose the interval and complete the scale.
4. Draw the bars to represent the number of points.

YOUR TURN!

Use the data in the table to create a bar graph.

The table shows the number of points scored last week by the top four players on the Giovanni Middle School girls' basketball team.

Number of Points Scored	
Name	**Points**
Barb	16
Elisa	18
Kanisha	10
Farah	6

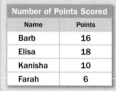
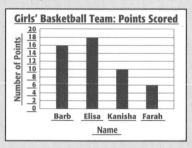

1. Write the title.
2. Label the horizontal and vertical axes.
3. Choose the interval and complete the scale.
4. Draw the bars to represent the number of points.

Intervention Strategy   Kinesthetic Learners

Make Graphs Three seventh-grade classrooms were surveyed about their favorite breakfast foods. The table below shows the results. Have students work in pairs. Distribute centimeter grid paper to each student, and tell them to create a bar graph for this data. Students should write a title, label the axes, decide on a scale that best fits the number of votes, and then draw the bars to represent each breakfast food.

Favorite Breakfasts	
Breakfast Food	**Number of Students**
Eggs	10
Pancakes	18
French Toast	16
Cereal	26
Oatmeal Bar	8

Example 2

Use the data in the table to create a double-bar graph.

The table shows the number of items collected last week by Room 101 and Room 102 in the Lincoln Middle School charity clothing drive.

1. Write the title.

2. Label the horizontal and vertical axes.

3. Choose the interval and complete the scale.

4. Draw the bars to represent the number of items.

5. Make a key to show the data for Room 101 and Room 102.

Clothing Drive Items		
	Number of Items	
Type of Clothing	Room 101	Room 102
Shirts	21	18
Pants	17	24
Coats	3	7
Pairs of shoes	16	11

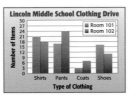

YOUR TURN!

Use the data in the table to create a double-bar graph.

The table shows the number of items collected last week by Grade 7 and Grade 8 in the Lincoln Middle School charity clothing drive.

1. Write the title.

2. Label the horizontal and vertical axes.

3. Choose the interval and complete the scale.

4. Draw the bars to represent the number of items.

5. Make a key to show the data for Grade 7 and Grade 8.

Clothing Drive Items		
	Number of Items	
Type of Clothing	Grade 7	Grade 8
Shirts	28	39
Pants	32	40
Coats	15	10
Pairs of shoes	19	27

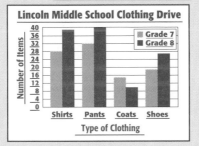

Lesson 7-5 Create Bar Graphs **307**

Additional *Example 2*

Use the data in the table to create a double-bar graph.

The table shows the number of summer camp programs attended by seventh graders.

Summer Camp Programs		
Type of Camp	Number of Participants	
	Girls	Boys
Sports	65	84
Church	46	38
Music	29	20
Scouts	53	75

1. Write the title.

2. Label the horizontal and vertical axes.

3. Choose the interval and complete the scale.

4. Draw the bars to represent the number of participants.

5. Make a key to show the data for girl and boy participants.

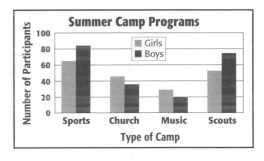

English Learner Strategy

Connections Use the table in Additional Example 2 to discuss summer camp programs. Encourage students to share any camp or summer adventure experiences, including details of their favorite activities. Survey which kinds of programs students have participated in and create a table with their results. Have students help you make a bar graph of their answers. Students should write a title, labels for the axes, and determine an appropriate scale for the graph. Evaluate the graph together.

③ Practice

Using Manipulatives

Unit Cubes   Use unit cubes and grid paper to create bar graphs. Students can build three-dimensional bar graphs by placing unit cubes on grid paper to represent the data in a given table. Use two different colors of unit cubes for a double-bar graph, and include these cubes in the key.

On-Hand Manipulatives   Students can use a ruler to create the bars in a bar graph. Model how to use the ruler to draw straight lines for each bar, or show how to trace the ruler itself to create a bar in the graph.

Who is Correct?

Use the values below to choose an interval for the scale of a bar graph.

19, 20, 16, 11, 7

Brett
Use an interval of 2 because the numbers in the data set are between 0 and 20.

Lorena
Use an interval of 20 because 20 is the largest number.

Bernard
Use an interval of 10 because most of the numbers are two-digit numbers.

Circle correct answer(s). Cross out incorrect answer(s).

Guided Practice

Use the data in the table to plan a bar graph. Sample answers provided.

The table shows the number of vehicles that were washed at the Jefferson Junior High School band fundraiser.

Jefferson JHS Band Car Wash	
Vehicle	Number Washed
Van	15
SUV	19
Sedan	11
Sports Car	3

1   What is a good title for the graph?
   Jefferson JHS Band Car Wash

2   What labels could be used for the x- and y-axes?
   Vehicle Type and Number Washed

3   What interval could be used for the scale?
   2

4   What will the height of each bar represent?
   the number of each type of vehicle washed

Who *is Correct?*
Diagnostic Teaching

- Brett is correct. He chose an appropriate interval and supported his answer.

- Lorena is incorrect. The interval she chose is too large for the data.

- Bernard is incorrect. The interval he chose is too large for the data.

Remind students to choose intervals that distribute the data evenly. If the interval is too large, the bars on the graph will be very short and possibly hard to read. If the intervals are too small, the bars become very tall.

Math Coach Notes

Intervals Help students practice choosing appropriate intervals by analyzing groups of numbers. Write groups of four numbers on the board and ask students to determine the interval to best showcase this data on a bar graph. Discuss how the bars representing the data would appear with different intervals, and consider the scale for each set. Compare the graph readability of using a small interval to using a larger interval.

Step by Step Practice

Use the data in the table on page 308 to create a bar graph.

5 Step 1 Write the title.

Step 2 Label the horizontal and vertical axes.

Step 3 Choose the interval and complete the scale.

Step 4 Draw the bars to represent the number of vehicles washed.

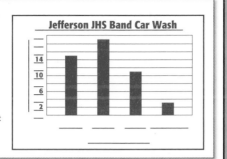

Jefferson JHS Band Car Wash

Use the data in each table to create a bar graph.

6 The table shows the number of instruments played in the Jefferson Junior High School orchestra.

Number of Instruments Played	
Instrument	Number
Woodwind	15
Brass	8
Percussion	7
String	19

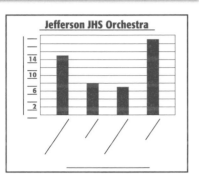

Jefferson JHS Orchestra

7 The table shows the number of singers in the Jefferson Junior High School choir.

Singers in Jefferson JHS Choir	
Type	Number
Soprano	15
Alto	12
Tenor	7
Bass	3

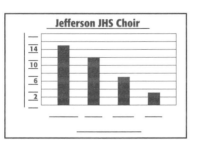

Jefferson JHS Choir

Lesson 7-5 Create Bar Graphs **309**

Are They Getting It?

Check students' understanding of creating bar graphs by writing the table and these problems on the board. Ask them to point out incorrect answers and explain their reasoning.

1. The horizontal axis of this bar graph will be labeled Number of Vehicles Sold. This is incorrect. The horizontal axis will show Type of Vehicle.

2. This data will produce a double-bar graph. This is correct.

3. The best interval for this data is 2. This is incorrect. A better interval is 5.

Vehicles Sold		
Type of Vehicle	Number of Vehicles Sold	
	New	Used
SUV	24	28
Truck	15	19
2-door car	25	38
4-door car	30	42

Common Error *Alert*

Exercises 8 and 9 Students may run into consistency issues when drawing the bars in a double-bar graph. Model how to draw the bars for one column and use colored pencils or markers to label that data before drawing the bars for the next column in the table. This way the two bars per category do not become confused or switched. Tell students to be consistent in assigning columns to specific locations, such as Grade 7 always being on the left and Grade 8 always being on the right in each category. Then the graph becomes easy and clear to read.

Step by Step *Problem-Solving Practice*

Use the data in the table to create a double-bar graph.

8 ASSEMBLIES The vice principal wanted to compare the favorite assemblies of the students at Grant Junior High School using data from the table. She will present the graph at the next parent-teacher meeting.

Favorite Grant JHS Assemblies		
Type of Assembly	Number of Votes	
	Grade 7	Grade 8
School Spirit	74	57
Music and the Arts	12	31
Health Education	10	4
Community Service	24	33

Understand Read the table. Write what you know.

The interval of the scale could be ___10___.

The key will show the data for

___Grade 7___ and ___Grade 8___.

Plan Pick a strategy. One strategy is to use a table.

Solve

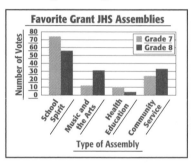

Check Check the length of each bar on the graph to be certain that it matches the data in the table.

Math Challenge

Survey for Data Challenge students to make a bar graph of their own. Tell them to create a survey for their classmates with at least five choices. Students should conduct their surveys and write the results in a table. Have them create a bar graph (or double-bar graph) from the data. Remind students to include a title, axes labels, an appropriate scale, and a key if necessary. Provide grid paper, colored pencils or markers, and rulers. Allow students to display their graphs in the room and share their products with classmates.

Use the data in the table to create a double-bar graph.

9 FIELD TRIPS   The vice principal wanted to compare the <u>favorite field trips</u> of the <u>boys and girls</u> from the table. She will present a <u>double-bar graph</u> at the next parent-teacher meeting. Check off each step.

Favorite Field Trips		
Type of Field Trip	Number of Votes	
	Boys	Girls
Aquarium	63	68
Science Museum	19	24
Ballet	11	3
Community Theater	25	32

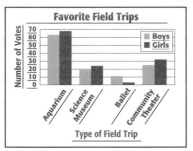

✔ Understand: I underlined key words.

✔ Plan: I will solve this problem by ____**using a table**____.

✔ Solve: The answer is ____**shown in the double-bar graph**____.

✔ Check: To check my answer I will ____**compare my graph to the table**____.

10 **Reflect**   How would the graph in Exercise 9 be different if zero girls had chosen the ballet as their favorite field trip?

Sample answer: The category would still be listed, but there would not be a bar for girls above the zero on the scale.

Note This!
Perceptions   Discuss how bar graphs are visual tools to relay information. Explain how manipulating intervals can be used as a persuasion tactic in the fields of advertising, reporting, and marketing.

Intervention Strategy   Auditory Learners

Explain Then Create   Write the following table on the board. Have students work in pairs. Tell students to explain how to create a bar graph from the data in the table. Explanations should include how to determine an appropriate interval and scale, identification of the parts of the graph, and what the graph would look like. Then have pairs create a double-bar graph from their explanations.

School Store Sales		
Item	Number of Items Sold	
	2008	2009
Pencils (12-pk)	110	150
Notebooks	85	120
T-shirts	40	65
Posters	35	42
School Decals	90	138

Lesson 7-5 Create Bar Graphs **311**

Odd/Even Assignments

Exercises 11 and 12 are structured so that students practice the same concepts whether they are assigned the odd or even problems.

In-Class Assignment

Have students complete Exercises 11 and 16 to ensure that they understand the concept.

 Skills, Concepts, and Problem Solving

Use the data in the table to create a bar graph.

11 The table shows the favorite types of music for Mr. Augayo's class.

Favorite Music of Mr. Augayo's Students	
Type	Number of Votes
Rock	5
Pop	17
R & B or Rap	7
Techno	1

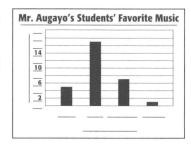

Use the data in the table to create a double-bar graph.

12 FUND-RAISING The principal wants to make a double-bar graph to compare the number of dollars raised at each fund-raising event at Martin Middle School in 2008 and 2009. She will present the graph at the next parent-teacher meeting.

Martin Middle School Fund-raisers		
Event	Dollars Raised	
	2008	2009
Car Wash	225	175
Gift Wrap Sales	200	250
Walk-A-Thon	75	100
Pizza Night	125	150

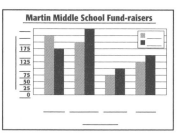

Vocabulary Check   Write the vocabulary word that completes each sentence.

13 The _____interval_____ is the difference between successive values on a scale.

14 The _____horizontal axis_____ is commonly the axis on which the categories or values are shown in a bar and line graph.

15 The _____vertical axis_____ is the axis on which the scale and interval are shown in a bar or line graph.

16 **Writing in Math** Suppose you are creating a bar graph. Choose a scale for the following numbers. Include information about the interval you would use. Explain your answer.

56, 97, 125, 79, 205, 152

Sample answer: A scale from 0 to 250 could be used. None of the numbers are

less than 0 or greater than 250. The scale could use intervals of 25 since most of

the values are close to multiples of 25.

 Spiral Review

Use the bar graph created in Exercise 12 to compare data. (Lesson 7-4, p. 297)

17 How much money was raised by the Walk-A-Thon in 2008?

$75

18 How much more money was raised by the car wash in 2008 than 2009?

$50

19 How much money was raised in gift wrap sales in 2008 and 2009?

$450

20 In which year was the most money raised?

2009

STOP

Ticket Out the Door

Creating Bar Graphs   Refer to the Favorite Vacations table in the Assess section above. As students approach the classroom door to exit, alternate asking them to name an appropriate interval for the graph, or give you one of the axes labels.

Accept intervals between 2 and 5.

Horizontal axis: Type of Vacation

Vertical axis: Number of Votes

Assess

See It, Do It, Say It, Write It

Step 1   Write the following table on the board.

Favorite Vacations		
Type of Vacation	**Number of Votes**	
	Girls	**Boys**
Theme Park	12	18
Beach Resort	16	12
Camping	5	14
Road Trip	7	6

Step 2   Ask students to create a double-bar graph from the information in the table.

Step 3   Have students work in pairs. Students should explain how they determined the scale and transferred the information from the table to the graph.

Step 4   Tell students to independently write an evaluation of their double-bar graph.

Looking Ahead: Pre-Teach

Interpret Line Graphs   In the next lesson, students will learn to interpret line graphs.

Example

What was the number of T-shirts sold in April?

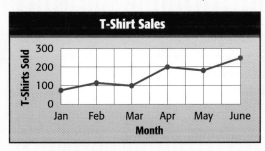

Look along the horizontal axis to find April. From the point for April, read the point along the vertical axis. The number of T-shirts sold is 200.

Formative Assessment

Use the Progress Check to assess students' mastery of the previous lessons. Have students review the lesson indicated for the problems they answered incorrectly.

Assignments

Exercises are structured so that students practice the concepts when they are assigned all the problems.

Chapter 7 Progress Check 2 (Lessons 7-4 and 7-5)

Use the bar graph "Carnival Sales" to compare data.

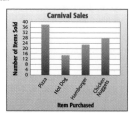

Carnival Sales

1 How many people purchased a slice of pizza at the carnival?

　　38

2 How many more people purchased a hamburger than purchased a hot dog?

　　8

3 How many more people purchased a slice of pizza than hot dogs and hamburgers combined?

　　0

4 How many items were sold at the carnival?

　104 items; 38 + 15 + 23 + 28 = 104

Use the data in the table to create a double-bar graph.

5 **MUSIC** Summer needs to create a double-bar graph for her math class. She recorded the songs that her friends downloaded last week. She will share the graph with her friends at school.

Number of Songs Downloaded		
Name	**Number of Songs**	
	Rock	**Pop**
Katie	16	5
Kiyo	6	12
Jocelyn	5	15
Tavio	19	0

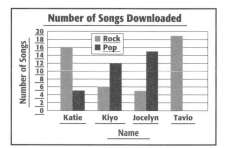

Number of Songs Downloaded

Data-Driven Decision Making

Students missing Exercises . . .	Have trouble with . . .	Should review and practice . . .
1–4	interpreting data in a bar graph.	SSG Lesson 7-4, p. 297 CRM Skills Practice, p. A147
5	creating a bar graph.	SSG Lesson 7-5, p. 305 CRM Skills Practice, p. A151

Lesson 7-6 Interpret Line Graphs

KEY Concept

A **line graph** is used to show how a set of data changes over a period of time. Like a bar graph, it has features such as a title, categories, and a scale.

The scale shown on a line graph is commonly set on the **vertical axis**.

The **horizontal axis** of the graph commonly shows the period of time such as hours, years, or decades.

Since the number of dollars raised each week in the graph below varies from 250 to 1,200, the **interval** on the scale is 250.

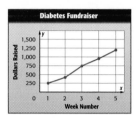

A double-line graph compares two sets of data. The lines of each set of data are a different color to make the graph easier to read. The line graph below compares the amount of money raised in 2008 and 2009.

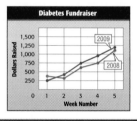

The points on a line graph are plotted like ordered pairs on a coordinate grid.

GO ON

VOCABULARY

horizontal axis
the axis on which the categories or values are shown in a bar and line graph

interval
the difference between successive values on a scale

line graph
a graph used to show how a set of data changes over a period of time

scale
the set of all possible values in a given measurement, including the least and greatest numbers in the set, separated by the intervals used

vertical axis
the axis on which the scale and interval are shown in a bar or line graph

Lesson 7-6 Interpret Line Graphs **315**

Intervention Strategy   Visual Learners

Read a Line Graph   Display the following line graph. Model how to identify the axes, title, and category labels. Discuss the scale and interval and what each plotted point represents. Use your finger to follow the line connecting the points to demonstrate whether the line is going up, down, or horizontally. Explain how to extend this line based on the trend. Have students help make a prediction about months 6 and 7.

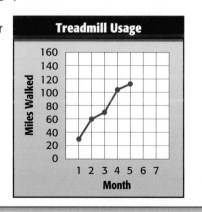

Lesson Planner

Objective   Interpret data in line graphs.

Vocabulary   horizontal axis, interval, line graph, scale, vertical axis

Materials/Manipulatives   centimeter grid paper, centimeter cubes

Chapter Resource Masters

CRM Vocabulary and English Language Development (p. A154)

CRM Skills Practice (p. A155)

CRM Problem-Solving Practice (p. A156)

CRM Homework Practice (p. A157)

 Introduce

Vocabulary

Trends   Describe a *trend* as a consistent change over time in statistical data. You can study the data in line graphs to make predictions based on the trend.

2 Teach

Key Concept

Foundational Skills and Concepts   After students have read through the Key Concept box, have them try these exercises.

1. When would you use a line graph instead of a bar graph? when you need to show a change in data over time

2. What typically is on the horizontal axis of a line graph? the time scale

3. What is an interval? the difference between values on a scale

Use the line graph "Max's Income" to compare data.

How much less does Max earn when he works 2 hours compared to 4 hours?

1. How much does Max earn for 4 hours of work? $30

2. how much does Max earn for 2 hours of work? $15

3. To find how much more money he makes, subtract.

$30 − $15 = $15

4. Max makes $15 more when he works 4 hours compared to 2 hours.

Use the double-line graph "Account Balance" to compare data.

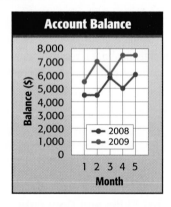

How much more did the account have after four months in 2009 compared to the same time period in 2008?

1. How much was in the account after the fourth month in 2009? $7,500

2. How much was in the account after the fourth month in 2008? $5,000

3. To find how much more was in the account after the fourth month in 2009, subtract.

$7,500 − $5,000 = $2,500

4. There was $2,500 more in the account in 2009.

Example 1

Use the line graph "Max's Income" to compare data.

How much more does Max earn after 5 hours of work compared to 4 hours of work?

1. How much did Max earn after 4 hours? $30

2. How much did Max earn after 5 hours? $37.50

3. To find how much more Max earned, subtract.

$37.50 − $30.00 = $7.50

4. Max earned $7.50 more.

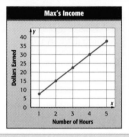

YOUR TURN!

Use the line graph "Max's Income" to compare data.

How much more does Max earn after 3 hours of work compared to 1 hour of work?

1. How much did Max earn after 3 hours? __$22.50__

2. How much did Max earn after 1 hour of work? __$7.50__

3. To find how much more he earned, __subtract__.

__$22.50__ − __$7.50__ = __$15.00__

4. Max earned __$15.00__ more.

Example 2

Use the double-line graph "School Spirit Sales" to compare data.

How much more was spent on T-shirts than on buttons in September?

1. How much was spent on T-shirts in September? $600

2. How much was spent on buttons in September? $100

3. To find the difference in sales, subtract.

$600 − $100 = $500

4. The amount spent on T-shirts was $500 more.

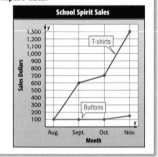

YOUR TURN!

Use the double-line graph "School Spirit Sales" to compare data.

How much more was spent on T-shirts in November than in August?

1. How much was spent on T-shirts in November? __$1,300__

2. How much was spent on T-shirts in August? __$100__

3. To find how much more was spent, __subtract__.

   __$1,300__ – __$100__ = __$1,200__

4. The amount spent on T-shirts in November was __$1,200__ more.

Who is Correct?

Use the double-line graph "School Spirit Sales" to compare data.

Compare the T-shirt sales and the button sales in September.

Andre
$100 – $100 = $0
There was no difference.

Michelle
$600 – $100 = $500
T-shirt sales were
$500 more.

Zacharias
$600 – $100 = $500
Button sales were
$500 less.

Circle correct answer(s). Cross out incorrect answer(s).

 Guided Practice

Use the line graph "Jason's Savings Account" to compare data.

1. What does the vertical axis of the bar graph represent?
   __the amount in Jason's savings account__

2. What is indicated on the horizontal axis?
   __months__

3. What does the dot on the horizontal axis indicate?
   __It indicates that in June, Jason has $0__
   __in his savings account.__

GO ON

Lesson 7-6 Interpret Line Graphs **317**

---

3 Practice

Using Manipulatives

Grid Paper   Practice plotting line graph points on grid paper. Compare this action to plotting points on a coordinate grid. Model how to set an interval and what it means when points are plotted between grid lines.

On-Hand Manipulatives   Have students use centimeter cubes on grid paper to plot points. Students can manipulate these cubes to make predictions.

Who *is Correct?*
Diagnostic Teaching

• **Andre is incorrect.** He compared August, not September.

• **Michelle is correct.** She correctly compared T-shirt and button sales.

• **Zacharias is also correct.** He correctly compared the sales data.

Remind students to look closely at double-line graphs to differentiate which line represents what. Tell students to use the key, when present, to keep the data separate and clear.

Predictions Tell students that determining a trend can help make predictions, or estimations of future results. These forecasts can be beneficial to companies or groups as they plan for growth and adjust to change.

Step by Step Practice

Use the line graph "Jason's Savings Account" on page 317 to compare data.

4 How much money does Jason take out of his savings during the month of February?

Step 1 The value of the account at the beginning of February is ___$40___.

Step 2 The value of the account at the beginning of March is ___$30___.

Step 3 To find the amount that was withdrawn, ___subtract___.
___$40___ – ___$30___ = ___$10___

Step 4 Jason withdrew ___$10___ in February.

Use the line graph "Janelle's Heart Rate" to compare data.

5 What is Janelle's heart rate at the 15-minute mark?
___140 beats per minute___

6 What is Janelle's heart rate at the 40-minute mark?
___140 beats per minute___

7 Compare Janelle's heart rate at the 10-minute mark to her heart rate at the 30-minute mark.
___Her heart rate is 70 beats___
___per minute higher at the 30-minute mark.___

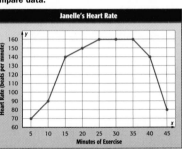

8 Compare Janelle's heart rate at the 5-minute mark to her heart rate at the 45-minute mark.
___Her heart rate is 10 beats per minute higher at the___
___45-minute mark.___

9 Describe the trend of the data. Does it increase, decrease, or stay the same over time?
___The trend of the data increases and then decreases.___

Are They Getting It?

Check students' understanding of interpreting line graphs by writing these problems on the board. Ask them to point out incorrect answers and explain their reasoning. Use the double-line graph Diabetes Fundraiser on page 315.

I. The graph shows that more money was raised in each week in 2009 compared to 2008. This is incorrect. In Week 1, more money was raised in 2008 than 2009.

2. The graph shows that nearly $250 more was raised in Week 4 in 2009 than in 2008. This is correct.

Step by Step Problem-Solving Practice

Use the double-line graph "Motor Vehicle Mileage" to compare data.

10 MILEAGE   Jordan created a line graph comparing the yearly mileage of Mr. Lane's semi-trailer truck and his personal vehicle. Compare the average annual mileage of the truck to his personal vehicle in 2010.

Problem-Solving Strategies
☐ Draw a diagram.
☑ Use a graph.
☐ Solve a simpler problem.
☐ Work backward.
☐ Look for a pattern.

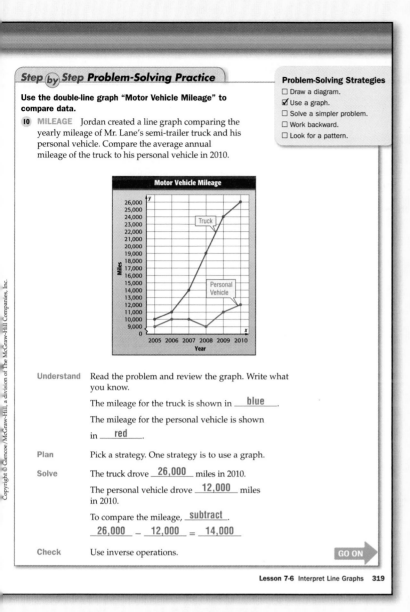

Understand   Read the problem and review the graph. Write what you know.

The mileage for the truck is shown in ___blue___.

The mileage for the personal vehicle is shown in ___red___.

Plan   Pick a strategy. One strategy is to use a graph.

Solve   The truck drove __26,000__ miles in 2010.

The personal vehicle drove __12,000__ miles in 2010.

To compare the mileage, __subtract__.

__26,000__ − __12,000__ = __14,000__

Check   Use inverse operations.

GO ON

Lesson 7-6 Interpret Line Graphs   **319**

Math Challenge

Independent Work

Display the following double-line graph. Have students write questions of various levels of difficulty about the graph. Tell them to include the answers to their questions on a separate piece of paper. Students can share their questions with classmates or post a few at a time in the room as Questions of the Day.

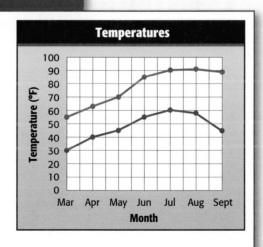

Odd/Even Assignments

Exercises 14–24 are structured so that students practice the same concepts whether they are assigned the odd or even problems.

In-Class Assignment

Have students complete Exercises 14, 17, 20, 22, and 26 to ensure that they understand the concept.

 Common Error *Alert*

Exercises 11–12, 20–22 Remind students to examine the key in a double-line graph. Having two sets of data to analyze can get confusing. By returning to the key, comparisons can be made accurately and clearly.

Use the double-line graph "Motor Vehicle Mileage" on page 319 to compare data.

11 TRUCKS   The owner of Tampera Trucking Company wants to compare the mileage Mr. Lane's truck traveled in 2010 to 2005. Check off each step.

　✔ Understand: I underlined key words.

　✔ Plan: I will solve this problem by ___using a graph___.

　✔ Solve: The answer is _16,000 miles more in 2010 than in 2005_

　✔ Check: To check my answer I will ___use inverse operations___.

12 VEHICLES   Compare the annual mileage of Mr. Lane's personal vehicle in 2006 and 2008.

10,000 − 9,000 = 1,000 Mr. Lane traveled 1,000 miles less

in his personal vehicle in 2008 than in 2006.

13 Reflect   What other interval could be used for the graph "Motor Vehicle Mileage?" How would this change the data?

Sample Answer: The scale could use an interval of every

500 miles instead of every thousand. More information

would be provided.

▶ Skills, Concepts, and Problem Solving

Use the line graph "Donations Collected by Amelia's Class" to compare data.

14 How much money did Amelia's class collect in September?

　___$5___

15 How much money did Amelia's class collect in June?

　___$55___

16 How much more was collected in March than in December?

　___$20___

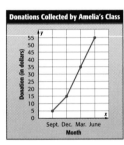

Donations Collected by Amelia's Class

320   Chapter 7 One-Variable Data

English Learner Strategy

Vocabulary   Use Exercises 10–12 to explain the meaning of the words *mileage*, *semi-trailer*, and *motor vehicles*. Give definitions and examples of each term or phrase. Discuss reasons why drivers would track their mileage, such as to monitor gas consumption, to gauge distances between locations, or to find more efficient routes for business, etc. Then examine the double-line graph titled "Motor Vehicle Mileage" together. Identify each part of the graph and discuss its meaning. Model how to make comparative statements about the graph, and encourage students to follow your examples by making their own evaluations.

Use the line graph "Donations Collected by Amelia's Class" on page 320 to compare data.

17 What is the interval of the scale? _5 dollars_

18 How much money was collected in March? _$35_

19 Describe the trend of the graph. Do the donations increase, decrease, or show no change?

The donations increase each quarter of the school year.

Use the double-line graph "Theater Rehearsal Time" to complete Exercises 20–22.

20 THEATER   The theater teacher made a graph of the rehearsal time at Monterrey High School over the past few weeks. Compare the number of minutes actors rehearsed during Week 3 to the number of minutes the stage crew rehearsed during Week 3.

During Week 3, actors rehearsed for 120 minutes

and the stage crew rehearsed for 60 minutes.

The actors rehearsed for 60 more minutes

than the stage crew.

21 STAGE CREW   Compare the number of minutes the stage crew spent in rehearsal during Week 4 to the number of minutes the stage crew spent in rehearsal during Week 1.

During Week 4, the stage crew rehearsed for 75 minutes and during Week 1,

the stage crew rehearsed for 30 minutes. The stage crew rehearsed for 45 more

minutes during Week 4 than during Week 1.

22 PATTERNS   If the trends continue, what would you expect the data to show for Week 5?

Sample answer: The trends for the number of minutes of theater rehearsal would

continue to increase. The number of minutes actors rehearse would continue

to outnumber the number of minutes that the stage crew spends in rehearsal.

Math Coach Notes

Change Over Time   Remind students that line graphs display data that changes over time. Examine the graphs titled "Janelle's Heart Rate," on page 318, and "Motor Vehicle Mileage," on page 319, together. Discuss what kind of time is passing in each graph.

See It, Do It, Say It, Write It

Step 1 Display the following graph.

Step 2 Ask students to answer the following questions:

- What is the interval for this graph? $100,000

- How much money was raised in 2005? $250,000

- How much more money was raised in 2008 compared to 2004? $400,000

- Describe the trend of the data. The amount of money raised increases each year.

Step 3 Have students work in pairs. Students should discuss their answers and explain how they found them.

Step 4 Tell students to independently write their evaluations of the line graph. Students should include the answers to the questions and their reasoning.

Looking Ahead: Pre-Teach

Create Line Graphs In the next lesson, students will learn how to create line graphs.

Choosing a scale and interval for the vertical axis on a line graph is done the same as choosing a scale and interval for a bar graph.

Use the double-line graph "Concession Stand Sales" to complete Exercises 23 and 24.

23 SALES The concession stand manager made a graph to compare sales of bottled water and hot cocoa during the football season. Compare the sales of water and cocoa in October.

During October, the cocoa sales were higher than the bottled water sales by $75.

24 PATTERNS If the trends continue, what would you expect the data to show for November?

Sample answer: The cocoa sales will continue to increase, and the bottled water sales will continue to decrease.

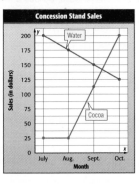

Vocabulary Check **Write the vocabulary word that completes the sentence.**

25 A _line graph_ is used to show how a set of data changes over a period of time.

26 Writing in Math Give a real-world example to explain when line graphs are used. Explain your answer.

Sample answer: Line graphs can be used to show sales of a particular product over time, the cost of a particular item over time, or other changes over time.

Spiral Review

Use the data in the table to plan a bar graph. (Lesson 7-5, p. 304)

The table shows the number of athletes at the Johnson Middle School. Sample answers provided.

27 What is a good title for the graph?

Johnson Middle School Athletes

28 What are the two main categories?

Sport and Number of Students

29 What interval could be used for the scale? __4__

Johnson Middle School Athletes	
Sport	Number of Students
Soccer	21
Baseball	19
Football	30
Basketball	37

STOP

Ticket Out the Door

Line Graphs Refer to the line graph titled "Money Raised Since 2004 in Annual Walk-a-thon" above. As students approach the classroom door to exit, ask them to make a prediction for 2010 based on the trend.

Accept all reasonable answers. Sample answer: $750,000

Create Line Graphs

KEY Concept

Information from a table can be used to create a **line graph**. The line graph below describes the number of miles Mr. Batista ran while he was training for a marathon. Notice that the title and the categories of the graph are similar to those shown in the table.

Marathon Training	
Month	Miles
January	5
February	12
March	18
April	21
May	25
June	30

The scale of the graph often starts at zero and the **interval** of the scale is determined by the range of the data.

A double-line graph can also be created using the information in a table. The double-line graph below compares donations to dog and cat rescue.

Donations (in thousands)		
Year	Dogs	Cats
2004	$3	$2
2005	$6	$6
2006	$8	$10
2007	$13	$8
2008	$12	$13
2009	$14	$16

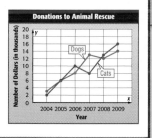

The lines in a double-line graph are often color-coded and labeled to indicate the categories.

VOCABULARY

horizontal axis
the axis on which the categories or values are shown in a bar or line graph

interval
the difference between successive values on a scale

line graph
a graph used to show how a set of data changes over a period of time

scale
the set of all possible values in a given measurement, including the least and greatest numbers in the set, separated by the intervals used

vertical axis
the axis on which the scale and interval are shown in a bar or line graph

---

Lesson Notes

Lesson Planner

Objective Display data in line graphs.

Vocabulary horizontal axis, interval, line graph, scale, vertical axis

Materials/Manipulatives centimeter grid paper, ruler, colored pencils or markers, push pins, yarn or string, index cards

Chapter Resource Masters

- CRM Vocabulary and English Language Development (p. A158)
- CRM Skills Practice (p. A159)
- CRM Problem-Solving Practice (p. A160)
- CRM Homework Practice (p. A161)

① Introduce

Vocabulary

Graphs Compare the vocabulary words for bar graphs and line graphs. Both kinds of graphs have axes, intervals, scales, and titles. Discuss the differences between the two types of graphs and how to determine which type of graph to use for a set of data.

② Teach

Key Concept

Foundational Skills and Concepts After students have read through the Key Concept box, have them try these exercises.

1. How is data plotted on a line graph? The data is graphed similar to points on a coordinate grid. A point is plotted where the two axes meet to indicate a data point.

2. How are the single and double-line graphs different? The double-line graph compares two sets of data using the same interval and categories.

3. How are two sets of data differentiated on a double-line graph? The lines are color-coded and labeled to separate the categories.

Intervention Strategy   Visual Learners

Create Line Graphs Use the data in the following table to make a line graph on a bulletin board. Have students help draw and label the axes and write a title for the graph. Labels can either be written right on the bulletin board or on index cards so the graph can be reused with other data. Discuss an appropriate scale and interval for the data. Model how to plot each point with a push pin. Use a piece of yarn or string to connect the points and create the line. Leave room for students to extend the graph, and demonstrate how to make predictions based on the trend.

Movie Passes					
Year	2005	2006	2007	2008	2009
Sales (in thousands)	575	550	480	390	340

Use the data in the table to create a line graph.

The table shows the newspaper sales over a four-hour period.

Newspaper Sales	
Time	Sales (in thousands)
2 PM	40
3 PM	65
4 PM	90
5 PM	125
6 PM	140

1. Write the title.

2. Label the horizontal and vertical axes.

3. Choose the interval and complete the scale.

4. Plot each point and connect the data points to create a line.

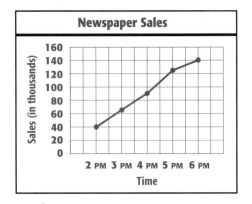

Example 1

Use the data in the table to create a line graph.

The table shows the number of hours Lucas spent completing his homework over a four-week period.

Lucas's Homework Log	
Week of	Hours
April 8	5
April 15	4
April 22	2
April 29	7

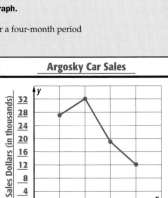

1. Write the title.
2. Label the horizontal and vertical axes.
3. Choose the interval and complete the scale.
4. Plot each point and connect the data points to create a line.

YOUR TURN!

Use the data in the table to create a line graph.

The table shows the number of cars sold over a four-month period by Argosky Auto Mall.

Argosky Car Sales	
Month	Sales Dollars (in thousands)
April	27
May	32
June	19
July	12

1. Write the title.
2. Label the horizontal and vertical axes.
3. Choose the interval and complete the scale.
4. Plot each point and connect the data points to create a line.

Argosky Car Sales

English Learner Strategy

Discuss Line Graphs   Write the following table on the board. Discuss what the table shows and define any unfamiliar words. Model how to set up a line graph and have students identify, say, and write the labels for the axes and the title. Talk about interval and ask students to consider the scale for this data. Offer a few choices and have students determine which one works the best. Model how to plot the first point and have students mimic your process with the other points to complete the graph.

Plant Growth				
Month	Jan	Feb	Mar	Apr
Height (cm)	25	30	40	45

Example 2

Use the data in the table to create a double-line graph.

The table shows the values of two houses of the same size in Kansas and Florida over a period of four years.

Housing Values		
Year	Value (in thousands)	
	Kansas	Florida
2006	95	150
2007	100	200
2008	120	250
2009	115	230

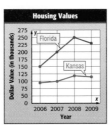

1. Write the title.

2. Label the horizontal and vertical axes.

3. Choose the interval and complete the scale.

4. Plot each point one line at a time.

5. Use a different color for each line and color-code each line's label.

YOUR TURN!

Use the data in the table to create a double-line graph.

The table shows the number of yards Amy and Isa walked in the Washington Middle School Walk-A-Thon.

Walk-A-Thon Results		
Number of Minutes	Yards Walked	
	Amy	Isa
10	14	19
20	30	36
30	44	54
40	54	66

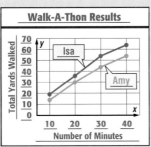

1. Write the title.

2. Label the horizontal and vertical axes.

3. Choose the interval and complete the scale.

4. Plot each point one line at a time.

5. Use a different color for each line and color-code each line's label.

GO ON

Lesson 7-7 Create Line Graphs **325**

Additional *Example 2*

Use the data in the table to create a double-line graph.

The table shows the mass of two samples over four days.

Daily Masses		
Day	Mass (kg)	
	Sample A	Sample B
1	15	20
2	23	35
3	27	25
4	30	33

I. Write the title.

2. Label the horizontal and vertical axes.

3. Choose the interval and complete the scale.

4. Plot each point for one line at a time.

5. Use a different color for each line and color-code each line's label.

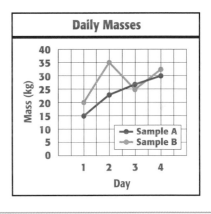

Intervention Strategy   Linguistic Learners

Communicate Graphs   Display the following table. Have students work in pairs. Distribute centimeter grid paper and colored pencils or markers to each group, and tell them to create a double-line graph for this data. After the graph is completed, students should write step-by-step directions instructing a classmate how to create this double-line graph. Have students read their directions aloud after they have written them to check for clarity and any missed steps.

Resting Heart Rates		
Time	Beats per Minute	
	Girls	Boys
9:00	50	58
9:05	55	56
9:10	58	54
9:20	52	57
9:25	54	59

Using Manipulatives

Grid Paper Have students use centimeter grid paper to create line graphs. The structured template enables students to create evenly-spaced intervals and plot points accurately.

On-Hand Manipulatives Model how to use a ruler to connect the points in a line graph. Explain that using a ruler helps make trends, predictions, and analyses easier.

Who is Correct?

Use the line graph "Walk-A-Thon Results" on page 325 to compare the data.

Describe the trend of the data. Do the number of yards increase, decrease, or stay the same over time?

Alicia
The data remains the same because Amy and Isa walk at the same rate.

Vidia
The data shows an increase over time because Amy and Isa continue to walk.

Tomás
The data decreases because Amy and Isa slow down.

Circle correct answer(s). Cross out incorrect answer(s).

▶ Guided Practice

Use the data in the table to plan a line graph. Sample answers provided.

The table shows the number of staffing hours at Phillips Bakery in a four-hour time period.

Phillips Bakery	
Time	Staffing Hours
7 A.M.	15
8 A.M.	34
9 A.M.	46
10 A.M.	56

1. What interval could be used for the scale?

   5

2. Describe the trend of the data. Do the number of staffing hours increase, decrease, or stay the same over time?

   the number of staffing hours increases

Step by Step Practice

Use the data in the table above to create a line graph.

3. **Step 1** Write the title.

   Step 2 Label the horizontal and vertical axes.

   Step 3 Choose the interval and complete the scale.

   Step 4 Plot each point and connect the data points to create a line.

Phillips Bakery

Who *is Correct?*
Diagnostic Teaching

- Alicia is incorrect. The walkers' rates are not the same. Isa and Amy continue to walk, so the number of yards is increasing.

- Vidia is correct. She identified the trend and supported her answer.

- Tomás is incorrect. Students are asked to compare the number of yards walked, not the rate.

Remind students to examine the pattern of the data to determine the trend. Have students follow the line with their fingers to conclude if the data is increasing, decreasing, or staying the same.

Step by Step Problem-Solving Practice

Use the data in the table to create a double-line graph.

4 **FINANCIAL LITERACY** Mr. and Mrs. Cho have been saving money to purchase a new couch. The table shows how much money each person has in their savings account at the end of each month.

Problem-Solving Strategies
☐ Draw a diagram.
☐ Work backward.
☐ Solve a simpler problem.
☑ Use a table.
☐ Look for a pattern.

Cho Family Savings		
Month	Number of Dollars ($)	
	Mr. Cho	Mrs. Cho
January	740	625
February	870	780
March	420	420
April	675	725

Understand Read the table. Write what you know.

The interval of the scale could be __100 dollars__.

The __dark line__ will show the data for __Mr. Cho__.

The __light line__ will show data for __Mrs. Cho__.

Plan Pick a strategy. One strategy is to use a table.

Solve

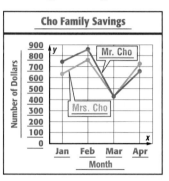

Check Check the color-coding on each line and compare the data on the graph to the data in the table.

GO ON

Are They Getting It?

Check students' understanding of creating line graphs by writing the table and these problems on the board. Ask them to point out incorrect answers and explain their reasoning.

1. A double-line graph can be made from this data. This is correct.

2. The best interval for this data is 5. This is incorrect. A better interval is 1.

3. The vertical axis for this line graph shows the kinds of sunflower plants. This is incorrect. The vertical axis shows the rate of growth in inches; the horizontal axis shows the day.

Sunflower Growth		
Day	Growth (in.)	
	Standard	Elf
1	1.5	0.5
2	3	1
3	4.5	1.5
4	6	2
5	7.5	2.5
6	9	3

Math Coach Notes

Estimation Sometimes the exact value of a plotted point in a line graph with a large scale is hard to discern. Explain to students how to estimate the most likely value if the data is not available in a table. Trends and predictions can still be made using estimation and projection.

Odd/Even Assignments

Exercises 7 and 8 are structured so that students practice the same concepts whether they are assigned the odd or even problems.

In-Class Assignment

Have students complete Exercises 7 and 11 to ensure that they understand the concept.

 Common Error *Alert*

Exercises 7 and 8 Determining an appropriate interval to fit all the data can be challenging for students. Choosing an interval that is too small can make plotting larger points difficult. Selecting one that is too large can make plotting points also difficult as it becomes harder to tell what the point represents. Tell students to select a scale and interval that allows them to easily read and comprehend the plotted points.

Use the data in the table to create a double-line graph.

5 HOMEWORK The PTA president will present a <u>double-line graph</u> showing the <u>average amount of study time per month</u> of the <u>boys and girls</u> at Huntsville Junior High School. Check off each step.

	Study Time	
Year	Number of Hours	
	Boys	Girls
2006	175	150
2007	150	175
2008	200	225
2009	175	200

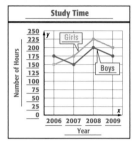

✔ Understand: I underlined key words.

✔ Plan: I will solve this problem by ___using a table___.

✔ Solve: The answer is ___shown in the double-line graph___.

✔ Check: To check my answer I will ___compare my graph to the table___.

6 Reflect Look at the line graph for Exercise 5. Describe the trend of the data. Do the number of hours studying increase, decrease, or show no relationship?

Sample Answer: The number of hours spent studying does not show a clear trend.

The average number of hours spent studying fluctuates for both boys and girls.

 Skills, Concepts, and Problem Solving

Use the data in the table to create a line graph.

7 The table shows Marka's hourly wages over a four-year time period.

Marka's Hourly Wages	
Year	Hourly Wages
2006	7
2007	10
2008	10
2009	12

Math Challenge

Questions and Graphs Have students make a line or double-line graph of their own. Students will need to make a table to plan their data before beginning. Remind them to include a title, axes labels, an appropriate scale, and a key if necessary. Provide grid paper, colored pencils or markers, and rulers for construction. When the graphs are complete, students should write several questions for their graph. Ask them to write answers for their questions on a separate piece of paper. Encourage students to share their work and have classmates try to answer the questions they have written about their graphs.

Use the data in the table to create a double-line graph.

8 SALES   The table shows the sales dollars for PWR 4 and RX 71 cell phones sold at Kingston Electronics over a four-month period.

Kingston Electronics Sales		
Month	Cell Phone Model	
	PWR 4	RX 71
May	$125,000	$175,000
June	$150,000	$75,000
July	$175,000	$100,000
August	$225,000	$150,000

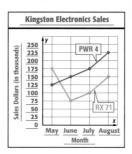

Kingston Electronics Sales

Vocabulary Check   Write the vocabulary word that completes each sentence.

9 The ___interval___ is the difference between successive values on a scale.

10 The ___vertical axis___ is commonly the axis on which the scale and interval are shown in a bar or line graph.

11 Writing in Math   Compare a bar graph and a line graph. Explain the differences and similarities between the two graphs.

Sample answer: Both a bar graph and a line graph have titles, categories, and scales provided in intervals. A bar graph is used to compare categories, while a line graph is used to show changes over a period of time.

 Spiral Review

Use the line graph created in Exercise 8 to compare data. (Lesson 7-6, p. 315)

12 What were the sales of RX 71 phones in August?

$150,000

13 How much higher were sales of PWR 4 phones than sales of RX 71 phones in June?

$75,000

14 Compare the sales of the PWR 4 and RX 71 phones. Which phone is more popular?

PWR 4

15 Describe the trend of the data for the PWR 4 phone. Do the sales increase, decrease, or stay the same over time?

increase

 STOP

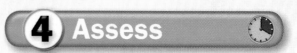

Assess

See It, Do It, Say It, Write It

Step 1   Write the following table on the board.

Photo Express Printers		
Year	Sales (in thousands)	
	Model 2E	Model 3A
1	$500	$90
2	$450	$175
3	$375	$375
4	$305	$450
5	$250	$530
6	$180	$625

Step 2   Ask students to create a double-line graph from the information in the table.

Step 3   Have students work in pairs. Students should identify the parts of their double-line graphs, explain how they determined the scale, and describe what the graph shows.

Step 4   Tell students to independently write an evaluation of their double-bar graph, including the discussion points from their partner exercise.

Ticket Out the Door

Creating Line Graphs   Use the Sunflower Growth table in the Are They Getting It section on page 327 of the Teacher's Edition. As students approach the classroom door to exit, alternate asking them to describe the trend or make a prediction about the expected height of a Standard sunflower or an Elf sunflower on Day 7.

The trend for Standard is 1.5 inches per day. The trend for the Elf is 0.5 inches per day.

Progress Check 3

Formative Assessment

Use the Progress Check to assess students' mastery of the previous lessons. Have students review the lesson indicated for the problems they answered incorrectly.

Odd/Even Assignments

Exercises 1–4 are structured so that students practice the same concepts whether they are assigned the odd or even problems.

Chapter 7 **Progress Check 3** (Lessons 7-6 and 7-7)

Use the double-line graph "Ares Amusement Parks Ticket Sales" to compare data.

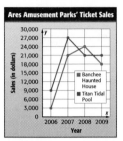

1. Describe the sales in 2007 for the Banchee Haunted House.

   $21,000

2. Compare the sales of the Titan Tidal Pool in 2008 to 2006.

   $12,000 more in 2008

3. Compare the sales of the Titan Tidal Pool to the Banchee Haunted House in 2008.

   Sales for the Banchee Haunted House were $3,000 higher.

4. Compare the sales of the Banchee Haunted House in 2007 to 2006.

   Sales were $18,000 higher in 2007.

Use the data in the table to create a line graph.

5. **SALES** Donavan needs to create a line graph for his boss. He recorded the number of cars that were sold at the dealership this week.

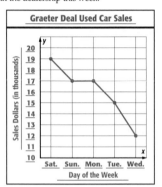

Graeter Deal Used Car Sales	
Day of the Week	Sales
Saturday	$19,000
Sunday	$17,000
Monday	$17,000
Tuesday	$15,000
Wednesday	$12,000

Data-Driven Decision Making

Students missing Exercises ...	Have trouble with ...	Should review and practice ...
1–4	interpreting data in a line graph.	SSG Lesson 7-6, p. 315 CRM Skills Practice, p. A155
5	creating a line graph.	SSG Lesson 7-7, p. 323 CRM Skills Practice, p. A159

Vocabulary and Concept Check

average, *p. 289*
bar graph, *p. 297*
data, *p. 281*
horizontal axis, *p. 297*
interval, *p. 297*
line graph, *p. 315*
mean, *p. 289*
measures of central tendency,
   p. 289
median, *p. 281*
mode, *p. 281*
outlier, *p. 289*
range, *p. 281*
scale, *p. 297*
sort, *p. 274*
Venn diagram, *p. 274*
vertical axis, *p. 297*

Write the vocabulary word that completes each sentence.

1. A(n) ___Venn diagram___ is a diagram that uses overlapping and separate circles or ellipses to organize and show data.

2. To group together items that have something in common is to _____sort_____ the items.

3. The _____median_____ is the middle number(s) in a set of data when the data are arranged in numerical order.

4. The number that appears most often in a set of data is called the _____mode_____.

5. A(n) _____line graph_____ is a graph that is used to show how a set of data changes over a period of time.

6. _____Data_____ is information gathered for statistical purposes.

Label the diagram with the correct vocabulary term.

7. ___vertical axis___

8. ___horizontal axis___

9. ___scale___

10. ___bar graph___

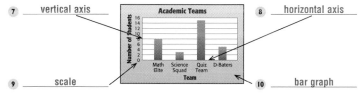

Vocabulary and Concept Check

If students have difficulty answering Exercises 1–10, remind them that they can use the page references to refresh their memories about the vocabulary terms.

Vocabulary Review Strategies

Word Search   Have students make a list of the vocabulary words for all the lessons in this chapter. Using grid paper, students can make a word search puzzle placing a single letter in each grid square. After the students have placed the letters for all vocabulary words intersecting words that have common letters, they should fill in the open grid squares randomly with letters. Students can trade their word lists and puzzles with another student and solve the puzzle.

Lesson Review

The examples walk the students through sorting and classifying items, finding mean, median, mode, and range of a data set, interpreting and creating bar graphs, and interpreting and creating line graphs. If the given examples are not sufficient to review the questions, have students design their own example from a particular section of the chapter. When finished, have them share their example and its solution with a partner.

Find **Extra Practice** for these concepts in the Practice Worksheets, pages A134–A161.

Classroom Management

Early Finishers   Have those students with extra time on their hands design additional practice questions for their classmates. You could give them an opportunity to come to the board and "teach" their example to the remainder of the class as time permits.

FOLDABLES Study Organizer — Dinah Zike's Foldables®

Review Remind students to complete and refer to their Foldables as they progress through the Chapter 7 Study Guide. Have students share and compare their completed Foldables with a partner. You may also choose to have them use their Foldable as a study aid in preparing for the Chapter Test. (For complete instructions, see Chapter Resource Masters, p. A131.)

7-1 Sort and Classify (pp. 274–280)

11 Create a Venn diagram to sort the numbers **4, 6, 7, 8, 9, 12**, and **14**. Classify them as multiples of 4 or odd numbers.

Multiples of 4: __4, 8, 12__
Odd numbers: __7, 9__
Neither: __6, 14__

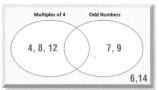

Multiples of 4 | Odd Numbers

4, 8, 12   7, 9

6, 14

Example 1

Create a Venn diagram to sort the numbers 2, 3, 7, 8, 9, 11, and 12. Classify them as multiples of 3 or as prime numbers.

1. Multiples of 3: 9, 12   3. Both: 3
2. Prime numbers: 2, 7, 11   4. Neither: 8

Multiples of 3 | Prime Numbers

9, 12   3   2, 7, 11

8

7-2 Mode, Median, and Range (pp. 281–288)

Find the mode and the range for each given set of data.

12 Jamari recorded the number of phone calls received each day.

12, 15, 17, 9, 15, 13, 11

The range is __8__.

The mode is __15__.

13 Mario recorded the number of hours he practiced piano each week.

5, 5, 7, 3, 7, 4, 7, 6, 3

The range is __4__.

The mode is __7__.

Example 2

Find the mode and the range for the given set of data.

Rafael recorded the number of siblings each of her teachers have.

2, 5, 2, 3, 4, 3, 1, 2, 0

1. Arrange the numbers in order from least to greatest.

0, 1, 2, 2, 2, 3, 3, 4, 5

2. The greatest number in the list is 5. The least number in the list is 0.

5 − 0 = 5

3. The range is 5.

4. The mode (the number listed most often) is 2.

7-3 Mean (pp. 289–295)

Find one missing number from a data set when the mean is given.

14 Mean: 6   Data set: 8, 3, 6, __7__

15 Mean: 14   Data set: 13, 18, 10, __15__

16 Mean: 27   Data set: 28, 28, 26, __26__

17 Mean: 4.1
Data set: 1.9, 2.8, 6.9, __4.8__

Example 3

The mean of five numbers is 6. Four of the numbers are 3, 7, 8 and 5. Find the missing number.

1. Find the total value of 5 numbers with a mean of 6.

   $5 \cdot 6 = 30$

2. Find the sum of the given numbers.

   $3 + 7 + 8 + 5 = 23$

3. Subtract the sum of the four numbers from the total sum.

   $30 - 23 = 7$

4. The missing number is 7.

7-4 Interpret Bar Graphs (pp. 297–304)

Use the double-bar graph "Favorite Spirit Day Apparel" to compare data.

18 Which apparel is preferred the least by boys?

   __hair accessories__

19 Which apparel is preferred the most by boys?

   __T-shirts__

20 How many more girls prefer face painting over T-shirts?

   __3 girls__

21 How many more boys than girls prefer T-shirts?

   __12 boys__

Example 4

Use the double-bar graph "Favorite Spirit Day Apparel" to compare data.

How many more girls chose face painting than hair accessories as their favorite Spirit Day apparel?

1. How many girls chose face painting? **11**
2. How many girls chose hair accessories? **5**
3. Subtract. $11 - 5 = 6$
4. Six more girls chose face painting.

Chapter 7 Study Guide **333**

Note This!

Scales Show students examples of a graph where the numerical scale does not start at 0. Illustrate the correct notation to indicate that the scale is not complete. Discuss reasons that the scale may not start at 0 such as the data itself, the space available to make the graph, and wanting to mislead the audience.

Math Coach Notes

Continuous Data Data appropriate to display in a line graph must be continuous. Discrete data should not be displayed using a line graph. An example of discrete data is the test scores for students in Mrs. Jones' class. An example of continuous data is the temperature recorded at each hour during the day.

7-5 Create Bar Graphs (pp. 305–313)

Example 5

Use the data in the table to create a bar graph.

Pet Adopt, Inc. took a survey of 500 pet owners to see what type of pets they own.

Pet Adopt, Inc. Survey	
Type of Pet	Number Owned
Dog	300
Horse	25
Cat	100
Fish	50
Bird	25

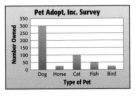

Use the data in the table to create a bar graph.

22 Starr City Library recorded the items that were checked out last week.

Starr City Library Circulation	
Item	Number Checked Out
Books	300
Audio Tapes	50
CDs	150
Books on Tape	100
DVDs	175

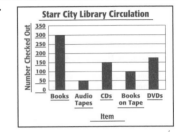

7-6 Interpret Line Graphs (pp. 315–322)

Use the double-line graph "Graphic T-Shirt Sales" to compare data.

23 Compare rock group T-shirt sales in June and April.

$5,000 more in June

24 Describe rock T-shirt sales in July.

$19,000

25 Compare sales of sports team T-shirts to rock group T-shirts in April.

$4,000 more sports team T-shirts

Example 6

Use the double-line graph "Graphic T-Shirt Sales" to compare data.

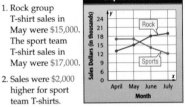

1. Rock group T-shirt sales in May were $15,000. The sport team T-shirt sales in May were $17,000.

2. Sales were $2,000 higher for sport team T-shirts.

7-7 Create Line Graphs (pp. 323–329)

Example 7

Use the data in the table to create a line graph.

Mr. Murphy recorded the gallons of paint his company used over a four-month period.

Murphy Home Improvement	
Month	Gallons of Paint
November	95
December	52
January	37
February	25

Use the data in the table to create a line graph.

26 Ms. Morales recorded the amount of money earned at Super-Fixer Auto Shop over a four-month period.

Super-Fixer Auto Shop	
Month	Money Earned
April	$72,000
May	$98,000
June	$81,000
July	$89,000

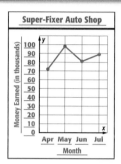

Use the data in the table to create a double-line graph.

27 Mr. Brooks recorded the sales trends of books and audio/visual products that his bookstore sells over a four-month period.

Brooks' Books Sales		
Month	Sales (in thousands)	
	Books	Audio/Visual
March	$12	$27
April	$14	$32
May	$16	$30
June	$19	$35

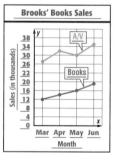

Chapter 7 Study Guide **335**

English Learner Strategy

Sample Data and Graphs For students whose native language is not English, ask them to bring in newspapers, magazine, or website addresses written in their languages. Have them locate examples of data tables, bar graphs, and line graphs in these publications. For each example of a data table found, students can determine an appropriate scale and interval. For each example of a graph found, students can identify the title, labels, and scales of each graph. Invite students to share these data tables and graphs with the class. Students can show each example and then explain the parts and data to the class.

Ticket Out the Door

Do These Problems Have students answer five problems of the following types:

(1) sorting and classifying items using a Venn diagram
(2) finding the median and range of a data set
(3) finding the mean of a data set
(4) creating and interpreting a bar graph
(5) creating and interpreting a line graph.

Chapter Resource Masters

Additional forms of the Chapter 7 Tests are available.

Test Format	Where to Find it
Chapter 7 Test	Math Online ⟩ glencoe.com
Blackline Masters	Assessment Masters, p. 107

ExamView®
Assessment Suite

Customize and create multiple versions of your chapter test and their answer keys. All of these questions from the chapter tests are available on ExamView® Assessment Suite.

Advance TRACKER

Online Assessment and Reporting
glencoe.com

This online assessment tool allows teachers to track student progress with easily-accessible, comprehensive reports available for every student. Assess students using any internet-ready computer.

Alternative Assessment

Use Portfolios   Ask students to create a bar graph and a line graph. Have them write three questions that can be answered by each graph. They should include the answers to their questions as well.

Chapter
7   **Chapter Test**

List the numbers in each category.

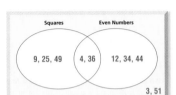

1 factors of 6 ___1, 2, 3, 6___

2 odd numbers ___1, 3, 5, 7, 9___

3 both ___1, 3___

4 neither ___0, 4, 8___

5 Create a Venn diagram to sort the numbers. Classify them as squares of whole numbers or even numbers.

3, 4, 9, 12, 25, 34, 36, 44, 49, 51

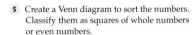

Squares   Even Numbers

9, 25, 49   4, 36   12, 34, 44

3, 51

Find the mode for each given set of data.

6 23, 17, 31, 39, 31 ___31___

7 97, 84, 57, 66, 97, 75, 97, 81, 68 ___97___

Find the median and the range for each given set of data.

8 Bianca asked seven students how many bedrooms are in their home.

3, 5, 2, 3, 2, 2, 4

The median is ___3___.   The range is ___3___.

9 George asked seven adults how many times they have moved.

5, 6, 1, 7, 6, 4, 12

The median is ___6___.   The range is ___11___.

Find the mean of the data set. Convert the remainder into a fraction or a decimal.

10 11, 9, 5, 7, 8, 5 ___7.5___   11 8, 11, 13, 9, 12, 10 ___10.5___

English Learner Strategy

Assessment   Allow students time to look over the assessment. Have the students take a close look at all the problem directions, as well as any tems in the word problems. Be sure the students understand what is being asked of them in each problem. If necesssary, provide them with dictionaries. Also have the students identify and list the vocabulary terms from the chapter as they read through the assessment. If necessary, review the meanings of all essential math vocabulary.

Find one missing number from a data set when the mean is given.

12 Mean: 9   Data set: 5, 12, 8, __11__

13 Mean: 12   Data set: 11.4, 9.7, 10.8, __16.1__

Use the bar graph "Betsy's Reading Log" to compare data.

14 What interval is used for the scale?

__10__

15 What does the height of each bar represent?

__The number of minutes Betsy read each day.__

Use the data in the table to create a double-line graph.

16 **DETERGENT** The table shows sales of two different laundry detergent brands at Save-Mart over a four-month period.

Save-Mart Sales		
Month	Laundry Detergent	
	Value	Brite
March	$75	$175
April	$125	$200
May	$125	$225
June	$175	$250

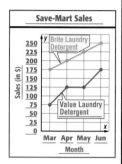

Correct the mistakes.

17 **VOTING** Khalil used the table below to make a double-bar graph. What was his mistake?

Student Council President Results		
Candidate	Number of Votes	
	Grade 7	Grade 8
Esmerelda	35	37
Minho	39	46
Demitri	46	23
Karena	29	38

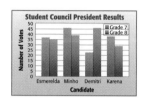

__The key does not match the data. Grade 7 is shown in blue and Grade 8__
__is shown in red.__

Learning from Mistakes

Diagnosing Errors   Review commonly missed questions or topics in small groups or as a class. Ask students to share their methods of answering each question. Try to find out if the mistakes are computational or whether they lack adequate understanding of the topic. Some further explanation may be required accordingly.

Data-Driven Decision Making

Students missing Exercises . . .	Have trouble with . . .	Should review and practice . . .
1–5	sorting and classifying numbers.	SSG Lesson 7-1, p. 274 CRM Skills Practice, p. A135
6–9	finding mode, median, and range.	SSG Lesson 7-2, p. 281 CRM Skills Practice, p. A139
10–13	finding mean.	SSG Lesson 7-3, p. 289 CRM Skills Practice, p. A143
14–15, 17	creating and interpreting bar graphs.	SSG Lessons 7-4 and 7-5, pp. 297 and 305 CRM Skills Practice, pp. A147 and A151
16	creating and interpreting line graphs.	SSG Lessons 7-6 and 7-7, pp. 315 and 323 CRM Skills Practice, pp. A155 and A159

Test Practice

![warning icon] **Diagnose Student Errors**

Survey student responses for each item. Class trends may indicate common errors and misconceptions.

1. A found mean
   B found median
   C guess
   Ⓓ correct

2. A guess
   Ⓑ correct
   C misinterpreted definition of mean
   D misinterpreted definition of mean

3. A found range
   Ⓑ correct
   C found mean
   D found greatest number of pounds

4. A misread graph; this is for grape juice
   Ⓑ correct
   C misread graph
   D guess

5. A found mode
   B found median
   C guess
   Ⓓ correct

6. A guess
   B found least grade
   C found median and/or mode
   Ⓓ correct

7. A difference between 10 A.M. and 11 A.M.
   Ⓑ correct
   C this is hours at 1 P.M.
   D this is sum of hours at 10 A.M. and 1 P.M., not difference

8. Ⓐ correct
   B this is April 2008 data
   C this is April 2009 data
   D this is for March or May, not April

9. A misinterpreted question
   Ⓑ correct
   C misclassified 36 as prime
   D did not classify 36 as a square number

Choose the best answer and fill in the corresponding circle on the sheet at right.

1 Francisco recorded the ages of 7 of his teachers. What is the mode of this data set?

32, 53, 23, 24, 31, 44, 23

A 32.9   C 30
B 31   Ⓓ 23

2 Miles recorded the number of students who play brass instruments in the school band. The mean is 6. What is the missing number of trumpet players in the table below?

Marcell Middle School Brass Section	
Instrument	Number of Players
Trumpet	
Trombone	6
Mellophone	3
Sousaphone	5

A 6 players   C 12 players
Ⓑ 10 players   D 24 players

3 Kelly recorded the number of pounds of bananas sold each hour. What is the median number of pounds?

54, 52, 54, 53, 56, 57, 59, 51, 58

A 8   C 54.5
Ⓑ 54   D 59

4 Use the bar graph, "Favorite Drinks" to compare data. How many more boys than girls chose chocolate milk as their favorite drink?

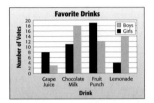

A 5 boys   C 9 boys
Ⓑ 7 boys   D 10 boys

5 The Census Bureau recorded the number of people that live in each house on Pine Street. What is the range of this data set?

9, 4, 6, 3, 6, 2, 4, 3, 3, 5, 7

A 3   C 5
B 4   Ⓓ 7

6 Mrs. Marcucci recorded Alexa's last seven quiz grades. What is the mean of this data set?

65, 77, 87, 91, 96, 77, 74

A 26   C 77
B 65   Ⓓ 81

7 Use the line graph, "Centertown Shipping" to compare data. How many more staffing hours were used at 1 P.M. than at 10 A.M.?

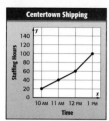

A 20 hours   **C** 100 hours

B 80 hours   **D** 120 hours

---

8 Use the double-line graph, "Bayside Boat Sales" to compare data. How much more was sold in April 2009 than in April 2008?

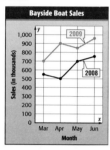

A $400,000   **C** $900,000

B $500,000   **D** $150,000

---

9 Beatriz is sorting a set of numbers into categories. In which category does the number 36 belong?

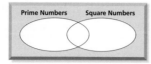

A prime numbers   **C** both

B square numbers   **D** neither

ANSWER SHEET

Directions: Fill in the circle of each correct answer.

1 (A) (B) (C) ●D
2 (A) ●B (C) (D)
3 (A) ●B (C) (D)
4 (A) ●B (C) (D)
5 (A) (B) (C) ●D
6 (A) (B) (C) ●D
7 (A) ●B (C) (D)
8 ●A (B) (C) (D)
9 (A) ●B (C) (D)

> **Success Strategy**
> If two answers seem correct, compare them for differences. Reread the problem to find the best answer between the two.

Diagnosing Student Errors and Misconceptions

Scoring Guides   Allowing students to use a scoring guide can help students build test-taking skills. Students can benefit from scoring responses of other students, as well as from checking and revising their own work. To protect students' privacy, be certain that papers to be scored do not indicate the students' names.

After students have scored their work, have them go back and take a look at the questions they missed. Ask them to try to find their mistakes, and once they do, have them try to make the appropriate corrections.

Chapter Overview

Chapter-at-a-Glance

Lesson	Math Objective	State/Local Standards
8-1 Percents (pp. 342–348)	Calculate percents for data in a set.	
8-2 Percents and Angle Measures (pp. 349–355)	Relate percents to angle measures.	
Progress Check 1 (p. 356)		
8-3 Interpret Circle Graphs (pp. 357–364)	Interpret data in a circle graph.	
8-4 Create Circle Graphs (pp. 365–372)	Display data in a circle graph.	
Progress Check 2 (p. 373)		

Content-at-a-Glance

The diagram below summarizes and unpacks Chapter 8 content.

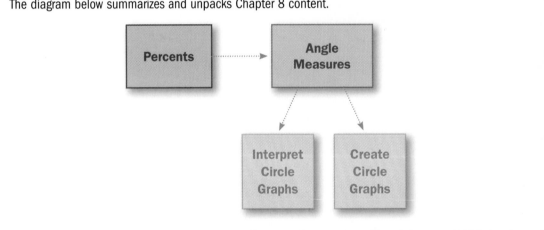

Chapter Assessment Manager

Diagnostic Diagnose students' readiness.

	Student/Teacher Editions	Assessment Masters	Technology
Course Placement Test		1	● ExamView® Assessment Suite
Book 3 Pretest		101	● ExamView® Assessment Suite
Chapter 8 Pretest		115	● ExamView® Assessment Suite
Quiz/Preview	SSG 341		Math Online ▷ glencoe.com StudentWorks™ Plus

Formative Identify students' misconceptions of content knowledge.

	Student/Teacher Editions	Assessment Masters	Technology
Progress Checks	SSG 356, 373		Math Online ▷ glencoe.com StudentWorks™ Plus
Vocabulary Review	SSG 374		Math Online ▷ glencoe.com
Lesson Assessments			● ExamView® Assessment Suite
Are They Getting It?	TE 345, 352, 360, 369		Math Online ▷ glencoe.com

Summative Determine student success in learning the concepts in the lesson, chapter, or book.

	Student/Teacher Editions	Assessment Masters	Technology
Chapter 8 Test	SSG 378	118	● ExamView® Assessment Suite
Test Practice	SSG 380	121	
Alternative Assessment	TE 378	124	● ExamView® Assessment Suite
See It, Do It, Say It, Write It	TE 347, 355, 364, 372		
Book 3 Test		137	● ExamView® Assessment Suite

Backmapping and Vertical Alignment **McGraw-Hill's** *Math Triumphs* intervention program was conceived and developed with the final results in mind: student success in grade-level mathematics, including Algebra 1 and beyond. The authors, using the **NCTM Focal Points and Focal Connections** as their guide, developed this brand-new series by backmapping from grade-level and Algebra 1 concepts, and vertically aligning the topics so that they build upon prior skills and concepts and serve as a foundation for future topics.

Chapter Resource Manager

	Lesson 8-1	Lesson 8-2	Lesson 8-3	Lesson 8-4
Concept	Percents	Percents and Angle Measures	Interpret Circle Graphs	Create Circle Graphs
Objective	Calculate percents for data in a set.	Relate percents to angle measures.	Interpret data in a circle graph.	Display data in a circle graph.
Math Vocabulary	equivalent fractions percent ratio	degree denominator percent sector simplest form	circle graph data degree percent sector	center circle graph data degree percent sector
Lesson Resources	**Materials** • Centimeter grid paper • Colored pencils **Manipulatives** • Fraction circles • Fraction tiles **Other Resources** [CRM] Vocabulary and English Language Development [CRM] Skills Practice [CRM] Problem-Solving Practice [CRM] Homework Practice	**Materials** • Compasses • Index cards **Manipulatives** • Fraction circles • Fraction tiles **Other Resources** [CRM] Vocabulary and English Language Development [CRM] Skills Practice [CRM] Problem-Solving Practice [CRM] Homework Practice	**Materials** • Calculators **Manipulatives** • Fraction circles **Other Resources** [CRM] Vocabulary and English Language Development [CRM] Skills Practice [CRM] Problem-Solving Practice [CRM] Homework Practice	**Materials** • Calculators • Compasses • Protractors **Manipulatives** • Fraction circles **Other Resources** [CRM] Vocabulary and English Language Development [CRM] Skills Practice [CRM] Problem-Solving Practice [CRM] Homework Practice
Technology	**Math Online** ▷ glencoe.com StudentWorks™ Plus ◉ ExamView® Assessment Suite	**Math Online** ▷ glencoe.com StudentWorks™ Plus ◉ ExamView® Assessment Suite	**Math Online** ▷ glencoe.com StudentWorks™ Plus ◉ ExamView® Assessment Suite	**Math Online** ▷ glencoe.com StudentWorks™ Plus ◉ ExamView® Assessment Suite

Intervention Strategy

Percents and Circle Graphs

Using real-world data to make a circle graph will show students the usefulness of these displays in everyday life. This hands-on activity will provide students with an anchoring experience when they learn how to make the graphs.

Step 1

To collect data for the circle graphs, ask students to name their favorite sport. Make a list of the sports and the numbers of students that prefer each. Make other lists for students' favorite foods, colors, school subjects, and seasons. If time permits, student groups can collect their own data.

Step 2

Divide the class into five small groups and assign one category of data collected to each group. Each student will make their own graph of their data.

Step 3

Students will list their categories and the percents for each category by dividing the part by the whole. For example, if there are 24 students and 9 like soccer, the percent will be:

$$\frac{9}{24} = 0.375 = 37.5\%$$

Tell students to round either to tenths or whole numbers. Remind them that percents must add up to 100% so they will have to round up or down as needed.

Step 4

Have students make their circle graphs by drawing a circle with a template, or using a paper plate. To determine the size of each sector, tell students to multiply 360° by the decimal form of the percent. For example, if 37.5% prefer soccer, then $360 \times 0.375 = 135$; the central angle of the sector for soccer will be 135°. Remind students that the central angles of all the sectors must add up to 360.

Step 5

Students will use a protractor to draw each sector to the correct degree. Tell students to label the sectors with the categories and percents.

Step 6

Student groups will present their circle graphs to the class and report their findings.

Chapter Notes

Real-World Applications

Shopping   Laura was shopping for a nice outfit when she came across the perfect outfit for the perfect price. She found a pink dress. The original price for the dress was $35.99; it was on sale for $28.99. What percentage did Laura save on the dress?

$35.99 – $28.99 = $7;
7 ÷ 35.99 = 0.1945; she saved about 20%.

Intervention Strategy
24 Hours in a Day

Step 1   As a class, brainstorm things that people spend time doing during a 24-hour day. List all suggestions.

Step 2   As a class, review the list and narrow it down to a list of ten categories in which every hour of a person's day can be classified.

Step 3   Individually, students should assign an average number of hours they spend per day on each of the ten activities on the list.

Step 4   Students should calculate the percent of their days spent doing each of the ten activities listed.

Step 5   Have students create a visual display to show the break down of how they spend a 24-hour period. Students can share their displays with the class. Compare the displays and determine which are easiest to read.

Percents and Circle Graphs

Percents can be used to compare values.

For example, 70% of the Earth's surface is covered with water. Surveys often show results in percents, such as 90% of dentists prefer a certain toothbrush. School systems also use percents to show the number of students who have graduated.

340   Chapter 8 Percents and Circle Graphs

Key Vocabulary

Find interactive definitions in 13 languages in the **eGlossary** at glencoe.com.

English   Español *Introduce the most important vocabulary terms from Chapter 8.*

circle graph   gráfica circular

a graph used to compare parts of a whole; the circle represents the whole and is separated into parts of a whole (p. 357)

data   datos

information, often numerical, which is gathered for statistical purposes (p. 357)

degree   grado

the most common unit of measure for an angle (p. 349)

percent   por ciento

a ratio that compares a number to 100 (p. 342)

ratio   razón

a comparison of two numbers by division (p. 342)

sector   sector

pie-shaped sections in a circle (p. 349)

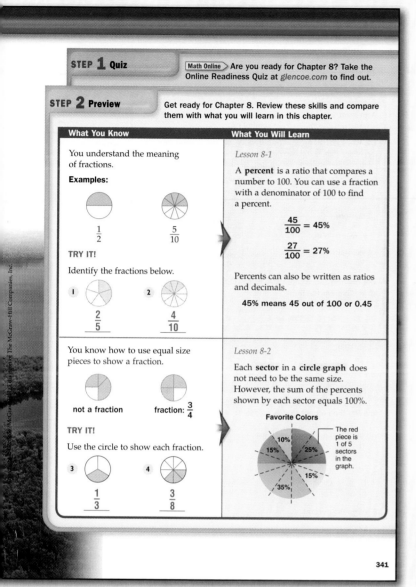

STEP 1 Quiz

Math Online > Are you ready for Chapter 8? Take the Online Readiness Quiz at *glencoe.com* to find out.

STEP 2 Preview

Get ready for Chapter 8. Review these skills and compare them with what you will learn in this chapter.

What You Know	What You Will Learn
You understand the meaning of fractions. **Examples:** $\frac{1}{2}$ $\frac{5}{10}$ **TRY IT!** Identify the fractions below. **1** $\frac{2}{5}$ **2** $\frac{4}{10}$	**Lesson 8-1** A **percent** is a ratio that compares a number to 100. You can use a fraction with a denominator of 100 to find a percent. $\frac{45}{100} = 45\%$ $\frac{27}{100} = 27\%$ Percents can also be written as ratios and decimals. **45% means 45 out of 100 or 0.45**
You know how to use equal size pieces to show a fraction. not a fraction fraction: $\frac{3}{4}$ **TRY IT!** Use the circle to show each fraction. **3** $\frac{1}{3}$ **4** $\frac{3}{8}$	**Lesson 8-2** Each **sector** in a **circle graph** does not need to be the same size. However, the sum of the percents shown by each sector equals 100%. **Favorite Colors** 10% 15% 25% 15% 35% The red piece is 1 of 5 sectors in the graph.

341

Step 1 Quiz

Pretest/Prescribe Students can take the Online Readiness Quiz or the Diagnostic Pretest in the Assessment Masters.

Step 2 Preview

Use this pre-chapter activity to activate students' prior knowledge, build confidence, and help students preview the lessons.

 **FOLDABLES** Study Organizer

Dinah Zike's Foldables

Guide students through the directions on p. A162 in the Chapter Resource Masters to create their own Foldable graphic organizer for use with this chapter.

Home Connections

- Have students look through their sock drawers. Have them find the percent of socks that are white and the percent of socks that are colored. They should make a circle graph of their findings.

Mc Graw Hill Professional Development

Targeted professional development has been articulated throughout **McGraw-Hill's** *Math Triumphs* intervention program. **The McGraw-Hill Professional Development Video Library** provides short videos that support the **NCTM Focal Points and Focal Connections**. For more information, visit glencoe.com.

Model Lessons   Instructional Strategies

Vocabulary Preview

- As students complete the Chapter Preview, have them make a list of important terms throughout the chapter.

- Have students use the list of key words along with the additional unfamiliar or important words throughout the chapter. Using index cards, have students write a vocabulary term on one side of each card. On the opposite side, students should write three to five words or phrases relating to the term.

- Once students are finished, pair them up to trade cards. Challenge them to determine the terms being described.

Lesson Notes

Lesson Planner

Objective Calculate percents for data in a set.

Vocabulary equivalent fractions, percent, ratio

Materials/Manipulatives centimeter grid paper, colored pencils, fraction circles or fraction tiles

Chapter Resource Masters

- CRM Vocabulary and English Language Development (p. A165)
- CRM Skills Practice (p. A166)
- CRM Problem-Solving Practice (p. A167)
- CRM Homework Practice (p. A168)

① Introduce

Vocabulary

Equivalent Comparisons Discuss how fractions, decimals, and percents are all *ratios*. Demonstrate how each term shows a comparison between a whole and a part of a whole. Model how one comparison can be expressed in several ways.

② Teach

Key Concept

Foundational Skills and Concepts After students have read through the Key Concept box, have them try these exercises.

1. What percent is equal to the ratio *65 out of 100*? 65%

2. Simplify $\frac{80}{100}$ to find an equivalent fraction. $\frac{4}{5}$

3. Express 28% as a simplified fraction. $\frac{7}{25}$

KEY Concept

A **percent** is a ratio that compares a number to 100. A percent is written using the percent symbol (%).

The word *percent* means "hundredths" or "out of 100." Percents can be written as fractions or decimals because they show the relationship between one whole (100%) and a part of a whole.

Describe the shaded area in different ways.

Ratio: 30 out of 100

Fraction: $\frac{30}{100}$

Percent: 30%

Decimal: 0.30

The fraction above could also be simplified to find an **equivalent fraction**.

$$30\% = \frac{30 \div 10}{100 \div 10} = \frac{3}{10}$$

VOCABULARY

equivalent fractions fractions that name the same number

percent a ratio that compares a number to 100

ratio a comparison of two numbers by division

You can use models to show the relationships between fractions and percents.

Example 1

Identify the percent that is modeled.

1. Find the fraction that is shaded.
   $1\frac{1}{4}$ or $\frac{5}{4}$

2. Find an equivalent fraction with a denominator of 100.
   $\frac{5 \cdot 25}{4 \cdot 25} = \frac{125}{100}$

3. Write the percent.
   125%

Additional *Example 1*

Identify the percent that is modeled.

1. Find the fraction that is shaded.
   $1\frac{7}{10}$ or $\frac{17}{10}$

2. Find an equivalent fraction with a denominator of 100.
   $\frac{17 \cdot 10}{10 \cdot 10} = \frac{170}{100}$

3. Write the percent. 170%

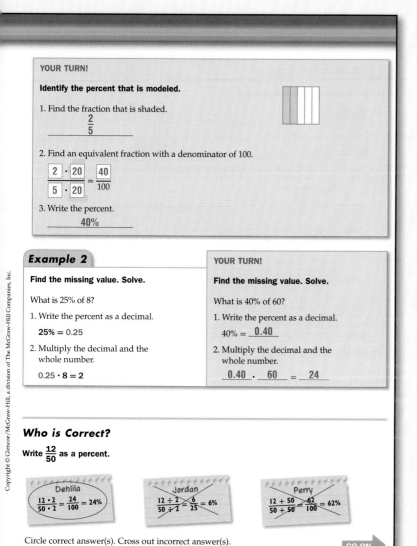

YOUR TURN!

Identify the percent that is modeled.

1. Find the fraction that is shaded.

$$\frac{2}{5}$$

2. Find an equivalent fraction with a denominator of 100.

$$\frac{2 \cdot 20}{5 \cdot 20} = \frac{40}{100}$$

3. Write the percent.

40%

Example 2

Find the missing value. Solve.

What is 25% of 8?

1. Write the percent as a decimal.

25% = 0.25

2. Multiply the decimal and the whole number.

$0.25 \cdot 8 = 2$

YOUR TURN!

Find the missing value. Solve.

What is 40% of 60?

1. Write the percent as a decimal.

40% = __0.40__

2. Multiply the decimal and the whole number.

__0.40__ · __60__ = __24__

Who is Correct?

Write $\frac{12}{50}$ as a percent.

Dehlila
$\frac{12 \cdot 2}{50 \cdot 2} = \frac{24}{100} = 24\%$

Jordan
$\frac{12 \div 2}{50 \div 2} = \frac{6}{25} = 6\%$

Perry
$\frac{12 + 50}{50 + 50} = \frac{62}{100} = 62\%$

Circle correct answer(s). Cross out incorrect answer(s).

GO ON

Copyright © Glencoe/McGraw-Hill, a division of The McGraw-Hill Companies, Inc.

Find the missing value. Solve.

What is 55% of 80?

1. Write the percent as a decimal.
55% = 0.55

2. Multiply the decimal and the whole number.
$0.55 \cdot 80 = 44$

Math Coach Notes

Large Percents For percents greater than 100, students may overlook the whole number and focus on just the fractional part. Explain how to translate the number in the hundreds place as the number of wholes and the remaining amount as the fractional part. Alternate using models as well as numerical examples to help students visualize this concept.

Who is Correct?
Diagnostic Teaching

- Dehlila is correct. She multiplied correctly to get a denominator of 100.

- Jordan is incorrect. She simplified the fraction and used the numerator incorrectly.

- Perry is incorrect. He used addition instead of multiplication to find a denominator of 100.

Practice

Using Manipulatives

Fraction Tiles   Use a set of rectangular or circular fraction tiles to practice converting among fractions, decimals, and percents.

On-Hand Manipulatives   Have students use centimeter grid paper and colored pencils to create models of percents and equivalent fractions and decimals.

Guided Practice

Identify each percent that is modeled.

1.

2.

Step by Step Practice

3. Identify the percent of green buttons in the total buttons.

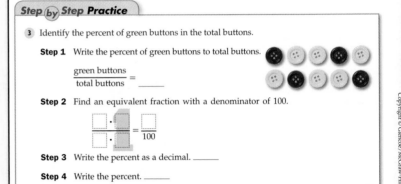

Step 1   Write the percent of green buttons to total buttons.

$$\frac{\text{green buttons}}{\text{total buttons}} = \underline{\hspace{1cm}}$$

Step 2   Find an equivalent fraction with a denominator of 100.

$$\frac{\square}{\square} \cdot \frac{\square}{\square} = \frac{\square}{100}$$

Step 3   Write the percent as a decimal. _____

Step 4   Write the percent. _____

Identify each percent that is modeled.

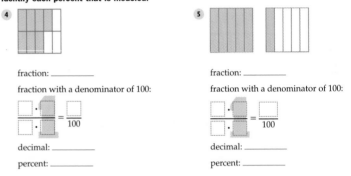

4.
fraction: _____

fraction with a denominator of 100:

$$\frac{\square}{\square} \cdot \frac{\square}{\square} = \frac{\square}{100}$$

decimal: _____

percent: _____

5.
fraction: _____

fraction with a denominator of 100:

$$\frac{\square}{\square} \cdot \frac{\square}{\square} = \frac{\square}{100}$$

decimal: _____

percent: _____

344   Chapter 8 Percents and Circle Graphs

Intervention Strategy   Naturalist Learners

Model Percents Have students work in small groups. Write several percents on the board. Tell groups to find three different ways to model each percent. Challenge students to use objects in their environment to represent the percents. Encourage examples such as glasses filled with water, containers filled with objects, children versus adults in a household, etc. Ask students to present their models to the class and explain how each demonstrates one of the percents on the board. Tell students to also express their models in equivalent

Find the missing value.

6 What is 30% of 20?

30% = __0.30__

__0.30__ · __20__ = __6__

7 What is 95% of 420?

95% = __0.95__

__0.95__ · __420__ = __399__

8 What is 110% of 46?

110% = __1.10__

__1.10__ · __46__ = __50.60__

9 What is 86% of 86?

86% = __0.86__

__0.86__ · __86__ = __73.96__

Step by Step *Problem-Solving Practice*

Solve.

10 **ELECTIONS** There are 300 students who voted for class president. Marcell won 34% of the vote, Antoinette won 29% of the vote, and Miranda won 37% of the vote. How many votes did each candidate receive?

Problem-Solving Strategies
☑ Use a table.
☐ Draw a diagram.
☐ Use logical reasoning.
☐ Solve a simpler problem.
☐ Work backward.

Understand Read the problem. Write what you know.

Marcell won __34%__ of the vote.
Antoinette won __29%__ of the vote.
Miranda won __37%__ of the vote.

Plan Pick a strategy. One strategy is to make a table.

Solve Complete the table to find the number of votes for each candidate.

To find the number of votes, write the percent as a __decimal__.

Then, multiply the __decimal__ times the __number of voters__.

Name	Percent	Calculation	Number of Votes
Marcell	34%	0.34 · 300 =	102
Antoinette	29%	0.29 · 300 =	87
Miranda	37%	0.37 · 300 =	111

Check Add the number of votes for each candidate. The sum should equal 300 votes.

GO ON

Note This!
Converting to Decimals In percents less than 10, remind students to move the decimal point *two* places to the left when converting to an equivalent decimal. Students may forget to write the zero placeholder. Demonstrate how this yields an entirely different fraction and decimal.

Common Error *Alert*

Exercises 6–9 Students may forget to place the decimal point in their answers. Emphasize the importance of this final step and model how the absence of the decimal point affects the answer. Remind students to check their answers by rereading the question to see if their answers make sense.

Math Coach Notes

Sum of the Parts Use Exercise 10 to point out that the sum of the parts needs to equal the whole number, just as the sum of the percents needs to equal 100%. This is a good way for students to check their calculations and the reasonableness of their answers.

Are They Getting It?

Check students' understanding of percents by writing these problems on the board. Ask them to point out incorrect answers and explain their reasoning.

1. An equivalent fraction for 84% is $\frac{13}{16}$. This is incorrect. $84\% = \frac{21}{25}$

2. 29% of 152 is 44.08. This is correct.

3. 25% of $46 is $11.25. This is incorrect. $0.25 \cdot \$46 = \$11.50$

Odd/Even Assignments

Exercises 14–29 are structured so that students practice the same concepts whether they are assigned the odd or even problems.

In-Class Assignment

Have students complete Exercises 14, 17, 20, 26, 27, and 32 to ensure that they understand the concept.

Solve.

11 SURVEYS The Sweet Tooth Ice Cream Company took a survey of 250 customers' favorite flavors. Forty-eight percent chose vanilla, twenty-four percent chose chocolate, and twenty-eight percent chose strawberry as their favorite. How many people chose each flavor?

Check off each step.

✔ Understand: I underlined key words.

✔ Plan: To solve this problem, I will ___make a table___

✔ Solve: The answer is ___vanilla: 120, chocolate: 60, strawberry: 70___

✔ Check: To check my answer, I will ___add the votes to___

___check for a sum of 250___

12 FINANCES Mrs. Arnold earns $2,075 dollars a month. If 40% of her salary is spent on rent, how much does she pay in rent each month?

$2{,}075 \cdot 0.40 = 830.00$; She pays $830.00 each month in rent.

13 Reflect Roald read 15 out of 25 books on his bookshelf. Explain how to find the percentage of books on the bookshelf that he has read.

$15 \div 25 = 0.60$; The decimal 0.60 equals 60%. He has read 60% of the books.

▶ Skills, Concepts, and Problem Solving

Identify each percent that is modeled.

14

71%

15

120%

Math Challenge

Construction   A foreman divides his construction crew of 450 workers among three projects. He sends 32% to fill potholes, 28% to pave the main road, and 40% to work on the bridge. How many more workers were sent to work on the bridge than to pave the main road?

54 workers

Identify each percent that is modeled.

16

fraction: $\dfrac{9}{25}$

fraction with a denominator of 100:

$\dfrac{9 \cdot 4}{25 \cdot 4} = \dfrac{36}{100}$

decimal: 0.36

percent: 36%

17

fraction: $1\dfrac{13}{20}$ or $\dfrac{33}{20}$

fraction with a denominator of 100:

$\dfrac{33 \cdot 5}{20 \cdot 5} = \dfrac{165}{100}$

decimal: 1.65

percent: 165%

18

fraction: $\dfrac{8}{20}$

fraction with a denominator of 100:

$\dfrac{8 \cdot 5}{20 \cdot 5} = \dfrac{40}{100}$

decimal: 0.40

percent: 40%

19

fraction: $1\dfrac{3}{4}$ or $\dfrac{7}{4}$

fraction with a denominator of 100:

$\dfrac{7 \cdot 25}{4 \cdot 25} = \dfrac{175}{100}$

decimal: 1.75

percent: 175%

Find the missing value.

20 What is 5% of 80?

0.05 · 80 = 4

21 What is 165% of 260?

1.65 · 260 = 429

22 What is 40% of 79?

0.40 · 79 = 31.6

23 What is 17% of 34?

0.17 · 34 = 5.78

24 What is 81% of 260?

0.81 · 260 = 210.6

25 What is 47% of 928?

0.47 · 928 = 436.16

GO ON

4 Assess

See It, Do It, Say It, Write It

Step 1 On the board, write a percent greater than 100.

Step 2 Tell students to draw a model that represents this percent.

Step 3 Ask students to work in pairs. Have students discuss how to write an equivalent fraction and decimal.

Step 4 Have students work alone to write an explanation of how to find an equivalent fraction and decimal. Encourage students to use correct vocabulary terms and clear language in their explanations.

Looking Ahead: Pre-Teach

Percents and Angle Measures   In the next lesson, students will learn the relationship between percents and sectors of a circle.

Example

What percent of a circle is one sector when the circle is divided into 5 equal sectors? What is the degree measure of each sector?

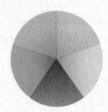

$100 \div 5 = 20$

One sector is 20% of the circle.

20% of $360° = 0.2 \cdot 360° = 72°$

Have students try each exercise below.

1. What percent of a circle is one sector when the circle is divided into 8 equal sectors?   12.5%

2. What is the degree measure of the sector in Question 1?   45°

Solve.

26 RAINFALL   On average, about 38 inches of precipitation falls in Arkansas City, Kansas. About 26% of the precipitation occurs in May and June. About how much precipitation occurs within this time period? Round to the nearest whole number.

   $0.26 \cdot 38 = 9.88$; about 10 inches

27 BUDGETS   Mr. Blackwell earns $1,275.00 each week. He budgets 3% of his earnings for his electric bill. How much money does Mr. Blackwell budget each week for his electric bill?

   $0.03 \cdot 1,275.00 = 38.25$; He budgets $38.25 each week for his electric bill.

28 FINANCIAL LITERACY   Alexis earned $57.00 this month. She has decided to deposit 10% of her earnings into a savings account. How much money will she deposit into savings?

   $0.10 \cdot 57 = 5.70$; She will deposit $5.70 into savings.

29 MUSEUMS   Twenty-seven percent of the paintings at the Archibald Museum of Art are watercolors. If the museum has a collection of 400 paintings, how many watercolors are in the museum?

   $0.27 \cdot 400 = 108$; 108 paintings

Vocabulary Check   **Write the vocabulary word that completes each sentence.**

30 A(n) _____ percent _____ is a ratio that compares a number to 100.

31 The numbers $\frac{2}{5}$ and $\frac{40}{100}$ are _equivalent fractions_

32 Writing in Math   Explain how to write the mixed number $1\frac{47}{50}$ as a percent.

   First, find the improper fraction. $\frac{50}{50} + \frac{47}{50} = \frac{97}{50}$. Then find the equivalent fraction

   with a denominator of 100. $\frac{97}{50} \cdot \frac{2}{2} = \frac{194}{100}$. Now, divide.$194 \div 100 = 1.94$

STOP

Ticket Out the Door

Equivalent Forms   Write 72% on the board. As students approach the classroom door to exit, alternate asking them to determine its equivalent ratio, simplified fraction, and decimal forms.

72 to 100, $\frac{18}{25}$, 0.72

KEY Concept

The relationship between percents, decimals, and fractions can be shown with a circle. Every circle is made of a total of 360°. The circle can be divided into pie-shaped sections called sectors.

The circle below shows 20 sectors of equal size. Each sector represents 5% of the circle.

Percent: 5%

Decimal: 0.05

Fraction: $\dfrac{5}{100}$

Simplest Form: $\dfrac{1}{20}$

To find the degree measure of each sector in the circle on the right, multiply the total degrees of the circle (360°) by the fraction in simplest form.

$$\dfrac{360°}{1} \cdot \dfrac{1}{20} = \dfrac{360°}{20} = 18°$$

Each 5% sector has a measure of 18°.

Another way to find the degreee measure of a 5% sector is to multiply 360° by the decimal 0.05.

$$360° \cdot 0.05 = 18°C$$

VOCABULARY

degree
the most common unit of measure for an angle

denominator
the bottom number in a fraction; it represents the number of parts in the whole

percent
the ratio that compares a number to 100

sector
pie-shaped sections in a circle

simplest form
the form of a fraction when the GCF of the numerator and the denominator is 1

Common percents, such as 5%, 10%, 25%, and 50%, can be used in combinations to make other useful percents and circle graphs.

Example 1

Find the degrees needed to show a 10% sector in a circle graph.

1. Write the percent as a fraction in simplest form.

$$10\% = \dfrac{10}{100} \div \dfrac{10}{10} = \dfrac{1}{10}$$

 $\frac{1}{10}$ of the circle is shaded.

2. Use the fraction to find the degree measure of a 10% sector.

$$\dfrac{360°}{1} \cdot \dfrac{1}{10} = \dfrac{360°}{10} = 36°$$

3. Check by multiplying 360° by the percent in decimal form.

$$360° \cdot 10\% = 360° \cdot 0.10 = 36°$$

GO ON

Additional *Example 1*

Find the degrees needed to show a 20% sector in a circle graph.

1. Write the percent as a fraction in simplest form.

$$20\% = \dfrac{20}{100} \div \dfrac{20}{20} = \dfrac{1}{5}$$

20%

2. Use the fraction to find the degree measure of a 20% sector.

$$\dfrac{360°}{1} \cdot \dfrac{1}{5} = \dfrac{360°}{5} = 72°$$

3. Check by multiplying 360° by the percent in decimal form.

$$360° \cdot 20\% = 360° \cdot 0.20 = 72°$$

Lesson Notes

Lesson Planner

Objective Relate percents to angle measures.

Vocabulary degree, denominator, percent, sector, simplest form

Materials/Manipulatives fraction circles, fraction tiles, compasses, index cards

Chapter Resource Masters

CRM Vocabulary and English Language Development (p. A169)

CRM Skills Practice (p. A170)

CRM Problem-Solving Practice (p. A171)

CRM Homework Practice (p. A172)

1 Introduce

Vocabulary

Relationships Draw several circles on the board. Divide each circle into a different number of equal sectors. Shade a few sectors in each circle, and practice describing each circle using vocabulary terms.

2 Teach

Key Concept

Foundational Skills and Concepts After students have read through the Key Concept box, have them try these exercises.

1. If 50% of a circle is shaded, what is the equivalent unit fraction for this sector? $\dfrac{1}{2}$

2. In a circle with 15 equal sectors, what is the degree measure of each sector? 24°

Use combinations to find the degrees needed to show a 45% sector in a circle graph.

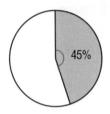

45%

1. Write 45% as a combination of percents.

20% + 25% = 45%

2. Find each percent in sector degrees.

$$20\% = \frac{360}{1} \cdot \frac{20}{100} = \frac{7200}{100} = 72°$$

$$25\% = \frac{360}{1} \cdot \frac{25}{100} = \frac{9000}{100} = 90°$$

3. Find the sum of the sector degrees.

20% + 25% = 45%

72° + 90° = 162°

Math Coach Notes

Calculating with Degrees Students have learned that percent means "per hundred." In working with degrees, they may miscalculate by dividing by 100 to find the number of specified sectors. Repeated practice with 360° will reinforce this new concept. Remind students that a right angle is 90° and four right angles are needed to create a circle.

YOUR TURN!

Find the degrees needed to show a 25% sector in a circle graph.

1. Write the percent as a fraction in simplest form.
   (Hint: What fraction of the circle is shaded?)

$$25\% = \frac{25}{100} \div \frac{25}{25} = \frac{1}{4}$$

25%

2. Use the fraction to find the degree measure of a 25% sector.

$$\frac{360°}{1} \cdot \frac{1}{4} = \frac{360°}{4} = 90°$$

3. Check by multiplying 360° by the percent in decimal form.

$$360° \cdot 25\% = 360° \cdot \underline{0.25} = \underline{90°}$$

Example 2

Use combinations to find the degrees needed to show a 35% sector in a circle graph.

35%

1. Write 35% as a combination of percents.

5% + 10% + 10% + 10% = 35%

2. Find each percent in sector degrees.

$$5\% = \frac{360}{1} \cdot \frac{5}{100} = \frac{1800}{100} = 18°$$

$$10\% = \frac{360}{1} \cdot \frac{10}{100} = \frac{3600}{100} = 36°$$

3. Find the sum of the sector degrees.

5% + 10% + 10% + 10% = 35%

18° + 36° + 36° + 36° = 126°

YOUR TURN!

Use combinations to find the degrees needed to show a 60% sector in a circle graph. Sample answers given.

60%

1. Write 60% as a combination of percents.

$$\underline{25\%} + \underline{25\%} + \underline{10\%} = \underline{60\%}$$

2. Find each percent in sector degrees.

$$25\% = \frac{360}{1} \cdot \frac{25}{100} = \frac{9000}{100} = \underline{90°}$$

$$10\% = \frac{360}{1} \cdot \frac{10}{100} = \frac{360}{100} = \underline{36°}$$

3. Show each percent in sector degrees.

$$\underline{25\%} + \underline{25\%} + \underline{10\%} = \underline{60\%}$$

$$\underline{90°} + \underline{90°} + \underline{36°} = \underline{216°}$$

Intervention Strategy   Linguistic Learners

Have students work in small groups. Tell each group to write a word problem for their peers to solve. Word problems must ask the solver to find the degree measures in a circle graph, the percent of the circle each sector represents, or both. Ask students to write an explanation of how to solve their problem and include an answer key. Allow groups to exchange their word problems, or display one problem at a time and challenge students to find the answer. Have students check their work with the group's answer key.

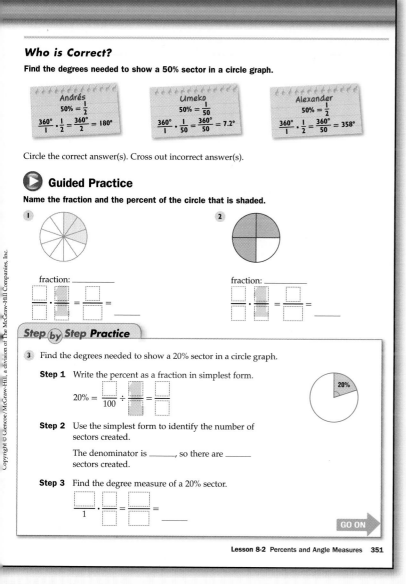

Who is Correct?

Find the degrees needed to show a 50% sector in a circle graph.

Andrés
$50\% = \frac{1}{2}$
$\frac{360°}{1} \cdot \frac{1}{2} = \frac{360°}{2} = 180°$

Umeko
$50\% = \frac{1}{50}$
$\frac{360°}{1} \cdot \frac{1}{50} = \frac{360°}{50} = 7.2°$

Alexander
$50\% = \frac{1}{2}$
$\frac{360°}{1} \cdot \frac{1}{2} = \frac{360°}{50} = 358°$

Circle the correct answer(s). Cross out incorrect answer(s).

▶ Guided Practice

Name the fraction and the percent of the circle that is shaded.

1

fraction: _____

$\dfrac{\square}{\square} \cdot \dfrac{\square}{\square} = \dfrac{\square}{\square} =$ _____

2

fraction: _____

$\dfrac{\square}{\square} \cdot \dfrac{\square}{\square} = \dfrac{\square}{\square} =$ _____

Step by Step Practice

3 Find the degrees needed to show a 20% sector in a circle graph.

Step 1 Write the percent as a fraction in simplest form.

$20\% = \dfrac{\square}{100} \div \dfrac{\square}{\square} = \dfrac{\square}{\square}$

20%

Step 2 Use the simplest form to identify the number of sectors created.

The denominator is _____, so there are _____ sectors created.

Step 3 Find the degree measure of a 20% sector.

$\dfrac{\square}{1} \cdot \dfrac{\square}{\square} = \dfrac{\square}{\square} =$ _____

GO ON

Using Manipulatives

Fraction Circles Have students practice finding percents and degree measures of shaded sectors using fraction circles. Model how to find the unit fraction for a tile and then find its degree measure.

On-Hand Manipulatives Model how to use a compass to draw a circle, or demonstrate this with two pencils, holding one point stationary and drawing the circle with the other point. Students can use these circles to make their own circular fraction tiles.

Who is Correct?
Diagnostic Teaching

• Andrés is correct. He multiplied the correct fraction by 360°.

• Umeko is incorrect. She did not multiply by the correct fraction.

• Alexander is incorrect. He used subtraction instead of division to find the sector measure.

Note This!
Consistency with Symbols Remind students to include symbols with every number when writing combinations. If percent or degrees signs are left off, calculation errors may occur or sums may become confused.

⚠️ **Common Error** *Alert*

Exercises 4 and 5 Remind students to consider the numerator when finding the degrees of a sector. They may focus on finding the degrees of each sector instead of a shaded region. Model how to check the answer by examining its reasonableness.

Math Coach Notes

Combination Computations For Exercises 7–10, encourage students to use increments of 5° or 10° to make their combinations. Explain that this makes their calculations simpler to do using mental math. Compare with an example using other increments to help students see this point.

Find the degrees needed to show each sector in a circle graph.

4
30%

$$30\% = \frac{30}{100} \div \frac{10}{10} = \frac{3}{10}$$

$$\frac{360°}{1} \cdot \frac{3}{10} = \frac{1080°}{10} = \underline{108°}$$

5
75%

$$75\% = \frac{75}{100} \div \frac{25}{25} = \frac{3}{4}$$

$$\frac{360°}{1} \cdot \frac{3}{4} = \frac{1080°}{4} = \underline{270°}$$

Use the answers to the previous exercises to complete the chart below.

6

Percent	Number of Sectors	Degree Measure of Each Sector
5	20	18°
10	10	36°
20	5	72°
25	4	90°
50	2	180°
100	1	360°

Use combinations from the values in the chart to find the degrees needed to show each sector in a circle graph.

7 15% **Sample answer:**

$$\underline{5\%} + \underline{10\%} = \underline{15\%}$$

$$\underline{18°} + \underline{36°} = \underline{54°}$$

8 85% **Sample answer:**

$$\underline{10\%} + \underline{25\%} + \underline{50\%} = \underline{85\%}$$

$$\underline{36°} + \underline{90°} + \underline{180°} = \underline{306°}$$

9 45% **Sample answer:**

$$\underline{20\%} + \underline{25\%} = \underline{45\%}$$

$$\underline{72°} + \underline{90°} = \underline{162°}$$

10 65% **Sample answer:**

$$\underline{5\%} + \underline{10\%} + \underline{50\%} = \underline{65\%}$$

$$\underline{18°} + \underline{36°} + \underline{180°} = \underline{234°}$$

Are They Getting It?

Check students' understanding of percents and angle measures by writing these problems on the board. Ask them to point out incorrect answers and explain their reasoning.

1. 35% of a circle graph equals 136°.

This is incorrect. 360° • 0.35 = 126°

2. $68\% = \frac{17}{25} = 0.68$ This is correct.

3. 50% of a circle graph is shaded, so this sector measures 50°.

This is incorrect. 360° • 0.50 = 180°

Math Coach Notes

Sum of Degrees Remind students how to check for calculation errors. The sum of percents in a circle graph is 100, while the sum of degrees equals 360°. Model how to check for computation errors by adding the percents and degrees columns in the chart.

Common Error *Alert*

Question Format Note to students that in Exercise 11 they are told to find the degree measure of each sector via a word sentence. In Exercise 12 they are asked the degree measure via a question. Students will find both formats on standardized tests.

Problem-Solving Strategies
- ☐ Use a table.
- ☐ Draw a diagram.
- ☐ Use logical reasoning.
- ☑ Use a formula.
- ☐ Work backward.

11 ELECTIONS Nita is writing an article on the recent election of the student body president. She includes a circle graph that shows how each class contributed to the voting. Of the votes cast, 30% were by 6th graders, 45% by 7th graders, and the rest by 8th graders. Find the degree measure of each sector in the circle graph.

Understand Read the problem. Write what you know.

The circle must show __30%__ for 6th graders, __45%__ for 7th graders, and __25%__ for 8th graders.

Plan Pick a strategy. One strategy is to use a formula. Use the decimal form of each percent to find the number of degrees in each sector.

Solve 6th graders: $360° \cdot$ __30%__ $= 360° \cdot$ __0.30__ $=$ __108°__

7th graders: $360° \cdot$ __45%__ $= 360° \cdot$ __0.45__ $=$ __162°__

8th graders: $360° \cdot$ __25%__ $= 360° \cdot$ __0.25__ $=$ __90°__

Check The sum of the degree measures should equal 360°.

__108°__ + __162°__ + __90°__ = __360°__

12 SURVEYS The eighth grade students voted on their choices for a class trip. The circle graph shows their choices. What is the degree measure of each sector in the circle graph?

Check off each step.

Class Trip

Mitchell Museum of Art 30%
Roller Coaster Kingdom 60%
Museum of History 10%

✔ Understand: I underlined key words.

✔ Plan: To solve the problem, I will __use a formula__

✔ Solve: The answer is __Roller Coaster Kingdom: 216°,__
__Mitchell Museum of Art: 108°, Museum of History: 36°__

✔ Check: I checked my answer by __adding the degrees of each sector__.

GO ON

Lesson 8-2 Percents and Angle Measures 353

Intervention Strategy   Auditory Learners

Tell students to work in pairs. Each pair should use index cards to make a deck of percent cards. On each card, students write a percent in increments of 5% up to 100%. Have students shuffle their deck of cards and take turns drawing a percent card. Each student should explain how to determine the number of sectors in a circle graph for each percent. Students should also find the degree measure of each sector. Students can use these cards to create combinations and number patterns for a drawn percent.

Odd/Even Assignments

Exercises 15–21 are structured so that students practice the same concepts whether they are assigned the odd or even problems.

In-Class Assignment

Have students complete Exercises 15, 17, 20, 21, and 24 to ensure that they understand the concept.

13 **LOGOS** Hi-Five Furniture wants to design a logo using a circle with 5 sectors of equal size. What percentage of the circle will each sector represent? What is the degree measure of each sector?

Each sector represents $\frac{1}{5}$ or $\frac{20}{100}$ of the circle. $\frac{20}{100} = 20\%$, so each sector is 20% of the circle. The degree measure of a 20% sector is 72°.

14 **Reflect** A 5% sector of a circle has a degree measure of 18°. How can you use this information to find the degree measure of a 25% sector?

Sample answer: Think: $5 + 5 + 5 + 5 + 5 = 25$ To find the degree measure of a 25% sector add the degree measure of a 5% sector 5 times.

$18° + 18° + 18° + 18° + 18° = 90°$, so the degree measure of a 25% sector is 90°.

▶ Skills, Concepts, and Problem Solving

Name the fraction and the percent of the circle that is shaded.

15

fraction: $\frac{7}{10}$

$\frac{7}{10} \cdot \frac{10}{10} = \frac{70}{100}$ ___70%___

16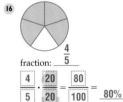

fraction: $\frac{4}{5}$

$\frac{4}{5} \cdot \frac{20}{20} = \frac{80}{100}$ ___80%___

Find the degrees needed to show each sector in a circle graph.

17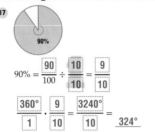

$90\% = \frac{90}{100} \div \frac{10}{10} = \frac{9}{10}$

$\frac{360°}{1} \cdot \frac{9}{10} = \frac{3240°}{10}$ ___324°___

18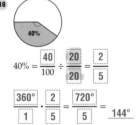

$40\% = \frac{40}{100} \div \frac{20}{20} = \frac{2}{5}$

$\frac{360°}{1} \cdot \frac{2}{5} = \frac{720°}{5} =$ ___144°___

Math Challenge

Favorite Music A survey of 500 eighth grade students reported their favorite kind of music. Use the information in the table to find the percent of responses, and the degree measure in a circle graph needed to display each survey answer.

Genre	Number of Votes	Percent of Responses	Degree Measure
Country	175	35%	126°
Rock	200	40%	144°
Hip Hop	75	15%	54°
Alternative	50	10%	36°

Use the chart from Exercise 6 to find the degrees needed to show each sector.

19 35% Sample answer:

$\underline{25\%}$ + $\underline{10\%}$ = $\underline{35\%}$

$\underline{90°}$ + $\underline{36°}$ = $\underline{126°}$

20 80% Sample answer:

$\underline{5\%}$ + $\underline{25\%}$ + $\underline{50\%}$ = $\underline{80\%}$

$\underline{18°}$ + $\underline{90°}$ + $\underline{180°}$ = $\underline{288°}$

Solve.

21 SUMMER SURVEY Mary Beth surveyed 250 students about their favorite summer vacation activity. Complete the table and find the degree measure in a circle graph needed to display each survey answer.

Activity	Responses	Degree Measure
Family Vacation	20%	72°
Outdoor Activities	45%	162°
Sleeping In	35%	126°

Vocabulary Check Write the vocabulary word that completes each sentence.

22 A(n) ____sector____ is a pie-shaped section in a circle.

23 The ___simplest form___ of $\frac{25}{100}$ is $\frac{1}{4}$.

24 Writing in Math Explain how you could use subtraction and commonly known percents to find the degree value of a 70% sector.

Sample answer: The degree measure of 75% sector is 270°. The degree measure of a 5% sector is 18°. Subtract these values. 270° − 18° = 252° A 70% sector has a degree measure of 252°.

 Spiral Review

Solve. (Lesson 8-1, p. 342)

25 CHARITY Maxwell earned $878.00 this month. He has decided to give 10% of his earnings to a local charity. How much money will he donate?

0.10 · 878 = 87.80; He will donate $87.80 to charity.

STOP

Ticket Out The Door

Percents to Degrees Write 95% on the board. Tell students to find the degrees needed to show this sector in a circle graph. As students approach the classroom door to exit, alternate asking them to name the equivalent simplified fraction or the number of degrees of this sector.

---

4 Assess

See It, Do It, Say It, Write It

Step 1 Write 10% on the board.

Step 2 Tell students to find the number of 10% sectors in a circle graph and how many would be shaded to represent a 10% sector. Then they should determine the degree measure of the shaded sector. 10; 1; 36°

Step 3 Ask students to work in pairs. Have students discuss how they found each part of their answer.

Step 4 Have students work alone to write an explanation of how they determined each part of their answer. Encourage students to use correct vocabulary terms and clear language in their explanations.

Looking Ahead: Pre-Teach

Interpret Circle Graphs In the next lesson, students will learn how to interpret circle graphs.

Example

A circle graph shows the results from a survey of 150 pet owners. The dog sector is 42% of the circle. The cat sector is 40%. The hamster sector is 8%. The other pets sector is 10%. How many people own hamsters?

$150 \times 0.08 = 12$

Twelve people of the 150 surveyed own hamsters.

Have students try each exercise below.

1. How many of those surveyed were cat owners? 60

2. How many of those surveyed were dog owners? 63

Formative Assessment

Use the Progress Check to assess students' mastery of the previous lessons. Have students review the lesson indicated for the problems they answered incorrectly.

Odd/Even Assignments

Exercises are structured so that students practice the same concepts whether they are assigned the odd or even problems.

Common Error Alert

Exercises 5 and 6 When multiplying fractions with greater numbers, encourage students to reduce any of the factors. As a result, they will be multiplying smaller numbers and will be less likely to make computational errors.

Chapter 8 Progress Check 1 (Lessons 8-1 and 8-2)

Identify the percent that is modeled.

1

fraction: $\dfrac{4}{5}$

fraction with a denominator of 100:

$$\dfrac{4 \cdot \boxed{20}}{5 \cdot \boxed{20}} = \dfrac{\boxed{20}}{100}$$

decimal: 0.80

percent: 80%

2

fraction: $1\dfrac{1}{4}$ or $\dfrac{5}{4}$

fraction with a denominator of 100:

$$\dfrac{5 \cdot \boxed{25}}{4 \cdot \boxed{25}} = \dfrac{\boxed{125}}{100}$$

decimal: 1.25

percent: 125%

Find the missing value. Round your answer to the nearest hundredth.

3 What is 7% of 210?

$\underline{0.07} \cdot \underline{210} = \underline{14.7}$

4 What is 23% of 241?

$\underline{0.23} \cdot \underline{241} = \underline{55.43}$

Find the degrees needed to show each sector in a circle graph.

5 70%

$70\% = \dfrac{70}{100} \div \dfrac{\boxed{10}}{\boxed{10}} = \dfrac{7}{\boxed{10}}$

$\dfrac{360°}{1} \cdot \dfrac{\boxed{7}}{\boxed{10}} = \dfrac{\boxed{2520°}}{\boxed{10}} = \underline{252°}$

6 50%

$50\% = \dfrac{50}{100} \div \dfrac{\boxed{50}}{\boxed{50}} = \dfrac{1}{\boxed{2}}$

$\dfrac{360°}{1} \cdot \dfrac{\boxed{1}}{\boxed{2}} = \dfrac{\boxed{360°}}{\boxed{2}} = \underline{180°}$

Solve.

7 **FINANCIAL LITERACY** Mr. Matthews had $3,000 in his savings account. If he withdrew 25%, how much did he withdraw?

$\underline{3{,}000 \cdot 0.25 = 750;\ \text{He withdrew } \$750.00.}$

356 Chapter 8 Percents and Circle Graphs

Data-Driven Decision Making

Students missing Exercises . . .	Have trouble with . . .	Should review and practice . . .
1–2	identifying the fraction and percent modeled.	**SSG** Lesson 8-1, p. 342 **CRM** Skills Practice, p. A166
3–4	finding the missing value in a percent problem.	**SSG** Lesson 8-1, p. 342 **CRM** Skills Practice, p. A166
5–6	finding the number of degrees in a sector.	**SSG** Lesson 8-2, p. 349 **CRM** Skills Practice, p. A170
7	solving word problems involving percents.	**CRM** Problem-Solving Practice, pp. A167 and A171

Lesson 8-3 Interpret Circle Graphs

KEY Concept

One way to represent data is in a **circle graph**. A circle graph has pie-shaped sections called **sectors**. Sectors can be used to compare the parts of a whole.

The circle graph shows the favorite sports of 200 students at Lincoln Middle School.

The whole circle represents the total of all the data, or 100% of the data. The sectors of the graph equal 100%.

Favorite Sports

Basketball 30%
Football 45%
Baseball 25%

$$45\% + 25\% + 30\% = 100\%$$

The table shows the relationship between the data that was collected and the percent in the chart.

Sport	Percent	Fractions	Number of Students
Football	45%	$\frac{45}{100} = \frac{90}{200}$	90
Baseball	25%	$\frac{25}{100} = \frac{50}{200}$	50
Basketball	30%	$\frac{30}{100} = \frac{60}{200}$	60

The percent equation can also be used to find the number of students who chose each sport.

$$\text{percent} \cdot \text{whole} = \text{part}$$
$$0.45 \cdot 200 = 90$$

The equation above shows that 90 students, out of 200, represents 45% of those surveyed.

VOCABULARY

circle graph
a graph used to compare parts of a whole; the circle represents the whole and is separated into parts of a whole

data
information, often numerical, which is gathered for statistical purposes

degree
the most common unit of measure for angles

percent
a ratio that compares a number to 100

sector
pie-shaped sections in a circle graph

To interpret the information in the circle graph above, it is important to know that 200 students were surveyed. This information is needed to find the number of responses to each choice.

GO ON

Intervention Strategy
Interpersonal Learners

Class Trip Choices on a Circle Graph Ask students to work in small groups. Draw the circle graph below and write the following problem on the board. Have students examine and discuss the graph together in their groups. Then tell groups to write 7–8 questions for the graph, including answers to their questions. Have groups share their questions with the class and answer them together.

Cedarville Middle School surveyed 200 eighth-grade students about where they would like to go for their class trip. The circle graph shows the percentage of each choice.

Class Trip Choices

Science Center 9%
History Museum 15%
City Hall 18%
State Capitol 31%
Art Museum 27%

Lesson Planner

Objective Interpret data in a circle graph.

Vocabulary circle graph, data, degree, percent, sector

Materials/Manipulatives fraction circles, calculators

Chapter Resource Masters

- CRM Vocabulary and English Language Development (p. A173)
- CRM Skills Practice (p. A174)
- CRM Problem-Solving Practice (p. A175)
- CRM Homework Practice (p. A176)

① Introduce

Vocabulary

Reviewing Terms Discuss how to examine a *circle graph* by looking at each of its parts. Review the relationship between fractions, decimals, percents, and *degrees*. Reinforce that each *sector* in a circle graph is a part of the whole.

② Teach

Key Concept

Foundational Skills and Concepts After students have read through the Key Concept box, have them try these exercises.

1. What is the sum of the percents in a circle graph? 100%

2. If given the percent of a sector, how do you find the number of data for that section? Multiply the decimal form of the percent by the total number of data collected.

3. Describe the relationship between fractions and the total number of data collected in a circle graph. The total number of data collected is the denominator in each fraction representing a sector in a circle graph.

Champion Wireless surveyed 200 customers about their favorite cell phone colors. Which two colors together were chosen as often as silver?

Cell Phone Colors

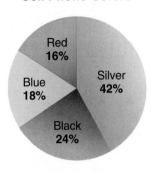

Red 16%
Silver 42%
Blue 18%
Black 24%

1. What percent of the cell phones were silver? 42%

2. Which two categories equal 42% when added together?

Black + Red = 24% + 16% = 40%
Red + Blue = 16% + 18% = 34%
Black + Blue = 24% + 18% = 42%

3. Black and blue together were chosen as often as silver.

Math Coach Notes

Examine, then Answer To help students fully interpret a circle graph, tell them to examine the graph first before reading the questions. Model how to read the title and the label for each section. Encourage students to figure out what the graph is displaying before working with any equations. This may help students better understand the questions about the graph.

Example 1

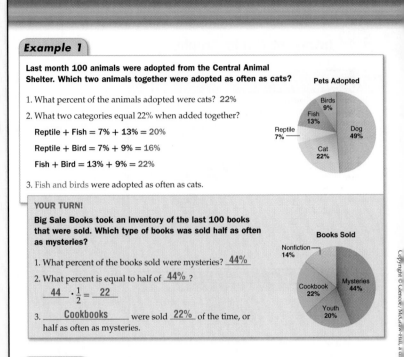

Last month 100 animals were adopted from the Central Animal Shelter. Which two animals together were adopted as often as cats?

Pets Adopted

1. What percent of the animals adopted were cats? 22%

2. What two categories equal 22% when added together?

Reptile + Fish = 7% + 13% = 20%
Reptile + Bird = 7% + 9% = 16%
Fish + Bird = 13% + 9% = 22%

3. Fish and birds were adopted as often as cats.

YOUR TURN!

Big Sale Books took an inventory of the last 100 books that were sold. Which type of books was sold half as often as mysteries?

Books Sold

1. What percent of the books sold were mysteries? _44%_

2. What percent is equal to half of _44%_ ?

$\underline{44} \cdot \frac{1}{2} = \underline{22}$

3. _Cookbooks_ were sold _22%_ of the time, or half as often as mysteries.

Example 2

Coconut Grove Consignment Shop sold 200 items of clothing last month. How many items were blue jeans?

Clothing Sold

1. What percent of the items were blue jeans? 43%

2. There were 200 total items sold.   This is the "whole."

3. Use the percent equation to solve.

percent • whole = part of clothing

43% • 200 items = part of clothing   Remember: 43% is the same as 0.43.

0.43 • 200 items = 86 blue jeans

Vick's Vehicles took an inventory of the last 400 new cars sold. How many cars had leather seats?

1. What percent of the new cars had leather seats? 21%

2. There were 400 new cars sold.

3. Use the percent equation to solve.

percent • whole = part

21% • 400 cars = part of cars sold

0.21 • 400 = 84 cars had leather seats

New Car Options

Satellite Radio 17%
Power Package 38%
Leather Seats 21%
Towing Hitch 24%

YOUR TURN!

Julieta spent $50 yesterday. How many dollars did Julieta spend on gasoline?

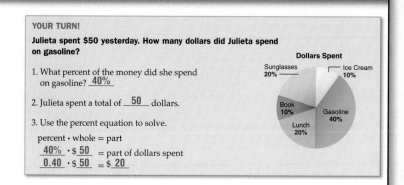

Dollars Spent

1. What percent of the money did she spend on gasoline? __40%__

2. Julieta spent a total of __50__ dollars.

3. Use the percent equation to solve.

percent · whole = part

__40%__ · $ __50__ = part of dollars spent

__0.40__ · $ __50__ = $ __20__

Who is Correct?

Refer to the circle graph above titled "Dollars Spent." How many dollars did Julieta spend on a book? Show your work.

Santos
percent · whole = part
0.10 · $100 = $10

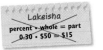

Lakeisha
percent · whole = part
0.30 · $50 = $15

Carmen
percent · whole = part
0.10 · $50 = $5

Guided Practice

The circle graph below shows the number of each type of home of 100 middle school teachers. Use the circle graph to answer the questions below.

ⅰ What is the title of the graph?

   __Home Sweet Home__

2 What type of home do the greatest number of teachers live in?

   __Apartment__

3 What percent of teachers do not live in a townhouse?

   __85%__

Home Sweet Home

Condo 5%
Townhouse 15%
Apartment 45%
House 35%

GO ON

Lesson 8-3 Interpret Circle Graphs **359**

Using Manipulatives

Fraction Circles Use fraction circles to practice finding the degrees needed for shaded sectors. This will reinforce the relationship between fractions, percents, and sectors.

On-Hand Manipulatives Ask students to check their work using calculators. Model how to examine an answer for its reasonableness.

Who *is Correct?*
Diagnostic Teaching

- Santos is incorrect. Julieta spent 10% of $50, not 10% of $100.

- Lakeisha is incorrect. She used the wrong percent for her equation.

- Carmen is correct. She multiplied the right percent correctly.

Math Coach Notes

Word Clues As students read a word problem, remind them to watch for word clues. Explain that emphasizing these words or phrases while reading can help students figure out the operation needed to solve the problem. Point out how capitalized or italicized words draw attention to which pieces of data to focus on or ignore.

Step by Step Practice

4 At the county fair, 200 votes were cast for three different peach pie makers. The person with the most votes won the blue ribbon. How many votes did Oda receive?

Blue Ribbon Results

Step 1 Oda received ____45%____ of the vote.

Step 2 There were ____200____ total votes cast.

Step 3 Use the percent equation to solve.

percent • whole = part

____0.45____ • ____200 votes____ = ____90 votes____

Step 4 Use division to check your work.
____90 ÷ 200____ = ____0.45 or 45%____

Big Sale Movies took an inventory of the last 100 movies that were sold. Use the circle graph to answer the questions below.

Movies Sold

5 What type of movie was sold half as often as action films?

What percent of the movies sold were action movies?

____36%____

What percent is equal to half of 36%?

____36%____ • $\frac{1}{2}$ = ____18%____

<u>Children's</u> movies were sold half as often as action movies.

The Fighting Falcons scored 100 points in last week's basketball game. Use the circle graph to answer the questions below.

Game Points

6 What type of shot was made twice as often as 3-point shots?

What percent of the points scored were from 3-point shots?

____24%____

What percent is two times 24%?

____24%____ • 2 = ____48%____

____2-point____ shots were made twice as often as 3-point shots.

360 Chapter 8 Percents and Circle Graphs

Are They Getting It? ?

Check students' understanding of interpreting circle graphs by writing these problems on the board. Ask them to point out incorrect answers and explain their reasoning.

1. Grape was the most popular choice of jelly bean. This is incorrect. Cherry has the largest sector and percent.

2. Lemon and licorice together were chosen as often as grape. This is correct. Lemon (13%) + Licorice (18%) = Grape (31%)

3. If 200 students were surveyed, 38 students voted for cherry. This is incorrect. 38% • 200 = 76 students

Favorite Jelly Bean Flavors

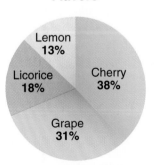

Step by Step Problem-Solving Practice

Solve.

7 DANCES Aisha is helping to plan the next school dance. In order to decide on a theme, she asks students which theme they like best: "70s Disco," "Barn Dance," or "Rock the Night."

A total of 300 students voted. How many students voted for the Barn Dance theme?

Understand Read the problem and review the circle graph. Write what you know.

Favorite Dance Theme

There were ___300___ votes.

"Rock the Night" is the favorite of ___40%___ of students.

"70s Disco" is the favorite of ___35%___ of students.

"Barn Dance" is the favorite of ___25%___ of students.

Plan Pick a strategy. One strategy is to make a table.

Solve Fill in the table.

percent of votes · total votes = votes for each theme

Theme	Rock the Night	70s Disco	Barn Dance
Percent	40%	35%	25%
Votes	120 votes	105 votes	75 votes

Check Add the votes for each theme. Does the sum equal total votes for the dance?

Problem-Solving Strategies
- ☐ Draw a diagram.
- ☑ Make a table.
- ☐ Work backward.
- ☐ Solve a simpler problem.
- ☐ Look for a pattern.

GO ON

Lesson 8-3 Interpret Circle Graphs **361**

⚠ Common Error Alert

Total Data Collected Students may overlook the total number of data collected, which will affect their computation. Have students circle or note the total number in a way that will draw their attention when they begin calculating the number of responses for each sector. Remind them that the sum of the number of responses must equal the total data collected.

True of False Statements Tell students to work in pairs. Ask them to interpret the following circle graph and determine if each sentence is true or false. If a statement is false, have students explain the incorrect part. Discuss the answers together as a class.

Carla's Casuals took an inventory of the last 300 pairs of shoes that were sold.

Shoes Sold

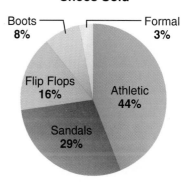

1. The store sold more athletic shoes than any other type of shoe. true
2. The store sold 26% more sandals than formal shoes. true
3. Flip flops and athletic shoes accounted for 75% of the total sales. false; flip flops (16%) + athletic shoes (44%) = 60% of total sales
4. Sandals sold more than flip flops, boots, and formal shoes combined. true
5. Of the last 300 pairs sold, 87 of them were boots. false; 24 pairs were boots, 0.08 · 300 = 24
6. The store sold 3 pairs of formal shoes. false; 0.03 · 300 = 9 pairs
7. Sandals did NOT sell twice as much as flip flops. true
8. The store sold 96 more pairs of athletic shoes than flip flops. false; athletic shoes = 0.44 · 300 = 132; flip flops = 0.16 · 300 = 48; 132 − 48 = 84 pairs

Common Error *Alert*

Exercises 11 and 21 Caution students to watch for the use of "NOT" in questions. Sometimes students will skip over this word and use the very data they are asked to ignore. Practice with Exercise 11, emphasizing the not and then restating the question for the data students *need* to use to answer the question. Have students mimic this strategy with Exercise 21.

---

8 **PARTIES** Colin's mom plans children's birthday parties. Last year she planned <u>400 parties</u>. <u>Use the circle graph</u> to find the number of <u>Petting Zoo</u> parties she planned.

Party Themes

Check off each step.

✔ Understand: I underlined key words.

✔ Plan: To solve this problem, I will ___**make a table**___.

✔ Solve: The answer is ___**24**___.

✔ Check: I checked my answer by ___**working backward**___.

CAFETERIA The school cafeteria manager wanted to know what vegetables to serve students. She asked 200 eighth graders to name their favorite vegetables. Use the circle graph to answer the questions below.

Favorite Vegetables

9 How many students chose broccoli as their favorite?

   0.22 • 200 = 44; 44 students

10 How many students chose peas or carrots as their favorites?

   10% + 42% = 52%; 0.52 • 200 = 104; 104 students

11 How many students did not choose green beans as their favorite?

   100% − 18% = 82%; 0.82 • 200 = 164; 164 students

12 How many students did not choose corn or carrots as their favorite?

   42% + 8% = 50%; 0.50 • 200 = 100; 100 students

13 **Reflect** Explain how you can use the idea that 200 equals 2 times 100 to find the number of students who chose broccoli as their favorite vegetable.

   Since 200 equals 2 times 100, you can think of the number of votes as 2 times the

   percent. Since 22% of the students chose broccoli, you can multiply 22 • 2 to

   find the number that voted for broccoli. 22 • 2 = 44; 44 students

---

Math Challenge

Have students read the following word problem, determine the missing data, and complete the table.

Five hundred eighth grade students were surveyed about which elective course they would like to see added to the curriculum.

Elective	Percent	Number of Votes
Orchestra	9%	45
Photography	47%	235
School Newspaper	15%	75
Spanish	29%	145

Assignments

Assign Exercises 14–24 so that students practice all the concepts presented in this lesson.

In-Class Assignment

Have students complete Exercises 14, 17, and 24 to ensure that they understand the concept.

▶ Skills, Concepts, and Problem Solving

The circle graph at the right shows the percentage of tickets given to each group for a high school football championship. Use the circle graph to answer the questions below.

Championship Tickets

Open Purchase 10%
Host 20%
East 35%
West 35%

14 What is the title of the graph?

___Championship Tickets___

15 What type of ticket will be sold the least?

___Open Purchase___

16 What percent of tickets will not go to the East or West division teams?

___30%___

Mr. Leapley used a circle graph to compare the number of students that played each instrument in the band. There are 200 students in the band. Use the circle graph to answer the questions below.

Instruments Played

Drums 21%
Flute 36%
Saxophone 12%
Clarinet 17%
Trumpet 9%
Trombone 5%

17 What type of instrument is played by four times as many band members as the trumpet?

What percent of the band members play trumpet?

___9%___

What percent is equal to four times 9%?

___9%___ · 4 = ___36%___

The ___flute___ is played by four times as many band members.

18 Which two instruments are played by as many band members as the clarinet?

What two percents equal ___17%___?

___12%___ + ___5%___ = ___17%___

The ___saxophone___ and the ___trombone___ are played by as many members as the clarinet.

The clarinet is played by ___17%___ of the band members.

GO ON

English Language Learner Strategy

Use Exercises 19–21 to discuss Field Day. Have students share their favorite events and activities. Ask students to compare this day to any similar native celebrations or traditions and share them with classmates.

(4) Assess

See It, Do It, Say It, Write It

Step 1 Draw the following circle graph on the board. Tell students 200 people were interviewed about the types of television shows they watched most.

TV Shows Watched

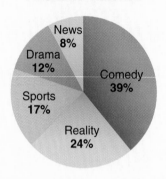

Step 2 Have students interpret the data in the circle graph. Then tell them to determine the number of responses each category received.

Step 3 Ask students to work with a partner. Have students discuss and interpret the circle graph together. They should explain how they found the number of responses for each category.

Step 4 Have students work alone to write their evaluations of the circle graph. Encourage students to write statements about the graph, using the information they obtained from their calculations.

Looking Ahead: Pre-Teach

Create Circle Graphs In the next lesson, students will learn how to put the skills of this chapter together to make circle graphs.

FIELD DAY MacMurray Middle School is planning the field day events. Fifty eighth graders were asked to name their favorite event. Use the circle graph to answer the questions below.

Favorite Field Day Event

19 How many students chose the long jump as their favorite event?

$0.18 \cdot 50 = 9$; 9 students

20 How many students chose the 100-Meter Race or the 400-Meter Relay as their favorites?

$14\% + 36\% = 50\%$; $0.50 \cdot 50 = 25$; 25 students

21 How many students did not choose the Field Course Challenge as their favorite?

$100\% - 32\% = 68\%$; $0.68 \cdot 50 = 34$; 34 students

AQUARIUMS Centerburg Aquarium has 500 animals. The circle graph compares the number of each type of animal. Use the circle graph to answer the questions below.

Aquarium Animals

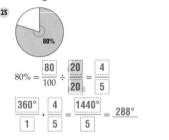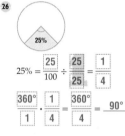

22 How many saltwater fish are at the aquarium?

$0.61 \cdot 500 = 305$; 305 saltwater fish

23 How many dolphins and sharks are at the aquarium?

$14\% + 8\% = 22\%$; $0.22 \cdot 500 = 110$; 110 dolphins and sharks

24 How many animals are not otters?

$100\% - 12\% = 88\%$; $0.88 \cdot 500 = 440$; 440 animals

▶ Spiral Review

Find the degrees needed to show each sector in a circle graph. *(Lesson 8-2, p. 349)*

25

$80\% = \dfrac{80}{100} \div \dfrac{20}{20} = \dfrac{4}{5}$

$\dfrac{360°}{1} \cdot \dfrac{4}{5} = \dfrac{1440°}{5} = 288°$

26

$25\% = \dfrac{25}{100} \div \dfrac{25}{25} = \dfrac{1}{4}$

$\dfrac{360°}{1} \cdot \dfrac{1}{4} = \dfrac{360°}{4} = 90°$

STOP

Ticket Out the Door

Interpreting Data Draw the following circle graph on the board. Tell students 100 elementary school teachers were asked what their favorite subject was when they were in school. As students approach the classroom door to exit, have them state one interpretative sentence from their analysis of the graph.

Favorite Subject

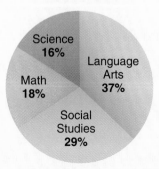

Lesson 8-4 Create Circle Graphs

KEY Concept

To create a circle graph, it can be helpful to use data from a table. The table shows the relationship between the data and the degree measures of the sectors in a circle graph.

Favorite Vacation Spots

Vacation Spots	Number of People	Percent Value	Degree Measure
Beach	15	15%	$0.15 \cdot 360 = 54°$
Camping	10	10%	$0.10 \cdot 360 = 36°$
Water Park	30	30%	$0.30 \cdot 360 = 108°$
Amusement Park	35	35%	$0.35 \cdot 360 = 126°$
Grand Canyon	10	10%	$0.10 \cdot 360 = 36°$
Total	**100**	**100%**	**360°**

To make the graph, start by dividing the circle into 10 equal pieces. Each mark represents 36°, or 10% of the circle.

Shade and label each sector working around the circle clockwise. To show 5%, cut a 10% section in half.

Favorite Vacation Spots

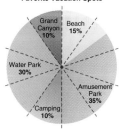

You can build a ratio table that provides a quick reference for many common percents and their degree measures.

GO ON

Lesson 8-4 Create Circle Graphs **365**

VOCABULARY

center
the given point from which all points on a circle are the same distance

circle graph
a graph used to compare parts of a whole; the circle represents the whole and is separated into parts of a whole

data
information, often numerical, which is gathered for statistical purposes

degree
the most common unit of measure for angles

percent
a ratio that compares a number to 100

sector
pie-shaped sections in a circle graph

Lesson Notes

Lesson 8-4

Lesson Planner

Objective   Display data in a circle graph.

Vocabulary   center, circle graph, data, degree, percent, sector

Materials/Manipulatives   compasses, protractors, calculators, fraction circles

Chapter Resource Masters

- CRM Vocabulary and English Language Development (p. A177)
- CRM Skills Practice (p. A178)
- CRM Problem-Solving Practice (p. A179)
- CRM Homework Practice (p. A180)

---

1 Introduce

Vocabulary

Relationships   Reinforce the relationships among fractions, decimals, and percents. Review the term *denominator* and explain its relevance to the total data collected in a survey. Then review the terms for the parts of a circle graph.

---

2 Teach

Key Concept

Foundational Skills and Concepts   After students have read through the Key Concept box, have them try these exercises.

1. What is the sum of the degrees in a circle graph? 360°

2. A circle graph is divided into 5 equal-sized sectors. How many degrees does each sector represent? 72°

3. One sector in a circle graph represents 40% of the data collected. Explain how to find the degree measure of this sector. Multiply 40% by 360° to find the degrees. $0.40 \cdot 360 = 144°$

Intervention Strategy   Logical Learners

Surveying Write the following data on the board. Tell students the table shows the results of a survey of 4,000 eighth-graders regarding the main language spoken at home. Have students work in pairs. Tell them to practice explaining how to find the decimal and percent values from the number surveyed. Then have students explain how to find the degree measure of each sector if this data were displayed in a circle graph. Discuss the answers together as a class when the pairs are finished.

Language	Number Surveyed	Decimal Value	Percent Value	Degree Measure
Chinese	600	$600 \div 4,000 = 0.15$	15%	54°
English	1,800	$1,800 \div 4,000 = 0.45$	45%	162°
German	200	$200 \div 4,000 = 0.05$	5%	18°
Italian	400	$400 \div 4,000 = 0.10$	10%	36°
Spanish	1,000	$1,000 \div 4,000 = 0.25$	25%	90°
Totals	**4,000**	**1.00**	**100%**	**360°**

Lesson 8-4 Create Circle Graphs **365**

English Learner Strategy

Circle Graphs in the Workplace Discuss careers in which compasses, protractors, or circle graphs are used. Encourage students to think of jobs where knowing how to use these tools and skills would be useful. Some examples may include advertising, finance, construction, architecture, politics, etc. Have students share when or where in their lives they have seen circle graphs outside of school, and what kinds of information the graphs displayed.

Example 1

Complete the table to show the decimal value, the percent, and the degree measure for each type of lunch.

Favorite Lunch	Number of People	Decimal Value	Percent Value	Degree Measure
Spaghetti	375	375 ÷ 1,500 = 0.25	25%	90°
Enchiladas	225	225 ÷ 1,500 = 0.15	15%	54°
Sloppy Joes	525	525 ÷ 1,500 = 0.35	35%	126°
Taco Salad	225	225 ÷ 1,500 = 0.15	15%	54°
Veggie Burgers	150	150 ÷ 1,500 = 0.10	10%	36°
Total	**1,500**	**1.00**	**100%**	**360°**

1. To write the decimal, divide the number for each lunch choice by the total surveyed.

2. Find the equivalent percent value for each decimal.

3. Change all percent values to degree measures.
   For example, 25% of 360° = 90°.

YOUR TURN!

Complete the table to show the decimal value, the percent, and the degree measure for each of Javier's income sources.

Source of Income	Dollars Earned	Decimal Value	Percent Value	Degree Measure
Babysitting	$555			
Summer Job	$1,850			
After School Tutoring	$1,110			
Holiday Gifts	$185			
Total	**3,700**	**1.00**	**100%**	**360°**

1. To write the decimal, divide the number for each source of income by the total dollars earned.

2. Find the equivalent percent value for each decimal.

3. Change all percent values to degree measures.

366 Chapter 8 Percents and Circle Graphs

Copyright © Glencoe/McGraw-Hill, a division of The McGraw-Hill Companies, Inc.

Additional *Example 1*

Complete the table to show the decimal value, the percent, and the degree measure for each type of healthy lifestyle habit.

Habit	Number of Students	Decimal Value	Percent Value	Degree Measure
Daily Exercise	84	84 ÷ 280 = 0.30	30%	108°
Balanced Diet	98	98 ÷ 280 = 0.35	35%	126°
Enough Sleep	70	70 ÷ 280 = 0.25	25%	90°
Stress Management	28	28 ÷ 280 = 0.10	10%	36°
Total Check	**280**	**1.00**	**100%**	**360°**

1. To write the decimal, divide the number for each habit by the total surveyed.

2. Find the equivalent percent value for each decimal.

3. Change all percent values to degree measures. For example, 30% of 360° = 108°.

366 Chapter 8 Percents and Circle Graphs

Example 2

Use the table in Example 1 on page 366 to create a circle graph.

1. Write a title for the graph.

2. Draw sector lines using 10% marks as guides.

3. Label the sectors of the circle for each category.

4. Color each sector a different color. Write the percent value in each sector.

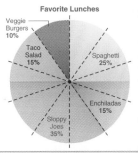

Favorite Lunches

Veggie Burgers 10%
Taco Salad 15%
Spaghetti 25%
Enchiladas 15%
Sloppy Joes 35%

YOUR TURN!

Use the table from Your Turn on page 366 to create a circle graph.

1. Write a title for the graph.

2. Draw sector lines using 10% marks as guides.

3. Label the sectors of the circle for each source of income.

4. Color each sector a different color. Write the percent value in each sector.

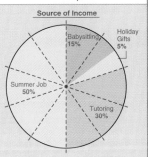

Source of Income

Babysitting 15%
Holiday Gifts 5%
Summer Job 50%
Tutoring 30%

Who is Correct?

A survey of 200 eighth graders, found that 56% of the students had a summer job last year. How many students had a summer job? Show your work.

Wesley
percent · whole = part
0.56 · 200 = 112
112 students

Taina
percent · whole = part
0.56 · 100 = 56
56 students

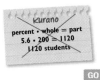

Kurano
percent · whole = part
5.6 · 200 = 1120
1120 students

GO ON

Additional *Example 2*

Use the table in Additional Example 1 on page 366 to create a circle graph.

1. Write a title for the graph.

2. Draw sector lines using 10° marks as guides.

3. Label the sectors of the circle for each "Habit" category.

4. Color each sector a different color. Write the percent value in each sector.

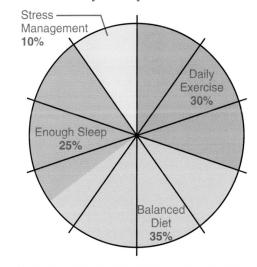

Healthy Lifestyle Habits

Stress Management 10%
Daily Exercise 30%
Enough Sleep 25%
Balanced Diet 35%

Who *is Correct?*
Diagnostic Teaching

• Wesley is correct. He multiplied the correct percent properly.

• Taina is incorrect. She used the wrong number for the whole in her equation.

• Kurano is incorrect. He did not move the decimal point over correctly in his equation.

③ Practice

Using Manipulatives

Compass   Model how to use a compass to draw a circle graph. Have students practice holding the point stationary while using the pencil to create the circle. Tell them the point around which the circle was created is the center.

On-Hand Manipulatives   Have students use calculators to find the percents and degree measures of a set of data.

Math Coach Notes

Note the Denominator   Remind students that the denominator used to find the decimal and percent values for a set of data is the total number of data collected. Reinforce the importance of checking the totals in each column to avoid calculation errors. The number of data in each sector should always equal the total number of data.

▶ Guided Practice

Write each percent as a decimal.

1 47%

_____

2 6%

_____

3 60%

_____

4 143%

_____

5 27%

_____

6 9%

_____

7 90%

_____

8 134%

_____

Step (by) Step Practice

9 Complete the table to show the decimal value, the percent, and the degree measure for each brand of shoe sold at the Fabulous Foot Shoe Store during a recent sale.

Shoe Type	Number Sold	Decimal Value	Percent Value	Degree Measure
Tennis	210			
Skateboard	168			
Basketball	252			
Soccer Cleats	126			
Running/Walking	84			
Total	**840**	**1.00**	**100**	**360°**

Step 1   To write the decimal, divide the number of each type of shoe by the total number of shoes sold.

Step 2   Find the equivalent percent value for each decimal.

Step 3   Change all percent values to degree measures.

Intervention Strategy   Interpersonal Learners

Classroom Survey Ask students to work in small groups. Tell them to create a topic or question for a classroom survey. Have students develop the question and 4–5 answer choices. Give groups time to collect their data by asking classmates to take their surveys. Students should create a table that shows their survey results, including decimal and percent values, and degree measures. Distribute a template of a circle graph to each group. Ask students to create a graph to display the results of their surveys. Remind students to label each sector with the sector name and percent, and to include a title for their graphs. Invite groups to share their results and graphs with the class.

Copyright © Glencoe/McGraw-Hill, a division of The McGraw-Hill Companies, Inc.

Complete the table to show the decimal value, the percent, and the degree measure.

10 Mr. Chiang analyzed the types of advertisements shown on children's TV shows. His team recorded advertisements shown on one Saturday morning.

Ad Type	Number Shown	Decimal Value	Percent Value	Degree Measure
Electronic Games	140	$140 \div 400 = 0.35$	35%	126°
Breakfast Cereals	40	$40 \div 400 = 0.10$	10%	36°
Fast Food	100	$100 \div 400 = 0.25$	25%	90°
Toys	120	$120 \div 400 = 0.30$	30%	108°
Total	**400**	**1.00**	**100**	**360°**

Step by Step Problem-Solving Practice

Use the table in Exercise 10 to create a circle graph.

11 RESEARCH   Mr. Chiang has been asked to present the research findings at a regional meeting. He has decided to make a circle graph.

Problem-Solving Strategies
☐ Draw a diagram.
☑ Use a table.
☐ Work backward.
☐ Solve a simpler problem.
☐ Look for a pattern.

Understand   Read the problem. Write what you know.

Electronic Game advertisements were shown ___35%___ of the time.

Breakfast Cereal advertisements were shown ___10%___ of the time.

Fast Food advertisements were shown ___25%___ of the time.

Toy advertisements were shown ___30%___ of the time.

Ads Shown
Breakfast Cereals 10%
Toys 30%
Electronic Games 35%
Fast Food 25%

Plan   Pick a strategy. One strategy is to use a table.

Solve   The title of the graph is ___Ads Shown___.

Draw sector lines using 10% marks as guides. Label the sectors of the circle for each category.

Color each sector a different color. Write the percent value in each sector.

Check   Add the percentages for each advertisement. Does the sum equal 100%?

GO ON ▶

Note This!
Reference Table   Have students make a ratio table for their personal reference. Model how to set up a table that shows several common percents and their degree measures. As students become used to these common measures, it will be easier for them to recognize if other measures are reasonable using mental math.

Are They Getting It? ?

Check students' understanding of creating circle graphs by writing these problems on the board. Ask them to point out incorrect answers and explain their reasoning.

1. A sector of a circle graph measures 25%. If 200 people were surveyed, this portion of the graph represents 25 people. This is incorrect. 25% of 200 is 0.25 • 200, or 50 people.

2. A circle graph is divided into 15 equal-sized sectors. Therefore, each sector measures 24°. This is correct. 360° ÷ 15 = 24°

3. One sector of a circle graph represents 65% of people surveyed. This means that this sector measures 65° on the graph. This is incorrect. 65% of 360° is 0.65 • 360, or 234°.

12 SALES   The store manager at Fabulous Foot shoe store has been asked to present his sales at a store meeting. He has decided to make a <u>circle graph</u>. Use the table in Exercise 9 on page 368 to create a circle graph. Check off each step.

✔ ___ Understand: I underlined key words.

✔ ___ Plan: To solve this problem, I will ___ use a table ___

✔ ___ Solve: The answer is ___ shown below ___

✔ ___ Check: I checked my answer by ___ adding the percents ___

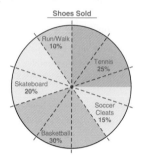

Shoes Sold

Run/Walk 10%
Tennis 25%
Skateboard 20%
Soccer Cleats 15%
Basketball 30%

13 **Reflect**   Maisie's table is missing some information. Explain how to use the known percent values to find the number of hours she spent on gymnastics last week.

Activity	Number of Hours	Decimal Value	Percent Value
Homework	15	15 ÷ 30 = 0.50	50%
Piano	3	3 ÷ 30 = 0.10	10%
Gymnastics	12	12 ÷ 30 = 0.40	40%
Totals	30	1.00	100

To find the percent value for gymnastics, subtract the sum of 50% and 10%

from 100%. Maisie spent 40% of her time on gymnastics. Then, multiply the

decimal value of 40% (0.40) by the total number of hours shown in the chart.

0.40 · 30 = 12 She spent 12 hours on gymnastics.

Math Challenge

Three hundred juniors were surveyed about their post-high school plans. Determine the missing data and complete the table.

Plan	Number Surveyed	Decimal Value	Percent Value	Degree Measure
Work Full Time	30	0.10	10%	36°
4-yr College	120	0.40	40%	144°
2-yr College	75	0.25	25%	90°
Armed Services	15	0.05	5%	18°
Not Sure	60	0.20	20%	72°
Totals	300	1.00	100%	360°

Which two plans have a combined measure of 90°? Armed Services and Not Sure

▶ Skills, Concepts, and Problem Solving

Complete the table to show the decimal value, the percent, and the degree measure.

14. Sell-A-Lot car dealership just finished their summer sales drive. The sales team recorded the sales in a table.

Vehicle Type	Number Sold	Decimal Value	Percent Value	Degree Measure
Convertible	104	$104 \div 260 = 0.40$	40%	144°
SUV	78	$78 \div 260 = 0.30$	30%	108°
Sedan	52	$52 \div 260 = 0.20$	20%	72°
Minivan	26	$26 \div 260 = 0.10$	10%	36°
Total	**260**	**1.00**	**100**	**360°**

15. **SALES** The store manager at Sell-A-Lot wants to present the sales results at the next team meeting. Use the table in Exercise 14 to create a circle graph.

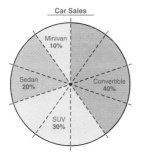

Car Sales

GO ON

! Common Error *Alert*

Exercises 14–16 Use these practice problems to reinforce the relationship between the decimal or percent value and the degree measure of a sector in a circle graph. The decimal and percent values are out of 100, while the degree measures are out of 360. Students may translate 40% to equal 40°. Remind them the wholes for each column add up to different amounts and to check their work by finding the sums of each measure.

Assignments

Assign Exercises 14–16 so that students practice all the concepts presented in this lesson.

In-Class Assignment

Have students complete Exercises 14 and 15 to ensure that they understand the concept.

See It, Do It, Say It, Write It

Recyclables Collected

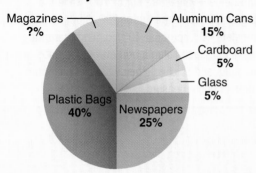

Magazines ?%

Aluminum Cans 15%

Cardboard 5%

Glass 5%

Plastic Bags 40%

Newspapers 25%

Step 1 Draw the circle graph above on the board. Tell students 50,000 items were collected in a recyclables drive.

Step 2 Have students study the graph and determine the missing percent.

Step 3 Ask students to work in pairs. Have students discuss how they found the missing percent. Then tell them to determine and then explain how to find the degree measure of each sector in the graph.

Step 4 Have students work alone to write their evaluations of the circle graph on the board. Evaluations should include how they determined the missing percent and degree measure of each sector.

Magazines, missing percent: 10%

Aluminum Cans: 54°
Cardboard: 18°
Glass: 18°
Newspapers: 90°
Plastic Bags: 144°
Magazines: 36°

16 **FARMER'S MARKET** Complete the table and create a circle graph to show the fruit sold at the local farmer's market.

Type of Fruit	Pounds	Decimal Value	Percent Value	Degree Measure
Apples	81	81 ÷ 180 = 0.45	45%	162°
Pears	45	45 ÷ 180 = 0.25	25%	90°
Peaches	36	36 ÷ 180 = 0.20	20%	72°
Plums	18	18 ÷ 180 = 0.10	10%	36°
Total	180	1.00	100%	360°

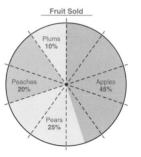

Fruit Sold

Plums 10%

Peaches 20%

Apples 45%

Pears 25%

▶ Spiral Review

17 **SURVEYS** The eighth-grade students voted on lunch choices for the last day of school. Find the degrees in each sector. (Lesson 8-2, p. 349)

Lunch Choices

Spaghetti 40%

Pizza 45%

Hamburger 15%

Pizza: 45%, 0.45 · 360° = 162°   Hamburger: 15%, 0.15 · 360° = 54°

Spaghetti: 40%, 0.40 · 360° = 144°   **STOP**

372 Chapter 8 Percents and Circle Graphs

Ticket Out the Door

Degree Measures Draw the following graph on the board. As students approach the classroom door to exit, alternate asking them to name the degree measure of one of the sectors in the circle graph.

Monthly Budget

Rent: 126°
Groceries: 90°
Utilities: 54°
Gas: 54°
Misc.: 36°

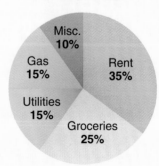

Misc. 10%

Gas 15%

Rent 35%

Utilities 15%

Groceries 25%

Chapter 8 · Progress Check 2 (Lessons 8-3 and 8-4)

The Big Buffet restaurant took an inventory of the last 200 meals that were served. Use the circle graph to answer the questions below.

Meals Served

Vegetarian 18%
Steak 26%
Turkey 13%
Pork 10%
Chicken 33%

1. What percent of the meals were steak dinners? __26%__

2. What percent is equal to half of 26%?
   __26%__ · $\frac{1}{2}$ = __13%__

3. What type of meal was sold half as often as steak dinners?
   __Turkey dinners__ were sold half as often as steak dinners.

4. How many meals were chicken or turkey dinners?
   __33% + 13% = 46% 0.46 · 200 = 92; 92 meals__

5. How many meals were not vegetarian?
   __100% − 18% = 82% 0.82 · 200 = 164; 164 meals__

Complete the table and create a circle graph to show the vegetables sold at the local farmer's market.

6.

Type of Vegetable	Pounds	Decimal Value	Percent Value	Degree Measure
Green Beans	72	72 ÷ 360 = 0.20	20%	72°
Carrots	90	90 ÷ 360 = 0.25	25%	90°
Corn	36	36 ÷ 360 = 0.10	10%	36°
Peas	162	162 ÷ 360 = 0.45	45%	162°
Total	360	1.00	100%	360°

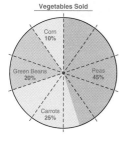

Vegetables Sold

Corn 10%
Peas 45%
Green Beans 20%
Carrots 25%

Progress Check 2

Chapter 8

Formative Assessment

Use the Progress Check to assess students' mastery of the previous lessons. Have students review the lesson indicated for the problems they answered incorrectly.

Assignments

Exercises are structured so that students practice the concepts only if they are assigned all the problems.

> ⚠ **Common Error Alert**
>
> **Find the Divisor** When the total of the whole is not given, students often think that they do not have all the information that they need to complete the problem. In a case such as Exercise 6, all of the information is in the problem, but the students need to realize that they need to compute the total of the whole. The total is the number of pounds listed in the *Pounds* column. Students need to total that column to know the number by which to divide to find the percent of each food.

Data-Driven Decision Making

Students missing Exercises . . .	Have trouble with . . .	Should review and practice . . .
1–5	interpreting a circle graph.	**SSG** Lesson 8-3, p. 357 **CRM** Skills Practice, p. A174
6	creating a circle graph.	**SSG** Lesson 8-4, p. 365 **CRM** Skills Practice, p. A178

Study Guide
Formative Assessment

Vocabulary and Concept Check

If students have difficulty answering Exercises 1–7, remind them that they can use the page references to refresh their memories about the vocabulary terms.

Vocabulary Review Strategies

Puzzles   Have students make a crossword puzzle to help them review key vocabulary words. They should interlock the words in the Vocabulary and Concept Check and then write clues that are used to determine the correct word. (For example: This is the bottom number in a fraction. *Answer: denominator*) Have them trade puzzles with another student for additional practice.

Lesson Review

Each example walks the students through identifying percents being modeled; writing percents as percents and fractions in simplest form; and creating and interpreting circle graphs. If the given examples are not sufficient to review the primary concepts of the chapter, remind students that the page references tell them where to review that topic in their textbooks.

Find **Extra Practice** for these concepts in the Practice Worksheets, pages A165–A180.

Classroom Management

Group Time   Have students who finish the review problems for each example create additional problems with solutions. Then have students gather in small groups to discuss their problems and explain the corresponding solutions. If there is ample time, you could have each group take turns presenting various problems from the different sections within the chapter.

Vocabulary and Concept Check

center, *p. 365*
circle graph, *p. 357*
data, *p. 357*
degree, *p. 349*
denominator, *p. 349*
equivalent fraction, *p. 342*
percent, *p. 342*
ratio, *p. 342*
sector, *p. 349*
simplest form, *p. 349*

Write the vocabulary word that completes each sentence.

1 A ratio that compares a number to 100 is called a(n) ____percent____.

2 ____Equivalent fractions____ are fractions that name the same number.

3 The bottom number in a fraction that represents the number of parts in the whole is called a(n) ____denominator____.

4 The most common unit of measure for an angle is a(n) ____degree____.

5 ____Data____ is information which is gathered for statistical purposes.

Label the diagram with the correct vocabulary term.

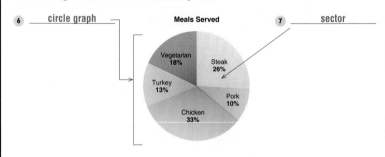

6 ____circle graph____   **Meals Served**   **7** ____sector____

Vegetarian 18%
Steak 26%
Turkey 13%
Pork 10%
Chicken 33%

Lesson Review

8-1 Percents (pp. 342–348)

Identify the percent that is modeled.

8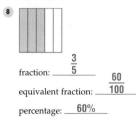

fraction: $\dfrac{3}{5}$

equivalent fraction: $\dfrac{60}{100}$

percentage: 60%

Identify the percent that is modeled.

1. Find the fraction that is shaded.

   $1\dfrac{7}{10}$ or $\dfrac{17}{10}$

2. Find an equivalent fraction with a denominator of 100.

   $\dfrac{17 \cdot 10}{10 \cdot 10} = \dfrac{170}{100}$

3. Write the percentage.

   170%

8-2 Percents and Angle Measures (pp. 349–355)

Use combinations to find the degrees needed to show each sector in a circle graph.

9

$75\% = \underline{50\%} + \underline{25\%} = 75\%$

$\underline{180°} + \underline{90°} = 270°$

10

$45\% = \underline{25\%} + \underline{20\%} = 45\%$

$\underline{90°} + \underline{72°} = 162°$

Example 2

Use combinations to find the degrees needed to show a 65% sector in a circle graph.

1. Write 65% as a combination of percents.

   50% + 10% + 5% = 65%

2. Show each percent in sector degrees.

   $50\% = \dfrac{360}{1} \cdot \dfrac{50}{100} = \dfrac{18,000}{100} = 180°$

   $10\% = \dfrac{360}{1} \cdot \dfrac{10}{100} = \dfrac{3,600}{100} = 36°$

   $5\% = \dfrac{360}{1} \cdot \dfrac{5}{100} = \dfrac{1,800}{100} = 18°$

3. Find the sum of the sector degrees.

   50% + 10% + 5% = 65%
   180° + 36° + 18° = 234°

Review Remind students to complete and refer to their Foldables as they progress through the Chapter 8 Study Guide. Have students share and compare their completed Foldables with a partner. You may also choose to have them use their Foldable as a study aid in preparing for the Chapter Test. (For complete instructions, see Chapter Resource Masters, p. A162.)

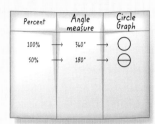

Note This!

Create a Checklist Help students create a study checklist. The checklist should include all of the following items:

- Notes from class
- Sketches, drawings, or number lines in their notebooks
- Foldables
- Vocabulary terms and definitions
- Lesson Examples
- Written assignments and quizzes
- Chapter 8 Study Guide

Intervention Strategy — Kinesthetic Learners

Hands On! Create a BINGO game in which you would say, for example: "B: 25%," and the students would have to look down their **B** columns for either a decimal or simplest fraction equivalent of 25%. You could also call out a decimal and have students look for its equivalent percent, or the simplified fraction. Another option is to call out a reduced fraction and have the students look for the equivalent decimal or percent on their BINGO card(s).

Note This!

Create a Checklist Help students create a study checklist. The checklist should include the following items:

- identifying a percent from a model
- finding the number of degrees represented by a sector in a circle
- interpreting a circle graph
- creating a circle graph

Students should put a checkmark next to each topic when they feel they have a good grasp of the process.

Math Coach Notes

Include the Equation Recommend to students that they start each percent problem by writing the word form of the percent equation.

$$\text{percent} \cdot \text{whole} = \text{part of the whole}$$

There are three values to each equation. To find the solution, two of the three need to be known. With the word equation written, students should substitute what is known into the equation. Students can then quickly know if they multiply the two numbers that they have or if they divide them. When the two known values are on the same side of the equals sign in the equation, the numbers need to be multiplied. When the two known values are on opposite sides of the equals sign, the numbers need to be divided where the number that stands alone is the dividend.

8-3 Interpret Circle Graphs (pp. 357–364)

Use the circle graph to answer the questions below.

Last year 300 students took art classes at the museum. At the end of each session students were asked to name their favorite project.

Favorite Project

11 What percent of students preferred pottery?

36%

12 What is $\frac{1}{2}$ of 36%?

$36\% \cdot 0.50 = 18\%$

13 What project was preferred by half as many students as pottery?

Stained Glass

14 How many students preferred pottery?

108 students

15 How many students preferred painting?

$0.12 \cdot 300 = 36$; 36 students

16 How many students did not prefer drawing?

$100 - 24 = 76\%$

$0.76 \cdot 300 = 228$ students

Example 3

Last month 200 visitors from five different states visited the art museum. The number of visitors from which two states was equal to the number of visitors from Florida?

Museum Visitors

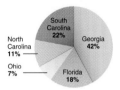

1. What percent of visitors were from Florida? 18%

2. What two states equal 18% when added together?

Ohio + North Carolina = 7% + 11% = 18%

Ohio and North Carolina were represented as often as Florida.

Example 4

How many visitors in the circle graph for Example 3 were from South Carolina?

1. What percent of the visitors were from South Carolina? 22%

There were 200 total visitors.

2. Use the percent equation to solve.

$0.22 \cdot 200$ visitors = 44 visitors

376 Chapter 8 Study Guide

8-4 Create Circle Graphs (pp. 365–372)

17 Complete the table and create a circle graph to show the Teacher of the Year results.

Name	Number	Percent	Degrees
Mrs. Sato	60		
Ms. Wilson	180		
Mr. Cruz	40		
Mr. Numkena	120		
Total	**400**	**100%**	**360°**

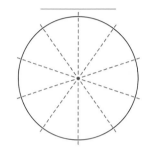

Example 5

Complete the table and create a circle graph to show the type of pets owned.

Pet Adopt, Inc. took a survey of 500 pet owners to see what type of pets they own.

Type of Pet	Number	Percent	Degrees
Dog	300	60%	216°
Horse	25	5%	18°
Cat	100	20%	72°
Fish	50	10%	36°
Bird	25	5%	18°
Total	**500**	**100%**	**360°**

1. To write the decimal, divide the number for each type of pet by the total number of pets.

2. Find the equivalent percent value for each decimal. Change all percent values to degree measures.

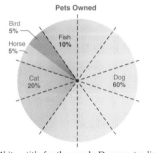

3. Write a title for the graph. Draw sector lines.

4. Label the sectors for each category. Color each sector a different color. Write the percent value for each sector.

Note This!

A Whole Circle   Students should get into the habit of checking their calculations to be certain that the degree measures they compute total 360° and that their percents total 100%. Caution students when rounding is necessary, the rounding process may cause the percent total to be 99% or 101%. When this situation occurs, students should double check their work and be certain that they are only off by ±1%.

Ticket Out the Door

One Equation, Multiple Questions   Write a number greater than 200 on the board, such as 248. Then have students randomly select a percent less than 100%. On their papers have students show the multiplication equation to find the percent of your total. Then students should write three questions, each with a different unknown using the numbers from their multiplication equation.

Chapter Resource Masters

Additional forms of the Chapter 8 Tests are available.

Test Format	Where to Find it
Chapter 8 Test	Math Online > glencoe.com
Blackline Masters	Assessment Masters, p. 118

ExamView®
Assessment Suite

Customize and create multiple versions of your chapter test and their answer keys. All of these questions from the chapter tests are available on ExamView® Assessment Suite.

Advance TRACKER

Online Assessment and Reporting
glencoe.com

This online assessment tool allows teachers to track student progress with easily-accessible, comprehensive reports available for every student. Assess students using any internet-ready computer.

Alternative Assessment

Use Portfolios   Ask students to create a circle graph and write three questions that can be answered from the circle graph in their portfolios. Then have the students write out each step of the solution needed to find the answer to each question. The goal is to have a very thorough, organized portfolio to be used as a reference later as needed.

Chapter 8 **Chapter Test**

Identify the percent that is modeled.

1.

fraction: $\dfrac{19}{20}$

fraction with a denominator of 100:

$\dfrac{19 \cdot \boxed{5}}{20 \cdot \boxed{5}} = \dfrac{\boxed{95}}{100}$

decimal: **0.95**

percent: **95%**

2.

fraction: $1\dfrac{3}{10}$ or $\dfrac{13}{10}$

fraction with a denominator of 100:

$\dfrac{13 \cdot \boxed{10}}{10 \cdot \boxed{10}} = \dfrac{\boxed{130}}{100}$

decimal: **1.30**

percent: **130%**

Find the degrees needed to show each sector in a circle graph.

3.

$60\% = \dfrac{60}{100} \div \dfrac{\boxed{20}}{\boxed{20}} = \dfrac{3}{5}$

$\dfrac{360°}{1} \cdot \dfrac{3}{5} = \dfrac{\boxed{1080°}}{\boxed{5}} = \underline{216°}$

4.

$10\% = \dfrac{10}{100} \div \dfrac{\boxed{10}}{\boxed{10}} = \dfrac{1}{10}$

$\dfrac{360°}{1} \cdot \dfrac{1}{10} = \dfrac{\boxed{360°}}{\boxed{10}} = \underline{36°}$

Find the missing value.

5. What is 7% of 50?

$\underline{0.07} \cdot \underline{50} = \underline{3.50}$

6. What is 45% of 360?

$\underline{0.45} \cdot \underline{360} = \underline{162}$

7. What is 75% of 350?

$\underline{0.75} \cdot \underline{350} = \underline{262.50}$

8. What is 170% of 90?

$\underline{1.70} \cdot \underline{90} = \underline{153}$

378   **Chapter 8** Test

English Learner Strategy

Assessment   Allow students time to look over the assessment. Have students take a close look at all the problem directions, as well as any terms in the word problems. Provide an opportunity for students to clarify any words they think they do not understand by conducting a brief question-and-answer period.

BICYCLES Smithtown Bike Shop has 400 bicycles. Use the circle graph to answer the questions below.

Bike Type

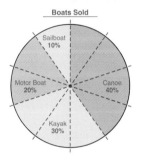

9 How many mountain bikes are at the bike shop?

$0.39 \cdot 400 = 156$; 156 mountain bikes

10 How many road bikes and hybrid bikes are at the bike shop?

$31\% + 17\% = 48\%$ $0.48 \cdot 400 = 192$; 192 bikes

11 How many bikes are not children's?

$100\% - 8\% = 92\%$ $0.92 \cdot 400 = 368$; 368 bikes

12 Complete the table and create a circle graph to show the boats sold at Boyd's Boat House.

Type of Boat	Number Sold	Decimal Value	Percent Value	Degree Measure
Canoe	104	$104 \div 260 = 0.40$	40%	144°
Kayak	78	$78 \div 260 = 0.30$	30%	108°
Motor Boat	52	$52 \div 260 = 0.20$	20%	72°
Sailboat	26	$26 \div 260 = 0.10$	10%	36°
Total	260	1.00	100%	360°

Boats Sold

Sailboat 10%

Motor Boat 20%

Canoe 40%

Kayak 30%

13 **TIPS**   Alida paid $17.00 for dinner. She has decided to tip the waiter 15% of the cost of her dinner. How much money will she use to tip the waiter?

$17 \cdot 0.15 = 2.55$; She will give a tip of $2.55.

Math Coach Notes

Test-Taking Tip   Ensure students read the sets of directions and the wording of the problems carefully. Specifically, it is important that students are able to interpret the circle graphs. Also, students should verify that their answers make sense in context.

Data-Driven Decision Making

Students missing Exercises . . .	Have trouble with . . .	Should review and practice . . .
1–2	identifying percents from models.	SSG Lesson 8-1, p. 342 CRM Skills Practice, p. A166
3–4	finding the number of degrees in a sector.	SSG Lesson 8-2, p. 349 CRM Skills Practice, p. A170
5–8	finding the percent of a number.	SSG Lesson 8-1, p. 342 CRM Skills Practice, p. A166
9–13	creating and interpreting circle graphs.	SSG Lessons 8-3 and 8-4, pp. 357 and 365 CRM Skills Practice, pp. A174 and A178

Test Practice

Chapter 8 **Test Practice**

Diagnose Student Errors

Survey student responses for each item. Class trends may indicate common errors and misconceptions.

1. A represents 5%
   B represents 25%
   C represents 40%
   D correct

2. A used percentage and dropped percent sign
   B correct
   C guess
   D used incorrect decimal; 28% = 0.28, not 2.8

3. A incorrectly used percent as degrees
   B represents 25%
   C correct
   D represents whole circle

4. A calculated 2% of 380
   B calculated 96% of 380
   C correct
   D calculated 102% of 380

5. A correct
   B used percent as number of pieces
   C is number of total pieces
   D added 20 and 75

6. A used percent as number of degrees
   B correct
   C represents half, not quarter circle
   D represents full circle

7. A percent of children's books, missed **not**
   B 76%, not 76 books
   C number of children's books, missed **not**
   D correct

8. A correct
   B moved decimal point in percent
   C subtracted discount from original price
   D added discount to original price

9. A guess
   B only considered second model
   C translated 3 parts as 3%
   D correct

Choose the best answer and fill in the corresponding circle on the sheet at right.

1 Which model represents 20%?

2 What is 28% of 250?
   A 28   C 75
   B 70   D 700

3 Amanda is making a circle graph of the votes for class president. Forty-five percent of the students voted for Horatio. How many degrees are needed for the sector of votes for Horatio?

   A 45°   C 162°
   B 90°   D 360°

4 What is 98% of 380?
   A 7.6   C 372.4
   B 364.8   D 387.6

380   Chapter 8 Test Practice

5 A large birthday cake was ordered for Patty's birthday. The cake had 75 pieces. Twenty percent of the cake was decorated with roses. How many pieces of cake were decorated with roses?
   A 15 pieces   C 75 pieces
   B 20 pieces   D 95 pieces

6 In a circle graph, how many degrees are needed to show a 25% sector?

   A 25°   C 180°
   B 90°   D 360°

7 Smalltown Library checked out 300 books last week. How many of the books were not children's books?

Book Type

   A 24 books   C 72 books
   B 76 books   D 228 books

10. A 4%, not 4 books
    B 4% of 300, not 200
    C correct
    D 4% of 300, not 1,000

11. A used incorrect decimal form of 5%
    B used degrees as decimal, then moved decimal point
    C used degrees as percent
    D correct

8 Picture frames are on sale for 25% off the original price. If the cost of a picture frame was $8.00, how much is the discount?

(A) $2.00   C $6.00

B $2.50   D $10.00

---

9 Which percent represents the shaded portion of the model?

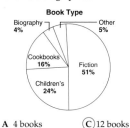

A 1.35%   C 103%

B 60%   (D) 160%

---

10 Smalltown Library checked out 300 books last week. How many of the books were biographies?

Book Type

Biography 4% — Other 5%

Cookbooks 16%

Fiction 51%

Children's 24%

A 4 books   (C) 12 books

B 8 books   D 40 books

---

11 One sector of a circle graph has a measure of 18°. What percent of the circle is represented by this sector?

A 0.5%   C 18%

B 1.8%   (D) 5%

ANSWER SHEET

Directions: Fill in the circle for each correct answer.

1 (A) (B) (C) **(D)**
2 (A) **(B)** (C) (D)
3 (A) (B) **(C)** (D)
4 (A) (B) **(C)** (D)
5 **(A)** (B) (C) (D)
6 (A) **(B)** (C) (D)
7 (A) (B) (C) **(D)**
8 **(A)** (B) (C) (D)
9 (A) (B) (C) **(D)**
10 (A) (B) **(C)** (D)
11 (A) (B) (C) **(D)**

Success Strategy

Read the entire question before looking at the answer choices. Make sure you know what the question is asking.

STOP

Diagnosing Student Errors and Misconceptions

Self-Check   After working on the Test Practice problems, have students score their own work by comparing their answers to the scoring guide provided. After they have scored their own problems, have them double-check the questions they missed.

Have students try to find and correct their mistakes. If they are still having trouble, try to determine whether or not the mistake was due to a basic computational error or whether there is a misunderstanding of the concept. If they are still having trouble figuring out their errors, have them work with a partner to see if together they can resolve any problems within the chapter.

If they seem to be having an issue with a topic covered in a previous chapter, then refer them to the pages in their text or to their portfolios.

Chapter Overview

Chapter-at-a-Glance

Lesson	Math Objective	State/Local Standards
9-1 Transition to Two-Variable Data (pp. 384–390)	Identify and describe the relationship between two variables within an equation.	
9-2 Scatter Plots (pp. 391–397)	Identify relationships using data in a scatter plot.	
Progress Check 1 (p. 398)		
9-3 Lines of Best Fit (pp. 399–405)	Determine and describe a line of best fit.	
Progress Check 2 (p. 406)		

Content-at-a-Glance

The diagram below summarizes and unpacks Chapter 9 content.

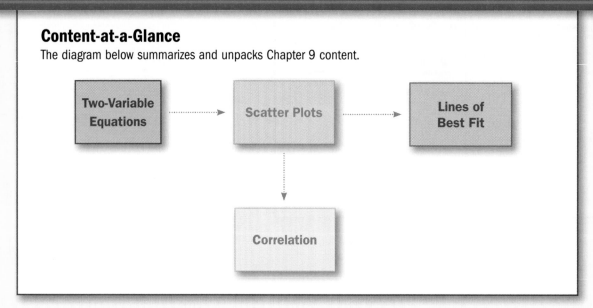

Chapter Assessment Manager

Diagnostic   Diagnose students' readiness.

	Student/Teacher Editions	Assessment Masters	Technology
Course Placement Test		1	💿 ExamView® Assessment Suite
Book 3 Pretest		101	💿 ExamView® Assessment Suite
Chapter 9 Pretest		126	💿 ExamView® Assessment Suite
Quiz/Preview	SSG 383		Math Online ▷ glencoe.com StudentWorks™ Plus

Formative   Identify students' misconceptions of content knowledge.

	Student/Teacher Editions	Assessment Masters	Technology
Progress Checks	SSG 398, 406		Math Online ▷ glencoe.com StudentWorks™ Plus
Vocabulary Review	SSG 407		Math Online ▷ glencoe.com
Lesson Assessments			💿 ExamView® Assessment Suite
Are They Getting It?	TE 387, 394, 402		Math Online ▷ glencoe.com

Summative   Determine student success in learning the concepts in the lesson, chapter, or book.

	Student/Teacher Editions	Assessment Masters	Technology
Chapter 9 Test	SSG 410	129	💿 ExamView® Assessment Suite
Test Practice	SSG 412	132	
Alternative Assessment	TE 410	135	💿 ExamView® Assessment Suite
See It, Do It, Say It, Write It	TE 389, 397, 405		
Book 3 Test		137	💿 ExamView® Assessment Suite

Backmapping and Vertical Alignment McGraw-Hill's *Math Triumphs* intervention program was conceived and developed with the final results in mind: student success in grade-level mathematics, including Algebra 1 and beyond. The authors, using the **NCTM Focal Points and Focal Connections** as their guide, developed this brand-new series by backmapping from grade-level and Algebra 1 concepts, and vertically aligning the topics so that they build upon prior skills and concepts and serve as a foundation for future topics.

Chapter Resource Manager

	Lesson 9-1	**Lesson 9-2**	**Lesson 9-3**
Concept	Transition to Two-Variable Data	Scatter Plots	Lines of Best Fit
Objective	Identify and describe the relationship between two variables within an equation.	Identify relationships using data in a scatter plot.	Determine and describe a line of best fit.
Math Vocabulary	ordered pair solution *x*-coordinate *y*-coordinate	coordinate grid scatter plot *x*-axis *y*-axis	data line of best fit scatter plot slope
Lesson Resources	**Materials** • Deck of cards • Colored pencils **Manipulatives** • Number cubes **Other Resources** CRM Vocabulary and English Language Development CRM Skills Practice CRM Problem-Solving Practice CRM Homework Practice	**Materials** • Centimeter grid paper • Rulers **Other Resources** CRM Vocabulary and English Language Development CRM Skills Practice CRM Problem-Solving Practice CRM Homework Practice	**Materials** • Butcher paper • Grid paper • Pipe cleaners • Rulers • String **Other Resources** CRM Vocabulary and English Language Development CRM Skills Practice CRM Problem-Solving Practice CRM Homework Practice
Technology	**Math Online** glencoe.com StudentWorks™ Plus ⊙ ExamView® Assessment Suite	**Math Online** glencoe.com StudentWorks™ Plus ⊙ ExamView® Assessment Suite	**Math Online** glencoe.com StudentWorks™ Plus ⊙ ExamView® Assessment Suite

Intervention Strategy

Scatter Plots

Making a scatter plot using real-world data will help students understand how data displays apply to the real world.

Step 1

Discuss with students the trends in scatter plots. Write their ideas on the board of what types of data they would expect to see have a negative trend, a positive trend, or no relationship.

Ideas for positive trends may include the average temperature for the first 6 months of the year, height and arm span, or distance traveled versus time traveling. Negative trends can be the time to swim one lap and the age or experience of the swimmer, hours of sunlight from June to December, or value of a car versus its age in years.

Step 2

Have students gather data for a scatter plot. Assign specific students data that will show a positive trend, negative trend, or no relationship. If time is short, students can create data.

Step 3

Students will make their scatter plots. When plots demonstrate a positive or negative trend, students can draw a line of best fit.

Step 4

Student pairs will present their scatter plots; discuss the trend and how they drew the line of best fit. Ask each student pair to make a projection using their lines.

Data is used to compare and predict trends.

Many people compare and predict trends of consumer purchases. Companies often predict purchases based on variables such as weather, season, or popularity of similar products. For example, outdoor markets and roadside vendors often sell more produce on days with pleasant weather conditions than on rainy or stormy days.

Real-World Applications

Stepping Through the Day   Imagine if every step you took for one day was recorded in a graph that showed a relationship, such as time and distance from home. Would the graph of your steps show when you were running? Would it show when you were standing still? Might it even show when you were not walking, but riding in a car? Try to illustrate your day on a coordinate grid. Are there parts of the graph steeper than other parts? Is any part a horizontal line? Are there any holes in the graph? Compare your graph to a classmate's graph.

Intervention Strategy

Telling Stories to Match a Graph

Step 1   Arrange students into groups of 3 students.

Step 2   Each group should look through newspapers, magazines, or on the Internet to find three different graphs. They should try to find a linear graph, a nonlinear graph, and a graph that they are not sure of the relationship illustrated. The group will use the graphs but not the information that accompanies the graphs.

Step 3   Each group should tell a story about situations that match each graph. For the linear graph, the story should involve a constant rate of change. For the nonlinear graph, the story will not involve a constant rate of change. After creating the stories, have the group decide if their third graph is linear or nonlinear.

Key Vocabulary

Find interactive definitions in 13 languages in the **eGlossary** at glencoe.com

English   Español *Introduce the most important vocabulary terms from Chapter 9.*

coordinate grid   cuadriculado de coordenadas

a grid in which a horizontal number line (*x*-axis) and a vertical number line (*y*-axis) intersect at their zero points (p. 391)

line of best fit   línea de ajuste óptimo

a line that is very close to most of the data points on a scatter plot (p. 399)

ordered pair   par ordenado

a pair of numbers used to locate a point in the coordinate system, the ordered pair is written in this form: (*x*-coordinate, *y*-coordinate) (p. 384)

scatter plot   nube de puntos

a graph in which two sets of data are plotted as ordered pairs in the coordinate plane (p. 391)

slope   pendiente

the rate of change between any two points on a line; the ratio of vertical change to horizontal change (p. 399)

solution   solución

the value of a variable that makes an equation true (p. 384)

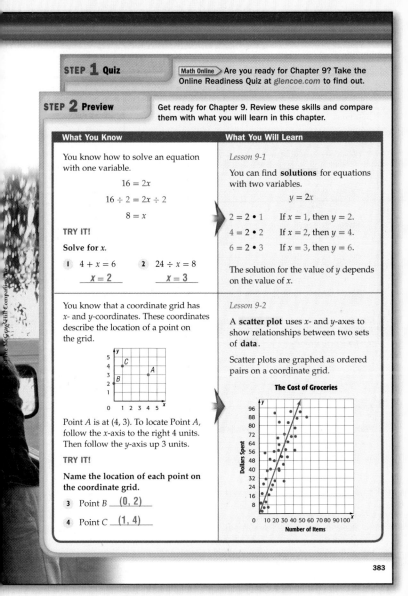

STEP **1** Quiz

Math Online ▸ Are you ready for Chapter 9? Take the Online Readiness Quiz at *glencoe.com* to find out.

STEP **2** Preview

Get ready for Chapter 9. Review these skills and compare them with what you will learn in this chapter.

What You Know	What You Will Learn
You know how to solve an equation with one variable. $16 = 2x$ $16 \div 2 = 2x \div 2$ $8 = x$ **TRY IT!** Solve for x. **1** $4 + x = 6$ **2** $24 \div x = 8$ $\underline{x = 2}$ $\underline{x = 3}$	*Lesson 9-1* You can find **solutions** for equations with two variables. $$y = 2x$$ $2 = 2 \cdot 1$ If $x = 1$, then $y = 2$. $4 = 2 \cdot 2$ If $x = 2$, then $y = 4$. $6 = 2 \cdot 3$ If $x = 3$, then $y = 6$. The solution for the value of y depends on the value of x.
You know that a coordinate grid has x- and y-coordinates. These coordinates describe the location of a point on the grid. Point A is at (4, 3). To locate Point A, follow the x-axis to the right 4 units. Then follow the y-axis up 3 units. **TRY IT!** **Name the location of each point on the coordinate grid.** **3** Point B $\underline{(0, 2)}$ **4** Point C $\underline{(1, 4)}$	*Lesson 9-2* A **scatter plot** uses x- and y-axes to show relationships between two sets of **data**. Scatter plots are graphed as ordered pairs on a coordinate grid.

383

Vocabulary Preview

- As students complete the Chapter Preview, have them make a list of important terms throughout the chapter.

- Have students use the key words as well as additional unfamiliar terms throughout the chapter to complete picture definitions.

- Students should complete one index card for each term.

- Students will write a term on one side of the index card and then draw a picture on the other side to describe the term.

Step 1   Quiz

Pretest/Prescribe   Students can take the Online Readiness Quiz online or the Diagnostic Pretest in the Assessment Masters.

Step 2   Preview

Use this pre-chapter activity to activate students' prior knowledge, build confidence, and help students preview the lessons.

 **Dinah Zike's Foldables**

Study Organizer

Guide students through the directions on p. A181 in the Chapter Resource Masters to create their own Foldable graphic organizer for use with this chapter.

Home Connections

- Have students draw two graphs, one showing a linear function and one showing a nonlinear function. Then have them relate each one with an event that happened during their day.

Mc Graw Hill Professional Development

Targeted professional development has been articulated throughout **McGraw-Hill's** *Math Triumphs* intervention program. **The McGraw-Hill Professional Development Video Library** provides short videos that support the **NCTM Focal Points and Focal Connections**. For more information, visit glencoe.com.

Model Lessons   Instructional Strategies

Lesson Notes

Lesson Planner

Objective   Identify and describe the relationship between two variables within an equation.

Vocabulary   ordered pair, solution, *x*-coordinate, *y*-coordinate

Materials/Manipulatives   deck of playing cards, number cubes, colored pencils

Chapter Resource Masters

- CRM Vocabulary and English Language Development (p. A184)

- CRM Skills Practice (p. A185)

- CRM Problem-Solving Practice (p. A186)

- CRM Homework Practice (p. A187)

① Introduce

Vocabulary

Coordinate System   Review how to locate and name *ordered pairs* in the first quadrant of a coordinate plane. Identify the *x*- and *y*-axes, and discuss how points are named with the *x-coordinate* first, and then the *y-coordinate*.

② Teach

Key Concept

Foundational Skills and Concepts   After students have read through the Key Concept box, have them try these exercises.

1. Is the ordered pair (3, 2) a solution of the equation $y = x - 1$? Explain. yes; When the variables are substituted into the equation, it yields a true sentence.

2. Describe the order of coordinates in an ordered pair. The *x*-coordinate is first, and the *y*-coordinate is second.

3. Is (4, 1) a solution of $y = \frac{1}{2}x$? Explain. no; When the variables are substituted into the equation, it yields a false sentence.

KEY Concept

Solutions for equations with two variables can vary. These solution sets consist of two numbers, one for each variable. Usually, the solution is expressed as an **ordered pair** (*x*, *y*).

One-Variable Equation	Two-Variable Equation
$8 = 2x$	$y = 2x$

unknown variable   unknown variables

To solve, divide each side by 2.

$$8 = 2x$$
$$\frac{8}{2} = \frac{2x}{2}$$
$$4 = x$$

The solution is 4.

To find solutions, make a table.

x	2x	y	(x, y)
0	2 • 0	0	(0, 0)
1	2 • 1	2	(1, 2)
2	2 • 2	4	(2, 4)

Three solutions are (0, 0), (1, 2), and (2, 4).

Finding a solution means finding values for the variables that make the sentence true.

VOCABULARY

ordered pair
a pair of numbers used to locate a point in the coordinate system; the ordered pair is written in this form: (*x*-coordinate, *y*-coordinate)

solution
the value of a variable that makes an equation true

x-coordinate
the first number of an ordered pair

y-coordinate
the second number of an ordered pair

Any ordered pair that makes an equation with two variables a true sentence is a solution of the equation. So, an equation with two variables has an infinite number of solutions.

Example 1

Which ordered pair, (3, 6) or (7, 4), is a solution of $y = x - 3$?

1. Substitute the values for *x* and *y* of (3, 6) into the equation.
$$y = x - 3$$
$$6 \stackrel{?}{=} 3 - 3$$
$$6 \neq 0 \; \textit{not a solution}$$

2. Substitute the values for *x* and *y* of (7, 4) into the equation.
$$y = x - 3$$
$$4 \stackrel{?}{=} 7 - 3$$
$$4 = 4 \; \checkmark \; \text{a solution}$$

3. The ordered pair (7, 4) is a solution of the equation $y = x - 3$.

Additional *Example 1*

Which ordered pair, (−2, 5) or (−1, −4), is a solution of $y = 3x - 1$?

1. Substitute the values for *x* and *y* of (−2, 5) into the equation.

$$5 \stackrel{?}{=} 3\,(-2) - 1$$
$$5 \stackrel{?}{=} (-6) - 1$$
$$5 \neq -7 \; \textit{not a solution}$$

2. Substitute the values for *x* and *y* of (−1, −4) into the equation.

$$-4 \stackrel{?}{=} 3\,(-1) - 1$$
$$-4 \stackrel{?}{=} (-3) - 1$$
$$-4 = -4 \; \checkmark \; \text{a solution}$$

3. The ordered pair (−1, −4) is a solution of the equation $y = 3x - 1$.

YOUR TURN!

Which ordered pair, $(-1, -1)$ or $(0, 2)$, is a solution of $y = 2x + 1$?

1. Substitute the values for x and y of $(-1, -1)$ into the equation.

$$\frac{-1}{-1} \overset{?}{=} 2 \frac{(-1)}{} + 1$$
$$\frac{-1}{-1} \overset{?}{=} \frac{-2}{} + 1$$
$$\frac{-1}{-1} \overset{=}{} \frac{-1}{}$$ Is $(-1, -1)$ a solution? __yes__

2. Substitute the values for x and y of $(0, 2)$ into the equation.

$$\frac{2}{2} \overset{?}{=} 2 \frac{(0)}{} + 1$$
$$\frac{2}{2} \overset{?}{=} \frac{0}{} + 1$$
$$\frac{2}{2} \overset{\neq}{} \frac{1}{}$$ Is $(0, 2)$ a solution? __no__

3. The ordered pair $\underline{(-1, -1)}$ is a solution of the equation $y = 2x + 1$.

Example 2

Complete the table for the equation $y = 4x + 5$.
Then find three solutions for the equation.

1. Make a table. Select three values for x.
   Substitute the values for x in the
   expression $4x + 5$.

2. Complete the table. Find y. Then
   write the ordered pairs.

x	4x + 5	y	(x, y)
0	4(0) + 5	5	(0, 5)
1	4(1) + 5	9	(1, 9)
2	4(2) + 5	13	(2, 13)

3. Three solutions of the equation $y = 4x + 5$ are $(0, 5)$, $(1, 9)$, and $(2, 13)$.

YOUR TURN!

Complete the table for the equation $y = -x + 7$.
Then find three solutions for the equation. Sample answers given.

1. Make a table. Select three values for x.
   Substitute the values for x in the
   expression $-x + 7$.

2. Complete the table. Find y. Then
   write the ordered pairs.

x	−x + 7	y	(x, y)
0	0 + 7	7	(0, 7)
1	−1 + 7	6	(1, 6)
2	−2 + 7	5	(2, 5)

3. Three solutions of the equation $y = -x + 7$ are $\underline{(0, 7)}$, $\underline{(1, 6)}$, and $\underline{(2, 5)}$.

GO ON

Additional *Example 2*

Complete the table for the equation $y = 2x - 8$.
Then find three solutions for the equation.

1. Make a table. Select three values for x.
   Substitute the values for x in the expression
   $2x - 8$.

x	2x − 8	y	(x, y)
0	2(0) − 8		
1	2(1) − 8		
2	2(2) − 8		

2. Complete the table. Find y. Write the
   ordered pairs.

x	2x − 8	y	(x, y)
0	2(0) − 8	−8	(0, −8)
1	2(1) − 8	−6	(1, −6)
2	2(2) − 8	−4	(2, −4)

3. Three solutions of the equation $y = 2x - 8$
   are $(0, -8)$, $(1, -6)$, and $(2, -4)$.

Math Coach Notes

Convenient Values   Remind students to select
convenient values for x-coordinates. Encourage them to
make their computations a little easier by choosing
x-values that are simpler to calculate, such as 0, 1,
or 2.

Intervention Strategy
Interpersonal/Kinesthetic Learners

Have students work in pairs. Distribute a deck of playing cards (minus
the face cards) to each pair. Ask students to create a table of
possible solutions for each of the following equations.

Students should draw a card from the deck. The drawn card
represents the x-coordinate. Pairs should work together to determine
the related y-coordinate for every draw.

Tell students to create a list of ordered-pair solutions for each
equation. Have groups check their ordered pairs with one another
after the exercise is finished.

$y = x + 4$

$y = -x - 6$

$y = 2x - 3$

Using Manipulatives

Number Cubes Roll a number cube for *x*-coordinates to practice finding ordered-pair solutions of equations.

On-Hand Manipulatives Have students use different colored pencils to write *x*- and *y*-coordinates. Use the coordinating colors when substituting for the variables to keep the pairs ordered correctly.

Math Coach Notes

Substitutions Use Exercises 1–3 to remind students to substitute correctly. Point out that the first variable in these equations is for the *y*-coordinate, not the *x*-coordinate. Demonstrate how switching the variables will lead to unequal equations, or false sentences.

Who is Correct?

Which ordered pair is a solution of $y = x + 12$?

Circle the correct answer(s). Cross out incorrect answer(s).

 Guided Practice

Determine which ordered pair, (2, 6) or (3, −1), is a solution of each equation.

1 $y = x - 4$

　　(3, −1)

2 $y = 3x$

　　(2, 6)

3 $y = 2x + 2$

　　(2, 6)

Step by Step Practice

4 Complete the table for the equation $y = 8x$.　　**Sample answers are given.**
　　Then find three solutions for the equation.

　　Step 1 Make a table. Select three values for *x*. Substitute these values for *x* in the expression $y = 8x$.

　　Step 2 Complete the table. Find *y*. Then write the ordered pairs.

x	8x	y	(x, y)
0	8 · 0	0	(0, 0)
1	8 · 1	8	(1, 8)
2	8 · 2	16	(2, 16)

　　Step 3 Three solutions are (0, 0), (1, 8), and (2, 16).

Complete the table for each equation.
Then find three solutions for each equation. Sample answers are given.

5 $y = -10x$

x	−10x	y
−2	−10(−2)	20
6	−10(6)	−60
7	−10(7)	−70

　　(−2, 20), (6, −60), (7, −70)

6 $y = x + 9$

x	x + 9	y
0	0 + 9	9
3	3 + 9	12
5	5 + 9	14

　　(0, 9), (3, 12), (5, 14)

386　Chapter 9 Two-Variable Data

Who *is Correct?*
Diagnostic Teaching

• Dominique is incorrect. She substituted or calculated incorrectly.

• Michael is incorrect. He substituted or calculated incorrectly.

• Cristina is correct. She substituted and computed correctly.

Remind students that the most convenient numbers to use when looking for ordered pair solutions are values such as 0 and 1.

Find three solutions for each equation. Sample answers are given.

7 $y = 3x + 2$

_(0, 2), (1, 5), (2, 8)_

8 $y = 5x - 5$

_(0, −5), (1, 0), (2, 5)_

Step by Step *Problem-Solving Practice*

Solve.

9 MUSIC The equation $y = 0.99x$ represents the total cost, y, of downloading x songs from an online music store. Find three solutions of the equation when x equals 2, 5, and 12. Describe what the solutions mean.

Problem-Solving Strategies
☐ Draw a diagram.
☐ Use logical reasoning.
☐ Solve a simpler problem.
☐ Work backward.
☑ Make a table.

Understand The variable x represents _the number of songs downloaded_.

The variable y represents _the total cost of downloading the songs_

The values of x are _2, 5, and 12_.

Plan Pick a strategy. One strategy is to make a table.

Solve

x	$0.99x$	y	(x, y)
2	$0.99 \cdot 2$	1.98	(2, 1.98)
5	$0.99 \cdot 5$	4.95	(5, 4.95)
12	$0.99 \cdot 12$	11.88	(12, 11.88)

The ordered pair solutions are _(2, 1.98), (5, 4.95), (12, 11.88)_.

This means that the cost of downloading 2 songs is _$1.98_.

The cost of downloading 5 songs is _$4.95_.

The cost of downloading 12 songs is _$11.88_.

Check Use estimation to check your answer. One song costs about $1, two songs cost about $2, and so on.

GO ON

Are They Getting It? ?

Check students' understanding of two-variable data by writing these problems on the board. Ask them to point out incorrect answers and explain their reasoning.

1. The ordered pair (0, 6) is a solution of $y = x - 6$.
This is incorrect. When substituted, this ordered pair yields a false sentence, $6 \neq -6$.

2. (1, 3) and (2, 4) are both solutions of $y = 2x + 1$.
This is incorrect. The ordered pair (2, 4) does not yield a true sentence.

3. (−2, 14) and (1, 5) are both solutions of $y = -3x + 8$.
This is correct.

10   PETS   The equation $y = 14 - x$ represents the number of puppies in a pet store, y, after x puppies are sold. Find three solutions of the equation when x equals 6, 10, and 13.

Check off each step.

✔ ___ Understand: I underlined key words.

✔ ___ Plan: To solve the problem, I will ___ make a table ___.

✔ ___ Solve: The answer is ___ 8 puppies, 4 puppies, 1 puppy ___.

✔ ___ Check: I checked my answer by ___ using logical

___ reasoning _____.

Solve.

11   MONEY   The equation $y = 6x + 5$ represents the amount of money Marissa has, y, after baby-sitting x hours. Find three solutions of the equation. Describe what the solutions mean.

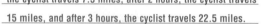

___ Sample answer: (1, 11), (2, 17), (3, 23); After baby-sitting 1 hour, Marissa has $11,

___ after baby-sitting 2 hours, she has $17, and after baby-sitting 3 hours, she has $23.

_____

12   CYCLING   The equation $d = 7.5t$ represents the distance, d, a cyclist travels after t hours. Find three solutions of the equation. Describe what the solutions mean.

___ Sample answers: (1, 7.5), (2, 15), (3, 22.5); After 1 hour,

___ the cyclist travels 7.5 miles, after 2 hours, the cyclist travels

___ 15 miles, and after 3 hours, the cyclist travels 22.5 miles.

_____

13   Reflect   The sum of Nate's and Ling's ages is 25. Let x represent Nate's age and let y represent Ling's age. Find four ordered pairs of numbers that represent their possible ages.

___ Sample answers: (10, 15), (11, 14), (12, 13), (13, 12)

Math Challenge

The sum of Marnie's and Nico's ages is 36. Let x represent Marnie's age and let y represent Nico's age. Marnie is older than 14 and younger than 18. Find the three ordered pairs of numbers that represent their possible ages.   (15, 21), (16, 20), (17, 19)

Skills, Concepts, and Problem Solving

Determine which ordered pair, (0, 0), (5, −9), or (1, 3), is a solution of each equation.

14 $y = 7x$

<u>(0, 0)</u>

15 $y = x + 2$

<u>(1, 3)</u>

16 $y = 5x − 2$

<u>(1, 3)</u>

17 $y = −x − 4$

<u>(5, −9)</u>

Complete the table for each equation.
Then find three solutions for each equation.

18 $y = 2x$

x	2x	y
0	2(0)	0
5	2(5)	10
9	2(9)	18

<u>(0, 0), (5, 10), (9, 18)</u>

19 $y = x + 15$

x	x + 15	y
−1	−1 + 15	14
3	(3) + 15	18
6	(6) + 15	21

<u>(−1, 14), (3, 18), (6, 21)</u>

20 $y = 6x − 5$

x	6x − 5	y
1	6(1) − 5	1
4	6(4) − 5	19
8	6(8) − 5	43

<u>(1, 1), (4, 19), (8, 43)</u>

21 $y = −x + 3$

x	−x + 3	y
1	−(1) + 3	2
2	−(2) + 3	1
3	−(3) + 3	0

<u>(1, 2), (2, 1), (3, 0)</u>

Find three solutions for each equation. Sample answers are given.

22 $y = x$

<u>(0, 0), (1, 1), (2, 2)</u>

23 $y = −4x$

<u>(0, 0), (1, −4), (2, −8)</u>

GO ON

English Language Learners

Ask the following questions to help students understand the process of finding ordered pair solutions for the equation $x + 2y = 18$.

• Is the ordered pair (2, 8) a solution to the equation? yes

• Is it the only solution? no

• What is the ordered pair solution when $x = 4$? (4, 7)

• Is the ordered pair (7, 4) also a solution? no

• What is the difference between the ordered pairs (4, 7) and (7, 4)?
In one ordered pair, $x = 4$ and in the other $x = 7$.

• Name one more solution. Possible answer: (8, 5)

Odd/Even Assignments

Exercises 14–29 are structured so that students practice the same concepts whether they are assigned the odd or even problems.

In-Class Assignment

Have students complete Exercises 14, 18, 23, 24, 28, and 32 to ensure that they understand the concept.

 **Assess**

See It, Do It, Say It, Write It

Step 1 Write the equation $y = −x + 3$ on the board. Under it, write ordered pairs (0, −3), (1, 2), and (2, −1).

Step 2 Tell students to determine which ordered pair is a solution of the equation. Then have them find three more ordered pair solutions to the equation.

Step 3 Ask students to work in pairs. Have students explain how they determined which ordered pair was one of the solutions of the equation. Students should share the three additional ordered pairs they found for the equation, and prove each yields a true sentence.

Step 4 Have students work alone to write an evaluation of the given ordered pairs. Tell students to include an explanation of how they determined the three additional ordered pairs.

Looking Ahead: Pre-Teach

In the next lesson, students will learn about scatter plots and explore the relationship between two sets of data.

Example

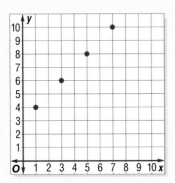

As the values of x increase, the values of y increase. This graph shows two sets of data with a positive relationship.

Exercise

1. Describe the relationship between the x- and y-values in the graph below.

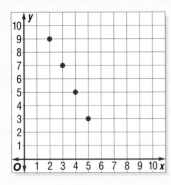

As the values of x increase, the values of y decrease.

Find three solutions for each equation. Sample answers are given.

24 $y = x + 11$

(0, 11), (1, 12), (2, 13)

25 $y = x - 5$

(0, −5), (1, −4), (2, −3)

26 $y = 4x + 2$

(0, 2), (1, 6), (2, 10)

27 $y = 10x - 3$

(0, −3), (1, 7), (2, 17)

Solve.

28 WATER   It costs a city about $10 per minute when a fire hydrant is running. This can be represented by the equation $C = 10m$, where C is the cost and m is the number of minutes. Find three solutions of the equation. Choose one solution and describe what it means.

Sample answer: (1, 10), (2, 20), (3, 30); (3, 30) means

that after 3 minutes, the cost of the water is $30.

29 GEOMETRY   The formula for the area of a rectangle is $A = \ell \cdot w$. The area of a rectangle is 48 square centimeters. Find three solutions of the equation. Choose one solution and describe what it means.

Sample answer: (6, 8), (12, 4), (24, 2); (6, 8) means that the rectangle is

6 centimeters long and 8 centimeters wide.

Vocabulary Check   Write the vocabulary word that completes each sentence.

30 A pair of numbers used to locate a point in the coordinate system is called a(n) ___ordered pair___.

31 The ordered pair (1, 7) is a(n) ___solution___ of the equation $y = 2x + 5$.

32 Writing in Math   What is the solution of the equation $3x + y = 14$ if $y = 2$? Explain your reasoning.

(4, 2); Substitute 2 for y in the equation and then solve for x. The result is $x = 4$.

So, the solution of the two-variable equation is (4, 2).

Ticket Out the Door

Equivalent Forms   Write $y = 3x - 2$ on the board. As students approach the classroom door to exit, alternate asking them to give the ordered pair solution when the x-coordinate equals 0, 1, or 2.

(0, −2), (1, 1), (2, 4)

Scatter Plots

KEY Concept

In a **scatter plot**, two sets of data are graphed as ordered pairs on a **coordinate grid**. A scatter plot shows the relationship, if any relationship exists, between the two sets of data.

Positive Relationship

As *x* increases, *y* increases.

Negative Relationship

As *x* increases, *y* decreases.

No Relationship

There is no obvious pattern.

If the points go up from left to right, the data show a positive relationship.

If the points go down from left to right, the data show a negative relationship.

If the points show no pattern from left to right, the data show no relationship.

VOCABULARY

coordinate grid
a grid in which a horizontal number line (*x*-axis) and a vertical number line (*y*-axis) intersect at their zero points

scatter plot
a graph in which two sets of data are plotted as ordered pairs in the coordinate grid

x-axis
the horizontal line of the two perpendicular number lines in a coordinate grid

y-axis
the vertical line of the two perpendicular number lines in a coordinate grid

Like line graphs, scatter plots are useful for interpreting data and making predictions. They often show trends in data.

GO ON

English Learner Strategy

The term *temperature* appears in many of the exercises. Have students use this word to describe the different seasons. Ask students to give examples of outdoor activities they could do during each season based on temperature. Encourage them to use the term in comparing activities, seasons, clothing, celebrations, etc. Point out the word whenever it appears in the examples and problems in the lesson.

Lesson Notes

Lesson Planner

Objective Identify relationships using data in a scatter plot.

Vocabulary coordinate grid , scatter plot , *x*-axis , *y*-axis

Materials/Manipulatives centimeter grid paper, rulers

Chapter Resource Masters

- CRM Vocabulary and English Language Development (p. A188)
- CRM Skills Practice (p. A189)
- CRM Problem-Solving Practice (p. A190)
- CRM Homework Practice (p. A191)

1 Introduce

Vocabulary

Trend Define *trend* as the general pattern formed by the points in a scatter plot. Tell students that a trend indicates a consistent change over time in a set of data, and can be used as the basis for predictions and projections.

2 Teach

Key Concept

Foundational Skills and Concepts After students have read through the Key Concept box, have them try these exercises.

1. Describe the relationship between two sets of data if one set increases while the other set decreases. This is a negative relationship.

2. If the points in a scatter plot show no definite pattern, describe the relationship between the data sets. There is no relationship.

Explain whether the scatter plot shows a *positive*, *negative*, or *no* relationship.

**Number of SportsAction
DVDs Sold**

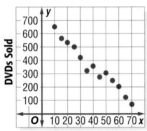

Days Since Release

1. Describe the two sets of data shown in the scatter plot.

The two sets of data are the days since release and the sales of SportsAction DVDs.

2. What do the *x*-axis and the *y*-axis represent?

The *x*-axis represents the days since release of the DVDs.

The *y*-axis represents the number of SportsAction DVDs sold.

3. As the number of days since release increases, what happens to the number of SportsAction DVDs sold?

The number of DVDs sold decreases.

4. The scatter plot shows a negative relationship between days since release and SportsAction DVDs sold.

Example 1

Explain whether the scatter plot shows a *positive*, *negative*, or *no* relationship.

1. Describe the two sets of data shown in the scatter plot.

   The two sets of data are the ages and the weights of thirty horses that are less than a year old.

2. What do the *x*-axis and the *y*-axis represent?

   The *x*-axis represents the ages of the horses.
   The *y*-axis represents the weights of the horses.

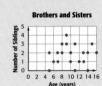

Growth of Horses

3. In general, as the ages of the horses increase, what happens to the weights of the horses?

   The weights increase.

4. The scatter plot shows a positive relationship between the ages and weights of the horses.

YOUR TURN!

Explain whether the scatter plot shows a *positive*, *negative*, or *no* relationship.

1. Describe the two sets of data shown in the scatter plot.

   The two sets of data are the ___ages of___ twenty students and the ___number of siblings they have___.

2. What do the *x*-axis and the *y*-axis represent?

   The *x*-axis represents the ___ages of the students___
   The *y*-axis represents the ___number of siblings___

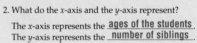

Brothers and Sisters

3. As the ages of the students increase, what happens to the number of siblings they have?

   ___There is no pattern.___

4. The scatter plot shows ___no___ relationship between the ages of the students and the number of siblings they have.

Example 2

Use the information in the table to create a scatter plot.

Create a scatter plot to show how the amount of snowfall affects the sales of sleds.

1. Set Snowfall (in.) on the *x*-axis.

2. Set Number of Sleds Sold on the *y*-axis.

3. Plot the points from the table.

Selling Sleds

Snowfall (in.)	0	0	1	2	3	3	4	4	5	6	6	7	7	8	9
Number of Sleds Sold	0	2	0	1	3	5	8	10	12	13	16	12	17	15	18

YOUR TURN!

Use the information in the table to create a scatter plot.

Create a scatter plot to show how the changes in outside temperature change over the course of seven hours.

1. Set <u>Number of Hours</u> on the *x*-axis.

2. Set <u>Temperature (in °F)</u> on the *y*-axis.

3. Plot the points from the table.

Outside Temperature

Number of Hours	1	2	3	4	5	6	7
Temperature (°F)	50	48	46	45	43	40	38

Who is Correct?

Explain whether the scatter plot "Selling Sleds" shows a *positive*, *negative*, or *no* relationship.

Addison
The points go down from left to right: negative relationship.

Tamyra
The points go up from left to right: positive relationship.

Carlos
The points show no pattern: no relationship.

Circle the correct answer(s). Cross out incorrect answer(s).

GO ON

Who is Correct?
Diagnostic Teaching

- Addison is incorrect. The points go up from left to right.

- Tamyra is correct. The points go up from left to right and the graph shows a positive relationship.

- Carlos is incorrect. The points do show a pattern.

Remind students that when both values increase, the relationship is positive.

Additional Example 2

Use the information in the table to create a scatter plot.

Create a scatter plot to show how the number in attendance of a baseball game affects the number of hot dogs sold.

1. Set Attendance (thousands) on the *x*-axis.

2. Set Number of Hot Dogs Sold on the *y*-axis.

3. Plot the points from the table.

Hot Dogs Sold at Baseball Games

Attendance (thousands)	4	5.2	6	7.1	9.5	10.4
Hot Dogs Sold	235	319	330	402	465	645

Attendance (thousands)	11.2	12.4	13.3	15.9	20.1
Hot Dogs Sold	649	635	757	872	1,127

3 Practice

Using Manipulatives

Centimeter Grid Paper   Have students use centimeter grid paper to practice plotting sets of data. Use the created graphs to determine if the relationships are positive, negative, or neither.

 On-Hand Manipulatives   Model how to use a ruler or straightedge to follow plotted points across and down to their corresponding labels.

Math Coach Notes

Outliers   Discuss how outliers in a data set can affect trends and predictions. Explain to students that when determining a trend, sometimes data falls outside the general range of gathered information. The outliers can skew trends or projections. Tell them to look at the data as a whole, or the larger picture the data represents.

⚠ Common Error Alert

Breaks in Scales   Students often do not see breaks in the scales of certain graphs. For example, in Exercise 1, the x-axis does not start at 0. The break indicates there is no data provided for 0 to 50.

 Guided Practice

Explain whether each scatter plot shows a *positive*, *negative*, or *no* relationship.

(1)   **Height of Students and Number of CDs**

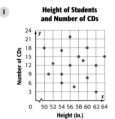

As the height increases, the number of CDs _show no pattern_____.

Describe the relationship between the height of students and the number of CDs that they own.

 _no relationship_____

(2)   **Lemonade Sales**

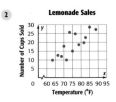

As the temperature increases, the number of cups sold _increase_____.

Describe the relationship between the temperature and the number of cups sold.

 _positive relationship_____

Step by Step Practice

Use the information in the table to create a scatter plot.

(3)   Create a scatter plot to show how the number of students in the Extreme Frisbee Club has changed over the course of six years.

Step 1   Set _____Year_____ on the x-axis.

Step 2   Set _Number of Students_ on the y-axis.

Step 3   Plot the points from the table.

Extreme Frisbee

Year	'03	'04	'05	'06	'07	'08	'09
Number of Students	4	9	13	16	23	25	30

 Are They Getting It?

Check students' understanding of scatter plots by writing these problems on the board. Ask them to point out incorrect answers and explain their reasoning.

T-Shirt Sales

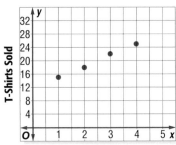

1. The data in the scatter plot shows a negative relationship. This is incorrect. The data shows a positive relationship.

2. During the second week about 18 T-shirts were sold. This is correct.

3. If the trend continues, the number of T-shirts sold during the fifth week will be about 22. This is incorrect. The predicted number of T-shirts sold will be about 29 or 30.

Echoing   Practice looking at a scatter plot and describing what it means with students. Explain what the x-axis shows, and have students explain it back to you in their own words. Do the same with the y-axis. Examine the plotted data to determine the relationship. Have students mimic this evaluation. Practice on several graphs, and eventually have students evaluate a scatter plot using their own words.

Use the information in the table to plan and create a scatter plot.

Year	'03	'04	'05	'06	'07	'08	'09
Number of Students	60	50	39	32	28	25	20

4 Set _____ on the x-axis.

5 Set _____ on the y-axis.

6

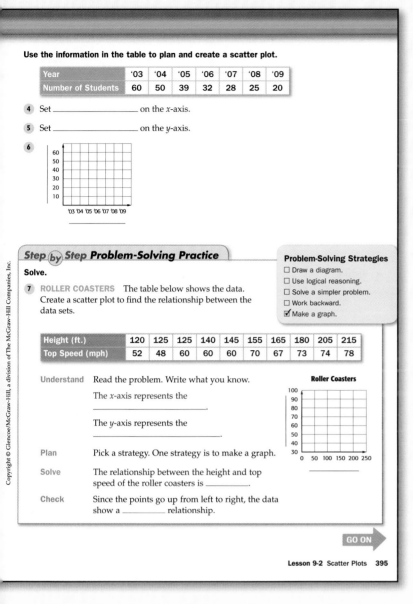

Step by Step Problem-Solving Practice

Solve.

7 ROLLER COASTERS   The table below shows the data. Create a scatter plot to find the relationship between the data sets.

Problem-Solving Strategies
☐ Draw a diagram.
☐ Use logical reasoning.
☐ Solve a simpler problem.
☐ Work backward.
☑ Make a graph.

Height (ft.)	120	125	125	140	145	155	165	180	205	215
Top Speed (mph)	52	48	60	60	60	70	67	73	74	78

Understand   Read the problem. Write what you know.

The x-axis represents the
_____.

The y-axis represents the
_____.

Plan   Pick a strategy. One strategy is to make a graph.

Solve   The relationship between the height and top speed of the roller coasters is _____.

Check   Since the points go up from left to right, the data show a _____ relationship.

Roller Coasters

GO ON

Intervention Strategy   Linguistic Learners

Scatter Plots and Predictions   Have students work in pairs. Tell them to use the data below to create a scatter plot on centimeter grid paper. Help students set up the x-and y-axis and model how to plot the first point. After the graphs are complete, ask pairs to discuss the scatter plots together. Have them write an explanation of the relationship shown and what the scatter plot means, including a prediction of how many $150-gift certificates would sell based on the trend.

Store Gift Certificates

Cost	$20	$25	$40	$50	$75	$100	$125
Number Sold	80	76	70	64	56	46	34

Assignments

Assign Exercises 10–12 so that students practice all the concepts presented in this lesson.

In-Class Assignment

Have students complete Exercises 10, 12, and 15 to ensure that they understand the concept.

Math Coach Notes

Correlations   Have students look at the scatter plot in Exercise 11. Ask them what it would mean in terms of the number of cups sold and the temperature, if the scatter plot showed a positive relationship. Have them predict the number of cups sold if the temperature was 60°F.

5 cups

---

8   PENCILS   Create a scatter plot to show the <u>number of weeks</u> that 20 pencils are used and the <u>pencil lengths</u>. Is the relationship *positive*, *negative*, or is there *no* relationship? Check off each step.

Time Used (Weeks)	0	0	1	1	2	2	3	3	3	4
Length (cm)	14	16	14	15	14	13	13	12	10	11

Time Used (Weeks)	4	$4\frac{1}{2}$	5	5	$5\frac{1}{2}$	6	6	6	$6\frac{1}{2}$	7
Length (cm)	10	8	9	7	7	8	7	6	6	7

Pencils

✔ ___ Understand: I underlined key words.

✔ ___ Plan: To solve the problem, I will _make a graph_

✔ ___ Solve: The answer is _____ _a negative relationship_

✔ ___ Check: I checked my answer by _looking at the points_

9   Reflect   A scatter plot shows the number of people in a family and their weekly grocery bill. Would you expect the graph of the data to show a positive, negative, or no relationship? Explain.

Positive; As the number of people in a family increases, the weekly grocery bill should also increase.

▶ Skills, Concepts, and Problem Solving

Explain whether each scatter plot shows a *positive*, *negative*, or *no* relationship.

10   As the ages increase, the weights _____ _increase_ .

Describe the relationship between the ages and weights of the gazelles.

positive relationship

Growth of Gazelles

11   As the temperature increases, the number of fans sold _____ _increases_ .

Describe the relationship between the temperature and fan sales.

positive relationship

Fan Sales

Math Challenge

Write and Support   Challenge students to write a situation that could be represented by a scatter plot showing a negative relationship. Include a graph to support the situation and a prediction based on the trend shown. For more proficient learners, challenge them to write a situation for each of the relationships discussed in this lesson.

---

12 **DROUGHT** A drought affects the depth of the pond. The table below shows the data. Create a scatter plot to find the relationship between the data sets.

Day	1	2	3	4	5	6	7	8
Depth (in.)	18.5	18.0	17.5	17.5	17.0	17.0	16.0	16.0

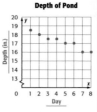
Depth of Pond

Describe the relationship between the number of days and depth of the pond.

negative relationship

Vocabulary Check Write the vocabulary word that completes each sentence.

13 A scatter plot displays two sets of data on the same graph.

14 If the points on a scatter plot appear to go downhill from left to right, then the data points show a negative relationship.

15 **Writing in Math** Describe how you can use a scatter plot to display two sets of related data.

Graph the two sets of data as ordered pairs, where the *x*-coordinate is a member

of one data set and the *y*-coordinate is a member of the other data set.

 Spiral Review (Lesson 9-1, p. 384)

Determine which ordered pair, (0, −5), (2, 10), or (−3, 15), is a solution of each equation.

16 $y = x + 8$

(2, 10)

17 $y = -5x$

(−3, 15)

18 $y = 3x - 5$

(0, −5)

Solve.

19 **FOOD** The equation $C = 2 + 1.5t$ represents the cost of a meal that includes a beverage and *t* tacos. Find three solutions of the equation. Describe what the solutions mean.

Sample answer: (1, 3.5), (2, 5), (3, 6.5); A meal with 1 taco costs $3.50,

a meal with 2 tacos costs $5.00, and a meal with 3 tacos costs $6.50.

 STOP

Lesson 9-2 Scatter Plots **397**

Ticket Out the Door

Relationships Tell students that a scatter plot shows the relationship between high school grade point averages and college application acceptances. As students approach the classroom door to exit, ask them to name the relationship represented in this graph.

See It, Do It, Say It, Write It

Step 1 Draw a scatter plot on the board, showing a positive relationship between the number of hours an employee worked and the number of books packaged.

Step 2 Tell students to determine the relationship shown in the scatter plot. Then they should predict the number of books packaged for a larger number of hours than shown on the graph.

Step 3 Have students work in pairs. Ask them to discuss what the scatter plot means and the type of relationship shown. They should share their predictions and explain their reasoning.

Step 4 Have students work alone to write an evaluation of the scatter plot on the board, including their prediction based on the trend. Encourage students to use correct vocabulary terms and clear language in their explanations.

Looking Ahead: Pre-Teach

In the next lesson, students will learn about lines of best fit.

Example

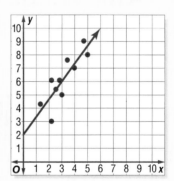

The blue line shows a line of best fit for the points in the scatter plot. Based on the graph, have students make conjectures about the meaning of the term "line of best fit."

Progress Check 1

Formative Assessment

Use the Progress Check to assess students' mastery of the previous lessons. Have students review the lesson indicated for the problems they answered incorrectly.

Odd/Even Assignments

Exercises are structured so that students practice the same concepts whether they are assigned the odd or even problems.

 Common Error *Alert*

Exercises 1–3 Caution students to pay close attention to the order in which they substitute values in for the variables. In all three equations, the *y* variable is listed first, but the second element of the ordered pairs given should be substituted for the *y*.

Exercises 6–8 Students may be confused about the directions for these problems because they must generate the values to substitute for *x*. Students need to understand there is an infinite number of ordered pairs that satisfy these equations. Encourage students to consider values that generate integral ordered pairs.

 Chapter 9

Progress Check 1 (Lessons 9-1 and 9-2)

Determine which ordered pair, (0, –4), (1, 5), or (4, 3), is a solution of each equation.

1 $y = x + 4$
(1, 5)

2 $y = x - 1$
(4, 3)

3 $y = 2x - 4$
(0, –4)

Complete the table for each equation. Then find three solutions for each equation.

4 $y = 5x$

x	5x	y
1	5(1)	5
4	5(4)	20
8	5(8)	40

(1, 5), (4, 20), (8, 40)

5 $y = 3x + 1$

x	3x + 1	y
–1	3(–1) + 1	–2
0	3(0) + 1	1
6	3(6) + 1	19

(–1, –2), (0, 1), (6, 19)

Find three solutions of each equation. Sample answers are given for Exercises 6–8.

6 $y = 12x$
(0, 0), (1, 12), (2, 24)

7 $y = x - 8$
(0, –8), (1, –7), (2, –6)

8 $y = 7x + 2$
(0, 2), (1, 9), (2, 16)

Solve.

9 **MEASUREMENT** The equation $P = 6s$ represents the perimeter of a regular hexagon with side length *s*. Find three solutions of the equation. Describe what the solutions mean.

Sample answer: (1, 6), (2, 12), (3, 18); The perimeter of a hexagon with a side length of 1 unit is 6 units. The perimeter of a hexagon with a side length of 2 units is 12 units. The perimeter of a hexagon with a side length of 3 units is 18 units.

Determine whether the scatter plot shows a *positive*, *negative*, or *no* relationship.

10 no relationship

Checking Out Library Items

Data-Driven Decision Making

Students missing Exercises . . .	Have trouble with . . .	Should review and practice . . .
1–3	determining if an ordered pair is a solution to an equation.	SSG Lesson 9-1, p. 384 CRM Skills Practice, p. A185
4–8	making a table for a given equation to find solutions.	SSG Lesson 9-1, p. 384 CRM Skills Practice, p. A185
9	describing solutions to an equation.	SSG Lesson 9-1, p. 384 CRM Skills Practice, p. A185
10	determining correlation from a scatter plot.	SSG Lesson 9-2, p. 391 CRM Skills Practice, p. A189

Lines of Best Fit

KEY Concept

If the points on a **scatter plot** come close to lying on a straight line, a **line of best fit** can be drawn to show the trend in the **data**. The line should be very close to most of the data points.

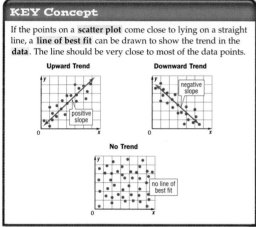

Upward Trend

positive slope

Downward Trend

negative slope

No Trend

no line of best fit

VOCABULARY

data
   information, often numerical, which is gathered for statistical purposes

line of best fit
   a line that is very close to most of the data points on a scatter plot

scatter plot
   in a scatter plot, two sets of related data are plotted as ordered pairs on the same graph

slope
   the rate of change between any two points on a line; the ratio of vertical change to horizontal change

A line of best fit is useful for showing trends in data and for making predictions. Since a line of best fit is an estimate, it is possible to draw slightly different lines for the same data.

Example 1

The scatter plot shows the length and weight of thirteen whale sharks. Draw a line of best fit. Then describe the slope of the line and the trend in the data.

1. Draw a line so that it runs through the center of the group of points.

2. The slope of the line of best fit is positive.

   It shows that there is an upward trend in the weight of whale sharks as the length increases.

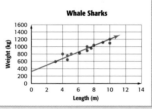

Whale Sharks

Weight (kg) / Length (m)

GO ON

Lesson 9-3 Lines of Best Fit **399**

Lesson Notes

Lesson Planner

Objective   Determine and describe a line of best fit.

Vocabulary   data, line of best fit, scatter plot, slope

Materials/Manipulatives   pipe cleaners, rulers, string, butcher paper, grid paper

Chapter Resource Masters

CRM Vocabulary and English Language Development (p. A192)

CRM Skills Practice (p. A193)

CRM Problem-Solving Practice (p. A194)

CRM Homework Practice (p. A195)

1 Introduce

Vocabulary

Predictions   Define *prediction* as the anticipation of a trend formed by studying statistical data. Predictions can be useful in projecting anticipated needs, preparing for growth, or adjusting to change.

2 Teach

Key Concept

Foundational Skills and Concepts   After students have read through the Key Concept box, have them try these exercises.

1. Define the term *line of best fit.* This is a line drawn on a scatter plot that is very close to most of the data points.

2. If the slope in a scatter plot increases from left to right, describe the trend represented. This indicates an upward trend, or positive relationship.

3. If the data in a scatter plot does not show a pattern, what does this mean about the data sets? There is no trend or relationship.

Additional *Example 1*

The scatter plot shows the height of sunflowers and the number of hours of daylight. Draw a line of best fit. Then describe the slope of the line and the trend in the data.

I. Draw a line so that it runs through the center of the group of points.

2. The slope of the line of best fit is positive. It shows there is an upward trend in the height of sunflowers as the number of hours of daylight increases.

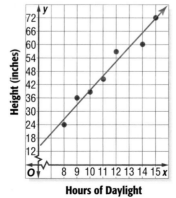

Height of Sunflowers

Height (inches) / Hours of Daylight

Lesson 9-3 Lines of Best Fit **399**

Additional *Example 2*

The scatter plot shows the weights of land animals and their speeds. Use the line of best fit shown to predict the speed an animal could move if it weighs about 2,000 pounds.

Speed of Animals

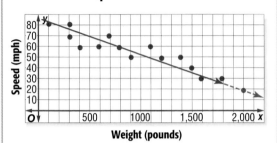

1. Use a ruler to extend the line.

2. Locate the point on the line that has an *x*-value of 2,000. Find the corresponding *y*-value.

   The corresponding *y*-value is about 20.

3. So, an animal that weighs about 2,000 pounds would travel at about 20 miles per hour.

YOUR TURN!

The scatter plot shows the number of pizzas that the school cafeteria sold during one lunch period. Draw a line of best fit. Then describe the slope of the line and the trend in the data.

1. Draw a line so that it runs through the center of the group of points.

2. The slope of a line of best fit is __negative__.

   It shows that there is a(n) __downward__ trend in the number of pizzas sold as the number of minutes increases.

Example 2

Use the line of best fit to predict the weight of a whale shark that is 13 meters long.

1. Use a ruler to extend the line.

2. Locate the point on the line that has an *x*-value of 13. Find the corresponding *y*-value.

   The corresponding *y*-value is about 1,500.

3. So, a whale shark that is 13 meters long would weigh about 1,500 kilograms.

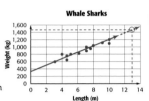

YOUR TURN!

Use the line of best fit shown to predict the length of the wait time for the ride at 9:30 P.M.

1. Use a ruler to extend the line.

2. Locate the point on the line that has an *x*-value of __9:30__. Find the corresponding *y*-value.

   The corresponding *y*-value is about __80__.

3. So, at 9:30, the wait time will be about __80 minutes__.

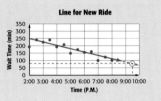

Intervention Strategy   Auditory Learners

Explaining to Others   Ask students to work in pairs. Tell them to discuss the scatter plot below. Tell them to explain what the graph means to their partners. Have pairs draw a line of best fit and describe the slope of the line and the trend in the data. Then ask groups to predict the test score for a student who slept 8 hours based on the trend. Discuss the predictions as a class.

Hours Slept

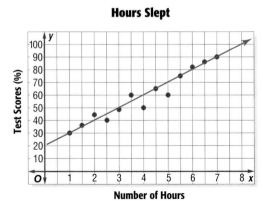

③ Practice

Using Manipulatives

Pipe Cleaners Have students practice finding lines of best fit using pipe cleaners. They can manipulate a pipe cleaner to determine the line that falls most closely along the plotted data. Then they can draw the line and use it to make predictions.

On-Hand Manipulatives Demonstrate how to determine the line of best fit using string. Draw a scatter plot on the board and model how to maneuver a piece of string to capture as many points above the string as below the string. Trace the string to draw the line of best fit on the graph.

Intervention Strategy   Interpersonal Learners

Scatter Plots Have students work in small groups. Tell them to discuss the scatter plot below. Ask them to explain the relationship shown and what the scatter plot means. Have the group develop a prediction about the population in 2010 based on the trend. Discuss the predictions as a class.

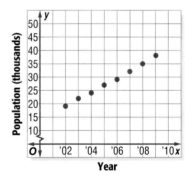

Population of Centerville

Who is Correct?

Describe the slope of the line and the trend in the data in the graph, "Line for New Ride."

Desmond — positive slope, upward trend

Martina — negative slope, no trend

Cassie — negative slope, downward trend

Circle the correct answer(s). Cross out incorrect answer(s).

▶ Guided Practice

Draw a line of best fit. Then describe the slope of the line and the trend in the data.

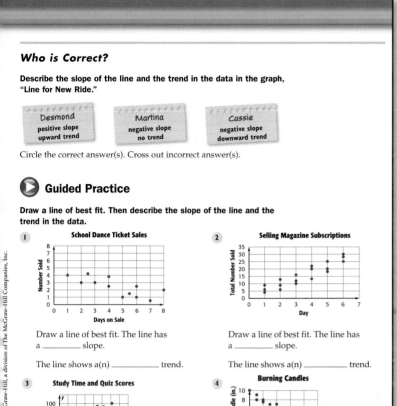

1. School Dance Ticket Sales

Draw a line of best fit. The line has a _____ slope.

The line shows a(n) _____ trend.

2. Selling Magazine Subscriptions

Draw a line of best fit. The line has a _____ slope.

The line shows a(n) _____ trend.

3. Study Time and Quiz Scores

Draw a line of best fit. The line has a _____ slope.

The line shows a(n) _____ trend.

4. Burning Candles

Draw a line of best fit. The line has a _____ slope.

The line shows a(n) _____ trend.

GO ON

Lesson 9-3 Lines of Best Fit **401**

Who *is Correct?*
Diagnostic Teaching

• Desmond is incorrect. The slope is negative.

• Martina is incorrect. A negative slope represents a downward trend.

• Cassie is correct.

Remind students that a negative slope goes downward from left to right, while a positive slope goes upward from left to right.

Copyright © Glencoe/McGraw-Hill, a division of The McGraw-Hill Companies, Inc.

Lesson 9-3 Lines of Best Fit **401**

Math Coach Notes

Estimations Remind students that the line of best fit is an estimate, so one student's line may not be exactly like another student's line. Try to find a line through the data that has about as many points above the line as below the line.

Use the line of best fit to predict how many pairs of new shoes a 15 year old will have.

5   The scatter plot shows the ages of fifteen children and the number of pairs of new shoes that they own.

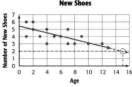

New Shoes

Step 1   Use a ruler to extend the line so that you can predict the *y*-value for an *x*-value of __15__.

Step 2   Locate the point on the line that has an *x*-value of __15__. Then move across to the *y*-axis to find the corresponding *y*-value.

The corresponding *y*-value is __2__.

Step 3   According to the scatter plot, a 15 year old will have about __2__ pairs of new shoes.

The scatter plot shows the number of blocks that students walked while participating in a walkathon.

6   Draw a line of best fit. Then describe the slope of the line and the trend in the data.

___positive slope; upward trend___

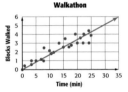

Walkathon

7   Use the line of best fit to predict how many blocks a student walked after 30 minutes.

___Sample answer: about 5 blocks___

Are They Getting It?

Check students' understanding of lines of best fit by writing these problems on the board. Ask them to point out incorrect answers and explain their reasoning.

1. The line of best fit shows a downward trend. This is correct.

2. As the recyclable bag sales increase, the number of plastic bags the store purchased also increase. This is incorrect. The purchase of plastic bags decreased.

Types of Bags

3. When the sales of recyclable bags reaches 50 boxes, the predicted number of plastic bags will be about 15 boxes. This is incorrect. The prediction will be closer to 5 boxes.

Step by Step Problem-Solving Practice

Solve.

8 SOCCER   The scatter plot shows the number of goals and the number of assists made by soccer players in a season. Use the line of best fit shown to predict how many assists a soccer player will have if she scores 25 goals.

Understand   Read the problem. Write what you know.

The points on the scatter plot represent the _number of goals_ and _number of assists_.

The line of best fit shows a(n) _upward trend_ in the number of assists as the number of goals increases.

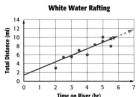

Plan   Pick a strategy. One strategy is to use a graph. Use a ruler to extend the line.

Solve   When the x-value is _25_, the corresponding y-value is about _30_.

So, if a soccer player scores 25 goals, you can predict that she will have about _30_ assists.

Check   Check your answer by plotting the point that you named on the scatter plot.

9 WHITE WATER RAFTING   The scatter plot shows the distances traveled by ten rafts on a river. Use the line of best fit to predict the total distance a raft will travel if it is on the river for 6.5 hours. Check off each step.

✔ Understand: I underlined key words.

✔ Plan: To solve the problem, I will _use a graph_.

✔ Solve: The answer is _about 11 miles_.

✔ Check: I checked my answer by _plotting_
_(6.5, 11)_

GO ON

Note This!
Neatness and Accuracy   Tell students when they create their own scatter plots, they need to work very neatly in order for the line of best fit to be as accurate as possible. This line is an estimate, but if the graph is not constructed carefully, the trends and predictions will be hard to decipher.

Intervention Strategy   Kinesthetic Learners

Using Butcher Paper   Have students work in small groups. Tell them to use the data below to create a scatter plot on large butcher paper. Remind students to label x- and y-axes and plot their ordered pairs carefully. After the graphs are complete, ask groups to discuss what the scatter plot means, determine a line of best fit, and predict how many participants will be involved in 2009. Have groups share the slopes of their lines, describe the trend, and tell their predictions.

Intramural Baseball Teams

Year	2003	2004	2005	2006	2007	2008	2009
Number of Participants	60	76	105	125	155	179	

Odd/Even Assignments

Exercises 11–16 are structured so that students practice the same concepts whether they are assigned the odd or even problems.

In-Class Assignment

Have students complete Exercises 11, 13, 15, 16, and 19 to ensure that they understand the concept.

Common Error *Alert*

Exercises 13–14   Remind students to take time to study the data and trend before making a prediction. Emphasize the importance of examining the scatter plot first before jumping right to the last ordered pair plotted. Consider any outliers and look at the graph as a whole.

Math Coach Notes

No Trend   Use Exercise 10 to discuss scatter plots that show no trend. Explain that sometimes two data sets have no correlation. For these plots you cannot draw a line of best fit to represent the data. Therefore, predictions also cannot be made based on the plot. Discuss examples of data sets that would show no trend, such as the height of a student and birth month, or a person's age and hair color.

---

10 **Reflect**   The scatter plot shows the amount of rain that fell during the first ten days of the month. Explain whether you can draw a line of best fit for the data.

There is no relationship between the days and the amount of rain. So, you cannot draw a line of best fit to represent the data.

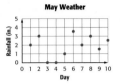

▶ Skills, Concepts, and Problem Solving

Draw a line of best fit. Then describe the slope of the line and the trend in the data.

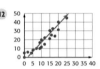

11

negative slope; downward trend

12

positive slope; upward trend

Use the line of best fit to make predictions.

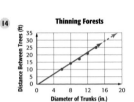

13 Lizards in Pet Store

Use the line of best fit to predict how many lizards will be in the pet store on the 12th day.

3 lizards

14 Thinning Forests

Use the line of best fit to predict the distance between trees if the trunks have a diameter of 16 inches.

30 ft

Math Challenge

Three Scatter Plots   Challenge students to create three scatter plots: one that shows an upward trend, one that shows a downward trend, and a third that shows no trend. Tell students to label the axes and plot the points carefully. Have them display their scatter plots for classmates to determine the lines of best fit and the trend in the data. Have proficient learners write questions that ask classmates to make predictions based on their trends. Tell students to include an answer key with their questions.

Solve.

15 **PLANTS** The scatter plot shows the height of plants that were planted from seeds. Draw a line of best fit. Then describe the slope of the line and the trend in the data.

<u>positive slope; upward trend</u>

Growth of Plants

16 Use the line of best fit that was drawn to predict the height of a plant after 8 weeks.

<u>about 8 centimeters</u>

Vocabulary Check **Write the vocabulary word that completes each sentence.**

17 A <u>line of best fit</u> is a line that is very close to most of the data points on a scatter plot.

18 If the slope of a line of best fit is positive, then the points on the scatter plot show a(n) <u>upward</u> trend.

19 **Writing in Math** Explain how to use a line of best fit to make a prediction.

<u>Sample answer: Use a ruler to extend the line so that it passes through the *x*-value</u>

<u>for which you want to predict. Locate the *x*-value on the line and determine the</u>

<u>corresponding *y*-value.</u>

▶ Spiral Review

The scatter plot shows the costs of used cars. (Lesson 9-2, p. 391)

20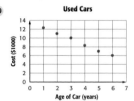

Used Cars

As the age of the car increases, the cost of the car <u>decreases</u>.

Describe the relationship between the age of the car and its cost.

<u>negative relationship</u>

STOP

④ Assess

See It, Do It, Say It, Write It

Step 1 Draw a scatter plot on the board, showing a negative relationship between the number of one-mile heats a runner practiced and the rate of speed of the runner.

Step 2 Tell students to draw a line of best fit for the scatter plot. Then they should describe the slope of the line and trend in the data, and predict the runner's rate of speed after 10 practices.

Step 3 Have students work in pairs. Ask them to discuss the slope of the line of best fit and their predictions based on the trend. Tell them to explain their reasoning for their predictions.

Step 4 Have students work alone to write an evaluation of the scatter plot's line of best fit, including their prediction based on the trend.

Ticket Out the Door

Trends Tell students that a scatter plot shows the relationship between leg length and natural stride length. As students approach the classroom door to exit, ask them to name the type of trend this data would show. This data would show a positive trend.

Progress Check 2

Formative Assessment

Use the Progress Check to assess students' mastery of the previous lessons. Have students review the lesson indicated for the problems they answered incorrectly.

Assignments

Exercises are structured so that students practice the same concepts whether they are assigned Exercises 1–4 or Exercises 5–8.

Chapter 9 **Progress Check** (Lesson 9-3)

Use the scatter plot to the right to complete Exercises 1–4.

1. As the time spent studying increases, do the test scores increase, decrease, or show no pattern?

   __increase__

2. Is there a relationship between the time spent studying and test scores? If so, describe the relationship.

   __yes; positive__

3. Draw a line of best fit on the scatter plot.

4. Use the line of best fit to predict the test score of a student who studies for 30 minutes.

   __Sample answer: 60__

Use the scatter plot to the right to complete Exercises 5–8.

5. As the number of meals eaten at home increases, does the number of meals eaten at a restaurant increase, decrease, or show no pattern?

   __decrease__

6. Is there a relationship between the number of meals eaten at home, and number of meals eaten at a restaurant? If so, describe the relationship.

   __yes; negative__

7. Draw a line of best fit on the scatter plot.

8. Use the line of best fit to find the number of meals eaten at home if there are 20 meals eaten at a restaurant.

   __Sample answer: 6 meals at home__

406　Chapter 9 Two-Variable Data

Data-Driven Decision Making

Students missing Exercises . . .	Have trouble with . . .	Should review and practice . . .
1, 5	finding a trend in a scatter plot.	SSG Lesson 9-3, p. 399 CRM Skills Practice, p. A193
2, 6	describing a data trend using a scatter plot.	SSG Lesson 9-3, p. 399 CRM Skills Practice, p. A193
3, 7	drawing a line of best fit.	SSG Lesson 9-3, p. 399 CRM Skills Practice, p. A193
4, 8	making a prediction using a line of best fit.	SSG Lesson 9-3, p. 399 CRM Skills Practice, p. A193

Vocabulary and Concept Check

coordinate grid, *p. 391*

data, *p. 399*

line of best fit, *p. 399*

ordered pair, *p. 384*

scatter plot, *p. 391*

slope, *p. 399*

solution, *p. 384*

x-axis, *p. 391*

x-coordinate, *p. 384*

y-axis, *p. 391*

y-coordinate, *p. 384*

Write the vocabulary word that completes each sentence.

1. A(n) __x-coordinate__ is the first number of an ordered pair.

2. Information which is gathered for statistical purposes is called __data__.

3. A(n) __solution__ is the value of a variable that makes an equation true.

4. The vertical line of the two perpendicular number lines in a coordinate grid is called the __y-axis__.

5. A(n) __coordinate grid__ is a grid in which a horizontal number line and a vertical number line intersect at their zero points.

Lesson Review

9-1 Transition to Two-Variable Data (pp. 384–390)

6. Which ordered pair, (3, 9) or (1, 6), is a solution of $y = x + 5$?

   __(1, 6)__

7. Which ordered pair, (2, 8) or (4, 10), is a solution of $y = 3x + 2$?

   __(2, 8)__

8. Which ordered pair, (2, −3) or (0, −5), is a solution of $y = 5x − 5$?

   __(0, −5)__

Example 1

Which ordered pair, (5, 4) or (1, 3), is a solution of $y = x − 1$?

1. Substitute the x- and y-values of (5, 4) into the equation.

   $y = x − 1$
   $4 \stackrel{?}{=} 5 − 1$
   $4 = 4 \checkmark$ a solution

2. Substitute the x- and y-values of (1, 3) into the equation.

   $y = x − 1$
   $3 \stackrel{?}{=} 1 − 1$
   $3 \neq 0$ not a solution

Classroom Management

Pair and Share   Pair a student who has a good grasp of the material with another student who could use some support. Have students take turns explaining the examples to each other. They will both benefit, whether by doing the explaining or having the material explained to them.

Study Guide
Formative Assessment

Vocabulary and Concept Check

If students have difficulty answering Exercises 1–5, remind them that they can use the page references to refresh their memories about the vocabulary terms.

Vocabulary Review Strategies

Vocabulary Flashcards   Have students create vocabulary flashcards for the words. On the set of cards, on one side state the definition and on the other side write the vocabulary term. If a picture can be drawn of the vocabulary term, then make a second card for these terms. Some of the terms may have both a *word* card and a *drawing* the student will have to recognize.

Students can use the flashcards as study tools by either looking at the vocabulary term and stating its definition (flipping the card over to see if they got the definition correct), or by reading the side with the definition or looking at the side with the picture and stating the corresponding vocabulary term, (flipping the card over to see if they got the correct term).

Lesson Review

The examples walk the students through determining if an ordered pair is a solution to an equation, finding solutions to equations, determining correlation from a scatter plot, and using a line of best fit. If the given examples are not sufficient to review the questions, have students design their own examples from a particular section of the chapter. When finished, have them share their examples and their solutions with a partner.

Find **Extra Practice** for these concepts in the Practice Worksheets, pages A184–A195.

Review Remind students to complete and refer to their Foldables as they progress through the Chapter 9 Study Guide. Have students share and compare their completed Foldables with a partner. You may also choose to have them use their Foldable as a study aid in preparing for the Chapter Test. (For complete instructions, see Chapter Resource Masters, p. A181.)

Two-Variable Data

Note This!

Create a Checklist Help students create a study checklist. The checklist should include all of the following items:

- Notes from class
- Sketches, drawings, or graphs in their notebooks
- Foldables
- Vocabulary terms and definitions
- Lesson Examples
- Written assignments and quizzes
- Chapter 9 Study Guide

Find three solutions for each equation. Sample answers:

9 $y = x + 4$

  (0, 4), (1, 5), (2, 6)

10 $y = 3x - 2$

  (0, −2), (1, 1), (2, 4)

11 $y = 2x + 7$

  (0, 7), (1, 9), (2, 11)

12 $y = -x - 2$

  (0, −2), (1, −3), (2, −4)

13 $y = -2x + 3$

  (0, 3), (1, 1), (2, −1)

Example 2

Find three solutions for the equation $y = 2x + 1$.

1. Make a table. Select three values for x. Substitute the values for x in the expression $2x + 1$.

2. Complete the table. Find y. Then write the ordered pairs.

x	$2x + 1$	y	(x, y)
0	2(0) + 1	1	(0, 1)
1	2(1) + 1	3	(1, 3)
2	2(2) + 1	5	(2, 5)

3. Three solutions of the equation $y = 2x + 1$ are (0, 1), (1, 3), and (2, 5).

9-2 Scatter Plots (pp. 391–397)

Explain whether each scatter plot shows a *positive*, *negative*, or *no* relationship.

14

Gas Mileage

negative

15

Weight Gain

positive

Example 3

Explain whether the scatter plot below shows a *positive*, *negative*, or *no* relationship.

The scatter plot shows the number of hours worked and the number of calls received by a customer service center.

Customer Service Calls

1. The x-axis represents the number of hours worked. The y-axis represents the calls received.

2. In general, as the number of hours worked increases, the calls received increases.

3. The scatter plot shows a positive relationship between the hours worked and the calls received.

408 Chapter 9 Study Guide

Intervention Strategy Logical Learners

Making Tables Suggest to students that even when problems do not include tables of values, it is a good idea to make tables and show their substitutions and computations in the tables. This provides a good starting point for anyone trying to help students study or troubleshoot an incorrect answer.

9-3 Lines of Best Fit (pp. 399–405)

Draw a line of best fit for each scatter plot. Then describe the slope of the line and the trend in the data.

16

Cookies Baked

positive; upward

17

Run Times

negative; downward

18 Use the line of best fit drawn in Exercise 16 to predict how many cookies 10 bakers will bake.

250 cookies

19 Use the line of best fit drawn in Exercise 17 to predict how many miles can be completed if it takes someone 20 minutes to run a mile.

3 miles

Example 5

Draw a line of best fit for each scatter plot. Then describe the slope of the line and the trend in the data.

The scatter plot shows the height and weight of the young men in a middle school.

Heights and Weights

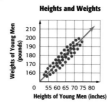

1. Draw a line so that it runs through the center of the group of points.

2. The slope of the line of best fit is positive. It shows that there is an upward trend in the young mens' weights as their heights increase.

Example 6

Use the line of best fit drawn in Example 5. Predict how much a young man who is 76 inches tall would weigh.

1. Use a ruler to extend the line.

2. Locate the point on the line with an x-value of 76. Then move across to the y-axis to find the corresponding y-value.

   The corresponding y-value is about 205.

3. So, a young man that is 76 inches tall would weigh about 205 pounds.

Chapter 9 Study Guide **409**

Note This!

Reference Graphs In their notebooks, students should include small graphs that show a positive relationship, negative relationship, and no relationship. With each graph, write the appropriate description.

For positive, as *x* increases, *y* increases.
For negative, as *x* increases, *y* decreases.
For none, no pattern visible.

Ticket Out the Door

Name the Ordered Pair Solution Write the equation $y = 5x - 11$ on the board. Tell students to spend a minute looking at the equation before leaving the classroom. As a student approaches the classroom door, name a value for *x*. The student should calculate the corresponding value of *y* and state the ordered pair solution to you.

Chapter Resource Masters

Additional forms of the Chapter 9 Tests are available.

Test Format	Where to Find it
Chapter 9 Test	Math Online > glencoe.com
Blackline Masters	Assessment Masters, p. 129

Customize and create multiple versions of your chapter tests and their answer keys. All of these questions from the chapter tests are available on ExamView® Assessment Suite.

Online Assessment and Reporting

glencoe.com

This online assessment tool allows teachers to track student progress with easily-accessible, comprehensive reports available for every student. Assess students using any Internet-ready computer.

Alternative Assessment

Showing Solutions and Non-Solutions   Ask students to use Exercises 3-6 from the Chapter Test to create pages for their portfolios. For each equation, students should create a table of values. In the table, have them select three values for x and find their corresponding values for y. Then students should select two different values for x with values of y that do not form ordered pair solutions. Tell them to explain why these ordered pairs are not solutions to the equation.

Chapter Test

Complete the table for each equation. Then find three solutions for each equation.

1 $y = x - 2$

x	x − 2	y
1	1 − 2	−1
3	3 − 2	1
5	5 − 2	3

(1, −1), (3, 1), (5, 3)

2 $y = -3x + 2$

x	−3x + 2	y
−2	−3(−2) + 2	8
2	−3(2) + 2	−4
4	−3(4) + 2	−10

(−2, 8), (2, −4), (4, −10)

Determine which ordered pair, (1, 2) or (2, 8), is a solution of each equation.

3 $y = x + 6$

(2, 8)

4 $y = 2x$

(1, 2)

5 $y = 3x + 2$

(2, 8)

6 $y = -2x + 4$

(1, 2)

Explain whether each scatter plot shows a *positive*, *negative*, or *no* relationship.

7

Chili Sales

As the temperature increases, the number of bowls of chili sold decreases.

Describe the relationship between the temperature and the number of bowls of chili sold.

negative relationship

8

Backyard Gardens

As yard lengths increase, the yard widths show no pattern.

Describe the relationship between the yard length and yard width.

no relationship

English Learner Strategy

Assessment   Allow students time to look over the assessment. Have the students take a close look at all the problem directions, as well as any terms in the word problems. Be sure the students understand what is being asked of them in each problem. If necessary, provide them with dictionaries. Also have the students identify and list the vocabulary terms from the chapter as they read through the assessment. If necessary, review the meanings of all essential math vocabulary.

Use the scatter plot of the number of students who drove to school from 2004 to 2009 to complete Exercises 9–10.

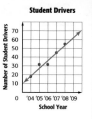

Student Drivers

9 Do the data in the scatter plot show a *positive*, *negative*, or *no* relationship? Explain.

  Positive; As the years increase, the number of
  students who drive to school increases.

10 Draw a line of best fit. Predict the number of students who will drive to school in 2009.

  Sample answer: 62 students

Solve.

11 **CELL PHONES** A local cell phone company charges a connection fee of $10. The company also charges 2 cents per minute for all calls. The equation $y = 0.02x + 10$ represents the total monthly cost (y) of using x minutes of air time. Find three solutions of the equation when $x = 10$, 100, and 1,000. Explain the solutions.

  (10, 10.2), (100, 12), (1000, 30); This means that 10 minutes of air time costs
  $10.20, 100 minutes costs is $12, and 1000 minutes costs $30.

12 The scatter plot shows the number of points scored and the number of assists made by basketball players in one season. Draw a line of best fit. Predict how many assists a basketball player will have if he scores 40 points.

  2 assists

2009–2010 Season

Correct the mistakes.

13 The equation $y = -2x + 1$ was written on the board. The teacher asked the class to give the solution if $x = -1$. Ken answered $(-1, 3)$, and Mila answered $(-1, -1)$. Who is correct? What mistake was made?

  Ken is correct. Mila substituted positive 1 for x when
  she should have substituted -1 for x.

STOP

Review Discuss commonly missed questions or topics in small groups or as a class. Ask students to share their methods of answering each question. Try to find out if the mistakes are computational or whether they lack adequate understanding of the topic. Some further explanation may be required accordingly.

Data-Driven Decision Making

Students missing Exercises . . .	Have trouble with . . .	Should review and practice . . .
1–2	making a table for a given equation to find solutions.	SSG Lesson 9-1, p. 384 CRM Skills Practice, p. A185
3–6	determining if an ordered pair is a solution to an equation.	SSG Lesson 9-1, p. 384 CRM Skills Practice, p. A185
7–8	describing a data trend using a scatter plot.	SSG Lessons 9-2 and 9-3, pp. 391 and 399 CRM Skills Practice, p. A189 and A193
9–10	drawing a line of best fit and making a prediction.	SSG Lesson 9-3, p. 399 CRM Skills Practice, p. A193
11–13	solving a word problem using a scatter plot.	CRM Problem-Solving Practice, pp. A186, A190, and A194

Diagnose Student Errors

Survey student responses for each item. Class trends may indicate common errors and misconceptions.

1. (A) correct
   B   data does not go down from left to right
   C   there is a pattern in the data
   D   guess

2. A   did not substitute correctly
   B   guess
   (C) correct
   D   did not substitute correctly

3. A   simplified incorrectly after substituting for *x*
   B   reversed *x* and *y*, miscalculated
   C   reversed *x* and *y*
   (D) correct

4. A   shows positive relationship
   (B) correct
   C   shows negative relationship
   D   shows negative relationship

5. (A) correct
   B   only considered first and last ordered pairs
   C   guess
   D   only considered first and last ordered pairs

6. A   did not consider negative sign
   B   guess
   C   guess
   (D) correct

7. A   used incorrect sign on *x*
   B   inverted negative signs
   (C) correct
   D   multiplied incorrectly

8. A   data does not go up from left to right
   B   data does not go down from left to right
   (C) correct
   D   guess

9. A   misinterpreted question
   B   chose last data point
   (C) correct
   D   incorrectly used line of best fit

Chapter 9 **Test Practice**

Choose the best answer and fill in the corresponding circle on the sheet at the right.

1 Which of the following best describes the relationship between the number of tickets and miles per hour over the speed limit in this scatter plot?

Speeding Tickets

(A) positive relationship

B   negative relationship

C   no relationship

D   unknown

---

2 Which is a solution of the equation $y = -2x + 5$?

A $(0, 3)$

B $(7, 0)$

(C) $(-1, 7)$

D $(1, -7)$

---

3 Find two solutions of the equation $y = x - 2$.

A $(1, -3), (2, -4)$

B $(3, 5), (0, 2)$

C $(-2, 0), (3, 5)$

(D) $(0, -2), (5, 3)$

---

4 Which of the following scatter plots shows no relationship between *x* and *y*?

A

(B)

C

D

---

5 Find three solutions of the equation $y = 2x + 3$.

(A) $(0, 3), (1, 5), (2, 7)$

B $(0, 3), (1, 1), (2, 7)$

C $(2, 3), (3, 4), (4, 5)$

D $(0, 3), (2, 3), (4, 11)$

6 (5, 10) is a solution to which of the following equations?

A $y = -2x$

B $y = x + 2$

C $y = x - 2$

D $y = 2x$

---

7 Which is a solution to the equation $y = -5x - 5$?

A $(-2, -15)$

B $(-2, 15)$

C $(2, -15)$

D $(2, 5)$

---

8 Which of the following best describes the relationship between age and amount of water consumed per day in this scatter plot?

Drinking Water Habits

A positive relationship

B negative relationship

C no relationship

D unknown

9 The scatter plot shows the temperature at various times of one day. Use a line of best fit to predict the temperature at 2:00 P.M.

Hourly Temperatures

A 40°

B 70°

C 80°

D 90°

ANSWER SHEET

Directions: Fill in the circle of each correct answer.

1 (A) (B) (C) (D)
2 (A) (B) (C) (D)
3 (A) (B) (C) (D)
4 (A) (B) (C) (D)
5 (A) (B) (C) (D)
6 (A) (B) (C) (D)
7 (A) (B) (C) (D)
8 (A) (B) (C) (D)
9 (A) (B) (C) (D)

Success Strategy

After answering all the questions, go back and check the signs and operations, making sure you worked each problem correctly.

STOP

Diagnosing Student Errors and Misconceptions

Polls When working on the Test Practice problems, have students show their work on a separate sheet of notebook paper that can be used later as a reference as needed. After the class has completed the Test Practice problems, randomly solicit answers to each question. After each question, take an informal poll of how many students answered the question correctly. If you notice that a significant number of students missed a particular question or questions, then review the method or strategy behind the question with the entire class.

A

Above-Level Suggestions, 9, 16, 25, 31, 37, 54, 55, 61, 68, 77, 86, 103, 110, 117, 124, 143, 150, 158, 166, 185, 191, 199, 206, 223, 229, 237, 245, 253, 279, 286, 294, 302, 310, 319, 328, 346, 354, 362, 370, 388, 396, 404

absolute value, 19

Academic Connections
chemistry, 45, 62
earth science, 208
geometry, 110, 205
health, 45, 221
science, 60, 222

Acceleration. *See Above-Level Suggestions*

acute angles, 138, 145

add
angles, 153–160
integers, 11–17

Addressing Individual Needs. *See Differentiated Instruction*

Advance, Online Assessment and Reporting, 2B, 44, 48B, 92, 96B, 132, 136B, 174, 178B, 212, 216B, 268, 272B, 336, 340B, 378, 382B, 410

Advanced Learners. *See Above-Level Suggestions*

algebra
evaluate expressions, 105–111
relate equations and formulas, 119–125
scatter plots, 391–397
solve equations, 113–118
transition to two-variable data, 384–390
write an equation, 259

algebraic expressions
defined, 105, 113
evaluate, 105–111
solve, 113–118

alternate exterior angles, 161

alternate interior angles, 161

Alternative Assessment
showing solutions and non-solutions, 410
use portfolios, 44, 92, 132, 174, 212, 268, 336, 378

angle measures, percents and, 349–355

angle relationships, 161

angles, 138–144
add, 153–160

Answer Sheet, 47, 95, 135, 177, 215, 271, 339, 381, 413

area, 119
real-world application, 238

Are They Getting It?, 7, 14, 23, 30, 35, 53, 59, 67, 75, 84, 101, 107, 115, 122, 141, 148, 156, 164, 183, 190, 197, 204, 220, 228, 235, 243, 251, 258, 277, 284, 293, 301, 309, 318, 327, 345, 352, 360, 369, 387, 394, 402

Are You Ready?
quiz, 3, 49, 97, 137, 179, 217, 273, 341, 383

Assessments
Alternative Assessment
showing solutions and non-solutions, 410
use portfolios, 44, 92, 132, 174, 212, 268, 336, 378
Diagnostic Assessment, 2B, 3, 48B, 49, 96B, 97, 136B, 137, 178B, 179, 216B, 217, 272B, 273, 340B, 341, 382B, 383
Formative Assessment
Are They Getting It?, 7, 14, 23, 30, 35, 53, 59, 67, 75, 84, 101, 107, 115, 122, 141, 148, 156, 164, 183, 190, 197, 204, 220, 228, 235, 243, 251, 258, 277, 284, 293, 301, 309, 318, 327, 345, 352, 360, 369, 387, 394, 402
Lesson Review, 40, 88, 127, 169, 209, 263, 331, 374, 407
Progress Check, 18, 39, 63, 87, 112, 126, 152, 168, 193, 208, 231, 247, 262, 296, 314, 330, 356, 373, 398, 406
Study Guide, 40, 88, 127, 169, 209, 263, 331, 374, 407
Vocabulary Review Strategies
color code, 127
flashcards, 209, 407
frames, 88, 263
games, 169
puzzles, 374
table, 40
word search, 331
Summative Assessment
Alternative Assessment
showing solutions and non-solutions, 410
use portfolios, 44, 92, 132, 174, 212, 268, 336, 378
Chapter Test, 44–45, 92–93, 132–133, 174–175, 212–213, 268–269, 336–337, 378–379, 410–411
See It, Do It, Say It, Write It, 10, 17, 26, 32, 38, 56, 62, 70, 78, 86, 104, 111, 118, 125, 144, 151, 160, 167, 186, 192, 200, 207, 224, 230, 238, 246, 254, 261, 280, 288, 295, 304, 313, 322, 329, 347, 355, 364, 372, 389, 397, 405
Test Practice, 46–47, 94–95, 134–135, 176–177, 214–215, 270–271, 338–339, 380–381, 412–413
Ticket Out the Door, 10, 17, 26, 32, 38, 43, 56, 62, 70, 78, 86, 91, 104, 111, 118, 125, 131, 144, 151, 160, 167, 173, 186, 192, 200, 207, 211, 224, 230, 238, 246, 254, 261, 267, 280, 288, 295, 304, 313, 322, 329, 335, 348, 355, 364, 372, 377, 390, 397, 405, 409

Assignments
In-Class Assignments, 8, 16, 25, 31, 37, 55, 61, 69, 77, 85, 103, 110, 117, 123, 143, 150, 158, 166, 185, 191, 199, 206, 222, 229, 237, 245, 253, 260, 278, 286, 294, 302, 312, 320, 328, 346, 354, 363, 371, 389, 396, 404
Odd/Even Assignments, 8, 16, 18, 25, 31, 37, 39, 55, 61, 63, 69, 77, 85, 87, 103, 110, 112, 117, 123, 126, 143, 150, 152, 158, 166, 168, 185, 191, 193, 199, 206, 208, 222, 229, 231, 237, 245, 247, 253, 260, 262, 278, 286, 294, 296, 302, 312, 314, 320, 328, 330, 346, 354, 356, 363, 371, 373, 389, 396, 398, 404, 406

Auditory Learners. *See Learning Styles*

average, 289

B

Back-Mapping, 2B, 48B, 96B, 136B, 178B, 216B, 272B, 340B, 382B

bar graphs
create, 305–313
interpret, 297–304

base, 98, 218

Below-Level Suggestions, 2, 2D, 5, 7, 8, 9, 12, 15, 19, 23, 24, 27, 30, 31, 34, 36, 41, 42, 48, 48D, 51, 55, 59, 60, 65, 66, 71, 73, 74, 75, 76, 79, 81, 82, 85, 96, 96D, 102, 104, 108, 116, 123, 129, 136, 136D, 138, 139, 142, 146, 149, 150, 153, 154, 155, 159, 161, 165, 166, 170, 171, 178, 178D, 184, 189, 198, 202, 204, 210, 216, 216D, 221, 223, 232, 236, 240, 241, 244, 249, 255, 259, 260, 266, 272, 274, 278, 279, 281, 287, 290, 292, 297, 300, 302, 305, 306, 311, 315, 323, 325, 333, 340, 340D, 344, 350, 353, 357, 361, 365, 368, 375, 382, 382D, 385, 395, 400, 401, 403, 408

C

calculator, use to check answer, 244

center, 365

Chapter Assessment Manager, 2B, 48B, 96B, 136B, 178B, 216B, 272B, 340B, 382B

Chapter-at-a-Glance, 2A, 48A, 96A, 136A, 178A, 216A, 272A, 340A, 382A

Chapter Notes, 2, 48, 96, 136, 178, 216, 272, 340, 382

Chapter Overview, 2A–2D, 48A–48D, 96A–96D, 136A–136D, 178A–178D, 216A–216D, 272A–272D, 340A–340D, 382A–382D

Chapter Preview, 3, 49, 97, 137, 139, 217, 273, 341, 383

Chapter Resource Manager, 2C–2D, 48C–48D, 96C–96D, 136C–136D, 178C–178D, 216C–216D, 272C–272D, 340C–340D, 382C–382D

Chapter Resource Masters, A1–A195

Chapter Test, 44–45, 92–93, 132–133, 174–175, 212–213, 268–269, 336–337, 378–379, 410–411

circle graphs
  create, 365–372
  interpret, 357–364

classify, triangle by sides and angles, 145

classify and sort, 274–280

Classroom Management
  early finishers, 127, 169, 209, 331
  group practice, 88, 263
  group time, 374
  pair and share, 40, 407

Common Error Alerts/Common Student Misconceptions, 10, 25, 35, 53, 55, 69, 74, 77, 83, 121, 123, 152, 157, 164, 168, 205, 208, 229, 231, 236, 251, 266, 277, 284, 296, 310, 320, 328, 345, 352, 356, 362, 371, 387, 398, 404
  absolute value, 21
  add integers with visual aids, 14
  add two negative numbers, 14
  breaks in scales, 394
  circle and check, 102
  correct formula, 260
  denominators, 190
  eliminate wrong answers, 47, 215
  find the divisor, 373
  graph lines, 262
  key words, 193
  labels, 254
  label variables, 63
  more with exponents, 85
  multi-step problems, 15, 24, 32, 38, 60, 117, 197, 222
  one step at a time, 112
  ordered pairs, 66
  plot a picture, 68
  question format, 353
  read the protractor, 140
  rewrite as addition, 42
  simplifying, 130
  simplifying steps, 128
  sizes of angles, 142
  slope, 262
  square root of 1, 227
  substitute correctly, 129
  substitute values for variables, 107
  tables, 279
  total data collected, 361
  use diagrams, 18
  use models, 126
  use self-guided questioning, 90
  watch the signs!, 39
  Who is Correct?, 82

Commutative Property of Addition, 11

complementary angles, 153

congruent, 145

congruent angles, 161

Content-at-a-Glance, 2A, 48A, 96A, 136A, 178A, 216A, 272A, 340A, 382A

convert, remainder into fraction, 290, 292, 294, 296

coordinate grid, 64, 71–78, 248, 391

Correct the Mistakes, 45, 93, 133, 175, 213, 269, 337, 411

corresponding angles, 161

cross product, 194

data, 281, 357, 365
  and creating circle graphs, 365–372
  interpret using circle graphs, 357–364
  and lines of best fit, 399–405
  and scatter plots, 391–397
  transition to two-variable, 384–390

Data-Driven Decision Making, 18, 39, 45, 63, 87, 93, 112, 126, 133, 152, 168, 175, 193, 208, 213, 231, 247, 262, 269, 296, 314, 330, 337, 356, 373, 379, 398, 406, 411

degree, 138, 349

denominator, 349

Diagnose Student Errors, 46, 94, 134, 176, 214, 270, 338, 380, 412

Diagnosing Student Errors and Common Misperceptions
  common errors, 135
  corrections, 47
  polls, 47, 95, 215, 413
  review, 177
  scoring guides, 271, 339
  self-check, 381

Diagnostic Assessment, 2B, 3, 48B, 49, 96B, 97, 136B, 137, 178B, 179, 216B, 217, 272B, 273, 340B, 341, 382B, 383

Diagnostic Teaching, 6, 13, 22, 29, 34, 52, 58, 65, 74, 82, 100, 106, 114, 121, 140, 147, 155, 163, 182, 188, 196, 203, 219, 226, 234, 242, 250, 257, 276, 283, 291, 299, 308, 326, 343, 351, 359, 367, 386, 393, 401

diagram, to write ratio, 212

Differentiated Instruction. See Above-Level Learners; Below-Level Learners; English Learner Strategy

distance formula, 97

divide, integers, 33–38

eGlossary, 2, 48, 96, 136, 178, 216, 272, 340, 382

English Learner Strategy
  angle vocabulary, 162
  assessment, 44, 92, 132, 174, 212, 268, 336, 378, 410
  background knowledge, 228
  circle graphs in the workplace, 366
  connections, 233, 300, 307
  develop multiplication skills, 28
  discuss line graphs, 324
  division language, 36

  explain the process, 114
  discuss line graphs, 324
  guiding questions, 7, 20, 195, 256, 275
  mode, median, and range, 282
  native celebrations, 364
  oral explanations, 116
  ordered pair solutions, 389
  ramps, 252
  reference cards, 108
  reference material, 102
  research, 239
  sample data and graphs, 335
  student as teacher, 60
  teaching in native language, 83
  temperature, 391
  terminology confusion, 120
  triangle sort, 145
  understand ratios, 181
  use a number line, 222
  vocabulary, 320
  word problems, 159

Enrichment. See Above-Level Suggestions

equation, 113, 259

equivalent fractions, 342

estimate, 232

evaluate, 105

Evaluation. See Assessment

ExamView Assessment Suite, 44, 92, 132, 174, 212, 268, 336, 378, 410

exponent, 98, 218

Extra Practice, 40, 88, 127, 169, 209, 263, 331, 374, 407

factor, 27, 218

finances, real-world application, 346

financial literacy
  budgets, 8
  checking accounts, 10
  investing, 38, 84
  money, 126
  real-world applications, 17, 26, 32, 36, 39, 45, 327
  saving, 84
  stocks, 16

Foldables, 3, 49, 97, 137, 179, 217, 273, 341, 383, A1, A24, A47, A66, A85, A104, A131, A162, A181
  review, 41, 89, 128, 170, 210, 264, 332, 375, 408

Formative Assessment
  Are They Getting It?, 7, 14, 23, 30, 35, 53, 59, 67, 75, 84, 101, 107, 115, 122, 141, 148, 156, 164, 183, 190, 197, 204, 220, 228, 235, 243, 251, 258, 277, 284, 293, 301, 309, 318, 327, 345, 352, 360, 369, 387, 394, 402
  Lesson Review, 40, 88, 127, 169, 209, 263, 331, 374, 407
  Progress Check, 18, 39, 63, 87, 112, 126, 152, 168, 193, 208, 231, 247, 262, 296, 314, 330, 356, 373, 398,

406
Study Guide, 40, 88, 127, 169, 209, 263, 331, 374, 407

formulas
algebraic equations and, 119–125
defined, 119
for slope, 255–261
use, 252, 353

Foundational Skills and Concepts, 4, 11, 19, 27, 33, 50, 57, 64, 71, 79, 98, 105, 113, 119, 138, 145, 153, 161, 180, 187, 194, 201, 218, 225, 232, 239, 248, 255, 274, 281, 289, 297, 305, 315, 323, 342, 349, 357, 365, 384, 391, 399

functions
defined, 57
introduction to, 57–62
linear and nonlinear, 79–86

function table, 57, 79

Games and Puzzles
Angle Accuracy, A67–A68
Compare to Win, A163–A164
Falling Off the Ends, A2–A3
Find a Proportion, A86–A87
Find a Solution, A182–183
Four in a Row!, A25–A26
Order Matters, A48–A49
Venn Diagram Game, A132–133
Where's My Line?, A105–A106

geometry
angle measures, percents and, 349–355
angles, 138–144
  add, 153–160
  alternate exterior, 161
  alternate interior, 161
  congruent, 161
  obtuse, 138, 145
  relationships and, 161
  right, 138, 145, 153
  straight, 138, 153
  supplementary, 153
hypotenuse, 239
protractor, 138
Pythagorean Theorem, 239–246
real-world applications, 110, 390
rectangles, 247
transversals, 161–167
triangles, 145–151

graph
bar, 297–304, 305–313
circle, 357–364, 365–372
coordinate grids, 71–78
determine slope of, 256
equation, 71
line, 315–322, 323–329
make a, 76, 395
ordered pair, 71–78
points on a line, 249
use a, 67, 319, 403
using a number line, 9, 18, 44

greatest common factor, 180

Guided Practice, 6, 13, 23, 29, 34, 52,

66, 74, 82, 100, 106, 115, 121, 141, 147, 156, 163, 182, 189, 197, 203, 220, 227, 235, 243, 250, 258, 276, 283, 292, 299, 308, 317, 326, 344, 351, 359, 368, 386, 394, 401

Guiding Questions, 7, 20, 195, 256, 275

Home Connections, 3, 49, 97, 137, 179, 217, 273, 341, 383

Homework Activities
Foldables, A1, A24, A47, A66, A85, A104, A131, A162, A181
Games and Puzzles, A2–A3, A25–A26, A48–A49, A67–A68, A86–A87, A105–A106, 132–A133, A163–164, A182–A183
Homework Practice, A7, A11, A15, A19, A23, A30, A34, A38, A42, A46, A53, A57, A61, A65, A72, A76, A80, A84, A91, A95, A99, A103, A110, A114, A118, A122, A126, A130, A137, A141, A145, A149, A153, A157, A161, A168, A172, A176, A180, A187, A191, A195
Problem-Solving Practice, A6, A10, A14, A18, A22, A29, A33, A37, A41, A45, A52, A56, A60, A64, A71, A75, A79, A83, A90, A94, A98, A102, A109, A113, A117, A121, A125, A129, A136, A140, A144, A148, A152, A156, A160, A167, A171, A175, A179, A186, A190, A194
Skills Practice, A5, A9, A13, A17, A21, A28, A32, A36, A40, A44, A51, A55, A59, A63, A70, A74, A78, A82, A89, A93, A97, A101, A108, A112, A116, A120, A124, A128, A135, A139, A143, A147, A151, A155, A159, A166, A170, A174, A178, A185, A189, A193
Vocabulary and English Language Development, A4, A8, A12, A16, A20, A27, A31, A35, A39, A43, A50, A54, A58, A62, A69, A74, A77, A81, A88, A92, A96, A100, A107, A111, A115, A119, A123, A127, A134, A138, A142, A146, A150, A154, A158, A165, A169, A173, A177, A184, A188, A192

horizontal axis, 297

hypotenuse, 239

In-Class Assignment, 8, 16, 25, 31, 37, 55, 61, 69, 77, 85, 103, 110, 117, 123, 143, 150, 158, 166, 185, 191, 199, 206, 222, 229, 237, 245, 253, 260, 278, 286, 294, 302, 312, 320, 328, 346, 354, 363, 371, 389, 396, 404

Instructional Planning and Support
Chapter Assessment Manager, 2B, 48B, 96B, 136B, 178B, 216B, 272B,

340B, 382B
Chapter Overview, 2A–2D, 48A–48D, 96A–96D, 136A–136D, 178A–178D, 216A–216D, 272A–272D, 340A–340D, 382A–382D
Chapter Resource Manager, 2C–2D, 48C–48D, 96C–96D, 136C–136D, 178C–178D, 216C–216D, 272C–272D, 340C–340D, 382C–382D
Mathematics Teacher Handbook, T1–T11

integers
add, 11–17
defined, 4
divide, 33–38
model, 4–10
multiply, 27–32
subtract, 19–26

Interpersonal Learners. See Learning Styles

interval, 297

Intervention Strategies
addition exercises, 155
all operations, 51
answer table, 240
better buy, 178
big number line, 232
classifying angle relationships, 161
classify shapes and angles, 171
classroom coordinate grid, 66
classroom sort, 279
class trip choices on a circle graph, 357
color codes, 202, 274
communicate graphs, 325
compare linear and nonlinear functions, 79
concept map, 146
concession stand sales, 96
construct a bar graph, 305
conversion equations, 73
correct the mistakes, 204
create figures, 150
create line graphs, 323
create subtraction models, 23
create word problems, 30
does the machine function?, 48D
draw percents in circle graphs, 353
evaluate bar graphs, 300
everyday angles, 166
everyday patterns, 48
explain then create, 311
explaining to others, 400
explanations, 15, 287
fact triangles, 116
find slope, 259, 260
find the missing angle, 165
function machine, 74
geoboard exercises, 123
graph an equation, 71
graph ordered pairs, 65
graph practice cards, 266
hands on, 375
human triangle, 136
identify rules of operations, 55
input/output, 76
input/output table, 75
integer bingo, 34

integer models, 9
integer work, 2
interpret a bar graph, 297
introductory activities, 255
lines and slopes, 249
make a table, 5
make graphs, 306
making tables, 408
mnemonic device, 102
model graphs, 82
model percents, 344
model proportions, 198
multiplication cards, 27
operations with integers, 2D
ordered pair solutions, 385
partner Venn diagrams, 278
percents and circle graphs, 340D
perfect squares to 15², 216
personal data, 210
plot points on a line graph, 323
prove it, 154
Pythagorean proof, 216D
questioning, 302
quick check, 139
ratio match up, 184
read a line graph, 315
real-world division, 36
real-world examples, 31, 244
real-world objects, 223
real-world triangles, 149
recognize perfect squares, 221
relationship of quantities, 60
relay functions, 59
represent data, 292
review game, 170
scatter plots, 382D, 401
scatter plots and predictions, 395
shade angles, 153
share-pair, 241
solve problems, 81
solving proportions, 178D
sort words, 278
square root to nearest whole, 236
student integers, 15
student proportions, 198
subtract and compare, 24
subtraction cards, 19
surveying, 272, 365, 368
talk, then write, 290
telling stories to match a graph, 382
terms and definitions, 136D
thermometers, 7
tic-tac-toe, 129
trade data, 333
true false statements, 361
24 hours in a day, 340
unit cost, 189
use color-coding, 108
use of counters or algebra tiles, 42
use of number lines, 41
use patty paper, 142
using butcher paper, 403
vertical line test, 85
visual integers, 12
why protractors work, 138
word problems and circle graphs, 350
words to numbers, 96D
write, exchange, and solve, 159
write integer examples, 8

inverse operations, 113, 225
Inverse Property of Addition, 11

K

Key Concept
    add angles, 153
    add integers, 11
    angles, 138
    approximate square roots, 232
    coordinate grid, 71
    create bar graphs, 305
    create circle graphs, 365
    create line graphs, 323
    divide integers, 33
    evaluate algebraic expressions, 105
    functions, 57
    interpret bar graphs, 297
    interpret circle graphs, 357
    interpret line graphs, 315
    introduction to slope, 248
    linear and nonlinear functions, 79
    lines of best fit, 399
    mean, 289
    mode, median, and range, 281
    model integers, 4
    multiply integers, 27
    number relationships, 50
    order of operations, 98
    ordered pairs, 64
    percents and angle measures, 349
    percents, 342
    proportions, 194
    Pythagorean Theorem, 239
    rates and unit costs, 187
    ratios, 180
    relate algebraic equations and
      formulas, 119
    scatter plots, 391
    slope formula, 255
    solve algebraic equations, 113
    solve problems using proportions, 201
    sort and classify, 274
    square roots, 225
    squaring a number, 218
    subtract integers, 19
    transition to two-variable data, 384
    transversals, 161
    triangles, 145
Key Vocabulary, 2, 48, 96, 136, 178, 216, 272, 340, 382
Kinesthetic Learners. *See* Learning Styles

L

Learning from Mistakes
    diagnosing errors, 337
    review, 175, 213, 411
Learning Styles
    Auditory Learners, 8, 15, 34, 60, 129, 139, 170, 287, 300, 311, 353, 400

Interpersonal Learners, 5, 9, 19, 24, 27, 51, 55, 73, 129, 159, 161, 184, 189, 204, 210, 241, 279, 333, 357, 368, 385, 401
Intrapersonal Learners, 31, 221, 266
Kinesthetic Learners, 12, 15, 23, 34, 42, 66, 82, 116, 123, 142, 154, 171, 184, 198, 221, 223, 232, 249, 278, 281, 292, 306, 375, 385, 403
Linguistic Learners, 8, 19, 24, 30, 36, 102, 204, 278, 290, 302, 325, 350, 395
Logical Learners, 5, 15, 19, 27, 34, 59, 71, 73, 74, 75, 76, 79, 81, 116, 158, 165, 204, 223, 240, 255, 259, 361, 365, 408
Naturalistic Learners, 9, 12, 23, 31, 36, 60, 166, 189, 244, 344
Visual Learners, 5, 7, 9, 12, 15, 23, 30, 36, 41, 65, 71, 75, 76, 79, 85, 108, 138, 139, 146, 149, 150, 153, 155, 165, 198, 202, 223, 236, 259, 260, 266, 274, 278, 297, 305, 315, 323, 333

legs of a triangle, 239

Lesson Notes, 4, 11, 19, 27, 33, 50, 57, 64, 71, 79, 98, 105, 113, 119, 138, 145, 153, 161, 180, 187, 194, 201, 218, 225, 232, 239, 248, 255, 274, 281, 289, 297, 305, 315, 323, 342, 349, 357, 365, 384, 391, 399

Lesson Planner, 4, 11, 19, 27, 33, 50, 57, 64, 71, 79, 98, 105, 113, 119, 138, 145, 153, 161, 180, 187, 194, 201, 218, 225, 232, 239, 248, 255, 274, 281, 289, 297, 305, 315, 323, 342, 349, 357, 365, 384, 391, 399

Lesson Preview, 3, 49, 97, 137, 179, 217, 273, 341, 383

Lesson Review, 40, 40–43, 88, 88–91, 127, 128–131, 169, 170–173, 209, 209–211, 263, 263–267, 331, 332–335, 374, 375–377, 407, 407–409

linear functions, 79

line graphs
    create, 323–329
    interpret, 315–322

lines of best fit, and data, 399–405

Linguistic Learners. *See* Learning Styles

Logical Learners. *See* Learning Styles

Looking Ahead: Pre-teach
    add angles, 151
    add integers, 10
    approximate square roots, 230
    coordinate grids, 70
    create bar graphs, 304
    create circle graphs, 364
    divide integers, 32
    evaluate algebraic expressions, 104
    graph linear and nonlinear functions, 78
    interpret bar graphs, 295
    interpret circle graphs, 355
    interpret line graphs, 313
    introduction to functions, 56
    introduction to slope, 246
    line graphs, 322

lines of best fit, 397
mean, 288
mode, median, and range, 280
multiply integers, 26
ordered pairs, 62
percents and angle measures, 348
proportions, 192
rates and unit costs, 186
relate algebraic equations and
  formulas, 118
scatter plots, 390
similarity, 200
slope formula, 254
solve algebraic equations, 111
square roots, 224, 238
subtract integers, 17
transversals, 160
triangles, 144

Manipulatives

algebra tiles, 4, 11, 19, 27, 33, 57,
  79, 98, 113, 194, 218
balance scale, 98, 113, 119
base-ten blocks, 218
bingo markers, 113
brass brads, 138
bulletin board, 248
butcher paper, 305, 399
calculator, 232, 289, 357, 365
card stock, 138
centimeter cubes, 289, 315
centimeter grid paper, 248, 297, 305,
  342, 391
colored pencils, 50, 161, 180, 194,
  201, 274, 305, 323, 342, 384
compasses, 349, 365
connecting cubes, 180
construction paper, 57, 218
coordinate grids, 64, 71, 79
counters, 4, 11, 19, 180, 194, 248,
  274, 281, 289
deck of playing cards, 281, 384
dried beans, 57, 281
dry erase markers
everyday objects, 105, 274
fraction circles, 342, 349, 357, 365
fraction tiles, 349
geoboards, 27, 33, 64, 119, 145, 201,
  218, 225, 255
grid paper, 64, 71, 79, 119, 201, 239,
  255, 315, 323, 399
household objects that have a price
  per unit, 187
hundreds chart, 27, 33
index cards, 57, 98, 105, 138, 145,
  153, 180, 218, 232, 239, 305, 323,
  349
masking tape, 232
money, 19, 180
multiplication facts chart, 225
multiplication tables, 27
number cubes, 218, 384
number lines, 4, 11, 19, 27, 33, 50
pattern blocks, 19, 145, 180, 274
patty paper, 138
pipe cleaners, 161, 399

plastic page covers, 64
poster board, 98
protractors, 138, 145, 153, 161, 239,
  365
push pins, 248, 323
rectangular or circular fraction tiles,
  342
rubber bands, 225
rulers, 4, 145, 153, 232, 239, 248,
  297, 305, 323, 391, 399
straight edge, 161
straws, 153
string, 399
tangrams, 180
thermometers, 4, 11, 19
two-color counters, 105, 113
unit cubes, 50, 119, 225, 281, 297,
  305
yarn or string, 323

Materials. *See* Manipulatives; Using
Manipulatives

Math Challenge

Analyze Graphs, 302
Applying Angle Relationships, 166
Area, 229
Card Addition, 16
Changing Data, 286
Complete the Table, 370
Construction, 346
Creating Mistakes, Correcting
  Mistakes, 103
Design of Slopes, 253
Determine the Missing Data, 362
Dividend of –48, 37
Double Classifications, 150
Expressions of 64, 31
Favorite Music, 354
Find the Measure, 245
Fractions in Sequences, 54
From 1 to 10 by the Year, 110
Graphing Calculators, 86
Independent Work, 319
Intersect Lines, 77
Logical Statements, 25
Make and Play Cards, 223
Matching Labels, 279
Math Scores, 294
Mileage Chart, 61
Ordered Pairs, 388
Partner Pictures, 68
Personal Data, 303
Plot Points, 9
Price Check, 191
Questions and Graphs, 328
Quilting, 237
Rectangle Dilemma, 124
Rectangle Ratios, 185
Rolled Ratios, 199
Similar Shapes, 206
Sums of Angles in Figures, 158
Three Scatter Plots, 404
Working Backward, 117
Write and Support, 396
Write Step-By-Step Instructions, 143

Math Coach Notes

addition in disguise, 21
analogies, 107
calculating with degrees, 350
change over time, 321

choosing the operation, 53
combination computations, 352
connect concepts, 76
connecting to previously learned
  material, 189
continuous data, 334
convenient values, 385
cooperative study, 245
correlations, 396
create a checklist, 211
discussions, 256
division as multiplication in disguise,
  34
echoing, 395
estimation, 327, 402
evaluate expressions, 101
examine, then answer, 358
finding the median, 284
flashcards, 221
fluency, 226
graphing tip, 72
include the equation, 376
intervals, 309
inverse operations, 121
isolating angles, 163
label arrays, 220
large percents, 343
make tables, 198
measures of central tendency, 292
more practice with functions, 63
multiply negative integers, 28
neatness and graph paper, 81
negative numbers, 5
note the denominator, 368
notice the graphs, 87
no trend, 404
number lines, 235
number properties, 12
outliers, 293, 394
partner practice, 164
placing the negative, 250
plotted points, 251
practice tips, 75, 149
proficient students, 258
proportions, 195, 202
Pythagorean triples, 241
quadrants, 69
real-world connections, 140
reasonable answers, 133
recite key information, 199
rising and running, 252
showing work, 109
signs, 12
similar figures, 203, 205
sort items, 176
slope m, 258
sort items, 176
SQ3R method, 54
squares, 244
strategies, 6, 14, 29, 35, 58, 115,
  141, 156, 184, 196, 221, 243
study tips, 9, 16, 24, 29, 36, 67, 91,
  172, 266
substituting values, 122
substitutions, 386
sum of the parts, 345
sums of degrees, 353
test-taking tip, 43, 45, 93, 269, 379
think aloud, 265

triangles, 203
verifying the rule, 51
word clues, 300, 360
write the steps, 67
See also On-hand Manipulatives; Using Manipulatives

Mathematical Reasoning. *See* Step-by-Step Problem-Solving Practice

Math Online
quiz, 3, 49, 97, 137, 179, 217, 273, 341, 383

mean, 289–295

measurement, real-world applications, 398

measures
add angles, 153–160
angles, 138–144
transversals, 161–167
triangles, 145–151

measures of central tendency, 289

median, 281–288

Mistakes, Learning from
diagnosing errors, 337
review, 175, 213, 411

mode, 281–288

model, use a, 228

model integers, 4–10

money
budgets, 8
checking accounts, 10
finance, 17, 26, 32, 36, 39, 45
investing, 38, 84
real-world applications, 126, 260, 388
saving, 84
stocks, 16

multiply, integers, 27–32

Multi-Step Problems, 15, 24, 32, 37, 60, 117, 197, 222

N

Naturalist Learner. *See* Learning Styles

negative number, 4

nonlinear function, 79

Note-Taking
tips on, 223

Note This!
add angles, 156
angles, 141
bar graph transparencies, 301
consistency with symbols, 352
converting to decimals, 345
Cornell Method, 157
correlations, 388
create a chart, 171
create a checklist, 41, 129, 170, 210, 333, 375, 376, 408
discrete data, 260
double-bar graph questions, 303
functions, 89
highlight text, 275
identify each rule, 54
identify the variable, 109
kinesthetic, 84

labeling triangles, 148
label units, 190
long data sets, 287
mnemonic devices, 285
multiplication facts, 124, 233
neatness and accuracy, 403
negative signs, 8
note-taking tips, 223
perceptions, 311
predictions, 318
reference graphs, 409
reference table, 369
reviewing congruency, 165
review materials, 149
scales, 334
simplest form, 183
sketch and label, 240
square root expressions, 228
strategies, 197
study strategies, 108
vocabulary sheets, 205
whole circle, 377

number, squaring a, 218–224

number line
find sums using, 18
graph integers on, 9
use to find sum and difference, 21

number relationships, 50–56

O

Objectives, learning, 2A, 48A, 96A, 136A, 178A, 216A, 272A, 340A, 382A

obtuse angles, 138, 145

Odd/Even Assignments, 8, 16, 18, 25, 31, 37, 39, 55, 61, 63, 69, 77, 85, 87, 103, 110, 112, 117, 123, 126, 143, 150, 152, 158, 166, 168, 185, 191, 193, 199, 206, 208, 222, 229, 231, 237, 245, 247, 253, 260, 262, 278, 286, 294, 296, 302, 312, 314, 320, 328, 330, 346, 354, 356, 363, 371, 373, 389, 396, 398, 404, 406

On-Hand Manipulatives
bulletin board, 250
calculator, 292, 359, 368
centimeter cubes, 317
centimeter grid paper, 344
colored construction paper, 197, 220
colored pencils or markers, 52, 203, 344, 386
compass, 351
dried beans, 283
everyday objects, 6, 13, 23, 59, 82, 106, 141, 182, 276
grid paper, 82, 243, 258
household objects that have a unit price, 189
hundreds chart, 29, 35
money, 23
notebook paper, 66, 74
number line, 235
push pins, 250
real-world items as triangles, 147
ruler, 394
rulers, 163, 299, 308, 326
stamper markers, 115
straws, 156

string, 401
thermometer, 13, 23
two-color counters, 106
unit cubes, 121, 227

Online Readiness Quiz, 3, 49, 97

opposites, 4, 19

ordered pair, 64–70
on coordinate grid, 71–78, 384

order of operations, 98–104, 105

origin, 64, 248

outlier, 289

Overviews, 2A–2D, 48A–48D, 96A–96D, 136A–136D, 178A–178D, 216A–216D, 272A–272D, 340A–340D, 382A–382D

P

parallel lines, 161

patterns
functions, introduction to, 57–62
linear and nonlinear functions, 79–86
look for, 60, 165
number relationships, 50–56
ordered pairs, 64–70
real-world application, 321

percents, 342–348
and angle measures, 349–355

positive number, 4

Practice. *See* Guided Practice; Step-by-Step Practice

Pretest/Prescribe, 3, 49, 97, 137, 179, 217, 273, 341, 383

Problem-Solving. *See* Step-by-Step Problem Solving

Problem-Solving Practice, A6, A10, A14, A18, A22, A29, A33, A37, A41, A45, A52, A56, A60, A64, A71, A75, A79, A83, A90, A94, A98, A102, A109, A113, A117, A121, A125, A129, A136, A140, A144, A148, A152, A156, A160, A167, A171, A175, A179, A186, A190, A194

Problem-Solving Strategies. *See* Step-by-Step Problem-Solving Practice

product, 27

Professional Development, 3, 49, 97, 137, 179, 217, 273, 341, 383

Program Organization, T6–T8

Progress Check, 18, 39, 63, 87, 112, 126, 152, 168, 193, 208, 231, 247, 262, 296, 314, 330, 356, 373, 398, 406

proportion, 194–200
defined, 194, 201
solve problems using, 201–207

protractor, 138

Pythagorean Theorem, 239–246

Q

quotient, 33

R

radical sign, 225
range, 281–288
rate
  defined, 187
  and unit costs, 187–192
ratio, 180–187, 342
ray, 138
  common, 153

Reaching All Learners. See Above-Level
Suggestions; Below-Level Suggestions;
English Learner Strategy; Learning Styles

Real-World Applications
  advertising, 118, 245
  ages, 133
  agriculture, 158
  airplanes, 32
  animals, 183, 296
  aquariums, 364
  architecture, 136, 151
  area, 238
  art, 150, 157, 213, 269
  assemblies, 310
  aviation, 37
  awards, 10
  basketball, 112, 293
  baskets, 184
  bicycling, 109, 379
  biking, 198
  book club, 261
  books, 104
  bridges, 167
  budgets, 8, 348
  business, 191, 199
  cafeteria, 301, 362
  calories, 18
  canoeing, 261
  carnival, 286
  cars, 133
  celebrations, 60
  cell phones, 411
  chairs, 231
  charity, 355
  checking accounts, 10
  chemistry, 45, 62
  chess, 185, 230
  cities, 68
  class supplies, 230
  clocks, 144
  clothes, 109
  collections, 104
  commuting, 70
  computers, 184
  construction, 148, 175, 245
  cooking, 93, 175
  crafts, 63, 87
  cross-country, 159
  cycling, 388
  dances, 361
  detergent, 337
  distance, 246
  doors, 175
  drought, 397
  earth science, 208
  elections, 345, 353
  elevation, 15

  entertainment, 125, 207
  erosion, 36
  evaporation, 30
  events, 206
  exercise, 117, 123, 124, 126, 133
  experiment, 295
  family, 61
  farmer's market, 372
  farming, 224
  fashion, 54
  field day, 364
  field trips, 311
  finance, 17, 26, 32, 36, 39, 45, 56,
    116, 118, 346
  financial literacy, 327, 348, 356
  fitness, 62, 207
  flags, 149, 247
  flowers, 183
  food, 110, 111, 199, 277, 279, 302,
    397
  football, 10, 18, 185, 303
  fund-raisers, 312
  games, 186, 230, 238
  gardening, 159
  gardens, 102, 228, 237
  gas mileage, 200
  gas prices, 24
  geometry, 110, 205, 390
  grades, 186
  health, 45, 221
  height, 285
  helicopters, 124
  hiking, 31
  home improvement, 244
  homework, 328
  interior design, 144, 221
  investing, 38, 84
  investment rates, 178
  jets, 124
  jogging, 78
  kites, 142
  labels, 175
  ladders, 254
  logos, 151, 354
  maps, 166
  measurement, 398
  mileage, 319
  money, 126, 260, 388
  movies, 262, 287
  museums, 348
  music, 59, 184, 314, 387
  name the integer, 2
  names, 293
  nature, 77, 190
  number sense, 278, 280
  nutrition, 26, 38
  office space, 224
  packaging, 269
  parties, 362
  patios, 236
  patterns, 321, 322
  pencils, 396
  pets, 55, 159, 198, 388
  photography, 102, 133
  pizza, 302
  plants, 405
  popcorn and peanuts, 96
  population, 32, 133, 191, 192, 200
  prices, 133, 259

  puzzles, 223, 231
  quilts, 165
  quiz scores, 295
  railroads, 165
  rainfall, 348
  ramps, 143, 252
  reading, 199
  recipes, 48
  recreation, 110
  rectangles, 247
  repairs, 168
  research, 369
  reunion, 224
  road signs, 142
  roller coasters, 395
  safety, 207
  sails, 254
  sales, 192, 322, 329, 330, 370, 371
  saving, 84
  scholarships, 10
  school, 59, 198
  science, 60, 222
  scuba diving, 8
  sculpture, 159
  service, 296
  shadows, 205, 254
  shapes, 78
  shipping, 117
  shopping, 112, 340
  skiing, 252
  soccer, 403
  space travel, 123
  spelling, 193
  sporting events, 17
  sports, 24, 26, 158, 184, 193, 303
  stage crew, 321
  stairs, 165
  stepping through the day, 382
  stocks, 16
  summer survey, 355
  supplies, 102
  surveys, 346, 353, 372
  swimming pools, 37
  taking the shortcut, 216
  tents, 167
  test scores, 293
  theater, 321
  theaters, 56
  tiles, 149, 228
  time, 152
  tips, 379
  towns, 69
  transportation, 101
  travel, 17, 39, 61, 67, 93, 208, 213,
    246
  trucks, 320
  TV Ratings, 272
  uniforms, 112
  vehicles, 320
  vending machines, 15
  video games, 76, 238, 287
  voting, 337
  water, 390
  weather, 7, 10, 25, 31, 38, 45
  white water rafting, 403
  work, 204
  writing, 213
  zoos, 55

rectangles, real-world application, 247

Reflect, 8, 16, 25, 31, 37, 55, 61, 68, 77, 85, 102, 110, 117, 123, 143, 149, 158, 165, 185, 191, 199, 206, 222, 229, 237, 245, 252, 260, 278, 286, 294, 302, 311, 320, 328, 346, 354, 362, 370, 388, 396, 404

Reteaching/Alternatve Approaches, 2, 2D, 5, 7, 8, 9, 12, 15, 19, 23, 24, 27, 30, 31, 34, 36, 41, 42, 48, 48D, 51, 55, 59, 60, 65, 66, 71, 73, 74, 75, 76, 79, 81, 82, 85, 96, 96D, 102, 104, 108, 116, 123, 129, 136, 136D, 138, 139, 142, 146, 149, 150, 153, 154, 156, 159, 161, 165, 166, 170, 171, 178, 178D, 184, 189, 198, 202, 204, 210, 216, 216D, 221, 223, 232, 236, 240, 241, 244, 249, 259, 260, 266, 272, 274, 278, 279, 281, 287, 290, 292, 297, 300, 302, 305, 306, 311, 315, 323, 325, 333, 340, 340D, 344, 350, 353, 357, 361, 365, 368, 375, 382, 382D, 385, 395, 400, 401, 403, 408

right angles, 138, 145, 153

roots, square, 225–230

rule, 50

scale, 297

scatter plots, 391–397

sector, 349, 357

See It, Do It, Say It, Write It, 10, 17, 26, 32, 38, 56, 62, 70, 78, 86, 104, 111, 118, 125, 144, 151, 160, 167, 186, 192, 200, 207, 224, 230, 238, 246, 254, 261, 280, 288, 295, 304, 313, 322, 329, 347, 355, 364, 372, 389, 397, 405

side, 145

similar figure, 201

simplest form, 180, 349

Skills, Concepts, and Problem Solving, 8, 16, 25, 31, 37, 55, 61, 69, 77, 85, 103, 110, 117, 123, 143, 150, 158, 166, 185, 191, 199, 206, 222, 229, 237, 245, 253, 260, 278, 286, 294, 302, 312, 320, 328, 346, 354, 363, 371, 389, 396, 404

Skills Practice, A5, A9, A13, A17, A21, A28, A32, A36, A40, A44, A51, A55, A59, A63, A70, A74, A78, A82, A89, A93, A97, A101, A108, A112, A116, A120, A124, A128, A135, A139, A143, A147, A151, A155, A159, A166, A170, A174, A178, A185, A189, A193

slope, 399
   formula for, 255–261
   introduction to, 248–254

Small Group Activities, 236, 241, 249, 281, 300, 325, 344, 350, 353, 357, 361, 365, 368, 385

solution, 384

sort and classify, 274–280

Spanish Vocabulary, 2, 48, 96, 136, 178, 216, 272, 340, 382

Spiral Review, 17, 26, 32, 38, 62, 70, 78, 86, 111, 118, 125, 151, 160, 167, 192, 200, 207, 230, 238, 246, 254, 261, 288, 295, 304, 313, 322, 329, 355, 364, 397, 405

square of a number, 218

square roots, 225–230
   approximate, 232–238

squaring a number, 218–224

Staff Development. See Professional Development

Step-by-Step Practice, 6, 14, 23, 35, 53, 59, 66, 75, 83, 100, 107, 115, 121, 141, 147, 156, 164, 183, 189, 197, 204, 220, 227, 235, 243, 251, 258, 276, 284, 292, 300, 309, 318, 326, 344, 351, 360, 368, 386, 394, 402

Step-by-Step Problem-Solving Practice
   act it out, 293
   draw a diagram, 7, 30, 221, 244, 277
   draw a picture, 15
   look for a pattern, 60, 165, 285
   make a graph, 76, 395
   make a list, 184
   make a table, 24, 54, 84, 198, 361, 387
   solve a similar problem, 157, 190
   solve a simpler problem, 301
   use a diagram, 142, 148
   use an equation, 109
   use a formula, 122, 252, 353
   use a graph, 67, 319, 403
   use logical reasoning, 236
   use a model, 36, 228
   use a table, 205, 310, 327, 345, 369
   write an equation, 259
   write an expression, 101, 116

straight angles, 138, 153

Struggling Students. See Below-Level Suggestions

straight angles, 138, 153

Study Guide, 40–43, 88–91, 127–131, 169–173, 209–211, 263–267, 331–335, 374–377, 407–409

subtract, integers, 19–26

Success Strategy, 47, 95, 135, 177, 215, 271, 339, 381, 413

sum, 11

Summative Assessment
   Alternative Assessment
     showing solutions and non-solutions, 410
      use portfolios, 44, 92, 132, 174, 212, 268, 336, 378
   Chapter Test, 44–45, 92–93, 132–133, 174–175, 212–213, 268–269, 336–337, 378–379, 410–411
   See It, Do It, Say It, Write It, 10, 17, 26, 32, 38, 56, 62, 70, 78, 86, 104, 111, 118, 125, 144, 151, 160, 167, 186, 192, 200, 207, 224, 230, 238, 246, 254, 261, 280, 288, 295, 304, 313, 322, 329, 347, 355, 364, 372, 389, 397, 405
   Test Practice, 46–47, 94–95, 134–135, 176–177, 214–215, 270–271, 338–339, 380–381, 412–413
   Ticket Out the Door, 10, 17, 26, 32, 38, 43, 56, 62, 70, 78, 86, 91, 104, 111, 118, 125, 131, 144, 151, 160, 167, 173, 186, 192, 200, 207, 211, 224, 230, 238, 246, 254, 261, 267, 280, 288, 295, 304, 313, 322, 329, 335, 348, 355, 364, 372, 377, 390, 397, 405, 409

supplementary angles, 153

table
   function, 57
   make a, 54, 75, 84, 198 , 361, 387
   use a, 205, 310, 327, 345, 369

TeacherWorks Plus, 2C, 48C, 96C, 136C, 178C, 216C, 272C, 340C, 382C

Technology, 2B, 2C, 48B, 48C, 96B, 96C, 136B, 136C, 178B, 178C, 216B, 216C, 272B, 272C, 340B, 340C, 382B, 382C
   eGlossary, 2, 48, 96, 136, 178, 216, 272, 340, 382
   Math Online
     quiz, 3, 49, 97, 137, 179, 217, 273, 341, 383
   TeacherWorks Plus, 2C, 48C, 96C, 136C, 178C, 216C, 272C, 340C, 382C

term, 50

Test Practice, 46–47, 94–95, 134–135, 176–177, 214–215, 270–271, 338–339, 380–381, 412–413

Ticket Out the Door, 10, 17, 26, 32, 38, 43, 56, 62, 70, 78, 86, 91, 104, 111, 118, 125, 131, 144, 151, 160, 167, 173, 186, 192, 200, 207, 211, 224, 230, 238, 246, 254, 261, 267, 280, 288, 295, 304, 313, 322, 329, 335, 348, 355, 364, 372, 377, 390, 397, 405, 409

transversals, 161–167

triangles, 145–151

two-variable data, transition to, 384–390

unit costs
   defined, 187
   and rates, 187–192

unit rate, 187

Universal Access. See Learning Styles; Differentiated Instruction; Small Group

Using Manipulatives
   algebra tiles, 6, 13, 23, 29, 59, 82, 100, 115, 220
   balance scale, 100, 121
   base-ten blocks, 220
   calculator, 235
   centimeter grid paper, 394
   circular fraction tiles, 351, 359
   compass, 368

connecting cubes, 182, 276
counters, 250, 292
fraction circles, 351, 359
fraction tiles, 344
geoboards, 29, 35, 66, 203, 220, 227, 258
grid paper, 66, 74, 82, 203, 317, 326
money, 182
number cubes, 386
number line, 6
pattern blocks, 23, 182, 276
pipe cleaners, 163, 401
protractors, 141, 147, 156
ruler, 6, 147
rulers and protractors, 243
tangrams, 182
two-color counters, 106, 115, 197
unit cubes, 52, 283, 299, 308
See also Manipulatives

variables, 113, 119

Venn diagram, 274

vertex, 138

Vertical Alignment, 2B, 48B, 96B, 136B, 178B, 216B, 272B, 340B, 382B

vertical axis, 297

Visual Learners. *See Learning Styles*

Vocabulary, 4, 11, 19, 27, 33, 50, 57, 64, 71, 79, 98, 105, 113, 119, 138, 145, 153, 161, 180, 187, 194, 201, 218, 225, 232, 239, 248, 255, 274, 281, 289, 297, 305, 315, 323, 342, 349, 357, 365, 384, 391, 399
  absolute value, 19
  access, 57, 79, 105, 274
  addition properties, 11
  arithmetic sequences, 50
  average, 289
  connect, 218
  coordinate plane, 297
  coordinate system, 384
  divide integers, 33
  equivalent, 342
  explore, 153, 239
  exponents, 225
  from left to right, 98
  function, 71
  graphing functions, 71
  graphs, 323
  interval, 305
  introduce, 180
  inverse actions, 113
  model, 138
  multiplication terms, 27
  predictions, 399
  prefix, 145
  preview, 3, 49, 97, 137, 179, 217, 273, 341, 383
  proportion, 194
  ratios, 180
  relationships, 349, 365
  review, 201, 357
  reviewing direction, 248
  statistics, 281
  trends, 315, 391

understanding terms, 4
unit cost, 187
use, 64
variables, 119
whole numbers, 232

Vocabulary Check, 10, 17, 26, 32, 38, 56, 62, 70, 78, 86, 104, 111, 118, 125, 144, 151, 160, 167, 186, 192, 200, 207, 224, 230, 246, 254, 261, 280, 288, 295, 304, 313, 322, 329, 348, 355, 390, 397, 405

Vocabulary and Concept Check, 40, 88, 127, 169, 209, 263, 331, 374, 407

Vocabulary and English Language Development, A4, A8, A12, A16, A20, A27, A31, A35, A39, A43, A50, A54, A58, A62, A69, A74, A77, A81, A88, A92, A96, A100, A107, A111, A115, A119, A123, A127, A134, A138, A142, A146, A150, A154, A158, A165, A169, A173, A177, A184, A188, A192

Vocabulary Review Strategies
  color code, 127
  flashcards, 209, 407
  frames, 88, 263
  games, 169
  puzzles, 374
  table, 40
  word search, 331

Who is Correct?, 6, 13, 22, 29, 34, 52, 58, 65, 74, 82, 100, 106, 114, 121, 140, 147, 155, 163, 182, 188, 196, 203, 219, 226, 234, 242, 250, 257, 276, 283, 291, 299, 308, 317, 326, 343, 351, 359, 367, 386, 393, 401

whole numbers, 4

Writing in Math, 10, 17, 26, 32, 38, 56, 62, 70, 78, 86, 104, 111, 118, 125, 144, 151, 160, 167, 186, 192, 200, 207, 224, 230, 246, 254, 261, 280, 288, 295, 304, 313, 322, 329, 348, 355, 390, 397, 405

***x*-axis,** 64, 391

***x*-coordinate,** 64, 248, 384

***x*-values,** 71

***y*-axis,** 64, 391

***y*-coordinate,** 64, 248, 384

Your Turn, 4–5, 11–13, 20–22, 28–29, 33–34, 51–52, 57–58, 65, 72–73, 80–81, 98–99, 105–106, 114, 120, 139–140, 146, 154–155, 162–163, 181–182, 187–188, 195–196, 202–203, 219, 226, 233–234, 240–242, 249, 256–257, 275, 282–283, 290–291, 298–299, 306–307, 316–317, 324–325, 343, 350, 358–359,

366–367, 385, 392–393, 400

***y*-values,** 71

Image Credits

Teacher Edition

All coins photographed by United States Mint.
All bills photographed by Michael Houghton/StudiOhio.
Cover Jupiterimages; **iv** (1 7 8)File Photo, (2 3)The McGraw-Hill Companies,
(4 5 6)Doug Martin; **ix** C. Borland/Getty Images; **vi** CORBIS; **vii** Digital Vision;
viii C. Borland/Getty Images; **x** CORBIS; **xi** PunchStock; **xii, xiii** CORBIS; **xiv**
PunchStock; **100** The McGraw-Hill Companies.

Student Edition

Book 1:

All coins photographed by United States Mint.
All bills photographed by Michael Houghton/StudiOhio.
Cover Jupiterimages; **vi** CORBIS; **vii** Digital Vision; **viii** C. Borland/Getty Images;
002-003 Rodger Klein/Peter Arnold; **008** Frank & Joyce Burek/Getty Images;
010 George Gojkovich/Getty Images; **015** Felicia Martinez/PhotoEdit; **017** Getty
Images; **018** Brand X Pictures; **025** Lee Foster/Alamy; **026** Scott Halleran/Getty
Images; **030** Ned Frisk/CORBIS; **031, 032** Alamy; **036** Tyrone Turner/Getty
Images; **038** James Steinberg/Photo Researchers Inc.; **039** Jack Hollingsworth/
Getty Images; **045** Getty Images; **048-049** David Madison/CORBIS; **049** (cw
from top)Jupiterimages, (2)PunchStock, (3)Getty Images; **054** Jose Luis Pelaez/
Jupiterimages; **055** G.K. & Vikki Hart/Getty Images; **056** CORBIS; **060** G.K. &
Vikki Hart/Getty Images; **062** (t)Ryan McVay/Getty Images, (b)Michael Newman/
PhotoEdit; **075** David Sacks/Getty Images; **077** Martin Ruegner/Getty Images;
093 Alamy; **096-097** John Giustina/Getty Images; **102** Getty Images;
104 CORBIS; **109** Siede Preis/Getty Images; **116** Jules Frazier/Getty Images;
117 Ken Cavanagh/The McGraw-Hill Companies; **118, 123** Getty Images;
124 Photolibrary; **133** (t)C. Borland/Getty Images; **133** (b)SuperStock.

Book 2:

All coins photographed by United States Mint.
All bills photographed by Michael Houghton/StudiOhio.
Cover Jupiterimages; **iv** (1 7 8)File Photo, (2 3)The McGraw-Hill Companies,
(4 5 6)Doug Martin; **vi** C. Borland/Getty Images; **vii** CORBIS; **viii** PunchStock;
136-137 CORBIS; **142** Getty Images; **149** (t)Alamy, (b)Getty Images; **150** Peter
Adams/CORBIS; **151, 158** CORBIS; **159** PunchStock; **178** SuperStock;
183, 184 CORBIS; **185** PunchStock; **189** John Flournoy/The McGraw-Hill
Companies; **190** (t)Steve Cohen/Jupiterimages, (bl)PunchStock, (br)Getty Images;
192 PunchStock; **198** CORBIS; **199** SuperStock; **204** Erik Dreyer/Getty Images;
206 Ken Cavanagh/The McGraw-Hill Companies; **207** Ryan McVay/Getty Images;
208 Charles Smith/CORBIS; **216-217** Jupiterimages; **221, 224** CORBIS;
228 Age Fotostock; **230** PunchStock; **237** D. Normark/Getty Images;
245 Jupiterimages; **246** Robert Glusic/Getty Images; **254** John Flournoy/
The McGraw-Hill Companies.

Book 3:

All coins photographed by United States Mint.
All bills photographed by Michael Houghton/StudiOhio.
Cover Jupiterimages; **iv** (1 7 8)File Photo, (2 3)The McGraw-Hill Companies,
(4 5 6)Doug Martin; **vi, vii** CORBIS; **viii** CORBIS; **viii** PunchStock;
272-273 Jupiterimages; **284** Getty Images; **286** Ed Kashi/CORBIS;
293 Kemberly Groue/U.S. Air Force; **334** AGE Fotostock; **340-341** Getty Images;
344 Ken Cavanagh/The McGraw-Hill Companies; **346** PunchStock; **347** CORBIS;
382-383 Masterfile; **388** (t)G.K. & Vikki Hart/Getty Images, (b)Getty Images;
390 Kent Knudson/Getty Images.

Chapter Resource Masters

Chapter 1

Foldables A1

Games and Puzzles A2-A3

Lesson 1-1 Worksheets A4-A7

Lesson 1-2 Worksheets A8-A11

Lesson 1-3 Worksheets A12-A15

Lesson 1-4 Worksheets A16-A19

Lesson 1-5 Worksheets A20-A23

Chapter 2

Foldables A24

Games and Puzzles A25-A26

Lesson 2-1 Worksheets A27-A30

Lesson 2-2 Worksheets A31-A34

Lesson 2-3 Worksheets A35-A38

Lesson 2-4 Worksheets A39-A42

Lesson 2-5 Worksheets A43-A46

Chapter 3

Foldables A47

Games and Puzzles A48-A49

Lesson 3-1 Worksheets A50-A53

Lesson 3-2 Worksheets A54-A57

Lesson 3-3 Worksheets A58-A61

Lesson 3-4 Worksheets A62-A65

Chapter 4

Foldables A66

Games and Puzzles A67-A68

Lesson 4-1 Worksheets A69-A72

Lesson 4-2 Worksheets A73-A76

Lesson 4-3 Worksheets A77-A80

Lesson 4-4 Worksheets A81-A84

Chapter 5

Foldables A85

Games and Puzzles A86-A87

Lesson 5-1 Worksheets A88-A91

Lesson 5-2 Worksheets A92-A95

Lesson 5-3 Worksheets A96-A99

Lesson 5-4 Worksheets A100-A103

Chapter 6

Foldables A104

Games and Puzzles A105-A106

Lesson 6-1 Worksheets A107-A110

Lesson 6-2 Worksheets A111-A114

Lesson 6-3 Worksheets A115-A118

Lesson 6-4 Worksheets A119-A122

Lesson 6-5 Worksheets A123-A126

Lesson 6-6 Worksheets A127-A130

Chapter Resource Masters

Chapter 7

Foldables A131

Games and Puzzles....................A132-A133

Lesson 7-1 Worksheets A134-A137

Lesson 7-2 Worksheets A138-A141

Lesson 7-3 Worksheets A142-A145

Lesson 7-4 Worksheets A146-A149

Lesson 7-5 Worksheets A150-A153

Lesson 7-6 Worksheets A154-A157

Lesson 7-7 Worksheets A158-A161

Chapter 8

Foldables A162

Games and Puzzles....................A163-A164

Lesson 8-1 Worksheets A165-A168

Lesson 8-2 Worksheets A169-A172

Lesson 8-3 Worksheets A173-A176

Lesson 8-4 Worksheets A177-A180

Chapter 9

Foldables A181

Games and Puzzles....................A182-A183

Lesson 9-1 Worksheets A184-A187

Lesson 9-2 Worksheets A188-A191

Lesson 9-3 Worksheets A192-A195

Answer Keys A196

Foldables Study Organizer

Dinah Zike's Foldables

Make this Foldable to help you organize information about integers.

1 Begin with one sheet of 11" × 17" paper. Fold the sheet of paper in sixths lengthwise.

2 Open and fold a 4" tab along the short side. Then fold the rest in half.

3 Draw lines along the folds and label as shown.

	Terms	Example(s)
Model Integers		
Add Integers		
Subtract Integers		
Multiply Integers		
Divide Integers		

TAKING NOTES

As you read through the chapter, describe concepts related to integers with terms and examples on the tabs of your Foldable.

USING YOUR FOLDABLE

As you study, check your understanding by writing additional examples that use integers in everyday life. An example could be a thermometer.

USING YOUR FOLDABLE

Work with a partner. Take turns writing examples of integer operations.

Games and Puzzles

Falling off the Ends

DIRECTIONS

- Let one number cube represent positive integers and the other number cube represent negative integers.
- Each player places a counter on zero.
- One player rolls both number cubes and adds the numbers shown. If the sum is positive, the player moves his or her counter right the number of spaces indicated by the sum. If the sum is negative, the player moves the counter left the number of spaces indicated by the sum.
- Players take turns rolling the number cubes and moving the counters.
- Who Wins? The first player to go off the sheet in either direction wins the game.

What You Need

- Falling Off the Ends Game Sheets
- 2 Different Colored Number Cubes
- 2 Different Colored Counters

Number of Players

2 or 4

NAME _____ DATE _____

Falling Off the Ends Game Sheet

−6	−5	−4	−3	−2	−1	0	1	2	3	4	5	6

Falling Off the Ends Game Sheet

−6	−5	−4	−3	−2	−1	0	1	2	3	4	5	6

Math Triumphs

**Lesson
1-1**

Vocabulary and
English Language Development

▶ Activate Prior Knowledge

Write the opposite of each word.

1 before _____

2 least _____

3 positive _____

4 subtract _____

5 interior _____

6 clockwise _____

▶ Definition Review

Integers are the whole numbers and their opposites: …−3, −2, −1, 0, 1, 2, 3,….
A **positive number** is a number that is greater than zero.
A **negative number** is a number that is less than zero.
Whole numbers are the counting numbers and zero.
Opposites are numbers that are the same distance from zero in opposite directions.

Identify each number as an *integer*, a *whole number*, or *both*.

7 62 _____

8 −41 _____

9 −36 _____

10 8 _____

Identify each number as *positive* or *negative*.

11 31 _____

12 86 _____

13 −42 _____

14 −75 _____

▶ Application

Follow the directions for the activity.

- Write each integer from −10 through 10 on separate pieces of paper. Put the pieces of paper in a bag, hat, or bowl.
- Have 5 student volunteers each pick a number from the bag.
- Instruct the volunteers to line up in front of the class according to their number from least to greatest.
- Ask the remaining students to verify whether or not the students in front of the class are in the correct order.
- Repeat the steps with each new group of students picking new numbers until each student has had a turn.
- As a variation, instruct some groups to line up from greatest to least.

Math Triumphs

Lesson 1-1

Skills Practice

Write the opposite of each number.

1 −3 _____

2 2 _____

3 7 _____

4 8 _____

5 −5 _____

6 4 _____

Graph the integers on a number line. Then write them in order from least to greatest.

7 −2, 1, 5, −4, −3 _____

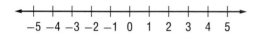

8 −3, −2, 1, −1, 3 _____

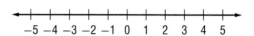

9 3, −1, 1, 4, −4 _____

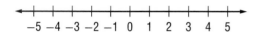

10 1, −2, 3, −4, 4 _____

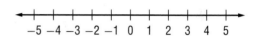

11 −1, 4, −5, −2, 3 _____

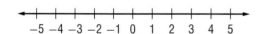

12 −4, −1, 2, −2, −3 _____

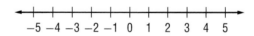

Write <, =, or > in each circle to make a true statement.

13 3 ◯ −4

14 −2 ◯ −7

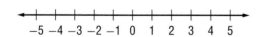

15 −2 ◯ 2

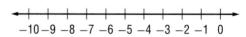

16 5 ◯ −1

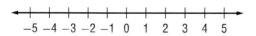

17 4 ◯ −5

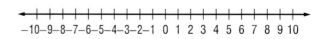

18 −1 ◯ −1

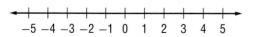
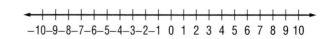

Math Triumphs

Lesson 1-1

Problem-Solving Practice

Solve.

1 **FINANCIAL LITERACY** Molly's bank statement showed an entry of −$25.00 on the 4th day of last month's statement. Did the entry −$25.00 represent a withdrawal or a deposit that Molly made?

_____

2 **PUZZLES** Write a negative integer that is more than 8 units from zero and less than 10 units from zero.

_____

3 **TEMPERATURE** On the Celsius temperature scale, 0° C is freezing. The thermometer at the right shows the current temperature outside. What is the temperature outside?

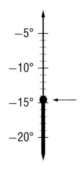

_____

4 **FOOTBALL** A running back was tackled 3 yards behind the line. What integer represents the change in yards by the team for that play?

_____

5 **TRAVEL** During summer vacation, Lamar and his family went camping and mountain climbing. The tallest mountain they climbed was 5,746 feet tall. What integer represents the height of the mountain that Lamar climbed with his family?

_____

6 **WEATHER** The temperature at 1:00 P.M. was 65°F. By 8:00 P.M., the temperature had dropped 19°F. What was the temperature at 8:00 P.M.?

_____

7 **BANKING** Jody wrote a check for $36. Then she made a deposit into her checking account of $24. What integer represents the net change in the balance of her checking account?

_____

Math Triumphs

Lesson 1-1

Homework Practice

Graph the integers on a number line.

1 Graph the integers between −3 and 5.

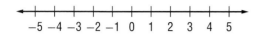

2 Graph the positive integers less than 4.

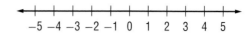

3 Graph the integers −5, −2 and 4.

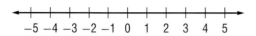

4 Graph the negative integers greater than −4.

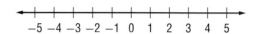

Write the integers from least to greatest.

5 −15, 9, −21, −16, 12 _____

6 45, −53, 47, −45, 54 _____

Write the integers from greatest to least.

7 72, −65, −74, −27, 67 _____

8 −34, 43, 41, 46, −43 _____

Write an integer to represent each statement.

9 A diver is 41 feet below sea level.

_____

10 Alisa's puppy gained 5 pounds.

_____

11 Marco earned $28 babysitting.

_____

12 A company reported a loss of $300 this quarter. _____

Solve.

13 **STOCK MARKET** The stock market had a very good day yesterday. It improved by 271 points. What integer represents yesterday's change in the stock market? _____

14 **BANKING** Sook withdrew $500 from his savings account this morning. What integer represents the change in Sook's bank account from this transaction? _____

Write the vocabulary word(s) that completes the sentence.

15 Integers that are greater than zero are called _____.

16 _____ are the whole numbers and their opposites.

Vocabulary and English Language Development

▶ Activate Prior Knowledge

Find each sum.

1 5 + 0 = _____

2 0 + 21 = _____

Inverse Property of Addition For any number, the sum of that number and its opposite is zero.

Commutative Property of Addition The order in which two numbers are added does not change the sum.

Example: $8 + 7 = 7 + 8$

▶ Definition Review

Match the equal expressions according to the Commutative Property of Addition.

3 10 + 15   22 + 3

4 8 + 17   15 + 10

5 3 + 22   11 + 14

6 14 + 11   17 + 8

Fill in the blank with the correct number.

7 16 + _____ = 0

8 −27 + _____ = 0

▶ Application

Follow the directions for the activity.

- Use masking tape to make a number line from −15 to 15 on the floor.
- Write each integer from −8 through 8 on separate pieces of paper. Put the pieces of paper in a bag, hat, or bowl.
- Student 1 picks a number from the bag and finds that number on the number line.
- Student 2 picks a number from the bag, and adds his or her number to the number of the other volunteer using the number line on the floor. What is the sum?
- Using the same numbers, Student 2 should find his or her number on the number line. Student 1 should find the sum using the number line. What is the sum? Is it the same?
- Repeat the steps with each new pair of students picking new numbers until each student has had a turn.

Math Triumphs

Lesson 1-2

Skills Practice

What is the opposite of each number? Write an addition sentence to show the Inverse Property of Addition.

1 −1 _____

2 −2 _____

3 9 _____

4 10 _____

5 6 _____

6 −7 _____

7 −12 _____

8 8 _____

Find each sum. Use the number line.

9 $4 + (-2) =$ _____

10 $-1 + (-3) =$ _____

11 $2 + (-7) =$ _____

12 $2 + (-3) =$ _____

13 $-3 + (-3) =$ _____

14 $-2 + 2 =$ _____

15 $-5 + 2 =$ _____

16 $1 + (-3) =$ _____

Find each sum.

17 $2 + (-5) =$ _____

18 $4 + (-4) =$ _____

19 $-1 + (-4) =$ _____

20 $-4 + 0 =$ _____

21 $-1 + 5 =$ _____

22 $-2 + (-8) =$ _____

23 $2 + (-2) =$ _____

24 $1 + (-3) =$ _____

Math Triumphs

Lesson 1-2

Problem-Solving Practice

Solve.

1. **FOOTBALL** During last week's football game, Nantan rushed for +7 yards, +3 yards and −2 yards. What were Nantan's total rushing yards for the game?

   _____

2. **GOLF** During a golf match, Marcel scores +2 (2 over par) on the first hole, +1 on the second hole, −1 (1 under par) on the third hole, and +1 on the fourth hole. What is Marcel's score after the fourth hole?

   _____

3. **TREASURE HUNT** Sachi is searching for buried treasure. The map says to take 25 steps forward from the tree, 10 steps backward, 3 steps forward, and finally 8 steps backward. Where is the treasure from the tree?

   _____

4. **HEALTH** When Joel eats a healthy meal, he gives himself 3 points. When he eats an unhealthy meal, he gives himself −5 points. On Thursday, he ate 2 healthy meals and 1 unhealthy meal. How many points should Joel give himself for that day?

   _____

5. **FINANCES** Maggie received $25 for her birthday. She paid her mother back the $25 that she had borrowed last week. How much money does Maggie have left?

   _____

6. **SPORTING EVENTS** Beth had $18 when she went to the basketball game. It cost her $5 to get into the game. How much money does Beth have left?

   _____

7. **GAME** Janet and Sandra made up their own scoring for a game they play with each other. For every shot they make they get 5 points, and for every shot they miss they lose 2 points. Who won the game? Explain.

Scoring		
	Janet	**Sandra**
Shots Made	6	5
Shots Missed	4	2

_____

_____

Math Triumphs

Lesson 1-2

Homework Practice

Find each sum. Use the number line.

1 −3 + (−5) = _____

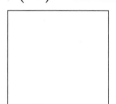

2 2 + (−6) = _____

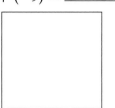

Find each sum. Use algebra tiles.

3 4 + (−7) = _____

4 3 + (−9) = _____

What is the opposite of each number? Use it to show the inverse Property of Addition.

5 −3 _____

6 4 _____

7 5 _____

8 −11 _____

Find each sum.

9 12 + (−9) = _____

10 −2 + (−8) = _____

11 6 + (−10) = _____

12 −3 + 3 = _____

Solve.

13 **BUS STOPS**   There were 15 riders on a bus. At the first stop, 3 people got off and 5 people got on. At the next stop, 7 people got off and 1 person got on. How many riders were now on the bus?   _____

14 **GAMES**   Corey moved 5 spaces forward on his first turn. He then moved 2 spaces forward on his next turn, but drew a card that said to move backward 3 spaces. How far had Corey advanced from the start?   _____

Write the vocabulary word that completes each sentence.

15 The _____ states that for any number, the sum of that number and its opposite is zero.

16 The _____ states that the order in which two numbers are added does not change the sum.

Lesson 1-3

Vocabulary and English Language Development

▶ Activate Prior Knowledge

Find each opposite.

1 +7 _____

2 −5 _____

3 −2 _____

4 −4 _____

5 +6 _____

6 +9 _____

▶ Definition Review

The **absolute value** of a number is the distance between the number and zero on a number line.

Opposites are numbers that are the same distance from zero in opposite directions.

Rewrite each subtraction as an addition expression.

7 7 − 10 _____

8 −3 − 5 _____

9 −8 − (−6) _____

10 9 − (−4) _____

▶ Application

Follow the directions for the activity.

- Use masking tape to make a number line from −15 to 15 on the floor.
- Write each integer from −8 through 8 on separate pieces of paper. Put the pieces of paper in a bag, hat, or bowl.
- Student 1 picks a number from the bag and finds that number on the number line.
- Student 2 picks a number from the bag, and subtracts his or her number from the number of the other volunteer using the number line on the floor. What is the difference?
- Using the same numbers, have Student 2 find the opposite of his or her number on the number line. Student 1 should find the sum using the number line. What is the sum? Is it the same?
- Repeat the steps with each new pair of students picking new numbers until each student has had a turn.

Math Triumphs

Lesson 1-3 Skills Practice

Find each absolute value.

1 $|8| =$ _____

2 $|2| =$ _____

3 $|-4| =$ _____

4 $|-6| =$ _____

5 $|15| =$ _____

6 $|9| =$ _____

7 $|-11| =$ _____

8 $|-1| =$ _____

9 $|-7| =$ _____

10 $|14| =$ _____

Find each difference. Use the number line.

11 $3 - (-4) =$ _____

```
<---+--+--+--+--+--+--+--+--+--+--+--->
  -10 -8 -6 -4 -2  0  2  4  6  8  10
```

12 $8 - 9 =$ _____

```
<---+--+--+--+--+--+--+--+--+--+--+--->
  -10 -8 -6 -4 -2  0  2  4  6  8  10
```

13 $-2 - 1 =$ _____

```
<--+--+--+--+--+--+--+--+--+--+-->
  -5 -4 -3 -2 -1  0  1  2  3  4  5
```

14 $-4 - (-2) =$ _____

```
<--+--+--+--+--+--+--+--+--+--+--+-->
 -6 -5 -4 -3 -2 -1  0  1  2  3  4  5  6
```

15 $-7 - (-3) =$ _____

```
<---+--+--+--+--+--+--+--+--+--+--+--->
  -10 -8 -6 -4 -2  0  2  4  6  8  10
```

16 $-9 - (-3) =$ _____

```
<---+--+--+--+--+--+--+--+--+--+--+--->
  -10 -8 -6 -4 -2  0  2  4  6  8  10
```

Find each difference.

17 $-5 - (-6) =$ _____

18 $-4 - (-7) =$ _____

19 $10 - (-3) =$ _____

20 $-1 - 6 =$ _____

21 $-8 - 4 =$ _____

22 $3 - (-3) =$ _____

23 $2 - (-3) =$ _____

24 $-9 - (-7) =$ _____

25 $7 - 11 =$ _____

26 $1 - 9 =$ _____

Lesson 1-3

Problem-Solving Practice

Solve.

1 **CONSTRUCTION** Ajay needs to dig a pit 12 inches deep for his new patio. On Monday, he digs an 8 inch hole. During the night it rains and 2 inches of dirt falls back into his pit. How much deeper does he still need to dig?

_____

2 **FOOTBALL** The home team needs to gain 8 yards for a touchdown. They gain 4 yards, lose 2 yards, and gain 5 yards. How many more yards does the home team need for a touchdown?

_____

3 **MINING** Maria travels down a mineshaft to 98 feet below sea level. The entrance of the mine is 25 feet below sea level. What integer describes her change in elevation?

_____

4 **SHOPPING** Tobias had a $35 in-store credit. After using his credit towards the purchase of a pair of jeans, he still owed the store $12. What was the cost of the jeans that Tobias purchased?

_____

5 **TEST** Leticia got her math test back. At the top of the page it said she had 12 points taken away for incorrect answers and she received 3 extra points for getting the bonus question correct. How many points were added or subtracted to get Leticia's final test score?

_____

6 **FOOD** A local restaurant had 2 dozen eggs when they opened on Wednesday morning. Later they received a delivery of more eggs. Throughout the day, the restaurant used a total of 5 dozen eggs. The restaurant had 8 dozen eggs left when they closed on Wednesday evening. How many dozen eggs were delivered to the restaurant?

_____

7 **FINANCES** Rudy borrowed $35 from his father last week. He earned $20 babysitting. He gave all of the babysitting money to his dad. What is Rudy's situation now?

_____

Math Triumphs

Lesson 1-3 Homework Practice

Find each difference. Use the number line.

1 $-4 - 3 = $ _____

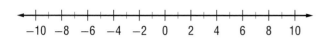

2 $1 - (-6) = $ _____

Find each difference. Use algebra tiles.

3 $-8 - 2 = $ _____

4 $-3 + 5 = $ _____

Which number has the greater absolute value?

5 -3 or 2 _____

6 4 or -4 _____

7 -6 or -9 _____

8 8 or 1 _____

Find each difference.

9 $6 - (-3) = $ _____

10 $-7 - 1 = $ _____

11 $-12 - (-8) = $ _____

12 $4 - 5 = $ _____

Solve.

13 **WEATHER** On the first day of February in upstate New York, the high
temperature was 3°F at 2:00 P.M. Over the next 5 hours, the temperature
dropped 10 degrees. What was the temperature at 7:00 P.M.? _____

14 **GEOGRAPHY** Taborri was at camp in Oregon where the elevation is
3,400 feet above sea level. Her mother was on a trip in California
where the elevation was 200 feet below sea level. What is the
difference in elevations? _____

Write the vocabulary word that completes each sentence.

15 Numbers that are the same distance from zero in opposite directions
are called _____.

16 The _____ of a number is the distance between the
number and zero on a number line.

Math Triumphs

Lesson 1-3 A15

Lesson 1-4 Vocabulary and English Language Development

▶ Activate Prior Knowledge

List all possible whole number factors of each number.

1 20 _____

2 36 _____

▶ Definition Review

A **product** is the answer or result to a multiplication problem. It also refers to expressing a number as the product of its factors.

A **factor** is a number that divides into a whole number with a remainder of zero. It is also a number that is multiplied by another number.

The **Zero Property of Multiplication** states that any number times zero is zero.

The **Identity Property of Multiplication** states that any number times 1 equals that number.

The **Commutative Property of Multiplication** states that the order in which numbers are multiplied does not change the product.

The **Associative Property of Multiplication** states that the manner in which factors are grouped does not change the product.

Find the missing number. Name the multiplication property.

3 $4 \cdot (-8) = $ _____ $\cdot 4$ _____

4 _____ $\cdot 1 = -7$ _____

5 $5 \cdot (6 \cdot 2) = (5 \cdot $ _____$) \cdot 2$ _____

6 $0 \cdot (-7) = $ _____ _____

▶ Application

Follow the directions for the activity.

- Write 20 integer multiplication problems.
- One problem at a time, read the problems aloud.
- If the product is a positive number, your partner should show thumbs up.
- If the product is zero, your partner should show thumbs between up and down.
- If the product is negative, your partner should show thumbs down.
- Determine the product.

NAME _____ DATE _____

Lesson 1-4 · Skills Practice

Find the missing number. Name the multiplication property.

1. $-8 \cdot 3 = 3 \cdot$ _____   _____

2. $-8(9 + 7) = (-8 \cdot$ _____$) + (-8 \cdot 7)$ _____

3. $-8 \cdot$ _____ $= -8$ _____

4. $(-8 \cdot 5) \cdot (-4) = -8 \cdot ($_____ $\cdot (-4))$ _____

5. $-8 \cdot$ _____ $= 0$ _____

Find each product. Use a number line.

6. $3 \cdot (-6) =$ _____

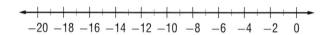

8. $2 \cdot (-8) =$ _____

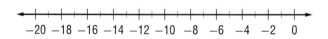

7. $4 \cdot (-3) =$ _____

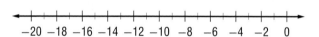

9. $2 \cdot (-5) =$ _____

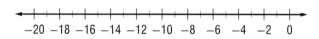

Find each product.

10. $-7 \cdot 3 =$ _____

11. $-10 \cdot 2 =$ _____

12. $5 \cdot (-5) =$ _____

13. $-8 \cdot (-8) =$ _____

14. $-6 \cdot 4 =$ _____

15. $2 \cdot (-9) =$ _____

16. $-7 \cdot (-8) =$ _____

17. $12 \cdot 3 =$ _____

18. $9 \cdot 5 =$ _____

19. $-4 \cdot 11 =$ _____

**Lesson
1-4 Problem-Solving Practice**

Solve.

1. **CELL PHONES** Mr. Owada tracks his family's cell phone use as negative minutes. His daughter said she talked on her phone 9 times last week, and each call lasted about 6 minutes. What integer should Mr. Owada record for his daughter's usage this past week? _____

2. **FINANCES** Leticia's parents allow her to borrow money to be paid back with future allowances. On Sunday, she borrowed money to purchase 3 books that cost $6 each. What is Leticia's balance? _____

3. **HEALTH** Mr. Larson lost 2 pounds each week for the past 2 weeks. What will be the overall change in Mr. Larson's weight if he maintains this rate for 3 more weeks? _____

4. **SCUBA DIVING** Gabe is scuba diving. He descends at a rate of 20 feet per minute. His diving partner times how long his descent takes. The stop watch shows 5 minutes and 0 seconds. What integer describes Gabe's change in depth? _____

5. **ENGINEERING** Howie documents power sources as positive current and devices that draw power as negative current. He has 5 small pumps in the machine that draw 8 amps of current. What integer will Howie use to document the total current of the pumps? _____

6. **STOCK MARKET** The stock market posted a loss of 10 points last week. An analyst said he expects this trend to continue for the next 6 weeks. What is the expected stock market change after the next 6 weeks? _____

7. **ENVIRONMENT** Haloke records the water level in the lake each week for the city. The water level has dropped 8 inches each week for the past 4 weeks. What has been the total change in the water level for this month? _____

Math Triumphs

NAME _____ DATE _____

Lesson 1-4 Homework Practice

Find each product. Use a number line.

1 $1 \cdot (-9) =$ _____

2 $4 \cdot (-4) =$ _____

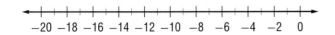

3 $3 \cdot (-3) =$ _____

4 $2 \cdot (-7) =$ _____

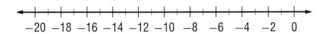 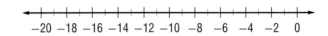

Find each product.

5 $9 \cdot (-7) =$ _____

6 $15 \cdot 2 =$ _____

7 $-4 \cdot 8 =$ _____

8 $6 \cdot (-7) =$ _____

9 $-12 \cdot (-3) =$ _____

10 $-8 \cdot 11 =$ _____

11 $4 \cdot (-5) =$ _____

12 $-2 \cdot (-9) =$ _____

Find the missing number. Name the multiplication property.

13 $-3 \cdot 1 =$ _____   _____

14 $-2 \cdot 6 =$ _____ $\cdot (-2)$ _____

15 $-8 \cdot 0 =$ _____   _____

16 $-2 \cdot [4 \cdot (-8)] = (-2 \cdot$ _____ $) \cdot (-8)$ _____

Solve.

17 **WEATHER** The daily high temperature has dropped 2° F each day for the past 7 days. What has the change in temperature been for the past week?   _____

18 **GOLF** On Saturday, Leon shot −1 (1 under par) for each of the first 3 holes. What is Leon's score after the first 3 holes?   _____

Write the vocabulary word that completes each sentence.

19 A _____ is a number that divides into a whole number evenly.

20 The answer or result of a multiplication problem is the _____.

Lesson
1-5

Vocabulary and
English Language Development

▶ Activate Prior Knowledge

Fill in the blank with *positive* or *negative*.

1 The temperature rose 5° each hour for 2 hours. The change in temperature is

_____.

2 Grace deposited $10 in her bank account each month for 6 months. The change in her bank balance is _____.

3 On a game show, a contestant loses $50 for each question answered incorrectly. James had won $400. Then he answered 4 questions incorrectly. The change in the amount of money he won is _____.

▶ Definition Review

A **dividend** is a number that is being divided.

A **divisor** is the number by which the dividend is being divided.

The **quotient** is the answer or result of a division problem.

Label the *dividend, divisor,* and *quotient* in each problem below.

4 _____

$$20 \div 5 = 4$$

_____   _____

5 _____

$$6 \overline{)18} ^{3}$$

_____   _____

▶ Application

Follow the directions for the activity.

- Write 10 integer division problems.
- One problem at a time, read the problems aloud.
- If the product is a positive number, your partner should make a plus sign with his or her hands.
- If the product is zero, your partner should make a zero with his or her hand.
- If the product is a negative number, your partner should make a negative sign with his or her hand.
- Determine the quotient, then switch roles and repeat the activity.

Math Triumphs

Lesson 1-5

Skills Practice

Find each quotient.

1 $10 \div (-1)$ _____

2 $10 \div 1$ _____

3 $-10 \div (-1)$ _____

4 $-10 \div 1$ _____

5 $14 \div (-2)$ _____

6 $\dfrac{49}{7}$ _____

7 $-55 \div (-11)$ _____

8 $\dfrac{28}{-4}$ _____

9 $15 \div (-3)$ _____

10 $-36 \div (-6)$ _____

11 $\dfrac{-9}{3}$ _____

12 $81 \div (-9)$ _____

13 $56 \div 7$ _____

14 $-42 \div (-6)$ _____

15 $100 \div (-25)$ _____

16 $60 \div 5$ _____

17 $-36 \div 4$ _____

18 $\dfrac{-16}{-4}$ _____

19 $0 \div (-8)$ _____

20 $75 \div 5$ _____

Lesson 1-5 Problem-Solving Practice

Solve. Explain your answer.

1 **WEATHER** The temperature dropped 18°F in the last 6 hours. How much did the temperature change in degrees per hour if the temperature changed the same amount each hour? _____

2 **RECREATION** Forty-eight people are going canoeing. If each canoe contains 4 people, how many canoes does the group need? _____

3 **INVESTING** The value of a share of stock has decreased by $2 over the last 5 hours. How much did the value of a share of stock change in dollars per hour if the value changed the same amount each hour? _____

4 **AVIATION** An airplane descended 4,000 feet in 8 minutes. How much did the airplane's altitude change in feet per minute if the altitude changed the same amount each minute? _____

5 **RECREATION** Sixty-six people are attending a family reunion. If each picnic table seats 6 people, how many tables are needed to seat everyone in the family? _____

6 **FOOTBALL** A team lost 25 yards for 5 penalties. How much did the team's position change in yards per penalty if the position changed the same amount for each penalty? _____

7 **FINANCE** Jack's stocks lost 18 points in 9 weeks. How much did the value of Jack's stocks change in points per week if the value changed the same amount each week? _____

Math Triumphs

Lesson 1-5 Homework Practice

Find each quotient.

1 $-5 \div (-1)$ _____

2 $-5 \div 1$ _____

3 $5 \div (-1)$ _____

4 $5 \div 1$ _____

5 $\dfrac{6}{-2}$ _____

6 $-18 \div (-3)$ _____

7 $-35 \div (-7)$ _____

8 $44 \div 11$ _____

9 $\dfrac{-54}{6}$ _____

10 $50 \div (-2)$ _____

11 $-25 \div (-5)$ _____

12 $\dfrac{-70}{-10}$ _____

Solve.

13 **MONEY** A group of 6 friends earned $90 doing yard work. They want to divide the money equally. How much money does each person get?

_____

14 **TRANSPORTATION** A submarine descends 600 feet in 2 minutes. How far does the submarine descend in 1 second?

Write the vocabulary word that completes each sentence.

15 A _____ is a number that is being divided.

16 A _____ is the number by which the dividend is being divided.

17 The _____ is the answer to a division problem.

Chapter 2 Foldables Study Organizer

Dinah Zike's Foldables

Make this Foldable to help you organize information about patterns and graphs.

1 Begin with five sheets of $8\frac{1}{2}''\times 11''$ paper. Fold a sheet of paper in half lengthwise. Cut a 1" tab along the left edge through one thickness.

2 Glue the 1" tab down. Write the title of the lesson on the front tab.

3 Repeat Steps 1–2 for the remaining sheets of paper. Label each sheet with the title of the lesson. Staple together to form a booklet.

TAKING NOTES

As you read through the chapter, record what you learn about patterns and graphs on the tabs of your Foldable. Use each tab to record notes for each lesson.

USING YOUR FOLDABLE

As you study, check your understanding by designing additional linear and nonlinear graphs.

USING YOUR FOLDABLE

Work in groups of four. Discuss examples of data from your own lives and compile in a table. Create a linear or nonlinear graph using the data you have collected.

Math Triumphs

Chapter 2

Games and Puzzles
Four in a Row!

DIRECTIONS:

- A player tosses the number cubes to make an ordered pair. For example, if the number cubes show 3 and 2, the player could choose to use the ordered pair (3, 2) or (2, 3).

- The player plots the ordered pair on the grid. If the ordered pair is already covered, the player rolls again. Players use different color counters.

- Repeat until someone plots four ordered pairs in a row, column, or diagonal. The player who connects four counters in a row wins.

What You Need

- 2 Number Cubes
- Four in a Row! Grid
- Counters in 2 Different Colors

Number of Players

2 or more

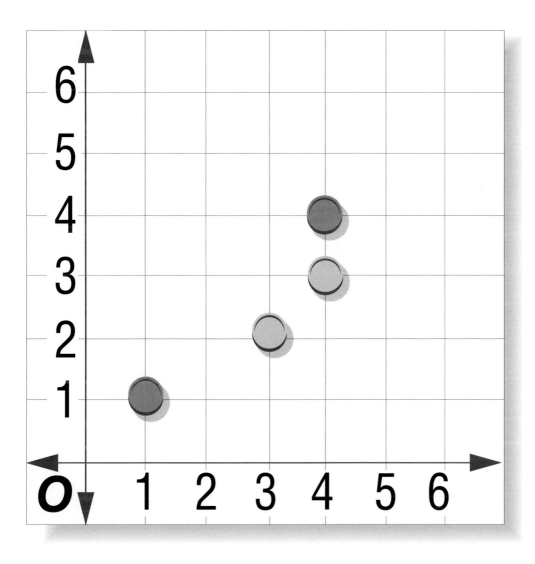

Chapter 2

Four in a Row! Grid

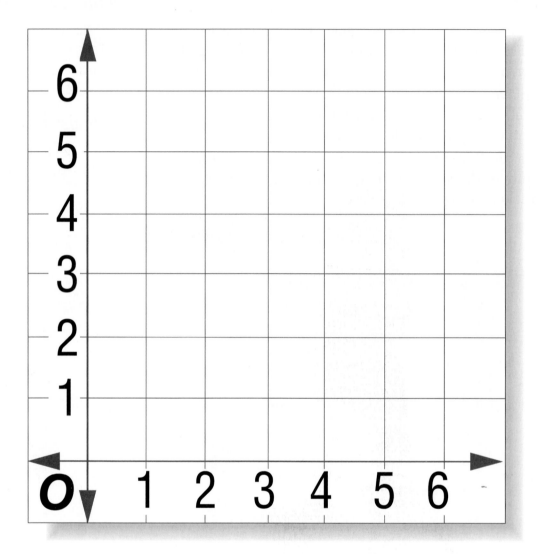

Math Triumphs

Lesson 2-1
Vocabulary and English Language Development

▶ Activate Prior Knowledge

Complete each sentence using the words *add*, *subtract*, *multiply*, or *divide*.

1 Carlos brushes his teeth three times a day. To find the number of times he brushes his teeth in a week, we can use the rule _____ 3 for each day.

2 Theo saves 2 pennies on Monday, 4 pennies on Tuesday, 8 pennies on Wednesday and so on. His rule for saving pennies is to _____ the previous day's savings by 2.

3 John buys a 32-ounce bottle of juice. He drinks 8 ounces of juice each day. To find the amount of juice left after 3 days, use the rule _____ 8.

4 Matilda is reading a book that is 240 pages long. After the first day of reading, she has 120 pages left. After the second day she has 60 pages left, and after the third day she has 30 pages left. To find the number of pages Matilda has left to read on the fourth day, we can _____ by 2.

▶ Definition Review

A **pattern** is a sequence of numbers, figures, or symbols that follows a rule or design.
A **rule** tells how numbers are related.
A **term** is each number in a sequence.

Match the pattern to its rule.

5 6, 21, 36, 51   Divide by 4.

6 64, 16, 4, 1   Add 300.

7 100; 400; 700; 1,000   Subtract 4.

8 2004, 2000, 1996, 1992   Add 15.

▶ Application

Follow the directions for the activity.

- A year is a leap year if it is divisible by 4. If the year is a year ending in 00, then it must be divisible by 400 to be a leap year.
- Students work individually.
- Determine if the following years are leap years:

2000 _____   2010 _____   2024 _____

Lesson 2-1

Skills Practice

Find a rule for each pattern.

1 10, 20, 30, 40 _____

2 100, 85, 70, 55 _____

3 1,600, 400, 100, 25 _____

4 25, 50, 100, 200 _____

5 12, 17, 22, 27 _____

In each sequence, find a rule. Then write the next three terms.

6 11, 21, 31, 41

Rule: _____

Next terms: _____, _____, _____

7 2,400,000; 240,000; 24,000

Rule: _____

Next terms: _____, _____, _____

8 62, 74, 86, 98

Rule: _____

Next terms: _____, _____, _____

9 6, 18, 54, 162

Rule: _____

Next terms: _____, _____, _____

Write the next three conversions in each pattern.

10

Number of Quarts	1	2	3	4
Number of Pints	2			

11

Number of Years	1	2	3	4
Number of Months	12			

12

Number of Yards	1	2	3	4
Number of Inches	36			

Lesson 2-1

Problem-Solving Practice

Solve.

1 **BANKING** Leo saves $4 each week. How much money does Leo save in 6 weeks? _____

Week	1	2	3	4	5	6
Amount Saved	$4					

2 **DESIGN** Candace created the pattern at the right. How many squares are in the 5th term of the pattern? 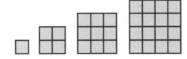 _____

3 **PIZZA** The Pizza Place sells a large pizza for $7.50. You can buy a second large pizza for $7.25, and a third for $7.00. If this pattern continues, how much would the fifth large pizza cost? _____

4 **VIDEO** Dion rented eight DVDs. Each rental costs $3. How much did Dion spend on all of the DVDs? _____

Number of DVDs	1	2	3	4	5	6	7	8
Cost	$3							

5 **COMMUTING** Mr. Harris drives 12 miles to and 12 miles from work each weekday. After 4 weeks, not including the weekends, how many miles has Mr. Harris commuted to and from work? _____

6 **PACKAGING** Jason bought 6 packages of cookies to share with the students in his grade. If each package contains 15 cookies, how many cookies did Jason buy? _____

7 **INTERIOR DESIGN** Cara is painting the following pattern on her kitchen wall.

If the pattern continues, how many dark triangles are in the sixth term? _____

How many light triangles are in the sixth term? _____

How many triangles are in the sixth term in all? _____

Lesson 2-1 Homework Practice

Find a rule for each pattern.

1 7, 21, 63, 189 _____

2 125, 100, 75, 50 _____

3 234, 245, 256, 267 _____

In each sequence, find a rule. Then write the next three terms.

4 189, 173, 157, 141

Rule: _____

Next terms: _____, _____, _____

5 729, 243, 81, 27

Rule: _____

Next terms: _____, _____, _____

Write the next three conversions in each pattern.

6

Number of Tricycles	1	2	3	4
Number of Wheels	3			

7

Number of Hours	1	2	3	4
Number of Minutes	60			

Solve.

8 **RACING** Lance is training for a bike race. Starting on Tuesday, each day he bikes 3 more miles than he did the day before. On Monday, he bikes 3 miles. How many miles does he bike on Friday? _____

Write the vocabulary word that completes each sentence.

9 A _____ tells how numbers are related to each other.

10 A _____ is a sequence of numbers, figures, or symbols that follows a rule or design.

11 A list of numbers in a specific order is a _____.

Math Triumphs

Lesson 2-2 Vocabulary and English Language Development

▶ Activate Prior Knowledge

Complete the table of values for the equations.

1 $y = x - 3$

x	y
−2	
−1	
0	
1	
2	

2 $y = 4x$

x	y
−2	
−1	
0	
1	
2	

3 $y = x + 2$

x	y
−4	
−2	
0	
2	
4	

▶ Definition Review

An **equation** is a mathematical sentence that contains an equal sign.
A **function** is a relationship in which one quantity depends upon another quantity (for every x-value there is exactly one y-value).
A **function table** is a table of ordered pairs that is based on a rule.
A **variable** is a symbol, usually a letter, used to represent a number.

Determine if each table of values represents a function.

4

x	y
1	−4
2	−3
3	−2
4	−1

_____

5

x	y
−1	3
−2	6
−1	0
−2	−3

_____

▶ Application

Follow the directions for the activity.

- Students work with a partner.
- Each student writes a function and creates a function table with only the input values shown.
- Each student gives their function and function table to their partner who must fill in the output values in the table using the given function.
- Return the completed function table to your partner who will check your work.
- If all your output values are correct you get 1 point, if your partner finds an error in your output values he or she gets 1 point.
- Repeat the activity three times. The student with the most points after four rounds is the winner.

Lesson 2-2 **Skills Practice**

Write a function to represent each situation.

1 Chad completed the race in half the time Jared did.   _____

2 Flor is 2 years younger than Hector.   _____

3 Each dining room table comes with 6 chairs.   _____

4 Amanda has $10 more than Meagan.   _____

Write a function and make a function table.

5 **TRAVEL**   Adina can paddle a canoe in still water at an average speed of 4 miles per hour. Let y = miles traveled and x = number of hours.

$y =$ _____

Number of Hours, x	1	2	3	4	5
Miles Traveled, y					

If Adina canoed for 4 hours, how many miles did Adina canoe?   _____

6 **FITNESS**   Kyle began exercising for 25 minutes each day. Each week, he increased the time of his workout by 5 minutes. Let y = length of workout in minutes and x = number of weeks.

$y =$ _____

Number of Weeks, x	1	2	3	4	5	6
Length of Workout, y						

What is the length of Kyle's daily workout after 6 weeks?   _____

7 **BABYSITTING**   Each Saturday evening, Jaylynn drives across town to babysit for a family with two children. She is paid $5 per hour plus $6 for gas. Let y = amount of money she receives and let x = number of hours she babysits.

$y =$ _____

Number of Hours Babysitting, x	2	3	4	5	6
Amount of Money Made, y					

Jaylynn babysat for 5 hours. How much money did she receive?   _____

Math Triumphs

Lesson 2-2 Problem-Solving Practice

Write a function and make a function table.

1 **BIOLOGY** During Biology class, Angie learns that spiders and scorpions each have 8 legs. Let y = the number of legs and x = the number of spiders or scorpions.

$y =$ _____

Number of Spiders or Scorpions, x	4	6	8	10	12
Number of Legs, y					

How many legs do 12 spiders have?   _____

2 **WAGES** Sergio works for a company that gives a raise every third year of employment. Sergio was 26 years old when he was hired. Let y = Sergio's age and x = the number of raises.

$y =$ _____

Number of Raises, x	1	2	3	4	5
Serio's Age, y					

How old will Sergio be when he gets his fourth raise?   _____

3 **MANAGEMENT** A manager works 1 hour longer each day than his employees. Let y = the number of hours worked by the manager and x = the number of hours worked by the employees.

$y =$ _____

Number of Hours Worked by Employees, x	2	4	6	8	10
Number of Hours Worked by Manager, y					

If the employees worked 8 hours one day, how many hours did the manager work?   _____

4 **SAVINGS** Trish is saving money to buy a new CD player. She already has $52 in her savings account and she is saving $4 each week. Let y = the total amount of money she has saved and let x = the number of weeks that she has been saving money.

$y =$ _____

Number of Weeks, x	4	6	8	10	12
Amount of Money Saved, y					

How much money will Trish have saved after 10 weeks?   _____

Lesson 2-2 Homework Practice

Write a function to represent each situation.

1 There are 8 notes in every octave.   _____

2 Frankie earns $5 more per hour than Doris.   _____

3 Nicole is 6 years younger than her sister.   _____

Write a function and make a function table.

4 **SCIENCE** In an experiment, a scientist used 3 times as much water as solution. Let y = amount of water and let x = amount of solution.

$y = $ _____

Amount of Solution, x	2	4	6	8	10
Amount of Water, y					

If 8 liters of solution are used, how many liters of water are used?   _____

5 **AGE** Ahanu is 22 years younger than his mother. Let y = Ahanu's age and x = Ahanu's mother's age.

$y = $ _____

Ahanu's Mother's Age, x	30	35	40	45	50
Ahanu's Age, y					

How old will Ahanu be when his mother is 45?   _____

6 **CALORIES** Jordan is counting the number of calories he consumes in a day. Yesterday he consumed 1,800 calories plus he drank several 8-ounce glasses of milk. Each 8-ounce glass of milk provides 120 calories. Let y = the total number of calories he consumed and let x = the number of 8-ounce glasses of milk he drank.

$y = $ _____

Number of 8-ounce Glasses of Milk, x	1	2	3	4	5
Total Number of Calories Consumed, y					

If Jordan drank five 8-ounce glasses of milk, how many calories did he consume that day?   _____

Write the vocabulary word that completes each sentence.

7 A symbol used to represent a number is a _____.

8 A relationship is a _____ if for every x-value there is exactly one y-value.

Math Triumphs

Lesson 2-3

Vocabulary and English Language Development

▶ Activate Prior Knowledge

Use a coordinate grid to locate and label points.

The city of Philadelphia was laid out in a grid pattern by William Penn and Thomas Holmes. Use a coordinate grid to find locations.

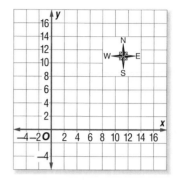

1 Locate and mark the origin. Label it "City Hall." Give its coordinates.

_____

2 Move east 9 blocks from City Hall. Mark the point and label it "Liberty Bell." Give its coordinates.

_____

3 Move south 1 block from Liberty Bell. Mark the point and label it "Independence Hall." Give its coordinates.

_____

4 Move east 3 blocks and north 2 blocks from Independence Hall. Mark the point and label it "Betsy Ross House." Give its coordinates.

_____

5 Move west 2 blocks from Betsy Ross House. Mark the point and label it "U.S. Mint." Give its coordinates.

_____

▶ Definition Review

Match the vocabulary word to its location on the graph.

6 origin _____

7 x-axis _____

8 y-axis _____

9 ordered pair _____

10 coordinate grid _____

▶ Application

Follow the directions to demonstrate plotting a point.

- Work as a class. Clear an area on a tile floor. Use tape to mark the x- and y-axes, and, if needed, to mark the grid lines. An auditorium, a gym, or an outdoor paved area could also be used.
- The teacher writes ordered pairs on the board.
- One at a time, students start at the origin and walk along the grid to the location of a specified ordered pair.
- Repeat until all students have graphed a point.

Math Triumphs

Lesson 2-3 **Skills Practice**

Name the ordered pair for each point.

1 A _____

2 B _____

3 C _____

4 D _____

5 E _____

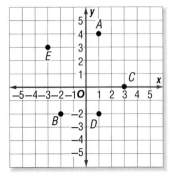

6 F _____

7 G _____

8 H _____

9 I _____

10 J _____

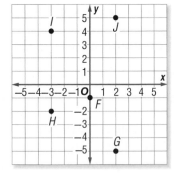

Graph the ordered pairs.

11 Graph the ordered pairs K (3, 1) and L (3, 4).
Then connect the points.

(3, 1) and (3, 4) are on a line parallel to the *y*-axis because
they have the same _____-coordinates.

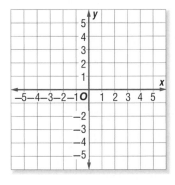

12 Graph the ordered pairs M (1, 4) and N (−3, 4).
Then connect the points.

(1, 4) and (−3, 4) are on a line parallel to the *x*-axis because
they have the same _____-coordinates.

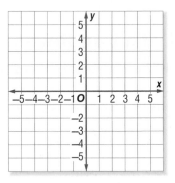

13 Graph the ordered pairs:

P (−2, −5)   Q (−2, 0)

R (3, 1)   S (−5, 2)

T (3, −2)   U (−4, −3)

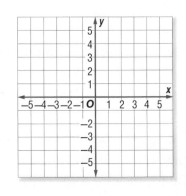

Math Triumphs

Lesson
2-3

Problem-Solving Practice

Lesson 2-3

Solve.

1 **CHESS** Della is playing chess. She moves her queen from position (8, 3) to position (1, 3). Graph the points. How many spaces did Della move her queen?

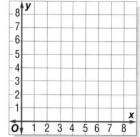

_____

2 **CITIES** Amanda has a map of her hometown. Each square represents one block. Give the coordinates of the fire station and the police station. How many blocks separate these buildings?

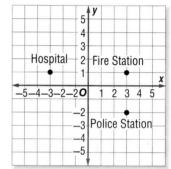

_____

3 **CITIES** Use the map of Amanda's hometown from Exercise 2 above. Give the coordinates of the hospital and the fire station. How many blocks separate these buildings?

_____

4 **BOARD GAMES** Blake and Juan are playing a military strategy game on a board which has been marked in a grid pattern. Blake attacked at location *A* on his first move and location *B* on his second move. Give the coordinates of each point and the number of spaces between Blake's first and second attacks.

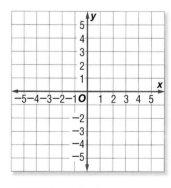

_____

5 **GRAPHING SENSE** Graph the points (−4, 2) and (5, 2) on the coordinate grid shown. What is the distance between these two points? Explain how this distance could be found without graphing the points.

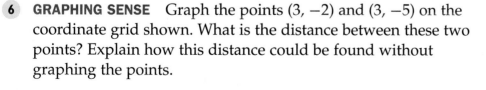

_____

_____

_____

6 **GRAPHING SENSE** Graph the points (3, −2) and (3, −5) on the coordinate grid shown. What is the distance between these two points? Explain how this distance could be found without graphing the points.

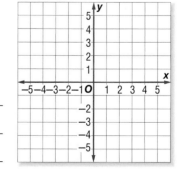

_____

_____

_____

Lesson 2-3

Homework Practice

Name the ordered pair for each point.

1 Z _____

2 Y _____

3 X _____

4 W _____

5 V _____

6 U _____

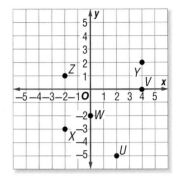

Graph the ordered pairs.

7 Graph the ordered pairs T (4, −1) and S (−1, −1).
Then connect the points.

(4, −1) and (−1, −1) are on a line parallel to the x-axis because

they have the same _____ -coordinate.

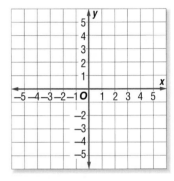

8 Graph the ordered pairs R (−1, 4) and Q (−1, 0).
Then connect the points.

(−1, 4) and (−1, 0) are on a line parallel to the y-axis because

they have the same _____ -coordinate.

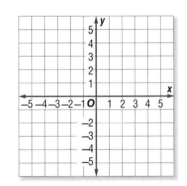

Write the vocabulary word that completes the sentence.

9 A _____ is a grid in which a horizontal number
line and a vertical number line intersect at their zero points.

Solve.

10 **GRAPHING SENSE** Graph the points (−2, 4) and (−2, −3)
on the coordinate grid shown. What is the distance
between these two points? Give two ways to find the distance.

_____

_____

_____

_____

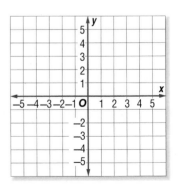

Lesson 2-4 Vocabulary and English Language Development

▶ Activate Prior Knowledge

Identify the table that corresponds to each equation.

1 $y = x + 2$ _____   **2** $y = 2x$ _____   **3** $y = x - 2$ _____   **4** $y = \dfrac{x}{2}$ _____

Table A

x	y
−2	−4
−1	−3
0	−2
1	−1

Table B

x	y
−4	−2
−2	0
0	2
2	4

Table C

x	y
−2	−4
−1	−2
0	0
1	2

Table D

x	y
−4	−2
−2	−1
0	0
2	1

▶ Definition Review

A **coordinate grid** is a grid in which a horizontal number line and a vertical number line intersect at their zero points.
An **ordered pair** is a pair of numbers that are the coordinates of a point in a coordinate grid, written in the order (horizontal coordinate, vertical coordinate).

Describe how to locate each ordered pair in a coordinate grid.

5 $(3, -2)$

_____

_____

6 $(-5, 4)$

_____

_____

▶ Application

Follow the directions to find the equation.

- Students work in pairs with paper and pencils.
- The first student thinks of an equation (for example: $y = 5x$ or $y = x - 4$) and creates a table for this equation.
- The first student gives the table to the second student, but does not reveal the equation.
- The second student examines the table and writes the equation he or she believes created the table.
- If the correct equation is found, the second student earns 1 point. If the equation is not found, the first student earns 1 point. If it is discovered that the table was incorrectly formed, the second student earns 1 point.
- Reverse roles and continue play until both students have created five equations. The student with the most points wins.

Lesson 2-4

Skills Practice

Make a table for each equation.

1 $y = x - 3$

x	x − 3	y	Ordered Pair
−2			
−1			
0			
1			
2			

2 $y = \dfrac{x}{2} + 3$

x	$\dfrac{x}{2} + 3$	y	Ordered Pair
−4			
−2			
0			
2			
4			

Graph each equation.

3 Graph the equation from Exercise 1.

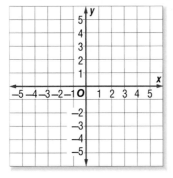

4 Graph the equation from Exercise 2.

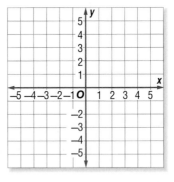

5 Graph $y = -\dfrac{x}{2} + 1$.

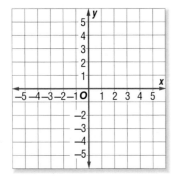

6 Graph $y = -2x + 1$.

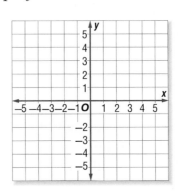

Math Triumphs

Lesson 2-4 Problem-Solving Practice

Solve.

1 **RECREATION** A local festival charges $1 per person plus a parking fee of $5 per car. Make a table to show the relationship between number of people and the total amount charged. How much does it cost for 3 people to drive to the festival in one car?

_____

x	x + 5	y	Ordered Pair
1			
2			
3			
4			
5			

2 **PIZZA** Meg hosted a party during which she served pizza. Each person at the party ate 2 slices of pizza. Make a table to show the relationship between the number of people at the party and the total amount of pizza. How many slices of pizza were eaten if 4 people attended the party?

_____

x	2x	y	Ordered Pair
1			
2			
3			
4			
5			

3 **MOVIES** Mr. Velez would like to take his kids and their friends to the movies. The matinee price for the movie is $3 each. Make a table to show the relationship between the number of tickets and the total cost. How much will the movies cost if Mr. Velez must pay for himself and 4 children?

_____

x	3x	y	Ordered Pair
1			
2			
3			
4			
5			

4 **SAVINGS** Evita has $5 in her savings bank. She wants to save $2 a week to buy some CDs. Make a table to show the relationship between the number of weeks and the total amount saved. How much will she save in 10 weeks?

_____

x	2x + 5	y	Ordered Pair
0			
5			
10			
15			
20			

Chapter 2

Lesson 2-4

Homework Practice

Make a table for each equation.

1 $y = \dfrac{x}{2} + 2$

x	y
−4	
−2	
0	
2	
4	

2 $y = -2x - 1$

x	y
−2	
−1	
0	
1	
2	

Graph each equation.

3 Graph the equation from Exercise 1.

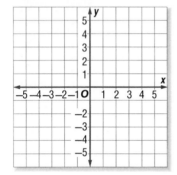

4 Graph the equation from Exercise 2.

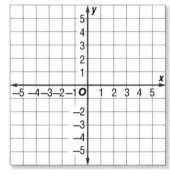

Solve.

5 The cost to go on rides at a fair is $x + 5$, where x is the total number of rides. Show the relationship between the number of rides and the total cost in a table and on a coordinate plane. How much money will it cost to go on 4 rides?

_____

x	x + 5	y	Ordered Pair
1			
2			
3			
4			
5			

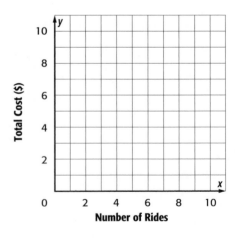

Write the vocabulary word(s) that completes the sentence.

6 A pair of numbers that is the coordinates of a point in a coordinate plane or grid is called an _____.

Lesson 2-5
Vocabulary and English Language Development

▶ Activate Prior Knowledge

Match the function to its graph.

A 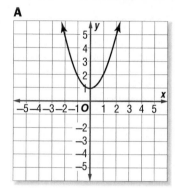 **B** 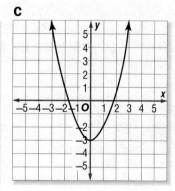 **C** **D**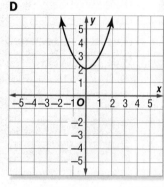

1 $y = x^2$ _____

2 $y = x^2 + 1$ _____

3 $y = x^2 + 2$ _____

4 $y = x^2 - 3$ _____

▶ Definition Review

A **function** is a relationship in which one quantity depends upon another.
A **function table** is a table of ordered pairs that is based on a rule.
A **linear function** is a function whose graph is a straight line.
A **nonlinear function** is a function whose graph is not a straight line.

Refer to the functions and graphs in Exercises 1–4.

5 How can you tell from the functions that they are not linear?

_____

6 How can you tell from the graphs that the functions are nonlinear?

_____

▶ Application

Follow the directions to explore nonlinear function graphs of the form $y = ax^2$.

- Students work in groups of 3 or 4.
- Each student writes a different function of the form $y = ax^2$, using a different integer between 1 and 10 for a.
- Each student creates and completes a function table for his/her function with values -2, -1, 0, 1, and 2 for x.
- Each student graphs his or her function.
- Compare graphs. Discuss similarities and differences.
- Repeat exercise using integers between -10 and -1 for a.

Math Triumphs

Skills Practice

Write a function, make a function table, and make a graph.
Is the function linear or nonlinear?

1 **INTERIOR DESIGN** Kaneesha is putting decorative tiles on the wall above her kitchen sink. The number of tiles is three times the square of the height (in decimeters) of the wall where the tile will go.

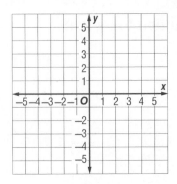

$y =$ _____

Height (in decimeters), x	3	4	5	6	7
Number of Tiles, y					

How many tiles are needed for a space with a height of 5 decimeters? _____

The function is _____.

Match each function with its function table and its graph.

2 $y = x$
function
table _____
graph _____

3 $y = 3x - 2$
function
table _____
graph _____

4 $y = -2x + 1$
function
table _____
graph _____

5 $y = x^2$
function
table _____
graph _____

A

x	−2	−1	0	1	2
y	−8	−5	−2	1	4

B

x	−2	−1	0	1	2
y	−2	−1	0	1	2

C

x	−2	−1	0	1	2
y	4	1	0	1	4

D

x	−2	−1	0	1	2
y	5	3	1	−1	−3

I

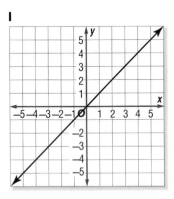

II

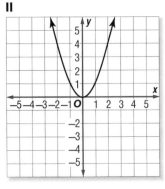

III

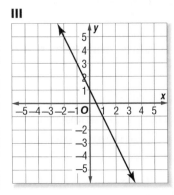

IV

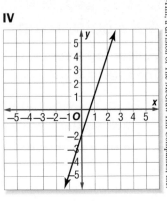

Lesson 2-5

Problem-Solving Practice

Write a function, make a function table, and make a graph.

1 **GEOMETRY** Volume is the amount of space an object occupies. The volume of a cube is the cube of the length of a side.

$y =$ _____

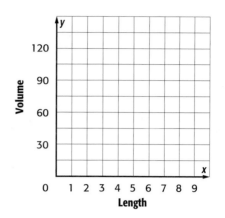

Length, x	1	2	3	4	5
Volume, y					

What is the volume of a cube with length 4 units? _____

2 **ROOFING** John is shingling a roof. He has already laid 100 shingles. He can lay 150 shingles each hour.

$y =$ _____

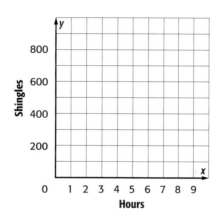

Hours, x	1	2	3	4	5
Shingles, y					

How many shingles will John have laid after 5 hours? _____

3 **MEMBERSHIP** Ian joined a gym. The cost of membership is a one-time fee of $50 plus $10 each month.

$y =$ _____

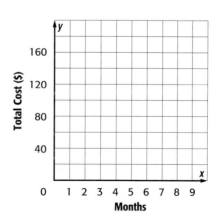

Months, x	2	4	6	8	10
Total Cost, y					

How much will Ian spend for 6 months of gym membership? _____

Lesson 2-5

Homework Practice

① **GEOMETRY** The surface area of a cube is 6 times the square of the length of one of its sides. What is the surface area of a cube with sides that are 4 yards long?

Make a function table using the rule $y =$ _____.

Length, x	1	2	3	4	5
Surface Area, y					

Graph the ordered pairs. Evaluate the rate of change. Connect the points.

A cube with sides 4 yards long has surface area of _____.

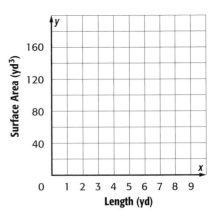

Match each function with its function table and its graph.

② $y = -x^2 + 3$

function table _____

graph _____

③ $y = x + 1$

function table _____

graph _____

④ $y = -x - 1$

function table _____

graph _____

⑤ $y = -2x^2 - 1$

function table _____

graph _____

A

x	−2	−1	0	1	2
y	−9	−3	−1	−3	−9

B

x	−2	−1	0	1	2
y	1	0	−1	−2	−3

C

x	−2	−1	0	1	2
y	−1	2	3	2	−1

D

x	−2	−1	0	1	2
y	−1	0	1	2	3

I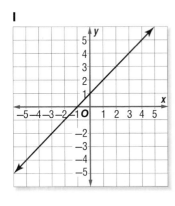

II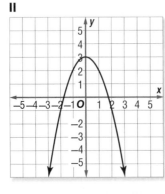

III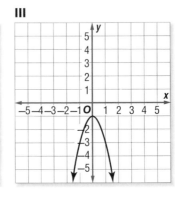

IV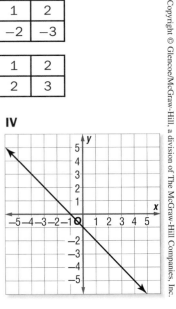

Write the vocabulary word(s) that completes the sentence.

⑥ A _____ is a function whose graph is not a straight line.

Math Triumphs

Foldables Study Organizer

Dinah Zike's Foldables

Make this Foldable to help you organize your notes about expressions and equations.

1 Begin with a sheet of 11″ × 17″ paper. Fold the short sides toward the middle.

2 Fold the top to the bottom. Open. Cut along the second fold to make four tabs.

3 Label each of the tabs as shown.

| 1. Simplify grouping symbols | 2. Find the values of all powers. |
| 3. Multiply and divide in order from left to right | 4. Add and subtract in order from left to right |

TAKING NOTES

As you read through the chapter, use your Foldable to write notes and record examples of each step in the order of operations.

USING YOUR FOLDABLE

As you study, simplify additional examples of expressions following the order of operations. Then, lift the tabs of your Foldable to check yourself.

USING YOUR FOLDABLE

Work with a partner. Write additional examples of expressions that can be simplified. Take turns explaining to one another the steps you would use to evaluate the expression. Make sure your partner is using the correct order of operations.

Chapter 3

Games and Puzzles
Order Matters

GET READY: Cut out the Order Matters cards.

DIRECTIONS

- Shuffle the cards. Then spread the cards facedown on the table.

- Player 1 flips an Order Matters card and rolls the number cube.

- Player 1 replaces the variable n on his or her Order Matters card with the number rolled and then evaluates the expression.

- If player 1 correctly evaluates the expression, he or she keeps the card.

- If player 1 incorrectly evaluates the expression, the card is returned facedown on the table.

- Player 2 takes a turn.

- Continue taking turns until all the Order Matters cards have been played correctly. Each player adds up the point value on his or her cards. The player with the most points wins.

- After a round of play, guide students into creating their own set of Order Matters cards. Point values on the cards should be from 1 to 5 with the level of difficulty becoming gradually harder with the increase in value. Create a total of ten cards: two cards worth 1 point each, two cards worth 2 points, two cards worth 3 points, two cards worth 4 points, and two cards worth 5 points.

- Play the game two additional times, once using the cards you made and once using the cards your partner made.

What You Need
- Order Matters cards
- Number cube
- Scissors
- Pencils
- Paper

Number of Players

2

NAME ____________________ DATE ____________

Order Matters Cards

$2n$ 1 point	$3n$ 1 point
$4n + 1$ 2 points	$5n - 3$ 2 points
$(4 + 1) \cdot n$ 3 points	$n \cdot (5 - 2)$ 3 points
$5 \cdot n \cdot (4 - 1)$ 4 points	$(3 + 2) \cdot 6 \cdot n$ 4 points
$(7 - n) \cdot (9 \div 3)$ 5 points	$8 \div 2 \cdot (n + 2)$ 5 points

Lesson 3-1 Vocabulary and English Language Development

▶ Activate Prior Knowledge

Find each sum, difference, product, or quotient.

1 $-3 + 7 =$ _____

2 $5 + (-8) =$ _____

3 $6 - 8 =$ _____

4 $-3 - 2 =$ _____

5 $-4 \cdot (-5) =$ _____

6 $-9 \cdot 8 =$ _____

7 $30 \div (-6) =$ _____

8 $-24 \div (-4) =$ _____

▶ Definition Review

In a power, the **base** is the number used as a factor.
In a power, the **exponent** is the number of times the base is used as a factor.
The **order of operations** are the rules that tell which operation to perform
first when more than one operation is used.

9 Use 1st, 2nd, 3rd, and 4th to put the steps in the correct order.

_____ Multiply and divide in order from left to right.

_____ Find the value within grouping symbols (parentheses).

_____ Add and subtract in order from left to right.

_____ Simplify terms with exponents.

▶ Application

- Work in pairs. Each student needs five index cards.
- Each student does the following on his or her index cards. On one side of each index card, write a numerical expression using four numbers from 1 to 20, three operation symbols, and at most one pair of grouping symbols and one exponent. Then calculate the value of the expression and write the value on the other side of the card. If the value is *not* a whole number, change your expression until a whole number value is obtained.
- Stack your five completed index cards with the expressions facing up. Trade your stack of cards with your partner, being sure to keep them with the expressions facing up.
- Calculate the value of the expression on each card, and record your values on a piece of paper. Compare your results to the values written on the back of the cards you received.
- If your value does not match the one on the back of the card, work with your partner to determine the correct value.

Math Triumphs

Lesson
3-1 **Skills Practice**

Name the step that should be performed first in each expression.

1 $8 \cdot 6 \div (4 + 2) - 4^2$

_____

2 $3 \cdot 6 + 3^2 + 9 \div 3$

_____

3 $5 \div 1 - 3 + 2 \cdot 6$

_____

4 $9 - 2 + (12 \cdot 6) + 9$

_____

5 $\dfrac{6 + 12}{11 - 2} + 7 \cdot 3$

_____

6 $10 \div 2 \cdot (5 - 1) + 4$

_____

Find the value of each expression.

7 $4 \cdot (2 + 6) - 30 + 4^2 = 4 \cdot \text{_____} - 30 + 4^2$

$= 4 \cdot \text{_____} - 30 + \text{_____}$

$= \text{_____} - 30 + \text{_____}$

$= \text{_____} + \text{_____}$

$= \text{_____}$

8 $9 + 7 \cdot 2 - 3^2 + (1 \cdot 8) = 9 + 7 \cdot 2 - 3^2 + \text{_____}$

$= 9 + 7 \cdot 2 - \text{_____} + \text{_____}$

$= 9 + \text{_____} - \text{_____} + \text{_____}$

$= \text{_____} - \text{_____} + \text{_____}$

$= \text{_____}$

9 $7 - 4 \div 2 + 5^2$

_____

10 $12 \div 4 \cdot 2^3 - (3 + 2)$

_____

11 $14 \cdot 2 \div (8 - 4) + 9$

_____

12 $10 - (12 \div 3) + 2 \cdot 5$

_____

13 $20 - 6 \cdot 3 \div (7 - 5)$

_____

14 $7 \div (5 - 4)^3 + 3 \cdot 2$

_____

Lesson 3-1 Problem-Solving Practice

Solve.

1   **KITTENS**   Carla has 2 cats. Each cat had 5 kittens. She found homes for 7 kittens. How many cats and kittens does Carla have left?

_____

2   **BAKERY**   A baker made 15 loaves of white bread, 12 loaves of wheat bread, and 10 loaves of rye bread. A customer bought 2 loaves of each of the 3 kinds of breads. How many loaves of bread are left?

_____

3   **EARNINGS**   On Monday, Colin worked 3 hours, earned $10 per hour, and spent $5 for lunch. On Tuesday, Colin worked 7 hours, earned $8 per hour, and spent $6 for lunch. How much money does Colin have now?

_____

4   **COOKIES**   Shamika baked 60 oatmeal cookies for a bake sale. She divided the cookies equally among 12 bags. At the bake sale she sold 7 bags of cookies. How many cookies does Shamika have left?

_____

5   **COMPUTERS**   Emilio received a $15 discount when he bought an ink-jet printer. He also bought 2 black printer cartridges, 1 color printer cartridge, and 5 reams of paper. His receipt is shown below. How much money did Emilio spend?

_____

Computer World

Ink-jet printer	1 @ $125.00
– Discount	–$15.00
Black printer cartridges	
	2 @ $35.00
Color printer cartridges	
	1 @ $35.00
Paper	5 @ $5.00

6   **AMUSEMENT PARK**   Lalana paid $12 for admission to an amusement park. She rode the roller coaster 3 times and the Ferris wheel 2 times. Each ride cost $2. She also bought a hamburger and 2 lemonade drinks during the day. How much money did Lalana spend?

_____

Lunch Menu

Hot Dog	$2.00
Hamburger	$3.00
French Fries	$1.00
Lemonade	$1.50
Water	$1.00

Math Triumphs

Lesson 3-1 Homework Practice

Name the step that should be performed first in each expression.

1 $7 + 9 - 2 + 4 \cdot 4^2$

_____

2 $3 \cdot 18 + (9 - 2) + 3^3 \div 3$

_____

3 $(9 + 4 \cdot 2) - 12 \div 3 + 8$

_____

4 $20 \div 4 \cdot 2 - 9 \cdot 2 + 5$

_____

Find the value of each expression.

5 $4^2 + 13 + (9 \div 3^2) \cdot 2$

_____

6 $15 \div (2^2 + 1^2) - 3 \cdot 1$

_____

7 $11 + 3 \cdot 2 + 8 - 8 \div 2$

_____

8 $(3 + 8 \cdot 2 - 18 + 3^2) \div 5$

_____

Solve.

9 SNACKS Marla bought 4 boxes of granola bars. Each box contains 6 granola bars. Marla ate 3 granola bars, and she gave her brother 4 granola bars. Marla then bought 2 more boxes of granola bars. How many granola bars does Marla have now?

_____

10 BOOKS Daniel has 65 books on a book shelf. He divides the books equally among 5 shelves. He then moves 5 books on the top shelf to the bottom shelf. He also buys 3 new books and puts them on the top shelf. How many books are on the top shelf?

_____

Chapter 3

Lesson 3-2 Vocabulary and English Language Development

▶ Activate Prior Knowledge

Circle the activities that need to be done in a specific order.

1 drive a mile and turn on the radio

2 read a book and write a book report

3 put on the left shoe and put on the right shoe

4 open the garage door and drive the car out of the garage

5 mix the ingredients and bake a cake

▶ Definition Review

Find the correct word(s) to complete each statement.

6 To find the value of an algebraic expression by replacing variables with numbers is called _____ the expression.

7 A(n) _____ is a combination of numbers, variables, and at least one operation.

Find the value of each expression.

8 $12 + 8 \div 2$ _____

9 $5 \cdot 8 + 3$ _____

10 $2 + 7 \cdot 4$ _____

11 $9 \div 3 - 1 + 6$ _____

▶ Application

Follow the directions for the activity.

- Students solve the following problems using the order of operations.
  1. $30 - 10 \div 2 + 14 - 3 \times 2$
  2. $7 \cdot 6 + 9 \div 3 + 10$
  3. $14 + 21 \div 7 + 8 \cdot 5$
- Students go back and solve the problems from left to right regardless of the order of operation rules.
- What are the solutions for each method?
- Did the solutions differ?
- Discuss the importance of the order of operations.

Math Triumphs

Lesson 3-2 Skills Practice

Evaluate each expression when $\triangle = 4$ and $\blacklozenge = 5$.

1 $3 \cdot \blacklozenge + 20 - (6 - 2) + \triangle$

Replace symbols with values: _____

Value of the expression: _____

2 $\blacklozenge \cdot 20 - \blacklozenge^2 + 10 - (\triangle + 2)$

Replace symbols with values: _____

Value of the expression: _____

3 $(\triangle \cdot 7 - \blacklozenge^2) \div 3$

Replace symbols with values: _____

Value of the expression: _____

Evaluate each expression when $\square = 8$.

4 $21 + \square$ _____

5 $64 \div \square$ _____

6 $5 \cdot \square$ _____

7 $\square + 14$ _____

8 $\square \div 2$ _____

9 $36 - \square$ _____

10 $2 \cdot \square + 17$ _____

11 $56 - 4 \cdot \square$ _____

12 $80 - 3 \cdot \square + 5$ _____

13 $3 \cdot \square + 24 \div \square$ _____

Evaluate each expression when $a = 3$ and $b = 4$.

14 $8a + b^2 - (55 \div 5)$ _____

15 $21 - b + 6 - a^2$ _____

16 $(18 + 7) + 12 \cdot (5 - b)$ _____

17 $10b + 5^2 - (16 - 7)$ _____

18 $12 - b \div 2 + (b + 5)^2$ _____

19 $9b \div 6 + 15 + (a \cdot b)^2$ _____

20 $(55 - 10a) \div 5 + 42$ _____

21 $b + 42 - (a \cdot b) + a^2$ _____

22 $10 - 5 + 12 - b + 9 \cdot 7$ _____

23 $14 + a^2 \cdot 7 - 6 + (b \div 2) - 8$ _____

Lesson 3-2

Problem-Solving Practice

Solve.

1. **EARNINGS** For a typical shift, Alex gets paid $5 per hour, plus $3 per hour in tips, and $40 per shift. The expression $5h + 3h + 40$ represents how much Alex can expect to make during a shift. Determine how much Alex should make if he works a 5-hour shift.   _____

2. **ALLOWANCE** Pelipa's parents give her points to determine her allowance. She gets 2 points for taking out the trash (t), 3 points for doing the dishes (d), and 5 points for feeding the dog each day of the week. The expression $2t + 3d + 5$ represents the total number of points she gets in a week. If Pelipa took out the trash once, washed the dishes 3 times, and fed the dog properly, determine the number of points she earned for the week.   _____

3. **GARDENING** Sujit was told to use 10 grams of fertilizer for each tomato plant and 8 grams for each pepper plant. The expression $10t + 8p$ represents how much fertilizer should be used. How much fertilizer does Sujit need if he has 2 tomato plants and 5 pepper plants?   _____

4. **ELECTRICITY** An air conditioner (A/C) unit consumes 2 kilowatts of electricity on low and 5 kilowatts of electricity on high. The expression $2l + 5h$ represents how much electricity the A/C unit uses. Leandro ran the A/C unit for 3 hours on low and 6 hours on high yesterday. How many kilowatts of electricity did the A/C unit consume?   _____

5. **SHOPPING** When Ayako goes shopping for clothes, she likes to buy complete outfits. She typically spends $20 for pants, p, $15 for shirts, s, and $3 for socks, c. The expression $20p + 15s + 3c$ represents how much she usually spends. This morning she went shopping and bought 4 pairs of pants, 4 shirts, and 4 pairs of socks. How much did Ayako spend?   _____

Math Triumphs

Lesson 3-2 **Homework Practice**

Evaluate each expression when □ = 2.

1 □ + 17 _____

2 □ − 1 _____

3 74 ÷ □ _____

4 26 · □ _____

5 47 − □ _____

6 □ + 139 _____

7 □ · 56 _____

8 46 ÷ □ _____

Evaluate each expression when $x = 8$ and $y = 9$.

9 $x^2 + 3 - 10 + y^2$ _____

10 $5y - (x \cdot 2) + 15$ _____

11 $7x + (3 \cdot y)$ _____

12 $20 - y + 5x$ _____

13 $(6 + y^2 + 12) \cdot (y - x)$ _____

14 $15 + (x + y) + y \cdot 10$ _____

15 $(y + 2)^2 + 4x$ _____

16 $4y \div 6 + x^2 - (y - x)^2$ _____

Solve.

17 **MUSIC** Jade likes to burn songs onto CDs. A CD can hold about 80 minutes of music. The expression $\frac{80}{s}$ represents how many minutes each song, s, can be to fit on the CD. Jade wants to put 20 songs on a CD. Evaluate the expression to determine how long each song can be. _____

18 **BAKING** Oya needs 10 minutes to set up and 40 minutes to bake each batch of bread. The expression $10b + 40b$ represents the time it takes for b batches of bread. Oya wants to make 5 batches of bread tomorrow. How many minutes will it take him? _____

Write the vocabulary word(s) that completes each sentence.

19 A(n) _____ is a combination of numbers, variables, and operation symbols.

20 The _____ is a set of rules that tells what order to follow in evaluating an expression.

Lesson 3-3 Vocabulary and English Language Development

▶ Activate Prior Knowledge

Solve.

1 **SAVINGS** Felipe has $12 and wants to buy a skateboard. How much more does Felipe need to save? _____

2 **SNACKS** Millie bought 3 of the same granola bar. The total cost was $1.95. Write the price of each granola bar on the price tags.

▶ Definition Review

Find the correct word(s) to complete each statement.

3 A combination of variables, numbers, and at least one operation is called a(n) _____.

4 A(n) _____ is a mathematical sentence that contains an equals sign.

▶ Application

Solve.

- Find the value of y in each equation.
- Use the key to determine what letters the different values of y represent.
- Write the letter that y represents above the question number.
- Use the key to answer the following question.

What area of math deals with representing numbers with letters and solving for the unknown?

_____ _____ _____ _____ _____ _____ _____
 5   3   1   6   2   4   5

KEY:							
A = 50	B = 16	C = 24	E = 82	F = 21	G = 28	I = 32	L = 25
M = 41	O = 85	R = 22	T = 13	V = 61	W = 35	Y = 10	Z = 17

5 $36 - y = 8$ $y =$ _____

6 $\dfrac{y}{4} = 4$ $y =$ _____

7 $\dfrac{y}{5} = 5$ $y =$ _____

8 $y + 20 = 42$ $y =$ _____

9 $5 \cdot y = 250$ $y =$ _____

10 $y - 80 = 2$ $y =$ _____

Math Triumphs

Lesson
3-3 Skills Practice

Find the value of each variable by modeling the equation.

1 $3 + \square = 8$

$\square = $ _____

2 $15 - n = 9$

$n = $ _____

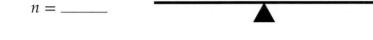

Find the value of each variable in each equation.

3 $\square + 12 = 19$

$\square = $ _____

4 $8 \cdot r = 24$

$r = $ _____

5 $\dfrac{y}{3} = 5$

$y = $ _____

6 $20 - a = 14$

$a = $ _____

7 $b \cdot 20 = 100$

$b = $ _____

8 $7 + \square = 32$

$\square = $ _____

9 $t - 14 = 16$

$t = $ _____

10 $\dfrac{\square}{5} = 8$

$\square = $ _____

Lesson 3-3

Problem-Solving Practice

Solve.

1 **TRAVEL** Mr. Davis is driving 350 miles to visit his friend. He drives 150 miles the first day of the trip. How many miles does Mr. Davis still need to drive?

_____

2 **TREES** Dion planted 20 fruit trees. He planted 8 apple trees. The rest of the trees were cherry trees. How many cherry trees did he plant?

_____

3 **COOKIES** Melody baked 84 cookies for a bake sale. She divided the cookies equally into 21 bags. How many cookies did Melody put into each bag?

_____

4 **TRAILS** Ruben hiked 2 trails over the weekend. He hiked a total of 22 miles. First Ruben hiked the Canyon Peak trail. What is the name of the second trail he hiked?

_____

Hiking Trails	
Name	**Length (miles)**
Canyon Peak	14
Winding Way	9
Lone Wolf	8
Blue Spring	11

5 **EARNINGS** Ivan worked 16 hours last week and earned $128. How much money did Ivan earn in one hour?

_____

6 **COLLECTIONS** Ally has 74 seashells in her collection. She gives 12 seashells to her sister. How many seashells are in her collection now?

_____

7 **THEATER** Sandra bought 8 tickets to the play *Now is the Time*. All the tickets were in the same section. If Sandra spent $96 on tickets, in what section did she buy the tickets?

_____

Ticket Prices for *Now is the Time*	
Section	**Price**
Lower Level	$15
Mezzanine	$14
Balcony	$12

8 **TENNIS** Jerry bought 6 cans of tennis balls. There are 3 tennis balls in each can. How many tennis balls did Jerry buy?

_____

Math Triumphs

Homework Practice

Find the value of each variable by modeling the equation.

1 $2 \cdot \square = 12$

$\square = _____$

2 $\dfrac{w}{4} = 3$

$w = _____$

Find the value of each variable in each equation.

3 $4 \cdot \square = 48$

$\square = _____$

4 $2z + 5 = 17$

$z = _____$

5 $\dfrac{a}{5} - 2 = 3$

$a = _____$

6 $16 - \square = 5$

$\square = _____$

Solve.

7 **TIRES** Reba bought 2 new tires for her bicycle. Each tire cost $15. She also bought a basket for her bike. Reba spent $38 in all. How much did the basket cost?

_____

8 **FIELD TRIP** Thirty-four students and adults went on a field trip to a museum. Eight adults went on the trip. How many students went?

_____

9 **EQUATIONS** Mrs. Ortega wrote the following equation on the board: $6 \cdot r = 42$. Jonah said the $r = 36$. Was Jonah correct? Explain.

_____

_____

Write the vocabulary word(s) that completes each sentence.

10 In the equation $4x + 6 = 14$, x is called the _____.

11 Subtraction is the _____ of addition.

Lesson 3-4

Vocabulary and English Language Development

▶ Activate Prior Knowledge

Find the value of each expression.

1 $8 - 12 \div 3 + (6 \cdot 3 + 1)$ _____

2 $6 \cdot 7 + (4 - 3) \cdot 8$ _____

3 $20 + (7 - 3) - 8 \cdot 2$ _____

4 $44 \div 4 + 9 \cdot 2^2 - 15$ _____

Name the step that should be performed first in each expression.

5 $50 - 20 \div 2 + (6 + 1)$ _____

6 $4^2 \cdot 3 + 4 - 3 \cdot 8$ _____

7 $35 \cdot 4 \div 5 + (8 - 3 + 2) - 12 \cdot 2$ _____

8 $10 \cdot 6 + 9 \cdot 2 - 15 + 3$ _____

▶ Definition Review

Area is the number of square units needed to cover the surface enclosed by a geometric figure.

An **equation** is a mathematical sentence that contains an equals sign.

A **formula** is an equation that shows a relationship among certain quantities.

A **variable** is a symbol, usually a letter, used to represent a number.

9 What formula should be used to find the length of the rectangle at the right? _____

10 The area of the rectangle is 36 square meters. Find the length of the rectangle. _____

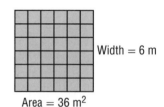

Width = 6 m

Area = 36 m²

▶ Application

Follow the directions for the activity.

- Students work with a partner.
- Each student creates six problems for their partner.
- Each problem must show a gridded rectangle like the one shown for Exercises 9 and 10. On two of the rectangles, give the area and the length; your partner must find the width. On two other rectangles, give the area and the width; your partner must find the length. On the last two rectangles, give the length and width; your partner must find the area.
- Exchange your six problems with your partner and solve the problems you receive. Return the completed problems to your partner. Check each other's work.

Math Triumphs

Skills Practice

Chapter 3

Find the value of m, when p = 18 and t = 6.

1 $p = m + t$

$m =$ _____

2 $t = m - p$

$m =$ _____

3 $t = p + m$

$m =$ _____

4 $p = m \cdot t$

$m =$ _____

Use the formula $A = \ell \cdot w$ to solve for ℓ, length.

5 The area of the rectangle is 36 square feet. Its width is 3 feet. What is the length of the rectangle?

$\ell =$ _____

6 The area of the rectangle is 18 square meters. Its width is 2 meters. What is the length of the rectangle?

$\ell =$ _____

Use the formula $A = \ell \cdot w$ to solve for w, width.

7 The area of the rectangle is 48 square meters. Its length is 12 meters. What is the width of the rectangle?

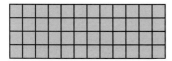

$w =$ _____

8 The area of the rectangle is 72 square feet. Its length is 9 feet. What is the width of the rectangle?

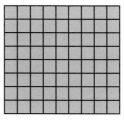

$w =$ _____

Use the formula $d = r \cdot t$ to solve for r, rate.

9 Melissa traveled 86 miles in 2 hours. What was her rate of speed?

$r =$ _____

10 Jeremy traveled 168 miles in 3 hours. What was his rate of speed?

$r =$ _____

Lesson 3-4

Problem-Solving Practice

Use the formula A = ℓ • w to solve for w, width.

1 **PHOTOGRAPH** Brad has a photograph of his favorite football team that he wants framed. It is rectangular in shape, with a length of 25 inches. The area of the photograph is 375 square inches. What is the width of the photograph?

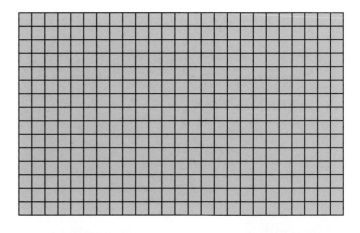

_____

2 **BLANKET** Rose is making a blanket for her friend for her birthday. She is using 48 square feet of material for the blanket. The length of the blanket is 8 feet. What is the width of the blanket Rose is making?

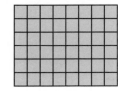

_____

Use the fact triangle shown at the right.

3 Write four related multiplication and division equations for the distance formula.

_____   _____

_____   _____

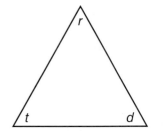

Use the formula d = r • t to solve for the missing variable.

4 **MOTORCYCLING** Mike rode his motorcycle a total of 944 miles on his vacation. It took him 16 hours to ride this distance. What was his rate of speed?

_____

5 **TREADMILL** Ben enjoys working out. He walks on the treadmill at a rate of 5 miles per hour. How long would it take Ben to walk 10 miles at this rate of speed?

_____

Math Triumphs

Lesson 3-4 Homework Practice

Find the value of c, when a = 3 and n = 24.

1. $n = c + a$ c = _____

2. $a = c - n$ c = _____

3. $n = c \cdot a$ c = _____

4. $a = n + c$ c = _____

Use the formula $A = \ell \cdot w$ to solve for ℓ, length.

5. The area of the rectangle is 55 square meters. Its width is 5 meters. What is the length of the rectangle?

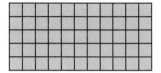

_____

6. The area of the rectangle is 192 square feet. Its width is 12 feet. What is the length of the rectangle?

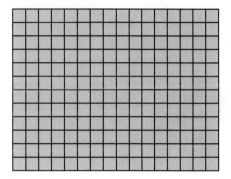

_____

Use the formula $d = r \cdot t$ to solve for t, time.

7. Mr. Mason is driving his car at a rate of 58 miles per hour. How long will it take him to travel 232 miles?

_____

8. Megan is biking at a rate of 14 miles per hour. How long will it take her to bike 98 miles?

_____

Use the formula $d = r \cdot t$ to solve for the missing variable.

9. **EXERCISE** Kevin is training to run in a marathon. He just finished running 9 miles. It took him $1\frac{1}{2}$ hours. What was his rate of speed?   _____

Write the vocabulary word that completes each sentence.

10. A ratio comparing two quantities with different kinds of units is called a(n) _____.

11. $A = \ell \cdot w$, an equation that shows a relationship among quantities, is an example of a(n) _____.

Chapter 3

Foldables Study Organizer

FOLDABLES®
Study Organizer

Dinah Zike's Foldables

Make this Foldable to help you organize information about angle measures.

1 Begin with four half sheets of notebook paper. Fold a sheet in half lengthwise. Then cut a 1" tab along the left edge through one thickness.

2 Glue the 1" tab down. Write the words *Angle Measures* on this tab and the lesson title on the front tab.

3 Write *Definitions* and *Examples* under the tab. Repeat Steps 1–3 for each lesson using the remaining paper. Staple them to form a booklet.

TAKING NOTES

As you read through the chapter, use your Foldable to organize information and write examples of angle measures from each lesson.

USING YOUR FOLDABLE

As you study, use the information in your Foldable to measure, identify, and draw additional angles.

USING YOUR FOLDABLE

Work with a partner. Take turns describing types of angles and how to classify them using your Foldable.

Math Triumphs

Games and Puzzles
Angle Accuracy

Chapter 4

DIRECTIONS

- Shuffle the Angle Accuracy Cards and place them face down.

- Turn the top card face up.

- Each player estimates the measure of the angle and records the number in the chart below. Players then work together to measure the angle and record this measure also.

- Each player finds the difference between his or her estimate and the actual measure of the angle. Players record that difference in the chart.

- The game repeats for each card. Players then total the six differences. The player with the lowest total after six rounds wins.

What You Need
- Angle Accuracy Cards
- Scissors
- Protractor

Number of Players
2 to 4

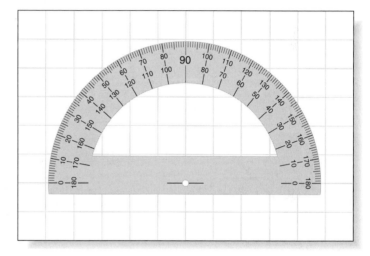

Angle Accuracy Recording Chart

Card	Estimate	Measure	Difference
1			
2			
3			
4			
5			
6			

TOTAL: _____

NAME _____ DATE _____

Angle Accuracy Cards

Vocabulary and English Language Development

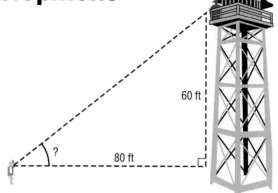

60 ft

? 80 ft

▶ Activate Prior Knowledge

Use a scale drawing to find an angle.

Stanley is waving at his brother in the fire tower. He is 80 feet away from the tower and his brother is standing 60 feet above him. Find the angle at which Stanley must look upward to see his brother.

1 Make a scale drawing on the back of this sheet. Let 10 feet in the problem equal 1 inch in the drawing. Use a ruler to draw a line segment 8 inches long. At the right endpoint of the segment, use a protractor to draw a right angle. Extend the vertical part of the right angle 6 inches. Connect the endpoints and form a triangle. This triangle is similar to the one in the problem and will have the same angle measures.

2 Use a protractor to measure the angle indicated. At what angle must Stanley look upward to see his brother in the fire tower? _____

▶ Definition Review

Complete each sentence by filling in the blanks.

3 A(n) _____ is formed by two rays with the same _____.

4 Angles are measured in _____. A(n) _____ can be used to make this measurement.

5 A(n) _____ is the common endpoint of the two rays that form an angle.

6 A part of a line that has one endpoint and extends indefinitely in one direction is called a(n) _____.

▶ Application

Follow the directions to estimate angle measures.

- Students play in groups of 3 or 4. Each student needs a piece of paper, a ruler, a pencil, and a protractor.
- The first student names an angle measure between 0° and 180°.
- Each student draws an angle estimated to have the given measure.
- Then students measure their angles with protractors.
- The student whose angle is closest to the actual measure wins the round.
- Repeat the game until all students have named an angle measure.

Chapter 4

Math Triumphs

Lesson 4-1 **Skills Practice**

Draw an angle with the given measurement.

1 40°

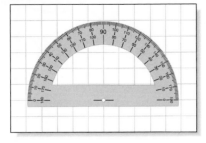

2 115°

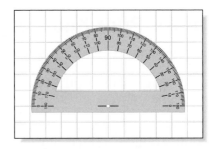

3 180°

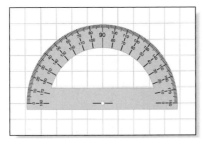

4 60°

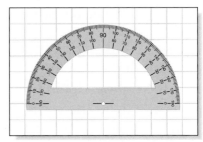

Measure and identify each angle.

5 ∠ABC measures _____. ∠ABC is a(n) _____ angle.

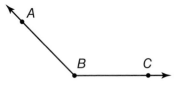

6 ∠MOP measures _____. ∠MOP is a(n) _____ angle.

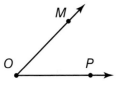

7 ∠XYZ measures _____. ∠XYZ is a(n) _____ angle.

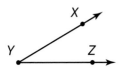

8 ∠NUT measures _____. ∠NUT is a(n) _____ angle.

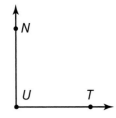

Math Triumphs

Problem-Solving Practice

Chapter 4

Solve.

1 SIGNS   What type of angle is shown on this sign?   _____

2 ALPHABET   Consider these letters of the alphabet. Which letters have a right angle?   _____

A   E   F   H   I

3 ALPHABET   Consider these letters of the alphabet. Which letters have an acute angle?   _____

K   L   M   N   T

4 ALPHABET   Consider these letters of the alphabet. Which letters have an obtuse angle?   _____

V   W   X   Y   Z

5 MAIL   When raising the flag on her mailbox, Annie noticed that the flag moved along an angle. What type of angle is formed with the raising of the mailbox flag?   _____

6 FURNITURE   Marlene placed this lounge chair on her patio. What type of angle is formed by the seat and back of the lounge chair?   _____

7 FLAGS   The state flag of Ohio is shown. It is the only state flag which is not a rectangle. What type of angle is formed along the right side of the flag?   _____

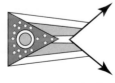

8 BOATING   A boat's steering wheel is shown. What is the measure of the highlighted angle on the wheel?   _____

Lesson
4-1
Homework Practice

Draw an angle with the given measurement.

1 70°

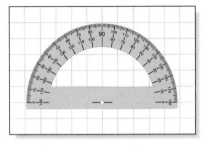

2 125°

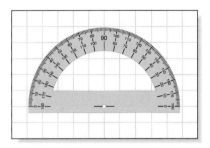

Measure and identify the angle.

3

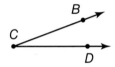

∠*TUV* measures _____. ∠*TUV* is a(n) _____ angle.

4

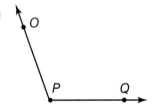

∠*BCD* measures _____. ∠*BCD* is a(n) _____ angle.

5

∠*OPQ* measures _____. ∠*OPQ* is a(n) _____ angle.

Solve.

6 **CLOCKS** Sarah had piano lessons at 2:30 PM. What type of angle is formed by the hands of the clock at this time? _____

7 **CARS** Mr. Johnson was cleaning his car. He moved the back of the driver's seat forward to a 45° angle. What type of angle was formed? _____

Write the vocabulary word that completes each sentence.

8 An angle that measures between 90° and 180° is a(n) _____ angle.

9 An angle that measures 180° is a _____ angle.

Lesson 4-2

Vocabulary and English Language Development

▶ Activate Prior Knowledge

Determine if each of the following triangles can be drawn. If it can, draw an example.

1 an equilateral, obtuse triangle

_____

2 an equilateral, right triangle

_____

3 a scalene, right triangle

_____

4 an obtuse, right triangle

_____

▶ Definition Review

An **acute angle** is an angle with a measure greater than 0° and less than 90°.
Line segments that have the same length or angles that have the same measure are **congruent**.
An **obtuse angle** is an angle with a measure greater than 90° but less than 180°.
A **right angle** is an angle that measures 90°.
A **side** is a ray that is part of an angle.
A **triangle** is a polygon with three sides and three angles.

Complete each statement.

5 A triangle with all three angles less than 90° is a(n) _____ triangle.

6 A triangle with three congruent sides is a(n) _____ triangle.

7 A triangle with no congruent sides is a(n) _____ triangle.

8 A triangle with at least two sides of the same length is a(n) _____ triangle.

▶ Application

- Pick a partner. Sketch a triangle.
- Ask your partner to identify the triangle as equilateral, isosceles, or scalene. Then identify the triangle as right, acute, or obtuse.
- Your partner sketches a triangle, and you identify the triangle by its sides and by its angles.
- Continue drawing different triangles and identifying them by sides and angles.

Math Triumphs

Chapter 4

Lesson 4-2

Skills Practice

Identify each angle as acute, obtuse, right, or straight.

1 117° _____

2 90° _____

3 3° _____

4 180° _____

5 164° _____

6 48° _____

Classify each triangle by the lengths of its sides.

7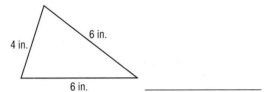

8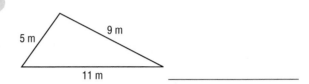

9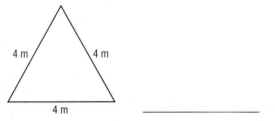

10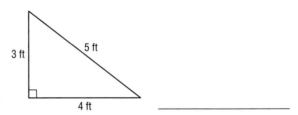

Classify each triangle by the measures of its angles.

11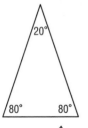

12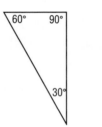

13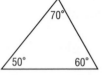

14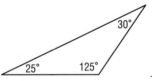

Classify each triangle by the measures of its angles and the lengths of its sides.

15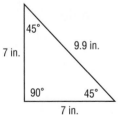

16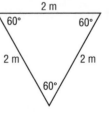

17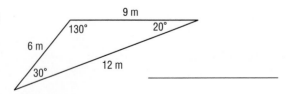

18

Math Triumphs

Lesson 4-2

Problem-Solving Practice

Solve.

1. **PENNANT**   Viktorio had a pennant that looked like the one shown below. Classify the shaded part of the pennant by the measures of its angles.

_____

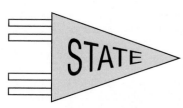

2. **YARD**   Eric's yard is in the shape of a triangle. One side is 100 feet, one side is 150 feet, and one side is 220 feet. Classify the shape of the yard by the lengths of its sides.

_____

3. **GARDEN**   Elias planted a garden of tulips as shown below. Classify the shape of the garden by the measures of its angles and the lengths of its sides.

_____

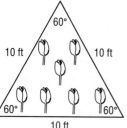

4. **RAMP**   Orville made a ramp for his miniature cars as shown. Classify the shape of the ramp by the lengths of its sides and the measures of its angles.

_____

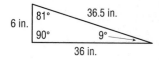

5. **STREET MAP**   Apple Lane, Peach Place, and Vine Street are shown below. Classify the shape of the figure formed by these three streets.

_____

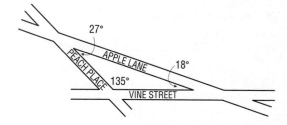

**Lesson
4-2** # Homework Practice

Identify each angle as acute, obtuse, or right.

1 56° _____

2 157° _____

3 92° _____

4 90° _____

Classify each triangle by the lengths of its sides.

5

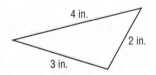

4 in.

2 in.

3 in.

_____

6

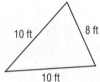

10 ft   8 ft

10 ft

_____

Classify each triangle by the measures of its angles.

7

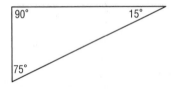

90°   15°

75°

_____

8

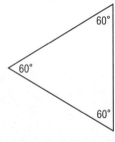

60°

60°

60°

_____

Classify each triangle by the lengths of its sides and the measures of its angles.

9

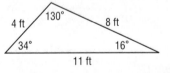

130°

4 ft   8 ft

34°   16°

11 ft

_____

10

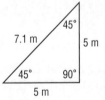

45°

7.1 m   5 m

45°   90°

5 m

_____

Solve.

11 **ART** Katrina is making a triangular frame for an art project. The measures of the angles of her frame are 30°, 30°, and 120°. Classify Katrina's frame by the measures of its angles.

_____

Write the vocabulary word that completes each sentence.

12 A triangle with one obtuse angle is a(n) _____ triangle.

13 A triangle with all three angles less than 90° is a(n) _____ triangle.

14 A triangle with one 90° angle is a(n) _____ triangle.

Math Triumphs

Vocabulary and English Language Development

▶ Activate Prior Knowledge

1 Measure each angle of the right, isosceles triangle.

$m\angle A =$ _____

$m\angle B =$ _____

$m\angle C =$ _____

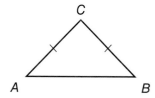

2 What do you notice about $m\angle A$ and $m\angle B$ in Exercise 1? _____

3 Explain how the angle measures in Exercise 1 could be found without using a protractor to measure the angles.

_____

_____

_____

▶ Definition Review

A **right angle** is an angle that measures 90°.
A **straight angle** is an angle that measures 180°.
The measures of two **supplementary angles** have a sum of 180°.
The measures of two **complementary angles** have a sum of 90°.

4
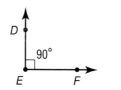

$\angle E$ is a _____ angle.

$\angle E$ measures _____.

5
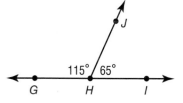

$\angle GHJ$ and $\angle JHI$ are _____ angles.

They have a sum of _____.

$\angle GHI$ is a _____ angle.

▶ Application

Follow the directions for the activity.

- Work in pairs.
- One student draws an acute triangle on paper and cuts it out.
- The other student tears off all three corners of the triangle.
- Place the corners together to form a line. Tape the corners in place.
- Discuss the number of degrees in a straight line, and how this relates to a triangle.
- Repeat the steps with an obtuse triangle and a right triangle.

Math Triumphs

Lesson 4-3 **Skills Practice**

Find the measure of each missing angle.

1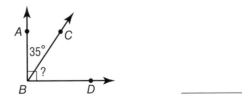

_____

2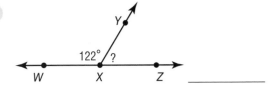

_____

3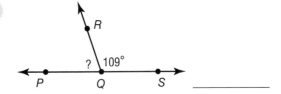

_____

4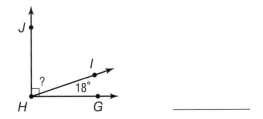

_____

Sketch each type of angle given.

5 Sketch supplementary angles when one angle's measure is 40°.

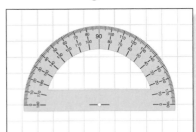

6 Sketch complementary angles when one angle's measure is 10°.

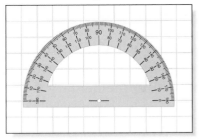

Find the measure of each missing angle.

7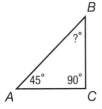

The measure of the missing angle is _____.

8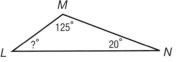

The measure of the missing angle is _____.

9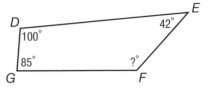

The measure of the missing angle is _____.

10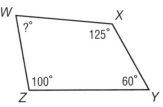

The measure of the missing angle is _____.

Math Triumphs

Lesson 4-3 Problem-Solving Practice

Solve.

1 **DRAWING** Tiffany drew a star that has triangular points. She found that the measure of each angle at the star's points is 38°. If the triangle is isosceles, what is the measure of each of the other angles in this triangle?

_____

2 **TOOLS** Architects use many tools to aid them in designing roads and structures. One of these is a drafting triangle which has angles that measure 90° and 60°. What is the measure of the third angle of this drafting triangle?

_____

3 **SHOPPING** The sides of a shopping cart in a grocery store are quadrilaterals. What is the measure of the missing angle?

_____

4 **GEOMETRY** A right triangle has one acute angle that measures 24°. What is the measure of the other acute angle?

_____

5 **CLEANING** While cleaning the house, Sandra's mom notices that the dustpan is a trapezoid. The non-parallel sides of the trapezoid are equal, so the angles on each side are equal. What is the measure of each of the missing angles?

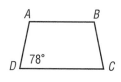

_____

6 **LADDERS** Ivan is painting the ceiling in his living room. He is standing on a ladder that opens at an angle of 40°. What angle is formed where the floor meets the leg of the ladder? HINT: The ladder forms an isosceles triangle.

_____

7 **LIGHTING** A light fixture is made of glass cut in various shapes, one of which is a quadrilateral. In this quadrilateral, one acute angle measures 75° and each of the obtuse angles measures 105°. What is the measure of the other acute angle?

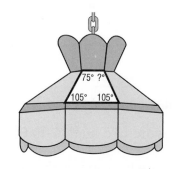

_____

Lesson 4-3

Homework Practice

Sketch each type of angle given.

1 Sketch supplementary angles.

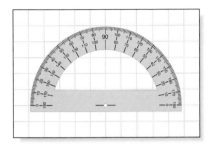

2 Sketch complementary angles.

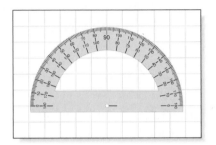

Find the measure of each missing angle.

3

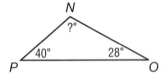

The measure of the missing

angle is _____.

4

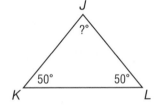

The measure of the missing

angle is _____.

5

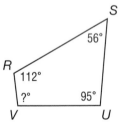

The measure of the missing

angle is _____.

6

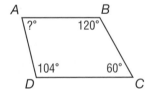

The measure of the missing

angle is _____.

Solve.

7 ROOF The roof of a house is an isosceles triangle. What is the measure of each of the missing roof angles?

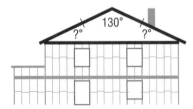

_____

Write the measurement that completes the sentence.

8 Complementary angles are two angles that have measures with a sum of _____.

9 Supplementary angles are two angles that have measures with a sum of _____.

Math Triumphs

Lesson 4-4

Vocabulary and English Language Development

▶ Activate Prior Knowledge

1 Measure each angle of the intersecting lines.

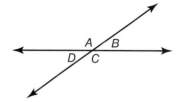

$m\angle A = 145°$ $m\angle B =$ _____

$m\angle C =$ _____ $m\angle D =$ _____

2 What do you notice about $m\angle A$ and $m\angle C$? _____

3 What do you notice about $m\angle B$ and $m\angle D$? _____

4 What is the sum of the measures of $\angle B$ and $\angle C$? _____

▶ Definition Review

Alternate exterior angles are exterior angles that lie on opposite sides of the transversal.

Alternate interior angles are interior angles that lie on opposite sides of the transversal.

Corresponding angles are angles that have the same position on two different parallel lines cut by a transversal.

Vertical angles are nonadjacent angles formed by a pair of lines that intersect.

5 Name two pairs of alternate interior angles.

_____

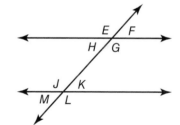

6 Name two pairs of alternate exterior angles.

_____

7 What type of angles are $\angle J$ and $\angle L$? _____

▶ Application

Follow the directions for the activity.

- Work in groups of three. Use masking tape to create two parallel lines and a transversal on the floor.
- One student tells the other two to locate a pair of vertical angles. The two students stand in the interiors of a pair of angles to indicate their selection.
- The student then tells the other two to locate a pair of corresponding angles, a pair of alternate interior angles, and a pair of alternate exterior angles.
- Repeat the activity so that each student has been the person instructing the other two students to locate each of the four pairs of angles.

Math Triumphs

Lesson 4-4 **Skills Practice**

Identify the measure of each angle indicated.

1

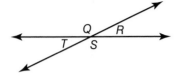

$m\angle R = 25°$, so $m\angle T =$ _____

2

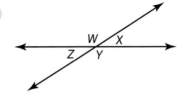

$m\angle W = 148°$, so $m\angle Y =$ _____

3

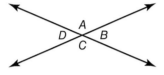

$m\angle B = 45°$, so $m\angle C =$ _____

4

$m\angle K = 87°$, so $m\angle J =$ _____

Name the alternate interior angles.

5

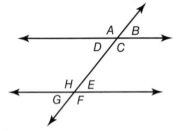

6

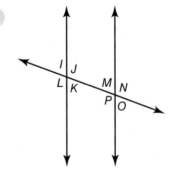

_____

_____

Name the alternate exterior angles.

7

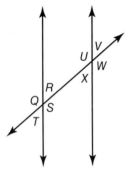

8

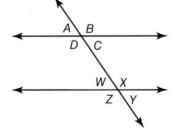

_____

_____

Math Triumphs

Lesson 4-4 Problem-Solving Practice

Solve.

1. **RAILROADS** Where a set of railroad tracks crosses a highway, the edge of the highway is the transversal to the rails of the track. What is the measure of ∠D?

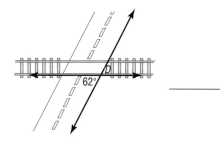

_____

2. **QUILTS** The quilt on Rhonda's bed has parallel gold stripes that run the width of the quilt. There is a broad blue stripe that runs at an angle across the quilt as shown in the figure. What is the value of x if the measure of ∠T is 70°?

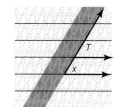

_____

3. **FARMING** The fields on both sides of a road have been plowed in preparation for planting. The furrows made by the plow model parallel lines. They meet the edge of the road at a 48°-angle. What is the measure of ∠R in the figure?

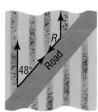

_____

4. **GIFTS** Samantha wrapped a gift for her mother. The wrapping had thin red stripes on it. She wrapped ribbon around the package. What is the value of y in the figure if the measure of ∠N is 52°?

_____

5. **WEATHER** During a winter storm, a snowdrift was created that crossed a fence line at a 115°-angle as shown in the figure. What is the measure of ∠L?

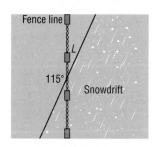

_____

6. **ALPHABET** Consider the following letters of the alphabet. Which letters model parallel lines cut by a transversal?

A C E F G H J K L N S V W Y Z

_____

Lesson
4-4 **Homework Practice**

Identify the measure of each angle indicated.

1

$m\angle H = 120°$, so $m\angle G =$ _____

2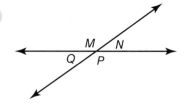

$m\angle N = 35°$, so $m\angle Q =$ _____

Name the alternate interior angles.

3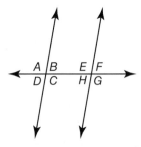

_____

4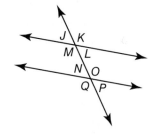

_____

Name the alternate exterior angles.

5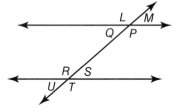

_____

6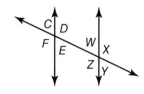

_____

Solve.

7 **AIRPLANES** A pair of jet airplanes were leaving two contrails that ran parallel to each other in the sky. Another jet airplane's contrail crossed the two parallel contrails. In the figure, angle C measures 60°. What is the measure of angle D?

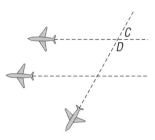

_____

Write the vocabulary word(s) that completes the sentence.

8 Exterior angles that lie on opposite sides of the transversal are

called _____.

Math Triumphs

Chapter 5 Foldables Study Organizer

Dinah Zike's Foldables

Make this Foldable to help you organize information about ratios, rates, and similarities.

1 Begin with a sheet of graph paper. Fold one sheet of graph paper in thirds lengthwise.

2 Unfold lengthwise and fold one-fourth down widthwise. Cut to make three tabs as shown.

3 Label the paper as shown. Unfold the tabs and label as shown.

TAKING NOTES

As you read through the chapter, use your Foldable to write about ratio, rate, and similarity.

 USING YOUR FOLDABLE

As you study, write definitions, take notes, record concepts, and write examples under the tabs about what you learn about ratio, proportion, and similar figures.

USING YOUR FOLDABLE

Trade Foldables with a partner. Compare each other's notes. Write your partner's notes and examples in your own Foldable.

Chapter

5 **Games and Puzzles**

Find a Proportion

What You Need

- 1-6 Number Cube
- Find a Proportion Game Sheet

Number of Players

2

DIRECTIONS

- Each player takes a turn and records the number of this turn in the Turn column. Toss the number cube four times. Write the number down each time in the Results column.

- Try to make a proportion using the numbers. Write the proportion in the Proportion column.

- If you cannot make a proportion, toss the number cube again. Keep tossing the number cube and recording each number in the Results column until you can write a proportion using *any* four of the numbers you have tossed so far.

- When you have written a proportion, you score the same number of points as the number of times you tossed the number cube. Write this number in the Points column.

- Continue playing until each player has written five proportions. Find your total score by adding the five numbers you have written in the Points column. The player with the lower score is the winner.

Example:

Turn	Results	Proportion	Points
#1	3, 4, 3, 1, 6, 2	$\frac{1}{3} = \frac{2}{6}$	6
#2	2, 1, 4, 2	$\frac{1}{2} = \frac{2}{4}$	4

Math Triumphs

NAME _____ DATE _____

Find a Proportion Game Sheet

Player 1: _____

Turn	Results	Proportion	Points

Player 2: _____

Turn	Results	Proportion	Points

Chapter 5

Lesson 5-1 Vocabulary and English Language Development

▶ Activate Prior Knowledge

1 Write a list of the names of your family members.

_____

2 Write a ratio of males to females in your family. _____

3 Write your ratio for Exercise 2 in simplest form. _____

▶ Definition Review

The **greatest common factor** is the greatest of the common factors of two or more numbers.

A **ratio** is a comparison of two numbers by division.

A fraction is in **simplest form** when the greatest common factor of the numerator and the denominator is one.

Match each group with the correct ratio.

4   The ratio of ladybugs to butterflies is 3 to 4.

5   The ratio of ladybugs to butterflies is 2 to 5.

Write the ratio as a fraction in simplest form.

6 $\dfrac{8}{10}$ _____

7 $\dfrac{3}{9}$ _____

8 $\dfrac{7}{14}$ _____

9 $\dfrac{20}{24}$ _____

▶ Application

Finding Ratios

- Students work individually.
- Students observe their classmates to find the following ratios:
  - The ratio of girls to boys in the class.
  - The ratio of boys to the total number of students in the class.
  - The ratio of students wearing red to students wearing blue.
  - The ratio of students with blond hair to students with black hair.
  - The ratio of students who do not have brown hair to the total number of students in the class.

Math Triumphs

Lesson 5-1 Skills Practice

Use the diagram to write each ratio as a fraction in simplest form.

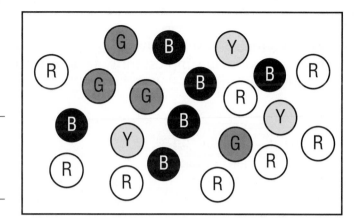

1 the number of yellow
marbles to the number
of red marbles _____

2 the number of black
marbles to the number
of green marbles _____

3 the number of green
marbles to the number
of red marbles _____

4 the number of red marbles to the number of black marbles _____

Write each ratio as a fraction in simplest form.

5 In a computer lab there are 15 desktop computers, 7 laptop
computers, and 5 printers. Write the ratio of printers to computers. _____

6 A tray of muffins contains 6 chocolate chip muffins, 3 blueberry
muffins, 4 pumpkin muffins, and 2 corn muffins. Write the ratio of
corn muffins to chocolate chip muffins. _____

7 Rebecca had 7 aces out of 10 serves in her volleyball game. Write the
ratio of aces to serves. _____

8 There were 8 cars and 3 buses in the parking lot. Write the ratio of
cars to the total number of vehicles. _____

9 In a classroom there are 15 boys and 13 girls. Write the ratio of boys
to the total number of students. _____

10 Write the ratio of the length
of the base to the height of
the triangle as a fraction in
simplest form.

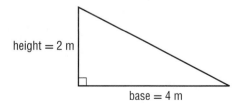

height = 2 m

base = 4 m

_____

Chapter 5

Lesson 5-1 Problem-Solving Practice

Solve.

1. **GARDENING** The dimensions of a flower garden are 15 feet long by 5 feet wide. In simplest form, what is the ratio of the garden's width to its length? _____

width = 5 feet

length = 15 feet

2. **HOBBIES** A jewelry-making kit contains 15 blue beads, 25 red beads, 10 yellow beads, and 30 black beads. In simplest form, what is the ratio of red beads to black beads? _____

3. **ELECTIONS** Carlos, Leona, and Kim ran for class president. The table below shows the number of votes each student received. In simplest form, what is the ratio of votes Carlos received to the total number of votes? _____

Votes Counted for Class President	
Carlos	ⅢⅡ ⅢⅡ ⅢⅡ ⅢⅡ II
Leona	ⅢⅡ ⅢⅡ ⅢⅡ ⅢⅡ I
Kim	ⅢⅡ ⅢⅡ III

4. **WEATHER** During the first 28 days of April, it rained on 8 days. If it rains the last two days of April, what will be the ratio of the number of rainy days in the month to the total number of days in the month? Write your answer in simplest form. _____

5. **BASEBALL** A baseball team played 120 games during a season. They won 80 games. What is the ratio of the number of games lost to the total number of games played? Write your answer in simplest form. _____

Math Triumphs

Lesson 5-1 Homework Practice

Use the diagram to write each ratio as a fraction in simplest form.

1 baseballs and tennis balls to the total number of balls _____

2 footballs and basketballs to tennis balls and baseballs _____

3 balls that are *not* tennis balls to the total number of balls _____

4 footballs to basketballs _____

Write each ratio as a fraction in simplest form.

5 Michele ran 3 out of 7 days this week. Write the ratio of days she ran to days she did *not* run. _____

6 A bowl of fruit contains 8 apples and 4 oranges. Write the ratio of apples to oranges. _____

Solve.

7 **SWIMMING** The dimensions of a rectangular swimming pool are 44 feet long by 20 feet wide. What is the ratio of the pool's width to its length?

width = 20 ft

length = 44 ft

_____

Write the vocabulary word(s) that completes each sentence.

8 A _____ is a comparison of two numbers by division.

9 The greatest number that divides evenly into two or more numbers is called the _____.

Chapter 5

Lesson 5-2

Vocabulary and English Language Development

▶ Activate Prior Knowledge

Circle the product with the lower unit cost in each group.

I

2

▶ Definition Review

A **rate** is a ratio comparing two quantities with different kinds of units.
A **ratio** is a comparison of two numbers by division.
Unit cost is the cost of a single item or unit.
A **unit rate** is a rate that has a denominator of 1.

Draw a line to match each rate to its unit rate.

3 18 miles in 3 hours   20 miles per hour

4 64 miles in 4 hours   60 miles per hour

5 300 miles in 15 hours   6 miles per hour

6 120 miles in 2 hours   16 miles per hour

Find each unit rate. Use the unit rate to find the unknown amount.

7 10 pages in 50 minutes; ☐ pages in 150 minutes _____

8 $75 for 3 hours; ☐ for 18 hours _____

▶ Application

Complete the graphic organizer.

Ratio	Rate
Examples	Examples
Unit Rate	**Unit Cost**
Examples	Examples

Lesson 5-2

Skills Practice

Write each rate as a fraction. Find each unit rate.

1

6 bottles of water
$3.00

_____

2

4 apples
$1.20

_____

3 250 envelopes in 10 minutes

_____

4 15 pages in 45 minutes

_____

Find each unit rate. Use the unit rate to find the unknown amount.

5 125 miles for 2 hours; ☐ miles for 5 hours _____

6 64 ounces for 8 people; ☐ ounces for 30 people _____

7 250 inches in 5 seconds; ☐ inches in 12 seconds _____

8 $65 for 4 CDs; ☐ for 7 CDs _____

Which product has the lower unit cost?

9 a 40-oz bag of dog food for $6.80 or a 24-oz bag of dog food for $3.60 _____

10 1 pound of pears for $0.99 or 5 pounds of pears for $4.60 _____

11 a 16-oz box of cereal for $4.32 or a 12-oz box of cereal for $3.00 _____

12 a pack of 6 pens for $4.74 or a pack of 15 pens for $12.75 _____

Lesson 5-2

Problem-Solving Practice

Solve.

1 **TECHNOLOGY** A laser printer can print 150 pages in 5 minutes. How many pages can the printer print in 22 minutes?

_____

2 **FITNESS** The table below shows the time and distance walked by Jenna and Theo. Which walker had the faster unit rate? Show your work.

_____

Jenna		Theo	
Time	Distance	Time	Distance
120 minutes	8 miles	90 minutes	6.5 miles

3 **FOOD** The diagrams below show the prices of large pizzas at two local restaurants. Which restaurant has the lower unit cost per pizza?

_____

Pizza Shack Specials	Leo's Pizza Parlor
Buy 2 large pizzas for $12.99 and get 1 large pizza free	Large Pizzas - $5.50 each

4 **AMUSEMENT PARKS** A Ferris wheel makes 10 revolutions in 4 minutes. How many revolutions does it make in 6 minutes?

_____

5 **PLANTS** A plant grows 4.5 inches in 3 months. At the same rate, how many inches will the plant grow in 8 months?

_____

6 **TRAVEL** A jet aircraft traveled 2,750 miles in 5 hours. Find a unit rate to describe its average speed.

_____

7 **POPULATION** Which state in the table below has the greatest population per square mile?

_____

State	2008 Estimated Population	Approximate Land Area (square miles)
Maryland	5,600,000	9,800
New York	19,500,000	47,000
Connecticut	3,500,000	5,000

Math Triumphs

Lesson 5-2 Homework Practice

Write each rate as a fraction. Find each unit rate.

1 110 miles in 2 hours _____

2 36 points scored in 3 games _____

3 90 customers served in 4.5 hours _____

4 12 pencils in 2 packs _____

Find each unit rate. Use the unit rate to find the unknown amount.

5 12 gallons in 5 minutes; ☐ gallons in 7 minutes

_____

6 140 heartbeats in 2 minutes; ☐ heartbeats in 5 minutes

_____

Which product has the lower unit cost?

7 a 6-pack of juice for $1.86 or a 12-pack of juice for $4.20 _____

8 2 pounds of granola for $2.50 or 5 pounds of granola for $6.30 _____

9 a box of 30 CDs for $10.80 or a box of 100 CDs for $34.00 _____

Solve.

10 **TRANSPORTATION** A car travels 144 miles on 6 gallons of gasoline. How many miles can the car travel on 15 gallons of gasoline? _____

Write the vocabulary word(s) that completes each sentence.

11 The _____ is the cost of a single item or unit.

12 A(n) _____ is a comparison of two numbers by division.

13 A(n) _____ is a ratio comparing two quantities with different kinds of units.

14 A(n) _____ is a rate that has a denominator of 1.

Chapter 5

Lesson 5-3 Vocabulary and English Language Development

▶ Activate Prior Knowledge

Complete the analogies.

1 Sock is to foot as _____ is to hand.

2 Car is to driver as _____ is to pilot.

▶ Definition Review

In a proportion, a **cross product** is the product of the numerator of one ratio and the denominator of the other ratio.

A **proportion** is an equation stating that two ratios are equivalent.

A **ratio** is a comparison of two quantities by division.

Determine whether the ratios are proportional. Write = or ≠ in each circle.

3 $\dfrac{3}{7} \bigcirc \dfrac{4}{8}$

4 $\dfrac{4}{6} \bigcirc \dfrac{20}{30}$

Match each proportion with its solution.

A $n = 21$ **B** $n = 4$ **C** $n = 1$ **D** $n = 6$

5 $\dfrac{2}{3} = \dfrac{4}{n}$ _____

6 $\dfrac{7}{8} = \dfrac{n}{24}$ _____

7 $\dfrac{n}{4} = \dfrac{2}{8}$ _____

8 $\dfrac{3}{n} = \dfrac{15}{20}$ _____

▶ Application

Follow the directions for the activity.

- Organize the class into groups of 4 to 5 students.
- Have each group create a fraction by rolling a number cube twice, picking two numbers out of a bag, or just choosing two numbers.
- Instruct each student to write a new fraction that is proportional to the fraction the group created.
- Have the students compare their fractions within their group.
- Are all the fractions within the group proportional?
- Have the groups repeat the process with new fractions as time allows.

Math Triumphs

Lesson
5-3 **Skills Practice**

Determine whether each pair of ratios is proportional. Write = or ≠ in each circle.

1 $\dfrac{14}{2} \bigcirc \dfrac{7}{1}$

2 $\dfrac{3}{4} \bigcirc \dfrac{9}{16}$

3 $\dfrac{3}{8} \bigcirc \dfrac{12}{32}$

4 $\dfrac{2}{5} \bigcirc \dfrac{12}{45}$

5 $\dfrac{3}{9} \bigcirc \dfrac{21}{42}$

6 $\dfrac{14}{16} \bigcirc \dfrac{49}{56}$

7 $\dfrac{10}{12} \bigcirc \dfrac{20}{24}$

8 $\dfrac{15}{21} \bigcirc \dfrac{35}{48}$

Solve each proportion.

9 $\dfrac{3}{9} = \dfrac{l}{21}$ $l =$ _____

10 $\dfrac{9}{12} = \dfrac{x}{28}$ $x =$ _____

11 $\dfrac{7}{10} = \dfrac{35}{r}$ $r =$ _____

12 $\dfrac{6}{15} = \dfrac{10}{k}$ $k =$ _____

13 $\dfrac{4}{n} = \dfrac{12}{18}$ $n =$ _____

14 $\dfrac{10}{m} = \dfrac{15}{18}$ $m =$ _____

15 $\dfrac{8}{2} = \dfrac{t}{4}$ $t =$ _____

16 $\dfrac{y}{5} = \dfrac{28}{70}$ $y =$ _____

17 $\dfrac{b}{11} = \dfrac{28}{44}$ $b =$ _____

18 $\dfrac{6}{14} = \dfrac{15}{a}$ $a =$ _____

Solve.

19 Twenty-eight cups of sugar are required for 14 cakes. How many cakes require 12 cups of sugar?   _____

20 Eighty flowers make 8 bouquets. How many flowers make 11 bouquets?   _____

21 Fifty-six buttons are used on 8 sweaters. How many sweaters use 63 buttons?   _____

22 Fifty-four balloons are in 3 bags. How many bags have 126 balloons?   _____

23 Seventy-five erasers are in 5 boxes. How many boxes have 120 erasers?   _____

24 Eighty-one books are on 9 shelves. How many shelves hold 36 books?   _____

Chapter 5

Lesson 5-3

Problem-Solving Practice

Solve.

1 **PACKAGING**   The Bracket Company sends out 6 screws with each order of 2 brackets. How many screws do they need to send out with an order for 500 brackets?

_____

2 **SCHOOL SUPPLIES**   Mr. Goetz hands out the same combination of pens and pencils to each person on the first day of school. He handed out 42 pens. How many pencils did Mr. Goetz hand out?

_____

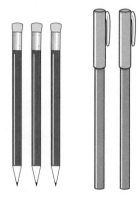

3 **FITNESS**   Awan's exercise routine includes repetitions of 20 push-ups and 30 sit-ups. On Tuesday, he did 100 push-ups. How many sit-ups did Awan do on Tuesday?

_____

4 **BIOLOGY**   Una is making media to culture cells. She uses 3 units of antibiotic for every 250 milliliters of media. She needs 1,000 milliliters of media. How many units of antibiotic does Una need to add?

_____

5 **MAPS**   Tulaya made a treasure map for her little brother. She says to take 6 steps for every 2 dashes on the map. If there are 5 dashes on the map, how many steps will her brother need to take?

_____

6 **ENGINEERING**   Ellis is designing heat ducts for a new building. The specifications for the system require ducts with 6 inches in diameter for every 10 cubic feet of air flow. One of the sections of the system has 40 cubic feet of air flow. What should the diameter of the duct be for this section?

_____

7 **ADVERTISING**   A beauty magazine needs to fill 6 pages with ads for every 9 pages of articles to meet their budget. This month's issue is projected to have 117 pages filled with articles. How many ad pages will the magazine have?

_____

Lesson 5-3 Homework Practice

Determine whether each pair of ratios is proportional. Write = or ≠ in each circle.

1 $\dfrac{6}{10} \bigcirc \dfrac{39}{62}$

2 $\dfrac{4}{16} \bigcirc \dfrac{16}{64}$

3 $\dfrac{6}{8} \bigcirc \dfrac{15}{20}$

4 $\dfrac{8}{14} \bigcirc \dfrac{28}{49}$

5 $\dfrac{8}{18} \bigcirc \dfrac{36}{72}$

6 $\dfrac{4}{9} \bigcirc \dfrac{72}{32}$

Solve each proportion.

7 $\dfrac{18}{21} = \dfrac{g}{28}$ $g =$ _____

8 $\dfrac{6}{k} = \dfrac{36}{42}$ $k =$ _____

9 $\dfrac{10}{25} = \dfrac{14}{r}$ $r =$ _____

10 $\dfrac{12}{16} = \dfrac{l}{36}$ $l =$ _____

11 $\dfrac{t}{4} = \dfrac{30}{60}$ $t =$ _____

12 $\dfrac{6}{8} = \dfrac{15}{a}$ $a =$ _____

13 $\dfrac{4}{y} = \dfrac{32}{56}$ $y =$ _____

14 $\dfrac{z}{10} = \dfrac{4}{20}$ $z =$ _____

Solve.

15 **FURNITURE** Lazaro is building chairs. He uses 4 legs and 6 supports for each chair. How many legs are used when 72 supports are used?   _____

16 **PAINTING** Latasha is painting a room in her house. The directions on the paint say that she needs 3 pints of paint for every 500 ft². How many pints of paint does Latasha need to paint 2,500 ft²?   _____

Write the vocabulary word(s) that completes each sentence.

17 An equation that states that two ratios are equivalent is a

_____.

18 In the proportion $\dfrac{2}{7} = \dfrac{12}{42}$, 2 · 42 is called a _____.

Lesson 5-4

Vocabulary and English Language Development

▶ Activate Prior Knowledge

Solve each proportion.

1. $\dfrac{3}{n} = \dfrac{6}{8}$ $n =$ _____

2. $\dfrac{6}{8} = \dfrac{12}{r}$ $r =$ _____

3. $\dfrac{4}{7} = \dfrac{p}{49}$ $p =$ _____

4. $\dfrac{t}{15} = \dfrac{18}{27}$ $t =$ _____

▶ Definition Review

A **proportion** is an equation stating that two ratios or rates are equivalent. **Similar figures** are figures that have the same shape but may have different sizes.

Determine whether the shapes are similar.

5. _____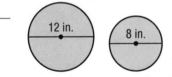

6. _____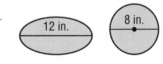

7. _____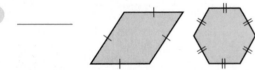

8. _____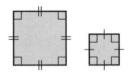

Use a proportion to solve each problem.

9. Tara can bike 7 miles in 30 minutes. How long will it take her to bike 28 miles?   _____

10. Jason bought 5 pounds of ground beef for $7.95. How much will 8 pounds of ground beef cost?   _____

▶ Application

Follow the directions for the activity.

- Organize the class so each person has a partner.
- Each partner creates 3 sets of figures that are either similar or not similar.
- Have partners exchange papers. Each partner determines if the figures are similar or not similar and explains why.
- Return the papers and have each partner check the answers.
- Each student gives a "thumbs up" if the figures are similar or a "thumbs down" if the figures are not similar.

Math Triumphs

Lesson 5-4

Skills Practice

Find the value of *x* in each pair of similar figures.

1 *x* = _____

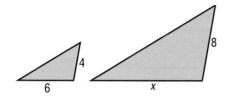

2 *x* = _____

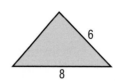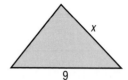

3 *x* = _____

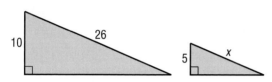

4 *x* = _____

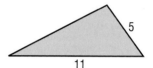

5 *x* = _____

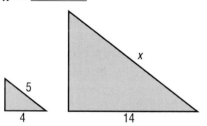

6 *x* = _____

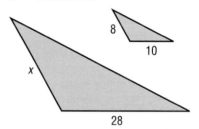

Use a proportion to solve.

7 Mary bought 3 cans of green beans for $1.20. What would it cost her to buy 7 cans of green beans? _____

8 Mr. Garcia drove 186 miles in 3 hours. At this rate, how long would it take him to travel 465 miles? _____

9 Amir sells handmade leather bracelets in packages of 3 for $25.00. A school fundraising group contacted him about making 75 bracelets for their members to sell. How much should he charge for 75 bracelets in order for the unit cost to be the same? _____

10 Kaitlin met with 5 clients in $2\frac{1}{2}$ hours at her investment agency this morning. At this rate, how many clients can she meet with in 4 hours this afternoon? _____

Chapter 5

Lesson 5-4 Problem-Solving Practice

Solve.

1 **SPA** Casey is filling her hot tub. The water fills the hot tub at a rate of 3 gallons per minute. Her hot tub has a capacity of 99 gallons. How long will it take for Casey to fill her hot tub?

_____

2 **TECHNOLOGY** Ernesto downloaded a picture from his friend. The picture downloaded at a rate of 90 kilobytes per second and took 10 seconds. What was the size of the picture?

_____

3 **TYPING** Marvin can type 52 words per minute. His boss gave him a 5-page report to type this morning. Marvin assumes that there are 250 words on each page. How long will it take him to type the report?

_____

4 **HOUSEKEEPING** Felicia can clean 10 hotel rooms in 2 hours. Her boss wants to know how long it will take her to clean all 15 rooms on the 8th floor. How long will it take Felicia to clean all of the rooms?

_____

5 **INCOME** Lakita is saving her money to buy a new computer. She gets paid $112.00 for 8 hours of work. How many hours will Lakita have to work to purchase a new computer?

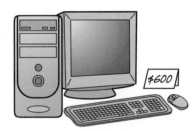

_____

6 **FISH** Areva's fish tank is gaining 7 parts per million of nitrate every 2 days. Areva was told to change the water when it reaches 28 parts per million of nitrate. How often should Areva expect to change the water?

_____

7 **UTILITIES** The Rollins family consists of 8 people. Mr. Rollins never has enough hot water for his shower. Their house has a 20-gallon hot water heater which runs out of hot water after 4 showers. Mr. Rollins wants to buy a larger water heater. Will everyone in the Rollins family be able to get a hot shower if Mr. Rollins buys a 35-gallon water heater? Explain.

_____

_____

_____

Math Triumphs

Lesson 5-4

Homework Practice

Find the value of x in each pair of similar figures.

1 x = _____

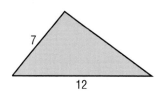

7
12
x
10.5

2 x = _____

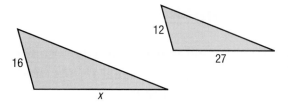

16
12
x
27

3 x = _____

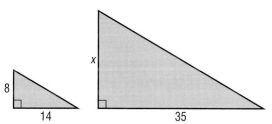

x
8
14
35

4 x = _____

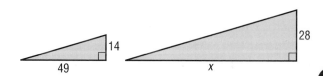

14
49
28
x

Use a proportion to solve.

5 Six kiwis cost a total of $3.30. What is the total cost of 11 kiwis? _____

6 The Min family uses 7 gallons of milk in 2 weeks. How many gallons of milk does the Min family use in 7 weeks? _____

Solve.

7 **LAUNDRY** Rosa needs $1\frac{1}{2}$ hours to do 2 loads of laundry. She has 3 loads this week. How long will it take Rosa to do her laundry this week? _____

8 **PHOTOGRAPHS** Paco has $6.00 to buy prints from his digital camera. The store offers 6 prints for $1.25. How many prints can Paco buy? _____

Write the vocabulary word(s) that completes each sentence.

9 The lengths of the corresponding sides of similar triangles can be used to write a _____.

10 The corresponding angles of _____ are congruent.

Chapter 5

Chapter 6 Foldables Study Organizer

FOLDABLES®
Study Organizer

Dinah Zike's Foldables

Make this Foldable to help you organize your notes about squares, square roots, and the Pythagorean Theorem.

1 Begin with two sheets of $8\frac{1}{2}'' \times 11''$ notebook paper. Fold one sheet in half from top to bottom. Cut along the fold from the edges to the margin.

2 Fold the other sheet in half. Cut along the fold between the margins.

3 Insert the first sheet through the second sheet and align the folds. Label each page with a lesson number and title.

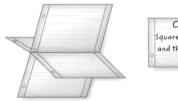
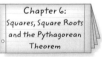

Chapter 6:
Squares, Square Roots
and the Pythagorean
Theorem

TAKING NOTES
As you read through the chapter, use your Foldable to write about squares, square roots, and the Pythagorean Theorem and its applications.

USING YOUR FOLDABLE
As you study, check your understanding by writing additional examples of squares and square roots. Then use your Foldable to check yourself.

USING YOUR FOLDABLE
Work with a partner. Take turns explaining your examples to one another. Alternate until you have both discussed each topic in your Foldable.

Math Triumphs

Chapter 6

Games and Puzzles
Where's My Line?

GET READY

- Players sit so they cannot see each others' papers.
- Each player draws a straight line on the graph paper.
- Players choose who will go first.

DIRECTIONS

- Player 1 calls out an ordered pair. Player 2 calls out "Hit!" if the ordered pair describes a point on his or her line, or "Miss!" if it does not.
- If Player 1 scores a hit, he or she takes another turn. If not Player 2 takes a turn.
- The first player to locate two points on the other player's line gets a point.
- A bonus point will be awarded if the player can give a function that represents the other player's line.
- The first player to earn 5 points wins.

What You Need
- Where's My Line? Graph Paper

Number of Players
2

Chapter 6

Where's My Line? Graph Paper

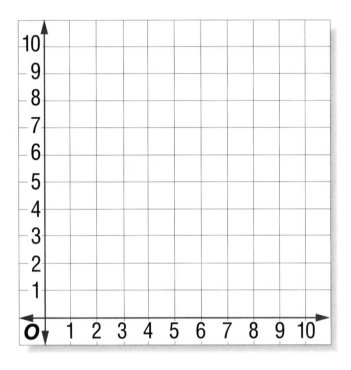

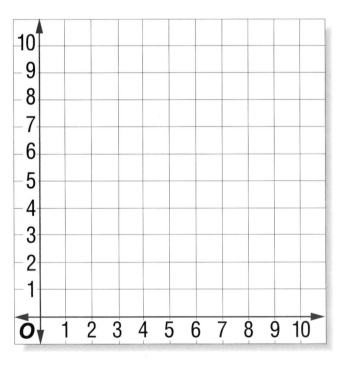

Lesson 6-1

Vocabulary and English Language Development

▶ Activate Prior Knowledge

Determine whether each figure is a square or a rectangle.

1 _____

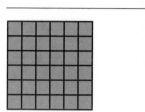

2 _____

3 _____

4 _____

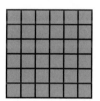

▶ Definition Review

Identify the *base* and the *exponent* of each expression.

5 7^5 base: _____
exponent: _____

6 8^4 base: _____
exponent: _____

7 10^6 base: _____
exponent: _____

8 3^9 base: _____
exponent: _____

9 5^3 base: _____
exponent: _____

10 2^7 base: _____
exponent: _____

▶ Application

Follow the directions for the activity.

- Draw a 3-inch by 3-inch square. Tell what expression is modeled.
- Divide the square into 1-inch squares.
- Count the small squares. What expression is modeled now?
- Repeat this activity for a 2-inch by 2-inch square.

Chapter 6

Lesson 6-1 **Skills Practice**

Write an equation using exponents to represent each model.

1 _____

2 _____

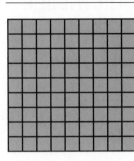

3 _____

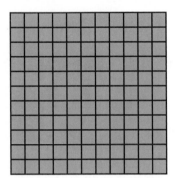

4 _____

Evaluate each expression.

5 11^2 base: _____

   exponent: _____

   $11^2 =$ _____ • _____ = _____

6 9^2 _____

7 1^2 _____

8 7^2 _____

9 2^2 _____

10 5^2 _____

11 10^2 _____

12 4^2 _____

13 12^2 _____

14 3^2 _____

15 6^2 _____

Lesson 6-1 Problem-Solving Practice

Solve.

1. **RESTAURANT** Mr. Agosto's restaurant has 2 large tables for bigger groups of people. The tables are big enough to accommodate 4 people on each side. How many people can sit at each of the big tables?

   _____

2. **CHEMISTRY** Pari made a hydrogen chloride solution in her chemistry lab. She poured 10 milliliters of solution into each of 10 test tubes. How many milliliters of hydrogen chloride did Pari make?

   _____

3. **PUZZLES** Write a number whose perfect square is the same as its base.

   _____

4. **MOVIES** Lucas and six of his friends went to the movies. Each of their tickets cost $7. What was the total cost of the tickets?

   _____

5. **DECORATING** Mapiya is putting tiles in her remodeled bathroom. Each tile is 1 inch by 1 inch. The tiles come connected in 1-square-foot sheets. Since there are 12 inches in 1 foot, how many tiles are in each sheet?

   _____

6. **CELEBRATIONS** Toya is having a party at her house. She plans to use 9 vases of fresh flowers for decoration. She wants to put 9 flowers in each vase. How many flowers will she need to buy?

   _____

7. **BABYSITTING** Lucas is babysitting next door. He charges $6 per hour. The parents said that they would be gone for 6 hours. How much can Lucas expect to earn?

   _____

8. **PAINTING** Noah is going to paint one wall in his bedroom. The wall is 8 feet wide and 8 feet high. He bought 1 quart of paint. The label says that the can of paint will cover 100 square feet. Does Noah have enough paint? Explain.

   _____

Lesson 6-1

Homework Practice

Write an equation using exponents to represent each model.

1 _____

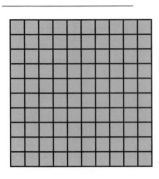

2 _____

3 _____

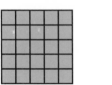

4 _____

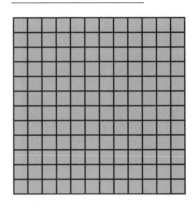

Evaluate each expression.

5 12^2 _____

6 10^2 _____

7 3^2 _____

8 6^2 _____

9 2^2 _____

10 7^2 _____

11 11^2 _____

12 9^2 _____

13 5^2 _____

14 8^2 _____

15 1^2 _____

16 4^2 _____

Solve.

17 **SCHOOL** Mr. Hatano's classroom has the same number of desks in each row. There is the same number of rows as there are desks in each row. There are 5 rows. How many desks are in Mr. Hatano's classroom?

_____

Math Triumphs

Lesson 6-2

Vocabulary and English Language Development

▶ Activate Prior Knowledge

Evaluate each expression.

1 4^2

_____

2 9^2

_____

3 15^2

_____

4 11^2

_____

5 1^2

_____

6 13^2

_____

▶ Definition Review

One of two equal factors of a number is called the **square root**.

The symbol used to indicate a nonnegative square root is called a **radical sign**.

Inverse operations are operations which undo each other.

7 Find the positive square root of 16. _____

8 What operation is the inverse of taking the square root of a number? _____

9 Draw a radical sign. _____

▶ Application

Follow the directions for the activity.

- Write 5 positive numbers.
- Find the square of each number.
- Then find the positive square root of each of your answers.
- Explain your results.

Math Triumphs

Lesson 6-2 Skills Practice

Find the positive square root using an area model.

1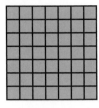

$\sqrt{49} =$ _____

2

$\sqrt{16} =$ _____

3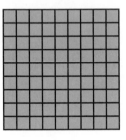

$\sqrt{81} =$ _____

4

$\sqrt{9} =$ _____

Find the positive square root of each number.

5 121

Write the expression.   _____

Name the factor pairs.   _____

Replace 121 with the set of identical factor pairs.   _____

$\sqrt{121} =$ _____

6 64

Write the expression.   _____

Name the factor pairs.   _____

Replace 64 with the set of identical factor pairs.   _____

$\sqrt{64} =$ _____

7 1

Write the expression.   _____

Name the factor pairs.   _____

Replace 1 with the set of identical factor pairs.   _____

$\sqrt{1} =$ _____

Lesson
6-2

Problem-Solving Practice

Solve.

1 **WINDOW** Mr. Trout has a patio window that has an area of
36 square feet. The length and width of the window are the same.
Use the positive square root of 36 to find the length of the window. _____

2 **FLOOR TILE** Humphrey is tiling the bathroom floor in his house.
He covers the floor with 64 square tiles. The length and width of
the bathroom are the same. Use the positive square root of 64 to
find the number of tiles in each row. _____

3 **TABLE COVER** Shelanda made a square card table cover. The area
of the cover is 1 square meter. Use the positive square root of 1 to
find the length of each side of the cover. _____

4 **SWIMMING POOL** Jacque has a square swimming pool. The area of
the pool is 169 square feet. Use the positive square root of 169 to
find the width of the pool. _____

5 **POSTER** Murphy is creating the poster
shown for art class. The area of the poster is
9 square feet. The length and width of the
poster are the same. Use the positive square
root of 9 to find the length of the poster.

_____

6 **GAME BOARD** A game board
consists of 49 squares as shown.
Use the positive square root of
49 to find the number of squares
in each row.

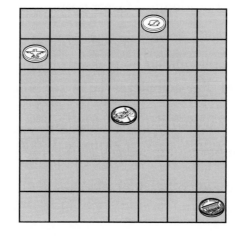

_____

Math Triumphs

Chapter 6

NAME _____ DATE _____

Homework Practice

Find the positive square root using an area model.

1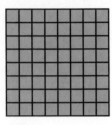

$\sqrt{64} =$ _____

2

$\sqrt{4} =$ _____

Find the positive square root of each number.

3 16

Write the expression. _____

Name the factor pairs. _____

Replace 16 with the set of identical factor pairs. _____

$\sqrt{16} =$ _____

4 4

Write the expression. _____

Name the factor pairs. _____

Replace 4 with the set of identical factor pairs. _____

$\sqrt{4} =$ _____

5 36

Write the expression. _____

Name the factor pairs. _____

Replace 36 with the set of identical factor pairs. _____

$\sqrt{36} =$ _____

Write the vocabulary word that completes each sentence.

6 A _____ is a number that is multiplied by another number.

7 The product of a number multiplied by itself is the _____.

8 Operations that undo each other are called _____.

Lesson 6-3

Vocabulary and English Language Development

▶ Activate Prior Knowledge

1 Round 28 to the nearest ten. _____

2 Round 225 to the nearest hundred. _____

3 Round 12.87 to the nearest tenth. _____

Write a whole number in the blank to make a true statement.

4 $12 < $ _____ $ < 16$

5 $25 < $ _____ $ < 28$

Find each value.

6 3^2

_____

7 $\sqrt{16} = $ _____

▶ Definition Review

A number close to an exact value is an **estimate**.

One of two equal factors of a number is the **square root** of the number.

8 Choose a reasonable estimate for $\sqrt{10}$.   3.1 or 3.8

9 Choose a reasonable estimate for $\sqrt{63}$.   7.2 or 7.9

▶ Application

Follow the directions for the activity.

- Students work in groups of 3. Each group needs a calculator.
- One student states a positive number between 0 and 200 whose square root is not a whole number, such as 14. This student finds the decimal approximation on the calculator, but does not show it to the other two students.
- The other two students each try to estimate the number to the nearest tenth.
- After they state their estimates, the student with the calculator then tells the value to the nearest tenth and the student who was closer gets one point.
- Rotate the calculator so that all students have an equal number of times at each role.
- The student with the greatest number of points wins.

Math Triumphs

Lesson 6-3 **Skills Practice**

Write an inequality using common square roots.

1 $\sqrt{\rule{1.5cm}{0pt}} < \sqrt{39} < \sqrt{\rule{1.5cm}{0pt}}$

2 $\sqrt{\rule{1.5cm}{0pt}} < \sqrt{130} < \sqrt{\rule{1.5cm}{0pt}}$

3 $\sqrt{\rule{1.5cm}{0pt}} < \sqrt{7} < \sqrt{\rule{1.5cm}{0pt}}$

4 $\sqrt{\rule{1.5cm}{0pt}} < \sqrt{190} < \sqrt{\rule{1.5cm}{0pt}}$

5 $\sqrt{\rule{1.5cm}{0pt}} < \sqrt{72} < \sqrt{\rule{1.5cm}{0pt}}$

6 $\sqrt{\rule{1.5cm}{0pt}} < \sqrt{23} < \sqrt{\rule{1.5cm}{0pt}}$

Estimate each square root to the nearest whole number. Plot each value on a number line.

7 $\sqrt{66}$ is close to the whole number

_____.

8 $\sqrt{116}$ is close to the whole number

_____.

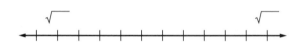

9 $\sqrt{28}$ is close to the whole number

_____.

10 $\sqrt{3}$ is close to the whole number

_____.

Choose a reasonable estimate for each square root.

11 $\sqrt{140}$

  10.6   11.8   12.2

12 $\sqrt{14}$

  3.1   3.4   3.7

13 $\sqrt{220}$

  14.8   15.2   15.8

14 $\sqrt{58}$

  6.8   7.2   7.6

15 $\sqrt{46}$

  6.4   6.8   7.2

16 $\sqrt{97}$

  9.8   10.3   10.8

Lesson 6-3 Problem-Solving Practice

Solve.

1. **FLOODING** The figure shows the square area that was flooded when the river overflowed last spring. The area is 10 square miles. Estimate the length and width of the flooded area to the nearest mile.

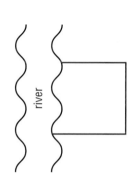

_____

2. **MIRROR** Sharon has a square mirror on her wall. The area of the mirror is 35 square feet. Estimate the length and width of the mirror.

_____

3. **WORKOUT ROOM** The picture shows a square workout room with area 160 square meters. Estimate the length and width to the nearest whole number of meters.

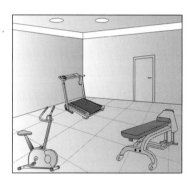

_____

4. **COLLAGE** Aaron created a photo collage by mounting 100 2-inch square pictures on a square piece of cardboard. If there is $\frac{1}{2}$-inch of cardboard around the edges of the pictures, what is the length and width of the cardboard?

_____

5. **BACKYARD** The backyard at Mrs. Miagi's condominium is a square with area 124 square meters. Estimate the length and width of the yard to the nearest meter.

_____

6. **MEDIA CENTER** Ryan has a media center in his basement. The area of the room is 200 square feet. Estimate the length and width of the room to the nearest whole number.

_____

Chapter 6

Lesson
6-3 **Homework Practice**

Write an inequality using common square roots.

1 $\sqrt{\rule{2em}{0pt}} < \sqrt{29} < \sqrt{\rule{2em}{0pt}}$

2 $\sqrt{\rule{2em}{0pt}} < \sqrt{84} < \sqrt{\rule{2em}{0pt}}$

3 $\sqrt{\rule{2em}{0pt}} < \sqrt{62} < \sqrt{\rule{2em}{0pt}}$

4 $\sqrt{\rule{2em}{0pt}} < \sqrt{12} < \sqrt{\rule{2em}{0pt}}$

Estimate each square root to the nearest whole number. Plot each value on a number line.

5 $\sqrt{23}$ is close to the whole number

_____.

6 $\sqrt{148}$ is close to the whole number

_____.

7 $\sqrt{53}$ is close to the whole number

_____.

8 $\sqrt{86}$ is close to the whole number

_____.

Choose a reasonable estimate for each square root.

9 $\sqrt{2}$

   1.0   1.4   1.8

10 $\sqrt{29}$

   4.8   5.1   5.4

11 $\sqrt{175}$

   13.2   13.6   13.9

12 $\sqrt{78}$

   7.6   8.8   9.2

13 **CALENDAR** Julie's square calendar has an area of 7 square inches. She estimated the length and width to be between 3 and 4 inches. Is she correct? Explain.

_____

Math Triumphs

Lesson 6-4

Vocabulary and English Language Development

▶ Activate Prior Knowledge

Evaluate each expression.

1 $\sqrt{49} =$ _____

2 $6^2 =$ _____

3 $9^2 =$ _____

4 $\sqrt{16} =$ _____

▶ Definition Review

The **square root** of a number is one of two equal factors of the number.
The **square of a number** is the product of the number multiplied by itself.

5 For a right triangle, $c^2 =$ _____

Complete each sentence using the words *square* or *square root*.

6 8 is the _____ of 64.

7 25 is the _____ of 5.

Determine whether or not the triangles are right triangles.

8

_____ + _____ ○ _____ _____

9

_____ + _____ ○ _____ _____

10

_____ + _____ ○ _____ _____

11

_____ + _____ ○ _____ _____

▶ Application

Follow the directions for the activity.

• Cut out a rectangle with a height of 3 inches and a width of 4 inches.
• Then cut the rectangles in half on the diagonal.
• Use the Pythagorean Theorem to find the length of the hypotenuse.
• Measure the hypotenuse of the triangle.
• Does the measurement match the calculation?
• Repeat the activity with a 5 cm by 12 cm rectangle.

Math Triumphs

Chapter 6

Lesson 6-4 **Skills Practice**

Find the length of the hypotenuse of the right triangle.

1
5
c
12

$c =$ _____ units

2
15
c
8

$c =$ _____ units

3
7
c
24

$c =$ _____ units

4
15
c
20

$c =$ _____ units

5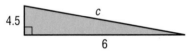
4.5
c
6

$c =$ _____ units

6
3
c
4

$c =$ _____ units

Find the length of the leg of each right triangle.

7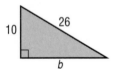
10
26
b

$b =$ _____ units

8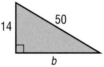
14
50
b

$b =$ _____ units

9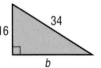
16
34
b

$b =$ _____ units

10
10.5
17.5
b

$b =$ _____ units

Determine if each triangle is a right triangle, using the Pythagorean Theorem.

11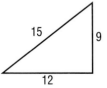
15
9
12

_____

12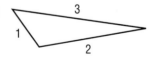
3
1
2

_____

Math Triumphs

Lesson 6-4

Problem-Solving Practice

Solve.

1 **ORAGAMI**   Dan is doing origami. He has a rectangular sheet of green paper that is 8 inches long and 6 inches wide. He cuts the paper in half diagonally to make 2 triangles. How long is the hypotenuse of each triangle?

_____

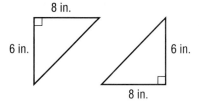

2 **ANTENNAS**   Amalia put an antenna on the roof of her house. The vertical distance from the top of the antenna to the base of the house is 50 feet. The network is 120 feet from base of the house. If a right triangle is created, how long is the hypotenuse?

_____

3 **SHORTCUTS**   To get to the pool, Carlos usually bikes north, then east. One day, Carlos discovered he can bike straight to the pool if he goes through the meadow. Look at the map. How far does Carlos have to bike through the meadow to get to the pool?

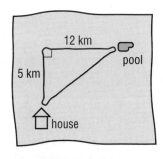

_____

4 **MAILBOX**   Sarit is building a mailbox. He needs to check the mailbox's support on the post. Using Sarit's diagram, determine the length of the support.

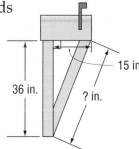

_____

Math Triumphs

Lesson 6-4 Homework Practice

Determine if each triangle is a right triangle, using the Pythagorean Theorem.

1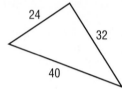

_____

2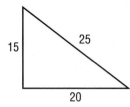

_____

Find the length of the leg or hypotenuse of each right triangle.

3

$c =$ _____ units

4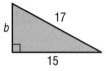

$b =$ _____ units

5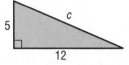

$c =$ _____ units

6

$b =$ _____ units

Solve.

7 **TELEVISION** Mr. Patel is buying a new television. He wants to figure out the biggest size television he can get. His cabinet has an opening that is 30 inches tall and 40 inches wide. What is the largest diagonal length of a television Mr. Patel can buy?

_____

8 **MAPS** Carisa is making a treasure map. The path from the starting point to the treasure is 28 paces forward then 21 paces to the left. How many paces would it be to go directly from the starting point to the treasure?

_____

Write the vocabulary word(s) that completes the sentence.

9 The _____ of a right triangle are the two sides that form the right angle.

10 The _____ is the side opposite the right angle in a right triangle.

Math Triumphs

Lesson 6-5
Vocabulary and English Language Development

▶ Activate Prior Knowledge

Name the ordered pair for each point.

1 A _____

2 B _____

3 C _____

4 D _____

5 E _____

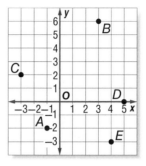

▶ Definition Review

A **coordinate grid** is a grid in which a horizontal number line and a vertical number line intersect at their zero points.

Slope is the ratio of vertical change to horizontal change. It is the rate of change between any two points on a line.

6 For $(3, -2)$, the x-coordinate is _____ and the y-coordinate is _____.

7 Find the slope of a line if the rise is $+6$ units and the run is $+5$ units. _____

8 Find the slope of a line if the rise is -3 units and the run is $+2$ units. _____

▶ Application

Form a human line.

- Clear the area on a floor with square tiles or use masking tape to form a grid on the floor.
- One student chooses a slope. Students arrange themselves on the grid so that they are points on a line with that slope.
- Another student chooses a different slope. Students rearrange themselves as needed.
- Repeat for several slopes. Use both positive and negative slopes. Use both fractional and whole number slopes as well.

Lesson 6-5 **Skills Practice**

Find the slope of each line.

1 The rise is _____ units.

2 The run is _____ units.

3 The slope is _____.

4 $\dfrac{\text{rise}}{\text{run}} = \dfrac{\boxed{}}{\boxed{}}$

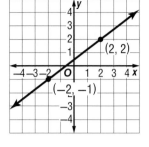

5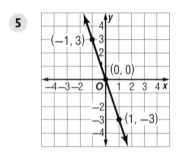

$\dfrac{\text{rise}}{\text{run}} = \dfrac{\boxed{}}{\boxed{}} =$ _____

6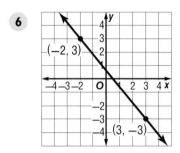

$\dfrac{\text{rise}}{\text{run}} = \dfrac{\boxed{}}{\boxed{}} =$ _____

Graph another point on each line, given one point on the line and the slope.

7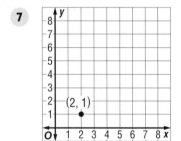

The slope is $\dfrac{1}{5}$.

8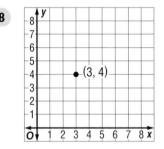

The slope is $-\dfrac{3}{2}$.

9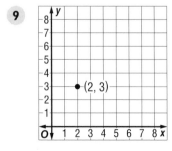

The slope is 4.

10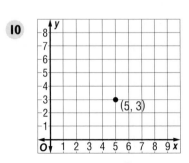

The slope is $\dfrac{3}{4}$.

Math Triumphs

Lesson 6-5 Problem-Solving Practice

Solve.

1 **SLEDDING** Max is sledding down the hill shown. What is the slope of the hill?

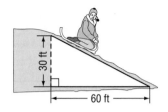

_____

2 **KITE** Bart is holding the string to a kite 4 feet above the ground. The kite is 100 feet above a point on the ground 32 feet from Bart. Find the slope of the kite string.

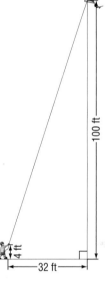

_____

3 **CLOTHESLINE** Leslie is stringing a clothesline from a pole that is 4 feet tall to a point on her garage 6 feet above the ground. The pole is 20 feet from the garage as shown in the diagram. Find the slope of the clothesline.

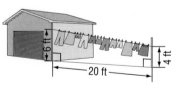

_____

4 **RAMPS** A ramp begins at a doorway that is 8 feet above the ground. The ramp runs a horizontal distance of 20 feet. A person leaving the building wants to know what the slope is. What would you say?

_____

Chapter 6

Lesson 6-5 **Homework Practice**

Find the slope of each line.

1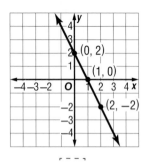

$$\frac{\text{rise}}{\text{run}} = \frac{\boxed{}}{\boxed{}} = \underline{}$$

2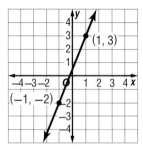

$$\frac{\text{rise}}{\text{run}} = \frac{\boxed{}}{\boxed{}}$$

Graph another point on each line, given one point on the line and the slope.

3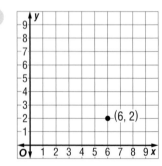

The slope is $-\frac{4}{3}$.

4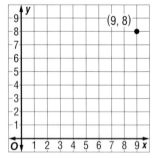

The slope is 2.

5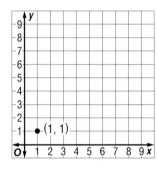

The slope is $\frac{3}{5}$.

6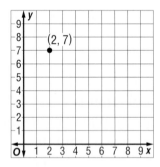

The slope is $-\frac{1}{2}$.

Solve.

7 **STAIRS** Each step on a flight of stairs has a height of 6 inches and a width of 9 inches. What is the slope of the stairs? _____

8 **LADDERS** A ladder is leaning against the side of a house. The bottom of the ladder is 12 feet away from the house and the top of the ladder is 15 feet above the ground. What is the slope of the ladder? _____

Math Triumphs

Lesson 6-6

Vocabulary and English Language Development

▶ Activate Prior Knowledge

Find the slope.

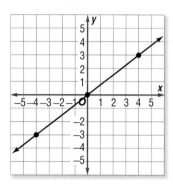

1 What is the rise? _____

2 What is the run? _____

3 What is the slope of the line? _____

▶ Definition Review

Slope is the rate of change between any two points on a line.

Complete the following.

4 Give the slope formula. _____

5 Explain how to find the slope using the terms "vertical" and "horizontal."

_____

▶ Application

Follow the directions for the activity.

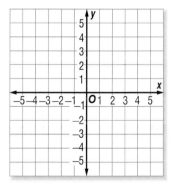

- Draw a line on the coordinate grid.
- Find two points on your line.
- Calculate the slope of the line using these two points and the slope formula.
- Repeat this activity for three other lines.

Chapter 6

Skills Practice

Graph each equation and determine its slope.

1 $y = \frac{1}{2}x + 3$

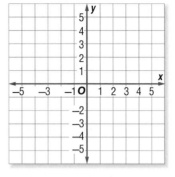

x	−4	0	4
y			

The slope is _____.

2 $y = -3x$

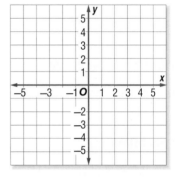

x	−1	0	1
y			

The slope is _____.

3 $y = -\frac{3}{4}x - 2$

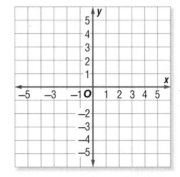

x	−4	0	4
y			

The slope is _____.

4 $y = 4x$

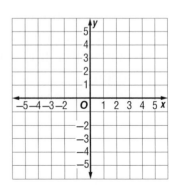

x	−1	0	1
y			

The slope is _____.

Math Triumphs

Lesson 6-6 Problem-Solving Practice

Solve.

1 **ANIMALS** Graph an equation to represent the data in the caption.

Write an equation.

Let x represent the number of hours and y represent the number of miles.

_____

The slope is _____.

A deer runs at a speed of approximately 30 miles per hour.

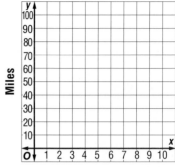

2 **MONEY** Luis earns \$8 per hour. Graph an equation to represent the amount he earns in x hours.

Write an equation.

Let x represent the number of hours and y represent dollars.

_____

The slope is _____.

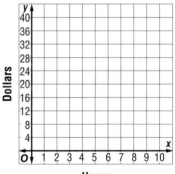

3 **SCHOOL** To complete a book for literature class, Aiden will read 5 pages every night. Graph an equation to represent the number of pages read after x nights.

Write an equation.

Let x represent the number of nights and y represent the number of pages.

_____

The slope is _____.

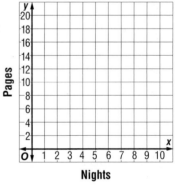

4 **BAKING** Julieta is baking cookies to give to her neighbors during the holidays. She bakes 3 batches of cookies every hour. Graph an equation to represent how many of batches she bakes in x hours.

Write an equation.

Let x represent the number of hours and y represent the number of cookie batches.

_____

The slope is _____.

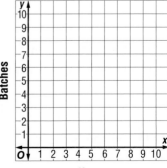

Chapter 6

Lesson
6-6 Homework Practice

Graph each equation and determine its slope.

1 $y = 2x + 1$

x	−3	−2	−1
y			

The slope is _____.

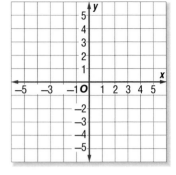

2 $y = -\frac{4}{5}x$

x	−5	0	5
y			

The slope is _____.

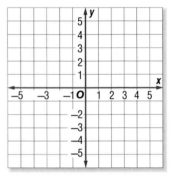

3 $y = \frac{2}{3}x + 2$

x	−3	0	3
y			

The slope is _____.

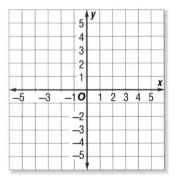

4 **ANIMALS** A pig can run at approximately 10 miles per hour. Graph an equation to represent how far a pig can run in x hours.

Write an equation. Let x represent the number of hours and y represent the number of miles.

_____

The slope is _____.

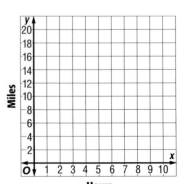

Math Triumphs

Chapter 7

Foldables Study Organizer

Dinah Zike's Foldables

Make this Foldable to help you organize information about one-variable data.

1. Begin with four sheets of graph paper. Fold each sheet of graph paper in half along the width.

2. Unfold each sheet and tape to form one long piece.

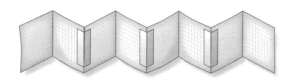

3. Label the pages with the lesson numbers as shown.

4. Refold the pages to form a journal.

TAKING NOTES

As you read through the chapter, use your Foldable to write about Mode, Median, Mean, Bar Graphs, and Line Graphs.

 USING YOUR FOLDABLE

As you study, use your Foldable to journal what you learn in each lesson. Take notes in the pages of your journal and use the appropriate journal page to study each lesson in the chapter.

USING YOUR FOLDABLE

Work with a partner. One student should give a set of data. The other student should create an example of the data in a bar graph.

Chapter 7

Chapter 7

Games and Puzzles
Venn Diagram Game

DIRECTIONS

- Have each team make a human Venn diagram for each set of clues. Use the yarn to form a circle. All of the team members who match the first clue should step into the circle. Then add additional circles and have team members step into them accordingly.

- The first team with everyone in the correct circles wins the round.

- Use the clues below found on the student page to facilitate the game.

ROUND	SET A	SET B	SET C
1	I like rock music.	I like rap music.	
2	I live in (your state).	I live in (your city).	
3	I was born in the U.S.	I live in the U.S.	
4	I am a sister.	I am a brother.	I am an only child.
5	I am female.	I am male.	I have used a calculator.
6	I am wearing red.	I am wearing blue.	I am wearing yellow.
7	I drank orange juice today.	I ate cereal today.	I drank a soft drink today.
8	I like to rollerblade.	I like to play soccer.	I like to play video games.
9	My favorite ice cream is chocolate.	My favorite ice creams are chocolate and vanilla.	My favorite ice cream is neither chocolate nor vanilla.
10	Set A: There is an *a* in my name. Set B: There is an *e* in my name.	Set C: There is an *i* in my name. Set D: There is an *o* in my name.	

Math Triumphs

Venn Diagram Game

Work in two teams.

- Each team makes a human Venn diagram for each set of clues. Use the yarn to form a circle. All of the team members who match the first clue should step into the circle. Then add additional circles and have team members step into them accordingly.

- The first team with everyone in the appropriate circles wins the round.

- Clues:

Round 1 **a.** I like rock music. **b.** I like rap music.	**Round 2** **a.** I live in (your state). **b.** I live in (your city).
Round 3 **a.** I was born in the U.S. **b.** I live in the U.S.	**Round 4** **a.** I am a sister. **b.** I am a brother. **c.** I am an only child.
Round 5 **a.** I am female. **b.** I am male. **c.** I have used a calculator.	**Round 6** **a.** I am wearing red. **b.** I am wearing blue. **c.** I am wearing yellow.
Round 7 **a.** I drank orange juice today. **b.** I ate cereal today. **c.** I drank a soft drink today.	**Round 8** **a.** I like to rollerblade. **b.** I like to play soccer. **c.** I like to play video games.
Round 9 **a.** My favorite ice cream is chocolate. **b.** My favorite ice creams are chocolate and vanilla. **c.** My favorite ice cream is neither chocolate nor vanilla.	**Round 10** **a.** There is an *a* in my name. **b.** There is an *e* in my name. **c.** There is an *i* in my name. **d.** There is an *o* in my name.

Lesson 7-1 Vocabulary and English Language Development

▶ Activate Prior Knowledge

Name a common feature by which each of the items could be sorted.

1 chair: _____

2 pizza: _____

3 swimming pool: _____

4 shoe: _____

▶ Definition Review

To **sort** is to put together items that have something in common.

A **Venn diagram** is a diagram that uses circles to display items of different sets.

Name a category by which each group could be sorted.

5 cats, dogs, hamsters, Guinea pigs _____

6 maple, oak, pine, birch _____

7 2, 4, 10, 16, 20 _____

8 ham, turkey, tuna, cheese _____

▶ Application

Follow the directions for the activity.

- Work individually. Each student needs two number cubes.
- Students roll both of the number cubes 8 times.
- For each roll, record the product of the two numbers rolled.
- Students then sort and classify the products as multiples of 3, multiples of 5, and neither.
- Draw a Venn diagram to show the results of sorting the numbers.
- Repeat the exercise, sorting the numbers into two different groups.

Lesson 7-1 Skills Practice

Sort the numbers into each category.

1, 2, 3, 4, 5, 6, 7, 8, 9, 10, 11, 12

I whole number factors of 18:

_____

2 prime numbers:

_____

3 both:

_____

4 neither:

_____

5 Create a Venn diagram to sort the numbers. Classify them as multiples of 10 or multiples of 25.

20, 25, 30, 35, 40, 50, 75, 80, 85, 100

Multiples of 10	Multiples of 25	Neither
_____	_____	_____

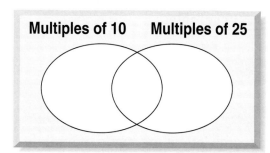

6 Create a Venn diagram to sort the numbers. Classify them as composite numbers or odd numbers.

0, 4, 6, 9, 11, 13, 17, 21, 31, 40

Composite Numbers	Odd Numbers	Neither
_____	_____	_____

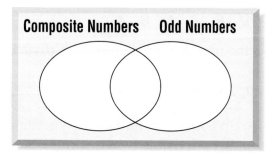

Math Triumphs

Chapter 7

Lesson 7-1 Problem-Solving Practice

Solve.

1 **SPORTS** In Mr. Rivera's class, some students play basketball, some play soccer, and some play both basketball and soccer. There are 30 people in the class. How many students do not play either basketball or soccer?

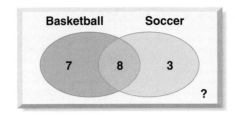

_____

2 **SHOPPING** Amber was shopping at the grocery store and noticed that some fruits and vegetables are red, some are green, and some can be either red or green. She wrote

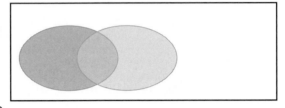

down the names of the fruits and vegetables in the list below. Create a Venn diagram to sort them into the categories red, green, both, or neither.

Fruits and Vegetables

Apples	Peppers
Oranges	Broccoli
Grapes	Beets
Celery	Grapefruit
Strawberries	Lemons

3 **ALPHABET** Ben noticed that some letters are made of straight lines and some are made of curved lines. Using the letters shown below, construct a Venn diagram to show how the letters are sorted into letters made with straight lines or letters made with curved lines.

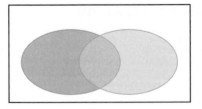

E O Z T U P D L B A

4 **NUMBER SENSE** Juan listed the first ten whole numbers divisible by 4:

4, 8, 12, 16, 20, 24, 28, 32, 36, 40

He noticed that some are also divisible by 6 and created a Venn diagram to sort them into numbers divisible by 4 or numbers divisible by 6. Which numbers are in both categories?

_____

Math Triumphs

Lesson 7-1

Homework Practice

List the numbers in each category.

1, 2, 3, 4, 5, 6, 7, 8, 9, 10

1 multiples of 5:

_____

2 even numbers:

_____

3 both:

_____

4 neither:

_____

5 Create a Venn diagram to sort the numbers. Classify them as prime numbers or even numbers.

2, 3, 8, 9, 17, 21, 25, 37, 41

Prime Numbers	Even Numbers	Neither
_____	_____	_____

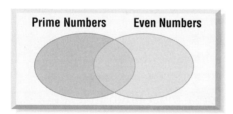

Solve.

6 **SURVEY** Malcolm took a survey to find out how many students have dogs, cats, or both pets. Malcolm surveyed 64 students and recorded his results in the Venn diagram shown below. Of the students surveyed, how many do not have a dog as a pet? _____

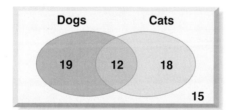

Write the vocabulary word that completes each sentence.

7 To put together items that have something in common is to _____.

8 A _____ uses overlapping circles to show common elements.

Chapter 7

Lesson 7-2 Vocabulary and English Language Development

▶ Activate Prior Knowledge

1 Arrange the following numbers in order from least to greatest.

11, 5, 3, 20, 2

_____

2 Which of the following numbers appears most often in the list?

0, 0, 2, 2, 4, 7, 7, 7, 9

_____

3 In the following list of numbers, which number is located in the middle of the list?

0, 1, 2, 5, 9

_____

▶ Definition Review

The **mode** is the number(s) or item(s) that appear most often in a set of data.

The difference between the greatest number and the least number in a set of data is the **range**.

The middle number in a set of data when the data are arranged in numerical order is the **median**.

4 Write a set of data with a mode of 2. _____, _____, _____, _____, _____

5 Write a set of data with a range of 5. _____, _____, _____, _____, _____

6 Write a set of data with a median of 5. _____, _____, _____, _____, _____

▶ Application

Follow the directions for the activity.

- Work in pairs.
- List 5 numbers where two of them are the same.
- Exchange numbers with your partner.
- Find the mode, median, and range of the numbers your partner wrote.
- Check your partner's answers.
- Repeat this activity three times using different numbers.

Math Triumphs

Lesson 7-2 Skills Practice

Find the mode for each given set of data.

1 1, 2, 0, 1, 2, 0, 1

_____

2 7, 3, 5, 2, 4, 3, 6, 10, 0

_____

3 3, 0, 0, 1, 2

_____

4 9, 3, 2, 5, 6, 3, 3, 7, 15

_____

Find the median for each given set of data.

5 Henry asked seven people what the last digit in their telephone number is.

2, 5, 9, 9, 7, 4, 3

Arrange the numbers in order: _____, _____, _____, _____, _____, _____, _____

The median is _____.

6 Christina asked five people how tall they were, in inches.

54, 63, 62, 48, 68

Arrange the numbers in order: _____, _____, _____, _____, _____

The median is _____.

7 Nathan recorded the low temperatures for each day one week.

34, 32, 41, 29, 42, 32, 50

Arrange the numbers in order: _____, _____, _____, _____, _____, _____, _____

The median is _____.

Find the range for each given set of data.

8 2, 5, 9, 9, 7, 4, 3

The range of digits in Exercise 5 is _____ − _____ = _____.

9 54, 63, 62, 48, 68

The range of heights in Exercise 6 is _____ − _____ = _____.

Chapter 7

Problem-Solving Practice

Solve.

1. **CLASS PERIODS** Leta surveyed 9 schools to find the length of their class periods in minutes. The results are shown below. Find the mode, median, and range of the times.

   90, 50, 45, 42, 55, 75, 80, 45, 60

   _____

2. **TELEVISION** Hans surveyed 11 classmates about how many minutes they spent watching television over the weekend. The results are shown below. Find the mode, median, and range of the times.

   180, 120, 135, 90, 30, 45, 0, 60, 90, 300, 90

   _____

3. **CHESS TOURNAMENT** The members of the Centerville Junior High School chess team recorded the number of games they won in each tournament in the table below. Find the mode, median, and range of the number of wins.

   _____

Tournament Number	1	2	3	4	5	6	7	8	9
Number of Wins	3	5	2	1	0	4	2	0	0

4. **COFFEE SHOP** Five friends had dinner at the local coffee shop. The prices of their dinners are shown below. Find the mode, median, and range of the prices.

   $5, $7, $4, $6, $7

   _____

5. **PETS** Wilhema asked 11 classmates how many pets they have. The results are shown in the table below. Find the mode, median, and range of the number of pets.

   _____

Name	Jack	Pete	Sue	Mary	Fred	Jeri	Ann	Teri	Cal	Mac	Amy
Number	0	2	4	3	1	1	1	2	3	5	0

Math Triumphs

Lesson 7-2

Homework Practice

Find the mode for each given set of data.

1 1, 3, 2, 2, 4, 3, 2, 4, 1

_____

2 7, 8, 5, 8, 4

_____

Find the median for each given set of data.

3 Barb counted the glasses in nine different kitchen cabinets.

11, 12, 4, 7, 9, 5, 13, 8, 12

Arrange the numbers in order:

_____, _____, _____, _____, _____, _____, _____, _____, _____

The median is _____.

4 Juan asked 13 students how many books they read over the summer.

0, 5, 15, 2, 11, 17, 8, 6, 5, 2, 0, 3, 2

Arrange the numbers in order:

____, ____, ____, ____, ____, ____, ____, ____, ____, ____, ____, ____, ____

The median is _____.

Find the range for each given set of data.

5 11, 12, 4, 7, 9, 5, 13, 8, 12

The range of glasses in Exercise 3 is _____ − _____ = _____.

6 0, 5, 15, 2, 11, 17, 8, 6, 5, 2, 0, 3, 2

The range of books in Exercise 4 is _____ − _____ = _____.

Solve.

7 **PAY** Julius kept track of the number of hours he worked per week for 15 weeks. The results are shown below. Find the mode, median, and range of the number of hours.

19, 16, 32, 30, 20, 40, 37, 10, 8, 0, 35, 40, 36, 12, 15

_____

Write the vocabulary word that completes the sentence.

8 Information gathered for statistical purposes is called _____.

Chapter 7

Lesson 7-3 Vocabulary and English Language Development

▶ Activate Prior Knowledge

Find the mode, median, and range of each data set.

1 The number of houses on different streets in a neighborhood.

6, 5, 2, 10, 9, 10, 4, 8, 7

mode: _____   median: _____   range: _____

2 The number of letters in the mail each day for five days.

5, 2, 0, 3, 5

mode: _____   median: _____   range: _____

▶ Definition Review

Fill in the blanks.

3 The _____ of a data set is the sum of the numbers in the set divided by the number of pieces of data.

4 A(n) _____ is a value that is much higher or much lower than the other values of a set of data.

5 Write a set of data with five numbers so that there is one outlier that is much higher than the other values. _____

6 Write a set of data with five numbers so that there is one outlier that is much lower than the other values. _____

▶ Application

Follow the directions for the activity.

- Students work in groups of 4 to 6. Each group should have a jar or bag of small identical items, like beans or pasta pieces.
- Each group member takes any number of items from the bag or jar. Each group member should lay their pieces in a pile in front of them.
- As a group, estimate the mean number of pieces a student took. Then find the mean by finding the sum of all the pieces and dividing by the number of piles. Confirm your answer by dividing the pieces into equal groups.
- Repeat this activity by taking a different number of pieces than before.

Math Triumphs

Lesson 7-3

Skills Practice

Find the mean of each data set.

1 6, 11, 15, 4

_____ + _____ + _____ + _____ = _____

_____ ÷ _____ = _____

The mean is _____.

2 16, 24, 32, 18, 10

_____

3 65, 42, 38, 27

_____

4 2.2, 3.5, 5, 4.1, 5.2

_____

5 34, 28, 30, 26, 22

_____

Find the mean of the data set. Convert the remainder into a fraction or a decimal.

6 12, 8, 5, 7, 9, 4

_____

7 8.3, 3.6, 9.4, 3.9

_____

8 9, 2, 1, 7, 17, 8

_____

9 48, 59, 72, 66

_____

Find one missing number from a data set when the mean is given.

10 Mean: 7   Data set: 5, 11, 2, _____

11 Mean: 4   Data set: 4.1, 4.3, 3.9, _____

12 Mean: 59   Data set: 56, 63, _____

13 Mean: 93   Data set: 99, 84, 88, 92, _____

Chapter 7

Lesson 7-3 Problem-Solving Practice

Solve.

1. **BASEBALL** The teams in the conference won the following number of games during the season: 6, 11, 7, 5, 16, 20, 18, 21, 7, 9, and 12. What is the mean of this data set? _____

2. **MATH COMPETITION** The schools in Douglas County qualified the following numbers of math team members for the state competition: 24, 5, 8, 16, 2. What is the mean of this data set? _____

3. **ENROLLMENT** Amos knows that the average enrollment in the courses listed in the table is 26, but he forgot to record the number of students enrolled in Computer Graphics. What is the missing amount in the table? _____

Course	Enrollment
Art	36
Metals	15
Computer Graphics	
Auto Shop	31

4. **SWIMMING** The number of laps that each member of the swim team swam during practice yesterday was 7, 12, 16, 26, and 19. What is the mean of this data set? _____

5. **ANIMALS** The maximum speeds, in mph, of certain animals are given in the table. What is the average speed of these animals? _____

Animal	Speed (mph)
Cheetah	70
Lion	50
Elk	45
Zebra	40
Grizzly bear	30

6. **GARDENING** Packages of tulip bulbs contained 36, 37, 28, and 31 bulbs. What was the mean number of bulbs in a package? _____

Lesson 7-3 Homework Practice

Find the mean of each data set.

1 60, 72, 56, 42, 80

_____

2 11, 16, 12

_____

3 5, 14, 25, 17, 14

_____

4 6.2, 3.8, 4.5, 5.5

_____

Find the mean of each set of data. Convert the remainder into a fraction or a decimal.

5 2, 7, 9, 4

_____

6 6.1, 8.2, 9.3, 7.6

_____

7 16, 30, 26, 14, 18

_____

8 2, 1, 9, 4, 0, 6

_____

Find one missing number from a data set when the mean is given.

9 Mean: 6   Data set: 2, 3, 10, _____

10 Mean: 7   Data set: 6.2, 5.2, 9.7, _____

11 Mean: 14.6 Data set: 19, 12, 10, 15, _____

12 Mean: 6   Data set: 4, 6, 3, 6, _____

13 **TEMPERATURE** Mark recorded the high temperature every day for five days. The temperatures were 52°F, 64°F, 57°F, 61°F, and 70°F. What was the mean high temperature for the week?   _____

Write the vocabulary word that completes each sentence.

14 The numbers that are often used to describe the center of a set of data are called the _____.

15 Another name for the mean of a set of data is the _____.

Chapter 7

Lesson 7-4 Vocabulary and English Language Development

▶ Activate Prior Knowledge

Pizza Places We Like

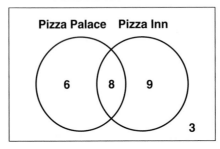

Use the Venn diagram to complete Exercises 1–4.

1 How many students like Pizza Inn?

_____

2 How many students like Pizza Palace?

_____

3 How many students like both Pizza Palace and Pizza Inn?

_____

4 How many students do not like either?

_____

▶ Definition Review

Write the letter of the definition that matches each term.

5 bar graph _____

6 horizontal axis _____

7 interval _____

8 scale _____

9 vertical axis _____

A The set of all possible values in a given measurement, separated by the intervals used.

B The axis on which the scale and interval are shown in a bar or line graph.

C A graph using bars to compare quantities.

D The axis on which the categories or values are shown in a bar or line graph.

E The difference between successive values on a scale.

▶ Application

Follow the directions for the activity.

- Bring to class an example of a bar graph found in a newspaper or in a magazine.
- Identify the title, categories, scale, and intervals on the graph.
- Write 3 questions about the data on your bar graph.
- Exchange your graph with that of a partner and answer the questions your partner wrote about his or her bar graph.
- Switch graphs with another pair of students and repeat the activity.

Math Triumphs

Skills Practice

Use the bar graph "My Classmates' Favorite Type of Book" to compare data.

1 How many students chose Mystery as their favorite

type of book? _____

2 How many chose Science Fiction? _____

3 How many chose Biography? _____

4 How many more students prefer Mysteries

than Classic Novels? _____

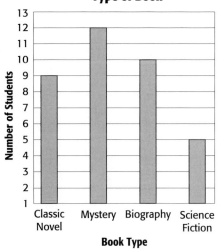

**My Classmates' Favorite
Type of Book**

Use the double-bar graph "My Classmates' Favorite Type of Book" to compare data.

5 How many girls chose Mystery as their favorite

type of book? _____

6 How many girls chose Classic Novel or

Biography? _____

7 How many more girls than boys chose

Classic Novels? _____

8 What type of book was preferred by the same

number of boys and girls? _____

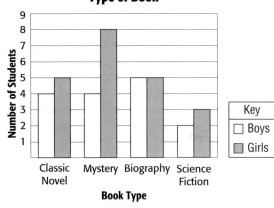

**My Classmates' Favorite
Type of Book**

Use the bar graph "Hours Ellen Volunteers at the Hospital" to compare data.

9 What are the categories? _____

10 How many more hours does Ellen volunteer on

Saturday than on Sunday? _____

11 How many hours does Ellen volunteer on Monday

and Tuesday together? _____

12 How many total hours does Ellen volunteer during

the week? _____

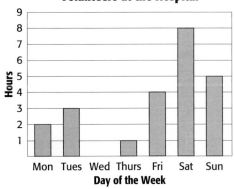

**Hours Ellen
Volunteers at the Hospital**

Chapter 7

Math Triumphs

Lesson 7-4 **Problem-Solving Practice**

Solve.

1 **CLASS TRIP**   The school activities director asked the eighth-graders where they should go for their class trip. How many boys prefer the amusement park or the beach compared to the number of boys that prefer the zoo or the museum?

_____

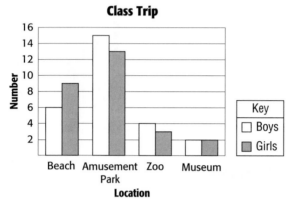

2 **ZOO**   Use the graph in Exercise 1. How many more boys than girls prefer going to the zoo?

_____

3 **SLEEP**   How many more students average 9 hours of sleep per night than 8 hours?

_____

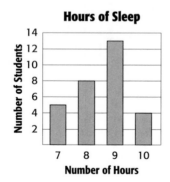

4 **ACTIVITIES**   How many more girls prefer to play sports or talk on the phone rather than playing video games or going to a movie?

_____

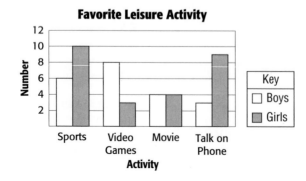

Math Triumphs

Lesson 7-4 Homework Practice

Use the double-bar graph "Quiz Grades" to compare data.

1 How many students earned A's?

_____

2 How many more boys earned B's than D's?

_____

3 How many girls earned A's or B's?

_____

4 A total of 11 students earned what grade?

_____

5 How many students took the quiz?

_____

6 How many more girls than boys earned a C?

_____

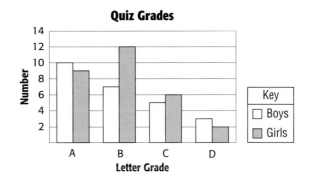

Use the bar graph "Favorite Ride" to compare data.

7 How many students were surveyed?

_____

8 How many students prefer the water rapids to the merry-go-round?

_____

9 How many students chose the Ferris wheel or the roller coaster as their favorite ride?

_____

10 What is the least favorite ride?

_____

11 How many more students prefer the roller coaster than the water rapids? _____

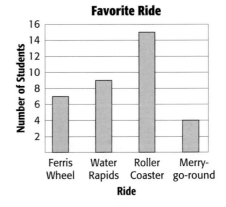

Chapter 7

Lesson 7-5

Vocabulary and English Language Development

▶ Activate Prior Knowledge

Use the bar graph "Favorite Type of Vacation" to compare data.

1 How many more students prefer a beach vacation than one in the mountains?

_____

2 What location is preferred by 8 students?

_____

3 What two locations were chosen as often as a beach vacation?

_____

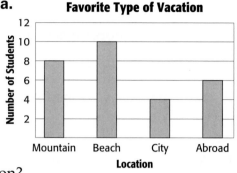

Favorite Type of Vacation

▶ Definition Review

Fill in the blanks.

4 The set of all possible values in a given measurement, including the least and greatest numbers in the set, separated by the intervals used is called the _____.

5 The axis on which the scale and interval are shown is the _____ axis while the axis on which the categories or values are shown is the _____ axis.

6 A graph using bars to compare quantities is called a _____.

7 The difference between successive values on a scale is called the _____.

▶ Application

Follow the directions for the activity.

- Work in groups of 2 or 3.
- Ask students in other groups what their favorite something is. For example: favorite type of fruit, favorite animal, favorite type of music.
- Make a bar graph to display your data.
- As a group, present your graph to the rest of the class. Discuss your findings as well as how you chose to make your graph, including the title, categories, scale, and intervals.

Lesson 7-5

Skills Practice

Use the data in the table to plan a bar graph.

The table shows the method students used to get to school.

1   What is a good title for the graph?

_____

2   What are the two main categories?

_____

3   What interval could be used for the scale?

_____

4   What will the height of each bar represent?

_____

Method of Getting to School	
Method	**Number of Students**
Car	36
Bus	44
Walk	24
Bike	18

Use the data in the table to create a bar graph.

5   The table shows the color of each mouse at Cassie's Pet Store.

Mice at Cassie's Pet Store	
Color	**Number**
White	10
Gray	8
Black	6
Brown	12

Use the data in the table to create a double-bar graph.

6   The table shows the number of fundraising items sold by the students in each grade.

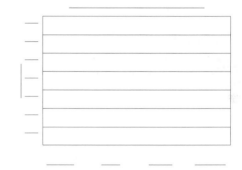

Items Sold in Fundraiser		
Item	**By Grade 7**	**By Grade 8**
Candles	17	24
Gift Wrap	30	20
Candy	16	22
Nuts	12	15

Chapter 7

Lesson
7-5 # Problem-Solving Practice

1 **ELECTION** A student reporter wants to make a double-bar graph to compare the number of boys and girls who said they voted for each candidate. Use the data in the table to create a double-bar graph.

Votes for Class President		
Candidate	**Boys**	**Girls**
Marcy	17	36
Brian	54	40
Lois	28	23
Tim	20	32

2 **TRACK AND FIELD** The track coach wants to compare the favorite events of the seventh and eighth graders on the track team. Use the data in the table to create a double-bar graph.

Favorite Track and Field Event		
Event	**7th Graders**	**8th Graders**
Hurdles	9	12
Relay Races	22	17
Long Jump	6	8
Discus Throw	4	9

3 **GREAT LAKES** Carl is doing a report on the Great Lakes and wants to compare their maximum depths. Use the data in the table to create a bar graph.

Maximum Depth of Great Lakes	
Lake	**Depth (feet)**
Erie	210
Huron	750
Michigan	925
Ontario	802
Superior	1,333

Math Triumphs

Lesson 7-5

Homework Practice

Use the data in the table to plan a bar graph.

1 What is a good title for the graph?

_____

2 What are the two main categories?

_____

_____

3 What interval could be used for the scale?

_____

4 What will the height of each bar represent?

_____

Education of 8th Graders' Parents	
Educational Level Attained	Number of Students
High School Diploma	17
Some College	29
College Degree	66
Graduate Level Degree	34

Use the data in the table to create a bar graph.

5 The table shows the favorite snack of students in summer school.

Favorite Snack	
Snack	Number of Students
Cookies	8
Veggies	15
Chips	9
Fruit	6
Milk	4

Use the data in the table to create a double-bar graph.

6 The table shows how many juniors and seniors prefer each location for their prom.

Preferred Location for Prom		
Location	Juniors	Seniors
School	10	6
Hotel	26	30
Museum	22	25
Railroad Station	15	19

Chapter 7

Lesson 7-6 Vocabulary and English Language Development

▶ Activate Prior Knowledge

Use the bar graph to answer the questions.

1 How many titles did Kwan win?

_____

2 How many more titles did Fleming win than Yamaguchi?

_____

3 How many titles did Hamill and Heiss win together?

_____

4 How many titles did all five skaters win together?

_____

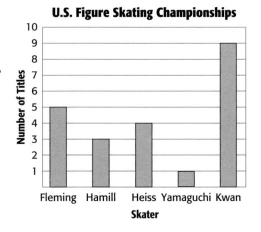

U.S. Figure Skating Championships

▶ Definition Review

A **line graph** is a graph used to show how a set of data changes over a period of time.

Circle yes if the data is best represented by a line graph.

5 The enrollment of a school every year from 2000 to 2008.   yes   no

6 The number of each type of animal on a farm.   yes   no

7 The outside temperature every hour from midnight to noon.   yes   no

▶ Application

Follow the directions for the activity.

- Work in pairs.
- Determine something you can keep track of in the classroom every minute for 10 minutes, such as the number of students who walk past the classroom door, or the number of cars that drive by.
- After recording the data, work with your partner to make a line graph of the data.
- Share your line graph with the rest of the class. Discuss why you chose the interval, scale, and title that you did. Discuss the general trend of the graph, if there is one.

Math Triumphs

Lesson 7-6

Skills Practice

Use the line graph "Jennifer's Savings" to compare data.

1 About how many dollars did Jennifer save in January?

_____

2 In which month did Jennifer save the most?

_____

3 What is the interval of the scale?

_____

4 For the months shown, in which month did Jennifer save the least?

_____

Jennifer's Savings

Use the double-line graph "Ice Cream Sales" to compare data.

5 In which month were more cones sold than shakes?

_____

6 In which month is there the greatest difference between the number of cones and number of shakes sold?

_____

7 In which month were the fewest number of shakes sold?

_____

8 Which month had the fewest number of sales combined?

_____

9 What is the trend of shakes sold from May through July?

_____

10 Describe the general trend of the graphs.

_____

_____

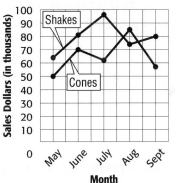

Ice Cream Sales

Chapter 7

Lesson 7-6

Problem-Solving Practice

Use the line graph "Minimum Wage" to compare data.

1   MINIMUM WAGE   For history class, Tamika created a line graph comparing the minimum wages throughout the years. Compare the minimum wage between 1970 and 1990.

_____

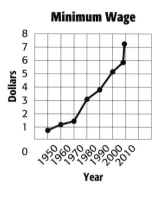

Use the line graph "Students in Sports" to compare data.

2   SPORTS   When was the only time the percent of students in sports decreased from one year to the next?

_____

3   REFLECT   What other interval could be used for the graph? Why might you prefer this interval?

_____

_____

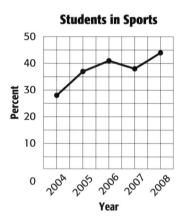

Use the double-line graph "CD Rates" to compare data.

4   RATES   A banker wants to compare the interest rates of two types of CDs (certificates of deposit) in past years. Compare the rates for a 6-month CD and a 24-month CD in 2005.

_____

5   YEARS   If the trend continues, what would you expect the data to show for 2009?

_____

_____

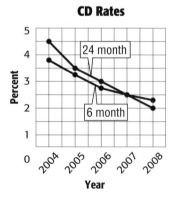

Math Triumphs

Lesson 7-6 Homework Practice

Use the line graph "Time to Finish Race" to compare data.

1. About how much faster was the time in 2008 than in 2002?

   _____

Time to Finish Race

2. In what year was the winning time the fastest?

   _____

3. Describe the trend of the graph. Do the times increase, decrease, or show no change?

   _____

4. If this trend continues, predict the time in 2010.

   _____

Use the double-line graph "Members of Spanish Club" to compare data.

5. How many more girls than boys were in Spanish Club in 2002?

   _____

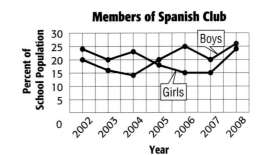

Members of Spanish Club

6. What percent of girls were in Spanish Club in 2004?

   _____

7. What percent of boys were in Spanish Club in 2007?

   _____

8. In what years was there a higher percentage of girls in Spanish Club?

   _____

9. What is the scale and what does it represent?

   _____

   _____

10. In which years are the percents of boys and girls the closest to each other?

   _____

Math Triumphs

Lesson 7-6 A157

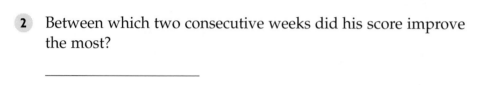

Lesson 7-7

Vocabulary and English Language Development

▶ Activate Prior Knowledge

Use the line graph "Video Game Scores" to compare data.

Video Game Scores

1   Describe how Mario's score changed from week 1 to week 5.

_____

2   Between which two consecutive weeks did his score improve the most?

_____

3   What is the trend of the data?

_____

▶ Definition Review

Fill in the blanks.

4   The axis on which the categories or values are shown is the

_____.

5   The difference between successive values on a

_____ is called the _____.

6   A _____ is used to show how a set of data changes over a period of time.

▶ Application

Follow the directions for the activity.

• Choose a company listed on the N.Y. Stock Exchange in the newspaper.
• Record the price of your stock every day for a week.
• Draw and label a line graph with this data.
• Discuss the graph you drew with your classmates.
• Find the change in price of your stock from the beginning of the week to the end.
• Find whose stock increased in value the most during the week and whose stock lost the most.
• Find whose stock had a noticeable trend (increasing or decreasing), whose has little to no change, and whose had both ups and downs during the week.

Math Triumphs

Lesson 7-7

Skills Practice

Use the data in the table to plan a line graph.

1 What is a good title for the graph?

   _____

2 What are the two main categories?

   _____

3 What interval could be used for the scale?

   _____

Digital Camera Ownership	
Year	Percent of Students
2005	7
2006	16
2007	21
2008	27
2009	32

4 Describe the trend of the data. Does the percent of students increase, decrease, or stay the same over time?

   _____

5 Use the data in the table to create a line graph.

Car Wash Fundraiser	
Time	Money Collected
8 A.M.	$150
10 A.M.	$70
12 P.M.	$230
2 P.M.	$120

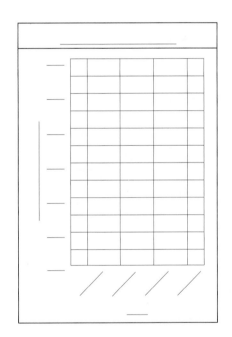

6 Use the data in the table to create a double-line graph.

Work Schedule		
Month	Hours Worked	
	Rob	Irena
March	28	17
April	26	16
May	23	12
June	22	10

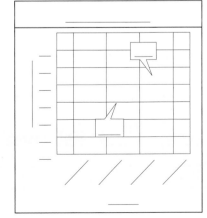

Math Triumphs

Problem-Solving Practice

Solve.

1 **SALES** The manager of a book store wants to compare the number of pens and pencils sold each day of the first week of school. Use the data in the table to create a double-line graph.

Bookstore Sales		
Day	Pens	Pencils
Monday	$240	$620
Tuesday	$190	$560
Wednesday	$120	$470
Thursday	$310	$320
Friday	$460	$650

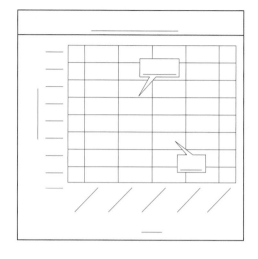

2 **TEST SCORES** A teacher wants to compare pre- and post-test scores to see how the new study program is working. Use the data in the table to create a double-line graph.

Average Test Scores		
Year	Pretest	Posttest
2005	32%	56%
2006	34%	58%
2007	39%	60%
2008	41%	64%
2009	43%	67%

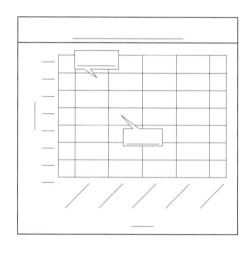

3 **PREDICTIONS** For the graph in Exercise 2, predict the average pretest and posttest scores in 2010.

4 **CUSTOMERS** A cafeteria manager wants to see how the dessert sales change throughout the week. Use the data in the table to create a line graph.

Dessert Sales						
Day	Mon	Tues	Wed	Thurs	Fri	Sat
Number	$52	$57	$46	$75	$98	$110

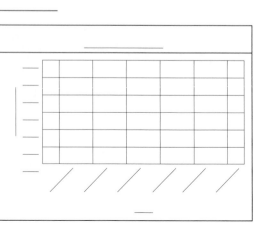

Copyright © Glencoe/McGraw-Hill, a division of The McGraw-Hill Companies, Inc.

Math Triumphs

Lesson 7-7 Homework Practice

Use the data in the table to plan a line graph.

1   What is a good title for the graph?

_____

2   What are the two main categories?

_____

3   What interval could be used for the scale?

_____

Amount Spent on Groceries	
Week	Amount
1	$68
2	$86
3	$135
4	$74
5	$91
6	$83

Use the data in the table to create a line or double-line graph.

4   A scientist records the amount of rain that fell in a city each day.

Amount of Rain	
Day of Week	Inches
Monday	0.25
Tuesday	0.10
Wednesday	0.00
Thursday	1.30
Friday	0.75

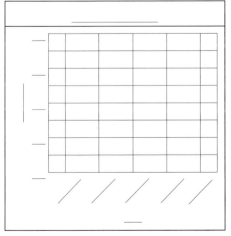

5   Ben and Betty's mother would like her children to keep track of how much money they save each month.

Amount Saved		
Month	Ben	Betty
January	$10	$15
February	$12	$22
March	$15	$13
April	$19	$11

Chapter 7

Chapter 8 Foldables Study Organizer

Dinah Zike's Foldables

Make this Foldable to help you organize information about percents and circle graphs.

1 Begin with one sheet of 11″ × 17″ paper. Fold a 2″ tab along the long side of the paper.

2 Unfold the paper and fold in thirds widthwise.

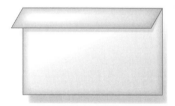

3 Draw lines along the folds and label the head of each column as shown. Label the front of the folded table with the chapter title.

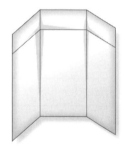

TAKING NOTES

As you read through the chapter, use your Foldable to write about percents and circle graphs.

USING YOUR FOLDABLE

As you study, check your understanding by designing additional circle graphs. Each graph should represent different percentages.

USING YOUR FOLDABLE

Work with a partner. One student should give a set of data. The other student should write an example of the data in a circle graph. Use your Foldable as reference to help create the circle graph.

Math Triumphs

Chapter 8

Games and Puzzles
Compare to Win

DIRECTIONS

- Choose one player to be the dealer.

- The dealer collects the cards, shuffles them, and then deals them one at a time to each of the players until all of the cards have been dealt.

- Starting at the left of the dealer, each player places one card face up on the table.

- The player with the card showing the fraction, decimal, or percent with the greatest value wins and keeps all of the cards.

- If two cards have the same greatest value, then those players place another card on the table until there is a winner.

- The game continues until one player has no cards left. The player with the most cards wins.

- Another way to play: The first person to get rid of all of their cards is the winner.

What You Need
- Compare to Win Cards

Number of Players
2 or 3

333%

2.05

0.75

$\dfrac{2}{5}$

80%

$\dfrac{1}{4}$

125%

Chapter 8

$\dfrac{2}{9}$	$\dfrac{1}{4}$	$\dfrac{5}{6}$
$\dfrac{8}{3}$	$\dfrac{4}{3}$	$\dfrac{13}{5}$
$\dfrac{2}{5}$	20%	80%
125%	333%	15%
7%	62.5%	0.625
0.75	1.3	2.05
2.5	3.14	4

Lesson 8-1

Vocabulary and English Language Development

▶ Activate Prior Knowledge

Complete each sentence.

The word "percent" is made from two parts: "per-" which means "out of" or "for every," and "-cent," which means "hundred." What other words do you know that uses "cent" to mean "hundred"?

1 There are 100 years in a _____.

2 There are 100 _____ in one dollar.

3 There are 100 _____ in one meter.

▶ Definition Review

Use the following words to complete each sentence.

   equivalent fractions   ratio   percent

4 A(n) _____ is a ratio that compares a number to 100.

5 A comparison of two numbers by division is a _____.

6 Fractions that name the same number are _____.

▶ Application

Complete each web.

7

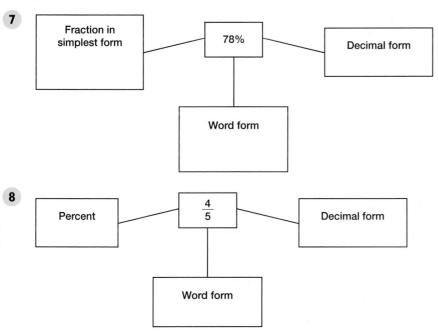

8

Math Triumphs

Lesson 8-1 Skills Practice

Identify each percent that is modeled.

1 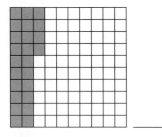 _____

2 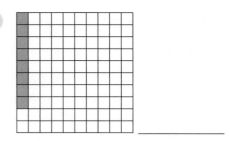 _____

3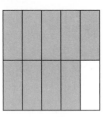

4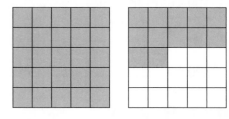

fraction: _____

fraction with a denominator of 100:

$$\frac{\cdot}{\cdot} = \frac{}{100}$$

decimal: _____

percent: _____

fraction: _____

fraction with a denominator of 100:

$$\frac{\cdot}{\cdot} = \frac{}{100}$$

decimal: _____

percent: _____

Find the missing value.

5 What is 25% of 36?

_____ • _____ = _____

6 What is 190% of 30?

_____ • _____ = _____

7 What is 30% of 84?

_____ • _____ = _____

8 What is 42% of 42?

_____ • _____ = _____

Solve.

9 **MOVIES** Mike watched 40% of the DVDs on his bookshelf. If there were 15 DVDs on the shelf, how many did Mike watch? _____

10 **ENTERTAINMENT** Fifteen percent of the people who entered a multi-media attraction at an amusement park yesterday chose to sit in the stationary seating section. If 4,420 people entered the attraction, how many sat in the stationary seating? _____

Lesson 8-1

Problem-Solving Practice

Solve.

1 **BASKETBALL** At practice, Ben made 22 out of 25 free throws. Kirk made 18 out of 20 free throws. Who made the greater percent?

_____

2 **SAVINGS** Jodi saves 20% of the money she earns. Serena saves 6% of the money she earns. If Jodi made $50 and Serena made $100, how much did each of them save?

_____

3 **JUGGLING** A juggler has two sets of juggling balls. The number of yellow balls and green balls in each set is shown. In which set is the greater percentage of yellow balls?

_____

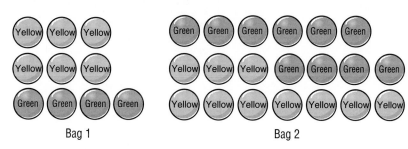

Bag 1   Bag 2

4 **SPORTS** The team has won 52 out of 80 games so far this season. Earlier in the season, they had won 42 out of 60 games. Has the team been doing better or worse? Explain.

_____

5 **SHOPPING** Which store is offering the greater percent discount on their shirts?

_____

Store A	Store B
Shirts Original price: $10.00 Buy 1, save $2	Shirts Original price: $12.00 Buy 1, save $3

6 **PATTERNS** Which pattern has the greater percentage of dark squares?

_____

Pattern A   Pattern B

7 **BOOKS** A school librarian asked all 300 students to name their favorite type of book. The responses are shown in the table. Find the number of students that named each type.

Type of book	Mystery	Fiction	Biography	Nonfiction
Percent of students	15%	44%	7%	34%

_____

Chapter 8

Homework Practice

Identify each percent that is modeled.

1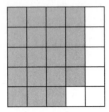

fraction: _____

fraction with denominator of 100:

$$\frac{ \cdot }{ \cdot } = \frac{}{100}$$

decimal: _____

percent: _____

2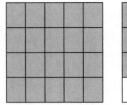

fraction: _____

fraction with denominator of 100:

$$\frac{ \cdot }{ \cdot } = \frac{}{100}$$

decimal: _____

percent: _____

Find the missing value.

3 What is 68% of 300?

_____ • _____ = _____

4 What is 3% of 50?

_____ • _____ = _____

5 What is 75% of 48?

_____ • _____ = _____

6 What is 15% of 60?

_____ • _____ = _____

Solve.

7 **PARKING** In section A of the mall parking lot, there are a total of 100 vehicles, of which 54 are minivans. In section B, there are 150 vehicles, of which 90 are minivans. Which section has the greater percentage of minivans?

_____

8 **SAVINGS** Marcos and Rosita each deposit 12% of their earnings into a savings account. One week, Marcos earned $80 and Rosita earned $115. Who deposited the greater amount into their savings account? Explain.

_____

Write the vocabulary word that completes each sentence.

9 A _____ is a comparison of two numbers by division.

10 A _____ is a ratio that compares a number to 100.

Math Triumphs

Lesson 8-2

Vocabulary and English Language Development

▶ Activate Prior Knowledge

1　A circle is a figure made of _____ degrees.

2　A unit fraction has a numerator of _____.

3　What unit fraction is equivalent to 20%?

_____

4　What unit fraction is equivalent to 5%?

_____

▶ Definition Review

Use the following words to complete each sentence.

degree　　percent　　sector　　simplest form　　denominator

5　The bottom number in a fraction is the _____; it represents the number of parts in the whole.

6　A(n) _____ is a pie-shaped section in a circle graph.

7　The most common unit of measure for an angle is a(n) _____.

8　When the greatest common factor (GCF) of the numerator and denominator of a fraction is 1, the fraction is in _____.

9　A ratio that compares a number to 100 is a(n) _____.

▶ Application

Follow these steps to find the degrees needed to show a 15% sector in a circle graph.

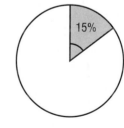

• Write 15% as a fraction in simplest form. _____

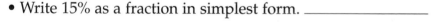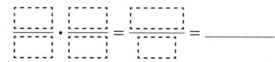

• Multiply 360° by the fraction.

• A 15% sector of a circle graph will have a measure of _____ degrees.

Math Triumphs

Chapter 8

Lesson 8-2

Skills Practice

1 Find the degrees needed to show a 40% sector in a circle graph.

$$40\% = \frac{\boxed{}}{100} \div \frac{\boxed{}}{\boxed{}} = \frac{\boxed{}}{\boxed{}}$$

$$\frac{\boxed{}}{1} \cdot \frac{\boxed{}}{\boxed{}} = \frac{\boxed{}}{\boxed{}} = \underline{}$$

2 Use combinations to find the degrees needed to show a 45% sector in a circle graph.

_____ + _____ + _____ = _____

_____ + _____ + _____ = _____

Name the fraction and the percent of the circle that is shaded.

3

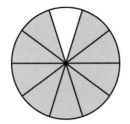

fraction: _____

$$\frac{\boxed{}}{\boxed{}} \cdot \frac{\boxed{}}{\boxed{}} = \frac{\boxed{}}{100} = \underline{}$$

4

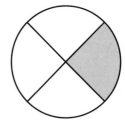

fraction: _____

$$\frac{\boxed{}}{\boxed{}} \cdot \frac{\boxed{}}{\boxed{}} = \frac{\boxed{}}{100} = \underline{}$$

Find the degrees needed to show each sector in a circle graph.

5

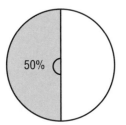

$$50\% = \frac{\boxed{}}{100} \div \frac{\boxed{}}{\boxed{}} = \frac{\boxed{}}{\boxed{}}$$

$$\frac{\boxed{}}{1} \cdot \frac{\boxed{}}{\boxed{}} = \frac{\boxed{}}{\boxed{}} = \underline{}$$

6

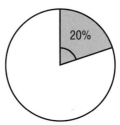

$$20\% = \frac{\boxed{}}{100} \div \frac{\boxed{}}{\boxed{}} = \frac{\boxed{}}{\boxed{}}$$

$$\frac{\boxed{}}{1} \cdot \frac{\boxed{}}{\boxed{}} = \frac{\boxed{}}{\boxed{}} = \underline{}$$

7 If you know that 5% of a circle has a degree measure of 18°, how can you use this information to find the degree measure of a 35% sector?

_____

_____

_____

Lesson 8-2

Problem-Solving Practice

Solve.

1 **LEISURE TIME** Cassy kept track of how she spent her leisure time. She made the circle graph shown at the right. How many degrees are in each sector of the graph used to show her data?

_____

_____

Leisure Time Activities

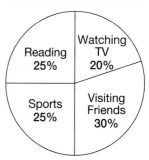

Leisure Time Activities

2 **FUNDRAISER** Hometown Middle School recently completed a fundraiser in which each class sold candles. Of the total number of candles sold, 20% were sold by the 6th graders, 45% by the 7th graders, and 35% by the 8th graders. Mrs. Apicella is making a circle graph of the sales. What is the degree measure of each sector?

_____

3 **LOANS** A credit union offers auto loans, home-equity loans, and personal loans. Of the total loans last month, 40% were for auto loans, 10% were home-equity loans, and 50% were personal loans. The loan officer is making a circle graph to show this data. What is the degree measure of each sector?

_____

4 **MUSIC** The eighth graders at a middle school were asked about their favorite type of music. The circle graph at the right shows the results of the survey. What is the degree measure of each sector?

_____

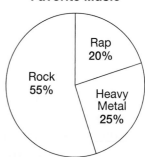

Favorite Music

5 **ART** Marsha wants to do an art project using a circle. She wants to use a circle with 10 sectors of equal size. What percent of the circle will each sector represent? What is the degree measure of each sector?

_____

Chapter 8

Lesson 8-2 Homework Practice

Use combinations to find the degrees needed to show each sector in a circle graph.

1 60% _____ + _____ = 60%

_____ + _____ = _____

2 15% _____ + _____ = 15%

_____ + _____ = _____

Name the fraction and the percent of the circle that is shaded.

3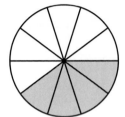

fraction: _____

$\dfrac{\boxed{}}{\boxed{}} \cdot \dfrac{\boxed{}}{\boxed{}} = \dfrac{\boxed{}}{100} =$ _____

4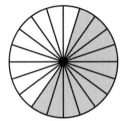

fraction: _____

$\dfrac{\boxed{}}{\boxed{}} \cdot \dfrac{\boxed{}}{\boxed{}} = \dfrac{\boxed{}}{100} =$ _____

Find the degrees needed to show each sector in a circle graph.

5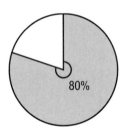

$80\% = \dfrac{\boxed{}}{100} \div \dfrac{\boxed{}}{\boxed{}} = \dfrac{\boxed{}}{\boxed{}}$

$\dfrac{\boxed{}}{1} \cdot \dfrac{\boxed{}}{\boxed{}} = \dfrac{\boxed{}}{\boxed{}} =$ _____

6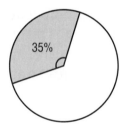

$35\% = \dfrac{\boxed{}}{100} \div \dfrac{\boxed{}}{\boxed{}} = \dfrac{\boxed{}}{\boxed{}}$

$\dfrac{\boxed{}}{1} \cdot \dfrac{\boxed{}}{\boxed{}} = \dfrac{\boxed{}}{\boxed{}} =$ _____

7 **PETS** Randy surveyed the students in his homeroom about the type of pet they have. Of his classmates, 20% have a dog, 30% have a cat, 10% have a fish, and 40% do not have a pet. He wants to make a circle graph to show this data. What is the degree measure of each sector?

_____

Write the vocabulary word that completes each sentence.

8 A pie-shaped section in a circle is called a(n) _____.

9 The bottom number in a fraction is called the _____.

Lesson 8-3

Vocabulary and English Language Development

▶ Activate Prior Knowledge

There are 50 cars in the parking lot of a department store. Of these cars, 15 are black, 20 are white, 10 are blue, and 5 are red.

1 What fraction of the cars are black?

_____

2 What fraction of the cars are white?

_____

3 What percent of the cars are red?

_____

4 What percent of the cars are blue?

_____

▶ Definition Review

Use the following words to complete each sentence.

data   circle graph   degree   percent   sector

5 The most common unit of measure for angles is the _____.

6 A pie-shaped section of a circle graph is called a _____.

7 Information, often numerical, which is gathered for statistical purposes, is called _____.

8 A graph used to compare parts of a whole is called a _____.

9 A ratio that compares a number to 100 is a _____.

▶ Application

The circle graph shows the results of a survey about 8th graders' favorite baseball teams. Use the circle graph to answer the questions below.

Favorite Baseball Team

Red Sox 25%

Yankees 50%

Cubs 25%

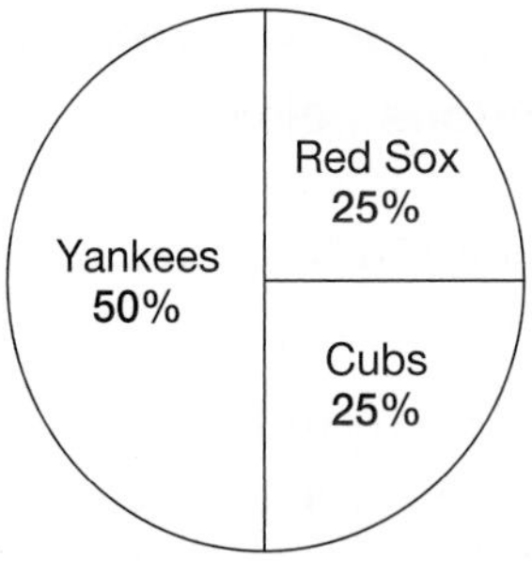

• What is the title of the graph?

_____

• What fraction of students named the Cubs? _____

• What fraction of students named the Yankees? _____

Chapter 8

Lesson 8-3 Skills Practice

1 **PET STORE**   There are 40 kittens at a pet store. The circle graph shows the percentage of each color. Which two colors together are the same percentage as that of the black kittens?

_____

Kitten Colors

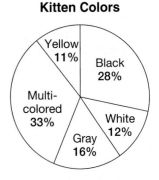

2 **BIRDHOUSES**   Pat has 50 birdhouses in her backyard. The percentage of each size of birdhouse is shown in the circle graph. What birdhouse size does Pat have twice as many of as compared to the number of medium birdhouses?

_____

Birdhouse Sizes

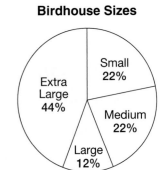

3 **TRAVEL**   Mr. Leonard asked the students in his geography class about their spring break plans. Twenty of the students were going on vacation. Their destinations are shown in the circle graph. How many are going to California?

_____

Spring Break Destination

Use the circle graph titled "Spring Break Destination" to answer the questions below.

4 How many more students are going to Florida than to Texas?   _____

5 The number of students going to which two states combined is the same as the number of students going to Texas?   _____

6 How many of the students going on vacation are not going to California or Hawaii?   _____

Math Triumphs

Lesson 8-3

Problem-Solving Practice

Solve.

1 **MASCOT** The 300 students at Washington Junior High School voted on a school mascot. The results of the voting are shown in the circle graph. Complete the table below. How many students voted for a jackrabbit?

Favorite Mascot

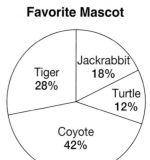

Mascot	Jackrabbit	Turtle	Coyote	Tiger
Percent				
Votes				

_____

2 **PARTY GUESTS** Becky was having a birthday party for her son. She invited 60 people. The age groups of the people who were invited are shown in the circle graph. How many teenagers were invited to the party?

Birthday Party Guests

_____

HOUSES There are 50 houses in a new housing development. The circle graph compares the three types of houses built there. Use the circle graph to answer the questions below.

Housing Development

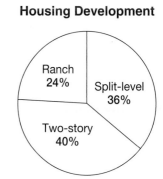

3 How many houses are ranch houses?

_____

4 How many houses are ranch or split-level houses?

_____

5 How many houses are not split-level houses?

_____

Chapter 8

Lesson 8-3

Homework Practice

MOVIES Lee sorted his 200 movies into categories. The circle graph shows the percentage of each type. Use the circle graph to answer the questions below.

Lee's Movies

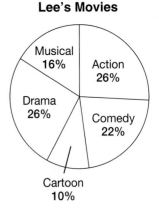

1 What is the title of the graph?

_____

2 Which two types of movies does he have the same number?

_____

3 Which two types of movies total the same as the percentage of action movies?

_____

4 How many cartoon movies does Lee have?

_____

5 How many more drama movies than comedy movies does Lee have?

_____

6 How many movies are not action movies?

_____

COIN COLLECTION Reba's coin collection includes 200 coins of different types. The circle graph shows the percentage of each type of coin. Use the circle graph to answer the questions below.

Reba's Coins

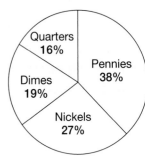

7 How many nickels has Reba collected?

_____

8 How many coins are not pennies?

_____

Write the vocabulary word(s) that complete each sentence.

9 A graph used to compare parts of a whole is called a _____.

10 Information, often numerical, which is gathered for statistical purposes, is called _____.

Math Triumphs

Lesson 8-4

Vocabulary and English Language Development

▶ Activate Prior Knowledge

SCOUTING A scout troop sold 300 geraniums as a fund-raiser for their annual jamboree trip. The circle graph shows the percentages of each color.

Geraniums

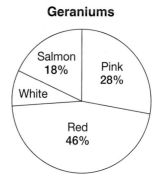

1 What is the title of the graph?

_____

2 When Samuel drew the graph, he forgot to include the percentage for white. What percent of the geraniums sold were white?

_____

3 How many red geraniums were sold?

_____

4 How many of the geraniums were not salmon?

_____

▶ Definition Review

Use the following words to complete each sentence.

    center   circle graph   percent   sector

5 A _____ is a ratio that compares a number to 100.

6 A pie-shaped section of a circle graph is called a _____.

7 The point from which all points on a circle are the same distance is called its _____.

8 A _____ is a graph used to compare parts of a whole.

▶ Application

Use the figure to answer the questions below.

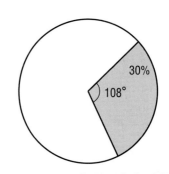

• What is the percentage of the shaded sector? _____

• How many degrees are in the shaded sector? _____

Chapter 8

Lesson 8-4 Skills Practice

1 Complete the table to show the decimal value, the percent, and the degree measure for each class president candidate.

Candidate	Number of Votes	Decimal Value	Percent	Degree Measure
Lucy	50			
Emil	70			
Irma	40			
Dale	40			
Total	200	1.00	100%	360°

2 **COLLECTIONS** Complete the table to show the decimal value, the percent, and the degree measure for each stuffed animal in Tami's collection.

Animal	Number	Decimal Value	Percent	Degree Measure
Bear	10			
Dog	20			
Rabbit	5			
Tiger	5			
Cat	10			
Total	50	1.00	100%	360°

3 Use the table in Exercise 1 to create a circle graph.

Election Results

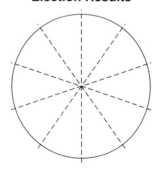

4 Use the table in Exercise 2 to create a circle graph.

Stuffed Animal Collection

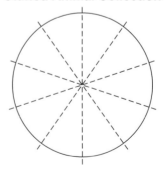

Math Triumphs

Lesson 8-4 Problem-Solving Practice

1 **BASKETBALL** The table below shows the points scored during a recent basketball game. Complete the table to show the decimal value, the percent, and the degree measure for each player.

Player	Points Scored	Decimal Value	Percent	Degree Measure
Mark	24			
Cuonzo	4			
Alfonze	8			
Robbie	16			
Chris	28			
Total	**80**	**1.00**	**100%**	**360°**

2 **SHOES** A shoe salesman recorded his sales during last month. Complete the table to show the decimal value, the percent, and the degree measure for each shoe type.

Shoe Type	Number	Decimal Value	Percent	Degree Measure
Cross-Training	150			
Running	200			
Walking	50			
Baseball	100			
Total	**500**	**1.00**	**100%**	**360°**

3 Use the table in Exercise 1 to create a circle graph.

Basketball Scoring

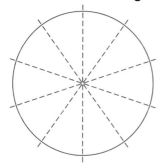

4 Use the table in Exercise 2 to create a circle graph.

Shoe Sales

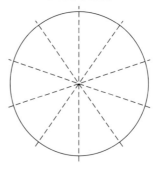

Chapter 8

Lesson 8-4 **Homework Practice**

1 Complete the table to show the decimal value, the percent, and the degree measure for each type of house for sale.

Number of Bedrooms	Number	Decimal Value	Percent	Degree Measure
Two	16			
Three	48			
Four	12			
Five	4			
Total	**80**	**1.00**	**100%**	**360°**

2 Complete the table to show the decimal value, the percent, and the degree measure for each type of transaction at a clothing store yesterday.

Transaction	Number	Decimal Value	Percent	Degree Measure
Cash	75			
Check	50			
Bank Credit Card	100			
Store Credit Card	150			
Debit Card	125			
Total	**500**	**1.00**	**100%**	**360°**

3 Use the table in Exercise 1 to create a circle graph.

Number of Bedrooms

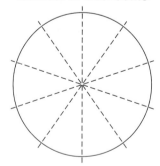

4 Use the table in Exercise 2 to create a circle graph.

Transaction Types

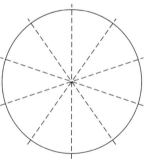

Math Triumphs

Chapter 9

Foldables Study Organizer

FOLDABLES®
Study Organizer

Dinah Zike's Foldables

Make this Foldable to help you organize your notes about two-variable data.

1. Begin with three sheets of $8\frac{1}{2}'' \times 11''$ paper. Fold a sheet in half lengthwise. Then cut a 1" tab along the left edge through one thickness.

2. Glue the 1" tab down. Write the title of the lesson on the front tab.

Two-Variable Data

3. Repeat Steps 1–2 and write examples of each topic on the remaining sheets of paper. Staple all of the sheets together to form a booklet.

Two-Variable Data

TAKING NOTES
As you read through the chapter, use your Foldable to write several examples of two-variable data, scatter plots, and lines of best fit.

USING YOUR FOLDABLE
As you study, use the information in your Foldable to identify and describe the relationship between two variables on a graph.

USING YOUR FOLDABLE
Trade Foldables with a partner. Compare each other's notes. Write your partner's notes and examples in your own Foldable.

Chapter 9

Chapter 9

Games and Puzzles
Find a Solution

What You Need
- Find a Solution Cards

Number of Players
2

DIRECTIONS

- Choose one player to be the dealer.

- The dealer collects the cards, shuffles them, and then deals five cards to each player.

- The dealer then places the remaining cards in a pile face down between them.

- The other player plays a pair of cards face-up where one card is an equation and the other is a solution to that equation. If that player does not have a pair of matching cards, he or she draws a card from the pile.

- Players take turns playing pairs of cards until one player has no cards left or the end of the pile is reached.

- The player with the greater number of pairs of cards face-up is the winner.

$y = 2x$

$y = x - 5$

$(4, 8)$

$(2, 7)$

$(12, 7)$

$y = 3x + 1$

Math Triumphs

Chapter 9

Find a Solution Cards

$y = 2x$	$y = x - 2$	**(1, 3)**
$y = x - 5$	$y = 10x$	**(4, 5)**
$y = 3x + 1$	$y = 4x - 3$	**(1, 6)**
$y = -x + 4$	$y = x + 5$	**(0, 6)**
$y = 2x - 3$	**(4, 8)**	**(5, 3)**
$y = 6x$	**(2, 7)**	**(7, 5)**
$y = 4x + 6$	**(12, 7)**	**(1, 10)**
$y = 8 - x$	**(3, 18)**	**(0, 0)**

Chapter 9

Lesson 9-1 Vocabulary and English Language Development

▶ Activate Prior Knowledge

Solve each equation.

1 $3x = 12$

_____

2 $x + 5 = 17$

_____

3 $x - 4 = 2$

_____

4 $\frac{x}{2} = 8$

_____

▶ Definition Review

Write the letter that matches the definition of each word.

5 ordered pair _____

A The value of a variable that makes an equation true

6 solution _____

B The first number of an ordered pair

7 x-coordinate _____

C A pair of numbers used to locate a point in the coordinate system

8 y-coordinate _____

D The second number of an ordered pair

▶ Application

9 Complete the table for the equation $y = 3x$.

x	3x	y	(x, y)
0	3(0) = 0	0	(0, 0)
1	3(_____) = _____		
2	3(_____) = _____		
5			

10 List four solutions of the equation $y = 3x$.

_____

Lesson
9-1 **Skills Practice**

Determine which ordered pair below is a solution of each equation.

(2, 12)   (10, 2)   (3, 9)   (8, 16)

1 $y = x + 6$ _____

2 $y = x - 8$ _____

Complete the table for the each equation. Then find three solutions for each equation.

3 $y = 2x + 6$

x	2x + 6	y	(x, y)
1	2(1) + 6		
2	2(____) + 6		
3	2(____) + 6		

_____

4 $y = 3x - 1$

x	3x − 1	y	(x, y)
−1	3(−1) − 1		
0	3(____) − 1		
1	3(____) − 1		

_____

5 $y = -4x + 2$

x	−4x + 2	y	(x, y)
0	−4(____) + 2		
2	−4(____) + 2		
4	−4(____) + 2		

_____

Find three solutions for each equation.

6 $y = x - 7$ _____

7 $y = -3x$ _____

8 $y = 5x + 4$ _____

Chapter 9

Lesson 9-1

Problem-Solving Practice

Solve.

1. **COOKIES** The equation $y = 50 - x$ represents the number of cookies left y after x cookies have been eaten. Complete the table for the equation. Find three solutions of the equation. Describe what the solutions mean.

x	50 − x	y	(x, y)
4	50 − ____		
12			
30			

_____

_____

_____

2. **TEXT MESSAGES** The equation $y = 0.15x$ represents the total cost y of sending x text messages. Find three solutions of the equation when $x = 6$, 10, and 22. Describe what the solutions mean.

_____

_____

_____

3. **READING** The equation $y = 50x + 20$ represents the number of pages Lou has read in his book y after x hours. Find three solutions of the equation when $x = 2$, 5, and 8. Describe what the solutions mean.

_____

_____

_____

4. **IRONING** The equation $y = 28 - 6x$ represents the number of shirts Ava has left to iron y after x hours. Find three solutions of the equation when $x = 1$, 2, and 3. Describe what the solutions mean.

_____

_____

Math Triumphs

Lesson 9-1 Homework Practice

Determine which ordered pair below is a solution of each equation.

(36, 4)   (2, 14)   (1, 10)   (0, 4)   (5, 16)   (2, 9)   (5, 2)   (6, 54)

1 $y = 9x$ _____

2 $y = x + 12$ _____

3 $y = 2x - 8$ _____

4 $y = 3x + 1$ _____

Complete the table for each equation. Then find three solutions for each equation.

5 $y = 4x - 1$

x	4x − 1	y
1	4(1) − 1	
3	4(____) − 1	
6	4(____) − 1	

_____

6 $y = 8x$

x	8x	y
1	8(____)	
2		
3		

_____

7 $y = -x + 10$

x	−x + 10	y
1		
2		
3		

_____

8 $y = 2x + 3$

x	2x + 3	y
0		
4		
7		

_____

Solve.

9 **PHOTOGRAPHS**   The equation $y = 12x$ represents the number of wallet-sized pictures y that can be printed on x sheets of photo paper. Find three solutions when $x = 2, 3,$ and 6. Explain what the solutions mean.

_____

_____

_____

Write the vocabulary word that completes the sentence.

10 The value of a variable that makes an equation true is called a _____.

Chapter 9

Lesson 9-2 Vocabulary and English Language Development

▶ Activate Prior Knowledge

Find three solutions of each equation.

1 $y = 2x - 4$

2 $y = 4x$

_____

_____

▶ Definition Review

Use the following words to complete each sentence.

coordinate grid   scatter plot   x-axis   y-axis

3 The _____ is the vertical line of the two perpendicular number lines in a coordinate grid.

4 The _____ is the horizontal line of the two perpendicular number lines in a coordinate grid.

5 A grid in which a horizontal number line and a vertical number line intersect at their zero points is called a _____.

6 A graph in which two sets of data are plotted as ordered pairs in the coordinate grid is called a _____.

▶ Application

• Graph and label these points on the coordinate grid.

   A (6, 2), B (3, 5), C (0, 4), D (1, 0)

• Give the coordinates of points E, F, G, and H.

_____

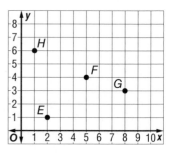

**Lesson
9-2**

Skills Practice

Explain whether each scatter plot shows a *positive*, *negative*, or *no* relationship.

1

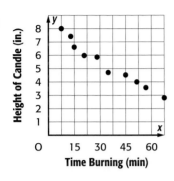

As the time increases, the height of

the candle _____.

Describe the relationship between the
time and the height of the candle.

_____

2

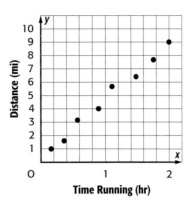

As the time increases, the distance

traveled _____.

Describe the relationship between the
time and the distance traveled.

_____

Solve.

3 **SNOWFALL** At a mountain resort in the Colorado Rockies,
it has been snowing for the past six days. The table below
shows the data. Create a scatter plot to find the relationship
between the data sets.

Day	1	2	3	4	5	6
Snowfall (in.)	2	3	2	4	3	5

Colorado Snow

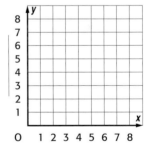

4 **SPELLING** Andrea learned her spelling words, but has not
continued to practice them. The table below shows the
number of words she can still spell correctly for certain days
after her test. Create a scatter plot to find the relationship
between the data sets.

Day	1	2	3	4	5
Number of Words Spelled Correctly	24	22	18	17	13

Andrea's Spelling List

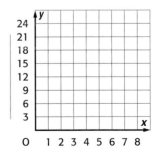

Chapter 9

Lesson 9-2 Problem-Solving Practice

Solve.

1 **MAKING COPIES** Explain whether the scatter plot shows a *positive*, *negative*, or *no* relationship.

_____

_____

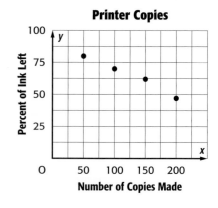

Printer Copies

2 **EARNINGS** Amanda recorded information about the earnings of several classmates for last week. The table below shows the data. Create a scatter plot to find the relationship between the data sets.

Hours Worked	2	2	3	4	4	5	5	6
Money Earned	$12	$14	$22	$24	$28	$30	$40	$42

Describe the relationship between the hours worked and the money earned.

_____

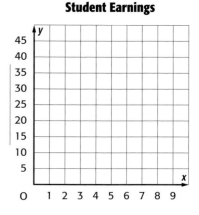

Student Earnings

3 **SWIMMING** The swim coach asked the swim team to track their calorie intake and minutes of exercise for the week. The table below shows the data. Create a scatter plot to find the relationship between the data sets.

Calories	1000	1200	1300	1400	1500	1600
Minutes of Exercise	60	45	45	60	30	60

Describe the relationship between the calorie intake and the minutes of exercise.

_____

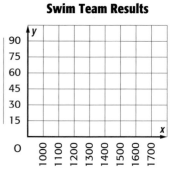

Swim Team Results

Math Triumphs

Lesson 9-2

Homework Practice

Solve.

I   TEMPERATURE   Mr. Ramirez recorded the temperature for July 17 at different elevations. The table below shows the data. Create a scatter plot to find the relationship between the data sets.

Data for July 17

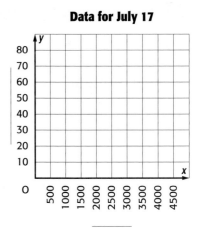

Temperature (°F)	500	1,000	1,500	2,000	2,500	3,000	3,500
Elevation (ft)	78	60	56	50	50	42	39

Describe the relationship between elevation and temperature.

_____

2   GASOLINE   Eric recorded his gas purchases over the last several months. The table below shows the data. Create a scatter plot to find the relationship between the data sets.

Eric's Gas Purchases

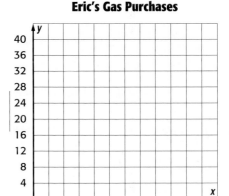

Gallons of Gasoline	2	3	4	5	5
Cost	$7	$11	$16	$17	$18

Gallons of Gasoline	6	7	7	7	9
Cost	$21	$23	$26	$27	$31

Describe the relationship between the gallons of gas purchased and the cost.

_____

Write the vocabulary word(s) that completes each sentence.

3   A(n) _____ is a graph in which two sets of data are plotted as ordered pairs in the coordinate plane.

4   A(n) _____ is a grid in which a horizontal number line and a vertical number line intersect at their zero points.

5   The horizontal line of the two perpendicular number lines in a coordinate grid is the _____.

Chapter 9

Lesson 9-3

Vocabulary and English Language Development

▶ Activate Prior Knowledge

The scatter plot at the right shows the number of minutes played and the number of points scored for several basketball players during last night's game.

Rockville Rockets

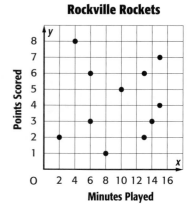

1 Is the relationship positive, negative, or is there no relationship?

_____

2 Explain how you know.

_____

_____

▶ Definition Review

Use the following words to complete each sentence.

          data   line of best fit   slope

3 The rate of change between any two points on a line is called the

_____.

4 Information, often numerical, which is gathered for statistical

purposes is called _____.

5 A line that is very close to most of the data points on a

scatter plot is called a _____.

▶ Application

Sketch a scatter plot showing each relationship.

6 positive

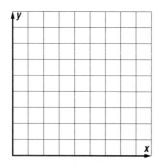

7 negative

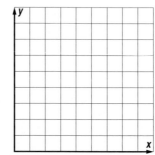

8 no relationship

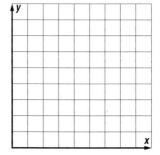

Math Triumphs

Lesson 9-3

Skills Practice

Draw a line of best fit. Then describe the slope of the line and the trend in the data.

1
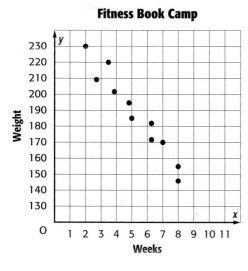
Fitness Book Camp

_____

2
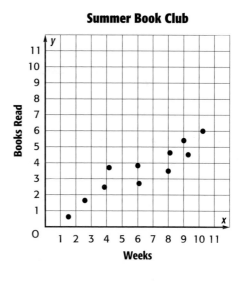
Summer Book Club

_____

Solve.

3 **PETS** The scatter plot at the right shows the weight and age of a pet rabbit. Draw a line of best fit. Then describe the slope of the line and the trend in the data.

_____

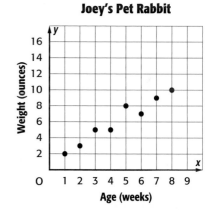
Joey's Pet Rabbit

4 Use the line of best fit for Exercise 3 to predict the weight of the rabbit when it is 10 weeks old.

_____

5 **CUSTOMER SERVICE** The scatter plot at the right shows the wait time to get your phone call answered by the appointment desk in a medical clinic at various times of the day. Draw a line of best fit.

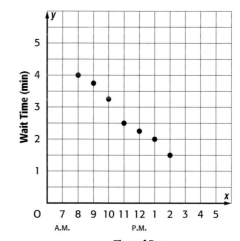

6 Use the line of best fit for Exercise 5 to predict the wait time at 4 P.M.

_____

Chapter 9

Problem-Solving Practice

Solve.

1. **INLINE SKATES** Reiko is using inline skates. The scatter plot shows the distance she has traveled since she started. Use the line of best fit shown to predict the total distance Reiko will have traveled after 3 hours.

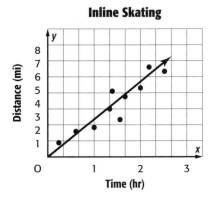

Inline Skating

_____

2. **GARDENING** Amber is designing a rectangular garden. The scatter plot shows the length and width that her garden could be. Use the line of best fit shown to predict the width when the length is 13 feet.

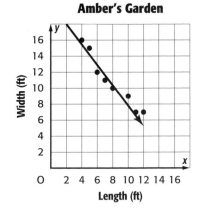

Amber's Garden

_____

3. **BANKING** The scatter plot shows the number of people who used an ATM machine at various times during the day. Explain whether you can draw a line of best fit for the data.

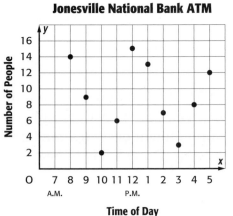

Jonesville National Bank ATM

_____

_____

_____

Lesson 9-3

Homework Practice

Draw a line of best fit. Then describe the slope of the line and the trend in the data.

1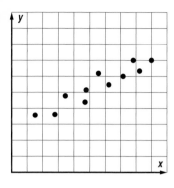

_____

2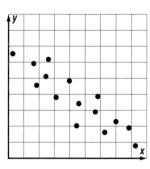

_____

Solve.

3 **CALLING PLANS** The scatter plot shows the cost of various cell phone calling plans. Draw a line of best fit. Then describe the slope of the line and the trend of the data.

_____

4 Use the line of best fit for Exercise 3 to predict the cost of a calling plan that includes 700 minutes.

_____

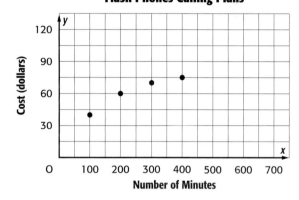

Flash Phones Calling Plans

5 **CAR SALES** The scatter plot shows the number of cars in a showroom for the first 10 days of the month. Use the line of best fit shown to predict how many cars will be in the showroom on the 14th day.

_____

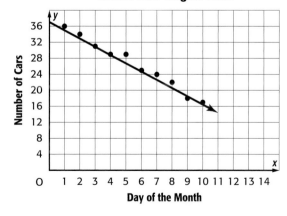

Carson Cars' August Sales

Write the vocabulary word that completes the sentence.

6 A line that is very close to most of the data points on a

scatter plot is called a _____ .

Chapter 9

Answer Key (Lesson 1-1)

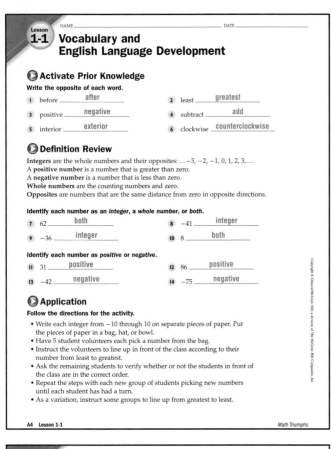

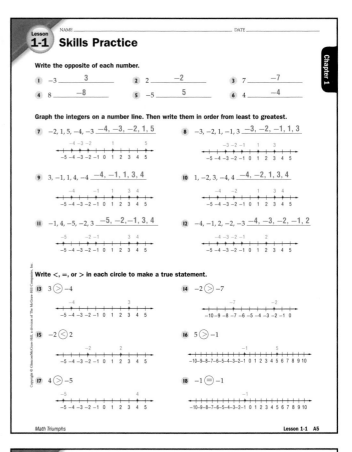

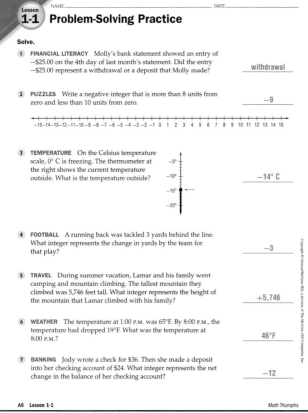

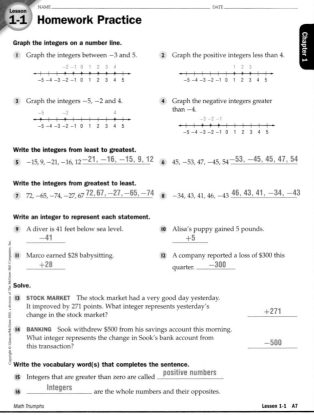

Answer Key (Lesson 1-2)

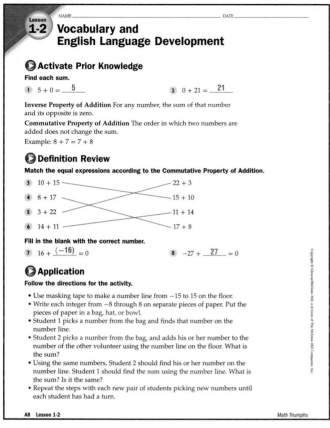

Vocabulary and English Language Development

▶ Activate Prior Knowledge

Find each sum.

1. $5 + 0 = $ __5__
2. $0 + 21 = $ __21__

Inverse Property of Addition For any number, the sum of that number and its opposite is zero.

Commutative Property of Addition The order in which two numbers are added does not change the sum.

Example: $8 + 7 = 7 + 8$

▶ Definition Review

Match the equal expressions according to the Commutative Property of Addition.

3. $10 + 15$ — $22 + 3$
4. $8 + 17$ — $15 + 10$
5. $3 + 22$ — $11 + 14$
6. $14 + 11$ — $17 + 8$

Fill in the blank with the correct number.

7. $16 + $ __(−16)__ $= 0$
8. $-27 + $ __27__ $= 0$

▶ Application

Follow the directions for the activity.

- Use masking tape to make a number line from −15 to 15 on the floor.
- Write each integer from −8 through 8 on separate pieces of paper. Put the pieces of paper in a bag, hat, or bowl.
- Student 1 picks a number from the bag and finds that number on the number line.
- Student 2 picks a number from the bag, and adds his or her number to the number of the other volunteer using the number line on the floor. What is the sum?
- Using the same numbers, Student 2 should find his or her number on the number line. Student 1 should find the sum using the number line. What is the sum? Is it the same?
- Repeat the steps with each new pair of students picking new numbers until each student has had a turn.

A8 Lesson 1-2   Math Triumphs

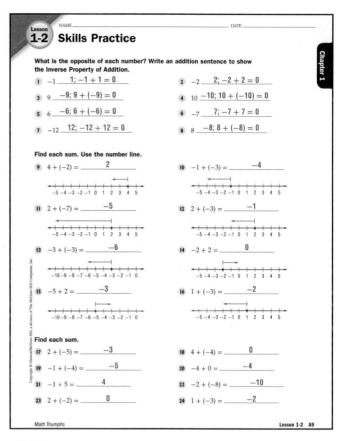

Skills Practice

What is the opposite of each number? Write an addition sentence to show the Inverse Property of Addition.

1. -1 __1; −1 + 1 = 0__
2. -2 __2; −2 + 2 = 0__
3. 9 __−9; 9 + (−9) = 0__
4. 10 __−10; 10 + (−10) = 0__
5. 6 __−6; 6 + (−6) = 0__
6. -7 __7; −7 + 7 = 0__
7. -12 __12; −12 + 12 = 0__
8. 8 __−8; 8 + (−8) = 0__

Find each sum. Use the number line.

9. $4 + (−2) = $ __2__
10. $-1 + (−3) = $ __−4__
11. $2 + (−7) = $ __−5__
12. $2 + (−3) = $ __−1__
13. $-3 + (−3) = $ __−6__
14. $-2 + 2 = $ __0__
15. $-5 + 2 = $ __−3__
16. $1 + (−3) = $ __−2__

Find each sum.

17. $2 + (−5) = $ __−3__
18. $4 + (−4) = $ __0__
19. $-1 + (−4) = $ __−5__
20. $-4 + 0 = $ __−4__
21. $-1 + 5 = $ __4__
22. $-2 + (−8) = $ __−10__
23. $2 + (−2) = $ __0__
24. $1 + (−3) = $ __−2__

Math Triumphs   Lesson 1-2   A9

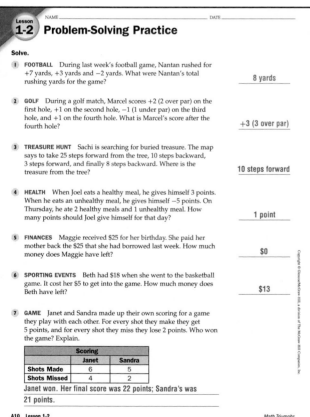

Problem-Solving Practice

Solve.

1. **FOOTBALL** During last week's football game, Nantan rushed for +7 yards, +3 yards and −2 yards. What were Nantan's total rushing yards for the game? __8 yards__

2. **GOLF** During a golf match, Marcel scores +2 (2 over par) on the first hole, +1 on the second hole, −1 (1 under par) on the third hole, and +1 on the fourth hole. What is Marcel's score after the fourth hole? __+3 (3 over par)__

3. **TREASURE HUNT** Sachi is searching for buried treasure. The map says to take 25 steps forward from the tree, 10 steps backward, 3 steps forward, and finally 8 steps backward. Where is the treasure from the tree? __10 steps forward__

4. **HEALTH** When Joel eats a healthy meal, he gives himself 3 points. When he eats an unhealthy meal, he gives himself −5 points. On Thursday, he ate 2 healthy meals and 1 unhealthy meal. How many points should Joel give himself for that day? __1 point__

5. **FINANCES** Maggie received $25 for her birthday. She paid her mother back the $25 that she had borrowed last week. How much money does Maggie have left? __$0__

6. **SPORTING EVENTS** Beth had $18 when she went to the basketball game. It cost her $5 to get into the game. How much money does Beth have left? __$13__

7. **GAME** Janet and Sandra made up their own scoring for a game they play with each other. For every shot they make they get 5 points, and for every shot they miss they lose 2 points. Who won the game? Explain.

Scoring	Janet	Sandra
Shots Made	6	5
Shots Missed	4	2

Janet won. Her final score was 22 points; Sandra's was 21 points.

A10   Lesson 1-2   Math Triumphs

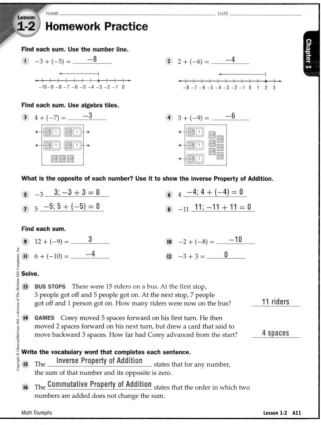

Homework Practice

Find each sum. Use the number line.

1. $-3 + (−5) = $ __−8__
2. $2 + (−6) = $ __−4__

Find each sum. Use algebra tiles.

3. $4 + (−7) = $ __−3__
4. $3 + (−9) = $ __−6__

What is the opposite of each number? Use it to show the inverse Property of Addition.

5. -3 __3; −3 + 3 = 0__
6. 4 __−4; 4 + (−4) = 0__
7. 5 __−5; 5 + (−5) = 0__
8. -11 __11; −11 + 11 = 0__

Find each sum.

9. $12 + (−9) = $ __3__
10. $-2 + (−8) = $ __−10__
11. $6 + (−10) = $ __−4__
12. $-3 + 3 = $ __0__

Solve.

13. **BUS STOPS** There were 15 riders on a bus. At the first stop, 3 people got off and 5 people got on. At the next stop, 7 people got off and 1 person got on. How many riders were now on the bus? __11 riders__

14. **GAMES** Corey moved 5 spaces forward on his first turn. He then moved 2 spaces forward on his next turn, but drew a card that said to move backward 3 spaces. How far had Corey advanced from the start? __4 spaces__

Write the vocabulary word that completes each sentence.

15. The __Inverse Property of Addition__ states that for any number, the sum of that number and its opposite is zero.

16. The __Commutative Property of Addition__ states that the order in which two numbers are added does not change the sum.

Math Triumphs   Lesson 1-2   A11

Answer Key (Lesson 1-3)

Copyright © Glencoe/McGraw-Hill, a division of The McGraw-Hill Companies, Inc.

Lesson 1-3 Vocabulary and English Language Development

▶ Activate Prior Knowledge

Find each opposite.

1. +7 __−7__
2. −5 __+5__
3. −2 __+2__
4. −4 __+4__
5. +6 __−6__
6. +9 __−9__

▶ Definition Review

The **absolute value** of a number is the distance between the number and zero on a number line.

Opposites are numbers that are the same distance from zero in opposite directions.

Rewrite each subtraction as an addition expression.

7. 7 − 10 __7 + (−10)__
8. −3 − 5 __−3 + (−5)__
9. −8 − (−6) __−8 + 6__
10. 9 − (−4) __9 + 4__

▶ Application

Follow the directions for the activity.

- Use masking tape to make a number line from −15 to 15 on the floor.
- Write each integer from −8 through 8 on separate pieces of paper. Put the pieces of paper in a bag, hat, or bowl.
- Student 1 picks a number from the bag and finds that number on the number line.
- Student 2 picks a number from the bag, and subtracts his or her number from the number of the other volunteer using the number line on the floor. What is the difference?
- Using the same numbers, have Student 2 find the opposite of his or her number on the number line. Student 1 should find the sum using the number line. What is the sum? Is it the same?
- Repeat the steps with each new pair of students picking new numbers until each student has had a turn.

A12   Lesson 1-3   Math Triumphs

Lesson 1-3 Skills Practice

Find each absolute value.

1. |8| = __8__
2. |2| = __2__
3. |−4| = __4__
4. |−6| = __6__
5. |15| = __15__
6. |9| = __9__
7. |−11| = __11__
8. |−1| = __1__
9. |−7| = __7__
10. |14| = __14__

Find each difference. Use the number line.

11. 3 − (−4) = __7__

−10 −8 −6 −4 −2 0 2 4 6 8 10

12. 8 − 9 = __−1__

−10 −8 −6 −4 −2 0 2 4 6 8 10

13. −2 − 1 = __−3__

−5 −4 −3 −2 −1 0 1 2 3 4 5

14. −4 − (−2) = __−2__

−6 −5 −4 −3 −2 −1 0 1 2 3 4 5 6

15. −7 − (−3) = __−4__

−10 −8 −6 −4 −2 0 2 4 6 8 10

16. −9 − (−3) = __−6__

−10 −8 −6 −4 −2 0 2 4 6 8 10

Find each difference.

17. −5 − (−6) = __1__
18. −4 − (−7) = __3__
19. 10 − (−3) = __13__
20. −1 − 6 = __−7__
21. −8 − 4 = __−12__
22. 3 − (−3) = __6__
23. 2 − (−3) = __5__
24. −9 − (−7) = __−2__
25. 7 − 11 = __−4__
26. 1 − 9 = __−8__

Math Triumphs   Lesson 1-3   A13

Lesson 1-3 Problem-Solving Practice

Solve.

1. **CONSTRUCTION**   Ajay needs to dig a pit 12 inches deep for his new patio. On Monday, he digs an 8 inch hole. During the night it rains and 2 inches of dirt falls back into his pit. How much deeper does he still need to dig?   __6 inches__

2. **FOOTBALL**   The home team needs to gain 8 yards for a touchdown. They gain 4 yards, lose 2 yards, and gain 5 yards. How many more yards does the home team need for a touchdown?   __1 yard__

3. **MINING**   Maria travels down a mineshaft to 98 feet below sea level. The entrance of the mine is 25 feet below sea level. What integer describes her change in elevation?   __−73 feet__

4. **SHOPPING**   Tobias had a $35 in-store credit. After using his credit towards the purchase of a pair of jeans, he still owed the store $12. What was the cost of the jeans that Tobias purchased?   __$47__

5. **TEST**   Leticia got her math test back. At the top of the page it said she had 12 points taken away for incorrect answers and she received 3 extra points for getting the bonus question correct. How many points were added or subtracted to get Leticia's final test score?   __−9 points; 9 points were subtracted.__

6. **FOOD**   A local restaurant had 2 dozen eggs when they opened on Wednesday morning. Later they received a delivery of more eggs. Throughout the day, the restaurant used a total of 5 dozen eggs. The restaurant had 8 dozen eggs left when they closed on Wednesday evening. How many dozen eggs were delivered to the restaurant?   __11 dozen eggs__

7. **FINANCES**   Rudy borrowed $35 from his father last week. He earned $20 babysitting. He gave all of the babysitting money to his dad. What is Rudy's situation now?   __−15 dollars; He still owes his dad $15.__

A14   Lesson 1-3   Math Triumphs

Lesson 1-3 Homework Practice

Find each difference. Use the number line.

1. −4 − 3 = __−7__

−10 −8 −6 −4 −2 0 2 4 6 8 10

2. 1 − (−6) = __7__

−10 −8 −6 −4 −2 0 2 4 6 8 10

Find each difference. Use algebra tiles.

3. −8 − 2 = __−10__

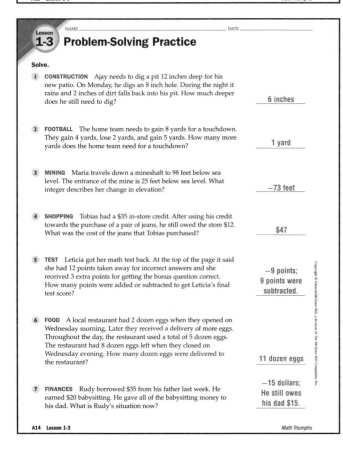

4. −3 + 5 = __2__

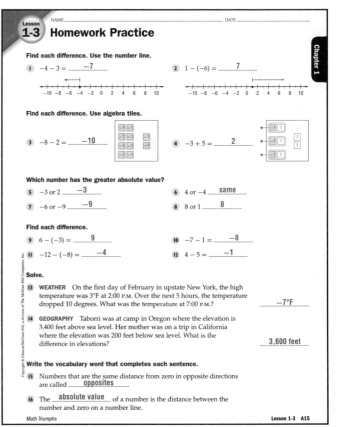

Which number has the greater absolute value?

5. −3 or 2 __−3__
6. 4 or −4 __same__
7. −6 or −9 __−9__
8. 8 or 1 __8__

Find each difference.

9. 6 − (−3) = __9__
10. −7 − 1 = __−8__
11. −12 − (−8) = __−4__
12. 4 − 5 = __−1__

Solve.

13. **WEATHER**   On the first day of February in upstate New York, the high temperature was 3°F at 2:00 P.M. Over the next 5 hours, the temperature dropped 10 degrees. What was the temperature at 7:00 P.M.?   __−7°F__

14. **GEOGRAPHY**   Taborri was at camp in Oregon where the elevation is 3,400 feet above sea level. Her mother was on a trip in California where the elevation was 200 feet below sea level. What is the difference in elevations?   __3,600 feet__

Write the vocabulary word that completes each sentence.

15. Numbers that are the same distance from zero in opposite directions are called __opposites__.

16. The __absolute value__ of a number is the distance between the number and zero on a number line.

Math Triumphs   Lesson 1-3   A15

Answer Key (Lesson 1-4)

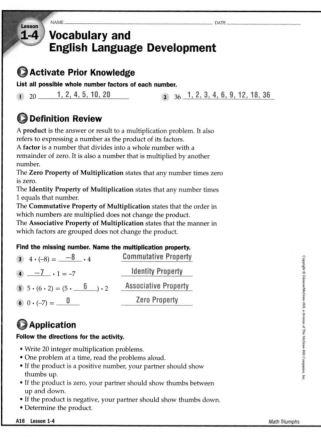

Lesson 1-4 Vocabulary and English Language Development

▶ Activate Prior Knowledge
List all possible whole number factors of each number.
1. 20   1, 2, 4, 5, 10, 20
2. 36   1, 2, 3, 4, 6, 9, 12, 18, 36

▶ Definition Review
A **product** is the answer or result to a multiplication problem. It also refers to expressing a number as the product of its factors.
A **factor** is a number that divides into a whole number with a remainder of zero. It is also a number that is multiplied by another number.
The **Zero Property of Multiplication** states that any number times zero is zero.
The **Identity Property of Multiplication** states that any number times 1 equals that number.
The **Commutative Property of Multiplication** states that the order in which numbers are multiplied does not change the product.
The **Associative Property of Multiplication** states that the manner in which factors are grouped does not change the product.

Find the missing number. Name the multiplication property.
3. 4 · (−8) = __−8__ · 4   Commutative Property
4. __−7__ · 1 = −7   Identity Property
5. 5 · (6 · 2) = (5 · __6__) · 2   Associative Property
6. 0 · (−7) = __0__   Zero Property

▶ Application
Follow the directions for the activity.
- Write 20 integer multiplication problems.
- One problem at a time, read the problems aloud.
- If the product is a positive number, your partner should show thumbs up.
- If the product is zero, your partner should show thumbs between up and down.
- If the product is negative, your partner should show thumbs down.
- Determine the product.

A16   Lesson 1-4   Math Triumphs

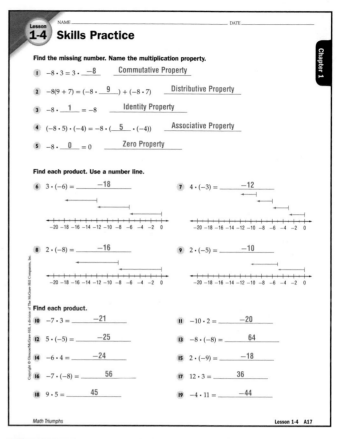

Lesson 1-4 Skills Practice

Find the missing number. Name the multiplication property.
1. −8 · 3 = 3 · __−8__   Commutative Property
2. −8(9 + 7) = (−8 · __9__) + (−8 · 7)   Distributive Property
3. −8 · __1__ = −8   Identity Property
4. (−8 · 5) · (−4) = −8 · (__5__ · (−4))   Associative Property
5. −8 · __0__ = 0   Zero Property

Find each product. Use a number line.
6. 3 · (−6) = __−18__
7. 4 · (−3) = __−12__
8. 2 · (−8) = __−16__
9. 2 · (−5) = __−10__

Find each product.
10. −7 · 3 = __−21__
11. −10 · 2 = __−20__
12. 5 · (−5) = __−25__
13. −8 · (−8) = __64__
14. −6 · 4 = __−24__
15. 2 · (−9) = __−18__
16. −7 · (−8) = __56__
17. 12 · 3 = __36__
18. 9 · 5 = __45__
19. −4 · 11 = __−44__

Math Triumphs   Lesson 1-4   A17

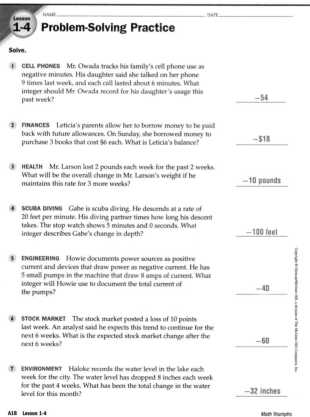

Lesson 1-4 Problem-Solving Practice

Solve.
1. **CELL PHONES** Mr. Owada tracks his family's cell phone use as negative minutes. His daughter said she talked on her phone 9 times last week, and each call lasted about 6 minutes. What integer should Mr. Owada record for his daughter's usage this past week?   −54

2. **FINANCES** Leticia's parents allow her to borrow money to be paid back with future allowances. On Sunday, she borrowed money to purchase 3 books that cost $6 each. What is Leticia's balance?   −$18

3. **HEALTH** Mr. Larson lost 2 pounds each week for the past 2 weeks. What will be the overall change in Mr. Larson's weight if he maintains this rate for 3 more weeks?   −10 pounds

4. **SCUBA DIVING** Gabe is scuba diving. He descends at a rate of 20 feet per minute. His diving partner times how long his descent takes. The stop watch shows 5 minutes and 0 seconds. What integer describes Gabe's change in depth?   −100 feet

5. **ENGINEERING** Howie documents power sources as positive current and devices that draw power as negative current. He has 5 small pumps in the machine that draw 8 amps of current. What integer will Howie use to document the total current of the pumps?   −40

6. **STOCK MARKET** The stock market posted a loss of 10 points last week. An analyst said he expects this trend to continue for the next 6 weeks. What is the expected stock market change after the next 6 weeks?   −60

7. **ENVIRONMENT** Haloke records the water level in the lake each week for the city. The water level has dropped 8 inches each week for the past 4 weeks. What has been the total change in the water level for this month?   −32 inches

A18   Lesson 1-4   Math Triumphs

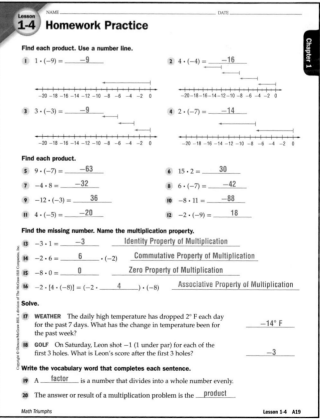

Lesson 1-4 Homework Practice

Find each product. Use a number line.
1. 1 · (−9) = __−9__
2. 4 · (−4) = __−16__
3. 3 · (−3) = __−9__
4. 2 · (−7) = __−14__

Find each product.
5. 9 · (−7) = __−63__
6. 15 · 2 = __30__
7. −4 · 8 = __−32__
8. 6 · (−7) = __−42__
9. −12 · (−3) = __36__
10. −8 · 11 = __−88__
11. 4 · (−5) = __−20__
12. −2 · (−9) = __18__

Find the missing number. Name the multiplication property.
13. −3 · 1 = __−3__   Identity Property of Multiplication
14. −2 · 6 = __6__ · (−2)   Commutative Property of Multiplication
15. −8 · 0 = __0__   Zero Property of Multiplication
16. −2 · [4 · (−8)] = (−2 · __4__) · (−8)   Associative Property of Multiplication

Solve.
17. **WEATHER** The daily high temperature has dropped 2° F each day for the past 7 days. What has the change in temperature been for the past week?   −14° F
18. **GOLF** On Saturday, Leon shot −1 (1 under par) for each of the first 3 holes. What is Leon's score after the first 3 holes?   −3

Write the vocabulary word that completes each sentence.
19. A __factor__ is a number that divides into a whole number evenly.
20. The answer or result of a multiplication problem is the __product__.

Math Triumphs   Lesson 1-4   A19

Answer Key (Lesson 1-5)

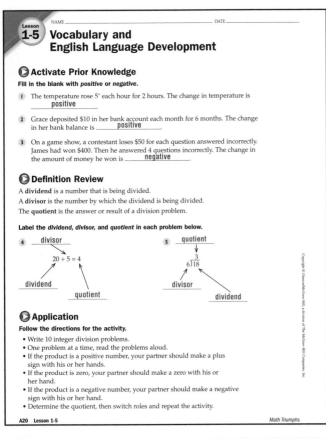

Vocabulary and English Language Development

▶ Activate Prior Knowledge

Fill in the blank with *positive* or *negative*.

1. The temperature rose 5° each hour for 2 hours. The change in temperature is __positive__

2. Grace deposited $10 in her bank account each month for 6 months. The change in her bank balance is __positive__

3. On a game show, a contestant loses $50 for each question answered incorrectly. James had won $400. Then he answered 4 questions incorrectly. The change in the amount of money he won is __negative__

▶ Definition Review

A **dividend** is a number that is being divided.
A **divisor** is the number by which the dividend is being divided.
The **quotient** is the answer or result of a division problem.

Label the *dividend*, *divisor*, and *quotient* in each problem below.

4.   divisor
   $20 \div 5 = 4$
   dividend   quotient

5.   quotient
   $6\overline{)18}$
   divisor   dividend

▶ Application

Follow the directions for the activity.
- Write 10 integer division problems.
- One problem at a time, read the problems aloud.
- If the product is a positive number, your partner should make a plus sign with his or her hands.
- If the product is zero, your partner should make a zero with his or her hand.
- If the product is a negative number, your partner should make a negative sign with his or her hand.
- Determine the quotient, then switch roles and repeat the activity.

A20   Lesson 1-5   Math Triumphs

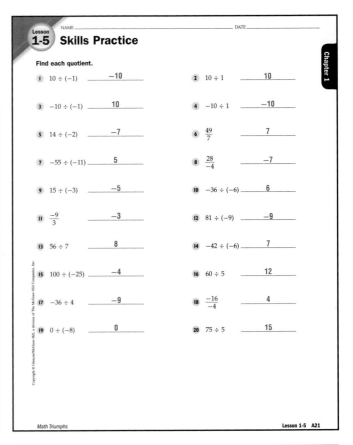

Skills Practice

Find each quotient.

1. $10 \div (-1)$ __−10__
2. $10 \div 1$ __10__
3. $-10 \div (-1)$ __10__
4. $-10 \div 1$ __−10__
5. $14 \div (-2)$ __−7__
6. $\frac{49}{7}$ __7__
7. $-55 \div (-11)$ __5__
8. $\frac{28}{-4}$ __−7__
9. $15 \div (-3)$ __−5__
10. $-36 \div (-6)$ __6__
11. $\frac{-9}{3}$ __−3__
12. $81 \div (-9)$ __−9__
13. $56 \div 7$ __8__
14. $-42 \div (-6)$ __7__
15. $100 \div (-25)$ __−4__
16. $60 \div 5$ __12__
17. $-36 \div 4$ __−9__
18. $\frac{-16}{-4}$ __4__
19. $0 \div (-8)$ __0__
20. $75 \div 5$ __15__

Math Triumphs   Lesson 1-5   A21

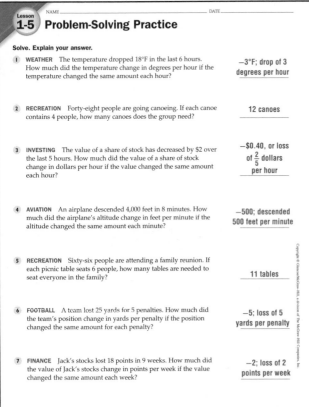

Problem-Solving Practice

Solve. Explain your answer.

1. **WEATHER** The temperature dropped 18°F in the last 6 hours. How much did the temperature change in degrees per hour if the temperature changed the same amount each hour?   **−3°F; drop of 3 degrees per hour**

2. **RECREATION** Forty-eight people are going canoeing. If each canoe contains 4 people, how many canoes does the group need?   **12 canoes**

3. **INVESTING** The value of a share of stock has decreased by $2 over the last 5 hours. How much did the value of a share of stock change in dollars per hour if the value changed the same amount each hour?   **−$0.40, or loss of $\frac{2}{5}$ dollars per hour**

4. **AVIATION** An airplane descended 4,000 feet in 8 minutes. How much did the airplane's altitude change in feet per minute if the altitude changed the same amount each minute?   **−500; descended 500 feet per minute**

5. **RECREATION** Sixty-six people are attending a family reunion. If each picnic table seats 6 people, how many tables are needed to seat everyone in the family?   **11 tables**

6. **FOOTBALL** A team lost 25 yards for 5 penalties. How much did the team's position change in yards per penalty if the position changed the same amount for each penalty?   **−5; loss of 5 yards per penalty**

7. **FINANCE** Jack's stocks lost 18 points in 9 weeks. How much did the value of Jack's stocks change in points per week if the value changed the same amount each week?   **−2; loss of 2 points per week**

A22   Lesson 1-5   Math Triumphs

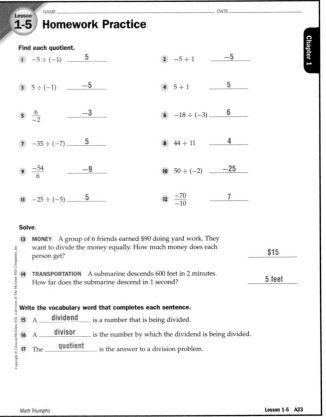

Homework Practice

Find each quotient.

1. $-5 \div (-1)$ __5__
2. $-5 \div 1$ __−5__
3. $5 \div (-1)$ __−5__
4. $5 \div 1$ __5__
5. $\frac{6}{-2}$ __−3__
6. $-18 \div (-3)$ __6__
7. $-35 \div (-7)$ __5__
8. $44 \div 11$ __4__
9. $\frac{-54}{6}$ __−9__
10. $50 \div (-2)$ __−25__
11. $-25 \div (-5)$ __5__
12. $\frac{-70}{-10}$ __7__

Solve.

13. **MONEY** A group of 6 friends earned $90 doing yard work. They want to divide the money equally. How much money does each person get?   __$15__

14. **TRANSPORTATION** A submarine descends 600 feet in 2 minutes. How far does the submarine descend in 1 second?   __5 feet__

Write the vocabulary word that completes each sentence.

15. A __dividend__ is a number that is being divided.

16. A __divisor__ is the number by which the dividend is being divided.

17. The __quotient__ is the answer to a division problem.

Math Triumphs   Lesson 1-5   A23

Answer Key (Lesson 2-1)

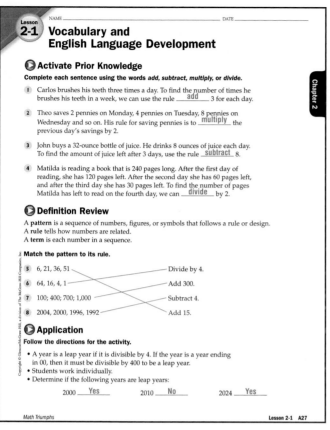

Vocabulary and English Language Development

Activate Prior Knowledge

Complete each sentence using the words *add, subtract, multiply,* or *divide*.

1. Carlos brushes his teeth three times a day. To find the number of times he brushes his teeth in a week, we can use the rule **add** 3 for each day.

2. Theo saves 2 pennies on Monday, 4 pennies on Tuesday, 8 pennies on Wednesday and so on. His rule for saving pennies is to **multiply** the previous day's savings by 2.

3. John buys a 32-ounce bottle of juice. He drinks 8 ounces of juice each day. To find the amount of juice left after 3 days, use the rule **subtract** 8.

4. Matilda is reading a book that is 240 pages long. After the first day of reading, she has 120 pages left. After the second day she has 60 pages left, and after the third day she has 30 pages left. To find the number of pages Matilda has left to read on the fourth day, we can **divide** by 2.

Definition Review

A **pattern** is a sequence of numbers, figures, or symbols that follows a rule or design.
A **rule** tells how numbers are related.
A **term** is each number in a sequence.

Match the pattern to its rule.

5. 6, 21, 36, 51 — Divide by 4.
6. 64, 16, 4, 1 — Add 300.
7. 100; 400; 700; 1,000 — Subtract 4.
8. 2004, 2000, 1996, 1992 — Add 15.

Application

Follow the directions for the activity.

- A year is a leap year if it is divisible by 4. If the year is a year ending in 00, then it must be divisible by 400 to be a leap year.
- Students work individually.
- Determine if the following years are leap years:

2000 **Yes**   2010 **No**   2024 **Yes**

Math Triumphs   Lesson 2-1   A27

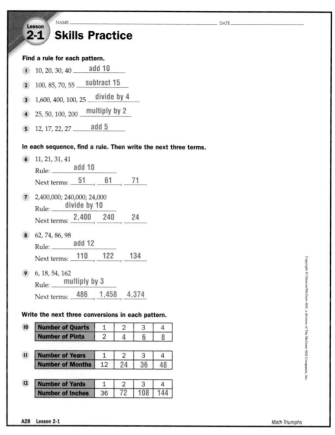

Skills Practice

Find a rule for each pattern.

1. 10, 20, 30, 40   **add 10**
2. 100, 85, 70, 55   **subtract 15**
3. 1,600, 400, 100, 25   **divide by 4**
4. 25, 50, 100, 200   **multiply by 2**
5. 12, 17, 22, 27   **add 5**

In each sequence, find a rule. Then write the next three terms.

6. 11, 21, 31, 41
   Rule: **add 10**
   Next terms: **51**, **61**, **71**

7. 2,400,000; 240,000; 24,000
   Rule: **divide by 10**
   Next terms: **2,400**, **240**, **24**

8. 62, 74, 86, 98
   Rule: **add 12**
   Next terms: **110**, **122**, **134**

9. 6, 18, 54, 162
   Rule: **multiply by 3**
   Next terms: **486**, **1,458**, **4,374**

Write the next three conversions in each pattern.

10.
Number of Quarts	1	2	3	4
Number of Pints	2	4	6	8

11.
Number of Years	1	2	3	4
Number of Months	12	24	36	48

12.
Number of Yards	1	2	3	4
Number of Inches	36	72	108	144

A28   Lesson 2-1   *Math Triumphs*

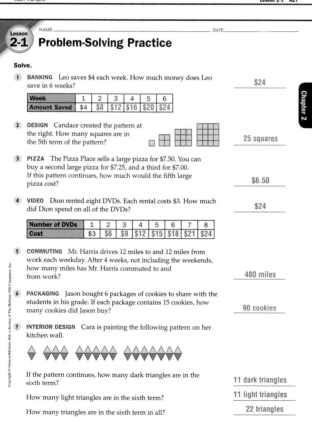

Problem-Solving Practice

Solve.

1. **BANKING** Leo saves $4 each week. How much money does Leo save in 6 weeks?   **$24**

Week	1	2	3	4	5	6
Amount Saved	$4	$8	$12	$16	$20	$24

2. **DESIGN** Candace created the pattern at the right. How many squares are in the 5th term of the pattern?   **25 squares**

3. **PIZZA** The Pizza Place sells a large pizza for $7.50. You can buy a second large pizza for $7.25, and a third for $7.00. If this pattern continues, how much would the fifth large pizza cost?   **$6.50**

4. **VIDEO** Dion rented eight DVDs. Each rental costs $3. How much did Dion spend on all of the DVDs?   **$24**

Number of DVDs	1	2	3	4	5	6	7	8
Cost	$3	$6	$9	$12	$15	$18	$21	$24

5. **COMMUTING** Mr. Harris drives 12 miles to and 12 miles from work each weekday. After 4 weeks, not including the weekends, how many miles has Mr. Harris commuted to and from work?   **480 miles**

6. **PACKAGING** Jason bought 6 packages of cookies to share with the students in his grade. If each package contains 15 cookies, how many cookies did Jason buy?   **90 cookies**

7. **INTERIOR DESIGN** Cara is painting the following pattern on her kitchen wall.

If the pattern continues, how many dark triangles are in the sixth term?   **11 dark triangles**

How many light triangles are in the sixth term?   **11 light triangles**

How many triangles are in the sixth term in all?   **22 triangles**

Math Triumphs   Lesson 2-1   A29

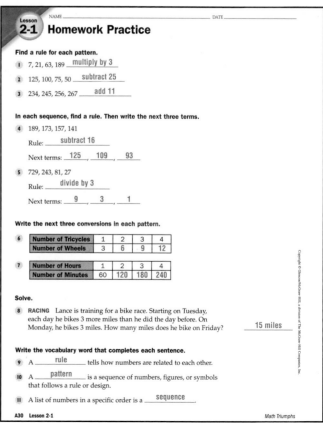

Homework Practice

Find a rule for each pattern.

1. 7, 21, 63, 189   **multiply by 3**
2. 125, 100, 75, 50   **subtract 25**
3. 234, 245, 256, 267   **add 11**

In each sequence, find a rule. Then write the next three terms.

4. 189, 173, 157, 141
   Rule: **subtract 16**
   Next terms: **125**, **109**, **93**

5. 729, 243, 81, 27
   Rule: **divide by 3**
   Next terms: **9**, **3**, **1**

Write the next three conversions in each pattern.

6.
Number of Tricycles	1	2	3	4
Number of Wheels	3	6	9	12

7.
Number of Hours	1	2	3	4
Number of Minutes	60	120	180	240

Solve.

8. **RACING** Lance is training for a bike race. Starting on Tuesday, each day he bikes 3 more miles than he did the day before. On Monday, he bikes 3 miles. How many miles does he bike on Friday?   **15 miles**

Write the vocabulary word that completes each sentence.

9. A **rule** tells how numbers are related to each other.

10. A **pattern** is a sequence of numbers, figures, or symbols that follows a rule or design.

11. A list of numbers in a specific order is a **sequence**.

A30   Lesson 2-1   *Math Triumphs*

Answer Key (Lesson 2-2)

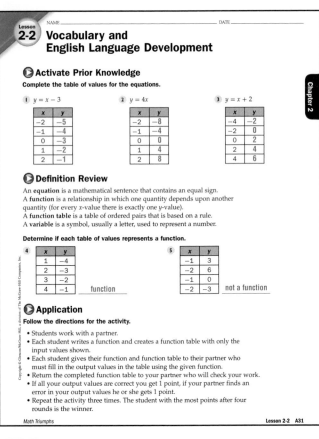

Lesson 2-2 Vocabulary and English Language Development

Activate Prior Knowledge

Complete the table of values for the equations.

1. $y = x - 3$

x	y
−2	−5
−1	−4
0	−3
1	−2
2	−1

2. $y = 4x$

x	y
−2	−8
−1	−4
0	0
1	4
2	8

3. $y = x + 2$

x	y
−4	−2
−2	0
0	2
2	4
4	6

Definition Review

An **equation** is a mathematical sentence that contains an equal sign.
A **function** is a relationship in which one quantity depends upon another quantity (for every x-value there is exactly one y-value).
A **function table** is a table of ordered pairs that is based on a rule.
A **variable** is a symbol, usually a letter, used to represent a number.

Determine if each table of values represents a function.

4.

x	y
1	−4
2	−3
3	−2
4	−1

function

5.

x	y
−1	3
−2	6
−1	0
−2	−3

not a function

Application

Follow the directions for the activity.

- Students work with a partner.
- Each student writes a function and creates a function table with only the input values shown.
- Each student gives their function and function table to their partner who must fill in the output values in the table using the given function.
- Return the completed function table to your partner who will check your work.
- If all your output values are correct you get 1 point, if your partner finds an error in your output values he or she gets 1 point.
- Repeat the activity three times. The student with the most points after four rounds is the winner.

Math Triumphs   Lesson 2-2   A31

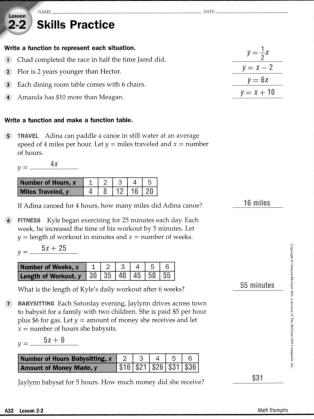

Lesson 2-2 Skills Practice

Write a function to represent each situation.

1. Chad completed the race in half the time Jared did. $y = \frac{1}{2}x$
2. Flor is 2 years younger than Hector. $y = x - 2$
3. Each dining room table comes with 6 chairs. $y = 6x$
4. Amanda has $10 more than Meagan. $y = x + 10$

Write a function and make a function table.

5. **TRAVEL** Adina can paddle a canoe in still water at an average speed of 4 miles per hour. Let y = miles traveled and x = number of hours.

   $y = \underline{\quad 4x \quad}$

Number of Hours, x	1	2	3	4	5
Miles Traveled, y	4	8	12	16	20

   If Adina canoed for 4 hours, how many miles did Adina canoe?   16 miles

6. **FITNESS** Kyle began exercising for 25 minutes each day. Each week, he increased the time of his workout by 5 minutes. Let y = length of workout in minutes and x = number of weeks.

   $y = \underline{\quad 5x + 25 \quad}$

Number of Weeks, x	1	2	3	4	5	6
Length of Workout, y	30	35	40	45	50	55

   What is the length of Kyle's daily workout after 6 weeks?   55 minutes

7. **BABYSITTING** Each Saturday evening, Jaylynn drives across town to babysit for a family with two children. She is paid $5 per hour plus $6 for gas. Let y = amount of money she receives and let x = number of hours she babysits.

   $y = \underline{\quad 5x + 6 \quad}$

Number of Hours Babysitting, x	2	3	4	5	6
Amount of Money Made, y	$16	$21	$26	$31	$36

   Jaylynn babysat for 5 hours. How much money did she receive? $31

A32   Lesson 2-2   *Math Triumphs*

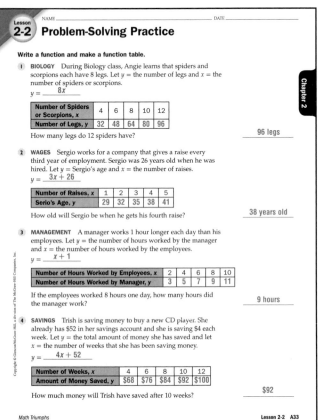

Lesson 2-2 Problem-Solving Practice

Write a function and make a function table.

1. **BIOLOGY** During Biology class, Angie learns that spiders and scorpions each have 8 legs. Let y = the number of legs and x = the number of spiders or scorpions.

   $y = \underline{\quad 8x \quad}$

Number of Spiders or Scorpions, x	4	6	8	10	12
Number of Legs, y	32	48	64	80	96

   How many legs do 12 spiders have?   96 legs

2. **WAGES** Sergio works for a company that gives a raise every third year of employment. Sergio was 26 years old when he was hired. Let y = Sergio's age and x = the number of raises.

   $y = \underline{\quad 3x + 26 \quad}$

Number of Raises, x	1	2	3	4	5
Serio's Age, y	29	32	35	38	41

   How old will Sergio be when he gets his fourth raise?   38 years old

3. **MANAGEMENT** A manager works 1 hour longer each day than his employees. Let y = the number of hours worked by the manager and x = the number of hours worked by the employees.

   $y = \underline{\quad x + 1 \quad}$

Number of Hours Worked by Employees, x	2	4	6	8	10
Number of Hours Worked by Manager, y	3	5	7	9	11

   If the employees worked 8 hours one day, how many hours did the manager work?   9 hours

4. **SAVINGS** Trish is saving money to buy a new CD player. She already has $52 in her savings account and she is saving $4 each week. Let y = the total amount of money she has saved and let x = the number of weeks that she has been saving money.

   $y = \underline{\quad 4x + 52 \quad}$

Number of Weeks, x	4	6	8	10	12
Amount of Money Saved, y	$68	$76	$84	$92	$100

   How much money will Trish have saved after 10 weeks? $92

Math Triumphs   Lesson 2-2   A33

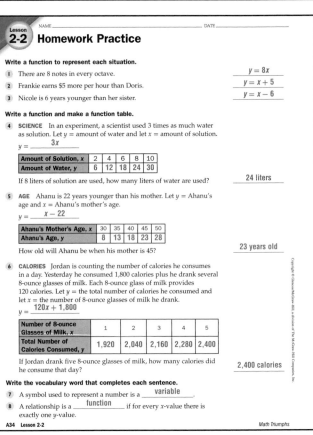

Lesson 2-2 Homework Practice

Write a function to represent each situation.

1. There are 8 notes in every octave. $y = 8x$
2. Frankie earns $5 more per hour than Doris. $y = x + 5$
3. Nicole is 6 years younger than her sister. $y = x - 6$

Write a function and make a function table.

4. **SCIENCE** In an experiment, a scientist used 3 times as much water as solution. Let y = amount of water and let x = amount of solution.

   $y = \underline{\quad 3x \quad}$

Amount of Solution, x	2	4	6	8	10
Amount of Water, y	6	12	18	24	30

   If 8 liters of solution are used, how many liters of water are used?   24 liters

5. **AGE** Ahanu is 22 years younger than his mother. Let y = Ahanu's age and x = Ahanu's mother's age.

   $y = \underline{\quad x - 22 \quad}$

Ahanu's Mother's Age, x	30	35	40	45	50
Ahanu's Age, y	8	13	18	23	28

   How old will Ahanu be when his mother is 45?   23 years old

6. **CALORIES** Jordan is counting the number of calories he consumes in a day. Yesterday he consumed 1,800 calories plus he drank several 8-ounce glasses of milk. Each 8-ounce glass of milk provides 120 calories. Let y = the total number of calories he consumed and let x = the number of 8-ounce glasses of milk he drank.

   $y = \underline{\quad 120x + 1,800 \quad}$

Number of 8-ounce Glasses of Milk, x	1	2	3	4	5
Total Number of Calories Consumed, y	1,920	2,040	2,160	2,280	2,400

   If Jordan drank five 8-ounce glasses of milk, how many calories did he consume that day?   2,400 calories

Write the vocabulary word that completes each sentence.

7. A symbol used to represent a number is a __variable__.
8. A relationship is a __function__ if for every x-value there is exactly one y-value.

A34   Lesson 2-2   *Math Triumphs*

Answer Key (Lesson 2-3)

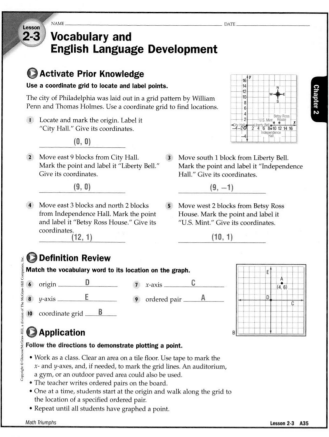

Lesson 2-3 Vocabulary and English Language Development

▶ Activate Prior Knowledge

Use a coordinate grid to locate and label points.

The city of Philadelphia was laid out in a grid pattern by William Penn and Thomas Holmes. Use a coordinate grid to find locations.

1. Locate and mark the origin. Label it "City Hall." Give its coordinates.

   (0, 0)

2. Move east 9 blocks from City Hall. Mark the point and label it "Liberty Bell." Give its coordinates.

   (9, 0)

3. Move south 1 block from Liberty Bell. Mark the point and label it "Independence Hall." Give its coordinates.

   (9, −1)

4. Move east 3 blocks and north 2 blocks from Independence Hall. Mark the point and label it "Betsy Ross House." Give its coordinates.

   (12, 1)

5. Move west 2 blocks from Betsy Ross House. Mark the point and label it "U.S. Mint." Give its coordinates.

   (10, 1)

▶ Definition Review

Match the vocabulary word to its location on the graph.

6. origin ___**D**___
7. x-axis ___**C**___
8. y-axis ___**E**___
9. ordered pair ___**A**___
10. coordinate grid ___**B**___

▶ Application

Follow the directions to demonstrate plotting a point.

- Work as a class. Clear an area on a tile floor. Use tape to mark the x- and y-axes, and, if needed, to mark the grid lines. An auditorium, a gym, or an outdoor paved area could also be used.
- The teacher writes ordered pairs on the board.
- One at a time, students start at the origin and walk along the grid to the location of a specified ordered pair.
- Repeat until all students have graphed a point.

Math Triumphs Lesson 2-3 A35

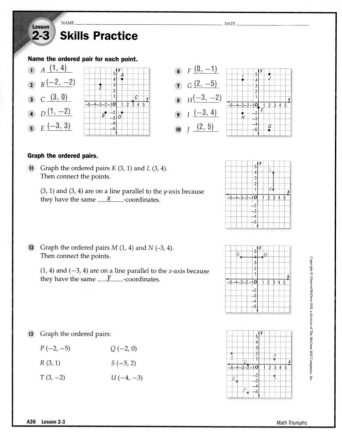

Lesson 2-3 Skills Practice

Name the ordered pair for each point.

1. A **(1, 4)**
2. B **(−2, −2)**
3. C **(3, 0)**
4. D **(1, −2)**
5. E **(−3, 3)**
6. F **(0, −1)**
7. G **(2, −5)**
8. H **(−3, −2)**
9. I **(−3, 4)**
10. J **(2, 5)**

Graph the ordered pairs.

11. Graph the ordered pairs K (3, 1) and L (3, 4). Then connect the points.

    (3, 1) and (3, 4) are on a line parallel to the y-axis because they have the same ___**x**___-coordinates.

12. Graph the ordered pairs M (1, 4) and N (−3, 4). Then connect the points.

    (1, 4) and (−3, 4) are on a line parallel to the x-axis because they have the same ___**y**___-coordinates.

13. Graph the ordered pairs:

    P (−2, −5)   Q (−2, 0)
    R (3, 1)   S (−5, 2)
    T (3, −2)   U (−4, −3)

A36 Lesson 2-3 *Math Triumphs*

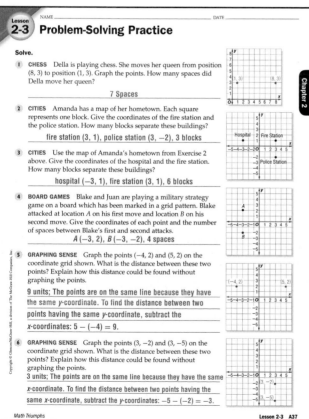

Lesson 2-3 Problem-Solving Practice

Solve.

1. **CHESS** Della is playing chess. She moves her queen from position (8, 3) to position (1, 3). Graph the points. How many spaces did Della move her queen?

   7 Spaces

2. **CITIES** Amanda has a map of her hometown. Each square represents one block. Give the coordinates of the fire station and the police station. How many blocks separate these buildings?

   fire station (3, 1), police station (3, −2), 3 blocks

3. **CITIES** Use the map of Amanda's hometown from Exercise 2 above. Give the coordinates of the hospital and the fire station. How many blocks separate these buildings?

   hospital (−3, 1), fire station (3, 1), 6 blocks

4. **BOARD GAMES** Blake and Juan are playing a military strategy game on a board which has been marked in a grid pattern. Blake attacked at location A on his first move and location B on his second move. Give the coordinates of each point and the number of spaces between Blake's first and second attacks.

   A (−3, 2), B (−3, −2), 4 spaces

5. **GRAPHING SENSE** Graph the points (−4, 2) and (5, 2) on the coordinate grid shown. What is the distance between these two points? Explain how this distance could be found without graphing the points.

   9 units; The points are on the same line because they have the same y-coordinate. To find the distance between two points having the same y-coordinate, subtract the x-coordinates: 5 − (−4) = 9.

6. **GRAPHING SENSE** Graph the points (3, −2) and (3, −5) on the coordinate grid shown. What is the distance between these two points? Explain how this distance could be found without graphing the points.

   3 units; The points are on the same line because they have the same x-coordinate. To find the distance between two points having the same x-coordinate, subtract the y-coordinates: −5 − (−2) = −3.

Math Triumphs Lesson 2-3 A37

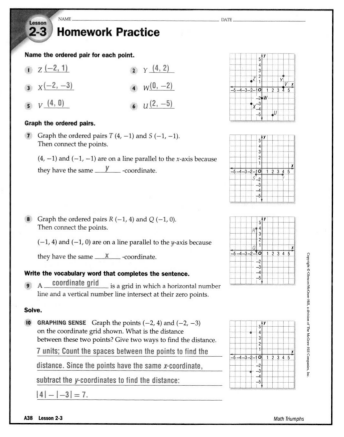

Lesson 2-3 Homework Practice

Name the ordered pair for each point.

1. Z **(−2, 1)**
2. Y **(4, 2)**
3. X **(−2, −3)**
4. W **(0, −2)**
5. V **(4, 0)**
6. U **(2, −5)**

Graph the ordered pairs.

7. Graph the ordered pairs T (4, −1) and S (−1, −1). Then connect the points.

   (4, −1) and (−1, −1) are on a line parallel to the x-axis because they have the same ___**y**___-coordinate.

8. Graph the ordered pairs R (−1, 4) and Q (−1, 0). Then connect the points.

   (−1, 4) and (−1, 0) are on a line parallel to the y-axis because they have the same ___**x**___-coordinate.

Write the vocabulary word that completes the sentence.

9. A ___**coordinate grid**___ is a grid in which a horizontal number line and a vertical number line intersect at their zero points.

Solve.

10. **GRAPHING SENSE** Graph the points (−2, 4) and (−2, −3) on the coordinate grid shown. What is the distance between these two points? Give two ways to find the distance.

    7 units; Count the spaces between the points to find the distance. Since the points have the same x-coordinate, subtract the y-coordinates to find the distance: |4| − |−3| = 7.

A38 Lesson 2-3 *Math Triumphs*

Answer Key (Lesson 2-4)

Panel 1

2-4 Vocabulary and English Language Development

▶ Activate Prior Knowledge

Identify the table that corresponds to each equation.

1. $y = x + 2$ __B__   2. $y = 2x$ __C__   3. $y = x - 2$ __A__   4. $y = \frac{x}{2}$ __D__

Table A

x	y
−2	−4
−1	−3
0	−2
1	−1

Table B

x	y
−4	−2
−2	0
0	2
2	4

Table C

x	y
−2	−4
−1	−2
1	2

Table D

x	y
−4	−2
−2	−1
0	0
2	1

▶ Definition Review

A **coordinate grid** is a grid in which a horizontal number line and a vertical number line intersect at their zero points.

An **ordered pair** is a pair of numbers that are the coordinates of a point in a coordinate grid, written in the order (horizontal coordinate, vertical coordinate).

Describe how to locate each ordered pair in a coordinate grid.

5. $(3, -2)$
From the origin, move 3 units right and then 2 units down.

6. $(-5, 4)$
From the origin, move 5 units left and then 4 units up.

▶ Application

Follow the directions to find the equation.

- Students work in pairs with paper and pencils.
- The first student thinks of an equation (for example: $y = 5x$ or $y = x - 4$) and creates a table for this equation.
- The first student gives the table to the second student, but does not reveal the equation.
- The second student examines the table and writes the equation he or she believes created the table.
- If the correct equation is found, the second student earns 1 point. If the equation is not found, the first student earns 1 point. If it is discovered that the table was incorrectly formed, the second student earns 1 point.
- Reverse roles and continue play until both students have created five equations. The student with the most points wins.

Panel 2

2-4 Skills Practice

Make a table for each equation.

1. $y = x - 3$

x	x − 3	y	Ordered Pair
−2	−2 − 3	−5	(−2, −5)
−1	−1 − 3	−4	(−1, −4)
0	0 − 3	−3	(0, −3)
1	1 − 3	−2	(1, −2)
2	2 − 3	−1	(2, −1)

2. $y = \frac{x}{2} + 3$

x	$\frac{x}{2} + 3$	y	Ordered Pair
−4	$\frac{-4}{2} + 3$	1	(−4, 1)
−2	$\frac{-2}{2} + 3$	2	(−2, 2)
0	$\frac{0}{2} + 3$	3	(0, 3)
2	$\frac{2}{2} + 3$	4	(2, 4)
4	$\frac{4}{2} + 3$	5	(4, 5)

Graph each equation.

3. Graph the equation from Exercise 1.

4. Graph the equation from Exercise 2.

5. Graph $y = -\frac{x}{2} + 1$.

6. Graph $y = -2x + 1$.

Panel 3

2-4 Problem-Solving Practice

Solve.

1. **RECREATION** A local festival charges $1 per person plus a parking fee of $5 per car. Make a table to show the relationship between number of people and the total amount charged. How much does it cost for 3 people to drive to the festival in one car?
$8

x	x + 5	y	Ordered Pair
1	1 + 5	6	(1, 6)
2	2 + 5	7	(2, 7)
3	3 + 5	8	(3, 8)
4	4 + 5	9	(4, 9)
5	5 + 5	10	(5, 10)

2. **PIZZA** Meg hosted a party during which she served pizza. Each person at the party ate 2 slices of pizza. Make a table to show the relationship between the number of people at the party and the total amount of pizza. How many slices of pizza were eaten if 4 people attended the party?
8 slices

x	2x	y	Ordered Pair
1	2(1)	2	(1, 2)
2	2(2)	4	(2, 4)
3	2(3)	6	(3, 6)
4	2(4)	8	(4, 8)
5	2(5)	10	(5, 10)

3. **MOVIES** Mr. Velez would like to take his kids and their friends to the movies. The matinee price for the movie is $3 each. Make a table to show the relationship between the number of tickets and the total cost. How much will the movies cost if Mr. Velez must pay for himself and 4 children?
$15

x	3x	y	Ordered Pair
1	3(1)	3	(1, 3)
2	3(2)	6	(2, 6)
3	3(3)	9	(3, 9)
4	3(4)	12	(4, 12)
5	3(5)	15	(5, 15)

4. **SAVINGS** Evita has $5 in her savings bank. She wants to save $2 a week to buy some CDs. Make a table to show the relationship between the number of weeks and the total amount saved. How much will she save in 10 weeks?
$25

x	2x + 5	y	Ordered Pair
0	2(0) + 5	5	(0, 5)
5	2(5) + 5	15	(5, 15)
10	2(10) + 5	25	(10, 25)
15	2(15) + 5	35	(15, 35)
20	2(20) + 5	45	(20, 45)

Panel 4

2-4 Homework Practice

Make a table for each equation.

1. $y = \frac{x}{2} + 2$

x	y
−4	0
−2	1
0	2
2	3
4	4

2. $y = -2x - 1$

x	y
−2	3
−1	1
0	−1
1	−3
2	−5

Graph each equation.

3. Graph the equation from Exercise 1.

4. Graph the equation from Exercise 2.

Solve.

5. The cost to go on rides at a fair is $x + 5$, where x is the total number of rides. Show the relationship between the number of rides and the total cost in a table and on a coordinate plane. How much money will it cost to go on 4 rides?
$9

x	x + 5	y	Ordered Pair
1	1 + 5	6	(1, 6)
2	2 + 5	7	(2, 7)
3	3 + 5	8	(3, 8)
4	4 + 5	9	(4, 9)
5	5 + 5	10	(5, 10)

Write the vocabulary word(s) that completes the sentence.

6. A pair of numbers that is the coordinates of a point in a coordinate plane or grid is called an __ordered pair__.

Answer Key (Lesson 2-5)

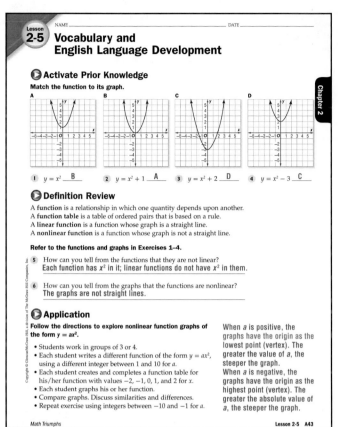

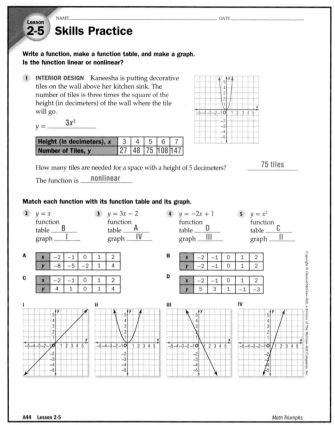

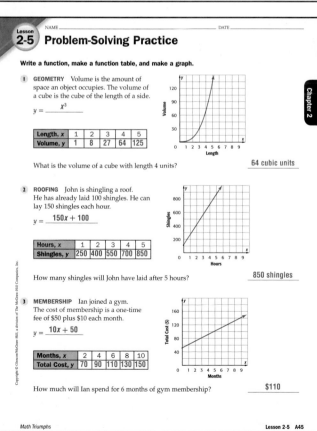

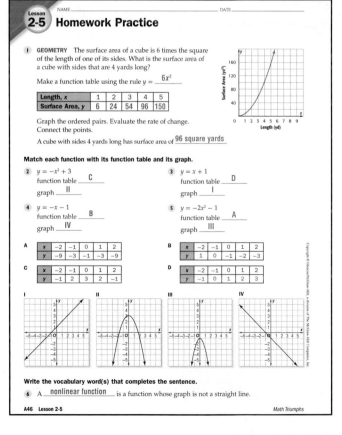

Answer Key (Lesson 3-1)

Vocabulary and English Language Development

NAME _____ DATE _____

Activate Prior Knowledge

Find each sum, difference, product, or quotient.

1. $-3 + 7 =$ __4__
2. $5 + (-8) =$ __-3__
3. $6 - 8 =$ __-2__
4. $-3 - 2 =$ __-5__
5. $-4 \cdot (-5) =$ __20__
6. $-9 \cdot 8 =$ __-72__
7. $30 \div (-6) =$ __-5__
8. $-24 \div (-4) =$ __6__

Definition Review

In a power, the **base** is the number used as a factor.
In a power, the **exponent** is the number of times the base is used as a factor.
The **order of operations** are the rules that tell which operation to perform first when more than one operation is used.

9. Use 1st, 2nd, 3rd, and 4th to put the steps in the correct order.

__3rd__ Multiply and divide in order from left to right.
__1st__ Find the value within grouping symbols (parentheses).
__4th__ Add and subtract in order from left to right.
__2nd__ Simplify terms with exponents.

Application

- Work in pairs. Each student needs five index cards.
- Each student does the following on his or her index cards. On one side of each index card, write a numerical expression using four numbers from 1 to 20, three operation symbols, and at most one pair of grouping symbols and one exponent. Then calculate the value of the expression and write the value on the other side of the card. If the value is *not* a whole number, change your expression until a whole number value is obtained.
- Stack your five completed index cards with the expressions facing up. Trade your stack of cards with your partner, being sure to keep them with the expressions facing up.
- Calculate the value of the expression on each card, and record your values on a piece of paper. Compare your results to the values written on the back of the cards you received.
- If your value does not match the one on the back of the card, work with your partner to determine the correct value.

A50 Lesson 3-1   *Math Triumphs*

Skills Practice

NAME _____ DATE _____

Name the step that should be performed first in each expression.

1. $8 \cdot 6 \div (4 + 2) - 4^2$
   addition
2. $3 \cdot 6 + 3^2 + 9 \div 3$
   exponent
3. $5 \div 1 - 3 + 2 \cdot 6$
   division
4. $9 - 2 + (12 \cdot 6) + 9$
   multiplication
5. $\frac{6 + 12}{11 - 2} + 7 \cdot 3$
   fraction bar
6. $10 \div 2 \cdot (5 - 1) + 4$
   subtraction

Find the value of each expression.

7. $4 \cdot (2 + 6) - 30 + 4^2 = 4 \cdot \underline{8} - 30 + 4^2$
$= 4 \cdot \underline{8} - 30 + \underline{16}$
$= \underline{32} - 30 + \underline{16}$
$= \underline{2} + \underline{16}$
$= \underline{18}$

8. $9 + 7 \cdot 2 - 3^2 + (1 \cdot 8) = 9 + 7 \cdot 2 - 3^2 + \underline{8}$
$= 9 + 7 \cdot 2 - \underline{9} + \underline{8}$
$= 9 + \underline{14} - \underline{9} + \underline{8}$
$= \underline{23} - \underline{9} + \underline{8}$
$= \underline{22}$

9. $7 - 4 \div 2 + 5^2$
   30
10. $12 \div 4 \cdot 2^3 - (3 + 2)$
   19
11. $14 \cdot 2 \div (8 - 4) + 9$
   16
12. $10 - (12 \div 3) + 2 \cdot 5$
   16
13. $20 - 6 \cdot 3 \div (7 - 5)$
   11
14. $7 \div (5 - 4)^3 + 3 \cdot 2$
   13

Math Triumphs   Lesson 3-1 A51

Problem-Solving Practice

NAME _____ DATE _____

Solve.

1. **KITTENS** Carla has 2 cats. Each cat had 5 kittens. She found homes for 7 kittens. How many cats and kittens does Carla have left?

   2 cats and 3 kittens

2. **BAKERY** A baker made 15 loaves of white bread, 12 loaves of wheat bread, and 10 loaves of rye bread. A customer bought 2 loaves of each of the 3 kinds of breads. How many loaves of bread are left?

   31 loaves

3. **EARNINGS** On Monday, Colin worked 3 hours, earned $10 per hour, and spent $5 for lunch. On Tuesday, Colin worked 7 hours, earned $8 per hour, and spent $6 for lunch. How much money does Colin have now?

   $75

4. **COOKIES** Shamika baked 60 oatmeal cookies for a bake sale. She divided the cookies equally among 12 bags. At the bake sale she sold 7 bags of cookies. How many cookies does Shamika have left?

   25 cookies

5. **COMPUTERS** Emilio received a $15 discount when he bought an ink-jet printer. He also bought 2 black printer cartridges, 1 color printer cartridge, and 5 reams of paper. His receipt is shown below. How much money did Emilio spend?

   $240

   Computer World
   Ink-jet printer   1 @ $125.00
   – Discount   –$15.00
   Black printer cartridges
                       2 @ $35.00
   Color printer cartridges
                       1 @ $35.00
   Paper   5 @ $5.00

6. **AMUSEMENT PARK** Lalana paid $12 for admission to an amusement park. She rode the roller coaster 3 times and the Ferris wheel 2 times. Each ride cost $2. She also bought a hamburger and 2 lemonade drinks during the day. How much money did Lalana spend?

   $28

   Lunch Menu
   Hot Dog $2.00
   Hamburger $3.00
   French Fries $1.00
   Lemonade $1.50
   Water $1.00

A52 Lesson 3-1   *Math Triumphs*

Homework Practice

NAME _____ DATE _____

Name the step that should be performed first in each expression.

1. $7 + 9 - 2 + 4 \cdot 4^2$
   exponent
2. $3 \cdot 18 + (9 - 2) + 3^3 \div 3$
   subtraction
3. $(9 + 4 \cdot 2) - 12 \div 3 + 8$
   multiplication
4. $20 \div 4 \cdot 2 - 9 \cdot 2 + 5$
   division

Find the value of each expression.

5. $4^2 + 13 + (9 \div 3^2) \cdot 2$
   31
6. $15 \div (2^2 + 1^2) - 3 \cdot 1$
   0
7. $11 + 3 \cdot 2 + 8 - 8 \div 2$
   21
8. $(3 + 8 \cdot 2 - 18 + 3^2) \div 5$
   2

Solve.

9. **SNACKS** Marla bought 4 boxes of granola bars. Each box contains 6 granola bars. Marla ate 3 granola bars, and she gave her brother 4 granola bars. Marla then bought 2 more boxes of granola bars. How many granola bars does Marla have now?

   29 granola bars

10. **BOOKS** Daniel has 65 books on a book shelf. He divides the books equally among 5 shelves. He then moves 5 books on the top shelf to the bottom shelf. He also buys 3 new books and puts them on the top shelf. How many books are on the top shelf?

   11 books

Math Triumphs   Lesson 3-1 A53

Answer Key (Lesson 3-2)

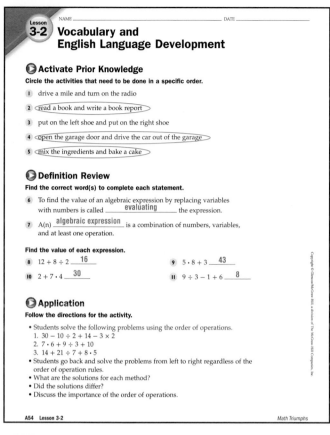

Lesson 3-2

Vocabulary and English Language Development

▶ Activate Prior Knowledge
Circle the activities that need to be done in a specific order.

1. drive a mile and turn on the radio
2. (read a book and write a book report)
3. put on the left shoe and put on the right shoe
4. (open the garage door and drive the car out of the garage)
5. (mix the ingredients and bake a cake)

▶ Definition Review
Find the correct word(s) to complete each statement.

6. To find the value of an algebraic expression by replacing variables with numbers is called __evaluating__ the expression.

7. A(n) __algebraic expression__ is a combination of numbers, variables, and at least one operation.

Find the value of each expression.

8. $12 + 8 \div 2$ __16__

9. $5 \cdot 8 + 3$ __43__

10. $2 + 7 \cdot 4$ __30__

11. $9 \div 3 - 1 + 6$ __8__

▶ Application
Follow the directions for the activity.

• Students solve the following problems using the order of operations.
1. $30 - 10 \div 2 + 14 - 3 \times 2$
2. $7 \cdot 6 + 9 \div 3 + 10$
3. $14 + 21 \div 7 + 8 \cdot 5$
• Students go back and solve the problems from left to right regardless of the order of operation rules.
• What are the solutions for each method?
• Did the solutions differ?
• Discuss the importance of the order of operations.

A54 Lesson 3-2   Math Triumphs

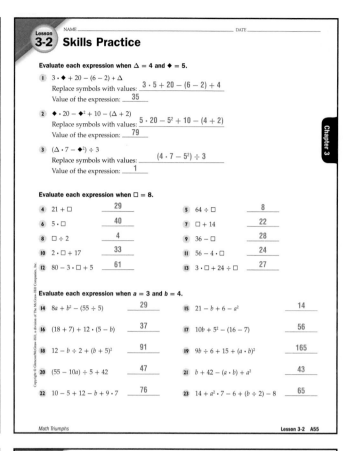

Lesson 3-2

Skills Practice

Evaluate each expression when △ = 4 and ◆ = 5.

1. $3 \cdot \blacklozenge + 20 - (6 - 2) + \triangle$
Replace symbols with values: $3 \cdot 5 + 20 - (6 - 2) + 4$
Value of the expression: __35__

2. $\blacklozenge \cdot 20 - \blacklozenge^2 + 10 - (\triangle + 2)$
Replace symbols with values: $5 \cdot 20 - 5^2 + 10 - (4 + 2)$
Value of the expression: __79__

3. $(\triangle \cdot 7 - \blacklozenge^2) \div 3$
Replace symbols with values: $(4 \cdot 7 - 5^2) \div 3$
Value of the expression: __1__

Evaluate each expression when □ = 8.

4. $21 + \square$ __29__
5. $64 \div \square$ __8__
6. $5 \cdot \square$ __40__
7. $\square + 14$ __22__
8. $\square \div 2$ __4__
9. $36 - \square$ __28__
10. $2 \cdot \square + 17$ __33__
11. $56 - 4 \cdot \square$ __24__
12. $80 - 3 \cdot \square + 5$ __61__
13. $3 \cdot \square + 24 \div \square$ __27__

Evaluate each expression when $a = 3$ and $b = 4$.

14. $8a + b^2 - (55 \div 5)$ __29__
15. $21 - b + 6 - a^2$ __14__
16. $(18 + 7) + 12 \cdot (5 - b)$ __37__
17. $10b + 5^2 - (16 - 7)$ __56__
18. $12 - b \div 2 + (b + 5)^2$ __91__
19. $9b \div 6 + 15 + (a \cdot b)^2$ __165__
20. $(55 - 10a) \div 5 + 42$ __47__
21. $b + 42 - (a \cdot b) + a^2$ __43__
22. $10 - 5 + 12 - b + 9 \cdot 7$ __76__
23. $14 + a^2 \cdot 7 - 6 + (b \div 2) - 8$ __65__

Math Triumphs   Lesson 3-2 A55

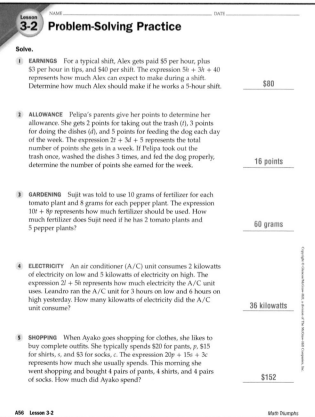

Lesson 3-2

Problem-Solving Practice

Solve.

1. **EARNINGS** For a typical shift, Alex gets paid $5 per hour, plus $3 per hour in tips, and $40 per shift. The expression $5h + 3h + 40$ represents how much Alex can expect to make during a shift. Determine how much Alex should make if he works a 5-hour shift.   __$80__

2. **ALLOWANCE** Pelipa's parents give her points to determine her allowance. She gets 2 points for taking out the trash (t), 3 points for doing the dishes (d), and 5 points for feeding the dog each day of the week. The expression $2t + 3d + 5$ represents the total number of points she gets in a week. If Pelipa took out the trash once, washed the dishes 3 times, and fed the dog properly, determine the number of points she earned for the week.   __16 points__

3. **GARDENING** Sujit was told to use 10 grams of fertilizer for each tomato plant and 8 grams for each pepper plant. The expression $10t + 8p$ represents how much fertilizer should be used. How much fertilizer does Sujit need if he has 2 tomato plants and 5 pepper plants?   __60 grams__

4. **ELECTRICITY** An air conditioner (A/C) unit consumes 2 kilowatts of electricity on low and 5 kilowatts of electricity on high. The expression $2l + 5h$ represents how much electricity the A/C unit uses. Leandro ran the A/C unit for 3 hours on low and 6 hours on high yesterday. How many kilowatts of electricity did the A/C unit consume?   __36 kilowatts__

5. **SHOPPING** When Ayako goes shopping for clothes, she likes to buy complete outfits. She typically spends $20 for pants, p, $15 for shirts, s, and $3 for socks, c. The expression $20p + 15s + 3c$ represents how much she usually spends. This morning she went shopping and bought 4 pairs of pants, 4 shirts, and 4 pairs of socks. How much did Ayako spend?   __$152__

A56 Lesson 3-2   Math Triumphs

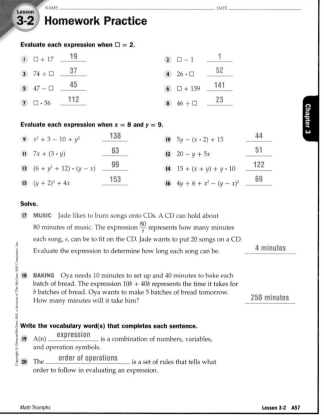

Lesson 3-2

Homework Practice

Evaluate each expression when □ = 2.

1. $\square + 17$ __19__
2. $\square - 1$ __1__
3. $74 \div \square$ __37__
4. $26 \cdot \square$ __52__
5. $47 - \square$ __45__
6. $\square + 139$ __141__
7. $\square \cdot 56$ __112__
8. $46 \div \square$ __23__

Evaluate each expression when $x = 8$ and $y = 9$.

9. $x^2 + 3 - 10 + y^2$ __138__
10. $5y - (x \cdot 2) + 15$ __44__
11. $7x + (3 \cdot y)$ __83__
12. $20 - y + 5x$ __51__
13. $(6 + y^2 + 12) \cdot (y - x)$ __99__
14. $15 + (x + y) + y \cdot 10$ __122__
15. $(y + 2)^2 + 4x$ __153__
16. $4y \div 6 + x^2 - (y - x)^2$ __69__

Solve.

17. **MUSIC** Jade likes to burn songs onto CDs. A CD can hold about 80 minutes of music. The expression $\frac{80}{s}$ represents how many minutes each song, s, can be to fit on the CD. Jade wants to put 20 songs on a CD. Evaluate the expression to determine how long each song can be.   __4 minutes__

18. **BAKING** Oya needs 10 minutes to set up and 40 minutes to bake each batch of bread. The expression $10b + 40b$ represents the time it takes for b batches of bread. Oya wants to make 5 batches of bread tomorrow. How many minutes will it take him?   __250 minutes__

Write the vocabulary word(s) that completes each sentence.

19. A(n) __expression__ is a combination of numbers, variables, and operation symbols.

20. The __order of operations__ is a set of rules that tells what order to follow in evaluating an expression.

Math Triumphs   Lesson 3-2 A57

Math Triumphs

Lesson 3-2 A207

Answer Key (Lesson 3-3)

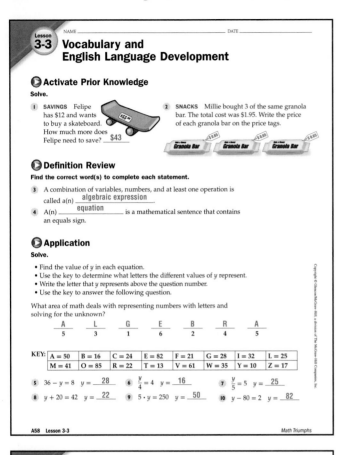

Activate Prior Knowledge

Solve.

1 **SAVINGS** Felipe has $12 and wants to buy a skateboard. How much more does Felipe need to save? $43

2 **SNACKS** Millie bought 3 of the same granola bar. The total cost was $1.95. Write the price of each granola bar on the price tags.

$0.65

Definition Review

Find the correct word(s) to complete each statement.

3 A combination of variables, numbers, and at least one operation is called a(n) ___algebraic expression___

4 A(n) ___equation___ is a mathematical sentence that contains an equals sign.

Application

Solve.

- Find the value of y in each equation.
- Use the key to determine what letters the different values of y represent.
- Write the letter that y represents above the question number.
- Use the key to answer the following question.

What area of math deals with representing numbers with letters and solving for the unknown?

A	L	G	E	B	R	A
5	3	1	6	2	4	5

KEY:

A = 50	B = 16	C = 24	E = 82	F = 21	G = 28	I = 32	L = 25
M = 41	O = 85	R = 22	T = 13	V = 61	W = 35	Y = 10	Z = 17

5 $36 - y = 8$ $y = $ 28

6 $\frac{y}{4} = 4$ $y = $ 16

7 $\frac{y}{5} = 5$ $y = $ 25

8 $y + 20 = 42$ $y = $ 22

9 $5 \cdot y = 250$ $y = $ 50

10 $y - 80 = 2$ $y = $ 82

A58   Lesson 3-3   Math Triumphs

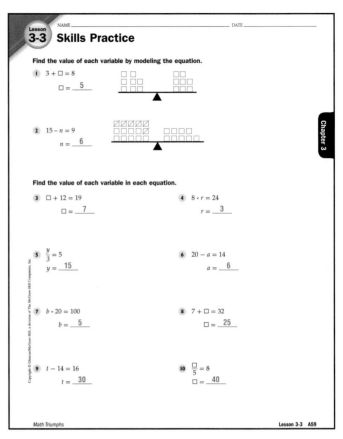

Find the value of each variable by modeling the equation.

1 $3 + \square = 8$ $\square = $ 5

2 $15 - n = 9$ $n = $ 6

Find the value of each variable in each equation.

3 $\square + 12 = 19$ $\square = $ 7

4 $8 \cdot r = 24$ $r = $ 3

5 $\frac{y}{3} = 5$ $y = $ 15

6 $20 - a = 14$ $a = $ 6

7 $b \cdot 20 = 100$ $b = $ 5

8 $7 + \square = 32$ $\square = $ 25

9 $t - 14 = 16$ $t = $ 30

10 $\frac{\square}{5} = 8$ $\square = $ 40

Math Triumphs   Lesson 3-3   A59

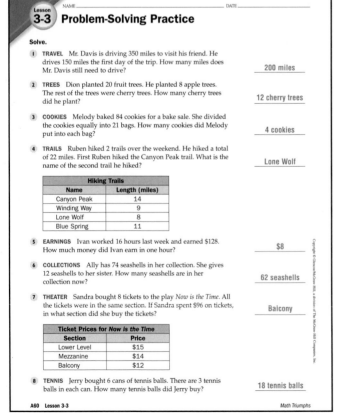

Solve.

1 **TRAVEL** Mr. Davis is driving 350 miles to visit his friend. He drives 150 miles the first day of the trip. How many miles does Mr. Davis still need to drive?   200 miles

2 **TREES** Dion planted 20 fruit trees. He planted 8 apple trees. The rest of the trees were cherry trees. How many cherry trees did he plant?   12 cherry trees

3 **COOKIES** Melody baked 84 cookies for a bake sale. She divided the cookies equally into 21 bags. How many cookies did Melody put into each bag?   4 cookies

4 **TRAILS** Ruben hiked 2 trails over the weekend. He hiked a total of 22 miles. First Ruben hiked the Canyon Peak trail. What is the name of the second trail he hiked?   Lone Wolf

Hiking Trails	
Name	Length (miles)
Canyon Peak	14
Winding Way	9
Lone Wolf	8
Blue Spring	11

5 **EARNINGS** Ivan worked 16 hours last week and earned $128. How much money did Ivan earn in one hour? $8

6 **COLLECTIONS** Ally has 74 seashells in her collection. She gives 12 seashells to her sister. How many seashells are in her collection now?   62 seashells

7 **THEATER** Sandra bought 8 tickets to the play *Now is the Time*. All the tickets were in the same section. If Sandra spent $96 on tickets, in what section did she buy the tickets?   Balcony

Ticket Prices for *Now is the Time*	
Section	Price
Lower Level	$15
Mezzanine	$14
Balcony	$12

8 **TENNIS** Jerry bought 6 cans of tennis balls. There are 3 tennis balls in each can. How many tennis balls did Jerry buy?   18 tennis balls

A60   Lesson 3-3   Math Triumphs

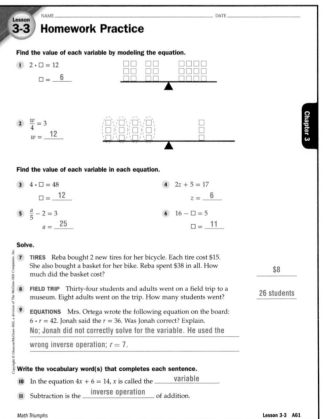

Find the value of each variable by modeling the equation.

1 $2 \cdot \square = 12$ $\square = $ 6

2 $\frac{w}{4} = 3$ $w = $ 12

Find the value of each variable in each equation.

3 $4 \cdot \square = 48$ $\square = $ 12

4 $2z + 5 = 17$ $z = $ 6

5 $\frac{a}{5} - 2 = 3$ $a = $ 25

6 $16 - \square = 5$ $\square = $ 11

Solve.

7 **TIRES** Reba bought 2 new tires for her bicycle. Each tire cost $15. She also bought a basket for her bike. Reba spent $38 in all. How much did the basket cost? $8

8 **FIELD TRIP** Thirty-four students and adults went on a field trip to a museum. Eight adults went on the trip. How many students went?   26 students

9 **EQUATIONS** Mrs. Ortega wrote the following equation on the board: $6 \cdot r = 42$. Jonah said the $r = 36$. Was Jonah correct? Explain.
No; Jonah did not correctly solve for the variable. He used the wrong inverse operation; $r = 7$.

Write the vocabulary word(s) that completes each sentence.

10 In the equation $4x + 6 = 14$, x is called the ___variable___

11 Subtraction is the ___inverse operation___ of addition.

Math Triumphs   Lesson 3-3   A61

Math Triumphs

Answer Key (Lesson 3-4)

Lesson 3-4 — Vocabulary and English Language Development

▶ Activate Prior Knowledge

Find the value of each expression.

1. $8 - 12 \div 3 + (6 \cdot 3 + 1)$ __23__

2. $6 \cdot 7 + (4 - 3) \cdot 8$ __50__

3. $20 + (7 - 3) - 8 \cdot 2$ __8__

4. $44 \div 4 + 9 \cdot 2^2 - 15$ __32__

Name the step that should be performed first in each expression.

5. $50 - 20 \div 2 + (6 + 1)$ __addition__

6. $4^2 \cdot 3 + 4 - 3 \cdot 8$ __exponent__

7. $35 \cdot 4 \div 5 + (8 - 3 + 2) - 12 \div 2$ __subtraction__

8. $10 \cdot 6 + 9 \cdot 2 - 15 \div 3$ __multiplication__

▶ Definition Review

Area is the number of square units needed to cover the surface enclosed by a geometric figure.

An **equation** is a mathematical sentence that contains an equals sign.

A **formula** is an equation that shows a relationship among certain quantities.

A **variable** is a symbol, usually a letter, used to represent a number.

9. What formula should be used to find the length of the rectangle at the right? __$A = \ell \cdot w$__

10. The area of the rectangle is 36 square meters. Find the length of the rectangle. __6 m__

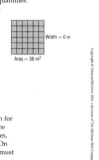

Width = 6 m

Area = 36 m²

▶ Application

Follow the directions for the activity.

- Students work with a partner.
- Each student creates six problems for their partner.
- Each problem must show a gridded rectangle like the one shown for Exercises 9 and 10. On two of the rectangles, give the area and the length; your partner must find the width. On two other rectangles, give the area and the width; your partner must find the length. On the last two rectangles, give the length and width; your partner must find the area.
- Exchange your six problems with your partner and solve the problems you receive. Return the completed problems to your partner. Check each other's work.

Lesson 3-4 — Skills Practice

Find the value of m, when p = 18 and t = 6.

1. $p = m + t$ $m =$ __12__

2. $t = m - p$ $m =$ __24__

3. $t = p + m$ $m =$ __−12__

4. $p = m \cdot t$ $m =$ __3__

Use the formula $A = \ell \cdot w$ to solve for ℓ, length.

5. The area of the rectangle is 36 square feet. Its width is 3 feet. What is the length of the rectangle?

$\ell =$ __12 ft__

6. The area of the rectangle is 18 square meters. Its width is 2 meters. What is the length of the rectangle?

$\ell =$ __9 m__

Use the formula $A = \ell \cdot w$ to solve for w, width.

7. The area of the rectangle is 48 square meters. Its length is 12 meters. What is the width of the rectangle?

$w =$ __4 m__

8. The area of the rectangle is 72 square feet. Its length is 9 feet. What is the width of the rectangle?

$w =$ __8 ft__

Use the formula $d = r \cdot t$ to solve for r, rate.

9. Melissa traveled 86 miles in 2 hours. What was her rate of speed?

$r =$ __43 miles per hour__

10. Jeremy traveled 168 miles in 3 hours. What was his rate of speed?

$r =$ __56 miles per hour__

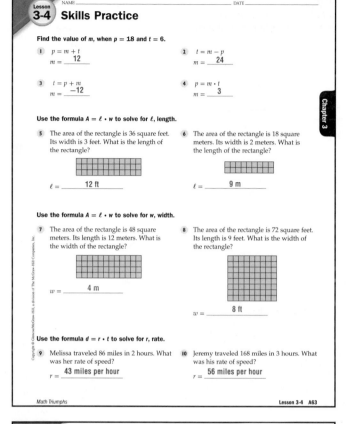

Lesson 3-4 — Problem-Solving Practice

Use the formula $A = \ell \cdot w$ to solve for w, width.

1. **PHOTOGRAPH** Brad has a photograph of his favorite football team that he wants framed. It is rectangular in shape, with a length of 25 inches. The area of the photograph is 375 square inches. What is the width of the photograph?

__$375 = 25 \cdot w$, so $w = 15$ in.__

2. **BLANKET** Rose is making a blanket for her friend for her birthday. She is using 48 square feet of material for the blanket. The length of the blanket is 8 feet. What is the width of the blanket Rose is making?

__$48 = 8 \cdot w$, so $w = 6$ ft__

Use the fact triangle shown at the right.

3. Write four related multiplication and division equations for the distance formula.

$d = r \cdot t$ $d = t \cdot r$

$t = d \div r$ $r = d \div t$

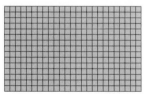

Use the formula $d = r \cdot t$ to solve for the missing variable.

4. **MOTORCYCLING** Mike rode his motorcycle a total of 944 miles on his vacation. It took him 16 hours to ride this distance. What was his rate of speed?

__59 miles per hour__

5. **TREADMILL** Ben enjoys working out. He walks on the treadmill at a rate of 5 miles per hour. How long would it take Ben to walk 10 miles at this rate of speed?

__2 hours__

Lesson 3-4 — Homework Practice

Find the value of c, when a = 3 and n = 24.

1. $n = c + a$ $c =$ __21__

2. $a = c - n$ $c =$ __27__

3. $n = c \cdot a$ $c =$ __8__

4. $a = n + c$ $c =$ __−21__

Use the formula $A = \ell \cdot w$ to solve for ℓ, length.

5. The area of the rectangle is 55 square meters. Its width is 5 meters. What is the length of the rectangle?

__$55 = \ell \cdot 5$, so $\ell = 11$ m__

6. The area of the rectangle is 192 square feet. Its width is 12 feet. What is the length of the rectangle?

__$192 = \ell \cdot 12$, so $\ell = 16$ ft__

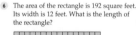

Use the formula $d = r \cdot t$ to solve for t, time.

7. Mr. Mason is driving his car at a rate of 58 miles per hour. How long will it take him to travel 232 miles?

__$232 = 58 \cdot t$, so $t = 4$ h__

8. Megan is biking at a rate of 14 miles per hour. How long will it take her to bike 98 miles?

__$98 = 14 \cdot t$, so $t = 7$ h__

Use the formula $d = r \cdot t$ to solve for the missing variable.

9. **EXERCISE** Kevin is training to run in a marathon. He just finished running 9 miles. It took him $1\frac{1}{2}$ hours. What was his rate of speed?

__6 miles per hour__

Write the vocabulary word that completes each sentence.

10. A ratio comparing two quantities with different kinds of units is called a(n) __rate__

11. $A = \ell \cdot w$, an equation that shows a relationship among quantities, is an example of a(n) __formula__

Answer Key (Lesson 4-1)

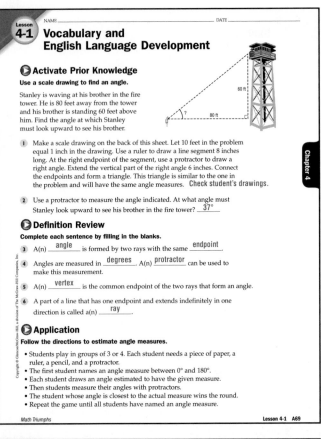

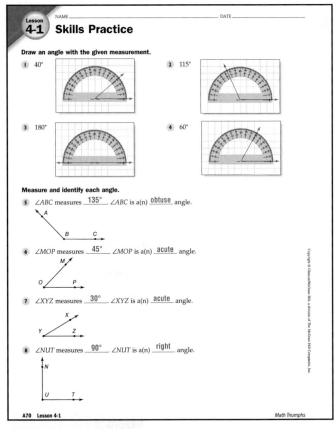

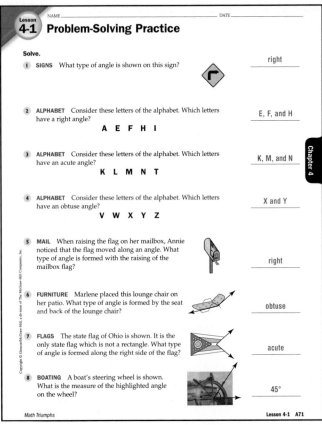

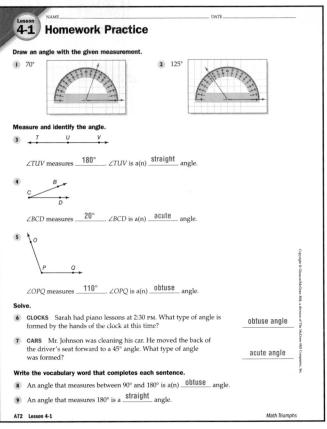

Answer Key (Lesson 4-2)

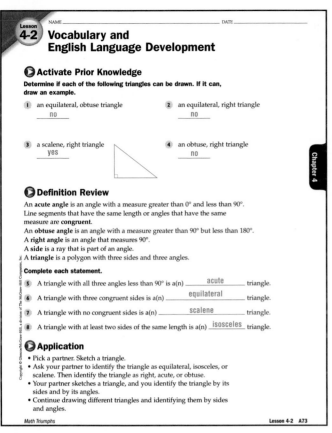

Vocabulary and English Language Development

Activate Prior Knowledge

Determine if each of the following triangles can be drawn. If it can, draw an example.

1. an equilateral, obtuse triangle
   no

2. an equilateral, right triangle
   no

3. a scalene, right triangle
   yes

4. an obtuse, right triangle
   no

Definition Review

An **acute angle** is an angle with a measure greater than 0° and less than 90°. Line segments that have the same length or angles that have the same measure are **congruent**.
An **obtuse angle** is an angle with a measure greater than 90° but less than 180°.
A **right angle** is an angle that measures 90°.
A **side** is a ray that is part of an angle.
A **triangle** is a polygon with three sides and three angles.

Complete each statement.

5. A triangle with all three angles less than 90° is a(n) **acute** triangle.

6. A triangle with three congruent sides is a(n) **equilateral** triangle.

7. A triangle with no congruent sides is a(n) **scalene** triangle.

8. A triangle with at least two sides of the same length is a(n) **isosceles** triangle.

Application

- Pick a partner. Sketch a triangle.
- Ask your partner to identify the triangle as equilateral, isosceles, or scalene. Then identify the triangle as right, acute, or obtuse.
- Your partner sketches a triangle, and you identify the triangle by its sides and by its angles.
- Continue drawing different triangles and identifying them by sides and angles.

Math Triumphs   Lesson 4-2   A73

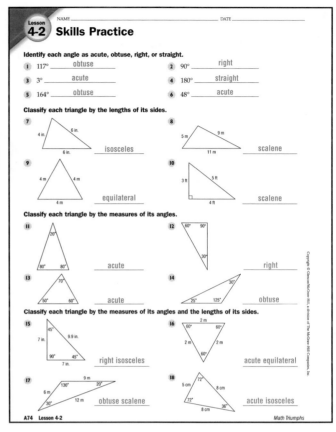

Skills Practice

Identify each angle as acute, obtuse, right, or straight.

1. 117° **obtuse**
2. 90° **right**
3. 3° **acute**
4. 180° **straight**
5. 164° **obtuse**
6. 48° **acute**

Classify each triangle by the lengths of its sides.

7. **isosceles**
8. **scalene**
9. **equilateral**
10. **scalene**

Classify each triangle by the measures of its angles.

11. **acute**
12. **right**
13. **acute**
14. **obtuse**

Classify each triangle by the measures of its angles and the lengths of its sides.

15. **right isosceles**
16. **acute equilateral**
17. **obtuse scalene**
18. **acute isosceles**

A74   Lesson 4-2   *Math Triumphs*

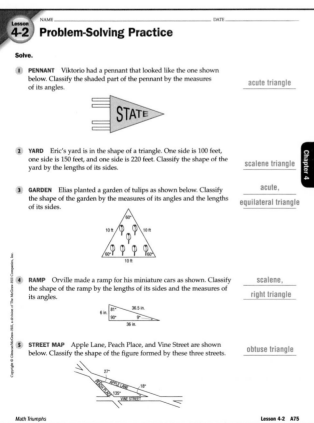

Problem-Solving Practice

Solve.

1. **PENNANT** Viktorio had a pennant that looked like the one shown below. Classify the shaded part of the pennant by the measures of its angles.

   acute triangle

2. **YARD** Eric's yard is in the shape of a triangle. One side is 100 feet, one side is 150 feet, and one side is 220 feet. Classify the shape of the yard by the lengths of its sides.

   scalene triangle

3. **GARDEN** Elias planted a garden of tulips as shown below. Classify the shape of the garden by the measures of its angles and the lengths of its sides.

   acute, equilateral triangle

4. **RAMP** Orville made a ramp for his miniature cars as shown. Classify the shape of the ramp by the lengths of its sides and the measures of its angles.

   scalene, right triangle

5. **STREET MAP** Apple Lane, Peach Place, and Vine Street are shown below. Classify the shape of the figure formed by these three streets.

   obtuse triangle

Math Triumphs   Lesson 4-2   A75

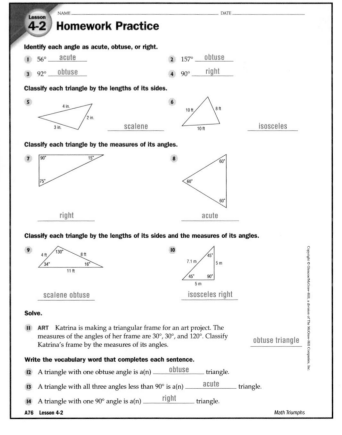

Homework Practice

Identify each angle as acute, obtuse, or right.

1. 56° **acute**
2. 157° **obtuse**
3. 92° **obtuse**
4. 90° **right**

Classify each triangle by the lengths of its sides.

5. **scalene**
6. **isosceles**

Classify each triangle by the measures of its angles.

7. **right**
8. **acute**

Classify each triangle by the lengths of its sides and the measures of its angles.

9. **scalene obtuse**
10. **isosceles right**

Solve.

11. **ART** Katrina is making a triangular frame for an art project. The measures of the angles of her frame are 30°, 30°, and 120°. Classify Katrina's frame by the measures of its angles.

   obtuse triangle

Write the vocabulary word that completes each sentence.

12. A triangle with one obtuse angle is a(n) **obtuse** triangle.

13. A triangle with all three angles less than 90° is a(n) **acute** triangle.

14. A triangle with one 90° angle is a(n) **right** triangle.

A76   Lesson 4-2   *Math Triumphs*

Math Triumphs

Answer Key (Lesson 4-3)

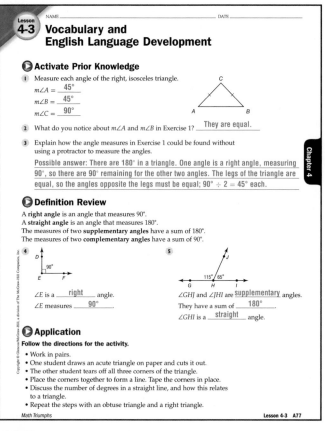

Lesson 4-3 Vocabulary and English Language Development

▶ Activate Prior Knowledge

1. Measure each angle of the right, isosceles triangle.

   $m\angle A =$ __45°__

   $m\angle B =$ __45°__

   $m\angle C =$ __90°__

2. What do you notice about $m\angle A$ and $m\angle B$ in Exercise 1? __They are equal.__

3. Explain how the angle measures in Exercise 1 could be found without using a protractor to measure the angles.

   Possible answer: There are 180° in a triangle. One angle is a right angle, measuring 90°, so there are 90° remaining for the other two angles. The legs of the triangle are equal, so the angles opposite the legs must be equal; 90° ÷ 2 = 45° each.

▶ Definition Review

A **right angle** is an angle that measures 90°.
A **straight angle** is an angle that measures 180°.
The measures of two **supplementary angles** have a sum of 180°.
The measures of two **complementary angles** have a sum of 90°.

4. $\angle E$ is a __right__ angle.

   $\angle E$ measures __90°__.

5. $\angle GHJ$ and $\angle JHI$ are __supplementary__ angles.

   They have a sum of __180°__.

   $\angle GHI$ is a __straight__ angle.

▶ Application

Follow the directions for the activity.

- Work in pairs.
- One student draws an acute triangle on paper and cuts it out.
- The other student tears off all three corners of the triangle.
- Place the corners together to form a line. Tape the corners in place.
- Discuss the number of degrees in a straight line, and how this relates to a triangle.
- Repeat the steps with an obtuse triangle and a right triangle.

Math Triumphs   Lesson 4-3   A77

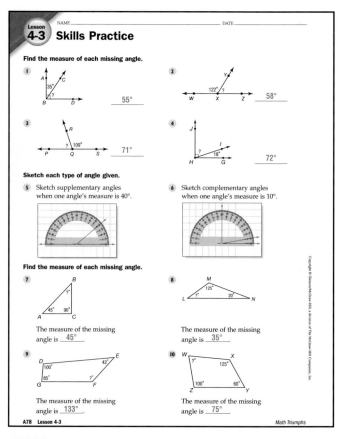

Lesson 4-3 Skills Practice

Find the measure of each missing angle.

1. __55°__

2. __58°__

3. __71°__

4. __72°__

Sketch each type of angle given.

5. Sketch supplementary angles when one angle's measure is 40°.

6. Sketch complementary angles when one angle's measure is 10°.

Find the measure of each missing angle.

7. The measure of the missing angle is __45°__.

8. The measure of the missing angle is __35°__.

9. The measure of the missing angle is __133°__.

10. The measure of the missing angle is __75°__.

A78   Lesson 4-3   Math Triumphs

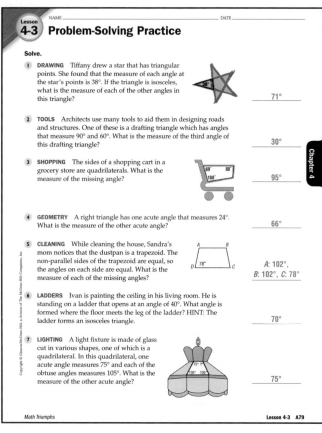

Lesson 4-3 Problem-Solving Practice

Solve.

1. **DRAWING** Tiffany drew a star that has triangular points. She found that the measure of each angle at the star's points is 38°. If the triangle is isosceles, what is the measure of each of the other angles in this triangle?   __71°__

2. **TOOLS** Architects use many tools to aid them in designing roads and structures. One of these is a drafting triangle which has angles that measure 90° and 60°. What is the measure of the third angle of this drafting triangle?   __30°__

3. **SHOPPING** The sides of a shopping cart in a grocery store are quadrilaterals. What is the measure of the missing angle?   __95°__

4. **GEOMETRY** A right triangle has one acute angle that measures 24°. What is the measure of the other acute angle?   __66°__

5. **CLEANING** While cleaning the house, Sandra's mom notices that the dustpan is a trapezoid. The non-parallel sides of the trapezoid are equal, so the angles on each side are equal. What is the measure of each of the missing angles?   __A: 102°, B: 102°, C: 78°__

6. **LADDERS** Ivan is painting the ceiling in his living room. He is standing on a ladder that opens at an angle of 40°. What angle is formed where the floor meets the leg of the ladder? HINT: The ladder forms an isosceles triangle.   __70°__

7. **LIGHTING** A light fixture is made of glass cut in various shapes, one of which is a quadrilateral. In this quadrilateral, one acute angle measures 75° and each of the obtuse angles measures 105°. What is the measure of the other acute angle?   __75°__

Math Triumphs   Lesson 4-3   A79

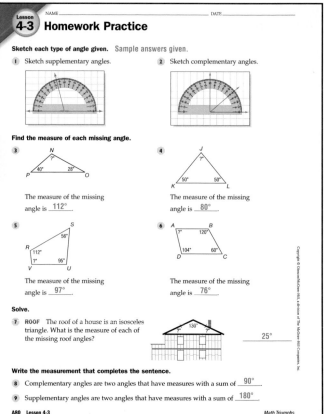

Lesson 4-3 Homework Practice

Sketch each type of angle given. Sample answers given.

1. Sketch supplementary angles.

2. Sketch complementary angles.

Find the measure of each missing angle.

3. The measure of the missing angle is __112°__.

4. The measure of the missing angle is __80°__.

5. The measure of the missing angle is __97°__.

6. The measure of the missing angle is __76°__.

Solve.

7. **ROOF** The roof of a house is an isosceles triangle. What is the measure of each of the missing roof angles?   __25°__

Write the measurement that completes the sentence.

8. Complementary angles are two angles that have measures with a sum of __90°__.

9. Supplementary angles are two angles that have measures with a sum of __180°__.

A80   Lesson 4-3   Math Triumphs

Answer Key (Lesson 4-4)

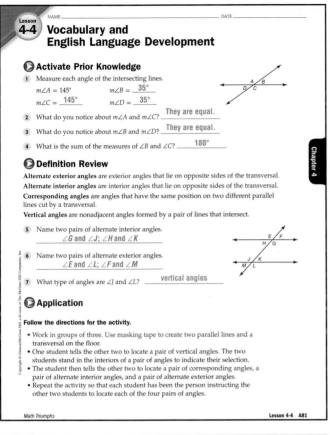

Lesson 4-4 Vocabulary and English Language Development

Activate Prior Knowledge

1. Measure each angle of the intersecting lines.

$m\angle A = 145°$ $m\angle B = \underline{35°}$

$m\angle C = \underline{145°}$ $m\angle D = \underline{35°}$

2. What do you notice about $m\angle A$ and $m\angle C$? **They are equal.**

3. What do you notice about $m\angle B$ and $m\angle D$? **They are equal.**

4. What is the sum of the measures of $\angle B$ and $\angle C$? **180°**

Definition Review

Alternate exterior angles are exterior angles that lie on opposite sides of the transversal.

Alternate interior angles are interior angles that lie on opposite sides of the transversal.

Corresponding angles are angles that have the same position on two different parallel lines cut by a transversal.

Vertical angles are nonadjacent angles formed by a pair of lines that intersect.

5. Name two pairs of alternate interior angles.
   $\angle G$ and $\angle J$; $\angle H$ and $\angle K$

6. Name two pairs of alternate exterior angles.
   $\angle E$ and $\angle L$; $\angle F$ and $\angle M$

7. What type of angles are $\angle J$ and $\angle L$? **vertical angles**

Application

Follow the directions for the activity.

- Work in groups of three. Use masking tape to create two parallel lines and a transversal on the floor.
- One student tells the other two to locate a pair of vertical angles. The two students stand in the interiors of a pair of angles to indicate their selection.
- The student then tells the other two to locate a pair of corresponding angles, a pair of alternate interior angles, and a pair of alternate exterior angles.
- Repeat the activity so that each student has been the person instructing the other two students to locate each of the four pairs of angles.

Math Triumphs   Lesson 4-4   A81

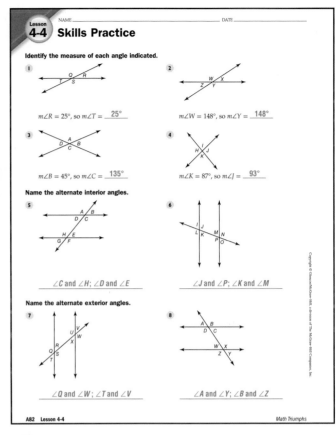

Lesson 4-4 Skills Practice

Identify the measure of each angle indicated.

1. $m\angle R = 25°$, so $m\angle T = \underline{25°}$

2. $m\angle W = 148°$, so $m\angle Y = \underline{148°}$

3. $m\angle B = 45°$, so $m\angle C = \underline{135°}$

4. $m\angle K = 87°$, so $m\angle J = \underline{93°}$

Name the alternate interior angles.

5. **$\angle C$ and $\angle H$; $\angle D$ and $\angle E$**

6. **$\angle J$ and $\angle P$; $\angle K$ and $\angle M$**

Name the alternate exterior angles.

7. **$\angle Q$ and $\angle W$; $\angle T$ and $\angle V$**

8. **$\angle A$ and $\angle Y$; $\angle B$ and $\angle Z$**

A82   Lesson 4-4   *Math Triumphs*

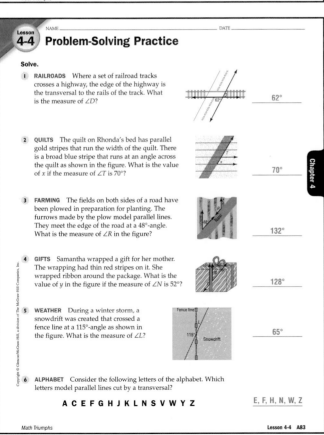

Lesson 4-4 Problem-Solving Practice

Solve.

1. **RAILROADS** Where a set of railroad tracks crosses a highway, the edge of the highway is the transversal to the rails of the track. What is the measure of $\angle D$?   **62°**

2. **QUILTS** The quilt on Rhonda's bed has parallel gold stripes that run the width of the quilt. There is a broad blue stripe that runs at an angle across the quilt as shown in the figure. What is the value of x if the measure of $\angle T$ is 70°?   **70°**

3. **FARMING** The fields on both sides of a road have been plowed in preparation for planting. The furrows made by the plow model parallel lines. They meet the edge of the road at a 48°-angle. What is the measure of $\angle R$ in the figure?   **132°**

4. **GIFTS** Samantha wrapped a gift for her mother. The wrapping had thin red stripes on it. She wrapped ribbon around the package. What is the value of y in the figure if the measure of $\angle N$ is 52°?   **128°**

5. **WEATHER** During a winter storm, a snowdrift was created that crossed a fence line at a 115°-angle as shown in the figure. What is the measure of $\angle L$?   **65°**

6. **ALPHABET** Consider the following letters of the alphabet. Which letters model parallel lines cut by a transversal?

   A C E F G H J K L N S V W Y Z   **E, F, H, N, W, Z**

Math Triumphs   Lesson 4-4   A83

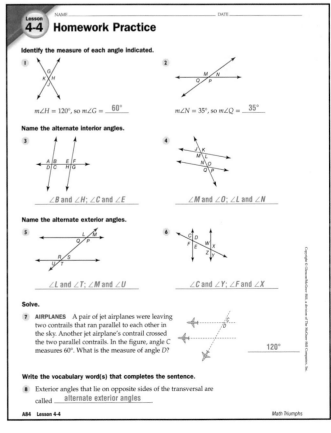

Lesson 4-4 Homework Practice

Identify the measure of each angle indicated.

1. $m\angle H = 120°$, so $m\angle G = \underline{60°}$

2. $m\angle N = 35°$, so $m\angle Q = \underline{35°}$

Name the alternate interior angles.

3. **$\angle B$ and $\angle H$; $\angle C$ and $\angle E$**

4. **$\angle M$ and $\angle O$; $\angle L$ and $\angle N$**

Name the alternate exterior angles.

5. **$\angle L$ and $\angle T$; $\angle M$ and $\angle U$**

6. **$\angle C$ and $\angle Y$; $\angle F$ and $\angle X$**

Solve.

7. **AIRPLANES** A pair of jet airplanes were leaving two contrails that ran parallel to each other in the sky. Another jet airplane's contrail crossed the two parallel contrails. In the figure, angle C measures 60°. What is the measure of angle D?   **120°**

Write the vocabulary word(s) that completes the sentence.

8. Exterior angles that lie on opposite sides of the transversal are called **alternate exterior angles**

A84   Lesson 4-4   *Math Triumphs*

Math Triumphs   **Lesson 4-4   A213**

Answer Key (Lesson 5-1)

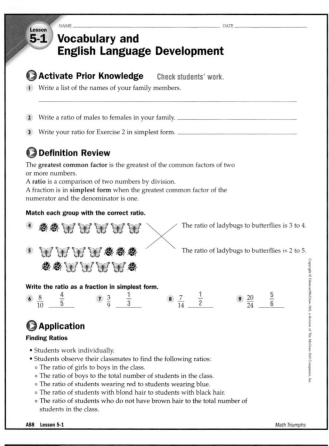

Vocabulary and English Language Development

Activate Prior Knowledge   Check students' work.

1 Write a list of the names of your family members.

2 Write a ratio of males to females in your family. _____

3 Write your ratio for Exercise 2 in simplest form. _____

Definition Review

The **greatest common factor** is the greatest of the common factors of two or more numbers.
A **ratio** is a comparison of two numbers by division.
A fraction is in **simplest form** when the greatest common factor of the numerator and the denominator is one.

Match each group with the correct ratio.

4 The ratio of ladybugs to butterflies is 3 to 4.

5 The ratio of ladybugs to butterflies is 2 to 5.

Write the ratio as a fraction in simplest form.

6 $\frac{8}{10}$ $\frac{4}{5}$ 7 $\frac{3}{9}$ $\frac{1}{3}$ 8 $\frac{7}{14}$ $\frac{1}{2}$ 9 $\frac{20}{24}$ $\frac{5}{6}$

Application

Finding Ratios

- Students work individually.
- Students observe their classmates to find the following ratios:
  ○ The ratio of girls to boys in the class.
  ○ The ratio of boys to the total number of students in the class.
  ○ The ratio of students wearing red to students wearing blue.
  ○ The ratio of students with blond hair to students with black hair.
  ○ The ratio of students who do not have brown hair to the total number of students in the class.

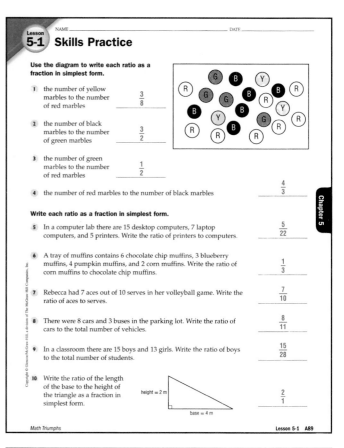

Skills Practice

Use the diagram to write each ratio as a fraction in simplest form.

1 the number of yellow marbles to the number of red marbles $\frac{3}{8}$

2 the number of black marbles to the number of green marbles $\frac{3}{2}$

3 the number of green marbles to the number of red marbles $\frac{1}{2}$

4 the number of red marbles to the number of black marbles $\frac{4}{3}$

Write each ratio as a fraction in simplest form.

5 In a computer lab there are 15 desktop computers, 7 laptop computers, and 5 printers. Write the ratio of printers to computers. $\frac{5}{22}$

6 A tray of muffins contains 6 chocolate chip muffins, 3 blueberry muffins, 4 pumpkin muffins, and 2 corn muffins. Write the ratio of corn muffins to chocolate chip muffins. $\frac{1}{3}$

7 Rebecca had 7 aces out of 10 serves in her volleyball game. Write the ratio of aces to serves. $\frac{7}{10}$

8 There were 8 cars and 3 buses in the parking lot. Write the ratio of cars to the total number of vehicles. $\frac{8}{11}$

9 In a classroom there are 15 boys and 13 girls. Write the ratio of boys to the total number of students. $\frac{15}{28}$

10 Write the ratio of the length of the base to the height of the triangle as a fraction in simplest form.   height = 2 m   base = 4 m $\frac{2}{1}$

Problem-Solving Practice

Solve.

1 GARDENING   The dimensions of a flower garden are 15 feet long by 5 feet wide. In simplest form, what is the ratio of the garden's width to its length? $\frac{1}{3}$

width = 5 feet
length = 15 feet

2 HOBBIES   A jewelry-making kit contains 15 blue beads, 25 red beads, 10 yellow beads, and 30 black beads. In simplest form, what is the ratio of red beads to black beads? $\frac{5}{6}$

3 ELECTIONS   Carlos, Leona, and Kim ran for class president. The table below shows the number of votes each student received. In simplest form, what is the ratio of votes Carlos received to the total number of votes? $\frac{11}{28}$

Votes Counted for Class President	
Carlos	JHT JHT JHT JHT II
Leona	JHT JHT JHT JHT I
Kim	JHT JHT III

4 WEATHER   During the first 28 days of April, it rained on 8 days. If it rains the last two days of April, what will be the ratio of the number of rainy days in the month to the total number of days in the month? Write your answer in simplest form. $\frac{1}{3}$

5 BASEBALL   A baseball team played 120 games during a season. They won 80 games. What is the ratio of the number of games lost to the total number of games played? Write your answer in simplest form. $\frac{1}{3}$

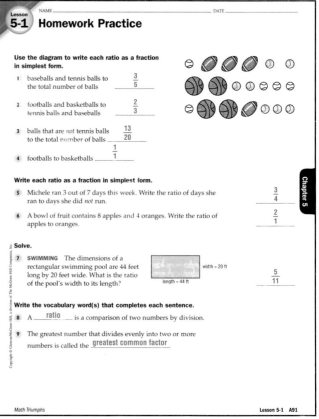

Homework Practice

Use the diagram to write each ratio as a fraction in simplest form.

1 baseballs and tennis balls to the total number of balls $\frac{3}{5}$

2 footballs and basketballs to tennis balls and baseballs $\frac{2}{3}$

3 balls that are *not* tennis balls to the total number of balls $\frac{13}{20}$

4 footballs to basketballs $\frac{1}{1}$

Write each ratio as a fraction in simplest form.

5 Michele ran 3 out of 7 days this week. Write the ratio of days she ran to days she did *not* run. $\frac{3}{4}$

6 A bowl of fruit contains 8 apples and 4 oranges. Write the ratio of apples to oranges. $\frac{2}{1}$

Solve.

7 SWIMMING   The dimensions of a rectangular swimming pool are 44 feet long by 20 feet wide. What is the ratio of the pool's width to its length?   width = 20 ft   length = 44 ft $\frac{5}{11}$

Write the vocabulary word(s) that completes each sentence.

8 A ___ratio___ is a comparison of two numbers by division.

9 The greatest number that divides evenly into two or more numbers is called the ___greatest common factor___

Answer Key (Lesson 5-2)

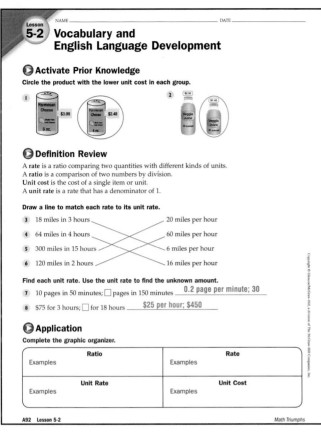

Lesson 5-2 Vocabulary and English Language Development

Activate Prior Knowledge
Circle the product with the lower unit cost in each group.

1. Parmesan Cheese $3.99 / 6 oz. — Parmesan Cheese $2.48 / 4 oz.
2. Veggie Juice $2.50 — Veggie Juice $1.48

Definition Review
A **rate** is a ratio comparing two quantities with different kinds of units.
A **ratio** is a comparison of two numbers by division.
Unit cost is the cost of a single item or unit.
A **unit rate** is a rate that has a denominator of 1.

Draw a line to match each rate to its unit rate.

3. 18 miles in 3 hours — 20 miles per hour
4. 64 miles in 4 hours — 60 miles per hour
5. 300 miles in 15 hours — 6 miles per hour
6. 120 miles in 2 hours — 16 miles per hour

Find each unit rate. Use the unit rate to find the unknown amount.

7. 10 pages in 50 minutes; ☐ pages in 150 minutes — 0.2 page per minute; 30
8. $75 for 3 hours; ☐ for 18 hours — $25 per hour; $450

Application
Complete the graphic organizer.

Ratio	Rate
Examples	Examples

Unit Rate	Unit Cost
Examples	Examples

A92   Lesson 5-2   Math Triumphs

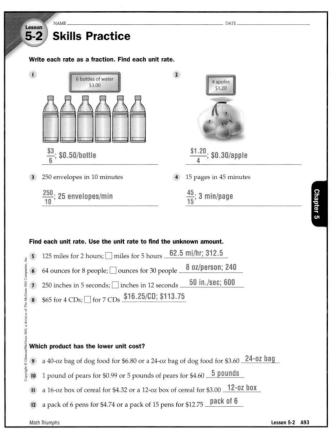

Lesson 5-2 Skills Practice

Write each rate as a fraction. Find each unit rate.

1. 6 bottles of water $3.00 — $\frac{$3}{6}$; $0.50/bottle
2. 4 apples $1.20 — $\frac{$1.20}{4}$; $0.30/apple
3. 250 envelopes in 10 minutes — $\frac{250}{10}$; 25 envelopes/min
4. 15 pages in 45 minutes — $\frac{45}{15}$; 3 min/page

Find each unit rate. Use the unit rate to find the unknown amount.

5. 125 miles for 2 hours; ☐ miles for 5 hours — 62.5 mi/hr; 312.5
6. 64 ounces for 8 people; ☐ ounces for 30 people — 8 oz/person; 240
7. 250 inches in 5 seconds; ☐ inches in 12 seconds — 50 in./sec; 600
8. $65 for 4 CDs; ☐ for 7 CDs — $16.25/CD; $113.75

Which product has the lower unit cost?

9. a 40-oz bag of dog food for $6.80 or a 24-oz bag of dog food for $3.60 — 24-oz bag
10. 1 pound of pears for $0.99 or 5 pounds of pears for $4.60 — 5 pounds
11. a 16-oz box of cereal for $4.32 or a 12-oz box of cereal for $3.00 — 12-oz box
12. a pack of 6 pens for $4.74 or a pack of 15 pens for $12.75 — pack of 6

Math Triumphs   Lesson 5-2   A93

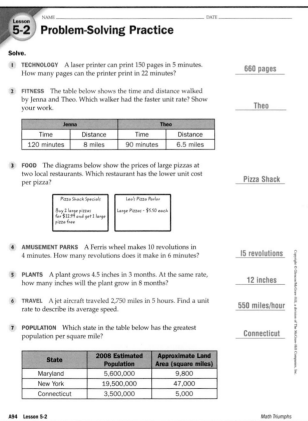

Lesson 5-2 Problem-Solving Practice

Solve.

1. **TECHNOLOGY**   A laser printer can print 150 pages in 5 minutes. How many pages can the printer print in 22 minutes? — 660 pages
2. **FITNESS**   The table below shows the time and distance walked by Jenna and Theo. Which walker had the faster unit rate? Show your work. — Theo

Jenna		Theo	
Time	Distance	Time	Distance
120 minutes	8 miles	90 minutes	6.5 miles

3. **FOOD**   The diagrams below show the prices of large pizzas at two local restaurants. Which restaurant has the lower unit cost per pizza? — Pizza Shack

Pizza Shack Specials — Buy 2 large pizzas for $12.99 and get 1 large pizza free

Leo's Pizza Parlor — Large Pizzas - $5.50 each

4. **AMUSEMENT PARKS**   A Ferris wheel makes 10 revolutions in 4 minutes. How many revolutions does it make in 6 minutes? — 15 revolutions
5. **PLANTS**   A plant grows 4.5 inches in 3 months. At the same rate, how many inches will the plant grow in 8 months? — 12 inches
6. **TRAVEL**   A jet aircraft traveled 2,750 miles in 5 hours. Find a unit rate to describe its average speed. — 550 miles/hour
7. **POPULATION**   Which state in the table below has the greatest population per square mile? — Connecticut

State	2008 Estimated Population	Approximate Land Area (square miles)
Maryland	5,600,000	9,800
New York	19,500,000	47,000
Connecticut	3,500,000	5,000

A94   Lesson 5-2   Math Triumphs

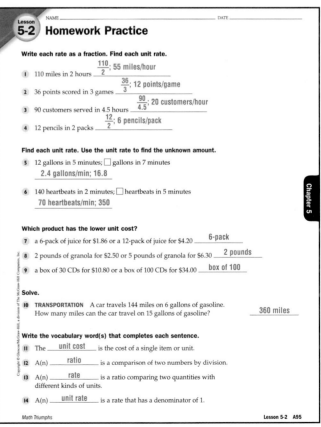

Lesson 5-2 Homework Practice

Write each rate as a fraction. Find each unit rate.

1. 110 miles in 2 hours — $\frac{110}{2}$; 55 miles/hour
2. 36 points scored in 3 games — $\frac{36}{3}$; 12 points/game
3. 90 customers served in 4.5 hours — $\frac{90}{4.5}$; 20 customers/hour
4. 12 pencils in 2 packs — $\frac{12}{2}$; 6 pencils/pack

Find each unit rate. Use the unit rate to find the unknown amount.

5. 12 gallons in 5 minutes; ☐ gallons in 7 minutes — 2.4 gallons/min; 16.8
6. 140 heartbeats in 2 minutes; ☐ heartbeats in 5 minutes — 70 heartbeats/min; 350

Which product has the lower unit cost?

7. a 6-pack of juice for $1.86 or a 12-pack of juice for $4.20 — 6-pack
8. 2 pounds of granola for $2.50 or 5 pounds of granola for $6.30 — 2 pounds
9. a box of 30 CDs for $10.80 or a box of 100 CDs for $34.00 — box of 100

Solve.

10. **TRANSPORTATION**   A car travels 144 miles on 6 gallons of gasoline. How many miles can the car travel on 15 gallons of gasoline? — 360 miles

Write the vocabulary word(s) that completes each sentence.

11. The __unit cost__ is the cost of a single item or unit.
12. A(n) __ratio__ is a comparison of two numbers by division.
13. A(n) __rate__ is a ratio comparing two quantities with different kinds of units.
14. A(n) __unit rate__ is a rate that has a denominator of 1.

Math Triumphs   Lesson 5-2   A95

Answer Key (Lesson 5-3)

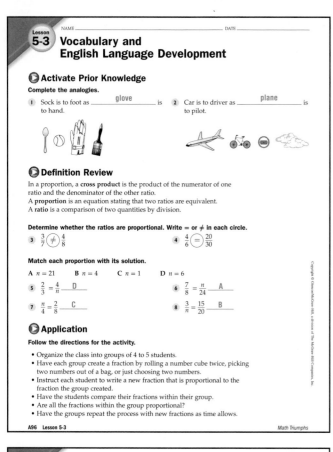

Vocabulary and English Language Development

▶ Activate Prior Knowledge

Complete the analogies.

1. Sock is to foot as ___glove___ is to hand.
2. Car is to driver as ___plane___ is to pilot.

▶ Definition Review

In a proportion, a **cross product** is the product of the numerator of one ratio and the denominator of the other ratio.

A **proportion** is an equation stating that two ratios are equivalent.

A **ratio** is a comparison of two quantities by division.

Determine whether the ratios are proportional. Write = or ≠ in each circle.

3. $\frac{3}{7} \neq \frac{4}{8}$
4. $\frac{4}{6} = \frac{20}{30}$

Match each proportion with its solution.

A $n = 21$ B $n = 4$ C $n = 1$ D $n = 6$

5. $\frac{2}{3} = \frac{4}{n}$ D
6. $\frac{7}{8} = \frac{n}{24}$ A
7. $\frac{n}{4} = \frac{2}{8}$ C
8. $\frac{3}{n} = \frac{15}{20}$ B

▶ Application

Follow the directions for the activity.

• Organize the class into groups of 4 to 5 students.
• Have each group create a fraction by rolling a number cube twice, picking two numbers out of a bag, or just choosing two numbers.
• Instruct each student to write a new fraction that is proportional to the fraction the group created.
• Have the students compare their fractions within their group.
• Are all the fractions within the group proportional?
• Have the groups repeat the process with new fractions as time allows.

A96   Lesson 5-3   Math Triumphs

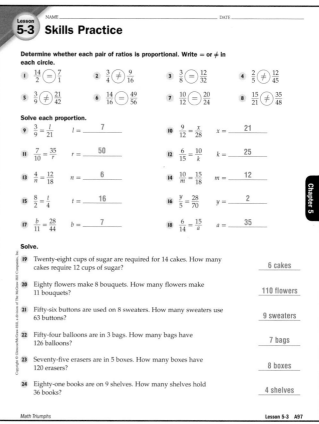

Skills Practice

Determine whether each pair of ratios is proportional. Write = or ≠ in each circle.

1. $\frac{14}{2} = \frac{7}{1}$
2. $\frac{3}{4} \neq \frac{9}{16}$
3. $\frac{3}{8} = \frac{12}{32}$
4. $\frac{2}{5} \neq \frac{12}{45}$
5. $\frac{3}{9} \neq \frac{21}{42}$
6. $\frac{14}{16} = \frac{49}{56}$
7. $\frac{10}{12} = \frac{20}{24}$
8. $\frac{15}{21} \neq \frac{35}{48}$

Solve each proportion.

9. $\frac{3}{9} = \frac{l}{21}$ $l = 7$
10. $\frac{9}{12} = \frac{x}{28}$ $x = 21$
11. $\frac{7}{10} = \frac{35}{r}$ $r = 50$
12. $\frac{6}{15} = \frac{10}{k}$ $k = 25$
13. $\frac{4}{n} = \frac{12}{18}$ $n = 6$
14. $\frac{10}{m} = \frac{15}{18}$ $m = 12$
15. $\frac{8}{2} = \frac{t}{4}$ $t = 16$
16. $\frac{y}{5} = \frac{28}{70}$ $y = 2$
17. $\frac{b}{11} = \frac{28}{44}$ $b = 7$
18. $\frac{6}{14} = \frac{15}{a}$ $a = 35$

Solve.

19. Twenty-eight cups of sugar are required for 14 cakes. How many cakes require 12 cups of sugar?   6 cakes
20. Eighty flowers make 8 bouquets. How many flowers make 11 bouquets?   110 flowers
21. Fifty-six buttons are used on 8 sweaters. How many sweaters use 63 buttons?   9 sweaters
22. Fifty-four balloons are in 3 bags. How many bags have 126 balloons?   7 bags
23. Seventy-five erasers are in 5 boxes. How many boxes have 120 erasers?   8 boxes
24. Eighty-one books are on 9 shelves. How many shelves hold 36 books?   4 shelves

Math Triumphs   Lesson 5-3   A97

Chapter 5

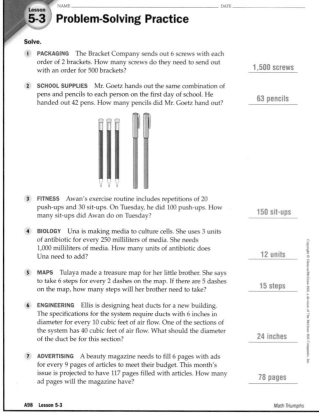

Problem-Solving Practice

Solve.

1. **PACKAGING** The Bracket Company sends out 6 screws with each order of 2 brackets. How many screws do they need to send out with an order for 500 brackets?   1,500 screws

2. **SCHOOL SUPPLIES** Mr. Goetz hands out the same combination of pens and pencils to each person on the first day of school. He handed out 42 pens. How many pencils did Mr. Goetz hand out?   63 pencils

3. **FITNESS** Awan's exercise routine includes repetitions of 20 push-ups and 30 sit-ups. On Tuesday, he did 100 push-ups. How many sit-ups did Awan do on Tuesday?   150 sit-ups

4. **BIOLOGY** Una is making media to culture cells. She uses 3 units of antibiotic for every 250 milliliters of media. She needs 1,000 milliliters of media. How many units of antibiotic does Una need to add?   12 units

5. **MAPS** Tulaya made a treasure map for her little brother. She says to take 6 steps for every 2 dashes on the map. If there are 5 dashes on the map, how many steps will her brother need to take?   15 steps

6. **ENGINEERING** Ellis is designing heat ducts for a new building. The specifications for the system require ducts with 6 inches in diameter for every 10 cubic feet of air flow. One of the sections of the system has 40 cubic feet of air flow. What should the diameter of the duct be for this section?   24 inches

7. **ADVERTISING** A beauty magazine needs to fill 6 pages with ads for every 9 pages of articles to meet their budget. This month's issue is projected to have 117 pages filled with articles. How many ad pages will the magazine have?   78 pages

A98   Lesson 5-3   Math Triumphs

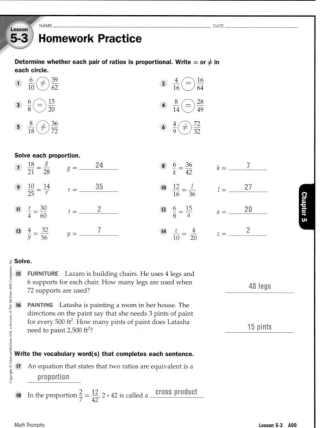

Homework Practice

Determine whether each pair of ratios is proportional. Write = or ≠ in each circle.

1. $\frac{6}{10} \neq \frac{39}{62}$
2. $\frac{4}{16} = \frac{16}{64}$
3. $\frac{6}{8} = \frac{15}{20}$
4. $\frac{8}{14} = \frac{28}{49}$
5. $\frac{8}{18} \neq \frac{36}{72}$
6. $\frac{4}{9} \neq \frac{72}{32}$

Solve each proportion.

7. $\frac{18}{21} = \frac{g}{28}$ $g = 24$
8. $\frac{6}{k} = \frac{36}{42}$ $k = 7$
9. $\frac{10}{25} = \frac{14}{r}$ $r = 35$
10. $\frac{12}{16} = \frac{l}{36}$ $l = 27$
11. $\frac{t}{4} = \frac{30}{60}$ $t = 2$
12. $\frac{6}{8} = \frac{15}{a}$ $a = 20$
13. $\frac{9}{y} = \frac{32}{56}$ $y = 7$
14. $\frac{z}{10} = \frac{4}{20}$ $z = 2$

Solve.

15. **FURNITURE** Lazaro is building chairs. He uses 4 legs and 6 supports for each chair. How many legs are used when 72 supports are used?   48 legs

16. **PAINTING** Latasha is painting a room in her house. The directions on the paint say that she needs 3 pints of paint for every 500 ft². How many pints of paint does Latasha need to paint 2,500 ft²?   15 pints

Write the vocabulary word(s) that completes each sentence.

17. An equation that states that two ratios are equivalent is a ___proportion___

18. In the proportion $\frac{2}{7} = \frac{12}{42}$, $2 \cdot 42$ is called a ___cross product___

Math Triumphs   Lesson 5-3   A99

Chapter 5

Answer Key (Lesson 5-4)

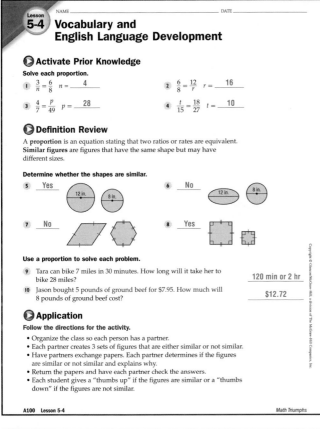

Lesson 5-4

Vocabulary and English Language Development

Activate Prior Knowledge

Solve each proportion.

1. $\frac{3}{n} = \frac{6}{8}$ $n = \underline{4}$

2. $\frac{6}{8} = \frac{12}{r}$ $r = \underline{16}$

3. $\frac{4}{7} = \frac{p}{49}$ $p = \underline{28}$

4. $\frac{t}{15} = \frac{18}{27}$ $t = \underline{10}$

Definition Review

A **proportion** is an equation stating that two ratios or rates are equivalent.
Similar figures are figures that have the same shape but may have different sizes.

Determine whether the shapes are similar.

5. Yes

6. No

7. No

8. Yes

Use a proportion to solve each problem.

9. Tara can bike 7 miles in 30 minutes. How long will it take her to bike 28 miles? **120 min or 2 hr**

10. Jason bought 5 pounds of ground beef for $7.95. How much will 8 pounds of ground beef cost? **$12.72**

Application

Follow the directions for the activity.

- Organize the class so each person has a partner.
- Each partner creates 3 sets of figures that are either similar or not similar.
- Have partners exchange papers. Each partner determines if the figures are similar or not similar and explains why.
- Return the papers and have each partner check the answers.
- Each student gives a "thumbs up" if the figures are similar or a "thumbs down" if the figures are not similar.

A100 Lesson 5-4

Math Triumphs

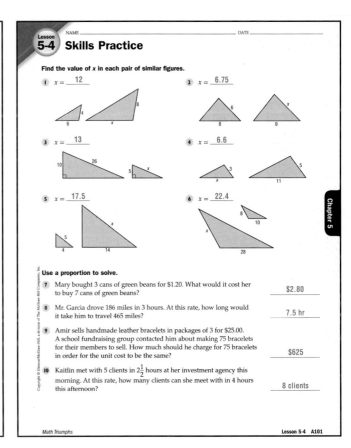

Lesson 5-4

Skills Practice

Find the value of *x* in each pair of similar figures.

1. $x = \underline{12}$

2. $x = \underline{6.75}$

3. $x = \underline{13}$

4. $x = \underline{6.6}$

5. $x = \underline{17.5}$

6. $x = \underline{22.4}$

Use a proportion to solve.

7. Mary bought 3 cans of green beans for $1.20. What would it cost her to buy 7 cans of green beans? **$2.80**

8. Mr. Garcia drove 186 miles in 3 hours. At this rate, how long would it take him to travel 465 miles? **7.5 hr**

9. Amir sells handmade leather bracelets in packages of 3 for $25.00. A school fundraising group contacted him about making 75 bracelets for their members to sell. How much should he charge for 75 bracelets in order for the unit cost to be the same? **$625**

10. Kaitlin met with 5 clients in $2\frac{1}{2}$ hours at her investment agency this morning. At this rate, how many clients can she meet with in 4 hours this afternoon? **8 clients**

Math Triumphs

Lesson 5-4 A101

Chapter 5

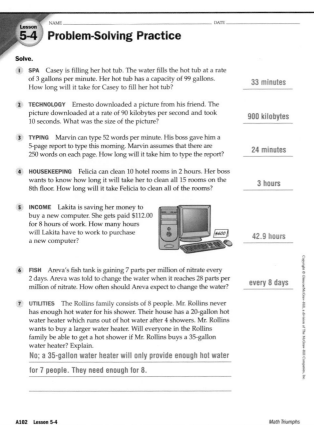

Lesson 5-4

Problem-Solving Practice

Solve.

1. **SPA** Casey is filling her hot tub. The water fills the hot tub at a rate of 3 gallons per minute. Her hot tub has a capacity of 99 gallons. How long will it take for Casey to fill her hot tub? **33 minutes**

2. **TECHNOLOGY** Ernesto downloaded a picture from his friend. The picture downloaded at a rate of 90 kilobytes per second and took 10 seconds. What was the size of the picture? **900 kilobytes**

3. **TYPING** Marvin can type 52 words per minute. His boss gave him a 5-page report to type this morning. Marvin assumes that there are 250 words on each page. How long will it take him to type the report? **24 minutes**

4. **HOUSEKEEPING** Felicia can clean 10 hotel rooms in 2 hours. Her boss wants to know how long it will take her to clean all 15 rooms on the 8th floor. How long will it take Felicia to clean all of the rooms? **3 hours**

5. **INCOME** Lakita is saving her money to buy a new computer. She gets paid $112.00 for 8 hours of work. How many hours will Lakita have to work to purchase a new computer? **42.9 hours**

6. **FISH** Areva's fish tank is gaining 7 parts per million of nitrate every 2 days. Areva was told to change the water when it reaches 28 parts per million of nitrate. How often should Areva expect to change the water? **every 8 days**

7. **UTILITIES** The Rollins family consists of 8 people. Mr. Rollins never has enough hot water for his shower. Their house has a 20-gallon hot water heater which runs out of hot water after 4 showers. Mr. Rollins wants to buy a larger water heater. Will everyone in the Rollins family be able to get a hot shower if Mr. Rollins buys a 35-gallon water heater? Explain.

No; a 35-gallon water heater will only provide enough hot water
for 7 people. They need enough for 8.

A102 Lesson 5-4

Math Triumphs

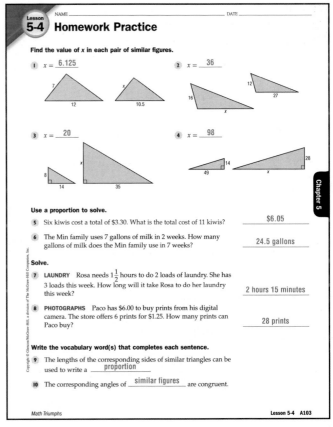

Lesson 5-4

Homework Practice

Find the value of *x* in each pair of similar figures.

1. $x = \underline{6.125}$

2. $x = \underline{36}$

3. $x = \underline{20}$

4. $x = \underline{98}$

Use a proportion to solve.

5. Six kiwis cost a total of $3.30. What is the total cost of 11 kiwis? **$6.05**

6. The Min family uses 7 gallons of milk in 2 weeks. How many gallons of milk does the Min family use in 7 weeks? **24.5 gallons**

Solve.

7. **LAUNDRY** Rosa needs $1\frac{1}{2}$ hours to do 2 loads of laundry. She has 3 loads this week. How long will it take Rosa to do her laundry this week? **2 hours 15 minutes**

8. **PHOTOGRAPHS** Paco has $6.00 to buy prints from his digital camera. The store offers 6 prints for $1.25. How many prints can Paco buy? **28 prints**

Write the vocabulary word(s) that completes each sentence.

9. The lengths of the corresponding sides of similar triangles can be used to write a **proportion**.

10. The corresponding angles of **similar figures** are congruent.

Math Triumphs

Lesson 5-4 A103

Chapter 5

Math Triumphs

Answer Key (Lesson 6-1)

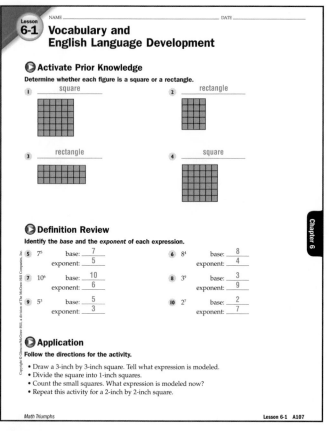

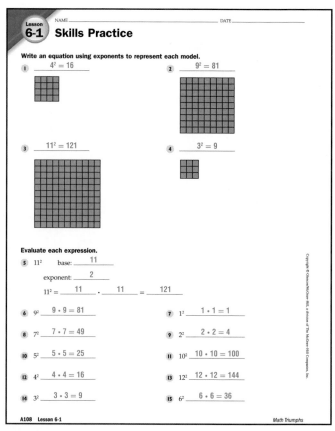

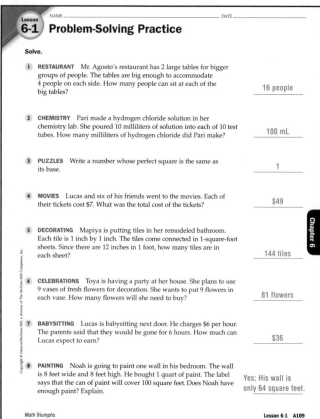

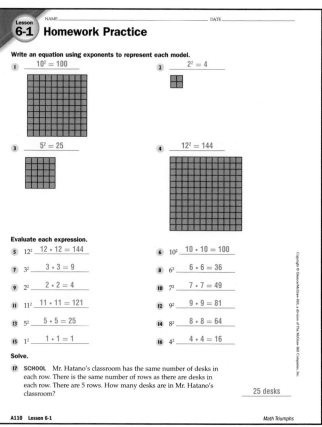

Answer Key (Lesson 6-2)

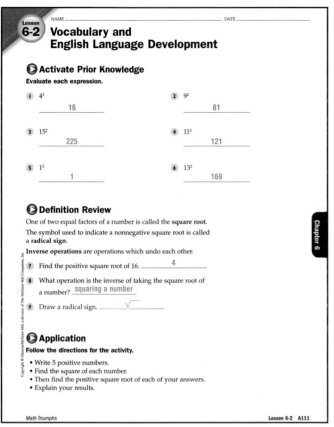

▶ Activate Prior Knowledge
Evaluate each expression.

1. 4^2 16

2. 9^2 81

3. 15^2 225

4. 11^2 121

5. 1^2 1

6. 13^2 169

▶ Definition Review
One of two equal factors of a number is called the **square root**.
The symbol used to indicate a nonnegative square root is called a **radical sign**.
Inverse operations are operations which undo each other.

7. Find the positive square root of 16.   4

8. What operation is the inverse of taking the square root of a number? squaring a number

9. Draw a radical sign. $\sqrt{}$

▶ Application
Follow the directions for the activity.
- Write 5 positive numbers.
- Find the square of each number.
- Then find the positive square root of each of your answers.
- Explain your results.

Math Triumphs   Lesson 6-2   A111

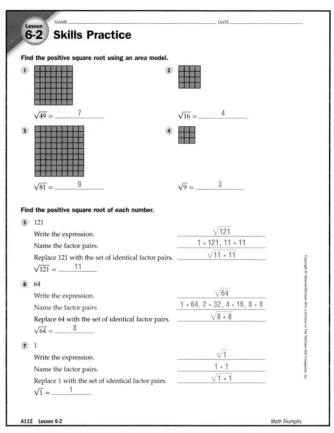

Find the positive square root using an area model.

1. $\sqrt{49} =$ 7

2. $\sqrt{16} =$ 4

3. $\sqrt{81} =$ 9

4. $\sqrt{9} =$ 3

Find the positive square root of each number.

5. 121

Write the expression.	$\sqrt{121}$
Name the factor pairs.	$1 \cdot 121, 11 \cdot 11$
Replace 121 with the set of identical factor pairs.	$\sqrt{11 \cdot 11}$

$\sqrt{121} =$ 11

6. 64

Write the expression.	$\sqrt{64}$
Name the factor pairs.	$1 \cdot 64, 2 \cdot 32, 4 \cdot 16, 8 \cdot 8$
Replace 64 with the set of identical factor pairs.	$\sqrt{8 \cdot 8}$

$\sqrt{64} =$ 8

7. 1

Write the expression.	$\sqrt{1}$
Name the factor pairs.	$1 \cdot 1$
Replace 1 with the set of identical factor pairs.	$\sqrt{1 \cdot 1}$

$\sqrt{1} =$ 1

A112   Lesson 6-2   *Math Triumphs*

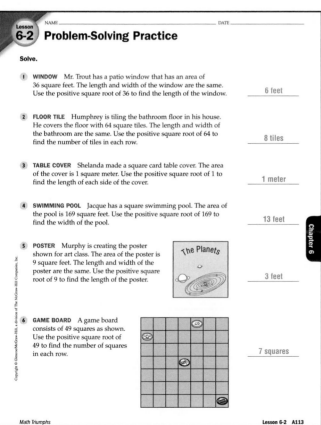

Solve.

1. **WINDOW** Mr. Trout has a patio window that has an area of 36 square feet. The length and width of the window are the same. Use the positive square root of 36 to find the length of the window.   6 feet

2. **FLOOR TILE** Humphrey is tiling the bathroom floor in his house. He covers the floor with 64 square tiles. The length and width of the bathroom are the same. Use the positive square root of 64 to find the number of tiles in each row.   8 tiles

3. **TABLE COVER** Shelanda made a square card table cover. The area of the cover is 1 square meter. Use the positive square root of 1 to find the length of each side of the cover.   1 meter

4. **SWIMMING POOL** Jacque has a square swimming pool. The area of the pool is 169 square feet. Use the positive square root of 169 to find the width of the pool.   13 feet

5. **POSTER** Murphy is creating the poster shown for art class. The area of the poster is 9 square feet. The length and width of the poster are the same. Use the positive square root of 9 to find the length of the poster.   3 feet

6. **GAME BOARD** A game board consists of 49 squares as shown. Use the positive square root of 49 to find the number of squares in each row.   7 squares

Math Triumphs   Lesson 6-2   A113

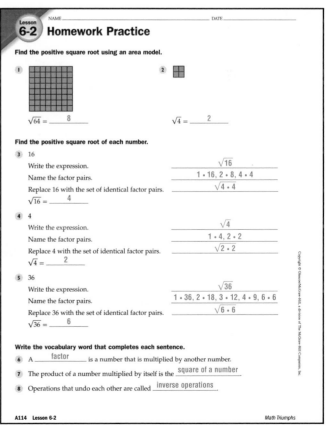

Find the positive square root using an area model.

1. $\sqrt{64} =$ 8

2. $\sqrt{4} =$ 2

Find the positive square root of each number.

3. 16

Write the expression.	$\sqrt{16}$
Name the factor pairs.	$1 \cdot 16, 2 \cdot 8, 4 \cdot 4$
Replace 16 with the set of identical factor pairs.	$\sqrt{4 \cdot 4}$

$\sqrt{16} =$ 4

4. 4

Write the expression.	$\sqrt{4}$
Name the factor pairs.	$1 \cdot 4, 2 \cdot 2$
Replace 4 with the set of identical factor pairs.	$\sqrt{2 \cdot 2}$

$\sqrt{4} =$ 2

5. 36

Write the expression.	$\sqrt{36}$
Name the factor pairs.	$1 \cdot 36, 2 \cdot 18, 3 \cdot 12, 4 \cdot 9, 6 \cdot 6$
Replace 36 with the set of identical factor pairs.	$\sqrt{6 \cdot 6}$

$\sqrt{36} =$ 6

Write the vocabulary word that completes each sentence.

6. A factor is a number that is multiplied by another number.

7. The product of a number multiplied by itself is the square of a number

8. Operations that undo each other are called inverse operations

A114   Lesson 6-2   *Math Triumphs*

Answer Key (Lesson 6-3)

6-3 Vocabulary and English Language Development

▶ Activate Prior Knowledge

1. Round 28 to the nearest ten. __30__

2. Round 225 to the nearest hundred. __200__

3. Round 12.87 to the nearest tenth. __12.9__

Write a whole number in the blank to make a true statement.

4. 12 < __13, 14, or 15__ < 16

5. 25 < __26 or 27__ < 28

Find each value.

6. 3^2

   __9__

7. $\sqrt{16} =$ __4__

▶ Definition Review

A number close to an exact value is an **estimate**.
One of two equal factors of a number is the **square root** of the number.

8. Choose a reasonable estimate for $\sqrt{10}$. __(3.1)__ or 3.8

9. Choose a reasonable estimate for $\sqrt{63}$. 7.2 or __(7.9)__

▶ Application
Follow the directions for the activity.

- Students work in groups of 3. Each group needs a calculator.
- One student states a positive number between 0 and 200 whose square root is not a whole number, such as 14. This student finds the decimal approximation on the calculator, but does not show it to the other two students.
- The other two students each try to estimate the number to the nearest tenth.
- After they state their estimates, the student with the calculator then tells the value to the nearest tenth and the student who was closer gets one point.
- Rotate the calculator so that all students have an equal number of times at each role.
- The student with the greatest number of points wins.

Math Triumphs   **Lesson 6-3 A115**

6-3 Skills Practice

Write an inequality using common square roots.

1. $\sqrt{\underline{36}} < \sqrt{39} < \sqrt{\underline{49}}$

2. $\sqrt{\underline{121}} < \sqrt{130} < \sqrt{\underline{144}}$

3. $\sqrt{\underline{4}} < \sqrt{7} < \sqrt{\underline{9}}$

4. $\sqrt{\underline{169}} < \sqrt{190} < \sqrt{\underline{196}}$

5. $\sqrt{\underline{64}} < \sqrt{72} < \sqrt{\underline{81}}$

6. $\sqrt{\underline{16}} < \sqrt{23} < \sqrt{\underline{25}}$

Estimate each square root to the nearest whole number. Plot each value on a number line.

7. $\sqrt{66}$ is close to the whole number __8__

8. $\sqrt{116}$ is close to the whole number __11__

9. $\sqrt{28}$ is close to the whole number __5__

10. $\sqrt{3}$ is close to the whole number __2__

Choose a reasonable estimate for each square root.

11. $\sqrt{140}$ 10.6   (11.8)   12.2

12. $\sqrt{14}$ 3.1   3.4   (3.7)

13. $\sqrt{220}$ (14.8)   15.2   15.8

14. $\sqrt{58}$ 6.8   7.2   (7.6)

15. $\sqrt{46}$ 6.4   (6.8)   7.2

16. $\sqrt{97}$ (9.8)   10.3   10.8

A116 Lesson 6-3   *Math Triumphs*

6-3 Problem-Solving Practice

Solve.

1. **FLOODING** The figure shows the square area that was flooded when the river overflowed last spring. The area is 10 square miles. Estimate the length and width of the flooded area to the nearest mile.

   3 miles

2. **MIRROR** Sharon has a square mirror on her wall. The area of the mirror is 35 square feet. Estimate the length and width of the mirror.

   6 feet

3. **WORKOUT ROOM** The picture shows a square workout room with area 160 square meters. Estimate the length and width to the nearest whole number of meters.

   13 meters

4. **COLLAGE** Aaron created a photo collage by mounting 100 2-inch square pictures on a square piece of cardboard. If there is $\frac{1}{2}$-inch of cardboard around the edges of the pictures, what is the length and width of the cardboard?

   21 inches

5. **BACKYARD** The backyard at Mrs. Miagi's condominium is a square with area 124 square meters. Estimate the length and width of the yard to the nearest meter.

   11 meters

6. **MEDIA CENTER** Ryan has a media center in his basement. The area of the room is 200 square feet. Estimate the length and width of the room to the nearest whole number.

   14 feet

Math Triumphs   **Lesson 6-3 A117**

6-3 Homework Practice

Write an inequality using common square roots.

1. $\sqrt{\underline{25}} < \sqrt{29} < \sqrt{\underline{36}}$

2. $\sqrt{\underline{81}} < \sqrt{84} < \sqrt{\underline{100}}$

3. $\sqrt{\underline{49}} < \sqrt{62} < \sqrt{\underline{64}}$

4. $\sqrt{\underline{9}} < \sqrt{12} < \sqrt{\underline{16}}$

Estimate each square root to the nearest whole number. Plot each value on a number line.

5. $\sqrt{23}$ is close to the whole number __5__

6. $\sqrt{148}$ is close to the whole number __12__

7. $\sqrt{53}$ is close to the whole number __7__

8. $\sqrt{86}$ is close to the whole number __9__

Choose a reasonable estimate for each square root.

9. $\sqrt{2}$ 1.0   (1.4)   1.8

10. $\sqrt{29}$ 4.8   5.1   (5.4)

11. $\sqrt{175}$ (13.2)   13.6   13.9

12. $\sqrt{78}$ 7.6   (8.8)   9.2

13. **CALENDAR** Julie's square calendar has an area of 7 square inches. She estimated the length and width to be between 3 and 4 inches. Is she correct? Explain.

   No; the square root of 7 is between 2 and 3.

A118 Lesson 6-3   *Math Triumphs*

Answer Key (Lesson 6-4)

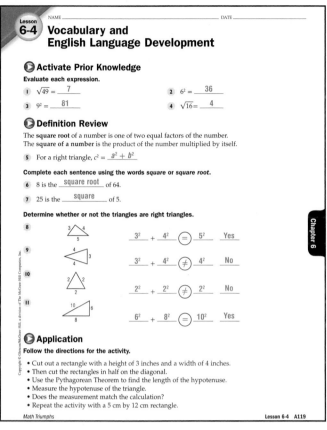

▶ Activate Prior Knowledge
Evaluate each expression.

1 $\sqrt{49} = \underline{7}$

2 $6^2 = \underline{36}$

3 $9^2 = \underline{81}$

4 $\sqrt{16} = \underline{4}$

▶ Definition Review
The **square root** of a number is one of two equal factors of the number.
The **square of a number** is the product of the number multiplied by itself.

5 For a right triangle, $c^2 = \underline{a^2 + b^2}$

Complete each sentence using the words *square* or *square root*.

6 8 is the __square root__ of 64.

7 25 is the __square__ of 5.

Determine whether or not the triangles are right triangles.

8 $\underline{3^2} + \underline{4^2} \bigcirc= \underline{5^2}$ Yes

9 $\underline{3^2} + \underline{4^2} \bigcirc\ne \underline{4^2}$ No

10 $\underline{2^2} + \underline{2^2} \bigcirc\ne \underline{2^2}$ No

11 $\underline{6^2} + \underline{8^2} \bigcirc= \underline{10^2}$ Yes

▶ Application
Follow the directions for the activity.
- Cut out a rectangle with a height of 3 inches and a width of 4 inches.
- Then cut the rectangles in half on the diagonal.
- Use the Pythagorean Theorem to find the length of the hypotenuse.
- Measure the hypotenuse of the triangle.
- Does the measurement match the calculation?
- Repeat the activity with a 5 cm by 12 cm rectangle.

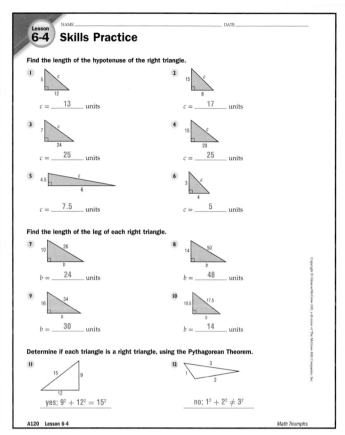

Find the length of the hypotenuse of the right triangle.

1 $c = \underline{13}$ units

2 $c = \underline{17}$ units

3 $c = \underline{25}$ units

4 $c = \underline{25}$ units

5 $c = \underline{7.5}$ units

6 $c = \underline{5}$ units

Find the length of the leg of each right triangle.

7 $b = \underline{24}$ units

8 $b = \underline{48}$ units

9 $b = \underline{30}$ units

10 $b = \underline{14}$ units

Determine if each triangle is a right triangle, using the Pythagorean Theorem.

11 yes; $9^2 + 12^2 = 15^2$

12 no; $1^2 + 2^2 \ne 3^2$

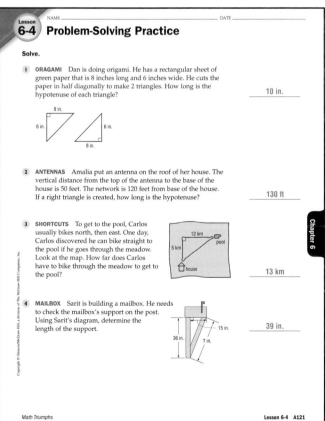

Solve.

1 **ORAGAMI** Dan is doing origami. He has a rectangular sheet of green paper that is 8 inches long and 6 inches wide. He cuts the paper in half diagonally to make 2 triangles. How long is the hypotenuse of each triangle?

__10 in.__

2 **ANTENNAS** Amalia put an antenna on the roof of her house. The vertical distance from the top of the antenna to the base of the house is 50 feet. The network is 120 feet from base of the house. If a right triangle is created, how long is the hypotenuse?

__130 ft__

3 **SHORTCUTS** To get to the pool, Carlos usually bikes north, then east. One day, Carlos discovered he can bike straight to the pool if he goes through the meadow. Look at the map. How far does Carlos have to bike through the meadow to get to the pool?

__13 km__

4 **MAILBOX** Sarit is building a mailbox. He needs to check the mailbox's support on the post. Using Sarit's diagram, determine the length of the support.

__39 in.__

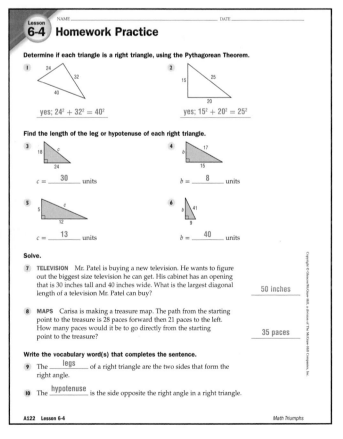

Determine if each triangle is a right triangle, using the Pythagorean Theorem.

1 yes; $24^2 + 32^2 = 40^2$

2 yes; $15^2 + 20^2 = 25^2$

Find the length of the leg or hypotenuse of each right triangle.

3 $c = \underline{30}$ units

4 $b = \underline{8}$ units

5 $c = \underline{13}$ units

6 $b = \underline{40}$ units

Solve.

7 **TELEVISION** Mr. Patel is buying a new television. He wants to figure out the biggest size television he can get. His cabinet has an opening that is 30 inches tall and 40 inches wide. What is the largest diagonal length of a television Mr. Patel can buy?

__50 inches__

8 **MAPS** Carisa is making a treasure map. The path from the starting point to the treasure is 28 paces forward then 21 paces to the left. How many paces would it be to go directly from the starting point to the treasure?

__35 paces__

Write the vocabulary word(s) that completes the sentence.

9 The __legs__ of a right triangle are the two sides that form the right angle.

10 The __hypotenuse__ is the side opposite the right angle in a right triangle.

Answer Key (Lesson 6-5)

Vocabulary and English Language Development

NAME _____ DATE _____

Activate Prior Knowledge

Name the ordered pair for each point.

1. A ___(−1, −2)___

2. B ___(3, 6)___

3. C ___(−3, 2)___

4. D ___(5, 0)___

5. E ___(4, −3)___

Definition Review

A **coordinate grid** is a grid in which a horizontal number line and a vertical number line intersect at their zero points.

Slope is the ratio of vertical change to horizontal change. It is the rate of change between any two points on a line.

6. For (3, −2), the x-coordinate is ___3___ and the y-coordinate is ___−2___

7. Find the slope of a line if the rise is +6 units and the run is +5 units. ___$\frac{6}{5}$___

8. Find the slope of a line if the rise is −3 units and the run is +2 units. ___$\frac{3}{2}$___

Application

Form a human line.

- Clear the area on a floor with square tiles or use masking tape to form a grid on the floor.
- One student chooses a slope. Students arrange themselves on the grid so that they are points on a line with that slope.
- Another student chooses a different slope. Students rearrange themselves as needed.
- Repeat for several slopes. Use both positive and negative slopes. Use both fractional and whole number slopes as well.

Math Triumphs   Lesson 6-5   A123

Skills Practice

NAME _____ DATE _____

Find the slope of each line.

1. The rise is ___3___ units.

2. The run is ___4___ units.

3. The slope is ___positive___

4. $\frac{rise}{run} = \frac{3}{4}$

5. $\frac{rise}{run} = \frac{-3}{1} = -3$

6. $\frac{rise}{run} = \frac{-6}{5} = \frac{6}{5}$

Graph another point on each line, given one point on the line and the slope.

7. The slope is $\frac{1}{5}$.

8. The slope is $-\frac{3}{2}$.

9. The slope is 4.

10. The slope is $\frac{3}{4}$.

A124   Lesson 6-5   *Math Triumphs*

Problem-Solving Practice

NAME _____ DATE _____

Solve.

1. **SLEDDING** Max is sledding down the hill shown. What is the slope of the hill?   ___$\frac{1}{2}$___

2. **KITE** Bart is holding the string to a kite 4 feet above the ground. The kite is 100 feet above a point on the ground 32 feet from Bart. Find the slope of the kite string.   ___3___

3. **CLOTHESLINE** Leslie is stringing a clothesline from a pole that is 4 feet tall to a point on her garage 6 feet above the ground. The pole is 20 feet from the garage as shown in the diagram. Find the slope of the clothesline.   ___$\frac{1}{10}$___

4. **RAMPS** A ramp begins at a doorway that is 8 feet above the ground. The ramp runs a horizontal distance of 20 feet. A person leaving the building wants to know what the slope is. What would you say?   ___$\frac{2}{5}$___

Math Triumphs   Lesson 6-5   A125

Homework Practice

NAME _____ DATE _____

Find the slope of each line.

1. $\frac{rise}{run} = \frac{-2}{1} = -2$

2. $\frac{rise}{run} = \frac{5}{2}$

Graph another point on each line, given one point on the line and the slope.

3. The slope is $-\frac{4}{3}$.

4. The slope is 2.

5. The slope is $\frac{3}{5}$.

6. The slope is $-\frac{1}{2}$.

Solve.

7. **STAIRS** Each step on a flight of stairs has a height of 6 inches and a width of 9 inches. What is the slope of the stairs?   ___$\frac{2}{3}$___

8. **LADDERS** A ladder is leaning against the side of a house. The bottom of the ladder is 12 feet away from the house and the top of the ladder is 15 feet above the ground. What is the slope of the ladder?   ___$\frac{5}{4}$___

A126   Lesson 6-5   *Math Triumphs*

Answer Key (Lesson 6-6)

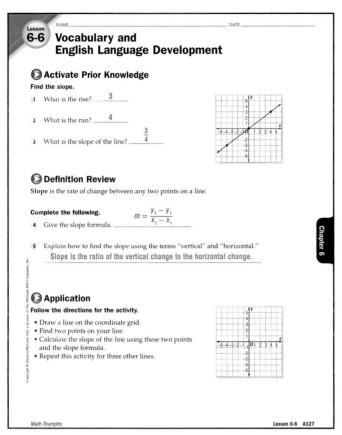

Lesson 6-6
Vocabulary and English Language Development

▶ Activate Prior Knowledge

Find the slope.

1. What is the rise? **3**

2. What is the run? **4**

3. What is the slope of the line? **$\frac{3}{4}$**

▶ Definition Review

Slope is the rate of change between any two points on a line.

Complete the following.

4. Give the slope formula. $m = \dfrac{y_2 - y_1}{x_2 - x_1}$

5. Explain how to find the slope using the terms "vertical" and "horizontal."
   Slope is the ratio of the vertical change to the horizontal change.

▶ Application

Follow the directions for the activity.

- Draw a line on the coordinate grid.
- Find two points on your line.
- Calculate the slope of the line using these two points and the slope formula.
- Repeat this activity for three other lines.

Math Triumphs   Lesson 6-6   A127

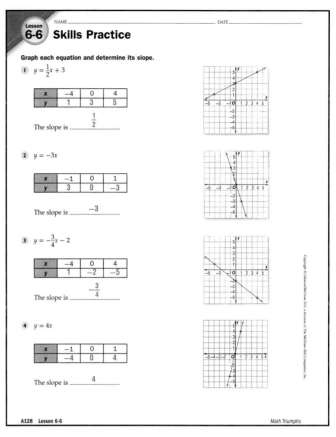

Lesson 6-6
Skills Practice

Graph each equation and determine its slope.

1. $y = \frac{1}{2}x + 3$

x	−4	0	4
y	1	3	5

The slope is **$\frac{1}{2}$**.

2. $y = -3x$

x	−1	0	1
y	3	0	−3

The slope is **−3**.

3. $y = -\frac{3}{4}x - 2$

x	−4	0	4
y	1	−2	−5

The slope is **$-\frac{3}{4}$**.

4. $y = 4x$

x	−1	0	1
y	−4	0	4

The slope is **4**.

A128   Lesson 6-6   Math Triumphs

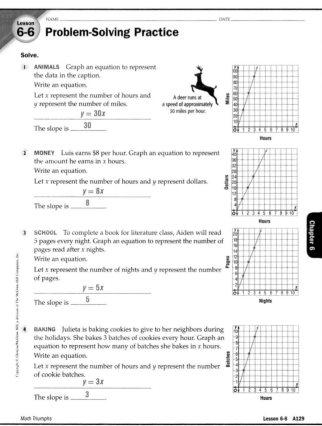

Lesson 6-6
Problem-Solving Practice

Solve.

1. **ANIMALS** Graph an equation to represent the data in the caption.
   Write an equation.
   Let x represent the number of hours and y represent the number of miles.
   y = 30x
   The slope is **30**.

   A deer runs at a speed of approximately 30 miles per hour.

2. **MONEY** Luis earns $8 per hour. Graph an equation to represent the amount he earns in x hours.
   Write an equation.
   Let x represent the number of hours and y represent dollars.
   y = 8x
   The slope is **8**.

3. **SCHOOL** To complete a book for literature class, Aiden will read 5 pages every night. Graph an equation to represent the number of pages read after x nights.
   Write an equation.
   Let x represent the number of nights and y represent the number of pages.
   y = 5x
   The slope is **5**.

4. **BAKING** Julieta is baking cookies to give to her neighbors during the holidays. She bakes 3 batches of cookies every hour. Graph an equation to represent how many of batches she bakes in x hours.
   Write an equation.
   Let x represent the number of hours and y represent the number of cookie batches.
   y = 3x
   The slope is **3**.

Math Triumphs   Lesson 6-6   A129

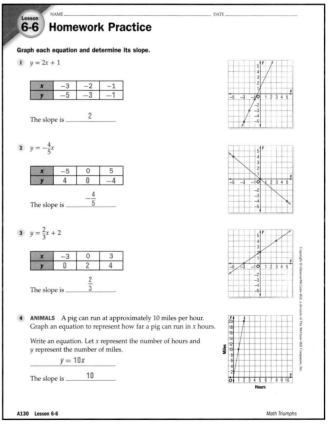

Lesson 6-6
Homework Practice

Graph each equation and determine its slope.

1. $y = 2x + 1$

x	−3	−2	−1
y	−5	−3	−1

The slope is **2**.

2. $y = -\frac{4}{5}x$

x	−5	0	5
y	4	0	−4

The slope is **$-\frac{4}{5}$**.

3. $y = \frac{2}{3}x + 2$

x	−3	0	3
y	0	2	4

The slope is **$\frac{2}{3}$**.

4. **ANIMALS** A pig can run at approximately 10 miles per hour. Graph an equation to represent how far a pig can run in x hours.
   Write an equation. Let x represent the number of hours and y represent the number of miles.
   y = 10x
   The slope is **10**.

A130   Lesson 6-6   Math Triumphs

Answer Key (Lesson 7-1)

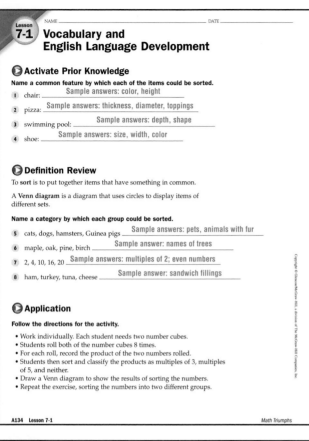

Vocabulary and English Language Development

Activate Prior Knowledge

Name a common feature by which each of the items could be sorted.

1. chair: _Sample answers: color, height_
2. pizza: _Sample answers: thickness, diameter, toppings_
3. swimming pool: _Sample answers: depth, shape_
4. shoe: _Sample answers: size, width, color_

Definition Review

To **sort** is to put together items that have something in common.

A **Venn diagram** is a diagram that uses circles to display items of different sets.

Name a category by which each group could be sorted.

5. cats, dogs, hamsters, Guinea pigs _Sample answers: pets, animals with fur_
6. maple, oak, pine, birch _Sample answer: names of trees_
7. 2, 4, 10, 16, 20 _Sample answers: multiples of 2; even numbers_
8. ham, turkey, tuna, cheese _Sample answer: sandwich fillings_

Application

Follow the directions for the activity.

- Work individually. Each student needs two number cubes.
- Students roll both of the number cubes 8 times.
- For each roll, record the product of the two numbers rolled.
- Students then sort and classify the products as multiples of 3, multiples of 5, and neither.
- Draw a Venn diagram to show the results of sorting the numbers.
- Repeat the exercise, sorting the numbers into two different groups.

A134 Lesson 7-1   Math Triumphs

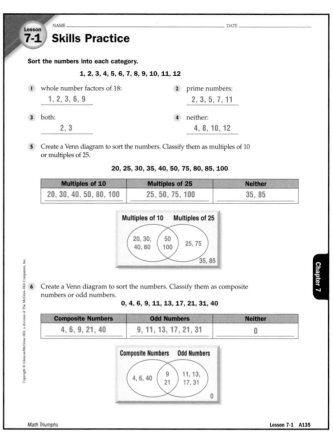

Lesson 7-1

Skills Practice

Sort the numbers into each category.

1, 2, 3, 4, 5, 6, 7, 8, 9, 10, 11, 12

1. whole number factors of 18: _1, 2, 3, 6, 9_
2. prime numbers: _2, 3, 5, 7, 11_
3. both: _2, 3_
4. neither: _4, 8, 10, 12_

5. Create a Venn diagram to sort the numbers. Classify them as multiples of 10 or multiples of 25.

20, 25, 30, 35, 40, 50, 75, 80, 85, 100

Multiples of 10	Multiples of 25	Neither
20, 30, 40, 50, 80, 100	25, 50, 75, 100	35, 85

6. Create a Venn diagram to sort the numbers. Classify them as composite numbers or odd numbers.

0, 4, 6, 9, 11, 13, 17, 21, 31, 40

Composite Numbers	Odd Numbers	Neither
4, 6, 9, 21, 40	9, 11, 13, 17, 21, 31	0

Math Triumphs   Lesson 7-1 A135

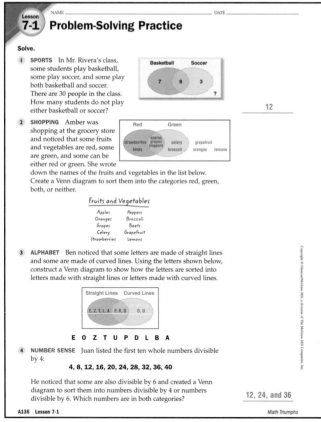

Lesson 7-1

Problem-Solving Practice

Solve.

1. **SPORTS** In Mr. Rivera's class, some students play basketball, some play soccer, and some play both basketball and soccer. There are 30 people in the class. How many students do not play either basketball or soccer? _12_

2. **SHOPPING** Amber was shopping at the grocery store and noticed that some fruits and vegetables are red, some are green, and some can be either red or green. She wrote down the names of the fruits and vegetables in the list below. Create a Venn diagram to sort them into the categories red, green, both, or neither.

   Fruits and Vegetables

Apples	Peppers
Oranges	Broccoli
Grapes	Beets
Celery	Grapefruit
Strawberries	Lemons

3. **ALPHABET** Ben noticed that some letters are made of straight lines and some are made of curved lines. Using the letters shown below, construct a Venn diagram to show how the letters are sorted into letters with straight lines or letters made with curved lines.

   E O Z T U P D L B A

4. **NUMBER SENSE** Juan listed the first ten whole numbers divisible by 4: _4, 8, 12, 16, 20, 24, 28, 32, 36, 40_

   He noticed that some are also divisible by 6 and created a Venn diagram to sort them into numbers divisible by 4 or numbers divisible by 6. Which numbers are in both categories? _12, 24, and 36_

A136 Lesson 7-1   Math Triumphs

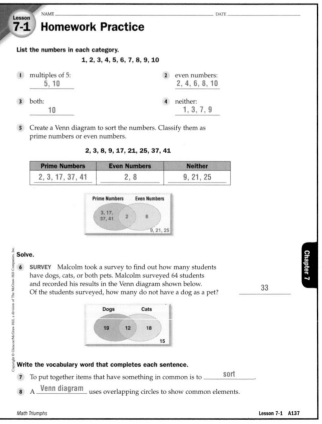

Lesson 7-1

Homework Practice

List the numbers in each category.

1, 2, 3, 4, 5, 6, 7, 8, 9, 10

1. multiples of 5: _5, 10_
2. even numbers: _2, 4, 6, 8, 10_
3. both: _10_
4. neither: _1, 3, 7, 9_

5. Create a Venn diagram to sort the numbers. Classify them as prime numbers or even numbers.

2, 3, 8, 9, 17, 21, 25, 37, 41

Prime Numbers	Even Numbers	Neither
2, 3, 17, 37, 41	2, 8	9, 21, 25

Solve.

6. **SURVEY** Malcolm took a survey to find out how many students have dogs, cats, or both pets. Malcolm surveyed 64 students and recorded his results in the Venn diagram shown below. Of the students surveyed, how many do not have a dog as a pet? _33_

Write the vocabulary word that completes each sentence.

7. To put together items that have something in common is to _sort_
8. A _Venn diagram_ uses overlapping circles to show common elements.

Math Triumphs   Lesson 7-1 A137

Answer Key (Lesson 7-2)

7-2 Vocabulary and English Language Development

Activate Prior Knowledge

1. Arrange the following numbers in order from least to greatest.

   11, 5, 3, 20, 2

   2, 3, 5, 11, 20

2. Which of the following numbers appears most often in the list?

   0, 0, 2, 2, 4, 7, 7, 7, 9

   7

3. In the following list of numbers, which number is located in the middle of the list?

   0, 1, 2, 5, 9

   2

Definition Review

The **mode** is the number(s) or item(s) that appear most often in a set of data.

The difference between the greatest number and the least number in a set of data is the **range**.

The middle number in a set of data when the data are arranged in numerical order is the **median**. Sample answers provided.

4. Write a set of data with a mode of 2. 1 2 2 4 2

5. Write a set of data with a range of 5. 3 3 4 7 8

6. Write a set of data with a median of 5. 1 3 5 6 9

Application

Follow the directions for the activity.

- Work in pairs.
- List 5 numbers where two of them are the same.
- Exchange numbers with your partner.
- Find the mode, median, and range of the numbers your partner wrote.
- Check your partner's answers.
- Repeat this activity three times using different numbers.

7-2 Skills Practice

Find the mode for each given set of data.

1. 1, 2, 0, 1, 2, 0, 1

   1

2. 7, 3, 5, 2, 4, 3, 6, 10, 0

   3

3. 3, 0, 0, 1, 2

   0

4. 9, 3, 2, 5, 6, 3, 3, 7, 15

   3

Find the median for each given set of data.

5. Henry asked seven people what the last digit in their telephone number is.

   2, 5, 9, 9, 7, 4, 3

   Arrange the numbers in order: 2, 3, 4, 5, 7, 9, 9

   The median is 5

6. Christina asked five people how tall they were, in inches.

   54, 63, 62, 48, 68

   Arrange the numbers in order: 48, 54, 62, 63, 68

   The median is 62

7. Nathan recorded the low temperatures for each day one week.

   34, 32, 41, 29, 42, 32, 50

   Arrange the numbers in order: 29, 32, 32, 34, 41, 42, 50

   The median is 34

Find the range for each given set of data.

8. 2, 5, 9, 9, 7, 4, 3

   The range of digits in Exercise 5 is 9 – 2 = 7

9. 54, 63, 62, 48, 68

   The range of heights in Exercise 6 is 68 – 48 = 20

Chapter 7

7-2 Problem-Solving Practice

Solve.

1. **CLASS PERIODS** Leta surveyed 9 schools to find the length of their class periods in minutes. The results are shown below. Find the mode, median, and range of the times.

   90, 50, 45, 42, 55, 75, 80, 45, 60

   45, 55, 48

2. **TELEVISION** Hans surveyed 11 classmates about how many minutes they spent watching television over the weekend. The results are shown below. Find the mode, median, and range of the times.

   180, 120, 135, 90, 30, 45, 0, 60, 90, 300, 90

   90, 90, 300

3. **CHESS TOURNAMENT** The members of the Centerville Junior High School chess team recorded the number of games they won in each tournament in the table below. Find the mode, median, and range of the number of wins.

   0, 2, 5

Tournament Number	1	2	3	4	5	6	7	8	9
Number of Wins	3	5	2	1	0	4	2	0	0

4. **COFFEE SHOP** Five friends had dinner at the local coffee shop. The prices of their dinners are shown below. Find the mode, median, and range of the prices.

   $5, $7, $4, $6, $7

   $7, $6, $3

5. **PETS** Wilhema asked 11 classmates how many pets they have. The results are shown in the table below. Find the mode, median, and range of the number of pets.

   1, 2, 5

Name	Jack	Pete	Sue	Mary	Fred	Jeri	Ann	Teri	Cal	Mac	Amy
Number	0	2	4	3	1	1	1	2	3	5	0

7-2 Homework Practice

Find the mode for each given set of data.

1. 1, 3, 2, 2, 4, 3, 2, 4, 1

   2

2. 7, 8, 5, 8, 4

   8

Find the median for each given set of data.

3. Barb counted the glasses in nine different kitchen cabinets.

   11, 12, 4, 7, 9, 5, 13, 8, 12

   Arrange the numbers in order:
   4, 5, 7, 8, 9, 11, 12, 12, 13

   The median is 9

4. Juan asked 13 students how many books they read over the summer.

   0, 5, 15, 2, 11, 17, 8, 6, 5, 2, 0, 3, 2

   Arrange the numbers in order:
   0, 0, 2, 2, 2, 3, 5, 5, 6, 8, 11, 15, 17

   The median is 5

Find the range for each given set of data.

5. 11, 12, 4, 7, 9, 5, 13, 8, 12

   The range of glasses in Exercise 3 is 13 – 4 = 9

6. 0, 5, 15, 2, 11, 17, 8, 6, 5, 2, 0, 3, 2

   The range of books in Exercise 4 is 17 – 0 = 17

Solve.

7. **PAY** Julius kept track of the number of hours he worked per week for 15 weeks. The results are shown below. Find the mode, median, and range of the number of hours.

   19, 16, 32, 30, 20, 40, 37, 10, 8, 0, 35, 40, 36, 12, 15

   40, 20, 40

Write the vocabulary word that completes the sentence.

8. Information gathered for statistical purposes is called _____ data _____

Chapter 7

Answer Key (Lesson 7-3)

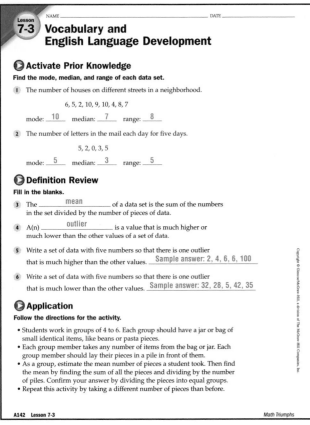

Vocabulary and English Language Development

Activate Prior Knowledge

Find the mode, median, and range of each data set.

1. The number of houses on different streets in a neighborhood.

    6, 5, 2, 10, 9, 10, 4, 8, 7

    mode: __10__ median: __7__ range: __8__

2. The number of letters in the mail each day for five days.

    5, 2, 0, 3, 5

    mode: __5__ median: __3__ range: __5__

Definition Review

Fill in the blanks.

3. The __mean__ of a data set is the sum of the numbers in the set divided by the number of pieces of data.

4. A(n) __outlier__ is a value that is much higher or much lower than the other values of a set of data.

5. Write a set of data with five numbers so that there is one outlier that is much higher than the other values. __Sample answer: 2, 4, 6, 6, 100__

6. Write a set of data with five numbers so that there is one outlier that is much lower than the other values. __Sample answer: 32, 28, 5, 42, 35__

Application

Follow the directions for the activity.

- Students work in groups of 4 to 6. Each group should have a jar or bag of small identical items, like beans or pasta pieces.
- Each group member takes any number of items from the bag or jar. Each group member should lay their pieces in a pile in front of them.
- As a group, estimate the mean number of pieces a student took. Then find the mean by finding the sum of all the pieces and dividing by the number of piles. Confirm your answer by dividing the pieces into equal groups.
- Repeat this activity by taking a different number of pieces than before.

A142   Lesson 7-3   Math Triumphs

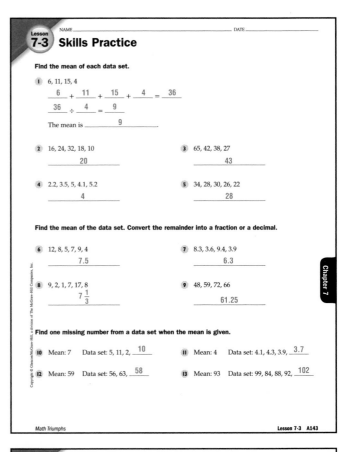

Skills Practice

Find the mean of each data set.

1. 6, 11, 15, 4

    $\frac{6}{} + \frac{11}{} + \frac{15}{} + \frac{4}{} = \frac{36}{}$

    $\frac{36}{} ÷ \frac{4}{} = \frac{9}{}$

    The mean is __9__.

2. 16, 24, 32, 18, 10   __20__

3. 65, 42, 38, 27   __43__

4. 2.2, 3.5, 5, 4.1, 5.2   __4__

5. 34, 28, 30, 26, 22   __28__

Find the mean of the data set. Convert the remainder into a fraction or a decimal.

6. 12, 8, 5, 7, 9, 4   __7.5__

7. 8.3, 3.6, 9.4, 3.9   __6.3__

8. 9, 2, 1, 7, 17, 8 $7\frac{1}{3}$

9. 48, 59, 72, 66   __61.25__

Find one missing number from a data set when the mean is given.

10. Mean: 7   Data set: 5, 11, 2, __10__

11. Mean: 4   Data set: 4.1, 4.3, 3.9, __3.7__

12. Mean: 59   Data set: 56, 63, __58__

13. Mean: 93   Data set: 99, 84, 88, 92, __102__

Math Triumphs   Lesson 7-3   A143

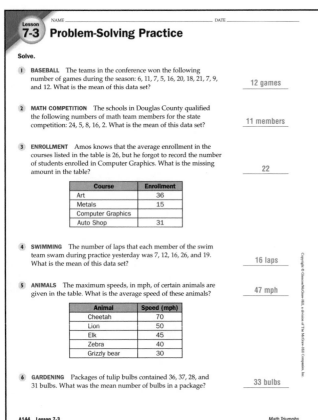

Problem-Solving Practice

Solve.

1. **BASEBALL** The teams in the conference won the following number of games during the season: 6, 11, 7, 5, 16, 20, 18, 21, 7, 9, and 12. What is the mean of this data set?   __12 games__

2. **MATH COMPETITION** The schools in Douglas County qualified the following numbers of math team members for the state competition: 24, 5, 8, 16, 2. What is the mean of this data set?   __11 members__

3. **ENROLLMENT** Amos knows that the average enrollment in the courses listed in the table is 26, but he forgot to record the number of students enrolled in Computer Graphics. What is the missing amount in the table?   __22__

Course	Enrollment
Art	36
Metals	15
Computer Graphics	
Auto Shop	31

4. **SWIMMING** The number of laps that each member of the swim team swam during practice yesterday was 7, 12, 16, 26, and 19. What is the mean of this data set?   __16 laps__

5. **ANIMALS** The maximum speeds, in mph, of certain animals are given in the table. What is the average speed of these animals?   __47 mph__

Animal	Speed (mph)
Cheetah	70
Lion	50
Elk	45
Zebra	40
Grizzly bear	30

6. **GARDENING** Packages of tulip bulbs contained 36, 37, 28, and 31 bulbs. What was the mean number of bulbs in a package?   __33 bulbs__

A144   Lesson 7-3   Math Triumphs

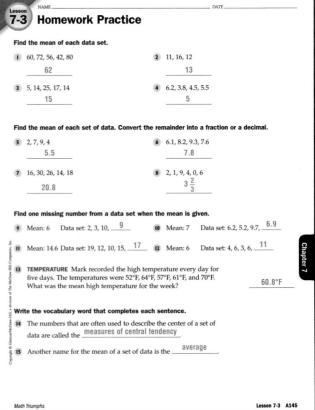

Homework Practice

Find the mean of each data set.

1. 60, 72, 56, 42, 80   __62__

2. 11, 16, 12   __13__

3. 5, 14, 25, 17, 14   __15__

4. 6.2, 3.8, 4.5, 5.5   __5__

Find the mean of each set of data. Convert the remainder into a fraction or a decimal.

5. 2, 7, 9, 4   __5.5__

6. 6.1, 8.2, 9.3, 7.6   __7.8__

7. 16, 30, 26, 14, 18   __20.8__

8. 2, 1, 9, 4, 0, 6 $3\frac{2}{3}$

Find one missing number from a data set when the mean is given.

9. Mean: 6   Data set: 2, 3, 10, __9__

10. Mean: 7   Data set: 6.2, 5.2, 9.7, __6.9__

11. Mean: 14.6 Data set: 19, 12, 10, 15, __17__

12. Mean: 6   Data set: 4, 6, 3, 6, __11__

13. **TEMPERATURE** Mark recorded the high temperature every day for five days. The temperatures were 52°F, 64°F, 57°F, 61°F, and 70°F. What was the mean high temperature for the week?   __60.8°F__

Write the vocabulary word that completes each sentence.

14. The numbers that are often used to describe the center of a set of data are called the __measures of central tendency__

15. Another name for the mean of a set of data is the __average__

Math Triumphs   Lesson 7-3   A145

Answer Key (Lesson 7-4)

7-4 Vocabulary and English Language Development

NAME _____ **DATE** _____

▶ Activate Prior Knowledge

Pizza Places We Like

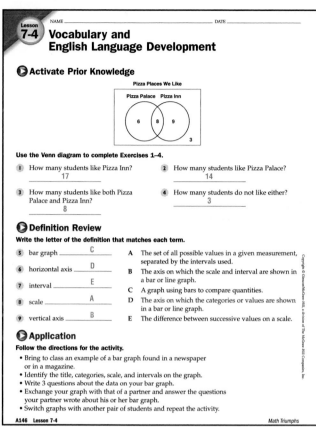

Use the Venn diagram to complete Exercises 1–4.

1. How many students like Pizza Inn?
   _____17_____

2. How many students like Pizza Palace?
   _____14_____

3. How many students like both Pizza Palace and Pizza Inn?
   _____8_____

4. How many students do not like either?
   _____3_____

▶ Definition Review

Write the letter of the definition that matches each term.

5. bar graph _____C_____
6. horizontal axis _____D_____
7. interval _____E_____
8. scale _____A_____
9. vertical axis _____B_____

A. The set of all possible values in a given measurement, separated by the intervals used.

B. The axis on which the scale and interval are shown in a bar or line graph.

C. A graph using bars to compare quantities.

D. The axis on which the categories or values are shown in a bar or line graph.

E. The difference between successive values on a scale.

▶ Application

Follow the directions for the activity.

- Bring to class an example of a bar graph found in a newspaper or in a magazine.
- Identify the title, categories, scale, and intervals on the graph.
- Write 3 questions about the data on your bar graph.
- Exchange your graph with that of a partner and answer the questions your partner wrote about his or her bar graph.
- Switch graphs with another pair of students and repeat the activity.

A146 Lesson 7-4 — Math Triumphs

7-4 Skills Practice

NAME _____ **DATE** _____

Use the bar graph "My Classmates' Favorite Type of Book" to compare data.

1. How many students chose Mystery as their favorite type of book? _____12_____

2. How many chose Science Fiction? _____5_____

3. How many chose Biography? _____10_____

4. How many more students prefer Mysteries than Classic Novels? _____3_____

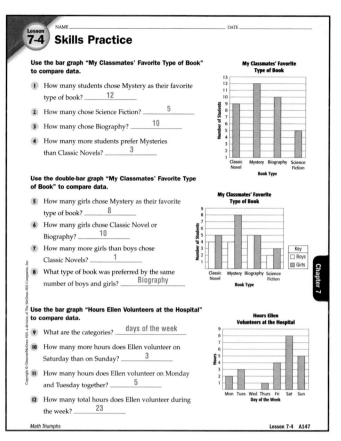

Use the double-bar graph "My Classmates' Favorite Type of Book" to compare data.

5. How many girls chose Mystery as their favorite type of book? _____8_____

6. How many girls chose Classic Novel or Biography? _____10_____

7. How many more girls than boys chose Classic Novels? _____1_____

8. What type of book was preferred by the same number of boys and girls? _____Biography_____

Use the bar graph "Hours Ellen Volunteers at the Hospital" to compare data.

9. What are the categories? _____days of the week_____

10. How many more hours does Ellen volunteer on Saturday than on Sunday? _____3_____

11. How many hours does Ellen volunteer on Monday and Tuesday together? _____5_____

12. How many total hours does Ellen volunteer during the week? _____23_____

Math Triumphs — Lesson 7-4 A147

Copyright © Glencoe/McGraw-Hill, a division of The McGraw-Hill Companies, Inc.

Chapter 7

7-4 Problem-Solving Practice

NAME _____ **DATE** _____

Solve.

1. **CLASS TRIP** The school activities director asked the eighth-graders where they should go for their class trip. How many boys prefer the amusement park or the beach compared to the number of boys that prefer the zoo or the museum? _____15 more_____

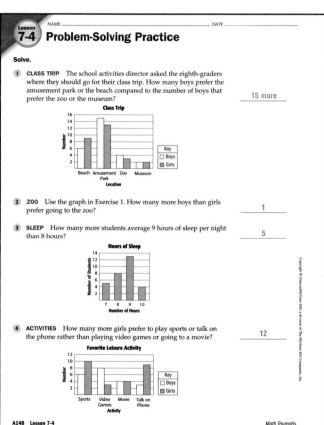

2. **ZOO** Use the graph in Exercise 1. How many more boys than girls prefer going to the zoo? _____1_____

3. **SLEEP** How many more students average 9 hours of sleep per night than 8 hours? _____5_____

4. **ACTIVITIES** How many more girls prefer to play sports or talk on the phone rather than playing video games or going to a movie? _____12_____

A148 Lesson 7-4 — Math Triumphs

7-4 Homework Practice

NAME _____ **DATE** _____

Use the double-bar graph "Quiz Grades" to compare data.

1. How many students earned A's?
   _____19_____

2. How many more boys earned B's than D's?
   _____4_____

3. How many girls earned A's or B's?
   _____21_____

4. A total of 11 students earned what grade?
   _____C_____

5. How many students took the quiz?
   _____54_____

6. How many more girls than boys earned a C?
   _____1_____

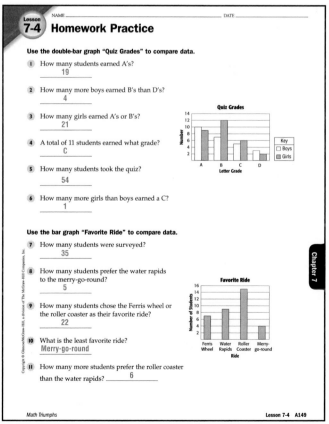

Use the bar graph "Favorite Ride" to compare data.

7. How many students were surveyed?
   _____35_____

8. How many students prefer the water rapids to the merry-go-round?
   _____5_____

9. How many students chose the Ferris wheel or the roller coaster as their favorite ride?
   _____22_____

10. What is the least favorite ride?
    _____Merry-go-round_____

11. How many more students prefer the roller coaster than the water rapids? _____6_____

Math Triumphs — Lesson 7-4 A149

Chapter 7

Answer Key (Lesson 7-5)

Lesson 7-5

Vocabulary and English Language Development

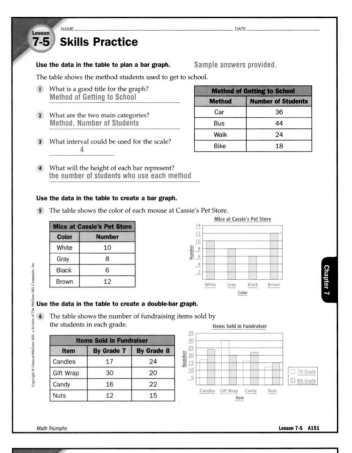

Activate Prior Knowledge

Use the bar graph "Favorite Type of Vacation" to compare data.

1 How many more students prefer a beach vacation than one in the mountains?
   2

2 What location is preferred by 8 students?
   mountains

3 What two locations were chosen as often as a beach vacation?
   city and abroad

Definition Review

Fill in the blanks.

4 The set of all possible values in a given measurement, including the least and greatest numbers in the set, separated by the intervals used is called the **scale**

5 The axis on which the scale and interval are shown is the **vertical** axis while the axis on which the categories or values are shown is the **horizontal** axis.

6 A graph using bars to compare quantities is called a **bar graph**

7 The difference between successive values on a scale is called the **interval**

Application

Follow the directions for the activity.

• Work in groups of 2 or 3.
• Ask students in other groups what their favorite something is. For example: favorite type of fruit, favorite animal, favorite type of music.
• Make a bar graph to display your data.
• As a group, present your graph to the rest of the class. Discuss your findings as well as how you chose to make your graph, including the title, categories, scale, and intervals.

A150   Lesson 7-5   Math Triumphs

Lesson 7-5

Skills Practice

Use the data in the table to plan a bar graph.   **Sample answers provided.**

The table shows the method students used to get to school.

1 What is a good title for the graph?
   Method of Getting to School

2 What are the two main categories?
   Method, Number of Students

3 What interval could be used for the scale?
   4

4 What will the height of each bar represent?
   the number of students who use each method

Method of Getting to School	
Method	Number of Students
Car	36
Bus	44
Walk	24
Bike	18

Use the data in the table to create a bar graph.

5 The table shows the color of each mouse at Cassie's Pet Store.

Mice at Cassie's Pet Store	
Color	Number
White	10
Gray	8
Black	6
Brown	12

Use the data in the table to create a double-bar graph.

6 The table shows the number of fundraising items sold by the students in each grade.

Items Sold in Fundraiser		
Item	By Grade 7	By Grade 8
Candles	17	24
Gift Wrap	30	20
Candy	16	22
Nuts	12	15

Math Triumphs   Lesson 7-5   A151

Lesson 7-5

Problem-Solving Practice

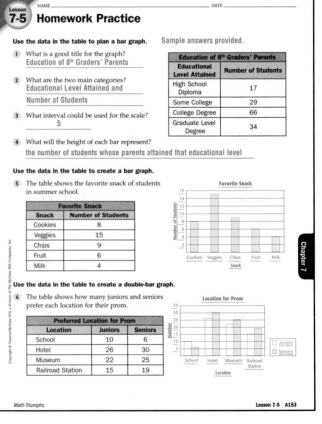

1 **ELECTION** A student reporter wants to make a double-bar graph to compare the number of boys and girls who said they voted for each candidate. Use the data in the table to create a double-bar graph.

Votes for Class President		
Candidate	Boys	Girls
Marcy	17	36
Brian	54	40
Lois	28	23
Tim	20	32

2 **TRACK AND FIELD** The track coach wants to compare the favorite events of the seventh and eighth graders on the track team. Use the data in the table to create a double-bar graph.

Favorite Track and Field Event		
Event	7th Graders	8th Graders
Hurdles	9	12
Relay Races	22	17
Long Jump	6	8
Discus Throw	4	9

3 **GREAT LAKES** Carl is doing a report on the Great Lakes and wants to compare their maximum depths. Use the data in the table to create a bar graph.

Maximum Depth of Great Lakes	
Lake	Depth (feet)
Erie	210
Huron	750
Michigan	925
Ontario	802
Superior	1,333

A152   Lesson 7-5   Math Triumphs

Lesson 7-5

Homework Practice

Use the data in the table to plan a bar graph.   **Sample answers provided.**

1 What is a good title for the graph?
   Education of 8ᵗʰ Graders' Parents

2 What are the two main categories?
   Educational Level Attained and Number of Students

3 What interval could be used for the scale?
   5

4 What will the height of each bar represent?
   the number of students whose parents attained that educational level

Education of 8ᵗʰ Graders' Parents	
Educational Level Attained	Number of Students
High School Diploma	17
Some College	29
College Degree	66
Graduate Level Degree	34

Use the data in the table to create a bar graph.

5 The table shows the favorite snack of students in summer school.

Favorite Snack	
Snack	Number of Students
Cookies	8
Veggies	15
Chips	9
Fruit	6
Milk	4

Use the data in the table to create a double-bar graph.

6 The table shows how many juniors and seniors prefer each location for their prom.

Preferred Location for Prom		
Location	Juniors	Seniors
School	10	6
Hotel	26	30
Museum	22	25
Railroad Station	15	19

Math Triumphs   Lesson 7-5   A153

Answer Key (Lesson 7-6)

Lesson 7-6

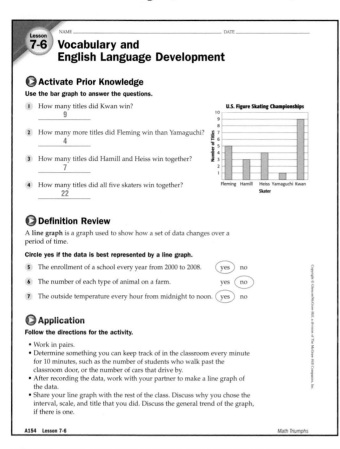

Vocabulary and English Language Development

▶ Activate Prior Knowledge
Use the bar graph to answer the questions.

1. How many titles did Kwan win?
   9

2. How many more titles did Fleming win than Yamaguchi?
   4

3. How many titles did Hamill and Heiss win together?
   7

4. How many titles did all five skaters win together?
   22

▶ Definition Review
A **line graph** is a graph used to show how a set of data changes over a period of time.

Circle yes if the data is best represented by a line graph.

5. The enrollment of a school every year from 2000 to 2008. **(yes)** no

6. The number of each type of animal on a farm. yes **(no)**

7. The outside temperature every hour from midnight to noon. **(yes)** no

▶ Application
Follow the directions for the activity.

- Work in pairs.
- Determine something you can keep track of in the classroom every minute for 10 minutes, such as the number of students who walk past the classroom door, or the number of cars that drive by.
- After recording the data, work with your partner to make a line graph of the data.
- Share your line graph with the rest of the class. Discuss why you chose the interval, scale, and title that you did. Discuss the general trend of the graph, if there is one.

A154 Lesson 7-6   Math Triumphs

Skills Practice

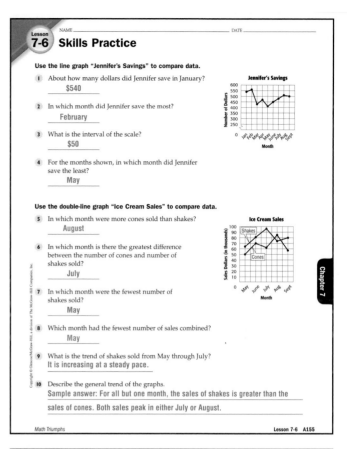

Use the line graph "Jennifer's Savings" to compare data.

1. About how many dollars did Jennifer save in January?
   $540

2. In which month did Jennifer save the most?
   February

3. What is the interval of the scale?
   $50

4. For the months shown, in which month did Jennifer save the least?
   May

Use the double-line graph "Ice Cream Sales" to compare data.

5. In which month were more cones sold than shakes?
   August

6. In which month is there the greatest difference between the number of cones and number of shakes sold?
   July

7. In which month were the fewest number of shakes sold?
   May

8. Which month had the fewest number of sales combined?
   May

9. What is the trend of shakes sold from May through July?
   It is increasing at a steady pace.

10. Describe the general trend of the graphs.
    Sample answer: For all but one month, the sales of shakes is greater than the sales of cones. Both sales peak in either July or August.

Math Triumphs   Lesson 7-6 A155

Problem-Solving Practice

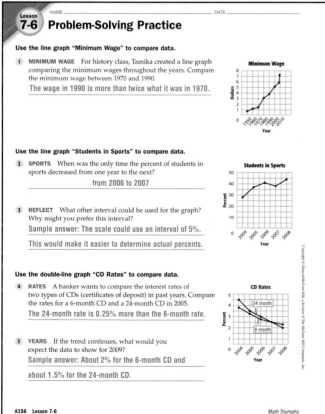

Use the line graph "Minimum Wage" to compare data.

1. **MINIMUM WAGE** For history class, Tamika created a line graph comparing the minimum wages throughout the years. Compare the minimum wage between 1970 and 1990.
   The wage in 1990 is more than twice what it was in 1970.

Use the line graph "Students in Sports" to compare data.

2. **SPORTS** When was the only time the percent of students in sports decreased from one year to the next?
   from 2006 to 2007

3. **REFLECT** What other interval could be used for the graph? Why might you prefer this interval?
   Sample answer: The scale could use an interval of 5%.
   This would make it easier to determine actual percents.

Use the double-line graph "CD Rates" to compare data.

4. **RATES** A banker wants to compare the interest rates of two types of CDs (certificates of deposit) in past years. Compare the rates for a 6-month CD and a 24-month CD in 2005.
   The 24-month rate is 0.25% more than the 6-month rate.

5. **YEARS** If the trend continues, what would you expect the data to show for 2009?
   Sample answer: About 2% for the 6-month CD and about 1.5% for the 24-month CD.

A156 Lesson 7-6   Math Triumphs

Homework Practice

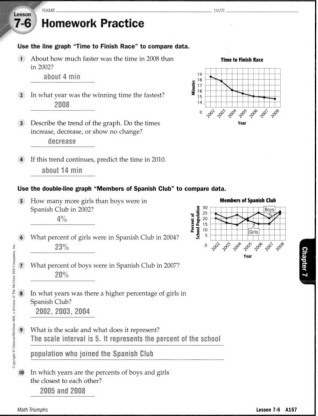

Use the line graph "Time to Finish Race" to compare data.

1. About how much faster was the time in 2008 than in 2002?
   about 4 min

2. In what year was the winning time the fastest?
   2008

3. Describe the trend of the graph. Do the times increase, decrease, or show no change?
   decrease

4. If this trend continues, predict the time in 2010.
   about 14 min

Use the double-line graph "Members of Spanish Club" to compare data.

5. How many more girls than boys were in Spanish Club in 2002?
   4%

6. What percent of girls were in Spanish Club in 2004?
   23%

7. What percent of boys were in Spanish Club in 2007?
   20%

8. In what years was there a higher percentage of girls in Spanish Club?
   2002, 2003, 2004

9. What is the scale and what does it represent?
   The scale interval is 5. It represents the percent of the school population who joined the Spanish Club

10. In which years are the percents of boys and girls the closest to each other?
    2005 and 2008

Math Triumphs   Lesson 7-6 A157

Math Triumphs   **Lesson 7-6   A229**

Answer Key (Lesson 7-7)

Vocabulary and English Language Development

▶ Activate Prior Knowledge

Use the line graph "Video Game Scores" to compare data.

Video Game Scores

1. Describe how Mario's score changed from week 1 to week 5.
   It doubled.

2. Between which two consecutive weeks did his score improve the most?
   week 2 and week 3

3. What is the trend of the data?
   increasing

▶ Definition Review

Fill in the blanks.

4. The axis on which the categories or values are shown is the **horizontal axis**

5. The difference between successive values on a **scale** is called the **interval**

6. A **line graph** is used to show how a set of data changes over a period of time.

▶ Application

Follow the directions for the activity.

- Choose a company listed on the N.Y. Stock Exchange in the newspaper.
- Record the price of your stock every day for a week.
- Draw and label a line graph with this data.
- Discuss the graph you drew with your classmates.
- Find the change in price of your stock from the beginning of the week to the end.
- Find whose stock increased in value the most during the week and whose stock lost the most.
- Find whose stock had a noticeable trend (increasing or decreasing), whose has little to no change, and whose had both ups and downs during the week.

Skills Practice

Use the data in the table to plan a line graph. **Sample answers provided.**

1. What is a good title for the graph?
   Digital Camera Ownership

2. What are the two main categories?
   Year and Percent of Students

3. What interval could be used for the scale?
   5

Digital Camera Ownership	
Year	Percent of Students
2005	7
2006	16
2007	21
2008	27
2009	32

4. Describe the trend of the data. Does the percent of students increase, decrease, or stay the same over time?
   the percent of students increases over time

5. Use the data in the table to create a line graph.

Car Wash Fundraiser	
Time	Money Collected
8 A.M.	$150
10 A.M.	$70
12 P.M.	$230
2 P.M.	$120

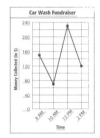

6. Use the data in the table to create a double-line graph.

Work Schedule		
Month	Hours Worked	
	Rob	Irena
March	28	17
April	26	16
May	23	12
June	22	10

Problem-Solving Practice

Solve.

1. **SALES** The manager of a book store wants to compare the number of pens and pencils sold each day of the first week of school. Use the data in the table to create a double-line graph.

Bookstore Sales		
Day	Pens	Pencils
Monday	$240	$620
Tuesday	$190	$560
Wednesday	$120	$470
Thursday	$310	$320
Friday	$460	$650

Bookstore Sales

2. **TEST SCORES** A teacher wants to compare pre- and post-test scores to see how the new study program is working. Use the data in the table to create a double-line graph.

Average Test Scores		
Year	Pretest	Posttest
2005	32%	56%
2006	34%	58%
2007	39%	60%
2008	41%	64%
2009	43%	67%

Average Test Scores

3. **PREDICTIONS** For the graph in Exercise 2, predict the average pretest and posttest scores in 2010.
   pretest: 45; posttest: 70

4. **CUSTOMERS** A cafeteria manager wants to see how the dessert sales change throughout the week. Use the data in the table to create a line graph.

Dessert Sales						
Day	Mon	Tues	Wed	Thurs	Fri	Sat
Number	$52	$57	$46	$75	$98	$110

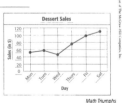

Dessert Sales

Homework Practice

Use the data in the table to plan a line graph. **Sample answers provided.**

1. What is a good title for the graph?
   Amount Spent on Groceries

2. What are the two main categories?
   Week and Amount

3. What interval could be used for the scale?
   $10

Amount Spent on Groceries	
Week	Amount
1	$68
2	$86
3	$135
4	$74
5	$91
6	$83

Use the data in the table to create a line or double-line graph.

4. A scientist records the amount of rain that fell in a city each day.

Amount of Rain	
Day of Week	Inches
Monday	0.25
Tuesday	0.10
Wednesday	0.00
Thursday	1.30
Friday	0.75

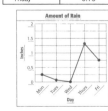

Amount of Rain

5. Ben and Betty's mother would like her children to keep track of how much money they save each month.

Amount Saved		
Month	Ben	Betty
January	$10	$15
February	$12	$22
March	$15	$13
April	$19	$11

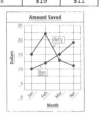

Amount Saved

Answer Key (Lesson 8-1)

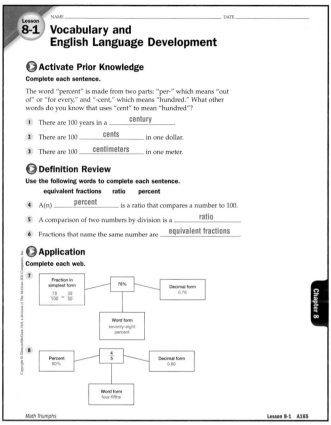

Lesson 8-1

Vocabulary and English Language Development

▶ Activate Prior Knowledge

Complete each sentence.

The word "percent" is made from two parts: "per-" which means "out of" or "for every," and "-cent," which means "hundred." What other words do you know that uses "cent" to mean "hundred"?

1. There are 100 years in a ___century___

2. There are 100 ___cents___ in one dollar.

3. There are 100 ___centimeters___ in one meter.

▶ Definition Review

Use the following words to complete each sentence.

equivalent fractions   ratio   percent

4. A(n) ___percent___ is a ratio that compares a number to 100.

5. A comparison of two numbers by division is a ___ratio___

6. Fractions that name the same number are ___equivalent fractions___

▶ Application

Complete each web.

7. Fraction in simplest form $\frac{78}{100} = \frac{39}{50}$ — 78% — Decimal form 0.78 — Word form seventy-eight percent

8. Percent 80% — $\frac{4}{5}$ — Decimal form 0.80 — Word form four-fifths

Math Triumphs Lesson 8-1 A165

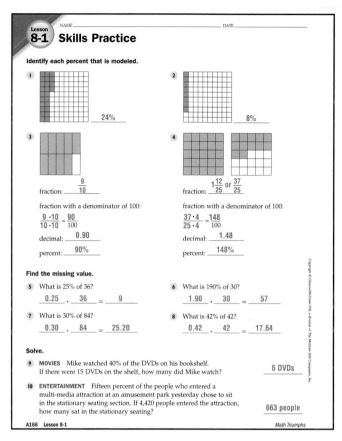

Lesson 8-1

Skills Practice

Identify each percent that is modeled.

1. 24%

2. 8%

3. fraction: $\frac{9}{10}$

fraction with a denominator of 100:
$\frac{9 \cdot 10}{10 \cdot 10} = \frac{90}{100}$

decimal: 0.90

percent: 90%

4. fraction: $1\frac{12}{25}$ or $\frac{37}{25}$

fraction with a denominator of 100:
$\frac{37 \cdot 4}{25 \cdot 4} = \frac{148}{100}$

decimal: 1.48

percent: 148%

Find the missing value.

5. What is 25% of 36?

$0.25 \cdot 36 = 9$

6. What is 190% of 30?

$1.90 \cdot 30 = 57$

7. What is 30% of 84?

$0.30 \cdot 84 = 25.20$

8. What is 42% of 42?

$0.42 \cdot 42 = 17.64$

Solve.

9. **MOVIES** Mike watched 40% of the DVDs on his bookshelf. If there were 15 DVDs on the shelf, how many did Mike watch? **6 DVDs**

10. **ENTERTAINMENT** Fifteen percent of the people who entered a multi-media attraction at an amusement park yesterday chose to sit in the stationary seating section. If 4,420 people entered the attraction, how many sat in the stationary seating? **663 people**

A166 Lesson 8-1 *Math Triumphs*

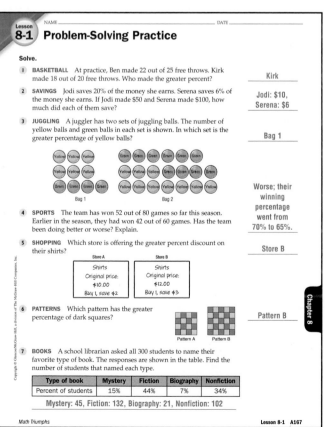

Lesson 8-1

Problem-Solving Practice

Solve.

1. **BASKETBALL** At practice, Ben made 22 out of 25 free throws. Kirk made 18 out of 20 free throws. Who made the greater percent? **Kirk**

2. **SAVINGS** Jodi saves 20% of the money she earns. Serena saves 6% of the money she earns. If Jodi made $50 and Serena made $100, how much did each of them save? **Jodi: $10, Serena: $6**

3. **JUGGLING** A juggler has two sets of juggling balls. The number of yellow balls and green balls in each set is shown. In which set is the greater percentage of yellow balls? **Bag 1**

   Bag 1   Bag 2

4. **SPORTS** The team has won 52 out of 80 games so far this season. Earlier in the season, they had won 42 out of 60 games. Has the team been doing better or worse? Explain. **Worse; their winning percentage went from 70% to 65%.**

5. **SHOPPING** Which store is offering the greater percent discount on their shirts? **Store B**

   Store A — Shirts Original price: $10.00 Buy 1, save $2

   Store B — Shirts Original price: $12.00 Buy 1, save $3

6. **PATTERNS** Which pattern has the greater percentage of dark squares? **Pattern B**

   Pattern A   Pattern B

7. **BOOKS** A school librarian asked all 300 students to name their favorite type of book. The responses are shown in the table. Find the number of students that named each type.

Type of book	Mystery	Fiction	Biography	Nonfiction
Percent of students	15%	44%	7%	34%

Mystery: 45, Fiction: 132, Biography: 21, Nonfiction: 102

Math Triumphs Lesson 8-1 A167

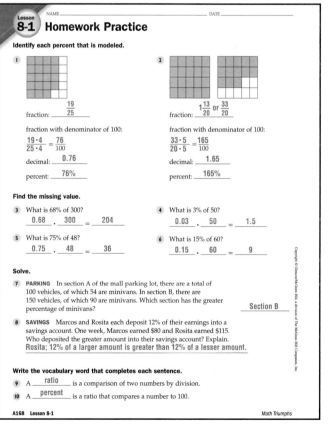

Lesson 8-1

Homework Practice

Identify each percent that is modeled.

1. fraction: $\frac{19}{25}$

fraction with denominator of 100:
$\frac{19 \cdot 4}{25 \cdot 4} = \frac{76}{100}$

decimal: 0.76

percent: 76%

2. fraction: $1\frac{13}{20}$ or $\frac{33}{20}$

fraction with denominator of 100:
$\frac{33 \cdot 5}{20 \cdot 5} = \frac{165}{100}$

decimal: 1.65

percent: 165%

Find the missing value.

3. What is 68% of 300?

$0.68 \cdot 300 = 204$

4. What is 3% of 50?

$0.03 \cdot 50 = 1.5$

5. What is 75% of 48?

$0.75 \cdot 48 = 36$

6. What is 15% of 60?

$0.15 \cdot 60 = 9$

Solve.

7. **PARKING** In section A of the mall parking lot, there are a total of 100 vehicles, of which 54 are minivans. In section B, there are 150 vehicles, of which 90 are minivans. Which section has the greater percentage of minivans? **Section B**

8. **SAVINGS** Marcos and Rosita each deposit 12% of their earnings into a savings account. One week, Marcos earned $80 and Rosita earned $115. Who deposited the greater amount into their savings account? Explain. **Rosita; 12% of a larger amount is greater than 12% of a lesser amount.**

Write the vocabulary word that completes each sentence.

9. A ___ratio___ is a comparison of two numbers by division.

10. A ___percent___ is a ratio that compares a number to 100.

A168 Lesson 8-1 *Math Triumphs*

Answer Key (Lesson 8-2)

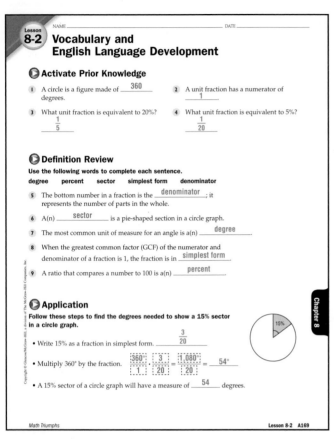

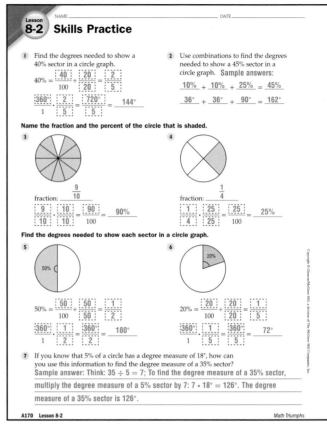

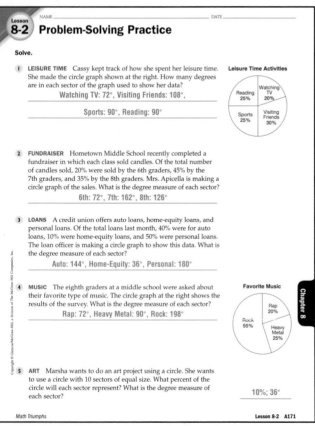

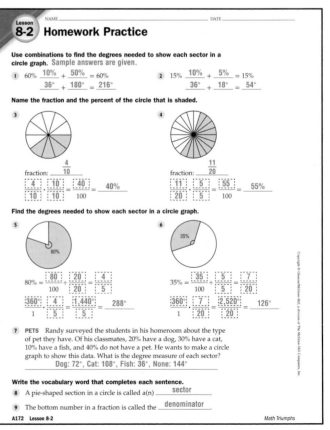

Answer Key (Lesson 8-3)

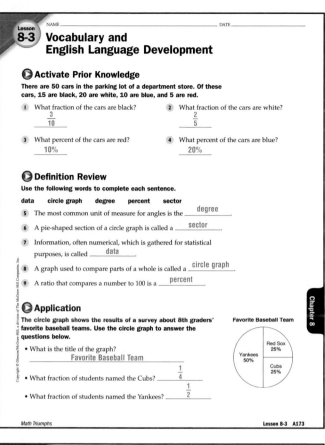

Vocabulary and English Language Development

▶ Activate Prior Knowledge

There are 50 cars in the parking lot of a department store. Of these cars, 15 are black, 20 are white, 10 are blue, and 5 are red.

1. What fraction of the cars are black?
   $\frac{3}{10}$

2. What fraction of the cars are white?
   $\frac{2}{5}$

3. What percent of the cars are red?
   10%

4. What percent of the cars are blue?
   20%

▶ Definition Review

Use the following words to complete each sentence.

data   circle graph   degree   percent   sector

5. The most common unit of measure for angles is the **degree**

6. A pie-shaped section of a circle graph is called a **sector**

7. Information, often numerical, which is gathered for statistical purposes, is called **data**

8. A graph used to compare parts of a whole is called a **circle graph**

9. A ratio that compares a number to 100 is a **percent**

▶ Application

The circle graph shows the results of a survey about 8th graders' favorite baseball teams. Use the circle graph to answer the questions below.

Favorite Baseball Team
Red Sox 25%, Yankees 50%, Cubs 25%

- What is the title of the graph?
  Favorite Baseball Team

- What fraction of students named the Cubs? $\frac{1}{4}$

- What fraction of students named the Yankees? $\frac{1}{2}$

Math Triumphs   Lesson 8-3   A173

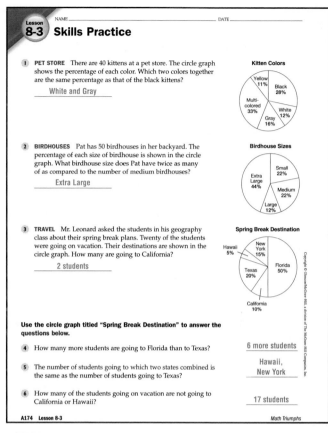

Skills Practice

1. **PET STORE** There are 40 kittens at a pet store. The circle graph shows the percentage of each color. Which two colors together are the same percentage as that of the black kittens?
   White and Gray

   Kitten Colors
   Yellow 11%, Black 28%, Multi-colored 33%, White 12%, Gray 16%

2. **BIRDHOUSES** Pat has 50 birdhouses in her backyard. The percentage of each size of birdhouse is shown in the circle graph. What birdhouse size does Pat have twice as many of as compared to the number of medium birdhouses?
   Extra Large

   Birdhouse Sizes
   Small 22%, Extra Large 44%, Medium 22%, Large 12%

3. **TRAVEL** Mr. Leonard asked the students in his geography class about their spring break plans. Twenty of the students were going on vacation. Their destinations are shown in the circle graph. How many are going to California?
   2 students

   Spring Break Destination
   Hawaii 5%, New York 15%, Florida 50%, Texas 20%, California 10%

Use the circle graph titled "Spring Break Destination" to answer the questions below.

4. How many more students are going to Florida than to Texas?
   6 more students

5. The number of students going to which two states combined is the same as the number of students going to Texas?
   Hawaii, New York

6. How many of the students going on vacation are not going to California or Hawaii?
   17 students

A174   Lesson 8-3   *Math Triumphs*

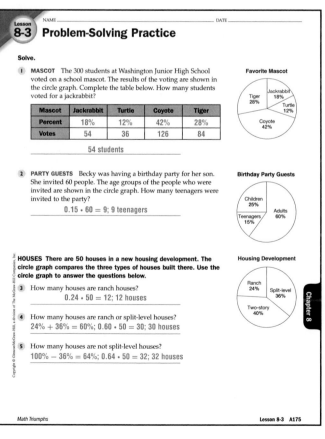

Problem-Solving Practice

Solve.

1. **MASCOT** The 300 students at Washington Junior High School voted on a school mascot. The results of the voting are shown in the circle graph. Complete the table below. How many students voted for a jackrabbit?

   Favorite Mascot
   Tiger 28%, Jackrabbit 18%, Turtle 12%, Coyote 42%

Mascot	Jackrabbit	Turtle	Coyote	Tiger
Percent	18%	12%	42%	28%
Votes	54	36	126	84

   54 students

2. **PARTY GUESTS** Becky was having a birthday party for her son. She invited 60 people. The age groups of the people who were invited are shown in the circle graph. How many teenagers were invited to the party?

   Birthday Party Guests
   Children 25%, Adults 60%, Teenagers 15%

   0.15 · 60 = 9; 9 teenagers

HOUSES There are 50 houses in a new housing development. The circle graph compares the three types of houses built there. Use the circle graph to answer the questions below.

Housing Development
Ranch 24%, Split-level 36%, Two-story 40%

3. How many houses are ranch houses?
   0.24 · 50 = 12; 12 houses

4. How many houses are ranch or split-level houses?
   24% + 36% = 60%; 0.60 · 50 = 30; 30 houses

5. How many houses are not split-level houses?
   100% − 36% = 64%; 0.64 · 50 = 32; 32 houses

Math Triumphs   Lesson 8-3   A175

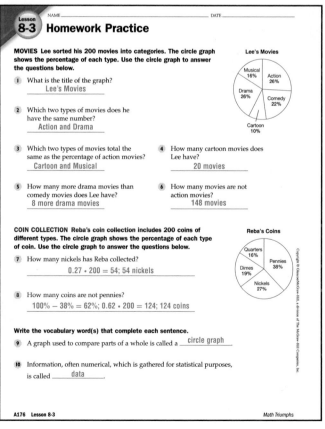

Homework Practice

MOVIES Lee sorted his 200 movies into categories. The circle graph shows the percentage of each type. Use the circle graph to answer the questions below.

Lee's Movies
Musical 16%, Action 26%, Drama 26%, Comedy 22%, Cartoon 10%

1. What is the title of the graph?
   Lee's Movies

2. Which two types of movies does he have the same number?
   Action and Drama

3. Which two types of movies total the same as the percentage of action movies?
   Cartoon and Musical

4. How many cartoon movies does Lee have?
   20 movies

5. How many more drama movies than comedy movies does Lee have?
   8 more drama movies

6. How many movies are not action movies?
   148 movies

COIN COLLECTION Reba's coin collection includes 200 coins of different types. The circle graph shows the percentage of each type of coin. Use the circle graph to answer the questions below.

Reba's Coins
Quarters 16%, Pennies 38%, Dimes 19%, Nickels 27%

7. How many nickels has Reba collected?
   0.27 · 200 = 54; 54 nickels

8. How many coins are not pennies?
   100% − 38% = 62%; 0.62 · 200 = 124; 124 coins

Write the vocabulary word(s) that complete each sentence.

9. A graph used to compare parts of a whole is called a **circle graph**

10. Information, often numerical, which is gathered for statistical purposes, is called **data**

A176   Lesson 8-3   *Math Triumphs*

Answer Key (Lesson 8-4)

Lesson 8-4

Vocabulary and English Language Development

Activate Prior Knowledge

SCOUTING A scout troop sold 300 geraniums as a fund-raiser for their annual jamboree trip. The circle graph shows the percentages of each color.

Geraniums

Salmon 18% | Pink 28%
White
Red 46%

1. What is the title of the graph?
   Geraniums

2. When Samuel drew the graph, he forgot to include the percentage for white. What percent of the geraniums sold were white?
   8%

3. How many red geraniums were sold?
   138 red geraniums

4. How many of the geraniums were not salmon?
   246 geraniums

Definition Review

Use the following words to complete each sentence.

center   circle graph   percent   sector

5. A __percent__ is a ratio that compares a number to 100.

6. A pie-shaped section of a circle graph is called a __sector__.

7. The point from which all points on a circle are the same distance is called its __center__.

8. A __circle graph__ is a graph used to compare parts of a whole.

Application

Use the figure to answer the questions below.

- What is the percentage of the shaded sector? __30%__
- How many degrees are in the shaded sector? __108°__

30%
108°

Lesson 8-4

Skills Practice

1. Complete the table to show the decimal value, the percent, and the degree measure for each class president candidate.

Candidate	Number of Votes	Decimal Value	Percent	Degree Measure
Lucy	50	0.25	25%	90°
Emil	70	0.35	35%	126°
Irma	40	0.20	20%	72°
Dale	40	0.20	20%	72°
Total	**200**	**1.00**	**100%**	**360°**

2. **COLLECTIONS** Complete the table to show the decimal value, the percent, and the degree measure for each stuffed animal in Tami's collection.

Animal	Number	Decimal Value	Percent	Degree Measure
Bear	10	0.20	20%	72°
Dog	20	0.40	40%	144°
Rabbit	5	0.10	10%	36°
Tiger	5	0.10	10%	36°
Cat	10	0.20	20%	72°
Total	**50**	**1.00**	**100%**	**360°**

3. Use the table in Exercise 1 to create a circle graph.

Election Results

4. Use the table in Exercise 2 to create a circle graph.

Stuffed Animal Collection

Lesson 8-4

Problem-Solving Practice

1. **BASKETBALL** The table below shows the points scored during a recent basketball game. Complete the table to show the decimal value, the percent, and the degree measure for each player.

Player	Points Scored	Decimal Value	Percent	Degree Measure
Mark	24	0.30	30%	108°
Cuonzo	4	0.05	5%	18°
Alfonze	8	0.10	10%	36°
Robbie	16	0.20	20%	72°
Chris	28	0.35	35%	126°
Total	**80**	**1.00**	**100%**	**360°**

2. **SHOES** A shoe salesman recorded his sales during last month. Complete the table to show the decimal value, the percent, and the degree measure for each shoe type.

Shoe Type	Number	Decimal Value	Percent	Degree Measure
Cross-Training	150	0.30	30%	108°
Running	200	0.40	40%	144°
Walking	50	0.10	10%	36°
Baseball	100	0.20	20%	72°
Total	**500**	**1.00**	**100%**	**360°**

3. Use the table in Exercise 1 to create a circle graph.

Basketball Scoring

4. Use the table in Exercise 2 to create a circle graph.

Shoe Sales

Lesson 8-4

Homework Practice

1. Complete the table to show the decimal value, the percent, and the degree measure for each type of house for sale.

Number of Bedrooms	Number	Decimal Value	Percent	Degree Measure
Two	16	0.20	20%	72°
Three	48	0.60	60%	216°
Four	12	0.15	15%	54°
Five	4	0.05	5%	18°
Total	**80**	**1.00**	**100%**	**360°**

2. Complete the table to show the decimal value, the percent, and the degree measure for each type of transaction at a clothing store yesterday.

Transaction	Number	Decimal Value	Percent	Degree Measure
Cash	75	0.15	15%	54°
Check	50	0.10	10%	36°
Bank Credit Card	100	0.20	20%	72°
Store Credit Card	150	0.30	30%	108°
Debit Card	125	0.25	25%	90°
Total	**500**	**1.00**	**100%**	**360°**

3. Use the table in Exercise 1 to create a circle graph.

Number of Bedrooms

4. Use the table in Exercise 2 to create a circle graph.

Transaction Types

Answer Key (Lesson 9-1)

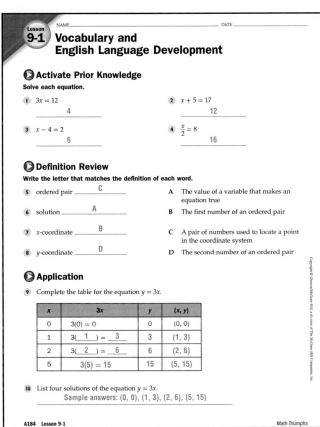

Lesson 9-1

Vocabulary and English Language Development

▶ Activate Prior Knowledge

Solve each equation.

1. $3x = 12$

   4

2. $x + 5 = 17$

   12

3. $x - 4 = 2$

   6

4. $\frac{x}{2} = 8$

   16

▶ Definition Review

Write the letter that matches the definition of each word.

5. ordered pair _____ C

6. solution _____ A

7. x-coordinate _____ B

8. y-coordinate _____ D

A The value of a variable that makes an equation true

B The first number of an ordered pair

C A pair of numbers used to locate a point in the coordinate system

D The second number of an ordered pair

▶ Application

9. Complete the table for the equation $y = 3x$.

x	3x	y	(x, y)
0	3(0) = 0	0	(0, 0)
1	3(_1_) = _3_	3	(1, 3)
2	3(_2_) = _6_	6	(2, 6)
5	3(5) = 15	15	(5, 15)

10. List four solutions of the equation $y = 3x$.
Sample answers: (0, 0), (1, 3), (2, 6), (5, 15)

A184   Lesson 9-1   Math Triumphs

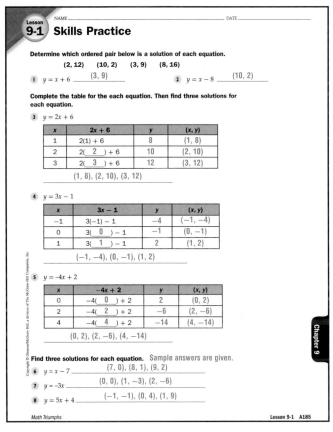

Lesson 9-1

Skills Practice

Determine which ordered pair below is a solution of each equation.

(2, 12)   (10, 2)   (3, 9)   (8, 16)

1. $y = x + 6$ _____ (3, 9)

2. $y = x - 8$ _____ (10, 2)

Complete the table for the each equation. Then find three solutions for each equation.

3. $y = 2x + 6$

x	2x + 6	y	(x, y)
1	2(1) + 6	8	(1, 8)
2	2(_2_) + 6	10	(2, 10)
3	2(_3_) + 6	12	(3, 12)

(1, 8), (2, 10), (3, 12)

4. $y = 3x - 1$

x	3x − 1	y	(x, y)
−1	3(−1) − 1	−4	(−1, −4)
0	3(_0_) − 1	−1	(0, −1)
1	3(_1_) − 1	2	(1, 2)

(−1, −4), (0, −1), (1, 2)

5. $y = -4x + 2$

x	−4x + 2	y	(x, y)
0	−4(_0_) + 2	2	(0, 2)
2	−4(_2_) + 2	−6	(2, −6)
4	−4(_4_) + 2	−14	(4, −14)

(0, 2), (2, −6), (4, −14)

Find three solutions for each equation. Sample answers are given.

6. $y = x - 7$ _____ (7, 0), (8, 1), (9, 2)

7. $y = -3x$ _____ (0, 0), (1, −3), (2, −6)

8. $y = 5x + 4$ _____ (−1, −1), (0, 4), (1, 9)

Math Triumphs   Lesson 9-1   A185

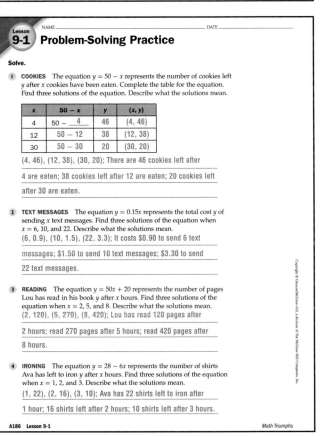

Lesson 9-1

Problem-Solving Practice

Solve.

1. **COOKIES** The equation $y = 50 - x$ represents the number of cookies left y after x cookies have been eaten. Complete the table for the equation. Find three solutions of the equation. Describe what the solutions mean.

x	50 − x	y	(x, y)
4	50 − _4_	46	(4, 46)
12	50 − 12	38	(12, 38)
30	50 − 30	20	(30, 20)

(4, 46), (12, 38), (30, 20); There are 46 cookies left after 4 are eaten; 38 cookies left after 12 are eaten; 20 cookies left after 30 are eaten.

2. **TEXT MESSAGES** The equation $y = 0.15x$ represents the total cost y of sending x text messages. Find three solutions of the equation when $x = 6$, 10, and 22. Describe what the solutions mean.
(6, 0.9), (10, 1.5), (22, 3.3); It costs $0.90 to send 6 text messages; $1.50 to send 10 text messages; $3.30 to send 22 text messages.

3. **READING** The equation $y = 50x + 20$ represents the number of pages Lou has read in his book y after x hours. Find three solutions of the equation when $x = 2$, 5, and 8. Describe what the solutions mean.
(2, 120), (5, 270), (8, 420); Lou has read 120 pages after 2 hours; read 270 pages after 5 hours; read 420 pages after 8 hours.

4. **IRONING** The equation $y = 28 - 6x$ represents the number of shirts Ava has left to iron y after x hours. Find three solutions of the equation when $x = 1$, 2, and 3. Describe what the solutions mean.
(1, 22), (2, 16), (3, 10); Ava has 22 shirts left to iron after 1 hour; 16 shirts left after 2 hours; 10 shirts left after 3 hours.

A186   Lesson 9-1   Math Triumphs

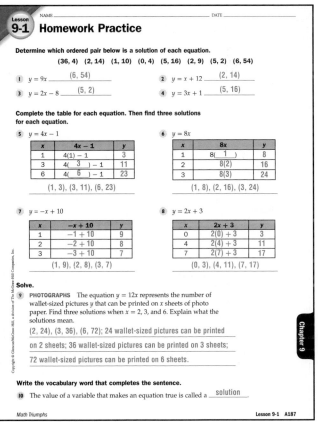

Lesson 9-1

Homework Practice

Determine which ordered pair below is a solution of each equation.

(36, 4)   (2, 14)   (1, 10)   (0, 4)   (5, 16)   (2, 9)   (5, 2)   (6, 54)

1. $y = 9x$ _____ (6, 54)

2. $y = x + 12$ _____ (2, 14)

3. $y = 2x - 8$ _____ (5, 2)

4. $y = 3x + 1$ _____ (5, 16)

Complete the table for each equation. Then find three solutions for each equation.

5. $y = 4x - 1$

x	4x − 1	y
1	4(1) − 1	3
3	4(_3_) − 1	11
6	4(_6_) − 1	23

(1, 3), (3, 11), (6, 23)

6. $y = 8x$

x	8x	y
1	8(_1_)	8
2	8(2)	16
3	8(3)	24

(1, 8), (2, 16), (3, 24)

7. $y = -x + 10$

x	−x + 10	y
1	−1 + 10	9
2	−2 + 10	8
3	−3 + 10	7

(1, 9), (2, 8), (3, 7)

8. $y = 2x + 3$

x	2x + 3	y
0	2(0) + 3	3
4	2(4) + 3	11
7	2(7) + 3	17

(0, 3), (4, 11), (7, 17)

Solve.

9. **PHOTOGRAPHS** The equation $y = 12x$ represents the number of wallet-sized pictures y that can be printed on x sheets of photo paper. Find three solutions when $x = 2$, 3, and 6. Explain what the solutions mean.
(2, 24), (3, 36), (6, 72); 24 wallet-sized pictures can be printed on 2 sheets; 36 wallet-sized pictures can be printed on 3 sheets; 72 wallet-sized pictures can be printed on 6 sheets.

Write the vocabulary word that completes the sentence.

10. The value of a variable that makes an equation true is called a _____ solution.

Math Triumphs   Lesson 9-1   A187

Math Triumphs   **Lesson 9-1   A235**

Answer Key (Lesson 9-2)

Lesson 9-2 Vocabulary and English Language Development

▶ Activate Prior Knowledge

Find three solutions of each equation. Sample answers are given.

1 $y = 2x - 4$
   (2, 0), (8, 12), (10, 16)

2 $y = 4x$
   (2, 8), (8, 32), (10, 40)

▶ Definition Review

Use the following words to complete each sentence.

coordinate grid   scatter plot   x-axis   y-axis

3 The __y-axis__ is the vertical line of the two perpendicular number lines in a coordinate grid.

4 The __x-axis__ is the horizontal line of the two perpendicular number lines in a coordinate grid.

5 A grid in which a horizontal number line and a vertical number line intersect at their zero points is called a __coordinate grid__.

6 A graph in which two sets of data are plotted as ordered pairs in the coordinate grid is called a __scatter plot__.

▶ Application

- Graph and label these points on the coordinate grid.
  A (6, 2), B (3, 5), C (0, 4), D (1, 0)
- Give the coordinates of points E, F, G, and H.
  E (2, 1), F (5, 4), G (8, 3), H (1, 6)

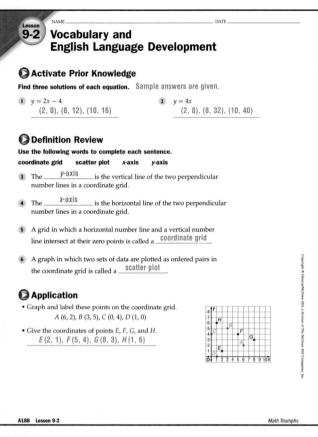

A188   Lesson 9-2   Math Triumphs

Lesson 9-2 Skills Practice

Explain whether each scatter plot shows a positive, negative, or no relationship.

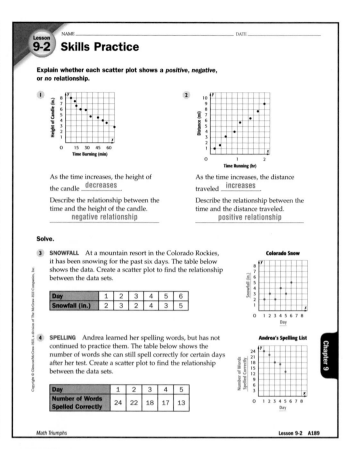

As the time increases, the height of the candle __decreases__

Describe the relationship between the time and the height of the candle.
__negative relationship__

As the time increases, the distance traveled __increases__

Describe the relationship between the time and the distance traveled.
__positive relationship__

Solve.

3 **SNOWFALL** At a mountain resort in the Colorado Rockies, it has been snowing for the past six days. The table below shows the data. Create a scatter plot to find the relationship between the data sets.

Day	1	2	3	4	5	6
Snowfall (in.)	2	3	2	4	3	5

Colorado Snow

4 **SPELLING** Andrea learned her spelling words, but has not continued to practice them. The table below shows the number of words she can still spell correctly for certain days after her test. Create a scatter plot to find the relationship between the data sets.

Day	1	2	3	4	5
Number of Words Spelled Correctly	24	22	18	17	13

Andrea's Spelling List

Math Triumphs   Lesson 9-2   A189

Lesson 9-2 Problem-Solving Practice

Solve.

1 **MAKING COPIES** Explain whether the scatter plot shows a positive, negative, or no relationship.
   __Negative; as more copies are made, the percent__
   __of ink left in the cartridge decreases.__

Printer Copies

2 **EARNINGS** Amanda recorded information about the earnings of several classmates for last week. The table below shows the data. Create a scatter plot to find the relationship between the data sets.

Hours Worked	2	2	3	4	4	5	5	6
Money Earned	$12	$14	$22	$24	$28	$30	$40	$42

Describe the relationship between the hours worked and the money earned.
__positive relationship__

Student Earnings

3 **SWIMMING** The swim coach asked the swim team to track their calorie intake and minutes of exercise for the week. The table below shows the data. Create a scatter plot to find the relationship between the data sets.

Calories	1000	1200	1300	1400	1500	1600
Minutes of Exercise	60	45	45	60	30	60

Describe the relationship between the calorie intake and minutes of exercise.
__no relationship__

Swim Team Results

A190   Lesson 9-2   Math Triumphs

Lesson 9-2 Homework Practice

Solve.

1 **TEMPERATURE** Mr. Ramirez recorded the temperature for July 17 at different elevations. The table below shows the data. Create a scatter plot to find the relationship between the data sets.

Temperature (°F)	500	1,000	1,500	2,000	2,500	3,000	3,500
Elevation (ft)	78	60	56	50	50	42	39

Describe the relationship between elevation and temperature.
__negative relationship__

Data for July 17

2 **GASOLINE** Eric recorded his gas purchases over the last several months. The table below shows the data. Create a scatter plot to find the relationship between the data sets.

Gallons of Gasoline	2	3	4	5	5
Cost	$7	$11	$16	$17	$18

Gallons of Gasoline	6	7	7	7	9
Cost	$21	$23	$26	$27	$31

Describe the relationship between the gallons of gas purchased and the cost.
__positive relationship__

Eric's Gas Purchases

Write the vocabulary word(s) that completes each sentence.

3 A(n) __scatter plot__ is a graph in which two sets of data are plotted as ordered pairs in the coordinate plane.

4 A(n) __coordinate grid__ is a grid in which a horizontal number line and a vertical number line intersect at their zero points.

5 The horizontal line of the two perpendicular number lines in a coordinate grid is the __x-axis__

Math Triumphs   Lesson 9-2   A191

Answer Key (Lesson 9-3)

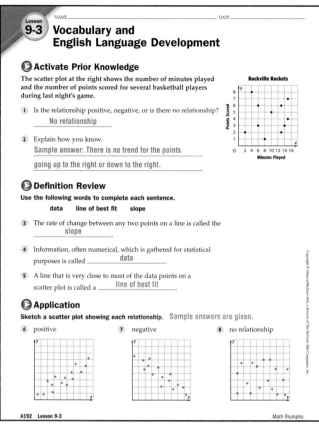

Lesson 9-3 Vocabulary and English Language Development

Activate Prior Knowledge

The scatter plot at the right shows the number of minutes played and the number of points scored for several basketball players during last night's game.

Rockville Rockets

1. Is the relationship positive, negative, or is there no relationship?
   No relationship

2. Explain how you know.
   Sample answer: There is no trend for the points
   going up to the right or down to the right.

Definition Review

Use the following words to complete each sentence.

data   line of best fit   slope

3. The rate of change between any two points on a line is called the
   slope

4. Information, often numerical, which is gathered for statistical
   purposes is called data

5. A line that is very close to most of the data points on a
   scatter plot is called a line of best fit

Application

Sketch a scatter plot showing each relationship. Sample answers are given.

6. positive   7. negative   8. no relationship

A192   Lesson 9-3   Math Triumphs

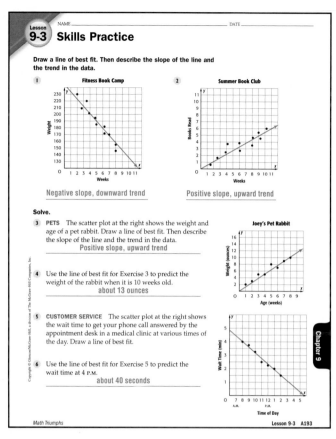

Lesson 9-3 Skills Practice

Draw a line of best fit. Then describe the slope of the line and the trend in the data.

1. **Fitness Book Camp**

2. **Summer Book Club**

Negative slope, downward trend   Positive slope, upward trend

Solve.

3. **PETS** The scatter plot at the right shows the weight and age of a pet rabbit. Draw a line of best fit. Then describe the slope of the line and the trend in the data.
   Positive slope, upward trend

   Joey's Pet Rabbit

4. Use the line of best fit for Exercise 3 to predict the weight of the rabbit when it is 10 weeks old.
   about 13 ounces

5. **CUSTOMER SERVICE** The scatter plot at the right shows the wait time to get your phone call answered by the appointment desk in a medical clinic at various times of the day. Draw a line of best fit.

6. Use the line of best fit for Exercise 5 to predict the wait time at 4 P.M.
   about 40 seconds

Math Triumphs   Lesson 9-3   A193

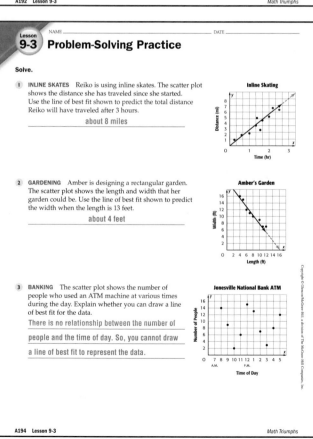

Lesson 9-3 Problem-Solving Practice

Solve.

1. **INLINE SKATES** Reiko is using inline skates. The scatter plot shows the distance she has traveled since she started. Use the line of best fit shown to predict the total distance Reiko will have traveled after 3 hours.
   about 8 miles

   Inline Skating

2. **GARDENING** Amber is designing a rectangular garden. The scatter plot shows the length and width that her garden could be. Use the line of best fit shown to predict the width when the length is 13 feet.
   about 4 feet

   Amber's Garden

3. **BANKING** The scatter plot shows the number of people who used an ATM machine at various times during the day. Explain whether you can draw a line of best fit for the data.
   There is no relationship between the number of
   people and the time of day. So, you cannot draw
   a line of best fit to represent the data.

   Jonesville National Bank ATM

A194   Lesson 9-3   Math Triumphs

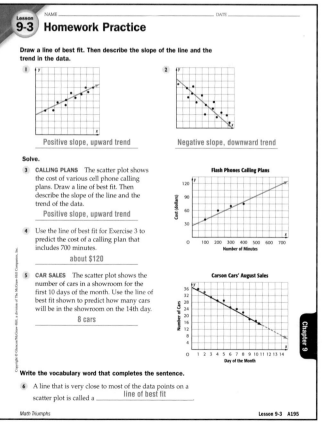

Lesson 9-3 Homework Practice

Draw a line of best fit. Then describe the slope of the line and the trend in the data.

1.   2.

Positive slope, upward trend   Negative slope, downward trend

Solve.

3. **CALLING PLANS** The scatter plot shows the cost of various cell phone calling plans. Draw a line of best fit. Then describe the slope of the line and the trend of the data.
   Positive slope, upward trend

   Flash Phones Calling Plans

4. Use the line of best fit for Exercise 3 to predict the cost of a calling plan that includes 700 minutes.
   about $120

5. **CAR SALES** The scatter plot shows the number of cars in a showroom for the first 10 days of the month. Use the line of best fit shown to predict how many cars will be in the showroom on the 14th day.
   8 cars

   Carson Cars' August Sales

Write the vocabulary word that completes the sentence.

6. A line that is very close to most of the data points on a
   scatter plot is called a line of best fit

Math Triumphs   Lesson 9-3   A195